TITLE CATALOG

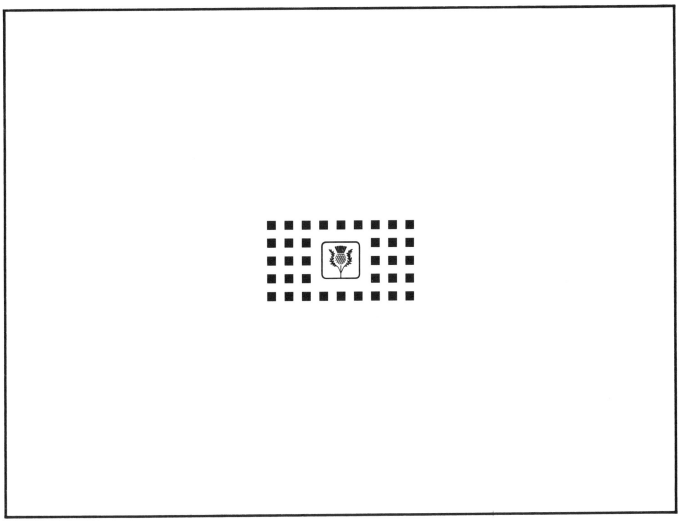

THE
MICROBOOK LIBRARY
OF
AMERICAN CIVILIZATION

TITLE CATALOG

LIBRARY RESOURCES INC
CHICAGO, 1971

INTRODUCTION

The Library of American Civilization is a collection of materials on microfiche relating to all aspects of American life and literature from their beginnings to the outbreak of World War I. Included in the library are pamphlets, periodicals, documents (both public and private), biographies and auto-biographies, fictional works, poetry, collections of various kinds, material of foreign origin relating to America, and many rare books not generally available.

Bibliographical access to the collection is provided in four ways, by means of an Author Catalog, a Title Catalog, a Subject Catalog, and a BIBLIOGUIDE™ Index. A description of the last may be found in the first of the two volumes in which the Index appears. A description of the three catalogs, together with some account of the mode of their preparation, follows.

The primary source of the bibliographic information used in the catalog entries was the *Library of Congress Official Catalog of Printed Cards.* Each entry was checked against the Official Catalog at the Library of Congress for revision and updating, and the latest information for main entries, birth and death dates, subject headings, added entries, etc., were supplied. This procedure was felt to be more effective than ordering printed cards from the Library of Congress, which, in addition to being often out of stock, frequently do not benefit from this continuous revision. Use of the Library of Congress Catalog was supplemented by original cataloging, *National Union Catalog* cards, and catalog cards supplied by libraries at the various film sites. The original cataloging, using a microfilmed copy of the book, was done on the basis of the *Anglo-American Cataloging Rules* (1967) and the *Subject Headings Used in the Dictionary Catalogs of the Library of Congress* (7th ed.)

The style of the catalog entries in the Library of American Civilization reflects over one hundred years of cataloging practice. An effort was made to bring the entries into a more uniform format, but minor inconsistencies remain in the notes, punctuation, use of italics, and style of imprint.

The Author Catalog contains the complete catalog entry for all personal and corporate (firms, institutions, societies) main entries, title main entries, and author added entries, interfiled in one alphabet. The arrangement, as is true of the title and subject catalogs, is based on the *A.L.A. Rules for Filing Catalog Cards* (2d ed.), adapted to the purposes of a divided catalog. Cross references have been made from pseudonyms and variants of names to the main entry and added entries, thus keeping the number of these "See" references to a useful minimum. Cross references were not always made, as, for example, from a woman's maiden name if she never published under or was known by that name. Similarly, cross references were deleted for entries that would file very close to their sources because of negligible differences. Despite the revision and updating, there remain some variations in the entries for the same author or corporate institution, such as open dates, varying fullness of names, errors of spelling or dates in the Library of Congress Catalog. Wherever the identity could be established, these author or institution entries have been interfiled.

The Title Catalog lists all titles and added titles, based on the original cataloging. The title of each book appears in bold type, followed by the body of the entry down to the imprint. The main entry has been brought down to a line below the citation, directing the reader to the Author Catalog, if fuller bibliographic description is needed.

The Subject Catalog is an alphabetical arrangement by subject of all the books in the Library of American Civilization. The entries, subarranged by author, appear in abbreviated form as in the Title Catalog. The subject headings and cross references are taken from *Subject Headings Used in the Dictionary Catalogs of the Library of Congress* (7th ed.) and its cumulative supplements. The reader may wish to consult that source for possible cross references to more specific subjects and to related subjects. References from terms that are not used to those that are used (*See* references) are provided in this catalog. Cross references for personal names, corporate bodies, and place names are also included where necessary.

This three-volume Book Catalog has been designed to provide easy bibliographic access to the materials in the Library. Although the information in the three volumes is complementary, each catalog can be utilized independently since every entry is identified by its LAC number.

LAC 20412

A. Bronson Alcott; his life and philosophy, by F. B. Sanborn and William J. T. Harris. Boston, Roberts Brothers, 1893.
Sanborn, Franklin Benjamin, 1831–1917.

LAC 10982

The A. P. A. movement. A sketch. Washington, The New century press, 1912.
Desmond, Humphrey Joseph, 1858–1932.

LAC 16174

The Aaron Burr conspiracy; a history largely from original and hitherto unused sources. New York, Dodd, Mead and company, 1903.
McCaleb, Walter Flavius, 1873–1967.

LAC 11497

"Abe" Lincoln's yarns and stories; a complete collection of the funny and witty anecdotes that made Lincoln famous as America's greatest story teller; with introduction and anecdotes, by Colonel Alexander K. McClure. The story of Lincoln's life told by himself in his stories...
Chicago, The Educational company, c1904.
McClure, Alexander Kelly, 1828–1909.

LAC 14659

The Abnakis and their history. Or, Historical notices on the aborigines of Acadia. By Rev. Eugene Vetromile. New York, J. B. Kirker, 1866.
Vetromile, Eugene, 1819–1881.

LAC 12848

The abolition crusade and its consequences, four periods of American history. New York, C. Scribner's sons, 1912.
Herbert, Hilary Abner, 1834–1919.

LAC 40006

Abolition of poverty; socialist versus ultramontane economics and politics. New York city, New York labor news co. [1911?]
DeLeon, Daniel, 1852–1914.

LAC 40077

The abolitionists vindicated in a review of Eli Thayers' paper on the New England emigrant aid company. Worcester, Mass., The Worcester society of antiquity, 1887.
Johnson, Oliver, 1809–1889.

LAC 15032

The aboriginal races of North America; comprising biographical sketches of eminent individuals, and an historical account of the different tribes, from the first discovery of the continent to the present period; with a dissertation on their origin, antiquities, manners and customs, illustrative narratives and anecdotes, and a copious analytical index, by Samuel G. Drake. 15th ed., rev., with valuable additions, by Prof. H. L. Williams. New York, Hurst & company [c1880]
Drake, Samuel Gardner, 1798–1875.

LAC 40051

Aborigines of the Ohio valley.
A discourse on the aborigines of the Ohio valley, in which the opinions of its conquest in the seventeenth century by the Iroquois or Six Nations, supported by Cadwallader Colden, Gov. Thomas Pownall, Dr. Benjamin Franklin, Hon. De Witt Clinton, and Judge John Haywood are examined and contested; to which are prefixed some remarks on the study of history. Prepared at the request of the Historical society of Ohio. With notes and an appendix. Chicago, Fergus printing company, 1883.
Harrison, William Henry, *pres. U.S.*, 1773–1841.

LAC 40070

Abraham and Lot. A sermon, on the way of peace, and the evils of war. Delivered at Salisbury, in New-Hampshire, on the day of the national fast, August 20, 1812. Concord, G. Hough, 1812.
Worcester, Noah, 1758–1837.

LAC 40059

Abram Lincoln and South Carolina. Philadelphia, D. E. Thompson, printer, 1861.
Jermon, J   Wagner.

LAC 14525

An abridgement of the History of New-England, for the use of young persons. Printed for the author, and for sale by B. & J. Homans, and John West. A. Newell, printer, Devonshire street, Boston. July, 1805.
Adams, Hannah, 1755–1832.

LAC 14129

An abridgment of the Indian affairs contained in four folio volumes, transacted in the colony of New York, from the year 1678 to the year 1751, by Peter Wraxall; ed. with an introduction by Charles Howard McIlwain. Cambridge, Harvard university press; [etc., etc.] 1915.
New York (*Colony*)

LAC 15333

Abstract of a course of lectures on mental & moral philosophy. Oberlin, J. Steele, 1840.
Mahan, Asa, 1800–1889.

LAC 40082

Absurdities of immaterialism; or, A reply to T. W. P. Taylder's pamphlet entitled "The materialism of the Mormons or Latter-day saints, examined and exposed."... [Liverpool, 1849]
Pratt, Orson, 1811–1881.

LAC 12946

Abyssinia of to-day; an account of the first mission sent by the American government to the court of the King of Kings (1903–1904) London, E. Arnold; New York, Longmans, Green & co., 1906.
Skinner, Robert Peet, 1866–

LAC 40003

Academic freedom. An address delivered before the New York Theta chapter of the Phi beta kappa society at Cornell university, May 29, 1907. Ithaca, New York [Press of Andrus & Church] 1907.
Eliot, Charles William, 1834–1926.

LAC 40029

An accidence to the English tongue, 1724. Menston (Yorks.), Scolar P., 1967.
Jones, Hugh, 1669–1760.

LAC 14911
Account of Arnold's campaign against Quebec, and of the hardships and sufferings of that band of heroes who traversed the wilderness of Maine from Cambridge to the St. Lawrence, in the autumn of 1775. Albany, J. Munsell, 1877.
Henry, John Joseph, 1758–1811.

LAC 11883
An account of Col. Crockett's tour to the North and down East, in the year of Our Lord one thousand eight hundred and thirty-four. His object being to examine the grand manufacturing establishments of the country; and also to find out the condition of its literature and morals, the extent of its commerce, and the practical operation of "The Experiment"... Written by himself. Philadelphia, E. L. Carey and A. Hart; Baltimore, Carey, Hart, and co., 1835.
Crockett, David, 1786–1836.

LAC 12251
An account of six years residence in Hudson's-bay from 1733 to 1736, and 1744 to 1747. Containing a variety of facts, observations, and discoveries about Hudson's-bay to Great Britain. And, II. The interested views of the Hudson's bay company; and the absolute necessity of laying open the trade. To which is added an appendix. London, Printed for J. Payne and J. Bouquet; [etc., etc.] 1752.
Robson, Joseph.

LAC 15483
An account of sundry missions performed among the Senecas and Munsees; in a series of letters. With an appendix. By Rev. Timothy Alden. New-York, Printed by J. Seymour, 1827.
Alden, Timothy, 1771–1839.

LAC 20774
An account of the European settlements in America. In six parts. I. A short history of the discovery of that part of the world. II. The manners and customs of the original inhabitants. III. Of the Spanish settlements. IV. Of the Portuguese. V. Of the French, Dutch, and Danish. VI. Of the English... 2d ed., with improvements. London, R. and J. Dodsley, 1758.
Burke, Edmund, 1729?–1797.

LAC 16616
An Account Of the First Voyages and Discoveries Made by the Spaniards in America. Containing The most Exact Relation hitherto publish'd, of their unparallel'd Cruelties on the Indians, in the destruction of above Forty Millions of people. With the Propositions offer'd to the King of Spain, to prevent the further Ruin of the West-Indies. By Don Bartholomew de las Casas. Illustrated with cuts. To which is added, The Art of Travelling, shewing how a Man may dispose his Travels to the best advantage. London, Printed by J. Darby for D. Brown, M.DC.XC.IX.
Casas, Bartolome de las, *bp. of Chiapa*, 1474–1566.

LAC 40123
An account of the Free-school society of New-York. New-York, Collins and co., 1814.
Public School Society of New York.

LAC 15143
An account of the history, manners, and customs, of the Indian nations, who once inhabited Pennsylvania and the neighbouring states. [Philadelphia. A. Small, 1819]
Heckewelder, John Gottlieb Ernestus, 1743–1823.

LAC 40113
An account of the late intended insurrection among a portion of the blacks of this city. Pub. by the authority of the corporation of Charleston. Charleston, Printed by A. E. Miller, 1822.
Charleston, *S.C.*

LAC 40012
An account of the late revolution in New-England. Together with the Declaration of the gentlemen, merchants, and inhabitants of Boston, and the country adjacent. April 18, 1689. Written by Mr. Nathanael Byfield. London, Printed by R. Chiswell, 1689.
Byfield, Nathaniel, 1653–1733.

LAC 40141
An account of the manners of the German inhabitants of Pennsylvania, written in 1789, by Benjamin Rush, M. D. Notes added by Prof. I. Daniel Rupp. Philadelphia, S. P. Town, 1875.
Rush, Benjamin, 1745–1813.

LAC 16220
An account of the New-York hospital. New-York, Printed by Collins & co., 1811.
Society of the New York Hospital.

LAC 22469
An account of the organization of the army of the United States; with biographies of distinguished officers of all grades. With thirty-six authentic portraits. Philadelphia, E. H. Butler & co., 1848.
Robinson, Fayette, *d.* 1859.

LAC 13795
An account of the people called Shakers: their faith, doctrines, and practice, exemplified in the life, conversations, and experience of the author during the time he belonged to the society. To which is affixed A history of their rise and progress to the present day. Troy, Printed by Parker and Bliss. Sold at the Troy bookstore; by Websters and Skinners, Albany; and by S. Wood, New-York, 1812.
Brown, Thomas, *b.* 1766.

LAC 14182
An account of the remarkable occurrences in the life and travels of Col. James Smith, during his captivity with the Indians, in the years 1755, '56, '57, '58, and '59. With an appendix of illustrative notes. By Wm. M. Darlington. Cincinnati, Robert Clarke, 1907.
Smith, James, 1737–1812.

LAC 40109
An account of the trial of Thomas Cooper, of Northumberland; on a charge of libel against the President of the United States; taken in short hand. With a preface, notes, and appendix, by Thomas Cooper. Philadelphia: Printed by John Bioren, no. 83, Chesnut street, for the author, April 1800.
Cooper, Thomas, 1759–1839, *defendant.*

LAC 13567
An account of the United States of America, derived from actual observation, during a residence of four years in that republic: including original communications... London, Printed at the Caxton press, by H. Fisher [1823]
Holmes, Isaac.

LAC 40012

An account of Virginia, its scituation, temperature, productions, inhabitants and their manner of planting and ordering tobacco &c. Communicated by Mr. Thomas Glover an ingenious chirurgion that hath lived some years in that country. Oxford, Reprinted from the Philosophical transactions of the Royal society, June 20, 1676 [by H. Hart, printer to the University] and sold by B. H. Blackwell, 1904.
Glover, Thomas, *fl.* 1676.

LAC 40012

An account, shewing the progress of the colony of Georgia in America, from it's first establishment. Pub. per order of the honorable the trustees. London, 1741; Maryland: Reprinted and sold by Jonas Green, at his printing-office, in Annapolis, 1742. [Washington, P. Force, 1835]
Georgia *(Colony)* Trustees for Establishing the Colony of Georgia in America.

LAC 13387

The acquisition of political, social and industrial rights of man in America. Cleveland, The Imperial press, 1903.
McMaster, John Bach, 1852–1932.

LAC 13295

Across America and Asia. Notes of a five years' journey around the world, and of residence in Arizona, Japan, and China. 5th ed., rev. New York, Leypoldt & Holt, 1871, [c1870]
Pumpelly, Raphael, 1837–1923.

LAC 13683

Across America: or, The great West and the Pacific coast. New York, Sheldon & company, 1874.
Rusling, James Fowler, 1834–1918.

LAC 16447

Across Russia, from the Baltic to the Danube. New York, C. Scribner's sons, 1892, [c1891]
Stoddard, Charles Augustus, 1833–1920.

LAC 13149

Across the continent: a summer's journey to the Rocky mountains, the Mormons, and the Pacific states, with Speaker Colfax. Springfield, Mass., S. Bowles & company; New York, Hurd & Houghton, 1866.
Bowles, Samuel, 1826–1878.

LAC 40072

Across the continent in 1865, as told in the diary of the late Colonel Henry McCormick. Harrisburg, Pa., Printed for private distribution, the Patriot company, 1937.
McCormick, Henry, 1831–1900.

LAC 13222

Across the plains and over the divide; a mule train journey from East to West in 1862, and incidents connected therewith. With map and illustrations. New York, Argosy-Antiquarian, 1964.
Hewitt, Randall Henry, 1840–

LAC 13319

Across the plains, with other memories and essays. New York, C. Scribner's sons, 1899, [c1892]
Stevenson, Robert Louis, 1850–1894.

LAC 16358

Active service; a novel. New York, International association of newspapers and authors, 1901.
Crane, Stephen, 1871–1900.

LAC 40041

Activities and publications. New York city, Dept. of surveys and exhibits [1915]
Russell Sage Foundation, *New York. Dept. of Surveys and Exhibits.*

LAC 10253

Acts and resolutions of the second session of the Provisional congress of the Confederate states, held at Montgomery, Ala. Richmond, Enquirer book and job press, by Tyler, Wise, Allegre & Smith, 1861.
Confederate States of America. *Laws, statutes, etc.*

LAC 12876

Acts of the anti-slavery apostles. Concord, N. H. [Clague, Wegman, Schlict, & co., printers] 1883.
Pillsbury, Parker, 1809–1898.

LAC 20530–35

Acts of the Privy council of England. Colonial series... London [etc.] 1908–1912.
Gt. Brit. *Privy Council.*

LAC 22139

The Adams-Jefferson letters; the complete correspondence between Thomas Jefferson and Abigail and John Adams. Edited by Lester J. Cappon. Chapel Hill, Published for the Institute of Early American History and Culture at Williamsburg, Va., by the University of North Carolina Press [1959]
Adams, John, *pres. U.S.*, 1735–1826.

LAC 16101

Adams's administration.
The history of the administration of John Adams, esq. late president of the United States. New-York printed: 1802.
Wood, John, 1775?–1822.

LAC 40100

An addition, of December 1818, to the memoir, of February and August 1817, on the subject of the cotton culture, the cotton commerce, and the cotton manufacture of the United States... By T. Coxe, of Philadelphia. [Philadelphia? 1818]
Coxe, Tench, 1755–1824.

LAC 40151

An address at the consecration of the National cemetery at Gettysburg, 19th November, 1863. Boston, Little, Brown, 1868.
Everett, Edward, 1794–1865.

LAC 40101

An address before the Society for the promotion of collegiate and theological education at the West, delivered in Tremont temple, Boston, Mass., May 30, 1855. By Rev. Lyman Whiting. Published by order of the directors. [Boston, Press of T. R. Marvin, 1855]
Whiting, Lyman, 1817–1906.

LAC 40021

An address before the Working-Men's Society of Dedham, delivered on the evening of September 7, 1831. Dedham, Mass., L. Powers, 1831.
Whitcomb, Samuel, *Jr.*

LAC 40077

An address, delivered at Springfield, before the Hampden colonization society, July 4th, 1828. Pub. by request of the society. Springfield, Printed by S. Bowles, 1828.
Peabody, William Bourn Oliver, 1799–1847.

LAC 40022

Address delivered at the meeting of the Association of American geologists and naturalists, held in Washington, May, 1844. New Haven, B. L. Hamlen, 1844.
Rogers, Henry Darwin, 1808–1866.

LAC 40008

Address delivered before the Agricultural society of Albemarle, Saturday, November 1st. 1845. Published by the society. Charlottesville, J. Alexander, printer, 1846.
Minor, Franklin, 1812–1867.

LAC 40032

An address delivered before the American dairymen's association, at Utica, N. Y., on Wednesday, January 10th, 1872... Condensed milk manufacture. [n.p., n.d.]
Willard, Xerxes Addison, 1820–1882.

LAC 40120

An address delivered before the Essex agricultural society, at the agricultural exhibition in Topsfield, Oct. 2, 1822. By Peter Eaton, D. D., of Boxford. Salem, Printed for the Society by J. D. and T. C. Cushing, jr., 1823.
Eaton, Peter, 1765–1848.

LAC 40021

Address delivered before the General trades' union of the city of New-York, at the Chatham-street chapel, Monday, December 2, 1833. By Ely Moore, president of the union. New-York, J. Ormond, printer [c1833]
Moore, Ely, 1798–1861.

LAC 12589

Address delivered on the centennial anniversary of the birth of Alexander von Humboldt, under auspices of the Boston society of natural history. With an account of the evening reception. Boston, Boston society of natural history, 1869.
Agassiz, Louis, 1807–1873.

LAC 40076

Address illustrative of the nature and power of the slave states, and the duties of the free states; delivered at the request of the inhabitants of the town of Quincy, Mass., on Thursday, June 5, 1856. Altered and enl. since delivery. Boston, Ticknor and Fields, 1856.
Quincy, Josiah, 1772–1864.

LAC 40043

Address of Charles Gayarre, to the people of the state, on the late frauds perpetrated at the election held on the 7th November, 1853, in the city of New Orleans. New Orleans [La.] Printed by Sherman & Wharton, 1853.
Gayarre, Charles Etienne Arthur, 1805–1895.

LAC 40019

Address of Edward Atkinson of Boston, Massachusetts, given in Atlanta, Georgia, in October, 1880, for the promotion of an international cotton exhibition. Boston, A. Williams and company, 1881.
Atkinson, Edward, 1827–1905.

LAC 40131

Address of Rufus B. Bullock to the people of Georgia. A review of the revolutionary proceedings of the late repudiating legislature. The slanders and misrepresentations of the committees exposed. A Republican administration contrasted with the corrupt and reckless action of the present usurping minority, under the lead of General Toombs. [n. p.] 1872.
Bullock, Rufus Brown, 1834–1907.

LAC 40086

Address of the National Labor Union, to the people of the United States, on money, land, and other subjects of national importance. Washington, McGill & Witherow, 1870.
National Labor Union.

LAC 40138

Address of the president of the New-Jersey society, for promoting the abolition of slavery, to the general meeting at Trenton, on Wednesday the 26th of September, 1804... Trenton, Printed by Sherman and Mershon, 1804.
New-Jersey Society for Promoting the Abolition of Slavery.

LAC 40033

Address of the trustees of the University of Maryland to the public. [n.p., 1830]
Maryland. University (1812–1920)

LAC 40004

Address on agricultural education, delivered before the N. Y. state agricultural society, at Albany, February 10, 1869. Published by the society. Albany, Printing house of C. Van Benthuysen & sons, 1869.
White, Andrew Dickson, 1832–1918.

LAC 40017

Address on civil government: delivered before the New York typographical society, February 25th, 1847. At the Society library lecture room. New-York, Printed by B. R. Barlow, 1847.
Moore, Ely, 1798–1861.

LAC 40047

An address on music; delivered before the Handel society, Dartmouth college, August, 1809. On occasion of their anniversary. Hanover, (N. H.) Printed by Charles and William S. Spear, 1810.
Brown, Francis, 1784–1820.

LAC 40028

An address on pauperism, its extent, causes, and the best means of prevention; delivered at the church in Bowdoin square, February 4, 1844. Pub. by the Society for the prevention of pauperism. Boston, C. C. Little and J. Brown, 1844.
Waterston, Robert Cassie, 1812–1893.

LAC 40152

An address, on the abolition of the slave-trade, delivered before the different African benevolent societies, on the 1st of January, 1816. Philadelphia, T. S. Manning, 1816.
Parrott, Russell, 1791–1824.

LAC 40048

Address on the government control of corporations and combinations of capital, by Charles G. Washburn, before the Economic club of Springfield, Massachusetts, Thursday, November 16, 1911. [Worcester? Mass., 1911]
Washburn, Charles Grenfill, 1857–1928.

LAC 40059

An address on the life and character of John Caldwell Calhoun. Delivered before the citizens of Montgomery, Alabama, on the Fourth July, 1850. Montgomery, Advertiser and gazette print, 1850.
Yancey, William Lowndes, 1814–1863.

LAC 40050

An address on the limits of education, read before the Massachusetts institute of technology, November 16, 1865. By Jacob Bigelow, M. D. Boston, E. P. Dutton & company, 1865.
Bigelow, Jacob, 1787–1879.

LAC 40008

An address on the opposite results of exhausting and fertilizing systems of agriculture, read before the South-Carolina institute, at its fourth annual fair, November 18th, 1852. Charleston, Press of Walker and James, 1853.
Ruffin, Edmund, 1794–1865.

LAC 40086

An address on the origin and progress of avarice, and its deleterious effects on human happiness, with a proposed remedy for the countless evils resulting from an inordinate desire for wealth. Delivered before the Union association of working men, in the Town hall, Charlestown, Mass., January 30, 1834. Boston, The author, 1834.
Luther, Seth.

LAC 40094

An address on the remedies for certain defects in American education, delivered before lyceums or institutes for education at Portsmouth and Exeter, N. H., Baltimore and Annapolis, Md. and Washington, D. C. Washington, D. C., W. Greer, printer, 1842.
Woodbury, Levi, 1789–1851.

LAC 12687

Address on the subject of a surveying and exploring expedition to the Pacific ocean and South seas. Delivered in the Hall of representatives on the evening of April 3, 1836. [New York, Harper & brothers, 1841]
Reynolds, Jeremiah N   1799–1858.

LAC 40028

Address on the truth, dignity, power and beauty of the principles of peace, and on the unchristian character and influence of war and the warrior: delivered ... at New Haven ... at the request of the Connecticut peace society ... the 6th of May, 1832. Hartford, Printed by G. F. Olmsted, 1832.
Grimke, Thomas Smith, 1786–1834.

LAC 40121

An address to Christians throughout the world. By a convention of ministers, assembled at Richmond, Va., April, 1863. Philadelphia, 1863.

LAC 40135

An address to farmers... To which is added an appendix, containing the most approved methods for the management and improvement of tillage, mowing and pasture lands; and for the practice of the art of husbandry in general. (Extracted principally from a variety of authors, who have written judiciously on these important subjects.) Salem, J. Dabney, 1796.
Dabney, John, 1752–1819, *comp.*

LAC 40027

An address to persons of fashion, containing some particulars relating to balls: and a few occasional hints concerning play-houses, card-tables, &c. In which is introduced the character of Lucinda... By a gentleman of the University of Oxford. 3d ed., rev., corr., and enl. London, G. Keith, 1761.
Hill, *Sir* Richard, *bart.*, 1732–1808.

LAC 40106

An address to the citizens of Philadelphia, on the great advantages which arise from the trade of the western country to the state of Pennsylvania at large, and to the city of Philadelphia in particular. On the danger of loosing those advantages, and on the means of saving them. By Messrs. Tarascon junr., James Berthoud and co. Philadelphia: Printed for the addressers, 1806. [Lexington, University of Kentucky, 1957]
Tarascon, Berthoud and Co., *firm, merchants, Philadelphia.*

LAC 40144

An address to the clergy of New-England, on their opposition to the rulers of the United States. By a layman. Concord, N. H., Printed by I. and W. R. Hill, 1814.
Plumer, William, 1759–1850.

LAC 40131

An address to the colored people of Georgia. Savannah, "Republican" job office, 1868.
Yulee, Elias.

LAC 11617

An address to the Congress of the United States, on the utility and justice of restrictions upon foreign commerce. With reflections on foreign trade in general, and the future prospects of America. Philadelphia: Published by C. & A. Conrad & co. Chesnut-street. John Binns, printer, 1809.
Brown, Charles Brockden, 1771–1810.

LAC 40099

Address to the inhabitants of New Mexico and California, on the omission by Congress to provide them with territorial governments, and on the social and political evils of slavery. New York, The Am. & for. anti-slavery society, 1849.
American and Foreign Anti-slavery Society.

LAC 40133

An address to the inhabitants of the British settlements on the slavery of the Negroes in America. 2d ed. Philadelphia, Printed and sold by J. Dunlap, 1773.
Rush, Benjamin, 1745–1813.

LAC 40040
An address to the people of England, Scotland, and Ireland, on the present important crisis of affairs. London, Printed by R. Cruttwell, in Bath, for E. and C. Dilly, 1775.
Macaulay, Catharine, 1731–1791.

LAC 40112
Address to the people of Louisiana on the state of parties. New Orleans, Printed by Sherman, Wharton, 1855.
Gayarre, Charles Etienne Arthur, 1805–1895.

LAC 40138
An address to the people of North Carolina, on the evils of slavery. By the friends of liberty and equality... William Swain, printer. Greensborough, N. C., 1830. [New York, N. Muller, printer, 1860]
Manumission Society of North Carolina.

LAC 40008
An address to the people of the United States, on the importance of encouraging agriculture and domestic manufactures... Together with an account of the improvements in sheep at Arlington, the native sheep of Smith's Island, and the plans proposed of extending this valuable race of animals, for the benefit of the country at large. Alexandria, Printed by S. Snowden [1808]
Custis, George Washington Parke, 1781–1857.

LAC 14838
Address to the people of the United States, on the measures pursued by the executive with respect to the batture at New-Orleans: to which are annexed, a full report of the cause tried in the Superior court of the terriry [!] of Orleans: the Memoire of Mr. Derbigny: an examination of the title of the United States: the opinion of counsel thereon: and a number of other documents necessary to a full understanding of this interesting case. New-Orleans:–Printed by Bradford & Anderson, 1808.
Livingston, Edward, 1764–1836.

LAC 40053
An address to the people of the United States, on the policy of maintaining a permanent navy. By an American citizen. Philadelphia, Printed by J. Humphreys for E. Bronson, 1802. Tarrytown, N. Y., Reprinted, W. Abbatt, 1921.

LAC 40111
An address to the people of West Virginia. Bridgewater, Va., The Green Bookman, 1933.
Ruffner, Henry, 1789–1861.

LAC 40088
Address to the students of the National academy of design, at the delivery of the premiums, Monday, the 18th of April, 1831. New-York, Printed by Clayton & Van Norden, 1831.
Dunlap, William, 1766–1839.

LAC 40136
An address to the workingmen of New England, on the state of education, and on the condition of the producing classes in Europe and America. With particular reference to the effect of manufacturing (as now conducted) on the health and happiness of the poor, and on the safety of our republic... Boston, The author, 1832.
Luther, Seth.

LAC 40084
An address upon the wool industry of the United States, delivered at the exhibition of the American institute in the city of New-York. October 5, 1869. New-York, S. W. Green, printer, 1869.
Bigelow, Erastus Brigham, 1814–1879.

LAC 15380
Addresses and essays on subjects of history, education, and government. Boston, Little, Brown, and company, 1900.
Hale, Edward Everett, 1822–1909.

LAC 14220
Addresses and miscellaneous writings. Cambridge, Metcalf and company, printers to the university, 1846.
Haddock, Charles Brickett, 1796–1861.

LAC 16084
Addresses and other papers. Philadelphia and London, W. B. Saunders & company, 1905.
Keen, William Williams, 1837–1932.

LAC 16043
Addresses and papers of Charles Evans Hughes, governor of New York, 1906–1908; with an introduction by Jacob Gould Schurman. New York and London, G. P. Putnam's sons, 1908.
Hughes, Charles Evans, 1862–1948.

LAC 10713
Addresses and papers on life insurance and other subjects. Newark, N. J., The Prudential insurance company of America, 1909.
Dryden, John Fairfield, 1839–1911.

LAC 40033
Addresses at the inauguration of Charles William Eliot as president of Harvard college, Tuesday, October 19, 1869. Cambridge, Sever and Francis, 1869.
Harvard University.

LAC 12518
Addresses on government and citizenship, by Elihu Root, collected and ed. by Robert Bacon and James Brown Scott. Cambridge, Harvard university press; [etc., etc.] 1916.
Root, Elihu, 1845–1937.

LAC 11238
Administration and educational work of American juvenile reform schools. [New York] 1907.
Snedden, David Samuel, 1868–1951.

LAC 15274
Administration of justice in the United States... Philadelphia, American academy of political and social science, 1910.
American Academy of Political and Social Science, *Philadelphia.*

LAC 13095
The administration of the aid-to-mothers law in Illinois, by Edith Abbott and Sophonisba P. Breckinridge. Washington, Govt. print. off., 1921.
Abbott, Edith, 1876–1957.

LAC 15697

The administration of the American revolutionary army. New York [etc.] Longmans, Green, and co., 1904.
Hatch, Louis Clinton, 1872–1931.

LAC 11681

Administration of the college curriculum. Boston, New York [etc.] Houghton Mifflin company [c1911]
Foster, William Trufant, 1879–1950.

LAC 11523

The administration of the colonies. (The 4th ed.) Wherein their rights and constitution are discussed and stated. London, Printed for J. Walter, 1768.
Pownall, Thomas, 1722–1805.

LAC 16853

Admiral Farragut. New York, D. Appleton and company, 1901.
Mahan, Alfred Thayer, 1840–1914.

LAC 16366

An admiral's log; being continued recollections of naval life. New York and London, D. Appleton and company, 1910.
Evans, Robley Dunglison, 1846–1912.

LAC 10594

Admission to college by certificate. New York city, Teachers college, Columbia university, 1912.
Henderson, Joseph Lindsey, 1869–

LAC 21294–95

Adolescence; its psychology and its relations to physiology, anthropology, sociology, sex, crime, religion and education. New York, D. Appleton and company, 1904.
Hall, Granville Stanley, 1844–1924.

LAC 40140

The adulateur; a tragedy, as it is now acted in Upper Servia. Boston: Printed and sold at the New printing-office, near Concert-hall, 1773. Tarrytown, N. Y., Reprinted, W. Abbatt, 1918.
Warren, Mercy, 1728–1814.

LAC 14406

Advance and retreat. Personal experiences in the United States and Confederate States armies. New Orleans, Pub. for the Hood orphan memorial fund, 1880.
Hood, John Bell, 1831–1879.

LAC 40095

Advancement of female education; or, A series of addresses, in favor of establishing at Athens, in Greece, a female seminary, especially designed to instruct female teachers. Published by the ladies of the "Troy society," for the benefit of the proposed institution. Troy [N. Y.] Printed by N. Tuttle, 1833.
Willard, Emma, 1787–1870.

LAC 40119

Advancing social and political organization in the United States. New Haven, Yale University press, 1914.
Sumner, William Graham, 1840–1910.

LAC 16137

Adventures in Mexico and the Rocky Mountains. New York, Harper, 1855.
Ruxton, George Frederick Augustus, 1820–1848.

LAC 14296

Adventures in the Apache country: a tour through Arizona and Sonora, with notes on the silver regions of Nevada. Illustrated by the author. New York, Harper & brothers, 1869.
Browne, John Ross, 1821–1875.

LAC 13249

Adventures in the wilds of North America. By Charles Lanman. Ed. by Charles Richard Weld. London, Longman, Green, Longman, Roberts, & Green, 1862.
Lanman, Charles, 1819–1895.

LAC 15290

The adventures of a blockade runner; or, Trade in time of war. By William Watson. Illustrated by Captain Byng, R. N. London, T. F. Unwin; New York, Macmillan & co., 1893.
Watson, William, of Skelmorlie, Scot.

LAC 13780

The adventures of a roving diplomatist. New York, W. P. Fetridge & co., 1857.
Wikoff, Henry, 1813–1884.

LAC 23458

Adventures of Alonso: containing some striking anecdotes of the present prime minister of Portugal. London, J. Bew, 1775.
Digges, Thomas Atwood, 1741–1821, supposed author.

LAC 16805

The adventures of Giuseppe Pignata, who escaped from the prisons of the inquisition of Rome, translated from the French by Arthur Symons. New York, Sears publishing company, inc. [1931]
Pignata, Giuseppe.

LAC 13303

Adventures of the first settlers on the Oregon or Columbia River; being a narrative of the expedition fitted out by John Jacob Astor to establish the "Pacific Fur Company"; with an account of some of the Indian tribes on the coast of the Pacific. London, Smith, Elder and co., 1849; Cleveland, Arthur H. Clark co., 1904.
Ross, Alexander, 1783–1856.

LAC 11458

The adventures of Uncle Sam, in search after his lost honor. Middletown [Conn.] Printed by S. Richards, 1816.
Fidfaddy, Frederick Augustus, pseud.

LAC 14734

Advice to shepherds and owners of flocks, on the care and management of sheep. Translated from the original French of M. Daubenton, by a gentleman of Boston. To which are added, explanations of the plates, and a table of contents. Boston, J. Belcher, 1811.
Daubenton, Louis Jean Marie, 1716–1799.

LAC 21316
Advice to the privileged orders in the several states of Europe, resulting from the necessity and propriety of a general revolution in the principle of government... London [J. Johnson, 1792]–93.
Barlow, Joel, 1754–1812.

LAC 11308
Advice to young men on their duties and conduct in life. Boston, Phillips, Sampson & co., 1853, [c1847]
Arthur, Timothy Shay, 1809–1885.

LAC 13854
Aequanimitas, with other addresses to medical students, nurses and practitioners of medicine. 3d impression, 2d ed., with three additional addresses. Philadelphia, P. Blakiston's son & co., 1914.
Osler, *Sir* William, *bart.*, 1849–1919.

LAC 40020
Aerial navigation. Washington, Govt. print. off., 1904.
Chanute, Octave, 1832–1910.

LAC 16769
Aesthetics; or, The science of beauty. Boston, Crosby and Ainsworth, 1867, [c1862]
Bascom, John, 1827–1911.

LAC 40102
The affairs of Rhode Island. A discourse delivered in the meeting-house of the First Baptist church, Providence, May 22, 1842. Boston, W. D. Ticknor, 1842.
Wayland, Francis, 1796–1865.

LAC 14544
Afloat on the Ohio.
On the storied Ohio; an historical pilgrimage of a thousand miles in a skiff, from Redstone to Cairo. Being a new and rev. ed. of "Afloat on the Ohio," with new preface, and full-page illustrations from photographs. Chicago, A. C. McClurg & co., 1903.
Thwaites, Reuben Gold, 1853–1913.

LAC 16135
Afoot and alone; a walk from sea to sea by the southern route. Adventures and observations in southern California, New Mexico, Arizona, Texas, etc. Hartford, Conn., Columbian book company, 1872.
Powers, Stephen.

LAC 12828
Africa and the American flag. By Commander Andrew H. Foote. New York, London, D. Appleton & co., 1854.
Foote, Andrew Hull, 1806–1863.

LAC 16246
Africa and the American negro. Addresses and proceedings of the Congress on Africa, held under the auspices of the Stewart missionary foundation for Africa of Gammon theological seminary, in connection with the Cotton states and international exposition, December 13–15, 1895. Edited by Prof. J. W. E. Bowen, secretary of the congress. Atlanta, Gammon theological seminary, 1896.
Congress on Africa, *Atlanta*, 1895.

LAC 40099
African colonization. Washington, American colonization society, 1869.
Roberts, Joseph Jenkins, *pres. of Liberia*, 1809–1876.

LAC 16871
The African preacher. An authentic narrative. Philadelphia, Presbyterian board of publication [c1849]
White, William Spottswood, 1800–1873.

LAC 40138
The African servant; an authentic narrative abridged. With a brief sketch of the life of the author by Rev. John Ayre. New York, American tract society [n.d.]
Richmond, Legh, 1772–1827.

LAC 40132
The African slave trade. A discourse delivered in the city of New-Haven, September 9, 1790, before the Connecticut' society for the promotion of freedom. New-Haven, Printed by T. and S. Green, 1791.
Dana, James, 1735–1812.

LAC 40132
The African slave trade. The secret purpose of the insurgents to revive it. No treaty stipulations against the slave trade to be entered into with the European powers. Judah P. Benjamin's intercepted instructions to L. Q. C. Lamar, styled commissioner, etc. Philadelphia, C. Sherman, 1863.

LAC 13939
Afro-American folk lore; told round cabin fires on the Sea islands of South Carolina. New York, Negro Universities Press [1969]
Christensen, A   M   H.

LAC 16466
The Afro-American press and its editors, by I. Garland Penn. With contributions by Hon. Frederick Douglass, Hon. John R. Lynch [etc.] Springfield, Mass., Willey & co., 1891.
Penn, Irvine Garland, 1867–1930.

LAC 15768
After icebergs with a painter: a summer voyage to Labrador and around Newfoundland. By Rev. Louis L. Noble. New York [etc.] D. Appleton and company, 1862, [c1861]
Noble, Louis Legrand, 1813–1882.

LAC 11529
After the war: a southern tour. May 1, 1865, to May 1, 1866. Cincinnati, New York, Moore, Wilstach & Baldwin; [etc., etc.] 1866.
Reid, Whitelaw, 1837–1912.

LAC 40083
After the war, what? A plea for a league of peace. New York, The Church peace union [1914?]
Fisher, Irving, 1867–1947.

LAC 12888
The aftermath of slavery; a study of the condition and environment of the American negro, by William A. Sinclair, with an introduction by Thomas Wentworth Higginson, LL. D. Boston, Small, Maynard & company, 1905.
Sinclair, William Albert, 1858–

LAC 11116

The age and the Church; being a study of the age, and of the adaptation of the church to its needs. Hartford, Conn., The student publishing co. [c1893]
Stuckenberg, John Henry Wilburn, 1835–1903.

LAC 14457

The age of fable. London, J. M. Dent; New York, E. P. Dutton [1912]
Bulfinch, Thomas, 1796–1867.

LAC 15154

The age of faith. Boston and New York, Houghton, Mifflin and company, 1901, [c1900]
Bradford, Amory Howe, 1846–1911.

LAC 40057

The agricultural activities of the Jews in America. New York, American Jewish committee, 1912.
Robinson, Leonard George, 1875–

LAC 15956

Agricultural depression in the United States. Its causes and remedies. [Ann Arbor, 1897]
Coutts, William Alexander.

LAC 40004

Agricultural education in New York state. Being a statement concerning certain charges made against Cornell university. [Ithaca, N. Y., 1904]
Bailey, Liberty Hyde, 1858–1954.

LAC 13049

Agricultural education in the United States
A history of agricultural education in the United States, 1785–1925. Washington, U. S. Govt. print. off., 1929.
True, Alfred Charles, 1853–1929.

LAC 15952

Agricultural, geological, and descriptive sketches of lower North Carolina, and the similar adjacent lands. Raleigh, Printed at the Institution for the deaf & dumb, & the blind, 1861.
Ruffin, Edmund, 1794–1865.

LAC 40135

Agricultural resources of Georgia. Address before the Cotton Planters Convention of Georgia at Macon, Dec. 13, 1860. Augusta, Ga., Steam Press of Chronicle & Sentinel, 1861.
Jones, Joseph, 1833–1896.

LAC 11753

Agriculture for the common schools. Atlanta, Ga., The Cultivator publishing company, 1903.
Hunnicutt, James Benjamin, 1836–

LAC 20596–97

Agriculture in some of its relations with chemistry. New York, C. Scribner's sons, 1888.
Storer, Francis Humphreys, 1832–1914.

LAC 40135

Agriculture of the United States, an address delivered 14th April, 1841, before the American institute, in New York. New York, H. A. Chapin & co.; Boston, Otis, Broaders & co.; [etc., etc.] 1841.
Colman, Henry, 1785–1849.

LAC 40135

Agriculture of the United States, or, An essay concerning internal improvement & domestic manufactures, shewing their inseperable [!] connection with the business and interests of agriculture... First published in Niles' register, of March 24, 1827. With additions. [n. p., 1827?]
Niles, Hezekiah, 1777–1839.

LAC 13095

Aid-to-mothers law.
The administration of the aid-to-mothers law in Illinois, by Edith Abbott and Sophonisba P. Breckinridge. Washington, Govt. print. off., 1921.
Abbott, Edith, 1876–1957.

LAC 14367

Alaska, and missions on the north Pacific coast. By Rev. Sheldon Jackson. New York, Dodd, Mead & company [c1880]
Jackson, Sheldon, 1834–1909.

LAC 40063

The Alaska purchase and Americo-Canadian relations. Morgantown, W. Va., Department of history and political science, West Virginia university, 1908.
Callahan, James Morton, 1864–

LAC 13101

Albert Brisbane, a mental biography, with a character study by his wife Redelia Brisbane. Boston, Arena, 1893.
Brisbane, Albert, 1809–1890.

LAC 11546

Albert Gallatin. Boston, New York, Houghton, Mifflin and company, 1884.
Stevens, John Austin, 1827–1910.

LAC 11228

Alcohol and the state; a discussion of the problem of law as applied to the liquor traffic. New York, National Temperance Society and Publication House, 1880, [c1877]
Pitman, Robert C.

LAC 15554

Alcuin; a dialogue, by Charles Brockden Brown; a type-facsimile reprint of the first edition, printed in 1798; with an introduction by LeRoy Elwood Kimball and photogravure reproductions of portraits of Charles Brockden Brown and Elihu Hubbard Smith. New Haven, C. & Margaret Rollins, 1935.
Brown, Charles Brockden, 1771–1810.

LAC 14371

Alexander H. Stephens in public and private. With letters and speeches before, during, and since the war. Philadelphia, Chicago, Ill. [etc.] National publishing company [c1866]
Cleveland, Henry.

LAC 12489

Alexander Hamilton. Boston, New York, Houghton, Mifflin and company, 1892.
Lodge, Henry Cabot, 1850–1924.

LAC 11436
Alexander Hamilton; an essay. New Haven, Yale university press; [etc., etc.] 1911.
Culbertson, William Smith, 1884–1966.

LAC 16333
Alexander's bridge. Boston and New York, Houghton Mifflin company, 1912.
Cather, Willa Sibert, 1873–1947.

LAC 20662
The Algerine captive; or, The life and adventures of Doctor Updike Underhill [*pseud.*] six years a prisoner among the Algerines... Walpole, N. H., Printed by D. Carlisle, jr., 1797.
Tyler, Royall, 1757–1826.

LAC 16433
The Alhambra and the Kremlin. The south and the north of Europe. New York, A. D. F. Randolph & company [1873]
Prime, Samuel Irenaeus, 1812–1885.

LAC 12090
Alice of old Vincennes, by Maurice Thompson. Illustrations by F. C. Yohn. Indianapolis, The Bobbs-Merrill company [c1900]
Thompson, Maurice, 1844–1901.

LAC 14865
The alien immigrant. With map and numerous illustrations from authors photographs. London, W. Heinemann; New York, C. Scribner's sons, 1903.
Evans-Gordon, *Sir* William Eden, 1857–

LAC 15509
Aliens or Americans? [By] Howard G. Grose; with introduction by Josiah Strong. New York, Toronto, Young people's missionary movement [c1906]
Grose, Howard Benjamin, 1851–

LAC 13746
All the Republican national conventions from Philadelphia, June 17, 1856. Proceedings, platforms, and candidates... Compiled and edited by Henry H. Smith. Washington, D. C., R. Beall, 1896.
Smith, Henry Harrison, 1842–   *ed.*

LAC 10789
Allan's Lone Star ballads. A collection of southern patriotic songs, made during Confederate times ... Comp. and rev. by Francis D. Allan. Galveston, Tex., J. D. Sawyer, 1874.
Allan, Francis D   *comp.*

LAC 14576
The almshouse, construction and management. New York, Charities publication committee, 1911.
Johnson, Alexander, 1847–

LAC 13312
Along Alaska's great river. A popular account of the travel of the Alaska exploring expediton of 1883, along the great Yukon river, from its source to its mouth, in the British North-west territory, and in the territory of Alaska. New York, Cassell & company, limited [c1885]
Schwatka, Frederick, 1849–1892.

LAC 16820
Alphabetical list of battles, 1754–1900; war of the rebellion, Spanish-American war, Philippine insurrection, and all old wars, with dates; summary of events of the war of the rebellion, 1860–1865; Spanish-American war, Philippine insurrection, 1898–1900; troubles in China, 1900; with other valuable information in regard to the various wars. Compiled from official records by Newton A. Strait. Washington, D. C., 1909.
Strait, Newton Allen, d. 1922, *comp.*

LAC 11094
Amana, the community of true inspiration. Iowa City, Ia., The State historical society of Iowa, 1908.
Shambaugh, Bertha Maud, 1871–

LAC 40084
The Amazon, and the Atlantic slopes of South America. A series of letters published in the National intelligencer and Union newspapers, under the signature of "Inca." Rev. and cor. by the author. Washington, F. Taylor, 1853.
Maury, Matthew Fontaine, 1806–1873.

LAC 12156
America: a four years' residence in the United States and Canada; giving a full and fair description of the country, as it really is, with the manners, customs, & character of the inhabitants; anecdotes of persons and institutions, prices of land and produce, state of agriculture and manufactures. Leeds, Printed for the author by Kemplay and Bolland, 1849.
Brown, William, *of Leeds.*

LAC 13616
America. A sketch of the political, social, and religious character of the United States of North America, in two lectures, delivered at Berlin, with a report read before the German church diet at Frankfort-on-the-Maine, Sept., 1854. By Dr. Philip Schaff. Tr. from the German. New York, C. Scribner, 1855.
Schaff, Philip, 1819–1893.

LAC 14232
America, and American Methodism. By the Rev. Frederick J. Jobson. With prefatory letters by the Rev. Thomas B. Sargent and the Rev. John Hannah. Illustrated from original sketches by the author. New York, Virtue, Emmins, 1857.
Jobson, Frederick James, 1821–1881.

LAC 11318
America and Europe. By Adam G. de Gurowski. New York, D. Appleton and company, 1857.
Gurowski, Adam, *hrabia*, 1805–1866.

LAC 12236
America and her commentators. With a critical sketch of travel in the United States. New York, C. Scribner, 1864.
Tuckerman, Henry Theodore, 1813–1871.

LAC 10366
America and her problems. New York, The Macmillan company, 1915.
Estournelles de Constant, Paul Henri Benjamin, *baron* d', 1852–1924.

LAC 13981

America and her resources; or, A view of the agricultural, commercial, manufacturing, financial, political, literary, moral and religious capacity and character of the American people. London, H. Colburn, 1818.
Bristed, John, 1778–1855.

LAC 10961

America, and the American church. By the Rev. Henry Caswall. London, Printed for J. G. & F. Rivington, 1839.
Caswall, Henry, 1810–1870.

LAC 12191

America by river and rail; or, Notes by the way on the New world and its people. London, J. Nisbet and co., 1856.
Ferguson, William.

LAC 20671–73

America, historical, statistic, and descriptive. London [etc.] Fisher, son, & co. [1841]
Buckingham, James Silk, 1786–1855.

LAC 12124

America in literature. New York and London, Harper & brothers, 1903.
Woodberry, George Edward, 1855–1930.

LAC 10680

America in the East; a glance at our history, prospects, problems, and duties in the Pacific ocean. London, James Clarke and company, 1899.
Griffis, William Elliot, 1843–1928.

LAC 15606

America in the forties; the letters of Ole Munch Raeder, translated and edited by Gunnar J. Malmin. Minneapolis, Pub. for the Norwegian-American historical association by the University of Minnesota press [c1929]
Raeder, Ole Munch, 1815–1895.

LAC 21389–90

America, its realities and resources: comprising important details connected with the present social, political, agricultural, commercial, and financial state of the country, its laws and customs, together with a review of the policy of the United States that led to the war of 1812, and peace of 1814–the "right of search," the Texas and Oregon questions, etc. etc. London, T. C. Newby, 1846.
Wyse, Francis.

LAC 16336

America of the fifties: letters of Fredrika Bremer, selected and edited by Adolph B. Benson. New York, The American-Scandinavian foundation; [etc., etc.] 1924.
Bremer, Fredrika, 1801–1865.

LAC 12258

America of to-morrow, by Abbe Felix Klein. Translated with approval by E. H. Wilkins; introductory note by Professor Charles R. Henderson. Chicago, A. C. McClurg & co., 1911.
Klein, Felix, 1862–1953.

LAC 10676

America: or, A general survey of the political situation of the several powers of the western continent, with conjectures on their future prospects... By a citizen of the United States. Philadelphia, H. C. Carey & I. Lea, 1827.
Everett, Alexander Hill, 1790–1847.

LAC 12217

America, the land of contrasts; a Briton's view of his American kin. [3d ed.] London and New York, J. Lane, 1902.
Muirhead, James Fullarton, 1853–1934.

LAC 11325

America, through the spectacles of an Oriental diplomat. With illustrations from sketches by the author and from photographs. New York, Frederick A. Stokes company [1914]
Wu, T'ing-fang, 1842–1922.

LAC 15254

America vindicated from European theologico-political and infidel aspersions. New York, Morgan & co., 1855.
Vaiden, Thomas J.

LAC 16051

American addresses at the second Hague peace conference delivered by Joseph H. Choate, General Horace Porter, James Brown Scott; ed., with introductory notes, by James Brown Scott. Boston and London, For the International school of peace, Ginn and company, 1910.
Scott, James Brown, 1866–   *ed.*

LAC 12654

American addresses, with a Lecture on the study of biology. New York, D. Appleton and company, 1877.
Huxley, Thomas Henry, 1825–1895.

LAC 10045

The American advertising directory, for manufacturers and dealers in American goods. For the year 1831. New York, Jocelyn, Darling & Co., 1831.

LAC 22223–38

The American almanac and repository of useful knowledge, for ... 1830–61. v. 1–32. Boston, Gray and Bowen; [etc., etc., c1829]–61.

LAC 13848

American and European railway practice in the economical generation of steam ... and in permanent way... New York, D. Van Nostrand; London, S. Low, son & co., 1867, [c1860]
Holley, Alexander Lyman, 1832–1882.

LAC 12155

The American angler's guide. Being a compilation from the works of popular English authors, from Walton to the present time; together with the opinions and practices of the best American anglers: containing every variety of mode adopted in ocean, river, lake and pond fishing; the necessary tackle and baits required; manner of making artificial flies ... By an American angler. New York, Burgess, Stringer & co., 1845.
Brown, John J

LAC 12965
An American anthology, 1787–1900; selections illustrating the editor's critical review of American poetry in the nineteenth century. [6th impression] Boston and New York, Houghton, Mifflin and company [c1900]
Stedman, Edmund Clarence, 1833–1908, *ed.*

LAC 30491–503
American anthropologist. v. 1–18; Jan. 1888–Dec. 1905. Lancaster, Pa. [etc.] American Anthropological Association.

LAC 14291
American antiquities and researches into the origin and history of the red race. New York, Dayton and Saxton; Boston, Saxton and Pierce, 1841.
Bradford, Alexander Warfield, 1815–1867.

LAC 16407
American apprenticeship and industrial education. New York, Columbia university; [etc., etc.] 1921.
Douglas, Paul Howard, 1892–

LAC 23973–93
American archives: consisting of a collection of authentick records, state papers, debates, and letters and other notices of publick affairs, the whole forming a documentary history of the origin and progress of the North American colonies; of the causes and accomplishment of the American revolution; and of the Constitution of government for the United States, to the final ratification thereof. In six series... By Peter Force. Prepared and published under authority of an act of Congress. [Washington, 1837–53]

LAC 14555
American artists. New York, London, C. Scribner's sons, 1923.
Cortissoz, Royal, 1869–1948.

LAC 14743
American bastile. A history of the illegal arrests and imprisonment of American citizens during the late civil war. 5th ed. Philadelphia, Evans, Stoddart & co., 1870.
Marshall, John A.

LAC 10284
American beer; glimpses of its history and description of its manufacture. New York, United States brewers' association, 1909.
Thomann, Gallus.

LAC 23496–502
American bibliography; a chronological dictionary of all books, pamphlets, and periodical publications printed in the United States of America from the genesis of printing in 1639 down to and including the year 1820. With bibliographical and biographical notes. Chicago, Priv. print. for the author by the Blakely Press, 1903–59.
Evans, Charles, 1850–1935.

LAC 20602–3
American biography. By Jeremy Belknap. With additions and notes by F. M. Hubbard. New-York, Harper & brothers, 1843, [c1841]
Belknap, Jeremy, 1744–1798.

LAC 13811
The American bird fancier; considered with reference to the breeding, rearing, feeding, management, and peculiarities of cage and house birds; with remarks on their diseases and remedies; drawn from authentic sources and personal observation. New York, Orange Judd & company [c1850]
Browne, Daniel Jay, *b.* 1804.

LAC 40010
The American birthright and the Philippine pottage. A sermon preached on Thanksgiving day, 1898... New York, Charles Scribner's sons [1898?]
Van Dyke, Henry, 1852–1933.

LAC 14546
American book-plates, a guide to their study with examples; by Charles Dexter Allen. With a bibliography by Eben Newell Hewins. Illustrated with many reproductions of rare and interesting book-plates... New York [etc.] Macmillan and co., 1894.
Allen, Charles Dexter, 1865–1926.

LAC 16287
American campaigns. Washington, B. S. Adams, 1909.
Steele, Matthew Forney, 1861–1953.

LAC 40150
American caricatures pertaining to the civil war; reproduced from the original lithographs published from 1856–1872, with introduction. New York, Brentano's, 1918.

LAC 10001
American cattle: their history, breeding and management. New York, Taintor brothers & co., 1868.
Allen, Lewis Falley, 1800–1890.

LAC 13118
American charities, by Amos G. Warner, revised by Mary Roberts Coolidge, with a biographical preface by George Elliott Howard. New York, T. Y. Crowell & company [1908]
Warner, Amos Griswold, 1861–1900.

LAC 23507–15
The American church history series, consisting of a series of denominational histories published under the auspices of the American society of church history; general editors, Rev. Philip Schaff, Rt. Rev. H. C. Potter, Rev. Samuel M. Jackson [and others] [New York, The Christian literature co., 1893–1916]

LAC 14548
American church silver of the seventeenth and eighteenth centuries, with a few pieces of domestic plate, exhibited at the Museum of fine arts, July to December, 1911. Boston, 1911.
Boston. Museum of Fine Arts.

LAC 40144
The American churches, the bulwarks of American slavery. 3d American ed., rev. Concord, P. Pillsbury, 1885.
Birney, James Gillespie, 1792–1857.

LAC 10766

The American city; a problem in democracy. New York, The Macmillan company; London, Macmillan and co., ltd., 1911, [c1904]
Wilcox, Delos Franklin, 1873–1928.

LAC 10406

The American coast pilot; containing the courses and distances between the principal harbours, capes and headlands, from Passamaquoddy through the Gulph of Florida, with directions for sailing into the same ... together with the courses and distances from Cape-Cod and Cape-Ann to Georges'-Bank ... with the latitudes and longitudes of the principal harbours on the coast. Together with a tide table. By Captain Lawrence Furlong. Cor. and improved by the most experienced pilots in the United States. 2d ed., largely improved... Newburyport, Mass., Printed by E. M. Blunt, 1798.

LAC 11662

American college athletics, by Howard J. Savage and Harold W. Bentley, John T. McGovern, Dean F. Smiley, M. D., with a preface by Henry S. Pritchett. New York, The Carnegie foundation for the advancement of teaching, 1929.
Savage, Howard James, 1886–

LAC 16018

The American college; criticism. New York, The Century co., 1908.
Flexner, Abraham, 1866–1959.

LAC 15993

The American colleges and the American public. New York, C. Scribner's sons [1878]
Porter, Noah, 1811–1892.

LAC 12747

The American colonial charter, a study of English administration in relation thereto, chiefly after 1688.
Kellogg, Louise Phelps, d. 1942.

LAC 15103

American colonial history illustrated by contemporary medals; by the late C. Wyllys Betts. Edited, with notes, by William T. R. Marvin and Lyman Haynes Low. New York, Scott stamp and coin company, l'd, 1894.
Betts, Charles Wyllys, 1845–1887.

LAC 21251–53

The American colonies in the eighteenth century. New York, Columbia university press, 1924.
Osgood, Herbert Levi, 1855–1918.

LAC 13478

American commercial legislation before 1789. [Philadelphia] University of Pennsylvania; New York, D. Appleton and company, agents, 1910.
Giesecke, Albert Anthony.

LAC 20112–14

The American commonwealth. London and New York, Macmillan and co., 1888.
Bryce, James Bryce, *viscount*, 1838–1922.

LAC 15711

American communities. Rev. ed., enl. to include additional societies, new and old, communistic, semi-communistic and cooperative. Chicago, C. H. Kerr & co., 1902.
Hinds, William Alfred, 1833–

LAC 22782–83

The American conflict: a history of the great rebellion in the United States of America, 1860–['65]: its causes, incidents, and results: intended to exhibit especially its moral and political phases, with the drift and progress of American opinion respecting human slavery from 1776 to the close of the war for the union. Hartford, O. D. Case & company; Chicago, G. & C. W. Sherwood, 1866, [c1864–66]
Greeley, Horace, 1811–1872.

LAC 10432

American contributions to civilization and other essays and addresses. New York, The Century co., 1897.
Eliot, Charles William, 1834–

LAC 14522

The American cotton industry; a study of work and workers, contributed to the Manchester guardian, by T. M. Young, with an introduction by Elijah Helm. New York, C. Scribner's sons, 1903.
Young, Thomas M.

LAC 10008

The American cotton spinner and managers' and carders' guide: a practical treatise on cotton spinning... Comp. from the papers of the late Robert H. Baird. Boston, Otis Perrin, 1854, [c1851]
Baird, Robert H.

LAC 23320

American criminal trials. Boston, T. H. Carter, 1844.
Chandler, Peleg Whitman, 1816–1889.

LAC 21957

The American crisis; or, Pages from the note-book of a state agent during the civil war. London, Saunders, Otley and co., 1867.
Peyton, John Lewis, 1824–1896.

LAC 40032

American dairying; its rise, progress, and national importance. Washington, Govt. print. off., 1866.
Willard, Xerxes Addison, 1820–1882.

LAC 10020

The American democrat; or, Hints on the social and civic relations of the United States of America. Cooperstown [N. Y.] H. & E. Phinney, 1838.
Cooper, James Fenimore, 1789–1851.

LAC 20664–65

An American dictionary of the English language: intended to exhibit, I. The origin, affinities and primary signification of English words, as far as they have been ascertained. II. The genuine orthography and pronunciation of words, according to general usage, or to just principles of analogy. III. Accurate and discriminating definitions, with numerous authorities and illustrations. To which are prefixed, an introductory dissertation on the origin, history and connection of the languages of Western Asia and of Europe, and a concise grammar of the English language. New York, S. Converse, 1828.
Webster, Noah, 1758–1843.

LAC 10208
American diplomacy and the furtherance of commerce. New York, C. Scribner's sons, 1886.
Schuyler, Eugene, 1840–1890.

LAC 13771
American diplomacy under Tyler and Polk. Baltimore, The Johns Hopkins press, 1907.
Reeves, Jesse Siddall, 1872–

LAC 10686
American diplomatic questions. New York, The Macmillan company; London, Macmillan & co., ltd., 1901.
Henderson, John Brooks, 1870–1923.

LAC 15365
The American doctrine of judicial supremacy. New York, The Macmillan company, 1914.
Haines, Charles Grove, 1879–1948.

LAC 40001
The American dollar; and the Anglo-German combination to make gold dearer. Richmond, Va., West, Johnston & co., 1885.
Hughes, Robert William, 1821–1901.

LAC 40128
The American driven well and Cowing & co.'s pumps, with a sketch of the well, description of the pumps, instructions to well drivers, price list, &c., &c. Manufactured at Seneca Falls, New York ... 1868. [New York, Bradstreet press, 1868]
Cowing & Co.

LAC 14226
American ecclesiastical law: the law of religious societies, church government and creeds, disturbing religious meetings, and the law of burial grounds in the United States. With practical forms. Albany, W. Gould, 1866.
Tyler, Ransom Hebbard, 1813–1881.

LAC 10589
American education, by Andrew S. Draper with an introduction by Nicholas Murray Butler. Boston, New York [etc.] Houghton Mifflin company [1909]
Draper, Andrew Sloan, 1848–1913.

LAC 14678
American education; or, Strictures on the nature, necessity, & practicability of a system of national education, suited to the United States. By Rev. Benjamin O. Peers. With an introductory letter by Francis L. Hawks, D. D. New-York, J. S. Taylor, 1838.
Peers, Benjamin Orrs, 1800–1842.

LAC 12689
American encyclopaedia of printing. Ed. by J. Luther Ringwalt. Philadelphia, Menamin & Ringwalt [etc.] 1871.
Ringwalt, John Luther, *ed*.

LAC 15832
American engineering, illustrated by large and detailed engravings embracing various branches of mechanical art, stationary, marine, river boat, screw propeller, locomotive, pumping and steam fire engines, rolling and sugar mills, tools, and iron bridges, of the newest and most approved construction. New York, 1861.
Weissenborn, Gustavus.

LAC 15352
American engravers and their works. Philadelphia, Gebbie & Barrie, 1875.
Baker, William Spohn, 1824–1897.

LAC 20919
American entomology, or Descriptions of the insects of North America. Illustrated by coloured figures from original drawings executed from nature. [Philadelphia] Philadelphia museum, S. A. Mitchell, 1824–28.
Say, Thomas, 1787–1834.

LAC 13801
American factories and their female operatives; with an appeal on behalf of the British factory population... By the Rev. William Scoresby. From the London ed. Boston, Ticknor, 1845.
Scoresby, William, 1789–1857.

LAC 10003
The American farm book; or, Compend of American agriculture... New York, Orange Judd & co. [1849]
Allen, Richard Lamb, 1803–1869.

LAC 12464
American farming and food. London, Longmans, Green and co., 1881.
Dun, Finlay.

LAC 10099
American farms; their condition and future. 2d ed. New York, & London, G. P. Putnam's sons, 1890.
Elliott, James Rupert.

LAC 40024
The American fast freight system.
Theory and practice of the American system of through fast freight transportation, as illustrated in the operations of the Empire transportation company. Philadelphia, Press of Helfenstein, Lewis & Greene, 1876.
Empire Transportation Company, *Philadelphia*.

LAC 40021
The American federation of labor. New York, Pub. for the American economic association by the Macmillan company; London, S. Sonnenschein & co., 1898.
Aldrich, Morton Arnold, 1874–

LAC 14293
American fights and fighters; stories of the first five wars of the United States, from the war of the revolution to the war of 1812. New York, McClure, Phillips & co., 1900.
Brady, Cyrus Townsend, 1861–

LAC 10141
American finance, with chapters on money and banking. New York, The American banker, 1901.
Bolles, Albert Sidney, 1846–1939.

LAC 12159
American football. With thirty-one portraits. New York, Harper & brothers, 1892, [c1891]
Camp, Walter Chauncey, 1859–1925.

LAC 12167
The American frugal housewife, dedicated to those who are not ashamed of economy. 30th ed., enl. and cor. by the author. New-York, Samuel S. & William Wood, 1844, [c1835]
Child, Lydia Maria, 1802–1880.

LAC 14742
The American fruit culturist, containing practical directions for the propagation and culture of fruit trees in the nursery, orchard, and garden. With descriptions of the principal American and foreign varieties cultivated in the United States. Illustrated with four hundred and eighty accurate figures. New York, W. Wood & co., 1867.
Thomas, John Jacobs, 1810–1895.

LAC 16243
The American fugitive in Europe; sketches of places and people abroad. With a memoir of the author. New York, Negro Universities Press [1969]
Brown, William Wells, 1815–1884.

LAC 21112–13
The American fur trade of the far West; a history of the pioneer trading posts and early fur companies of the Missouri valley and the Rocky mountains and of the overland commerce with Santa Fe... New York, F. P. Harper, 1902.
Chittenden, Hiram Martin, 1858–1917.

LAC 16010
The American gardener; or, A treatise on the situation, soil, fencing and laying-out of gardens; on the making and managing of hot-beds and green-houses; and on the propagation and cultivation of the several sorts of vegetables, herbs, fruits and flowers. Claremont, N. H. Manufacturing company, Simeon Ide, Ag't. [1819]
Cobbett, William, 1763–1835.

LAC 15885
An American garland, being a collection of ballads relating to America, 1563–1759; ed. with introduction and notes by C. H. Firth. Oxford, B. H. Blackwell, 1915.
Firth, Charles Harding, 1857–1936, ed.

LAC 12216
The American gazetteer, exhibiting, in alphabetical order, a much more full and accurate account than has been given, of the states, provinces, counties, cities, towns ... on the American continent, also of the West India islands, and other islands appendant to the continent, and those newly discovered in the Pacific ocean ... with a particular description of the Georgia western territory... Collected and comp. ... by, and under the direction of Jedidiah Morse. 2d ed., cor., illustrated with seven new and improved maps. To which are added, facts and calculations respecting the population and territory of the United States of America... Printed in Boston, New England; London, Reprinted for J. Stockdale [etc.] 1798.
Morse, Jedidiah, 1761–1826, comp.

LAC 40014
American general education; a short study of its present condition and needs. Princeton, Princeton university press, 1932.
West, Andrew Fleming.

LAC 20653–54
An American glossary, being an attempt to illustrate certain Americanisms upon historical principles. London, Francis & co., 1912.
Thornton, Richard Hopwood, 1845–1925.

LAC 14724
The American government, national and state. New and rev. ed. Chicago, New York, Werner school book company [c1895]
Hinsdale, Burke Aaron, 1837–1900.

LAC 10116
American grape growing and wine making. New and enl. ed. With several added chapters on the grape industries of California. New York, Orange Judd company, 1888, [c1883]
Husmann, George, 1827–1902.

LAC 14294
American hero-myths. A study in the native religions of the western continent. Philadelphia, H. C. Watts & co., 1882.
Brinton, Daniel Garrison, 1837–1899.

LAC 10182
American highways; a popular account of their conditions, and of the means by which they may be bettered. New York, The Century co., 1896.
Shaler, Nathaniel Southgate, 1841–1906.

LAC 22771–72
American history told by contemporaries... New York, Macmillan, 1906–1917.
Hart, Albert Bushnell, 1854–   ed.

LAC 40088
American houses: a variety of original designs for rural buildings. Illustrated by twenty-six colored engravings, with descriptive references. Philadelphia, The Author, 1861.
Sloan, Samuel, 1815–1884.

LAC 23553
American husbandry; being a series of essays on agriculture. Comp. principally from "The Cultivator" and "The Genesee farmer." With additions by Willis Gaylord and Luther Tucker. New York, Harper & brothers, 1840.
Gaylord, Willis, 1792–1844.

LAC 12022
American ideas for English readers, by James Russell Lowell; with introduction by Henry Stone. Boston, J. G. Cupples co. [c1892]
Lowell, James Russell, 1819–1891.

LAC 16911
An American in Iceland. An account of its scenery, people, and history. With a description of its millennial celebration in August, 1874; with notes on the Orkney, Shetland, and Faroe islands, and the great eruption of 1875. Boston, Lockwood, Brooks, and company, 1876.
Kneeland, Samuel, 1821–1888.

LAC 20704
The American in Paris. Philadelphia, Carey & Hart, 1839.
Sanderson, John, 1783–1844.

LAC 13870
The American Indian as a product of environment, with special reference to the Pueblos. Boston, Little, Brown, and company, 1907.
Fynn, Arthur John, 1857–1930.

LAC 13946
The American Indian (Uh-nish-in-na-ba)... Chicago, The Mas-sin-na-gan company, 1888.
Haines, Elijah Middlebrook, 1822–1889.

LAC 10793
The American Indians and their music. New York, The Womans press [c1926]
Densmore, Frances, 1867–1957.

LAC 11606
American industrial conditions and competition; reports of the commissioners appointed by the British iron trade association, to enquire into the iron, steel, and allied industries of the United States. Ed. by J. Stephen Jeans. London, The British iron trade association, 1902.
British Iron Trade Association.

LAC 16003
The American Irish and their influence on Irish politics. London, K. Paul, Trench & co., 1882.
Bagenal, Philip Henry Dudley, 1850–

LAC 16662
American irrigation farming; a systematic and practical treatment of every phase of irrigation farming, including its history, with statistical tables and formulas. Chicago, A. C. McClurg & co., 1913.
Olin, Walter Herbert, 1862–

LAC 15510
The American Japanese problem; a study of the racial relations of the East and West. New York, C. Scribner's sons, 1914.
Gulick, Sidney Lewis, 1860–1945.

LAC 14844
American-Japanese relations; an inside view of Japan's policies and purposes. New York, Chicago [etc.] Fleming H. Revell company [c1912]
Kawakami, Kiyoshi Karl, 1875–1949.

LAC 11307
The American jest book, being a chaste collection of anecdotes, bon mots, and epigrams, original and selected, for the amusement of the young and old of both sexes. Philadelphia, Hogan and Thompson, 1833.

LAC 16293
The American Jew; an expose of his career... New York, The Minerva publishing company [c1888]
Timayenis, Telemachus Thomas, 1853–

LAC 14335
The American Jew as patriot, soldier and citizen, by Simon Wolf; ed. by Louis Edward Levy. Philadelphia, The Levytype company; New York [etc.] Brentano's, 1895.
Wolf, Simon, 1836–1923.

LAC 15358
The American Joe Miller: a collection of Yankee wit and humour. Compiled by Robert Kempt. London, Adams and Francis, 1865.

LAC 30252–56
American Journal, and Annals of Education and Instruction.
American Journal of Education. v. 1–4, Jan. 1826-Dec. 1829; new ser. v. 1, Jan.-Dec. 1830. Boston, Wait, Greene, and Co., 1826–1830.

LAC 30252–56
American Journal of Education. v. 1–4, Jan. 1826-Dec. 1829; new ser. v. 1, Jan.-Dec. 1830. Boston, Wait, Greene, and Co., 1826–1830.

LAC 30894–928
The American journal of education. Ed. by Henry Barnard, LL. D. v. 1–32; Aug. 1855–1882. Hartford, F. C. Brownell; [etc., etc.] 1856–82.

LAC 16703
American journey.
Moreau de St. Mery's American journey (1793–1798) translated and edited by Kenneth Roberts and Anna M. Roberts. Preface by Kenneth Roberts. Introduction by Stewart L. Mims. Frontispiece painting by James Bingham. Garden City, N. Y., Doubleday & company, inc., 1947.
Moreau de Saint-Mery, Mederic Louis Elie, 1750–1819.

LAC 11384
The American judiciary. New York, The Century co., 1905.
Baldwin, Simeon Eben, 1840–1927.

LAC 10104
The American kitchen gardener; containing practical directions for the culture of vegetables. Also, garden fruits, strawberry, raspberry, gooseberry, currants, melons, &c., &c. Rev. from the 35th ed., and adapted to the use of families, by a practical gardener. New York, C. M. Saxton, 1852.
Fessenden, Thomas Green, 1771–1837.

LAC 13893
American labor; its great wrongs, and how it can redress them, and obtain for itself great and lasting prosperity; restore harmony to the country and purity to the government. St. Joseph, Mo., Steam printing co., 1877.
Warren, Marvin.

LAC 40055
The American landscape, no. 1. Containing the following views: Weehawken, Catskill mountains, Fort Putnam, Delaware water-gap, falls of the Sawkill, Winnipiseogee lake. Engraved from original and accurate drawings; executed from nature expressly for this work, and from well authenticated pictures; with historical and topographical illustrations. New-York, E. Bliss, 1830.
Bryant, William Cullen, 1794–1878.

LAC 30889–93
The American Law Journal. By John E. Hall, esq. v. 1–6 (no. 1–24); 1808–17. Philadelphia, W. P. Farrand and co.; Boston, Farrand, Mallory and co.; [etc., etc.] 1808–17.

LAC 30889–93
The American Law Journal and Miscellaneous Repertory.
The American Law Journal. By John E. Hall, esq. v. 1–6 (no. 1–24); 1808–17. Philadelphia, W. P. Farrand and co.; Boston, Farrand, Mallory and co.; [etc., etc.] 1808–17.

LAC 40112
American liberty, its sources–its dangers,–and the means of its preservation: an oration, delivered at the Broadway Tabernacle, in New-York, before the Order of United Americans, on the 22nd of February, A. D. 1850, being the 118th anniversary of the birthday of Washington. New-York, B'S Seaman & Dunham, 1850.
Ely, Alfred Brewster, 1817–1872.

LAC 40005
American life.
Uncollected lectures by Ralph Waldo Emerson; reports of lectures on American life and Natural religion, reprinted from the Commonwealth. Edited by Clarence Gohdes. New York, W. E. Rudge, 1932.
Emerson, Ralph Waldo, 1803–1882.

LAC 15901
American life, translated from the French by A. J. Herbertson. Paris, New York, Firmin-Didot & co., 1892.
Rousiers, Paul de, 1857–1934.

LAC 12969
American literature, and other papers, by Edwin Percy Whipple, with introductory note by John Greenleaf Whittier. Boston, Ticknor and company, 1887.
Whipple, Edwin Percy, 1819–1886.

LAC 14466
The American Lutheran church, historically, doctrinally and practically delineated, in several occasional discourses. 4th ed. Springfield [O.] D. Harbaugh, 1852.
Schmucker, Samuel Simon, 1799–1873.

LAC 40123
The American lyceum, or society for the improvement of schools and diffusion of useful knowledge. [Boston, Directors of the Old South work, 1903]
Holbrook, Josiah, 1788–1854.

LAC 10706
American marine; the shipping question in history and politics. Boston and New York, Houghton Mifflin company [c1892]
Bates, William Wallace, 1827–1912.

LAC 14551
American masters of painting; being brief appreciations of some American painters. New York, Doubleday, Page & company, 1902.
Caffin, Charles Henry, 1854–1918.

LAC 20265
American medical botany, being a collection of the native medicinal plants of the United States, containing their botanical history and chemical analysis, and properties and uses in medicine, diet and the arts, with coloured engravings. By Jacob Bigelow, M. D., Rumford professor and lecturer on materia medica and botany in Harvard university. Boston: Published by Cummings and Hilliard, at the Boston bookstore, no. 1, Cornhill. University press.... Hilliard and Metcalf, 1817–20.
Bigelow, Jacob, 1787–1879.

LAC 10319
An American merchant in Europe, Asia, and Australia: series of letters from Java, Singapore, China, Bengal, Egypt, the Holy Land... etc. By Geo. Francis Train. With an introduction by Freeman Hunt. New York, G. P. Putnam & co., 1857.
Train, George Francis, 1829–1904.

LAC 11801
The American merchant marine; its history and romance from 1620 to 1902. New York, C. Scribner's sons, 1902.
Marvin, Winthrop Lippitt, 1863–

LAC 11111
American Methodism.
A compendious history of American Methodism. Abridged from the author's "History of the Methodist Episcopal church." New York, Hunt & Eaton, 1889, [c1867]
Stevens, Abel, 1815–1897.

LAC 14013
The American miller, and millwrights' assistant. A new ed. Revised, with much additional matter. Philadelphia, H. C. Baird; London, Trubner & co., 1862.
Hughes, William Carter.

LAC 15323
American mural painting; a study of the important decorations by distinguished artists in the United States. Boston, Noyes, Platt & company, 1902.
King, Pauline.

LAC 20902–3
American natural history... Part 1.–Mastology. 2d ed. Philadelphia, Key and Mielkie, 1831.
Godman, John Davidson, 1794–1830.

LAC 13065
The American Negro; what he was, what he is, and what he may become; a critical and practical discussion. New York, The Macmillan company; London, Macmillan & co., ltd., 1901.
Thomas, William Hannibal, 1843–

LAC 12600
American nervousness, its causes and consequences, a supplement to Nervous exhaustion (neurasthenia). New York, G. P. Putnam's sons, 1881.
Beard, George Miller, 1839–1883.

LAC 16878
American newspapers, 1821–1936; a union list of files available in the United States and Canada, edited by Winifred Gregory under the auspices of the Bibliographical Society of America. New York, H. W. Wilson Co., 1937.

LAC 20270–71
American orations; studies in American political history, edited with introductions by Alexander Johnston. Re-edited with historical and textual notes by James Albert Woodburn. New York, London, G. P. Putnam's sons [c1896–98]
Johnston, Alexander, 1849–1889, *ed.*

LAC 22901-2
American ornithology; or, The natural history of the birds of the United States. By Alexander Wilson and Charles Lucian Bonaparte. Edited by Robert Jameson. Edinburgh, Constable and co.; [etc., etc.] 1831.
Wilson, Alexander, 1766-1813.

LAC 21150-51
American ornithology; or, The natural history of the birds of the United States: illustrated with plates, engraved and colored from original drawings taken from nature. Philadelphia [etc.] Bradford and Inskeep, 1808-25.
Wilson, Alexander, 1766-1813.

LAC 15125
American painters: with eighty-three examples of their work engraved on wood. New York, D. Appleton, 1879, [c1878]
Sheldon, George William, 1843-1914.

LAC 14107
American pauperism and the abolition of poverty, by Isador Ladoff. With a supplement "Jesus or Mammon," by J. Felix. Chicago, C. H. Kerr & company, 1904.
Ladoff, Isador.

LAC 20023-24
The American petroleum industry... By Raymond Foss Bacon and William Allen Hamor. 1st ed. New York, McGraw-Hill book company, inc.; [etc., etc.] 1916.
Bacon, Raymond Foss, 1880-

LAC 11622
The American pharos, or Light-house guide: founded on official reports received at the Treasury department; also, a general view of the coast, from the St. Lawrence to the Sabine. To which is added an appendix, containing an account of the light houses on the gulf and river St. Lawrence, with sailing directions for the St. Lawrence: founded on official reports from the Trinity board of Quebec, in 1832... Washington, Thompson & Homans, 1832.
Mills, Robert, 1781-1855.

LAC 15770
The American pictorial home book; or, Housekeeper's encyclopedia... For the special use of families and nurses, in city and country; restaurants, boarding houses and hotels. St. Louis, Mo., Historical publishing co., 1883.
Suddoth, Harriet Almaria Baker.

LAC 13480
The American plutocracy, by M. W. Howard. Illustrations by A. A. Cobb. New York, Holland publishing company [c1895]
Howard, Milford Wriarson, 1862-

LAC 15763
American poems, selected and original. vol. I. Litchfield: [Conn.] Printed by Collier and Buel [1793]

LAC 14096
American policy; the Western hemisphere in its relation to the Eastern. New York, C. Scribner's sons, 1914.
Bigelow, John, 1854-1936.

LAC 13980
American political economy; including strictures on the management of the currency and the finances since 1861, with a chart showing the fluctuations in the price of gold. New York, C. Scribner & co., 1870.
Bowen, Francis, 1811-1890.

LAC 10511
American political ideas viewed from the standpoint of universal history: three lectures delivered at the Royal institution of Great Britain in May, 1880. New York, Harper & brothers, 1885.
Fiske, John, 1842-1901.

LAC 11558-59
American politics (non-partisan) from the beginning to date. Embodying a history of all the political parties, with their views and records on all important questions. Great speeches on all great issues, the text of all existing political laws... Also a complete federal blue book... By Hon. Thomas V. Cooper and Hector T. Fenton. Chicago, C. R. Brodix [1882?]
Cooper, Thomas Valentine, 1835-1909.

LAC 16517
American population before the federal census of 1790, by Evarts B. Greene and Virginia D. Harrington. Gloucester, Mass., Peter Smith, 1966, [c1932]
Greene, Evarts Boutell, 1870-1947.

LAC 10782
The American preceptor; being a new selection of lessons for reading and speaking. Designed for the use of schools. 2d ed. Published according to act of Congress. Printed at Boston, by I. Thomas and E. T. Andrews, for the author, 1795.
Bingham, Caleb, 1757-1817, *comp.*

LAC 15065
The American prejudice against color. New York, Arno Press, 1969.
Allen, William G.

LAC 13624
American Presbyterianism; its origin and early history. Together with an appendix of letters and documents, many of which have recently been discovered. New York, C. Scribner's, 1885.
Briggs, Charles Augustus, 1841-1913.

LAC 40005
An American primer, by Walt Whitman, with facsimiles of the original manuscript; ed. by Horace Traubel. Boston, Small, Maynard & company, 1904.
Whitman, Walt, 1819-1892.

LAC 11343
American primitive music, with especial attention to the songs of the Ojibways. New York, Moffat, Yard and company, 1909.
Burton, Frederick Russell, 1861-1909.

LAC 40066
American principles. A review of Works of Fisher Ames, compiled by a number of his friends. First published in the Boston patriot. Boston: Published by Everett and Munroe, 1809.
Adams, John Quincy, *pres. U.S.*, 1767-1848.

LAC 15879
American prose masters: Cooper-Hawthorne-Emerson-Poe-Lowell-Henry James. New York, C. Scribner's sons, 1909.
Brownell, William Crary, 1851-1928.

LAC 40139
American psalmody; or, Titles of books, containing tunes printed in America from 1721-1820. New York, C. F. Heartman, 1917.
Metcalf, Frank Johnson, 1865-1945, *comp.*

LAC 13044
American public schools; history and pedagogics. New York, Cincinnati [etc.] American book company [c1900]
Swett, John, 1830-1913.

LAC 30257-72
The American quarterly review. v. 1-22; Mar. 1827-Dec. 1837. Philadelphia, Carey, Lea & Carey [etc.]

LAC 40040
The American querist: or, Some questions proposed relative to the present disputes between Great Britain, and her American colonies. By a North-American. Printed in North America, in 1774. London, Reprinted for T. Caddel, 1775.
Chandler, Thomas Bradbury, 1726-1790.

LAC 40056
American question... A letter from a calm observer, to a noble lord, on the subject of the late declaration relative to the Orders in council. London, Printed by A. J. Valpy, 1812.

LAC 14295
The American race: a linguistic classification and ethnographic description of the native tribes of North and South America. New York, N. D. C. Hodges, 1891.
Brinton, Daniel Garrison, 1837-1899.

LAC 10300
An American railroad builder. John Murray Forbes. Boston and New York, Houghton Mifflin company, 1911.
Pearson, Henry Greenleaf, 1870–

LAC 10010
American railroad law. Boston, Little, Brown, and company, 1904.
Baldwin, Simeon Eben, 1840-1927.

LAC 11656
American railroads as investments. A handbook for investors in American railroad securities. New-York, G. P. Putnam's sons; [etc., etc.] 1893.
Oss, Salomon Frederik van, 1868–

LAC 11334
American railway guide, and pocket companion for the United States; containing correct tables, for time of starting from all stations, distances, fares, etc. on all the railway lines in the United States, together with a complete railway map; also many principal steamboat and stage lines running in connection with railroads. Charles Cobb, comp. New York, Curran Dinsmore & co., 1851.

LAC 40035
The American rebellion. Some facts and reflections for the consideration of the English people... By an American citizen. London, Beadle and company [c1861]
Victor, Orville James, 1827-1910.

LAC 15246
The American reformed cattle doctor; containing ... information for preserving the health and curing the diseases of oxen, cows, sheep, and swine, with a great variety of original recipes, and valuable information in reference to farm and dairy management... Boston, J. G. Tilton and company, 1851.
Dadd, George H   *b.* 1813.

LAC 14397
American renaissance; a review of domestic architecture, illustrated by ninety-six half-tone plates, by Joy Wheeler Dow, architect. New York, W. T. Comstock, 1904.
Dow, Joy Wheeler.

LAC 30738-47
The American review... v. 1-6, Jan. 1845-Dec. 1847; v. 7-10 (new ser., v. 1-4) Jan. 1848-Dec. 1849. New York, Wiley and Putnam [etc.] 1845-1849.

LAC 40152
The American revolution. [New York, Kraus reprint corporation, 1965]
Osgood, Herbert Levi, 1855-1918.

LAC 13443
The American revolution: a constitutional interpretation. Ithaca, N. Y., Cornell University Press [1966]
McIlwain, Charles, 1871–

LAC 12913
The American revolution, 1776-1783. New York and London, Harper & brothers [c1933]
Van Tyne, Claude Halstead, 1869-1930.

LAC 12176
American scenes and Christian slavery; a recent tour of four thousand miles in the United States. London, J. Snow, 1849.
Davies, Ebenezer, 1808-1882.

LAC 10090
The American settler's guide: a popular exposition of the public land system of the United States of America. 2d ed. Washington, D.C., Pub. by the editor, 1882.
Copp, Henry Norris, 1843-1912.

LAC 15960
The American shepherd: being a history of the sheep, with their breeds, management, and diseases. Illustrated with portraits of different breeds, sheep barns, sheds, &c. With an appendix, embracing upwards of twenty letters from eminent woolgrowers and sheep-fatteners of different states, detailing their respective modes of management. New York, Harper & brothers, 1851, [c1845]
Morrell, Luke A.

LAC 40053
American ships; their past and future, and the question of wood or iron for their construction, reviewed. In two parts. Part I. Chicago, The author, 1870.
Bates, William Wallace, 1827–1912.

LAC 14848
The American Siberia; or, Fourteen years' experience in a southern convict camp. Chicago, Donohue, Henneberry & co. [c1891]
Powell, J   C.

LAC 11774
The American silk grower's guide; or, The art of raising the mulberry and silk, and the system of successive crops in each season. 2d ed., enl. and improved. Boston, Weeks, Jordan & co., 1839.
Kenrick, William, b. 1789.

LAC 10470
The American silk industry and the tariff. Cambridge, Mass., American economic association; [etc., etc.] 1910.
Mason, Frank Richardson.

LAC 12832
The American slave code in theory and practice: its distinctive features shown by its statutes, judicial decisions, and illustrative facts... New-York, American and foreign anti-slavery society, 1853.
Goodell, William, 1792–1878.

LAC 12804
American slavery and colour. London, W. & R. Chambers; New York, Dix and Edwards, 1857.
Chambers, William, 1800–1883.

LAC 20967–70
American slavery and the Negro.
Judicial cases concerning American slavery and the Negro, edited by Helen Tunnicliff Catterall (Mrs. Ralph C. H. Catterall)... Washington, D. C., Carnegie institution of Washington, 1926–37.
Catterall, Helen Honor, 1870–1933, ed.

LAC 10047
American slavery as it is: testimony of a thousand witnesses... New York, American anti-slavery society, 1839.
American anti-slavery society.

LAC 12886
American slavery distinguished from the slavery of English theorists, and justified by the law of nature. By Rev. Samuel Seabury. New York, Mason-brothers, 1861.
Seabury, Samuel, 1801–1872.

LAC 15478
American social and religious conditions. New York, Chicago [etc.] Fleming H. Revell company [c1912]
Stelzle, Charles, 1869–1941.

LAC 14001
American socialism of the present day, by Jessie Wallace Hughan, Ph. D. With an introduction, by John Spargo. New York, John Lane company, 1911.
Hughan, Jessie Wallace, 1875–

LAC 14988
The American spirit. New York, The Century co., 1913.
Straus, Oscar Solomon, 1850–

LAC 15258
American state papers bearing on Sunday legislation. Rev. and enl. ed. Compiled and annotated by William Addison Blakeley. Revised edition edited by Willard Allen Colcord. Foreword by Judge Thomas M. Cooley. Washington, D. C., The Religious liberty association, 1911.
Blakely, William Addison, ed.

LAC 16242
American states, churches, and slavery. By the Rev. J. R. Balme. 3d ed. London, Hamilton, Adams & co., 1864.
Balme, Joshua Rhodes.

LAC 20429–30
American supremacy; the rise and progress of the Latin American republics and their relations to the United States under the Monroe doctrine. New York, Brentano's, 1908.
Crichfield, George Washington, 1862–

LAC 11262
American syndicalism; the I. W. W. New York, The Macmillan company, 1913.
Brooks, John Graham, 1846–1938.

LAC 20851
American tariff controversies in the nineteenth century. Boston and New York, Houghton, Mifflin and company, 1903.
Stanwood, Edward, 1841–1923.

LAC 40129
American textile machinery: its early history, characteristics, contributions to the industry of the world, relations to other industries, and claims for national recognition. Cambridge, University press, John Wilson and son, 1879.
Hayes, John Lord, 1812–1887.

LAC 13544
An American town; a sociological study. New York [The James Kempster printing company] 1906.
Williams, James Mickel, 1876–

LAC 12219
American traits from the point of view of a German. Boston and New York, Houghton, Mifflin and co., 1901.
Munsterberg, Hugo, 1863–1916.

LAC 40105
The American traveller and emigrant's guide, containing a description of the British possessions in North America... Shrewsbury, C. Hulbert, 1817.

LAC 12244
The American traveller: or, Observations on the present state, culture and commerce of the British colonies in America, and the further improvements of which they are capable; with an account of the exports, imports and returns of each colony respectively,–and of the num-

bers of British ships and seamen, merchants, traders and manufacturers employed by all collectively: together with the amount of the revenue arising to Great-Britain therefrom. In a series of letters written originally to the Right Honourable the Earl of ——— By an old and experienced trader. London, Printed for E. and C. Dilly [etc.] 1769.
Cluny, Alexander.

LAC 40056
American treaty.
Observations on the American treaty. First published in "The Sun," under the signature of Decius. London, J. Budd, 1808.
Courtenay, Thomas Peregrine, 1782–1841.

LAC 40003
The American university and the American man: second commencement address, Leland Stanford junior university, May 31, 1893. Palo Alto, Cal., The University, 1893.
Howard, George Elliott, 1849–1928.

LAC 40101
The American university. When shall it be? Where shall it be? What shall it be? An essay. Boston, Ginn, Heath, & co., 1884.
Burgess, John William, 1844–1931.

LAC 40015
The American village, a poem by Philip Freneau, reprinted in facsimile from the original edition published at New York in 1772, with an introduction by Harry Lyman Koopman and Bibliographical data by Victor Hugo Paltsits. Providence, R. I. [Standard printing company] 1906.
Freneau, Philip Morin, 1752–1832.

LAC 20384
American war ballads and lyrics: a collection of the songs and ballads of the colonial wars, the revolution, the war of 1812–15, the war with Mexico, and the civil war. New York and London, G. P. Putnam's sons [c1889]
Eggleston, George Cary, 1839–1911, ed.

LAC 30749-52
The American Whig review... v. 11–16, May 1850–Dec. 1852; (new ser., v. 5–10) New York, 1850–1852.

LAC 12143
The American woman's home: or, Principles of domestic science; being a guide to the formation and maintenance of economical, healthful, beautiful, and Christian homes. By Catharine E. Beecher and Harriet Beecher Stowe. New York, J. B. Ford and company; Boston, H. A. Brown. & co.; [etc., etc.] 1869.
Beecher, Catherine Esther, 1800–1878.

LAC 16832
American women in civic work. With portraits. New York, Dodd, Mead and company, 1915.
Bennett, Helen Christine.

LAC 12036
American writers, a series of papers contributed to Blackwood's magazine (1824–1825) by John Neal; edited with notes and bibliography by Fred Lewis Pattee. Durham, N. C., Duke university press, 1937.
Neal, John, 1793–1876.

LAC 11348
American writers and compilers of sacred music. New York, Cincinnati, The Abingdon press [c1925]
Metcalf, Frank Johnson, 1865–1945.

LAC 12918
The Americanisation of the world, or The trend of the twentieth century... New York [etc.] H. Markley [1902]
Stead, William Thomas, 1849–1912.

LAC 40007
Americanische reiss-beschreibung nach den Caribes Insslen, und Neu-Engelland. Verrichtet und aufgesezt durch Felix-Christian Spori, schnitt- und wund-artzet von Zurich. In verlegung Johann Wilhelm Simlers, und Johann Rudolff Rhanen. Getrukt zu Zurich, bey M. Schauffelbergers sel. erbin. durch J. Bachmann, 1677.
Sporri, Felix Christian.

LAC 15909
Americanism contrasted with foreignism, Romanism, and bogus democracy, in the light of reason, history, and Scripture; in which certain demagogues in Tennessee, and elsewhere, are shown up in their true colors. Nashville, Tenn., Pub. for the author, 1856.
Brownlow, William Gannaway, 1805–1877.

LAC 40052
Americanization. St. Paul, Keller publishing co., 1919.
Aronovici, Carol, 1881–

LAC 15506
The Americanization of Carl Schurz. Chicago, Ill., The University of Chicago press [c1929]
Easum, Chester Verne.

LAC 12218
The Americans, by Hugo Munsterberg, tr. by Edwin B. Holt. New York, McClure, Phillips & co., 1905.
Munsterberg, Hugo, 1863–1916.

LAC 22728-29
The Americans at home; or, Byeways, backwoods, and prairies. Ed. by the author of "Sam Slick." London, Hurst and Blackett, 1854.
Haliburton, Thomas Chandler, 1796–1865.

LAC 12211
The Americans at home: pen and ink sketches of American men, manners, and institutions. Popular ed. —rev. Glasgow, J. S. Marr, 1879.
Macrae, David, 1837–1907.

LAC 16621
Americans in Europe. By one of them. New York, Tait, sons & company [c1893]
Royce, George Monroe, 1850–

LAC 11588
Americans in process; a settlement study by residents and associates of the South End house ... North and west ends, Boston. Boston and New York, Houghton, Mifflin and company, 1902.
Woods, Robert Archey, 1865–1925, ed.

LAC 15906

Americans of 1776. New York, Dodd, Mead and company, 1906.
Schouler, James, 1839–1920.

LAC 13788

Americans of to-day and to-morrow. Philadelphia, Henry Altemus company [c1908]
Beveridge, Albert Jeremiah, 1862–1927.

LAC 10649

America's economic supremacy. New York, The Macmillan company; London, Macmillan & co., ltd., 1900.
Adams, Brooks, 1848–1927.

LAC 12963

America's foreign policy; essays and addresses by Theodore Salisbury Woolsey... New York, The Century co., 1898.
Woolsey, Theodore Salisbury, 1852–1929.

LAC 40027

America's greatest indoor sport.
Two in a bed: America's greatest indoor sport; or, The super-specialist's handbook on bundling with the Pennsylvania Dutch. Harrisburg, Pa., Aurand press [c1930]
Aurand, Ammon Monroe, 1895–

LAC 13617

America's national game; historic facts concerning the beginning, evolution, development and popularity of base ball, with personal reminiscences of its vicissitudes, its victories and its votaries, by Albert G. Spalding; cartoons by Homer C. Davenport. New York, American sports publishing company, 1911.
Spalding, Albert Goodwill, 1850–1915.

LAC 22180–81

America's successful men of affairs. An encyclopedia of contemporaneous biography. [New York] The New York tribune, 1895–96.
Hall, Henry, 1845–   *ed.*

LAC 13399

America's working people. [2d ed.] New York, London and Bombay, Longmans, Green, and co., 1900.
Spahr, Charles Barzillai, 1860–1904.

LAC 40125

Les amities americaines de madame d'Houdetot, d'apres sa correspondance inedite avec Benjamin Franklin et Thomas Jefferson. Paris, E. Champion, 1924.
Chinard, Gilbert, 1881–

LAC 10607

Among country schools. Boston, New York [etc.] Ginn & company [c1906]
Kern, Olly Jasper, 1861–

LAC 14773

Among Jews, sketches by M. Salmonson. With a preface by Dr. Emil G. Hirsch and a copy of an etching by the Danish painter, Carl Bloch (1834–1890) Chicago, Meyer & brother [c1907]
Salmonsen, Morris, 1843–

LAC 16375

Among our sailors. With an appendix containing extracts from the laws and consular regulations governing the United States merchant service. New York, Harper & brothers, 1874.
Jewell, J   Grey.

LAC 15987

Among the cotton thieves. Detroit, The Free press steam book and job printing house, 1867.
Bacon, Edward, 1830–1901.

LAC 14289

Among the Indians. Eight years in the far West, 1858–1866. By Henry A. Boller. Edited by Milo Milton Quaife. Chicago, R. R. Donnelley & sons co., 1959.
Boller, Henry A.

LAC 40003

Analysis of some statistics of collegiate education; a paper read before the Trustees of Columbia college, New York, January 3, 1870, by the president of the college. [New York] Printed for the use of the Trustees [1870]
Barnard, Frederick Augustus Porter, 1809–1889.

LAC 40019

Analysis of the cotton plant and seed, with suggestions as to manures, &c. Columbia, Allen, M'Carter & co.; Charleston, J. Russell, 1848.
Summer, Thomas J.

LAC 40081

An analysis of the social structure of a western town; a specimen study according to Small and Vincent's method. Chicago, The University of Chicago press, 1896.
Dunn, Arthur William, 1868–1927.

LAC 14972

Anarchism: its philosophy and scientific basis as defined by some of its apostles... Chicago, Mrs. A. R. Parsons [c1887]
Parsons, Albert R   1848–1887.

LAC 13400

Anarchist case. Advance sheets of the Illinois reports: comprising pages 1 to 267, inclusive, of volume 122. Issued by Norman L. Freeman, reporter of the Supreme court. November 6, 1887. Springfield, 1887.
Spies, August-Vincent Theodore, 1855–1887, *plaintiff in error.*

LAC 13738

The anarchist's conspiracy; or, The blight of 3770. A true history of the experience of Daniel Hines as a knight of labor. Boston, 1887.
Hines, Thomas R.

LAC 12059

The anatomy of negation. London, Edinburgh, Williams and Norgate, 1886.
Saltus, Edgar Evertson, 1855–1921.

LAC 13420

The Ancient and honorable mechanical company of Baltimore. Organized, September 22d, 1763. Provincial charter, June 26th, 1764. Incorporated by act of assembly, no. 127, 1827... Historical sketch by George W. McCreary. [Baltimore, Md., Kohn & Pollock, 1901]
McCreary, George Washington.

LAC 13126

"The ancient city." A history of Annapolis, in Maryland. 1649–1887. Annapolis Record printing office, 1887.
Riley, Elihu Samuel, 1845–

LAC 40142

Ancient history, or Annals of Kentucky; with a survey of the ancient monuments of North America, and a tabular view of the principal languages and primitive nations of the whole earth. Frankfort, Ky., Printed for the author, 1824.
Rafinesque, Constantine Samuel, 1783–1840.

LAC 14470

Ancient society; or, Researches in the lines of human progress from savagery through barbarism to civilization. Chicago, C. H. Kerr, 1907.
Morgan, Lewis Henry, 1818–1881.

LAC 22175–79

Anderson's Historical and chronological deduction of the origin of commerce, from the earliest accounts. Containing an history of the great commercial interests of the British empire. To which is prefixed, an introduction, exhibiting a view of the ancient and modern state of Europe; of the importance of our colonies; and of the commerce, shipping, manufactures, fisheries, &c. of Great-Britain and Ireland; and their influence on the landed interest. With an appendix, containing the modern politico-commercial geography of the several countries of Europe. Carefully rev., cor., and continued to the year 1789, by Mr. Coombe. Dublin, Printed by P. B. Byrne, 1790.
Anderson, Adam, 1692?–1765.

LAC 40148

Anderson's narrative of a ride to the Rocky mountains in 1834, edited by Albert J. Partoll. [Missoula, Mont., 1938]
Anderson, William Marshall, 1807–1881.

LAC 14487

Andersonville: a story of Rebel military prisons, fifteen months a guest of the so-called southern confederacy. A private soldier's experience in Richmond, Andersonville, Savannah, Millen, Blackshear and Florence. Toledo, D. R. Locke, 1879.
McElroy, John, 1846–1929.

LAC 13646

Andersonville diary, escape, and list of the dead, with name, co., regiment, date of death and no. of grave in cemetery. John L. Ransom, author and publisher. Auburn, N. Y., 1881.
Ransom, John L.

LAC 30509–27

The Andover review; a religious and theological monthly. v. 1–19; 1884–93. Editors, Egbert C. Smyth, William J. Tucker, J. W. Churchill, George Harris, Edward Y. Hincks, professors in Andover theological seminary, with the assistance of their colleagues in the faculty. Boston, New York, Houghton, Mifflin and co., 1884–93.

LAC 10636

Andrew Carnegie: the man and his work. New York, Doubleday, Page & co., 1902.
Alderson, Bernard.

LAC 14176

Andrew Gregg Curtin: his life and services. Ed. by William H. Egle, M. D. Philadelphia, Avil printing company, 1895.
Egle, William Henry, 1830–1901, *ed.*

LAC 12542

Andrew Jackson as a public man: what he was, what chances he had, and what he did with them. Boston, New York, Houghton, Mifflin and company, 1888, [c1882]
Sumner, William Graham, 1840–1910.

LAC 40140

Androboros. A bographical [!] farce in three acts, viz. The senate, The consistory, and The apotheosis. [New York] Printed [by William Bradford] at Monoropolis since August, 1714.
Hunter, Robert, d. 1734.

LAC 40127

Andros records. [Worcester, American ́antiquarian society, 1901]
Toppan, Robert Noxon, 1836–1901.

LAC 23191–92

Anecdotes of painters, engravers, sculptors and architects, and curiosities of art. New York, G. P. Putnam & co., 1853.
Spooner, Shearjashub, 1809–1859.

LAC 20221

Anecdotes of public men. New York, Harper & brothers [c1873–81]
Forney, John Wien, 1817–1881.

LAC 15303

The angels preparing to sound the trumpets.
Manuductio ad ministerium; directions for a candidate of the ministry, by Cotton Mather. Reproduced from the original edition, Boston, 1726, with a bibliographical note by Thomas J. Holmes and Kenneth B. Murdock. New York, Pub. for the Facsimile text society by Columbia university press, 1938.
Mather, Cotton, 1663–1728.

LAC 14021

The Anglican episcopate and the American colonies. New York, London [etc.] Longmans, Green, and co., 1902.
Cross, Arthur Lyon, 1873–1940.

LAC 13932

Anglican humanitarianism in colonial New York. Philadelphia, The Church historical society [c1940]
Klingberg, Frank Joseph, 1883–

LAC 40056

Anglo-American alliance.
The proposed Anglo-American alliance; an address delivered before the American social science association at its annual meeting at Saratoga, August 31st, 1898. New York & London, G. P. Putnam's sons, 1898.
Gardiner, Charles Alexander, 1855–

LAC 14809

Anglo-American memories. London, Duckworth & co., 1911.
Smalley, George Washburn, 1833–1916.

LAC 15283
The Anglo-Saxon century and the unification of the English-speaking people. New York and London, G. P. Putnam's sons, 1903.
Dos Passos, John Randolph, 1844–1917.

LAC 10216
The Angora goat: its origin, culture, and products. Containing the most recent observations of eminent breeders. With an appendix on the Alpaca and its congeners; or, The wool-bearing animals of the cordilleras of the Andes. New York, Orange Judd company, 1882.
Hayes, John Lord, 1812–1887.

LAC 13943
Ann Lee (the founder of the Shakers), a biography, with memoirs of William Lee, James Whittaker, J. Hocknell, J. Meacham, and Lucy Wright; also a compendium of the origin, history, principles, rules, and regulations, government and doctrines of the United society of believers in Christ's second appearing. 4th ed. ... London, J. Burns; Mount Lebanon, New York, F. W. Evans [1869?]
Evans, Frederick William, 1808–1893.

LAC 30848–70
Annals. v. 1–26; July 1890–Dec. 1905. Philadelphia.
American Academy of Political and Social Science, *Philadelphia.*

LAC 10907
Annals, comprising memoirs, incidents and statistics of Harrisburg. From the period of its first settlement. Harrisburg, G. A. Brooks, 1858.
Morgan, George Hallenbrooke, 1828–   *comp.*

LAC 14311
Annals of a fortress. By E. Viollet-Le-Duc. Translated by Benjamin Bucknall. Boston, J. R. Osgood and company, 1876.
Viollet-Le-Duc, Eugene Emmanuel, 1814–1879.

LAC 23844–48
The annals of Albany. Albany, J. Munsell, 1850–59.
Munsell, Joel, 1808–1880.

LAC 20123–24
The annals of America, from the discovery by Columbus in the year 1492, to the year 1826. 2d ed. ... Cambridge, Hilliard and Brown, 1829.
Holmes, Abiel, 1763–1837.

LAC 40009
The annals of Chicago: a lecture delivered before the Chicago lyceum, January 21, 1840. Republished from the original edition of 1840, with an introduction, written by the author in 1876, and also a review of the lecture, published in the Chicago tribune in 1872. Chicago, Fergus printing company, 1876.
Balestier, Joseph Neree.

LAC 13022
Annals of fifty years; a history of Abbot Academy, Andover, Mass., 1829–1879, by Philena McKeen and Phebe F. McKeen. With an introd. by Edwards A. Park. Andover, W. F. Draper, 1880.
McKeen, Philena, *d.* 1898.

LAC 21302–3
Annals of King's chapel from the Puritan age of New England to the present day. Boston, Little, Brown and co., 1882–96.
Foote, Henry Wilder, 1838–1889.

LAC 10803
Annals of music in America; a chronological record of significant musical events, from 1640 to the present day, with comments on the various periods into which the work is divided. Boston, Marshall Jones company, 1922.
Lahee, Henry Charles, 1856–

LAC 10805
Annals of music in Philadelphia and history of the Musical fund society from its organization in 1820 to the year 1858; comp. by Louis C. Madeira, edited by Philip H. Goepp. Philadelphia, J. B. Lippincott company, 1896.
Madeira, Louis Cephas.

LAC 14571
The annals of Newtown, in Queens county, New-York: containing its history from its first settlement, together with many interesting facts concerning the adjacent towns; also, a particular account of numerous Long island families now spread over this and various other states of the Union. By James Riker, jr. New-York, D. Fanshaw, 1852.
Riker, James, 1822–1889.

LAC 11710
Annals of Pennsylvania, from the discovery of the Delaware. 1609–1682. Philadelphia, Hazard & Mitchell, 1850.
Hazard, Samuel, 1784–1870.

LAC 20573–74
Annals of Philadelphia, and Pennsylvania, in the olden time; being a collection of memoirs, anecdotes, and incidents of the city and its inhabitants, and of the earliest settlements of the inland part of Pennsylvania... By John F. Watson. Enlarged, with many revisions and additions, by Willis P. Hazard. Philadelphia, E. S. Stuart, 1884.
Watson, John Fanning, 1779–1860.

LAC 10357
Annals of Portsmouth, comprising a period of two hundred years from the first settlement of the town; with biographical sketches of a few of the most respectable inhabitants. Portsmouth [N. H.] The author, 1825.
Adams, Nathaniel, 1756–1829.

LAC 10800
Annals of St. Louis in its early days under the French and Spanish dominations; comp. by Frederic L. Billon, from authentic data. St. Louis, Printed for the Author, 1886.
Billon, Frederic Louis, 1801–1895.

LAC 10802
Annals of St. Louis in its territorial days, from 1804 to 1821; being a continuation of the author's previous work, the Annals of the French and Spanish period. St. Louis, Printed for the author, 1888.
Billon, Frederic Louis, 1801–1895.

LAC 12381
The annals of Tennessee to the end of the eighteenth century: comprising its settlement, as the Watauga association, from 1769 to 1777; a part of North Carolina, from 1777 to 1784; the state of Franklin, from 1784–1788; a part of North-Carolina, from 1788–1790; the territory of the U. States, south of the Ohio, from 1790 to 1796; the state of Tennessee, from 1796 to 1800. Charleston, J. Russell, 1853.
Ramsey, James Gettys McGready, 1797–1884.

LAC 20468–76
Annals of the American pulpit; or, Commemorative notices of distinguished American clergymen of various denominations, from the early settlement of the country to the close of the year eighteen hundred and fifty-five. With historical introductions. New York, R. Carter and brothers, 1857–[69]
Sprague, William Buell, 1795–1876.

LAC 15627
Annals of the Boston Primary school committee, from its first establishment in 1818, to its dissolution in 1855. Comp. by Joseph M. Wightman. Boston, G. C. Rand & Avery, city printers, 1860.
Wightman, Joseph Milner.

LAC 15350
Annals of the City of Kansas: embracing full details of the trade and commerce of the great western plains, together with statistics of the agricultural, mineral and commercial resources of the country west, south, and south-west, embracing western Missouri, Kansas, the Indian country, and New Mexico. Kansas City, Van Horn & Abeel's printing house, 1858.
Spalding, Charles Carroll.

LAC 21603–45
Annals of the Congress of the United States.
The debates and proceedings in the Congress of the United States; with an appendix, containing important state papers and public documents, and all the laws of a public nature; with a copious index... [First to] Eighteenth Congress.-first session: comprising the period from [March 3, 1789] to May 27, 1824, inclusive. Comp. from authentic materials. Washington, Gales and Seaton, 1834–56.
U.S. *Congress.*

LAC 11107
Annals of the Evangelical association of North America and history of the United Evangelical church... Harrisburg, Pa., Pub. house of the United Evangelical church, 1900, [c1896]
Stapleton, Ammon, 1850–1916.

LAC 14689
Annals of the first African church, in the United States of America, now styled the African Episcopal church of St. Thomas, Philadelphia, in its connection with the early struggles of the colored people to improve their condition, with the co-operation of the Friends, and other philanthropists; partly derived from the minutes of a beneficial society, established by Absalom Jones, Richard Allen and others, in 1787, and partly from the minutes of the aforesaid church. By the Rev. Wm. Douglass, rector. Philadelphia, King & Baird, printers, 1862.
Douglass, William, *of Philadelphia.*

LAC 14101
Annals of the great strikes in the United States. A reliable history and graphic description of the causes and thrilling events of the labor strikes and riots of 1877. By Hon. J. A. Dacus. Chicago, L. T. Palmer & co.; Philadelphia, W. R. Thomas; [etc., etc.] 1877.
Dacus, Joseph A

LAC 10575
Annals of the Redwood library and athenaeum, Newport, R. I. Newport, R. I., Redwood library, 1891.
Mason, George Champlin, 1820–1894.

LAC 16782
Annals of the Swedes on the Delaware, from their first settlement in 1636, to the present time. 2d ed., cor. and enl. Philadelphia, F. Foster, 1858.
Clay, Jehu Curtis, 1792–1863.

LAC 10362
Annals of the town of Providence, from its first settlement, to the organization of the city government, in June, 1832. Providence, Printed by Knowles and Vose, 1843.
Staples, William Read, 1798–1868.

LAC 14228
Annals of the United States Christian commission. By Rev. Lemuel Moss, home secretary to the commission. Philadelphia, J. B. Lippincott & co., 1868.
Moss, Lemuel, 1829–1904.

LAC 14902
The annals of the war written by leading participants north and south. Originally pub. in the Philadelphia weekly times. Philadelphia, The Times publishing company, 1879.

LAC 13288–89
Annals of the West: embracing a concise account of principal events which have occurred in the western states and territories, from the discovery of the Mississippi valley to the year eighteen hundred and fifty-six. Comp. from the most authentic sources, and pub. by James R. Albach. Pittsburgh, W. S. Haven, book and job printer, 1858, [c1856]
Perkins, James Handasyd, 1810–1849.

LAC 13794
Annals of witchcraft in New England, and elsewhere in the United States, from their first settlement. Drawn up from unpublished and other well authenticated records of the alleged operations of witches and their instigator, the devil. Boston, W. E. Woodward, 1869.
Drake, Samuel Gardner, 1798–1875.

LAC 12982
Annals of Yale college, in New Haven, Connecticut, from its foundation, to the year 1831. With an appendix, containing statistical tables, and exhibiting the present condition of the institution. New Haven, H. Howe, 1831.
Baldwin, Ebenezer, d. 1837.

LAC 12995
The annals or history of Yale-college, in New Haven, in the colony of Connecticut, from the first founding thereof, in the year 1700, to the year 1766: with an appendix, containing the present state of the College, the method of instruction and government, with the officers, benefactors, and graduates. New-Haven, Printed for J. Hotchkiss and B. Mecom, 1766.
Clap, Thomas, 1703–1767.

LAC 15665
Annee 1791. Le theatre-francais, a la Nlle Orleans. Essai historique. Annee 1906. [Nouvelle-Orleans, Imprimerie G. Muller, 1906]
Baroncelli, Joseph Gabriel de, 1857–

LAC 40067
The annexation of Hawaii, an address by Hermann Eduard von Holst, delivered before the Commercial club of Chicago at its 140th regular dinner at the Auditorium hotel, January 29, 1898. [Chicago, 1898]
Holst, Hermann Eduard von, 1841–1904.

LAC 40063
The annexation of Mexico the means of paying the national debt. Letter to President Johnson, from Andrew J. Wilcox. [Baltimore? 1865?]
Wilcox, Andrew Jackson, 1835–1870.

LAC 12948
The annexation of Texas. New York, Macmillan, 1919, [c1911]
Smith, Justin Harvey, 1857–1930.

LAC 13835
Annexation, The law and policy of.
The law and policy of annexation, with special reference to the Philippines, together with observations on the status of Cuba. New York [etc.] Longmans, Green, & co., 1901.
Randolph, Carman Fitz, 1856–1920.

LAC 15308
Annie Kilburn, a novel by William D. Howells. New York, Harper & brothers, 1889.
Howells, William Dean, 1837–1920.

LAC 40020
Anniversary address on the progress of the natural sciences in the United States: delivered before the Lyceum of natural history of New York, Feb. 1826. New York, G. & C. Carvill, 1826.
De Kay, James Ellsworth, 1792–1851.

LAC 20705–15
Annual of scientific discovery: or, Year-book of facts in science and art, for [1850]–71, exhibiting the most important discoveries and improvements in mechanics, useful arts, natural philosophy, chemistry, astronomy, geology, biology, botany, mineralogy, meteorology, geography, antiquities, etc., together with notes on the progress of science ... a list of recent scientific publications; obituaries of eminent scientific men, etc. ... Boston, Gould and Lincoln; [etc., etc.] 1850–71.

LAC 12671
Annual of the National academy of sciences for 1863–1864. Cambridge [Mass.] Welch, Bigelow, 1865.
National Academy of Sciences, *Washington, D. C.*

LAC 23337–38
Annual report... 1st–6th; 1834–39. New-York.
American Anti-slavery Society.

LAC 21505–13
Annual report. 1st–15th, 1863–64 to 1877–78. Boston, 1865–79.
Massachusetts. *Board of State Charities.*

LAC 23578–601
Annual report 1891–1906. Washington, Govt. print. off., 1892–1908.
American Historical Association.

LAC 21106
Annual report of the board of managers. 1st, 3d–4th, 13th; 1833, 1835–36, 1845. Boston, 1833–1845.
Massachusetts Anti-slavery Society.

LAC 21886–936
Annual report of the Bureau of American ethnology to the secretary of the Smithsonian institution. 1st–48th; 1879–80 to 1930–31. Washington, Govt. print. off., 1881–1933.
U.S. *Bureau of American Ethnology.*

LAC 21514–46
Annual report of the commissioner of labor. The first–twenty-fifth. March, 1886–1910. Washington, Govt. print. off., 1886–1911.
U.S. *Bureau of Labor.*

LAC 12576
Annual report of the secretary of commerce. 1913. Washington, Govt. print. off., 1913.
U.S. *Dept. of Commerce.*

LAC 16267
Annual reports of the commissioners of emigration of the state of New York, from the organization of the Commission, May 5, 1847, to 1860, inclusive: together with tables and reports, and other official documents. Comp. and prepared under resolution adopted by the Board, August 29, 1860. New York, 1861.
New York *(State) Commissioners of Emigration.*

LAC 16756
Annual reports on education. Boston, Horace B. Fuller, 1868.
Mann, Horace, 1796–1859.

LAC 40060
Answer of Robert F. Stockton in behalf of the joint board of the D. & R. canal and C. & A. R. R. companies, to a committee of the Senate of New Jersey, in relation to surrendering the works of the companies to the state. Read and ordered to be printed. Trenton, Printed at the True American office, 1854.
Stockton, Robert Field, 1795–1866.

LAC 40092
An answer to Alexander Hamilton's Letter, concerning the public conduct and character of John Adams, esq., president of the United States. By a citizen of New-York. New-York: Printed by P. R. Johnson & J. Stryker, at the Literary Printing Office, no. 29 Gold-Street, 1800.
Cheetham, James, 1772–1810.

LAC 40090
Answer to interrogatories in case no. 396, Mary C. Paschal et al., vs. Theodore Evans, District court of McCulloch County, Texas... [Austin, Texas, Pemberton Press] c1894, [1964]
Meusebach, John O.

LAC 40090
An answer to the question what is to be done with the unemployed labourers of the United Kingdom? London, Printed by Stewart and Murray, 1847.
Godley, John Robert.

LAC 13725
The anthracite coal combination in the United States, with some account of the early development of the anthracite industry. Cambridge, Harvard university press [etc., etc.] 1914.
Jones, Eliot, 1887–

LAC 13394
Anthracite coal communities; a study of the demography, the social, educational and moral life of the anthracite regions. New York, The Macmillan company; London, Macmillan & co., ltd., 1904.
Roberts, Peter, 1859–

LAC 11642
The anthracite coal industry; a study of the economic conditions and relations of the co-operative forces in the development of the anthracite coal industry of Pennsylvania, by Peter Roberts, PH. D., with an introduction by W. G. Sumner. New York, The Macmillan company; London, Macmillan & co., ltd., 1901.
Roberts, Peter, 1859–

LAC 12521
Anticipations of the future, to serve as lessons for the present time. In the form of extracts of letters from an English resident in the United States, to the London Times, from 1864 to 1870. With an appendix, on the causes and consequences of the independence of the South... Richmond, J. W. Randolph, 1860.
Ruffin, Edmund, 1794–1865.

LAC 40010
Anti-imperialism. Los Angeles, Public ownership review, 1899.
Swift, Morrison Isaac, 1856–

LAC 13915
Antiqvitates americanae; sive, Scriptores septentrionales rerum ante-columbianarum in America. Samling af de i nordens oldskrifter indeholdte efterretninger om de gamle Nordboers opdagelsesreiser til America fra det 10de til det 14de aarhundrede. Edidit Societas regia antiqvariorum septentrionalium. Hafniae, typis officinae Schultzianae, 1837.
Rafn, Carl Christian.

LAC 40036
Anti-slavery catechism. 2d ed. Newburyport, C. Whipple, 1839.
Child, Lydia Maria, 1802–1880.

LAC 40139
The anti-slavery harp; a collection of songs for anti-slavery meetings. 4th ed. Boston, B. Marsh, 1854.
Brown, William Wells, 1815–1884, *comp.*

LAC 16485
Anti-slavery in America, from the introduction of African slaves to the prohibition of the slave trade, 1619–1808. Gloucester, Mass., P. Smith, 1965, [c1901]
Locke, Mary Stoughton.

LAC 13061
Anti-slavery manual, containing a collection of facts and arguments on American slavery. By Rev. La Roy Sunderland. New-York, S. W. Benedict, 1837.
Sunderland, La Roy, 1802–1885.

LAC 12877
Anti-slavery opinions before the year 1800; read before the Cincinnati literary club, November 16, 1872, by William Frederick Poole, to which is appended a facsimile reprint of Dr. George Buchanan's Oration on the moral and political evil of slavery, delivered at a public meeting of the Maryland society for promoting the abolition of slavery, Baltimore, July 4, 1791. Cincinnati, R. Clarke & co., 1873.
Poole, William Frederick, 1821–1894.

LAC 20979
The anti-slavery papers of James Russell Lowell. Boston and New York, Houghton Mifflin and company, 1902.
Lowell, James Russell, 1819–1891.

LAC 40118
The anti-slavery poems of John Pierpont... Boston, O. Johnson, 1843.
Pierpont, John, 1785–1866.

LAC 15877
The anti-trust act and the Supreme court. New York and London, Harper & brothers, 1914.
Taft, William Howard, *pres. U.S.*, 1857–1930.

LAC 14296
Apache country.
Adventures in the Apache country: a tour through Arizona and Sonora, with notes on the silver regions of Nevada. Illustrated by the author. New York, Harper & brothers, 1869.
Browne, John Ross, 1821–1875.

LAC 15100
Apercu sur la situation politique des Etats-Unis d'Amerique. Par le general Turreau. Paris, F. Didot, 1815.
Turreau de Linieres, Louis Marie, *baron*, 1756–1816.

LAC 13931
Apologetica historia de las Indias, de Fr. Bartolome de las Casas por M. Serrano y Sanz. Madrid, Bailly, Bailliere e hijos, 1909.
Casas, Bartolome de las, *bp. of Chiapa*, 1474–1566.

LAC 16113
An apology for the Bible, in a series of letters, addressed to Thomas Paine, author of a book entitled, The age of reason, part the second, being an investigation of true and of fabulous theology. New-Brunswick [N. J.]: Printed by Abraham Blauvelt, 1796.
Watson, Richard, *bp. of Llandaff*, 1737–1816.

LAC 15110
An apology for the life of James Fennell. Written by himself. Philadelphia, Pub. by Moses Thomas, no. 52, Chestnut-street, J. Maxwell, printer, 1814.
Fennell, James, 1766–1816.

LAC 12959

An appeal from the judgments of Great Britain respecting the United States of America. Part first, containing an historical outline of their merits and wrongs as colonies; and strictures upon the calumnies of the British writers. Philadelphia, Mitchell, Ames, and White, 1819.
Walsh, Robert, 1784–1859.

LAC 40065

An appeal from the new to the old Whigs, in consequence of the Senate's course, and particularly of Mr. Webster's speech upon the executive patronage bill. By a Whig of the old school. Boston, Russell, Ordiorne, and company, 1835.
Adams, Charles Francis, 1807–1886.

LAC 13104

An appeal in favor of that class of Americans called Africans. Boston, Allen and Ticknor, 1833.
Child, Lydia Maria, 1802–1880.

LAC 40083

An appeal in vindication of peace principles, and against resistance by force of arms. A review, in opposition to an address, delivered by the company chaplain, William J. Mullen, at the First Baptist church in Passyunk, Philadelphia, on the occasion of a sword presentation to Lieutenant Fink, Company E, Third regiment, Reserve grays, P. V., June 17th, 1861. Philadelphia, Maas & Vogdes, printers, 1862.
Love, Alfred H.

LAC 12895

An appeal to Caesar. New York, Fords, Howard, & Hulbert, 1884.
Tourgee, Albion Winegar, 1838–1905.

LAC 40107

Appeal to the Christian community on the condition and prospects of the New-York Indians, in answer to a book entitled The case of the New-York Indians, and other publications, of the Society of Friends. By Nathaniel T. Strong, a chief of the Seneca tribe. New York, E. B. Clayton, printer, 1841.
Strong, Nathaniel T.

LAC 40076

Appeal to the Christian women of the South. New York, Arno press, 1969.
Grimke, Angelina Emily, 1805–1879.

LAC 15479

An appeal to the learned, being a vindication of the right of visible saints to the Lords supper... Boston, B. Green, 1709.
Stoddard, Solomon, 1643–1729.

LAC 40139

An appeal to the people of the United States, in behalf of art, artists, and the public weal... New-York [J. J. Reed, printer] 1854.
Spooner, Shearjashub, 1809–1859.

LAC 40136

Appeal to the wealthy of the land, ladies as well as gentlemen, on the character, conduct, situation, and prospects of those whose sole dependence for subsistence is on the labour of their hands. 3d ed., improved. Philadelphia, Stereotyped by L. Johnson, 1833.
Carey, Mathew, 1760–1839.

LAC 40036

An appeal to the women of the nominally free states, issued by an anti-slavery convention of American women. Held by adjournments from the 9th to the 12th of May, 1837... 2d ed. Boston, I. Knapp, 1838.
Anti-slavery Convention of American Women. *1st, New York*, 1837.

LAC 21369–75

Appletons' cyclopaedia of American biography, ed. by James Grant Wilson and John Fiske. New York, D. Appleton, 1894–1900.

LAC 21350–51

Appleton's dictionary of machines, mechanics, engine-work, and engineering... New York, D. Appleton & company, 1852.

LAC 30754–68

Appletons' journal of literature, science and art. v. 2–15, Aug. 1869–June 1876; new ser. v. 1, July–Dec. 1876. New York, D. Appleton and company.

LAC 31168–76

Appleton's popular science monthly. v. 48–56; Nov. 1895–April 1900. New York, D. Appleton and company.

LAC 15720

Applications of the science of mechanics to practical purposes. New-York, Harper & brothers, 1844.
Renwick, James, 1790–1863.

LAC 13085

Applied Christianity; moral aspects of social questions. Boston and New York, Houghton, Mifflin and company, 1886.
Gladden, Washington, 1836–1918.

LAC 40079

The appreciation of money: its effects on debts, industry, and national wealth. Embracing the substance of a discourse delivered at Xenia, Ohio, with additions, together with essays on financial questions written at various times. Philadelphia, H. C. Baird & co., 1877.
Warner, Adoniram Judson, 1834–1910.

LAC 16020

Apprenticeship & apprenticeship education in colonial New England & New York. New York City, Teachers college, Columbia university, 1917.
Seybolt, Robert Francis, 1888–1951.

LAC 11971

April hopes. New York, Harper & brothers, 1888, [c1887]
Howells, William Dean, 1837–1920.

LAC 40015

April twilights: poems by Willa Sibert Cather. Boston, R. G. Badger, 1903.
Cather, Willa Sibert, 1873–1947.

LAC 14561
Apropos of women and theatres. With a paper or two on Parisian topics. New York, Carleton; London, S. Low, son, & co., 1869.
Logan, Olive, 1839–1909.

LAC 10693
Arator; being a series of agricultural essays, practical & political: in sixty one numbers. 2d ed., rev. and enl. By Col. John Taylor, of Caroline county, Virginia, Georgetown, Columbia, Printed and published by J. M. Carter, 1814.
Taylor, John, 1753–1824.

LAC 13849
Archaeological studies among the ancient cities of Mexico. Chicago [1895–97]
Holmes, William Henry, 1846–1933.

LAC 14699
Archibald Robertson, lieutenant-general Royal engineers, his diaries and sketches in America, 1762–1780; edited with an introduction by Harry Miller Lydenberg. New York, The New York public library, 1930.
Robertson, Archibald, *ca.* 1745–1813.

LAC 14133
The architectural heritage of the Merrimack; early houses & gardens... by John Mead Howells, with an introduction by William Graves Perry. New York, N. Y., Architectural book publishing company, inc. [c1941]
Howells, John Mead, 1868–1959.

LAC 40122
An architectural monograph on domestic architecture in Massachusetts, 1750–1800, with text by Julian A. Buckly, prepared for publication by Russell F. Whitehead. [Saint Paul, White pine bureau] 1916.
Buckly, Julian A   1872–1918.

LAC 40122
An architectural monograph on early wood built houses of central New York, with text by Carl C. Tallman; prepared for publication by Russell F. Whitehead. [Saint Paul, White pine bureau] 1918.
Tallman, Carl Cornwell, 1884–

LAC 30769–76
Architectural record. v. 1–12; July 1891–Dec. 1902. New York.

LAC 40122
Architecture in the United States, an article in four parts. New Haven, 1830.
Silliman, Benjamin, 1779–1864.

LAC 13884
The architecture of colonial America, by Harold Donaldson Eberlein; illustrated from photographs by Mary H. Northend and others. Boston, Little, Brown, and company, 1915.
Eberlein, Harold Donaldson.

LAC 16014
The architecture of country houses; including designs for cottages, farm houses, and villas, with remarks on interiors, furniture, and the best modes of warming and ventilating. With three hundred and twenty illustrations. New York, D. Appleton & co.; Philadelphia, G. S. Appleton, 1850.
Downing, Andrew Jackson, 1815–1852.

LAC 22914–72
Archives of Maryland ... pub. by authority of the state, under the direction of the Maryland historical society. v. [1]–70. Baltimore, Maryland historical society, 1883–1964.

LAC 13145
Arctic experiences: containing Capt. George E. Tyson's wonderful drift on the ice-floe, a history of the Polaris expedition, the cruise of the Tigress, and rescue of the Polaris survivors. To which is added a general Arctic chronology. New York, Harper & brothers, 1874.
Blake, Euphemia, 1817–1904, *ed.*

LAC 21132
Arctic explorations: the second Grinnell expedition in search of Sir John Franklin, 1853, '54, '55. Illustrated by upwards of three hundred engravings, from sketches by the author... Philadelphia, Childs & Peterson; [etc., etc.] 1856–1857.
Kane, Elisha Kent, 1820–1857.

LAC 14946
The ardent eighties.
Reminiscences of an interesting decade, the ardent eighties, by Gregory Weinstein. With a foreword by Lillian D. Wald. New York, The International press [c1928]
Weinstein, Gregory, 1864–

LAC 30626–39
The Arena. v. 1–14; Dec. 1889–Nov. 1895. Boston, The Arena publishing company, 1890–1895.

LAC 40152
An argument addressed to His Excellency, the governor of Pennsylvania, in support of the bill to incorporate the Pennsylvania fiscal agency. [Philadelphia, 1859]
Green, Duff, 1791–1875.

LAC 15279
An argument on the unconstitutionality of slavery, embracing an abstract of the proceedings of the national and state conventions on this subject. Boston, Saxton & Peirce, 1841.
Mellen, George W   F.

LAC 16714
Arise take thy journey... New York, New Harlem publishing company, 1903.
Toler, Henry Pennington.

LAC 10537
Aristocracy and evolution; a study of the rights, the origin, and the social functions of the wealthier classes. New York, The Macmillan company; London, Macmillan & co., ltd., 1898.
Mallock, William Hurrell, 1849–1923.

LAC 20492
Aristocracy in America. From the sketch-book of a German nobleman. Ed. by Francis J. Grund. London, R. Bentley, 1839.
Grund, Francis Joseph, 1805–1863.

LAC 14532

Arizona and Sonora: the geography, history, and resources of the silver region of North America. 3d ed., rev. and enl. New York, Harper & brother, 1864.
Mowry, Sylvester.

LAC 13225

Arizona as it is.
Arizona as it was, 1877. [Chicago] R[io] G[rande Press, 1962]
Hodge, Hiram C.

LAC 13225

Arizona as it was, 1877. [Chicago] R[io] G[rande Press, 1962]
Hodge, Hiram C.

LAC 40047

The Arkansas traveller's songster: containing the celebrated story of the Arkansas traveller, with the music for violin or piano, and also an extensive and choice collection of new and popular comic and sentimental songs. New York, Dick & Fitzgerald [c1863]

LAC 14695

The army correspondence of Colonel John Laurens in the years 1777–8, now first printed from original letters to his father, Henry Laurens, president of Congress; with a memoir by Wm. Gilmore Simms. New York, 1867.
Laurens, John, 1754–1782.

LAC 14912

Army life in a black regiment. Boston, Fields, Osgood & co., 1870.
Higginson, Thomas Wentworth, 1823–1911.

LAC 15173

Army life in Virginia. Letters from the Twelfth Vermont regiment and personal experiences of volunteer service in the war for the Union, 1862–63. Burlington, Free press association, 1895.
Benedict, George Grenville, 1826–1907.

LAC 14635

Army life on the Pacific; a journal of the expedition against the northern Indians, the tribes of the Coeur d'Alenes, Spokans, and Pelouzes, in the summer of 1858. By Lawrence Kip, second lieutenant of the Third regiment of artillery, U.S. army. New York, Redfield, 1859.
Kip, Lawrence, 1836–1899.

LAC 40121

The Army of the Potomac, and its mismanagement; respectfully addressed to Congress. By Charles Ellet, jr. Washington, Printed by L. Towers & co., 1861.
Ellet, Charles, 1810–1862.

LAC 14897

The Army of the Potomac: its organization, its commander, and its campaign. By the Prince de Joinville. Tr. from the French, with notes, by William Henry Hurlbert. New York, A. D. F. Randolph, 1862.
Joinville, Francois Ferdinand Philippe Louis Marie d'Orleans, *prince* de, 1818–1900.

LAC 14700

The army of the United States; historical sketches of staff and line with portraits of generals-in-chief, ed. by Theo. F. Rodenbough and William L. Haskin. New York, Maynard, Merrill, & co., 1896.
Rodenbough, Theophilus Francis, 1838–1912, *ed.*

LAC 11754

Around an old homestead; a book of memories. Cincinnati, Jennings and Graham; New York, Eaton and Mains [c1906]
Huston, Paul Griswold.

LAC 13366

Arredondo's historical proof of Spain's title to Georgia; a contribution to the history of one of the Spanish borderlands, edited by Herbert E. Bolton. Berkeley, Calif., University of California press, 1925.
Arredondo, Antonio de.

LAC 15669

Art and artists in Connecticut. Boston, Lee and Shepard; New York, C. T. Dillingham, 1879.
French, Henry Willard, 1854–

LAC 16359

Art and common sense. New York, C. Scribner's sons, 1913.
Cortissoz, Royal, 1869–1948.

LAC 13057

Art and industry as represented in the exhibition at the Crystal Palace, New York—1853–4, showing the progress and state of the various useful and esthetic pursuits. From the New York Tribune. Rev. and ed. by Horace Greeley. New York, Redfield, 1853.
Greeley, Horace, 1811–1872.

LAC 14589

Art and scenery in Europe, with other papers; being chiefly fragments from the port-folio of the late Horace Binney Wallace. Philadelphia, Parry & McMillan, 1857, [c1856]
Wallace, Horace Binney, 1817–1852.

LAC 14552

Art for life's sake; an application of the principles of art to the ideals and conduct of individual and collective life. New York, Chicago [etc.] The Prang company [c1913]
Caffin, Charles Henry, 1854–1918.

LAC 16676

Art hand-book, sculpture, architecture, painting. Official handbook of architecture and sculpture and art catalogue to the Pan-American exposition... Buffalo, N. Y., D. Gray, 1901.
Gray, David, 1870–1968, *ed.*

LAC 15319

Art-hints. Architecture, sculpture, and painting. New York, Harper & brothers, 1855.
Jarves, James Jackson, 1818–1888.

LAC 15320

The art-idea: sculpture, painting, and architecture in America. 3d ed. New York, Hurd and Houghton, 1866, [c1864]
Jarves, James Jackson, 1818–1888.

LAC 15667
Art in America; a critical and historical sketch. New York, Harper & brothers, 1880.
Benjamin, Samuel Greene Wheeler, 1837–1914.

LAC 14556
Art-life of William Morris Hunt. With illustrations from his works. Boston, Little, Brown and company, 1900, [c1899]
Knowlton, Helen Mary, 1832–

LAC 11484
The art of amusing. Being a collection of graceful arts, merry games, odd tricks, curious puzzles, and new charades. Together with suggestions for private theatricals, tableaux, and all sorts of parlor and family amusements... With nearly 150 illustrations by the author. New York, Carleton; London, S. Low, son & co., 1866.
Bellew, Frank.

LAC 40054
The art of fiction. Boston, Cupples and Hurd [1884]
Besant, *Sir* Walter, 1836–1916.

LAC 40048
The art of money getting; or, Golden rules for money getting. Chicago, L. P. Miller, 1882.
Barnum, Phineas Taylor, 1810–1891.

LAC 11621
The art of money making; or, The road to fortune: a universal guide for honest success. New York, International publishing company [c1872]
Mills, James D.

LAC 10331
The art of newspaper making; three lectures. New York, D. Appleton and company, 1895.
Dana, Charles Anderson, 1819–1897.

LAC 40027
The art of swimming; containing instructions and cautions to learners. To which are added, Dr. Franklin's advice to swimmers... London, W. Mason [1815?]
Frost, J

LAC 15581
The art of tanning leather... 3d ed., with additions. New York, Baker & Godwin, printers, 1857.
Kennedy, David H.

LAC 15321
Art thoughts; the experiences and observations of an American amateur in Europe. New York, Hurd and Houghton, 1870, [c1869]
Jarves, James Jackson, 1818–1888.

LAC 11838
Artemus Ward, his book... New York, Carleton, 1862.
Browne, Charles Farrar, 1834–1867.

LAC 11841
Artemus Ward; his travels... With comic illustrations by Mullen. New York, Carleton; [etc., etc.] 1865.
Browne, Charles Farrar, 1834–1867.

LAC 11967
Arthur Bonnicastle; an American novel. By J. G. Holland, with twelve full-page illustrations by Mary A. Hallock. New York, Scribner, Armstrong & co., 1873.
Holland, Josiah Gilbert, 1819–1881.

LAC 13407
Articles and discussions on the labor question, including the controversy with Mr. Lyman J. Gage on the ethics of the Board of trade; and also the controversy with Mr. Hugh O. Pentecost, and others, on the single tax question. Chicago, The Open court publishing company, 1890.
Trumbull, Matthew Mark, *d.* 1894.

LAC 15134
Artist-life: or, Sketches of American painters. New-York, D. Appleton & company; Philadelphia, Geo. S. Appleton, 1847.
Tuckerman, Henry Theodore, 1813–1871.

LAC 21874
Artistic houses; being a series of interior views of a number of the most beautiful and celebrated homes in the United States, with a description of the art treasures contained therein... New York, Printed for the subscribers by D. Appleton and company, 1883–84.

LAC 12678
The artist's guide and mechanic's own book, embracing the portion of chemistry applicable to the mechanic arts, with abstracts of electricity, galvanism, magnetism, pneumatics, optics, astronomy, and mechanical philosophy. Also mechanical exercises in iron, steel, lead, zinc, copper, and tin soldering and a variety of useful receipts, extending to every profession and occupation of life; particularly dyeing, silk, woollen, cotton, and leather. Boston, Sanborn, Carter, and Bazin, 1856, [c1841]
Pilkington, James, *fl.* 1841.

LAC 14559
The artists of America: a series of biographical sketches of American artists; with portraits and designs on steel. New-York, Baker & Scribner, 1846.
Lester, Charles Edwards, 1815–1890.

LAC 15133
The arts & crafts in New England, 1704–1775; gleanings from Boston newspapers relating to painting, engraving, silversmiths, pewterers, clockmakers, furniture, pottery, old houses, costume, trades and occupations, &c... Topsfield, Mass., The Wayside press, 1927.
Dow, George Francis, 1868–1936.

LAC 15329
The arts & crafts in Philadelphia, Maryland and South Carolina ... gleanings from newspapers, collected by Alfred Coxe Prime. [Topsfield, Mass.] The Walpole society, 1929.
Prime, Alfred Coxe, 1883–1926, *comp.*

LAC 22629
Arts of design in the United States.
History of the rise and progress of the arts of design in the United States. New York, G. P. Scott and co., printers, 1834.
Dunlap, William, 1766–1839.

LAC 15594

As I remember; recollections of American society during the nineteenth century. New York and London, D. Appleton and company, 1911.
Gouverneur, Marian.

LAC 13431

As it is in the Philippines, by Edgar G. Bellairs [*pseud.*] New York, Lewis, Scribner & co., 1902.
Ballentine, Charles, 1861?–

LAC 11712

As we see it. Washington, D. C., Press of C. F. Sudwarth, 1910.
Waring, Robert Lewis, 1863–

LAC 13863

Asa Turner; a home missionary patriarch and his times, by George F. Magoun. Introduction by A. H. Clapp, D. D. Boston and Chicago, Congregational Sunday-school and publishing society [c1889]
Magoun, George Frederic, 1821–1896.

LAC 13322

The ascent of Denali (Mount McKinley); a narrative of the first complete ascent of the highest peak in North America. New York, C. Scribner's sons, 1914.
Stuck, Hudson, 1863–1920.

LAC 12629

Ascent of man.
The Lowell lectures on the ascent of man. New York, J. Pott & co., 1894.
Drummond, Henry, 1851–1897.

LAC 13175

The Ashley-Smith explorations and the discovery of a central route to the Pacific, 1822–1829, with the original journals, ed. by Harrison Clifford Dale. Cleveland, The Arthur H. Clark company, 1918.
Dale, Harrison Clifford, 1885–

LAC 15522

Asia at the door; a study of the Japanese question in continental United States, Hawaii and Canada, by Kiyoshi K. Kawakami. With a prologue by Doremus Scudder and an epilogue by Hamilton W. Mabie. New York, Chicago [etc.] Fleming H. Revell company [c1914]
Kawakami, Kiyoshi Karl, 1875–

LAC 16079

Aspirations of nature. New York, J. B. Kirker, 1857.
Hecker, Isaac Thomas, 1819–1888.

LAC 40075

The assassination of President Lincoln. A sermon preached in St. James church, Birmingham, Ct., April 19th, 1865. New York, G. W. Carleton, 1865.
Chamberlain, Nathan Henry, 1830 (*ca.*)–1901.

LAC 14023

The associate creed of Andover theological seminary. Boston, Franklin press: Rand, Avery & co., 1883.
Park, Edwards Amasa, 1808–1900.

LAC 15940

Association and Christianity, exhibiting the anti-moral and anti-Christian character of the churches and the social relations in present Christendom, and urging the necessity of industrial association, founded on Christian brotherhood and unity... Pittsburgh, J. W. Cook, 1845.
Van Amringe, Henry Hamlin.

LAC 20656

Astoria; or, Enterprise beyond the Rocky mountains. Philadelphia, Carey, Lea & Blanchard, 1836.
Irving, Washington, 1783–1859.

LAC 20881

The asylum; or, Alonzo and Melissa. An American tale, founded on fact. By I. Mitchell. Poughkeepsie, J. Nelson, 1811.
Jackson, Daniel, *b.* 1790.

LAC 20383

Athanase de Mezieres and the Louisiana-Texas frontier, 1768–1780; documents pub. for the first time, from the original Spanish and French manuscripts, chiefly in the archives of Mexico and Spain; tr. into English; ed. and annotated, by Herbert Eugene Bolton. Cleveland, The Arthur H. Clark company, 1914.
Bolton, Herbert Eugene, 1870–1953, *ed.*

LAC 11583

Atheism in philosophy, and other essays. Boston, Roberts brothers, 1884.
Hedge, Frederic Henry, 1805–1890.

LAC 10203

The Atlantic ferry, its ships, men, and working. London, Whittaker and co.; New York, Macmillan and co., 1892.
Maginnis, Arthur J.

LAC 30099

The Atlantic index; a list of articles, with names of authors appended, published in "The Atlantic monthly," from its establishment in 1857 to the close of the sixty-second volume in 1888. Boston, Houghton, Mifflin and company, 1889.

LAC 30099

The Atlantic index supplement.
The Atlantic index; a list of articles, with names of authors appended, published in "The Atlantic monthly," from its establishment in 1857 to the close of the sixty-second volume in 1888. Boston, Houghton, Mifflin and company, 1889.

LAC 30001–98

The Atlantic monthly. v. 1–96; Nov. 1857–Dec. 1905. Boston.

LAC 16576

Atlantis arisen; or, Talks of a tourist about Oregon and Washington. Philadelphia, J. B. Lippincott company, 1891.
Victor, Frances, 1826–1902.

LAC 40099
An attempt to demonstrate the practicability of emancipating the slaves of the United States of North America, and of removing them from the country, without impairing the right of private property, or subjecting the nation to a tax. By a New-England man. New-York, G. &. C. Carvil, 1825.

LAC 13370
Attitude of American courts in labor cases; a study in social legislation. New York, Longmans, Green & co., agents; [etc., etc.] 1911.
Groat, George Gorham, 1871–

LAC 20883-84
Audubon and his journals, by Maria R. Audubon, with zoological and other notes by Elliott Coues. New York, C. Scribner's sons, 1897.
Audubon, John James, 1785–1851.

LAC 13367
Audubon's western journal: 1849–1850; being the ms. record of a trip from New York to Texas, and an overland journey through Mexico and Arizona to the gold fields of California, by John W. Audubon, with biographical memoir by his daughter, Maria R. Audubon; introduction, notes, and index by Frank Heywood Hodder. With folded map, portrait, and original drawings. Cleveland, The A. H. Clark company, 1906.
Audubon, John Woodhouse, 1812–1862.

LAC 15766
Avgvstvs Saint-Gavdens. Boston and New York, Houghton, Mifflin and company, 1907.
Cortissoz, Royal, 1869–1948.

LAC 15119
Augustus Saint-Gaudens. [New York] The International studio, John Lane company, 1908.
Hind, Charles Lewis, 1862–1927.

LAC 15017
Aunt Becky's army-life.
The story of Aunt Becky's army-life. New York, New York printing company, 1871, [1867]
Palmer, Sarah A.

LAC 16241
Aunt Sally; or, The cross the way to freedom. A narrative of the slave-life and purchase of the mother of Rev. Isaac Williams, of Detroit, Michigan... Cincinnati, American reform tract and book society, 1858.

LAC 40149
Authentic account of the proceedings of the congress held at New-York, in MDCCLXV, on the subject of the American stamp act. [London, Printed for J. Almon] 1767.
Stamp Act Congress, *New York*, 1765.

LAC 20176
An authentic and comprehensive history of Buffalo, with some account of its early inhabitants, both savage and civilized, comprising historic notices of the Six nations, or Iroquois Indians, including a sketch of the life of Sir William Johnson, and of other prominent white men, long resident among the Senecas. Arranged in Chronological order. Buffalo, N. Y., Rockwell, Baker & Hill, printers, 1864–65.
Ketchum, William.

LAC 40043
Authentic biography of Col. Richard M. Johnson, of Kentucky. Boston, Pub. for the proprietor, 1834.
Emmons, William, *b.* 1792.

LAC 40058
An authentic narrative of the piratical descents upon Cuba made by hordes from the United States, headed by Narciso Lopez, a native of South America; to which are added, some interesting letters and declarations from the prisoners, with a list of their names, &c. Havana, 1851.
Wilson, Thomas William.

LAC 11912
Authors and friends. London, T. Fisher Unwin, 1896.
Fields, Annie, 1834–1915.

LAC 11273
Autobiographical sketches and recollections, during a thirty-five years' residence in New Orleans. Boston, Phillips, Sampson & company, 1857.
Clapp, Theodore, 1792–1866.

LAC 16794
Autobiography. [Brooklyn, c1942]
Carey, Mathew, 1760–1839.

LAC 16745
Autobiography. Edited, and with an introd., by Stuart Gerry Brown, with the assistance of Donald G. Baker. [Syracuse] Syracuse University Press [1959]
Monroe, James, *pres. U.S.*, 1758–1831.

LAC 13629
Autobiography and letters of Orville Dewey, D. D. Edited by his daughter, Mary E. Dewey. Boston, Roberts brothers, 1883.
Dewey, Orville, 1794–1882.

LAC 11190
Autobiography and personal recollections of John B. Gough, with twenty-six years' experience as a public speaker. Illustrated by George Cruikshank and others. Springfield, Mass., Bill, Nichols & co.; Chicago, Ill., Bill & Heron; [etc., etc.] 1870.
Gough, John Bartholomew, 1817–1886.

LAC 14252-53
Autobiography and personal reminiscences of Major-General Benj. F. Butler; Butler's book. By Benj. F. Butler. A review of his legal, political, and military career. Boston, A. M. Thayer & co., 1892.
Butler, Benjamin Franklin, 1818–1893.

LAC 21422-23
Autobiography, correspondence, etc. Edited by Charles Beecher. New York, Harper & Bros., 1864–1865.
Beecher, Lyman, 1775–1863.

LAC 20372-73
Autobiography, memories and experiences of Moncure Daniel Conway... Boston and New York, Houghton, Mifflin and company, 1904.
Conway, Moncure Daniel, 1832–1907.

LAC 11786
Autobiography of a farm boy. Ithaca, N.Y., Cornell university press, 1946.
Roberts, Isaac Phillips, 1833–1928.

LAC 16935
Autobiography of a fugitive negro: his anti-slavery labours in the United States, Canada, & England. London, J. Snow, 1855.
Ward, Samuel Ringgold, b. 1817.

LAC 11729
The autobiography of a Pennsylvanian. Philadelphia, The J. C. Winston company, 1918.
Pennypacker, Samuel Whitaker, 1843–1916.

LAC 10996
Autobiography of a Shaker, and Revelation of the Apocalypse. With an appendix. New York, American news company [1869]
Evans, Frederick William, 1808–1893.

LAC 10718
Autobiography of Adin Ballou. 1803–1890. Containing an elaborate record and narrative of his life from infancy to old age. With appendixes. Completed and ed. by his son-in-law, William S. Heywood. Lowell, Mass., The Vox populi press, 1896.
Ballou, Adin, 1803–1890.

LAC 15332
Autobiography of an actress; or, Eight years on the stage. By Anna Cora Mowatt. Boston, Ticknor, Reed, and Fields, 1854.
Ritchie, Anna Cora Mowatt, 1819–1870.

LAC 16546
Autobiography of an English soldier in the United States army. Comprising observations and adventures in the States and Mexico. New York, Stringer & Townsend, 1853.
Ballentine, George, b. 1812?

LAC 14192
The autobiography of an ex-colored man. Boston, Sherman, French & company, 1912.
Johnson, James Weldon, 1871–1938.

LAC 16326
Autobiography of Andrew Carnegie... Boston and New York, Houghton Mifflin company [c1920]
Carnegie, Andrew, 1835–1919.

LAC 20441–42
Autobiography of Andrew Dickson White... New York, The Century co., 1907, [c1905]
White, Andrew Dickson, 1832–1918.

LAC 15835
Autobiography of August Bondi, 1833–1907. Published by his sons and daughters for its preservation. Galesburg, Ill., Wagoner printing company, 1910.
Bondi, August, 1833–1907.

LAC 13684
Autobiography of Charles Biddle, vice-president of the Supreme executive council of Pennsylvania. 1745–1821. (Privately printed.) Philadelphia, E. Claxton and company, 1883.
Biddle, Charles, 1745–1821.

LAC 13753
Autobiography of Charles Caldwell, M. D., with a preface, notes, and appendix, by Harriot W. Warner. Philadelphia, Lippincott, Grambo and co., 1855.
Caldwell, Charles, 1772–1853.

LAC 16036
The autobiography of Colonel John Trumbull, patriot-artist, 1756–1843; edited by Theodore Sizer. Containing a supplement to [the editor's] The works of Colonel John Trumbull. New Haven, Yale University Press, [etc.,] 1953.
Trumbull, John, 1756–1843.

LAC 14894
The autobiography of Commodore Charles Morris, U. S. N., with portrait and explanatory notes. Boston, A. Williams & co., 1880.
Morris, Charles, 1784–1856.

LAC 14350
Autobiography of George Dewey, admiral of the navy... New York, C. Scribner's sons, 1913.
Dewey, George, 1837–1917.

LAC 13229
The autobiography of Gurdon Saltonstall Hubbard, Pa-pa-ma-ta-be, "The swift walker"; with an introduction by Caroline M. McIlvaine. Chicago, R. R. Donnelley & sons company, 1911.
Hubbard, Gurdon Saltonstall, 1802–1886.

LAC 40043
Autobiography of John Chambers, ed. by John Carl Parish. Iowa City, Ia., The State historical society of Iowa, 1908.
Chambers, John, 1780–1852.

LAC 12362
Autobiography of John E. Massey; ed. by Elizabeth H. Hancock. New York and Washington, The Neale publishing company, 1909.
Massey, John Edward, 1819–1901.

LAC 16247
Autobiography of John G. Fee, Berea, Kentucky. Chicago, Ill., National Christian association, 1891.
Fee, John Gregg, b. 1816.

LAC 15322
The autobiography of Joseph Jefferson. New York, The Century co. [c1890]
Jefferson, Joseph, 1829–1905.

LAC 14004
The autobiography of Joseph Le Conte; edited by William Dallam Armes. New York, D. Appleton and company, 1903.
Le Conte, Joseph, 1823–1901.

LAC 10317
The autobiography of Levi Hutchins: with a preface, notes, and addenda, by his youngest son. (Private ed.) Cambridge [Mass.] Riverside press, 1865.
Hutchins, Levi, 1761–1855.

LAC 15634
Autobiography of Ma-ka-tai-me-she-kia-kiak, or Black Hawk, embracing the traditions of his nation, various wars in which he has been engaged, and his account of the cause and general history of the Black Hawk war of 1832, his surrender, and travels through the United States. Dictated by himself. Antoine LeClair, U.S. interpreter. J. B. Patterson, editor and amanuensis. Rock Island, Illinois, 1833. Also, life, death and burial of the old chief, together with a history of the Black Hawk war, by J. B. Patterson. [St. Louis, Press of Continental printing co.] 1882.
Black Hawk, *Sauk chief*, 1767–1838.

LAC 13747
The autobiography of Martin Van Buren, ed. by John C. Fitzpatrick. Washington, Govt. print. off., 1920.
Van Buren, Martin, *pres. U.S.*, 1782–1862.

LAC 22286–87
Autobiography of Oliver Otis Howard, major general, United States army. New York, The Baker & Taylor company, 1907.
Howard, Oliver Otis, 1830–1909.

LAC 16659
The autobiography of Parley Parker Pratt, one of the twelve apostles of the Church of Jesus Christ of latter-day saints, embracing his life, ministry and travels, with extracts ... from his miscellaneous writings. Edited by his son, Parley P. Pratt. Chicago, Published for Pratt bros. by Law, King & Law, 1888, [c1874]
Pratt, Parley Parker, 1807–1857.

LAC 16237
The autobiography of Peggy Eaton; with a preface by Charles F. Deems. New York, C. Scribner's sons, 1932.
Eaton, Margaret L   Timberlake, 1799?–1879.

LAC 10959
Autobiography of Peter Cartwright, the backwoods preacher. Ed. by W. P. Strickland. Cincinnati, L. Swormstedt & A. Poe, 1860, [c1856]
Cartwright, Peter, 1785–1872.

LAC 10997
Autobiography of Rev. James B. Finley; or, Pioneer life in the West. Edited by W. P. Strickland, D. D. Cincinnati, Printed at the Methodist book concern, for the author, 1854, [c1853]
Finley, James Bradley, 1781–1856.

LAC 15196
Autobiography of Samuel S. Hildebrand, the renowned Missouri "bushwhacker" ... being his complete confession, recently made to the writers, and carefully compiled by James W. Evans and A. Wendell Keith. Together with all the facts connected with his early history. Jefferson City, Mo., State times printing house, 1870.
Hildebrand, Samuel S   1836–1872.

LAC 20800
Autobiography of seventy years. New York, C. Scribner's sons, 1903.
Hoar, George Frisbie, 1826–1904.

LAC 16320
The autobiography of Sir Henry Morton Stanley. Ed. by his wife, Dorothy Stanley. With sixteen photogravures and a map. Boston and New York, Houghton Mifflin company [c1909]
Stanley, *Sir* Henry Morton, 1841–1904.

LAC 10971
Autobiography of the first forty-one years of the life of Sylvanus Cobb, D. D., to which is added a memoir, by his eldest son, Sylvanus Cobb, jr. Boston, Universalist publishing house, 1867.
Cobb, Sylvanus, 1798–1866

LAC 12511
The autobiography of Thomas Collier Platt, with twenty portraits in sepia photogravure, comp. and ed. by Louis J. Lang, with addenda. New York, B. W. Dodge & company, 1910.
Platt, Thomas Collier, 1833–1910.

LAC 15891
Autobiography of Thomas Jefferson, 1743–1790, together with a summary of the chief events in Jefferson's life, an introduction and notes by Paul Leicester Ford, and a foreword by George Haven Putnam. New York and London, G. P. Putnam's sons [1914]
Jefferson, Thomas, *pres. U.S.*, 1743–1826.

LAC 16566
The autobiography of Thomas Shepard, the celebrated minister of Cambridge, N. E. With additional notices of his life and character, by Nehemiah Adams. Boston, Pierce and Parker, 1832.
Shepard, Thomas, 1605–1649.

LAC 12840
Autographs for freedom. [2d series] Ed. by Julia Griffiths. Auburn, Alden, Beardsley & co.; Rochester, Wanzer, Beardsley & co., 1854.
Griffiths, Julia, *ed.*

LAC 11866
The awakening. Chicago & New York, H. S. Stone & company, 1899.
Chopin, Kate, 1851–1904.

LAC 13722
Awful disclosures of Maria Monk; or, The hidden secrets of a nun's life in a convent exposed. London, Camden Publishing Company [1939]
Monk, Maria, *d. ca.* 1850.

LAC 15424
B. and M. Gratz, merchants in Philadelphia, 1754–1798; papers of interest to their posterity and the posterity of their associates. Jefferson City, Mo., The Hugh Stephens printing co., 1916.
Byars, William Vincent, 1857–1938. *ed.*

LAC 11915
Back country poems, by Sam Walter Foss; illustrated by Bridgman. Boston, Lee and Shepard [c1894]
Foss, Sam Walter, 1858–1911.

LAC 14874
The background of Swedish immigration, 1840–1930... [Chicago, Ill., The University of Chicago press, 1931]
Janson, Florence Edith.

LAC 13580
Bakers and baking in Massachusetts, including the flour, baking supply and kindred interests, from 1620 to 1909. Boston, By authority of the Master bakers' association of Massachusetts, 1909.
Brayley, Arthur Wellington, 1863–

LAC 12080
Ballads and poems relating to the Burgoyne campaign; annotated by William L. Stone. Albany, J. Munsell's sons, 1893.
Stone, William Leete, 1835–1908, *comp.*

LAC 40047
Ballads of the western mines and others. New York, Cochrane publishing company, 1910.
Fitch, Anthony.

LAC 20163–64
Baltimore; its history and its people, by various contributors... New York, Chicago, Lewis historical publishing company, 1912.

LAC 16598
Baltimore: past and present. With biographical sketches of its representative men. Baltimore, Richardson & Bennett, 1871.

LAC 13710
The Bancroft naturalization treaties with the German states... Being a collection of documents and opinions relating to the subject... An appeal to the German-American citizens... By Charles Munde. Wurzburg, Sold by A. Stuber; New York, W. Radde; [etc., etc.] 1868.
Munde, Carl.

LAC 16284
The banditti of the plains; or, The cattlemen's invasion of Wyoming in 1892... [n.p., c1894]
Mercer, Asa Shinn, 1839–1917.

LAC 16117
The banditti of the prairies; a tale of the Mississippi valley. Chicago, W. B. Conkey company [189?]
Bonney, Edward, 1807–1864.

LAC 10016
The bank and the Treasury. New York [etc.] Longmans, Green, and co., 1905.
Cleveland, Frederick Albert, 1865–1946.

LAC 14204
Banking and currency and the money trust. [Washington, D. C., National capital press, inc., c1913]
Lindbergh, Charles August, 1859–1924.

LAC 40026
Banking and currency legislation. Letter from the chairman of the Committee on banking and currency United States Senate, Sixty-third Congress, first session, relative to the bill S. 2639, a bill to provide for the establishment of federal reserve banks, for furnishing an elastic currency, affording means of rediscounting commercial paper, and to establish a more effective supervision of banking in the United States, and for other purposes... Washington [Govt. print. off.] 1913.
U.S. *Congress. Senate. Committee on Banking and Currency.*

LAC 11570
The banking & currency problem in the United States. New York, North American review publishing co., 1909.
Morawetz, Victor, 1859–1938.

LAC 40026
Banking, its history, commercial importance, and social and moral influence. A lecture, before the Mechanics institute, of the city of Chicago, delivered Thursday evening, Feb. 24, 1852. Chicago, Langdon & Rounds, 1852.
Bross, William, 1813–1890.

LAC 10041
Banking problems... Philadelphia, American academy of political and social science, 1910.
American Academy of Political and Social Science, *Philadelphia.*

LAC 10327
The banking system of the state of New York, with notes and references to adjudged cases; including also an account of the New York clearing house. New York, J. S. Voorhies, 1857.
Cleaveland, John.

LAC 40126
Banks and a paper currency: their effects upon society. By a friend of the people. Philadelphia, 1832.
Ronaldson, James.

LAC 20062
Banks and banking in the United States. Boston, Ticknor, Reed, and Fields, 1853.
Baker, Henry Felt, 1797–1857.

LAC 15810
Banks, banking, and paper currencies; in three parts. I. History of banking and paper money. II. Argument for open competition in banking. III. Apology for one-dollar notes. Boston, Whipple & Damrell, 1840.
Hildreth, Richard, 1807–1865.

LAC 10059
The banks of New-York, their dealers, the clearing-house, and the panic of 1857... New-York, Appleton, 1859.
Gibbons, James Sloan, 1810–1892.

LAC 20345–46
The Baptist encyclopaedia; a dictionary of the doctrines, ordinances, usages, confessions of faith, sufferings, labors, and successes, and of the general history of the Baptist denomination in all lands. With numerous biographical sketches of distinguished American and foreign Baptists, and a supplement. Rev. ed. Philadelphia, Louis H. Everts, 1883, [c1880]
Cathcart, William, 1826–1908, *ed.*

LAC 40144
The Baptists and slavery, 1840–1845. Ann Arbor, Mich., George Wahr, 1913.
Putnam, Mary Burnham.

LAC 40046
Barbarism the first danger. A discourse for home missions. New York, Printed for the American home missionary society, 1847.
Bushnell, Horace, 1802–1876.

LAC 40019
Barberry bushes and wheat. Reprinted from the Publications of the Colonial society of Massachusetts, vol. XI. Cambridge [Mass.] J. Wilson and son, 1907.
Davis, Andrew McFarland, 1833–1920.

LAC 15195
The bark covered house; or, Back in the woods again; edited by Milo Milton Quaife. Chicago, The Lakeside press, R. R. Donnelley & sons co., 1937.
Nowlin, William, b. 1821.

LAC 30894–928
Barnard's American journal of education.
The American journal of education. Ed. by Henry Barnard, LL. D. v. 1–32; Aug. 1855–1882. Hartford, F. C. Brownell; [etc., etc.] 1856–82.

LAC 12056
Barriers burned away. New and rev. ed. New York, Dodd & Mead [c1885]
Roe, Edward Payson, 1838–1888.

LAC 11385
The Barrington-Bernard correspondence and illustrative matter, 1760–1770, drawn from the "Papers of Sir Francis Bernard" (sometime governor of Massachusetts-Bay) ed. by Edward Channing ... and Archibald Cary Coolidge. Cambridge, Harvard university; [etc., etc.] 1912.
Barrington, William Wildman Barrington, *2d viscount*, 1717–1793.

LAC 14777
The basic outline of universology. An introduction to the newly discovered science of the universe; its elementary principles; and the first stages of their development in the special sciences. Together with preliminary notices of alwato (*ahl-wah-to*), the newly discovered scientific universal language, resulting from the principles of universology. New York, D. Thomas, 1872.
Andrews, Stephen Pearl, 1812–1886.

LAC 13865
Basis of American history, 1500–1900. New York and London, Harper & brothers, 1904.
Farrand, Livingston, 1867–1939.

LAC 22883–84
The Bath archives. A further selection from The diaries and letters of Sir George Jackson, K. C. H. from 1809 to 1816. Ed. by Lady Jackson. London, R. Bentley and son, 1873.
Jackson, *Sir* George, 1785–1861.

LAC 40054
The battle of Brooklyn; a farce in 2 acts. Brooklyn, Reprinted, 1873.

LAC 15289
The battle of Buena Vista, with the operations of the "Army of occupation" for one month. New York, Harper and brothers, 1848.
Carleton, James Henry, 1814–1873.

LAC 16370
The battle of Chancellorsville; the attack of Stonewall Jackson and his army upon the right flank of the Army of the Potomac at Chancellorsville, Virginia, on Saturday afternoon, May 2, 1863. Bangor, Me., The author, 1896.
Hamlin, Augustus Choate, 1829–1905.

LAC 40035
The battle of Fort Sumter and first victory of the southern troops, April 13th, 1861. Full accounts of the bombardment, with sketches of the scenes, incidents, etc. Comp. chiefly from the detailed reports of the Charleston press... Charleston, Steam-power presses of Evans & Cogswell, 1861.

LAC 15059
The battle of New Orleans, including the previous engagements between the Americans and the British, the Indians, and the Spanish which led to the final conflict on the 8th of January, 1815. Louisville, Ky., J. P. Morton & company, printers, 1904.
Smith, Zachariah Frederick, 1827–1911.

LAC 16108
The battle of Seven Pines. New York, C. G. Crawford, printer, 1891.
Smith, Gustavus Woodson, 1822–1896.

LAC 16559
The battle of the Big Hole. A history of General Gibbon's engagement with Nez Perces Indians in the Big Hole valley, Montana, August 9th, 1877. By G. O. Shields. ("Coquina") Chicago and New York, Rand, McNally & company, 1889.
Shields, George O   1846–1925.

LAC 40118
The battle of the kegs. [Philadelphia] Oakwood press, 1866.
Hopkinson, Francis, 1737–1791.

LAC 16408
Battle-pieces and aspects of the war. New York, Harper & brothers, 1866.
Melville, Herman, 1819–1891.

LAC 10756
The battle with the slum. New York, The Macmillan company; London, Macmillan & co., ltd., 1902.
Riis, Jacob August, 1849–1914.

LAC 11947
The battleground, by Ellen Glasgow; illustrated by W. F. Baer and W. Granville Smith. New York, Doubleday, Page & co., 1902.
Glasgow, Ellen Anderson Gholson, 1874–1945.

LAC 22387–90

Battles and leaders of the civil war ... being for the most part contributions by Union and Confederate officers. Based upon "The Century war series". Ed. by R. U. Johnson and C. C. Buel. New-York, The Century co. [c1887–88]

LAC 13414

The battles of labor; being the William Levi Bull lectures for the year 1906. Philadelphia, G. W. Jacobs & co. [c1906]
Wright, Carroll Davidson, 1840–1909.

LAC 14415

Battles of the American revolution, 1775–1781. Historical and military criticism, with topographical illustration... New York, Chicago [etc.] A. S. Barnes & co., 1876.
Carrington, Henry Beebee, 1824–1912.

LAC 23861–62

The Bay of San Francisco, the metropolis of the Pacific coast, and its suburban cities. A history... Chicago, The Lewis publishing company, 1892.

LAC 11867

Bayou folk. Boston and New York, Houghton, Mifflin and company, 1894.
Chopin, Kate, 1851–1904.

LAC 15442

The beast, by Judge Ben B. Lindsey and Harvey J. O'Higgins. New York, Doubleday, Page & company, 1910.
Lindsey, Benjamin Barr, 1869–1943.

LAC 16969

Beauchampe, or, The Kentucky tragedy. A sequel to Charlemont. New and rev. ed. Chicago, Donohue, Henneberry, 1890.
Simms, William Gilmore, 1806–1870.

LAC 40048

Beauties of the monopoly system of New Jersey. By a citizen of Burlington. Philadelphia, C. Sherman, 1848.
Carey, Henry Charles, 1793–1879.

LAC 14354

The beautiful life of Frances E. Willard, a memorial volume by Anna A. Gordon. Introduction by Lady Henry Somerset, with character sketches and memorial tributes by the general officers of the World's and the National W. C. T. U., English leaders and other distinguished persons. Chicago, Woman's temperance publishing association [c1898]
Gordon, Anna Adams, 1853–

LAC 10056

Beet-root sugar and cultivation of the beet. Boston, Lee and Shepard, 1867.
Grant, E   B.

LAC 16480

Befo' de war; echoes in Negro dialect, by A. C. Gordon and Thomas Nelson Page. New York, C. Scribner's sons, 1901, [c1888]
Gordon, Armistead Churchill, 1855–1931.

LAC 14851

Before and after the treaty of Washington: the American civil war and the war in the Transvaal; an address delivered before the New York historical society on its ninety-seventh anniversary, Tuesday, November 19, 1901. New York, Printed for the Society, 1902.
Adams, Charles Francis, 1835–1915.

LAC 11428

The beginners of a nation; a history of the source and rise of the earliest English settlements in America, with special reference to the life and character of the people. New York, D. Appleton and company, 1900, [c1896]
Eggleston, Edward, 1837–1902.

LAC 40104

The beginning of Central park, New York. A fragment of autobiography. By the late Frederick Law Olmsted, with introductory note by his son, Frederick Law Olmsted. [Albany, J. B. Lyon, 1914]
Olmsted, Frederick Law, 1822–1903.

LAC 40047

The beginning of grand opera in Chicago (1850–1859) Chicago, The Laurentian publishers, 1913.
Hackett, Karleton Spalding, 1867–

LAC 40042

The beginning, progress, and conclusion of Bacon's rebellion in Virginia, in the years 1675 and 1676. [Rochester, G. P. Humphrey, 1897]
Mathew, Thomas, *d.* 1705 *or* 6.

LAC 16009

The beginnings of agriculture in America. 1st ed. New York [etc.] McGraw-Hill book company, inc., 1923.
Carrier, Lyman, 1877–

LAC 12103

Beginnings of literary culture in the Ohio valley, historical and biographical sketches. Cincinnati, R. Clarke & co., 1891.
Venable, William Henry, 1836–1920.

LAC 10584–85

The beginnings of public education in North Carolina; a documentary history, 1790–1840. Raleigh, Edwards & Broughton printing company, 1908.
Coon, Charles Lee, 1868–1927, *ed.*

LAC 23867

The beginnings of San Francisco from the expedition of Anza, 1774, to the city charter of April 15, 1850; with biographical and other notes. San Francisco, Z. S. Eldredge, 1912.
Eldredge, Zoeth Skinner, 1846–

LAC 11494

Behind the scenes in Washington. Being a complete and graphic account of the Credit mobilier investigation, the congressional rings, political intrigues, workings of the lobbies, etc. ... with sketches of the leading senators, congressmen, government officials, etc., and an accurate description of the splendid public buildings of the federal capital. By Edward Winslow Martin [*pseud.*]... [New York] Continental publishing company [c1873]
McCabe, James Dabney, 1842–1883.

LAC 12856
Behind the scenes. Or, Thirty years a slave, and four years in the White House. New York, G. W. Carleton & co., 1868.
Keckley, Elizabeth, 1824–1907.

LAC 14494
Belden, the white chief; or, Twelve years among the wild Indians of the plains. From the diaries and manuscripts of George P. Belden... Ed. by Gen. James S. Brisbin, U. S. A. Cincinnati and New York, C. F. Vent; [etc., etc.] 1870.
Belden, George P.

LAC 15937
Belief in God: an examination of some fundamental theistic problems. By M. J. Savage. To which is added an address on The intellectual basis of faith, by W. H. Savage. 2d ed. Boston, G. H. Ellis, 1900.
Savage, Minot Judson, 1841–1918.

LAC 40144
The belief in one God. Philadelphia, S. B. Weston [1901]
Sheldon, Walter Lorenzo, 1858–1907.

LAC 14823
Beliefs and superstitions of the Pennsylvania Germans. Philadelphia, American germanica press, 1915.
Fogel, Edwin Miller, 1874–

LAC 12424
Belle Boyd in camp and prison, written by herself. With an introduction, by George Augusta [!] Sala. New York, Blelock & company, 1865.
Boyd, Belle, 1844–1900.

LAC 10250
A belle of the fifties; memories of Mrs. Clay, of Alabama, covering social and political life in Washington and the South,1853–66, put into narrative form by Ada Sterling. Illustrated from contemporary portraits. New York, Doubleday, Page & company, 1905.
Clay-Clopton, Virginia, 1825–1915.

LAC 14840
Belligerent and sovereign rights as regards neutrals during the war of secession. Argument before the Mixed commission on British and American claims, under the 12th article of the treaty of Washington... Boston, A. Mudge a [!] son, printers, 1873.
Lawrence, William Beach, 1800–1881.

LAC 11178
Beneath two flags. A study in mercy and help methods. 4th ed. Cincinnati, Cranston and Curts, 1894.
Booth, Maud Ballington, 1865–1948.

LAC 16314
Benjamin Franklin. Boston, New York [etc.] Houghton, Mifflin and company [c1900]
More, Paul Elmer, 1864–1937.

LAC 14517
Benjamin Franklin as a man of letters. Boston, New York, Houghton, Mifflin and company, 1887.
McMaster, John Bach, 1852–1932.

LAC 40110
Benjamin Franklin's Letters to Madame Helvetius and Madame La Frete, with an explanatory note by Luther S. Livingston. Cambridge [Printed at the Harvard university press] 1924.
Franklin, Benjamin, 1706–1790.

LAC 40110
Benjamin Franklin's life and writings. A bibliographical essay on the Stevens' collection of books and manuscripts relating to Doctor Franklin. By Henry Stevens of Vermont, F. S. A. London, Printed by Messrs. Davy & sons, 1881.
Stevens, Henry, 1819–1886.

LAC 40050
Benjamin Franklin's Proposals for the education of youth in Pennsylvania, 1749. Ann Arbor [Mich.] The William L. Clements library, 1927.
Franklin, Benjamin, 1706–1790.

LAC 14751
Benjamin Tompson, 1642–1714, first native-born poet of America; his poems, collected with an introduction by Howard Judson Hall. Boston and New York, Houghton Mifflin company, 1924.
Tompson, Bejamin, 1642–1714.

LAC 15318
Benjamin West, his life and work; a monograph by Henry E. Jackson, with a letter by Henry Van Dyke; twelve illustrations. Philadelphia, The J. C. Winston co., 1900.
Jackson, Henry Ezekiel, 1869–

LAC 10164
Benner's prophecies of future ups and downs in prices. What years to make money on pig-iron, hogs, corn, and provisions. 3rd ed. Cincinnati, Robert Clarke company, 1884.
Benner, Samuel.

LAC 12029
The Berber: or, The mountaineer of the Atlas. A tale of Morocco. New-York, G. P. Putnam's sons, 1873.
Mayo, William Starbuck, 1812–1895.

LAC 16300
The Berean: a manual for the help of those who seek the faith of the primitive church. Putney, Vt., Office of the Spiritual magazine, 1847.
Noyes, John Humphrey, 1811–1886.

LAC 20765–66
The Berkeley manuscripts. The lives of the Berkeleys, lords of the honour, castle and manor Berkeley, in the county of Gloucester, from 1066 to 1618; with a description of the hundred of Berkeley and of its inhabitants, by John Smyth of Nibley. Ed. by Sir John Maclean for the Bristol and Gloucestershire archaeological society. Gloucester, Printed by J. Bellows for the subscribers, 1883–85.
Smyth, John, 1567–1640.

LAC 12132
Bernard Lile; an historical romance, embracing the periods of the Texas revolution, and the Mexican war. Philadelphia, J. B. Lippincott & co., 1856.
Clemens, Jeremiah, 1814–1865.

LAC 14134
Bertram Grosvenor Goodhue, architect and master of many arts; the text by Hartley Burr Alexander, Ralph Adams Cram, George Ellery Hale, Lee Lawrie, C. Howard Walker, Charles Harris Whitaker, edited by Charles Harris Whitaker. New York city, Press of the American institute of architects, inc., 1925.
Whitaker, Charles Harris, 1872–1938, *ed.*

LAC 14264
Bethany; a story of the old South. New York, D. Appleton and company, 1905, [c1904]
Watson, Thomas Edward, 1856–1922.

LAC 13473
The better city; a sociological study of a modern city. Los Angeles, The Neuner company press, 1907.
Bartlett, Dana Webster, 1860–

LAC 40136
Better homes for workingmen. Prepared for the Twelfth National Conference of Charities, held at Washington, June, 1885. [n.p., n.d.]
White, Alfred Tredway, 1846–1921.

LAC 13537
Better homes for workingmen, 1855.
Improved dwellings for the working classes, 1877. 1879; Better homes for workingmen, 1885; Riverside buildings, 1890. [n.p., 1891?]
White, Alfred Tredway, 1846–1921.

LAC 11236
Between eras from capitalism to democracy, a cycle of conversations and discourses with occasional side-lights upon the speakers. Kansas City, Mo., Intercollegiate press [c1913]
Small, Albion Woodbury, 1854–1926.

LAC 15869
Between the ocean and the Lakes; the story of Erie. New York, J. S. Collins, 1901.
Mott, Edward Harold, 1845–1920.

LAC 15912
The Bible against slavery. An inquiry into the patriarchal and Mosaic systems on the subject of human rights. 4th ed. New-York, The American anti-slavery society, 1838.
Weld, Theodore Dwight, 1803–1895.

LAC 15476
Bible defence of slavery, by Rev. Josiah Priest. To which is added, a faithful exposition of that system of pseudo philanthropy, or fanaticism, yclept modern abolitionism, which threatens to dissolve the Union; and proposing a plan of national colonization... Glasgow, Ky., W. S. Brown, 1851.
Priest, Josiah, 1788–1851.

LAC 10835
The Bible in the public schools. Arguments in the case of John D. Minor et al. *versus* **the Board of education of the city of Cincinnati et al. Superior court of Cincinnati. With the opinions and decision of the court.** Cincinnati, R. Clarke & co., 1870.
Minor, John D., *et al., plaintiffs.*

LAC 40011
The Bible, the rod, and religion, in common schools. The ark of God on a new cart: a sermon, by Rev. M. Hale Smith. A review of the sermon, by Wm. B. Fowle. Strictures on the sectarian character of the Common school journal, by a member of the Mass. board of education. Correspondence between the Hon. Horace Mann, sec. of the Board of education, and Rev. Matthew Hale Smith. Boston, Redding & co., 1847.
Smith, Matthew Hale, 1810–1879, *ed.*

LAC 10348–49
Bibliography of American historical societies (the United States and the dominion of Canada) 2d ed., rev. and enl. [Washington, Govt. print. off., 1907]
Griffin, Appleton Prentiss Clark, 1852–1926.

LAC 15382
Bibliography of college, social, university and church settlements. Comp. by Caroline Williamson Montgomery, for the College settlements association. 5th ed., rev. and enl. Chicago [Blakely press] 1905.

LAC 13029
Bibliography of education. New York, D. Appleton and company, 1897.
Monroe, Will Seymour, 1863–1939.

LAC 40042
Bibliography of Rhode Island history. Boston, The Mason publishing company, 1902.
Brigham, Clarence Saunders, 1877–1963.

LAC 20575–76
A bibliography of the state of Maine from the earliest period to 1891. In two volumes. Portland, The Thurston print, 1896.
Williamson, Joseph, 1828–1902.

LAC 20951–55
Biblioteca hispano-americana (1493–1810). Santiago de Chile, 1898–1907.
Medina, Jose Toribio, 1852–1930.

LAC 11463
Bibliotheca Hamiltoniana; a list of books written by, or relating to Alexander Hamilton. New York, Printed for the author, The Knickerbocker press, 1886.
Ford, Paul Leicester, 1865–1902.

LAC 13579
Bibliotheca Jeffersoniana: a list of books written by or relating to Thomas Jefferson. New York and London, G. P. Putnam's sons, 1887.
Tompkins, Hamilton Bullock, 1843–1921.

LAC 30532–71
Bibliotheca sacra. v. 1–40; Feb. 1844–Oct. 1883. Andover, Mass., 1844–1883.

LAC 11383
Bibliotheca Washingtoniana; a descriptive list of the biographies and biographical sketches of George Washington. Philadelphia, R. M. Lindsay, 1889.
Baker, William Spohn, 1824–1897.

LAC 14807-08
Bi-centennial history of Albany. History of the county of Albany, N.Y., from 1609 to 1886. With portraits, biographies and illustrations. [By] Howell [and] Tenney. Assisted by local writers. New York, W. W. Munsell & co., 1886.
Howell, George Rogers, 1833-1899, *ed.*

LAC 12049
The big bear of Arkansas, and other sketches, illustrative of characters and incidents in the South and Southwest. Ed. by William T. Porter. With illustrations by Darley. Philadelphia, T. B. Peterson and Brothers [c1843]
Porter, William Trotter, 1809-1858, *ed.*

LAC 15762
Bill Arp: from the uncivil war to date, 1861-1903. 2d ed., Atlanta, Ga., The Byrd printing company, 1903.
Smith, Charles Henry, 1826-1903.

LAC 12072
Bill Arp's peace papers. With illustrations by Matt O'Brian. New York, G. W. Carleton & co.; [etc., etc.] 1873.
Smith, Charles Henry, 1826-1903.

LAC 15028
"Billy" Sunday, the man and his message, with his own words which have won thousands for Christ, by William T. Ellis. Authorized ed. [Philadelphia, The John C. Winston company, c1914]
Sunday, William Ashley, 1862-1935.

LAC 12051
Biographical and critical miscellanies. London, R. Bentley, 1845.
Prescott, William Hickling, 1796-1859.

LAC 14545
Biographical and historical sketches of early Indiana. Indianapolis, Hammond & co., 1883.
Woollen, William Wesley, 1828-

LAC 14938-40
Biographical directory of the American Congress, 1774-1949: the Continental Congress, September 5, 1774 to October 21, 1788, and the Congress of the United States from the First to the Eightieth Congress, March 4, 1789 to January 3, 1949, inclusive. James L. Harrison, compiler. Washington, Govt. print. off., 1949.
U.S. *Congress.*

LAC 11009
Biographical memoirs of the late Rev. John Gano, of Frankfort (Kentucky.) formerly of the city of New York. Written principally by himself. New York, Printed by Southwick and Hardcastle for J. Tiebout, 1806.
Gano, John, 1727-1804.

LAC 22472-74
Biographical register of the officers and graduates of the U.S. Military Academy at West Point, N. Y., from its establishment, in 1802, to 1890. With The early history of the United States Military Academy. 3d ed., rev. and extended. Boston, Houghton, Mifflin, 1891.
Cullum, George Washington, 1809-1892.

LAC 40004
A biographical sketch of Elkanah Watson, founder of agricultural societies in America, and the projector of canal communication in New York state, with a brief genealogy of the Watson family, early settled in Plymouth colony. Albany [N.Y.] J. Munsell, 1864.
Deane, William Reed, 1809-1871.

LAC 11483
A biographical sketch of Henry A. Wise, with a history of the political campaign in Virginia in 1855. To which is added a review of the position of parties in the Union, and a statement of the political issues: distinguishing them on the eve of the presidential campaign of 1856. Richmond, Va., J. W. Randolph, 1856.
Hambleton, James Pinkney.

LAC 12418
Biographical sketch of Linton Stephens, (late associate justice of the Supreme court of Georgia,) containing a selection of his letters, speeches, state papers, etc. Ed. by James D. Waddell. Atlanta, Ga., Dodson & Scott, 1877.
Waddell, James D   *ed.*

LAC 16132
A biographical sketch of the life of William B. Ide: with a minute and interesting account of one of the largest emigrating companies ... from the East to the Pacific coast. And ... account of "the virtual conquest of California, in June, 1846, by the Bear flag party," as given by its leader, the late Hon. William Brown Ide... [Claremont, N. H., S. Ide, 1880]
Ide, Simeon, 1794-1889.

LAC 22470-71
Biographical sketches of loyalists of the American revolution, with an historical essay. Boston, Little, Brown and company, 1864.
Sabine, Lorenzo, 1803-1877.

LAC 10271
Biographical sketches of the Bordley family, of Maryland, for their descendants... By Mrs. Elizabeth Bordley Gibson, ed. by her niece, Elizabeth Mifflin. Philadelphia, Printed by H. B. Ashmead, 1865.
Gibson, Elizabeth, 1777-1863.

LAC 10920
Biographical sketches of the founder and principal alumni of the Log college. Together with an account of the revivals of religion under their ministry. Collected and ed. by Archibald Alexander, D. D. Philadelphia, Presbyterian board of publication [c1851]
Alexander, Archibald, 1772-1851.

LAC 24074-79
Biographical sketches of the graduates of Yale college with annals of the college history... New York, H. Holt and company, 1885-1912.
Dexter, Franklin Bowditch, 1842-1920.

LAC 12574
Biographies of successful Philadelphia merchants. Philadelphia, J. K. Simon, 1864.
Winslow, Stephen Noyes, 1826-

LAC 15033
Biography and history of the Indians of North America; comprising a general account of them, and details in the lives of all the most distinguished chiefs, and others who have been noted, among the various Indian nations ... also a history of their wars; their manners and customs; and the most celebrated speeches of their orators... Likewise exhibiting an analysis of the ... authors who have written upon ... the first peopling of America... 3d ed., with large additions and corrections. Boston, O. L. Perkins [etc.] New York, Collins, Hannay & co., 1834.
Drake, Samuel Gardner, 1798–1875.

LAC 11676
Biography of Andrew Jackson, president of the United States, formerly major general in the Army of the United States. Hartford, S. Andrus and son, 1847.
Goodwin, Philo Ashley, 1807–1873.

LAC 11112
The biography of Eld. Barton Warren Stone, written by himself: with additions and reflections. By Elder John Rogers. Cincinnati, Published for the author by J. A. & U. P. James, 1847, [c1846]
Stone, Barton Warren, 1772–1844.

LAC 40102
A biography of Fernando Wood. A history of the forgeries, perjuries, and other crimes of our "model" mayor. No. 1... [New York, 1856]
Ingraham, Abijah.

LAC 11449
Biography of James G. Blaine. By Gail Hamilton [*pseud.*]. Norwich, Conn., The Henry Bill publishing company, 1895.
Dodge, Mary Abigail, 1833–1896.

LAC 10931
Biography of Rev. Hosea Ballou. By his youngest son, Maturin M. Ballou. Boston, A. Tompkins, 1852.
Ballou, Maturin Murray, 1820–1895.

LAC 15225
Biography of Samuel Lewis, first superintendent of common schools for the state of Ohio. Cincinnati, Printed at the Methodist book concern, 1857.
Lewis, William G   W.

LAC 11645
Biography of Stephen Girard, with his will affixed ... together with a detailed history of his banking and financial operations for the last twenty years... Philadelphia, T. L. Bonsal, 1832.
Simpson, Stephen, 1789–1854.

LAC 21108
The biography of the principal American military and naval heroes; comprehending details of their achievements during the revolutionary and late wars. Interspersed with authentic anecdotes not found in any other work... 2d ed., rev. ... New-York, Low, 1822.
Wilson, Thomas, 1768–1828?

LAC 20628
A biography of William Cullen Bryant, with extracts from his private correspondence. New York, D. Appleton and company, 1883.
Godwin, Parke, 1816–1904.

LAC 16635
Biography, songs and musical compositions of Stephen C. Foster. By his brother Morrison Foster. Pittsburgh, Pa., Percy F. Smith printing and lithographing company, 1896.
Foster, Stephen Collins, 1826–1864.

LAC 14376
Birth of the federal Constitution. A history of the New Hampshire convention for the investigation, discussion, and decision of the federal Constitution: and of the Old North meeting-house of Concord, in which it was ratified by the ninth state, and thus rendered operative ... on ... the 21st of June, 1788. Boston, Cupples & Hurd, 1888.
Walker, Joseph Burbeen, 1822–1912.

LAC 21860–61
Bishop Chase's Reminiscences: an autobiography. Second edition: comprising a history of the principal events in the author's life to A. D. 1847... Boston, J. B. Dow; [etc., etc.] 1848.
Chase, Philander, *bp.*, 1775–1852.

LAC 40130
Bismarck and Motley, with correspondence till now unpublished. [New York, 1898]
Grund, James Pemberton.

LAC 11600
Bits of old China. Taipei, Ch'eng-Wen publishing co., 1966 [London, Kegan Paul, Trench, 1855]
Hunter, William C   1812–1891.

LAC 15186
The bitter cry of the children, by John Spargo; with an introduction by Robert Hunter. New York, The Macmillan company; London, Macmillan & co., ltd., 1906.
Spargo, John, 1876–1966.

LAC 12813
Black America: a study of the ex-slave and his late master. Reprinted with large additions, from "The Times." London [etc.] Cassell & company, limited, 1891.
Clowes, *Sir* William Laird, 1856–1905.

LAC 13895
Black and white. A journal of a three months' tour in the United States. London, Macmillan and co., 1867.
Latham, Henry, 1828 *or* 29–1871.

LAC 12825
Black and white in the southern states; a study of the race problem in the United States from a South African point of view. London, New York [etc.] Longmans, Green and co., 1915.
Evans, Maurice Smethurst, 1854–1920.

LAC 16471
Black and white: land, labor, and politics in the South. New York, Fords, Howard, & Hulbert, 1884.
Fortune, T   Thomas.

LAC 16785
Black-belt diamonds; gems from the speeches, addresses, and talks to students of Booker T. Washington. Selected and arr. by Victoria Earle Matthews. Introd. by T. Thomas Fortune. New York, Negro Universities Press [1969]
Washington, Booker Taliaferro, 1859?–1915.

LAC 12878
Black diamonds gathered in the darkey homes of the South. New-York, Pudney & Russell, 1859.
Pollard, Edward Alfred, 1831–1872.

LAC 14041
The Black Hawk war, including a review of Black Hawk's life; illustrated with upward of three hundred rare and interesting portraits and views. Chicago, Ill., F. E. Stevens, 1903.
Stevens, Frank Everett, 1856–

LAC 16574
The Black Hills; or, The last hunting ground of the Dakotahs. A complete history of the Black Hills of Dakota, from their first invasion in 1874 to the present time. St. Louis, Nixon-Jones printing co., 1899.
Tallent, Annie D.

LAC 40108
The black laws, speech of Hon. B. W. Arnett of Greene County, in the Ohio House of Representatives, March 10, 1886. [n.p., 1886]
Arnett, Benjamin William, bp., 1838–1906.

LAC 16254
'Black mammy,' a song of the sunny South, in three cantos; and "My village home." Cheyenne, Wyo. [Sun steam print.] 1885.
Visscher, William Lightfoot, 1842–1924.

LAC 12793
The black man, his antecedents, his genius, and his achievements. New York, T. Hamilton; Boston, R. F. Wallcut, 1863.
Brown, William Wells, 1815–1884.

LAC 12415
The black man of the South, and the Rebels; or, The characteristics of the former, and the recent outrages of the latter. New York, Negro Universities Press [1969]
Stearns, Charles.

LAC 12904
The black phalanx; a history of the negro soldiers of the United States in the wars of 1775–1812, 1861–'65. 56 illustrations. Springfield, Mass., Winter & co., 1888.
Wilson, Joseph Thomas, 1836–1891.

LAC 16685
The black side; a partial history of the business, religious, and educational side of the Negro in Atlanta, Ga. Atlanta, 1894.
Carter, Edward R.

LAC 13944
Blackfoot lodge tales; the story of a prairie people. New York, C. Scribner's sons, 1892.
Grinnell, George Bird, 1849–1938.

LAC 40038
Black list. A list of those Tories who took part with Great-Britain, in the revolutionary war, and were attainted of high treason, commonly called the Black list! To which is prefixed the legal opinions of Attorney Generals Mc.Kean & Dallas, &c. Philadelphia, Printed for the proprietor, 1802.

LAC 40098
Blacklisting [by] Grover G. Huebner. Prepared with the co-operation of the Political science department of the University of Wisconsin. Madison, Wis., Wisconsin free library commission, Legislative reference dep't, 1906.
Huebner, Grover Gerhardt, 1884–

LAC 11397
The Blaine and Logan campaign of 1884. Blaine's speeches during the canvass, and some of his public letters... Comp. by T. B. Boyd. Chicago, Printed by J. L. Regan & co., 1884.
Boyd, Thomas B   comp.

LAC 40075
Blaine, Conkling and Garfield; a reminiscence and a character study. New York, G. E. Stechert, 1919.
Brigham, Johnson, 1846–1936.

LAC 12966
The blameless prince, and other poems. Boston, Fields, Osgood, & co., 1869.
Stedman, Edmund Clarence, 1833–1908.

LAC 20039
The Bland papers: being a selection from the manuscripts of Colonel Theodorick Bland, jr. To which are prefixed an introduction, and a memoir of Colonel Bland. Ed. by Charles Campbell. Petersburg [Va.] Printed by E. & J. C. Ruffin, 1840–43.
Bland, Theodorick, 1742–1790.

LAC 12524
The Blennerhassett papers, embodying the private journal of Harman Blennerhassett, and the hitherto unpublished correspondence of Burr, Alston, Comfort Tyler, Devereaux, Dayton, Adair, Miro, Emmett, Theodosia Burr Alston, Mrs. Blennerhassett, and others, their contemporaries; developing the purposes and aims of those engaged in the attempted Wilkinson and Burr revolution; embracing also the first account of the "Spanish association of Kentucky", and a memoir of Blennerhassett. Cincinnati, Moore, Wilstach & Baldwin, 1864.
Safford, William Harrison, 1821–1903.

LAC 11826
The blindman's world and other stories, by Edward Bellamy; with a prefatory sketch by W. D. Howells. Boston and New York, Houghton, Mifflin and company, 1898.
Bellamy, Edward, 1850–1898.

LAC 10287
Blix. New York, Doubleday, Page & co., 1905, [c1899]
Norris, Frank, 1870–1902.

LAC 15060
The blockade and the cruisers. New York, C. Scribner's sons, 1887, [c1883]
Soley, James Russell, 1850–1911.

LAC 11326
A blockaded family: life in southern Alabama during the civil war. Boston and New York, Houghton, Mifflin and co., 1888.
Hague, Parthenia Antoinette, 1838–

LAC 12677

The bloudy tenent of persecution for cause of conscience discussed: and Mr. Cotton's letter examined and answered. Edited for the Hanserd Knollys Society by Edward Bean Underhill. London, Printed for the Society by J. Haddon, 1848.
Williams, Roger, 1604?–1683.

LAC 15655

Blue laws.
The code of 1650, being a compilation of the earliest laws and orders of the General court of Connecticut: also, the constitution, or civil compact, entered into and adopted by the towns of Windsor, Hartford, and Wethersfield, in 1638–9. To which is added, some extracts from the laws and judicial proceedings of New-Haven colony, commonly called Blue laws. Hartford, S. Andrus [1822]
Connecticut *(Colony) Laws, statutes, etc.*

LAC 14721

Body and mind: a history and a defense of animism. New York, The Macmillan company, 1911.
McDougall, William, 1871–1938.

LAC 11850

Bonaventure, a prose pastoral of Acadian Louisiana. New York, International association of newspapers and authors, 1901.
Cable, George Washington, 1844–1925.

LAC 16249

Bond and free; a true tale of slave times. Harrisburg [Pa.] E. K. Meyers, printer, 1886.
Howard, James H   W.

LAC 14120

Bon ifacius: an essay ... to do good. (1710) A facsimile reproduction with an introd. by Josephine K. Piercy. Gainesville, Fla., Scholar's Facsimiles & Reprints, 1967.
Mather, Cotton, 1663–1728.

LAC 12223

The book of American pastimes, containing a history of the principal base-ball, cricket, rowing, and yachting clubs of the United States. New York, The author, 1866.
Peverelly, Charles A.

LAC 40058

The book of blood. An authentic record of the policy adopted by modern Spain to put an end to the war for the independence of Cuba. (October, 1868, to November 10, 1873.) New York, N. Ponce de Leon, translator and printer, 1873.
Ponce de Leon y Laguardia, Nestor, 1837–1899.

LAC 16202

The book of corn; a complete treatise upon the culture, marketing and uses of maize in America and elsewhere, for farmers, dealers, manufacturers and others–a comprehensive manual upon the production, sale, use and commerce of the world's greatest crop. Prepared under the direction of Herbert Myrick, by the most capable specialists. 2d rev. ed. New York, Chicago, Orange Judd company, 1904.
Myrick, Herbert, 1860–1927, *ed.*

LAC 16710

The book of Mormon: an account written by the hand of Mormon upon plates taken from the plates of Nephi... Translated by Joseph Smith, jun.; division into chapters and verses, with references, by Orson Pratt, sen. 4th electrotype ed. Kansas City, Mo., Southwestern States Mission, 1902.
Book of Mormon.

LAC 11342

The book of popular songs, being a compendium of the best sentimental, comic, Negro, Irish, Scotch, national, patriotic, military, naval, social, convivial and pathetic songs, ballads and melodies, as sung by the most celebrated opera and ballad singers, negro minstrels and comic vocalists of the day. Philadelphia, G. G. Evans, 1861, [c1859]

LAC 40074

The book of prices of the House carpenters and joiners of the city of Cincinnati. Adopted, Monday, January 4, 1819. Carefully revised and enlarged, February, 1844. By Louis H. Shally. Cincinnati, L'Hommedieu & co., printers, 1844.
Master Carpenters' and Joiners' Society of Cincinnati.

LAC 15127

Book of the artists. American artist life, comprising biographical and critical sketches of American artists: preceded by an historical account of the rise and progress of art in America. With an appendix containing an account of notable pictures and private collections. New York, G. P. Putnam & sons; [etc., etc.] 1867.
Tuckerman, Henry Theodore, 1813–1871.

LAC 11646

The book of the great railway celebrations of 1857; embracing a full account of the opening of the Ohio & Mississippi, and the Marietta & Cincinnati railroads, and the Northwestern Virginia branch of the Baltimore and Ohio railroad, with ... an account of the subsequent excursion to Baltimore, Washington and Norfolk... 1st ed. New York, D. Appleton & co., 1858.
Smith, William Prescott, 1822?–1872.

LAC 10095

The book of wheat; an economic history and practical manual of the wheat industry. New York, Orange Judd company, 1912, [c1908]
Dondlinger, Peter Tracy, 1877–

LAC 10038

Book-trade bibliography in the United States in the XIXth century; to which is added A catalogue of all the books printed in the United States, with the prices, and place where published, annexed. Published by the booksellers in Boston, January, 1804. New York, Printed for the Dibdin club, 1898.
Growoll, Adolf, 1850–1909.

LAC 12819

Booker T. Washington, the master mind of a child of slavery: an appealing life story rivaling in its picturesque simplicity and power those recounted about the lives of Washington and Lincoln. A biographical tale destined to live in history and furnish an inspiration for present and future generations: a human interest story depicting the life achievements of a great leader of a rising race... By Frederick E. Drinker, editor and author. Splendidly illustrated with photographic pictures. Memorial ed. [Philadelphia. Printed by National publishing co., c1915]
Drinker, Frederick E.

LAC 12052
Books and men. Boston and New York, Houghton, Mifflin and company, 1888.
Repplier, Agnes, 1858–1950.

LAC 14428
The boomerang; or, Bryan's speech with the wind knocked out. A dialogue, including the full text of Bryan's famous Madison square garden speech, together with complete answers to each argument by various significant characters. New York, J. S. Barcus & co., 1896.
Barcus, James S.

LAC 15544
Boonesborough; its founding, pioneer struggles, Indian experiences, Transylvania days and revolutionary annals; with full historical notes and appendix. Louisville, Ky., J. P. Morton & company, printers, 1901.
Ranck, George Washington, 1841–1900.

LAC 14616
"Boots and saddles"; or, Life in Dakota and General Custer. With portrait and map. New York, Harper & brothers [c1885]
Custer, Elizabeth, 1842–1933.

LAC 16960
Border beagles; a tale of Mississippi. New and rev. ed. Chicago, Donohue, Henneberry, 1890.
Simms, William Gilmore, 1806–1870.

LAC 40150
The border ruffian code in Kansas. [New York, Tribune office, 1856]

LAC 14708
Border warfare in Pennsylvania during the revolution; presented to the Faculty of philosophy of the University of Pennsylvania by Lewis S. Shimmell, in partial fulfillment of the requirements of doctor of philosophy. Harrisburg, Pa., R. L. Myers & co., 1901.
Shimmell, Lewis Slifer, 1852–1914.

LAC 14622
The border wars of New England, commonly called King William's and Queen Anne's wars. New York, C. Scribner's sons, 1910, [c1897]
Drake, Samuel Adams, 1833–1905.

LAC 15167
Border wars of the West: comprising the frontier wars of Pennsylvania, Virginia, Kentucky, Ohio, Indiana, Illinois, Tennessee, and Wisconsin; and embracing individual adventures among the Indians, and exploits of Boone, Kenton, Clark, Logan, Brady, Poe, Morgan, the Whetzels, and other border heroes of the West. New York and Auburn, Miller, Orton & Mulligan, 1856.
Frost, John, 1800–1859.

LAC 15823
The boss. An essay upon the art of governing American cities. By Henry Champernowne [*pseud.*] New York, G. H. Richmond & co., 1894.
Means, David MacGregor, 1847–1931.

LAC 14073
Boston. London and New York, Longmans, Green, and co., 1891.
Lodge, Henry Cabot, 1850–1924.

LAC 10461
The Boston herald and its history. How, when and where it was founded. Its early struggles and hard-won successes... Boston, Mass., 1878.
Perry, Edwin A.,

LAC 13542
Boston in 1682 and 1699; A trip to New-England, by Edward Ward, and A letter from New England, by J. W. Reprinted, with an introduction and notes, by George Parker Winship. Providence, R. I. [Club for colonial reprints] 1905.
Winship, George Parker, 1871–   *ed.*

LAC 30528–31
The Boston quarterly review. v. 1–5; Jan. 1838–Oct. 1842. Boston, B. H. Greene, 1838–42.

LAC 10872
Boston railways; their condition and prospects. Boston, Little, Brown, and company, 1856.
Grant, E   B.

LAC 11005
Boston Unitarianism, 1820–1850; a study of the life and work of Nathaniel Langdon Frothingham. A sketch. New York & London, G. P. Putnam's sons, 1890.
Frothingham, Octavius Brooks, 1822–1895.

LAC 12642
The botanical text-book... 2d ed. New York, Wiley and Putnam, 1845, [c1842]
Gray, Asa, 1810–1888.

LAC 12645
The botanists of Philadelphia and their work. Philadelphia [Press of T. C. Davis & son] 1899.
Harshberger, John William, 1869–1929.

LAC 12604
Botany for high schools and colleges. New York, H. Holt and company, 1880.
Bessey, Charles Edwin, 1845–1915.

LAC 12641
Botany for young people and common schools. How plants grow, a simple introduction to structural botany. With a popular flora, or an arrangement and description of common plants, both wild and cultivated. Illustrated by 500 wood engravings. New York, Ivison, Blakeman, Taylor, & co. [c1858]
Gray, Asa, 1810–1888.

LAC 40072
Bounty lands of Illinois.
A description of the bounty lands in the state of Illinois: also, the principal roads and routes, by land and water, through the territory of the United States; extending from the province of New-Brunswic, in Nova Scotia, to the Pacific Ocean... Cincinnati, Looker, Reynolds & co., printers, 1819.
Dana, Edmund.

LAC 11365
The boy, how to help him succeed; a symposium of successful experiences, by Nathaniel C. Fowler, jr. assisted by three hundred and nineteen American men of marked accomplishment. Boston, Mass., Oakwood publishing company [c1902]
Fowler, Nathaniel Clark, 1858–1918.

LAC 11939
Boy life on the prairies. Border edition. New York and London, Harper & brothers [c1899]
Garland, Hamlin, 1860–1940.

LAC 14043
Boycotts and the labor struggle; economic and legal aspects, by Harry W. Laidler; with an introduction by Henry R. Seager. New York, John Lane company; London, John Lane; [etc., etc.] 1914.
Laidler, Harry Wellington, 1884–

LAC 12168
The boy's own book; a complete encyclopedia of all athletic, scientific, recreative, outdoor and indoor, exercises and diversions. 5th ed. rev. Boston, Munroe and Francis, 1851.
Clarke, William, 1800–1838.

LAC 15309
A boy's town, described for "Harper's young people." New York, Harper & brothers, 1890.
Howells, William Dean, 1837–1920.

LAC 11743
Bradford's history "of Plimoth plantation." From the original manuscript. With a report of the proceedings incident to the return of the manuscript to Massachusetts... Boston, Wright & Potter printing co., state printers, 1898.
Bradford, William, 1588–1657.

LAC 16039
Bradford's history of Plymouth plantation, 1606–1646; ed. by William T. Davis. With a map and three facsimiles. New York, C. Scribner's sons, 1908.
Bradford, William, 1588–1657.

LAC 16691
Braman's information about Texas. Carefully prepared by D. E. E. Braman. Philadelphia, J. B. Lippincott & co., 1857.
Braman, D   E   E.

LAC 10828
The brass industry in Connecticut; a study of the origin and the development of the brass industry in the Naugatuck valley. Shelton, Conn., W. G. Lathrop, 1909.
Lathrop, William Gilbert, 1865–

LAC 13556
The bread-winners; a social study. New York, Harper & brothers, 1893, [c1883]
Hay, John, 1838–1905.

LAC 10657
The break-up of China; with an account of its present commerce, currency, waterways, armies, railways, politics, and future prospects, by Lord Charles Beresford. New York and London, Harper & brothers, 1899.
Beresford, Charles William De la Poer Beresford, 1st baron, 1846–1919.

LAC 11761
The breeds of live stock, and the principles of heredity... Chicago, J. H. Sanders publishing company, 1887.
Sanders, James Harvey, 1832–1899.

LAC 13486
The brewing industry and the brewery workers' movement in America. Cincinnati, O., International union of united brewery workmen of America, 1910.
Schluter, Hermann, fl. 1907–1918.

LAC 12092
Bricks without straw; a novel. New York, Fords, Howard, & Hulbert; [etc., etc., c1880]
Tourgee, Albion Winegar, 1838–1905.

LAC 15586
Bride and bridegroom: a series of letters to a young married couple. By Julia C. R. Dorr. Cincinnati, Hitchcock and Walden; New York, Nelson and Phillips, 1873.
Dorr, Julia Caroline, 1825–1913.

LAC 40093
A brief account of the province of East-New-Jarsey [!] in America: published by the Scots proprietors having interest there. 1683. Morrisania, N. Y. [Broadstreet press] 1867.

LAC 40012
A briefe and true report of the new found land of Virginia, by Thomas Hariot; reproduced in facsimile from the first edition of 1588, with an introductory note by Luther S. Livingston. New York, Dodd, Mead & company, 1903.
Harriot, Thomas, 1560–1621.

LAC 16147
A brief biographic memorial of Joh. Jonas Rupp, and complete genealogical family register of his lineal descendants, from 1756 to 1875. With an appendix. W. Philadelphia, Pa., L. W. Robinson [1875]
Rupp, Israel Daniel, 1803–1878.

LAC 40145
A brief description and historical account of the Caribee Islands in North-America, and their present state. [London, 1746]
Barbot, Jean.

LAC 40093
A briefe discription of New England and the severall townes therein, together with the present government thereof. (From a manuscript written in 1660 by Samuel Maverick, and recently discovered in the British museum by Henry F. Waters) [Boston, Press of D. Clapp & son] 1885.
Maverick, Samuel, 1602?–1670?

LAC 40009
A brief description of New-York. Reproduced from the original edition, with a bibliographical note, by Victor Hugo Paltsits. New York, Pub. for the Facsimile text society by Columbia university press, 1937.
Denton, Daniel, fl. 1656–1696.

LAC 40016
A brief description of the canals and rail roads of the United States: comprehending notices of all the most important works of internal improvement throughout the several states. Philadelphia, The author, 1834.
Tanner, Henry Schenck, 1786–1858.

LAC 14242
A brief enquiry into the true nature and character of our federal government: being a review of Judge Story's commentaries on the Constitution of the United States. Republished and reprinted from the original Petersburg edition of 1840. Philadelphia, J. Campbell, 1863.
Upshur, Abel Parker, 1790–1844.

LAC 21939
A brief history of epidemic and pestilential diseases; with the principal phenomena of the physical world, which precede and accompany them, and observations deduced from the facts stated... Hartford: Printed by Hudson & Goodwin, 1799. [Published according to act of Congress.]
Webster, Noah,1758–1843.

LAC 14218
A brief history of Rocky mountain exploration, with especial reference to the expedition of Lewis and Clark. New York, D. Appleton and company, 1914, [c1904]
Thwaites, Reuben Gold, 1853–1913.

LAC 16632
A brief history of the Pequot war: especially of the memorable taking of their fort at Mistick in Connecticut in 1637, by Major John Mason. With an introduction and ... notes by Rev. Thomas Prince. Boston, S. Kneeland and T. Green, 1736.
Mason, John, 1600–1672.

LAC 16800
A brief history of the sheep industry in the United States. [Washington, Govt. print. off., 1921]
Connor, Louis George, 1883–

LAC 13465
A brief history of the United States. For schools... New York and Chicago, A. S. Barnes & company [c1881]
Steele, Joel Dorman, 1836–1886.

LAC 12925
A brief illustration of the principles of war and peace, showing the ruinous policy of the former, and the superior efficacy of the latter, for national protection and defence; clearly manifested by their practical operations and opposite effects upon nations, kingdoms and people. By Philanthropos [pseud.] Albany, Printed by Packard and Van Benthuysen, 1831.
Ladd, William, 1778–1841.

LAC 13081
A brief inquiry into the origin and principles of free masonry. Portland [Me.] Printed by A. Shirley, 1820.
Greenleaf, Simon, 1783–1853.

LAC 40109
A brief narrative of the case and tryal of John Peter Zenger, printer of the New-York weekly journal. [Colophon: New-York, Printed and sold by John Peter Zenger. MDCCXXXVI]
Zenger, John Peter, 1680?–1746, defendant.

LAC 20910–11
A brief retrospect of the eighteenth century. Part first; in two volumes: containing a sketch of the revolutions and improvements in science, art, and literature, during that period. New-York: Printed by T. and J. Swords, no. 160 Pearl-street, 1803.
Miller, Samuel, 1769–1850.

LAC 40069
A brief review of the financial history of Pennsylvania, and of the methods of auditing public accounts. With lists of the finance committees and accounting officers of the province and state, from the inception of the government to the present time. 1682–1881. Harrisburg, L. S. Hart, state printer, 1881.
Nead, Benjamin Matthias, 1847–1923.

LAC 10456
A brief sketch of George Peabody, and a history of the Peabody education fund through thirty years. Cambridge [Mass.] University press, 1898.
Curry, Jabez Lamar Monroe, 1825–1903.

LAC 40115
A brief sketch of some of the blunders in the engineering practice of the Bureau of steam engineering, in the U.S. navy. By an engineer. New York, Metropolitan job printing establishment, 1868.

LAC 15200
A brief sketch of the early history of the Catholic church on the island of New York. By the Rev. J. R. Bayley. 2d ed., rev. and enl. New York, The Catholic publication society, 1870.
Bayley, James Roosevelt, abp., 1814–1877.

LAC 13035
Brief sketch of the life and labors of Rev. Alexander Bettis; also an account of the founding and development of the Bettis academy. Trenton, S.C., The author, 1913.
Nicholson, Alfred William, 1861–

LAC 40042
A brief state of the province of Pennsylvania. By William Smith, D. D. New York, Reprinted for J. Sabin, 1865.
Smith, William, 1727–1803.

LAC 40077
A brief statement of the rise and progress of the testimony of the religious society of Friends, against slavery and the slave trade. Pub. by direction of the Yearly meeting, held in Philadelphia, in the fourth month, 1843. Philadelphia, Printed by J. and W. Kite, 1843.
Friends, Society of. Philadelphia Yearly Meeting.

LAC 40072
A brief topographical & statistical manual of the state of New-York: exhibiting the situation and boundaries of the several counties ... and designating the principal places and the seat of the courts... Albany, Pub. by J. Frary, State-street, 1811.
Goodenow, Sterling.

LAC 11451
A brief treatise upon constitutional and party questions, and the history of political parties, as I received it orally from the late Senator Stephen A. Douglas... By J. Madison Cutts. New York, D. Appleton and company, 1866.
Douglas, Stephen Arnold, 1813–1861.

LAC 40085

A brief view of the conduct of Pennsylvania, for the year 1755; so far as it affected the general service of the British colonies, particularly the expedition under the late General Braddock. With an account of the shocking inhumanities, committed by incursions of the Indians upon the province in October and November; which occasioned a body of the inhabitants to come down, while the Assembly were sitting, and to insist upon an immediate suspension of all disputes, and the passing of a law for the defence of the country. Interspers'd with several interesting anecdotes and original papers, relating to the politics and principles of the people called Quakers: being a sequel to a late well-known pamphlet, intitled, A brief state of Pennsylvania. In a second letter to a friend in London... London, Printed for R. Griffiths in Paternoster row; and Sold by Mr. Bradford in Philadelphia, 1756.
Smith, William, 1727–1803.

LAC 12741

A brief view of the Constitution of the United States, addressed to the Law academy of Philadelphia. Published by and for the Academy. Philadelphia, E. G. Dorsey, printer, 1834.
Du Ponceau, Peter Stephen, 1760–1844.

LAC 40060

Brief view of the system of internal improvement of the state of Pennsylvania; containing a glance at its rise, progress, retardation,–the difficulties it underwent,–its present state,–and its future prospects... Pub. by order of the Society for the promotion of internal improvement. Philadelphia, Printed by L. Bailey, 1831.
Carey, Mathew, 1760–1839.

LAC 15398

The bright side of prison life; experiences, in prison and out, of an involuntary sojourner in rebeldom. Baltimore, Press of Fleet, McGinley [c1897]
Swiggett, S   A.

LAC 12133

Bright skies and dark shadows. New York, C. Scribner's sons, 1890.
Field, Henry Martyn, 1822–1907.

LAC 15049

The British colonist in North America; a guide for intending emigrants. London, S. Sonnenschein & co., 1890.

LAC 14852

British diplomatic correspondence concerning the Republic of Texas, 1838–1846; ed. by Ephraim Douglass Adams. Austin, Tex., The Texas state historical association [1918?]
Gt. Brit. *Foreign office.*

LAC 40038

The British in Boston, being the diary of Lieutenant John Barker of the King's own regiment from November 15, 1774 to May 31, 1776; with notes by Elizabeth Ellery Dana. Cambridge, Harvard university press, 1924.
Barker, John, *fl.* 1775.

LAC 10228

British interests and activities in Texas, 1838–1846. Baltimore, The John Hopkins press, 1910.
Adams, Ephraim Douglas, 1865–1930.

LAC 14614

The British invasion from the north. The campaigns of generals Carleton and Burgoyne, from Canada, 1776–1777, with the journal of Lieut. William Digby, of the 53d, or Shropshire regiment of foot. Illustrated with historical notes, by James Phinney Baxter, A. M. Albany, N. Y., J. Munsell's sons, 1887.
Digby, William, *fl.* 1776.

LAC 14462

The British mechanic's and labourer's hand book, and true guide to the United States; with ample notices respecting various trades and professions. London, C. Knight and co., 1840.

LAC 15466

The broad pennant: or, A cruise in the United States flag ship of the Gulf squadron, during the Mexican difficulties; together with sketches of the Mexican war, from the commencement of hostilities to the capture of the city of Mexico. By Rev. Fitch W. Taylor. New York, Leavitt, Trow & co., 1848.
Taylor, Fitch Waterman, 1803–1865.

LAC 16609

Brokerage. New York, Universal business institute, inc., c1910.
Nourse, Edwin Griswold, 1883–

LAC 13649

Bronson Alcott at Alcott house, England, and Fruitlands, New England (1842–1844) Cedar Rapids, Ia., The Torch press, 1908.
Sanborn, Franklin Benjamin, 1831–1917.

LAC 10727

Brook Farm; historic and personal memoirs. Boston, Arena publishing company, 1894.
Codman, John Thomas.

LAC 10761

Brook Farm; its members, scholars, and visitors. New York, The Macmillan company; London, Macmillan & co., ltd., 1908, [c1900]
Swift, Lindsay, 1856–1921.

LAC 10788

Brookline; the history of a favored town. Brookline, Mass., C. A. W. Spencer, 1897.
Bolton, Charles Knowles, 1867–1950.

LAC 14149

The Brooks and Baxter war: a history of the reconstruction period in Arkansas. St. Louis, Slawson printing co., 1893.
Harrell, John Mortimer.

LAC 15117

Browere's life masks of great Americans. [New York] Printed at the De Vinne press for Doubleday and McClure company, 1899.
Hart, Charles Henry, 1847–1918.

LAC 16801
The brownies: their book. New York, The Century co. [c1887]
Cox, Palmer, 1840–1924.

LAC 40054
Brutus; or, The fall of Tarquin. An historical tragedy, in five acts. First represented at the Theatre Royal, Drury-Lane. On Thursday evening, December 3, 1818. 3d ed. London, R. White, 1818.
Payne, John Howard, 1791–1852.

LAC 12118
Bryant, and his friends: some reminiscences of the Knickerbocker writers... New York, Fords, Howard & Hulbert, 1886, [c1885]
Wilson, James Grant, 1832–1914.

LAC 16104
The buccaneers of America; a true account of the most remarkable assaults committed of late years upon the coasts of the West Indies by the buccaneers of Jamaica and Tortuga (both English and French) Wherein are contained more especially the unparalleled exploits of Sir Henry Morgan... By John Esquemeling, one of the buccaneers who was present at those tragedies. Now faithfully rendered into English. With facsimiles of all the original engravings, etc. London, S. Sonnenschein & co. [1898]
Exquemelin, Alexandre Olivier.

LAC 40152
Buckwheat crops of the United States, 1866–1906. Prepared under the direction of Charles C. Clark. Washington, Govt. print. off., 1908.
U.S. *Bureau of Statistics (Dept. of Agriculture)*

LAC 13349
Buffalo land: an authentic narrative of the adventures and misadventures of a late scientific and sporting party upon the great plains of the West. With full descriptions of the country traversed, the Indian as he is, the habits of the buffalo, wolf, and wild horse, etc., etc. Also an appendix, constituting the work a manual for sportsmen and hand-book for emigrants seeking homes. By W. E. Webb. Illustrated from original drawings by Henry Worrall, and actual photographs. Cincinnati and Chicago, E. Hannaford & company, 1872.
Webb, William Edward.

LAC 10952
Building eras in religion. New York, C. Scribner's sons, 1881.
Bushnell, Horace, 1802–1876.

LAC 14057
Buildings and structures of American railroads. A reference book for railroad managers, superintendents, master mechanics, engineers, architects, and students. New York, J. Wiley & sons, 1893.
Berg, Walter Gilman, 1858–1908.

LAC 14766
Bull moose trails: supplement to "Rooseveltian fact and fable". New York, The author [c1912]
Hale, Annie Riley, 1859–

LAC 22790–821
Bulletin. no. [1]–199. Washington, Govt. print. off., 1887–1967.
U.S. *Bureau of American Ethnology.*

LAC 13424
Bulletin, no. 53, July 1904. Washington, Govt. print. off., 1904.
U.S. *Bureau of Labor.*

LAC 15297
Bulletin, no. 56, January 1905. Washington, U.S. Government Printing Office, 1905.
U.S. *Bureau of Labor.*

LAC 13425
Bulletin no. 77, July 1908. Washington, Govt. print. off., 1908.
U.S. *Bureau of Labor.*

LAC 13426
Bulletin no. 81, March, 1909. Washington [Govt. print. off.] 1909.
U.S. *Bureau of Labor.*

LAC 10185
Bulls and bears of New York, with the crisis of 1873, and the cause. Hartford, J. B. Burr, 1875.
Smith, Matthew Hale, 1810–1879.

LAC 12232
Bundling; its origin, progress and decline in America. Albany, Knickerbocker Publishing Company, 1871.
Stiles, Henry Reed, 1832–1909.

LAC 40038
Bunker Hill: the story told in letters from the battlefield by British officers engaged. With an introduction and sketch of the battle. Boston, Nichols & Hall, 1875.
Drake, Samuel Adams, 1833–1905.

LAC 13397
The Burlington strike: its motives and methods, including the causes of the strike, remote and direct, and the relations to it, of the organizations of Locomotive engineers, Locomotive firemen, Switchmen's M. A. A., and action taken by order Brotherhood R. R. brakemen, order Railway conductors, and Knights of labor. The great dynamite conspiracy; ending with a sketch by C. H. Frisbie: forty-seven years on a locomotive... Comp. by C. H. Salmons. Aurora, Ill., Bunnell and Ward, 1889.
Salmons, Charles H   *comp.*

LAC 11598
Burnham's new poultry book. A practical work on selecting, housing, and breeding domestic fowls. Illustrated with drawings of modern popular varieties, plans of poultry houses, &c. Boston, Lee & Shepard [c1877]
Burnham, George Pickering, 1814–1902.

LAC 15481
The burning of the convent. A narrative of the destruction, by a mob, of the Ursuline school on mount Benedict, Charlestown, as remembered by one of the pupils. Cambridge, Mass., Welch, Bigelow, 1877.
Whitney, Louisa, 1819–1883.

LAC 40006
The burning question of trades unionism. A lecture delivered at Newark, N. J., on April 21, 1904. New York city, National executive committee, Socialist labor party, 1919.
De Leon, Daniel, 1852–1914.

LAC 40092
Burr bibliography. A list of books relating to Aaron Burr. Brooklyn, N. Y., Historical printing club, 1892.
Tompkins, Hamilton Bullock, 1843–

LAC 10143
Business–a profession, by Louis D. Brandeis; with a foreword by Ernest Poole. Boston, Small, Maynard & company [c1914]
Brandeis, Louis Dembitz, 1856–1941.

LAC 40098
Business morals. Madison, Wis., 1910.
Edwards, Richard Henry, 1877–1954, *ed.*

LAC 16178
By way of Cape Horn; four months in a Yankee clipper. Illustrated from photographs taken by the author. Philadelphia, J. B. Lippincott company, 1899.
Stevenson, Paul Eve, 1868–1910.

LAC 12826
Cabin and plantation songs, as sung by the Hampton students, arranged by Thomas P. Fenner, Frederic G. Rathbun and Miss Bessie Cleaveland. 3d ed., enl. by the addition of forty-four songs... New York and London, G. P. Putnam's sons, 1901.
Fenner, Thomas P.   *comp.*

LAC 12066
The cabin book: or, National characteristics. By Charles Sealsfield. Tr. from the German by Sarah Powell. With numerous engravings. London, Ingram, Cooke, & co., 1852.
Sealsfield, Charles, 1793–1864.

LAC 40067
Cable dispatches from General Otis, etc. Message from the President of the United States, transmitting ... copies of cable dispatches from General Otis relative to efforts of Aguinaldo to bring about a conclusion of hostilities; also copies of correspondence with Admiral George Dewey relative to alleged saluting of the flag of the Philippine republic. [Washington, Govt. print. off., 1900]
U.S. *Congress. Senate. Committee on the Philippines.*

LAC 12318
Cabot bibliography; with an introductory essay on the careers of the Cabots based upon an independent examination of the sources of information... London, H. Stevens, son & Stiles; New York, Dodd, Mead & company, 1900.
Winship, George Parker, 1871–1952.

LAC 12315
Cabot's discovery of North America. London, J. Macqueen, 1897.
Weare, George Edward.

LAC 14239
Cadwallader Colden; a representative eighteenth century official. New York, The Columbia university press, The Macmillan company, agents; [etc., etc.] 1906.
Keys, Alice Mapelsden.

LAC 10738
Caesar's column; a story of the twentieth century, by Edmund Boisgilbert, M. D. (Ignatius Donnelly) Chicago, F. J. Schulte & co., 1891, [c1890]
Donnelly, Ignatius, 1831–1901.

LAC 12972
Calamus, a series of letters written during the years 1868–1880, by Walt Whitman to a young friend (Peter Doyle); edited with an introduction by Richard Maurice Bucke. Boston, L. Maynard, 1897.
Whitman, Walt, 1819–1892.

LAC 14975
Calculations and statements relative to the trade between Great Britain and the United States of America... London, E. Wilson, 1833.
Reuss, W   F.

LAC 15657
Calendar of Council minutes 1668–1783... Albany, University of the state of New York, 1902.
New York *(Colony) Council.*

LAC 23818–43
Calendar of state papers, Colonial series... Preserved in the Public record office... London, 1860–1926.
Gt. Brit. *Public Record Office.*

LAC 16817
California: a history of Upper and Lower California from their first discovery to the present time, comprising an account of the climate, soil, natural productions, agriculture, commerce, & c. A full view of the missionary establishments and condition of the free and domesticated Indians. With an appendix relating to steam navigation in the Pacific. Illustrated with a new map, plans of the harbours, and numerous engravings. London, Smith, Elder and co., 1839.
Forbes, Alexander, 1778–1862.

LAC 15729
California and the Oriental: Japanese, Chinese and Hindus. Report of State board of control of California to Gov. Wm. D. Stephens, June 19, 1920. Rev. to January 1, 1922. Sacramento, California state printing office, 1922.
California. *State Board of Control.*

LAC 13278
California: for health, pleasure, and residence. A book for travellers and settlers. New York, Harper & brothers, 1872.
Nordhoff, Charles, 1830–1901.

LAC 13304
California, from the conquest in 1846 to the second vigilance committee in San Francisco [1856]. A study of American character. Boston and New York, Houghton, Mifflin and company, 1886.
Royce, Josiah, 1855–1916.

LAC 16391
California gold book; first nugget, its discovery and discoverers, and some of the results proceeding therefrom; by W. W. Allen and R. B. Avery. San Francisco and Chicago, Donohue & Henneberry, printers, 1893.
Allen, William Wallace.

LAC 16894
California illustrated; including a description of the Panama and Nicaragua routes. 4th thousand. New York, R. T. Young, 1853.
Letts, John M.

LAC 40148
California in 1837. Diary of Col. Philip L. Edwards containing an account of a trip to the Pacific coast. Pub. in "Themis" by authority of the Board of state library trustees of the state of California. Sacramento, A. J. Johnston & co., 1890.
Edwards, Philip Leget, 1812–1869.

LAC 13633
California life illustrated. By William Taylor, of the California conference. 21st thousand. New York, Pub. for the author, by Carlton & Porter, 1861, [c1858]
Taylor, William, 1821–1902.

LAC 16187
California three hundred and fifty years ago. Manuelo's narrative, tr. from the Portuguese, by a pioneer. San Francisco, S. Carson & co.; New York, C. T. Dillingham, 1888.
Cole, Cornelius, 1822–1924.

LAC 16933
The call of the wild, by Jack London. Illustrated by Philip R. Goodwin and Charles Livingston Bull. Decorated by Chas. Edw. Hooper. New York, London, The Macmillan company, 1903.
London, Jack, 1876–1916.

LAC 11509
A call to action. An interpretation of the great uprising, its source and causes. Des Moines, Iowa printing co., 1892.
Weaver, James Baird, 1833–1912.

LAC 40040
A calm address to our American colonies. London, Printed by R. Howes [1775]
Wesley, John, 1703–1791.

LAC 40099
Calumny refuted by facts from Liberia; with extracts from the inaugural address of the coloured President Roberts; an eloquent speech of Hilary Teage, a coloured senator; and extracts from a discourse by H. H. Garnett, a fugitive slave, on the past and present condition, and destiny of the coloured race. Presented to the Boston Anti-slavery bazaar, U.S., by the author of "A tribute for the negro". London, C. Gilpin; New York, W. Harned, Anti-slavery office; [etc., etc.] 1848.
Armistead, Wilson, 1819?–1868.

LAC 40029
The Cambridge high school; history and catalogue, by William F. Bradbury, with its early history, by Elbridge Smith, illustrated. Cambridge, Mass., M. King, 1882.
Bradbury, William Frothingham, 1829–1914.

LAC 10353
The cameralists, the pioneers of German social polity. Chicago, The University of Chicago press; [etc., etc.] 1909.
Small, Albion Woodbury, 1854–1926.

LAC 16931
Camp, field and prison life; containing sketches of service in the South, and the experience, incidents and observations connected with almost two years' imprisonment at Johnson's Island, Ohio... With an introd. by L. M. Lewis and a Medical history of Johnson's Island by I. G. W. Steedman. Saint Louis, Southwestern Book and Pub. Co., 1870.
Wash, W   A

LAC 15396
Camp, march and battle-field; or, Three years and a half with the Army of the Potomac. By Rev. A. M. Stewart. Philadelphia, J. B. Rodgers, 1865.
Stewart, Alexander Morrison, 1814–1875.

LAC 14411
A campaign in New Mexico with Colonel Doniphan. With a map of the route, and a table of the distances traversed. Philadelphia, Carey and Hart, 1847.
Edwards, Frank S.

LAC 16372
Campaign sketches of the war with Mexico. By Capt. W. S. Henry. New York, Harper & brothers, 1847.
Henry, William Seaton, 1816–1851.

LAC 16086
The campaign text book of the Democratic party for the presidential election of 1892. Prepared by authority of the Democratic national committee... New York, 1892.
Democratic Party. *National Committee*, 1892–1896.

LAC 14633
Campaigning in Cuba. New York, The Century co., 1899.
Kennan, George, 1845–1924.

LAC 14696
Campaigning with Grant. New York, The Century co., 1897.
Porter, Horace, 1837–1921.

LAC 14636
Campaigns of the Army of the Potomac; a critical history of operations in Virginia, Maryland and Pennsylvania, from the commencement to the close of the war, 1861–5. New York, C. B. Richardson, 1866.
Swinton, William, 1833–1892.

LAC 22203-7
Campaigns of the civil war... New York, C. Scribner's sons, 1881–83.

LAC 16384
Campaigns of the Rio Grande and of Mexico. With notices of the recent work of Major Ripley. By Brevet-Major Isaac I. Stevens, U.S. army. New York, D. Appleton and co., 1851.
Stevens, Isaac Ingalls, 1818–1862.

LAC 16449
Campaigns of the war of 1812-15, against Great Britain, sketched and criticised; with brief biographies of the American engineers, by Bvt. Major-General George W. Cullum. New York, J. Miller, 1879.
Cullum, George Washington, 1809-1892.

LAC 12410
Camp-fire and cotton-field: southern adventure in time of war. Life with the Union armies, and residence on a Louisiana plantation. New York, Blelock and company; Chicago, A. Kidder, 1865.
Knox, Thomas Wallace, 1835-1896.

LAC 16928
Camp-fires of the Afro-American; or, The colored man as a patriot, soldier, sailor, and hero, in the cause of free America: displayed in colonial struggles, in the revolution, the war of 1812, and in later wars, particularly the great civil war-1861-5, and the Spanish-American war-1898: concluding with an account of the war with the Filipinos-1899... By Chaplain Jas. M. Guthrie. Philadelphia, Afro-American pub. co., 1899.
Guthrie, James M.

LAC 14691
Camps and prisons. Twenty months in the department of the Gulf. New York, 1865.
Duganne, Augustine Joseph Hickey, 1823-1884.

LAC 13368
Camps in the Rockies. Being a narrative of life on the frontier, and sport in the Rocky mountains, with an account of the cattle ranches of the West. With an original map based on the most recent U.S. government survey. New York, C. Scribner's sons, 1884, [c1882]
Baillie-Grohman, William Adolph, 1851-1921.

LAC 12947
Canada and the Canadian question. Popular ed., with map. Toronto, Hunter, Rose; London and New York, Macmillan, 1892.
Smith, Goldwin, 1823-1910.

LAC 20440
Canada in 1837-38; showing, by historical facts, the causes of the late attempted revolution, and of its failure; the present condition of the people, and their future prospects, together with the personal adventures of the author, and others who were connected with the revolution. Philadelphia, H. F. Anners; New York, J. & H. G. Langley, 1841.
Theller, Edward Alexander, 1804-1859.

LAC 40037
Canada in the seventeenth century. From the French of Pierre Boucher. By Edward Louis Montizambert. Montreal, G. E. Desbarats, 1883.
Boucher, Pierre, *sieur de Boucherville*, 1620?-1717.

LAC 12281
Canadian types of the old regime, 1608-1698. New York, H. Holt and company, 1908.
Colby, Charles William, 1867-

LAC 16377
The Canadian war of 1812. Oxford, Clarendon press, 1906.
Lucas, *Sir* Charles Prestwood, 1853-1931.

LAC 15513
Les Canadiens-Francais de la Nouvelle-Angleterre, par E. Hamon, S. J. Quebec, N. S. Hardy, 1891.
Hamon, E.

LAC 11470
A candid examination of the mutual claims of Great-Britain, and the colonies: with a plan of accommodation, on constitutional principles. By the author of Letters to a nobleman on the conduct of the American war. New-York: printed by James Rivington, early in MDCCLXXV. [London] Republished by G. Wilkie and R. Faulder, 1780.
Galloway, Joseph, 1731-1803.

LAC 40084
A candid examination of the objections to the treaty of amity, commerce, and navigation, between the United States and Great-Britain, as stated in the report of the committee appointed by the citizens of the United States, in Charleston, South-Carolina. By a citizen of South-Carolina. Addressed to citizens of South-Carolina. Charleston: Printed. New-York: Re-printed for James Rivington, No. 156 Pearl-street, 1795.
Smith, William Loughton, 1758-1812.

LAC 15633
The Cane Ridge meeting-house, by James R. Rogers; to which is appended the autobiography of B. W. Stone, and a sketch of David Purviance by William Rogers. 2d ed. Cincinnati, The Standard publishing company [c1910]
Rogers, James Richard, 1840-

LAC 12827
Cannibals all! or, Slaves without masters. Richmond, Va., A. Morris, 1857.
Fitzhugh, George, 1806-1881.

LAC 16821
Cannon and camera; sea and land battles of the Spanish-American war in Cuba; camp life, and the return of the soldiers. Described and illustrated by John C. Hemment. With index, and an introduction by W. I. Lincoln Adams. New York, D. Appleton and company, 1898.
Hemment, John C.

LAC 16509
The Canton Chinese; or, The American's sojourn in the Celestial empire. By Osmond Tiffany, jr. Boston and Cambridge, J. Munroe and company, 1849.
Tiffany, Osmond, 1823-

LAC 13363
A canyon voyage; the narrative of the second Powell expedition down the Green-Colorado River from Wyoming, and the explorations on land, in the years 1871 and 1872, by Frederick S. Dellenbaugh, artist and assistant topographer of the expedition. With fifty illustrations. New York and London, G. P. Putnam's sons, 1908.
Dellenbaugh, Frederick Samuel, 1853-1935.

LAC 40015
Canzoni & ripostes of Ezra Pound whereto are appended the complete poetical works of T. E. Hulme. London, E. Mathews, 1913.
Pound, Ezra Loomis, 1885-

LAC 40013
Capital and labor. Constitutional convention of Pennsylvania. Report of the Committee on industrial interests and labor. H. C. Carey, chairman. Philadelphia, Collins, printer, 1873.
Pennsylvania. *Constitutional Convention, 1872–1873. Committee on Industrial Interests and Labor.*

LAC 14785
Capital and population: a study of the economic effects of their relations to each other. New York, D. Appleton and company, 1882.
Hawley, Frederick Barnard, 1843–

LAC 13120
Capital and profits. Springfield, Mass., The Hazard company [c1914]
Reid, David Collins, 1857–

LAC 14878
The capitulation.
War on the Detroit; the chronicles of Thomas Vercheres de Boucherville and The capitulation, by an Ohio volunteer, edited by Milo Milton Quaife. Chicago, The Lakeside press, R. R. Donnelley & sons co., 1940.
Vercheres de Boucherville, Rene Thomas.

LAC 12863
Captain Canot; or, Twenty years of an African slaver; being an account of his career and adventures on the coast, in the interior, on shipboard, and in the West Indies. Written out and edited from the captain's journals, memoranda and conversations, by Brantz Mayer. New York, D. Appleton and company, 1855, [c1854]
Conneau, Theophile.

LAC 16938
Captain Craig; a book of poems. Rev. ed. with additional poems. New York, The Macmillan company, 1915.
Robinson, Edwin Arlington, 1869–1935.

LAC 12006
The captain of Company K, by Joseph Kirkland; illustrated from drawings by Hugh Capper. Chicago, Dibble publishing company, 1891.
Kirkland, Joseph, 1830–1894.

LAC 11940
The captain of the gray-horse troop, a novel. New York and London, Harper & brothers [c1902]
Garland, Hamlin, 1860–1940.

LAC 40080
The capture of Mount Washington, November 16th, 1776, the result of treason. New York, 1877.
De Lancey, Edward Floyd, 1821–1905.

LAC 16289
The capture, the prison pen, and the escape, giving a complete history of prison life in the South... By Willard W. Glazier. Hartford, Conn., H. E. Goodwin, 1868.
Glazier, Willard, 1841–1905.

LAC 15604
The care and culture of men: a series of addresses on the higher education. San Francisco, The Whitaker & Ray company, 1896.
Jordan, David Starr, 1851–1931.

LAC 13112
The care of destitute, neglected and delinquent children. New York, The Macmillan company; London, Macmillan & co., ltd., 1902.
Folks, Homer, 1867–

LAC 15355
Caricature and other comic art in all times and many lands. With 203 illustrations. New York, Harper & brothers, 1878, [c1877]
Parton, James, 1822–1891.

LAC 15749
Carl Schurz, militant liberal. [Evansville, Wis., The Antes press, c1930]
Schafer, Joseph, 1867–1941.

LAC 15176
Carolana.
A description of the English province of Carolana. By the Spaniards call'd Florida, and by the French, La Louisiane... To which is added a large and accurate map of Carolana, and of the river Meschacebe. [London] Printed for and sold by O. Payne, 1741.
Coxe, Daniel, 1673–1739.

LAC 12189
Carolina sports, by land and water; including incidents of devil-fishing, wild-cat, deer and bear hunting, etc. New York, Derby & Jackson, 1859.
Elliott, William, 1788–1863.

LAC 12718
Cartier to Frontenac... Geographical discovery in the interior of North America in its historic relations, 1534–1700; with full cartographical illustrations from contemporary sources. Boston and New York, Houghton, Mifflin and company, 1894.
Winsor, Justin, 1831–1897.

LAC 15890
Cartoons. By Margaret J. Preston. Boston, Roberts brothers, 1875.
Preston, Margaret, 1820–1897.

LAC 16655
Cartoons by McCutcheon; a selection of one hundred drawings. Chicago, A. C. McClurg & co., 1903.
McCutcheon, John Tinney, 1870–

LAC 13432
Cartoons of the Spanish-American war, by Bart [*pseud.*] with dates of important events; from the Minneapolis Journal, January 1899. Minneapolis, Minn., The Journal printing company, 1899.
Bartholomew, Charles Lewis, 1869–1949.

LAC 11165
The case of Mexico and the policy of President Wilson. Tr. from the Spanish by Andre Tridon. New York, A. and C. Boni, 1914.
Zayas Enriquez, Rafael de, 1848–1932.

LAC 40042
The case of the planters of tobacco in Virginia, as represented by themselves; signed by the president of the council, and speaker of the house of burgesses. To which is added, A vindication of the said representation. London, Printed for J. Roberts, 1733.

LAC 15725

The case of the Seneca Indians in the state of New York. Illustrated by facts. Printed for the information of the Society of Friends, by direction of the joint committees on Indian affairs, of the four yearly meetings of Friends of Genesee, New York, Philadelphia, and Baltimore. Philadelphia, Merrihew and Thompson, 1840.
Friends, Society of. *(Hicksite) Executive Committee of the Yearly Meetings.*

LAC 13439

Cases of contested elections in Congress, from 1834 to 1865, inclusive. Comp. by D. W. Bartlett, clerk to the Committee of elections. Washington, Govt. print. off., 1865.
U.S. *Congress. House. Committee on Elections.*

LAC 11822

Castine.
Tales of the Puritans. The regicides.–The fair Pilgrim.–Castine. New-Haven, A. H. Maltby; New-York, G. and C. and H. Carvill, and J. Leavitt; [etc., etc.] 1831.
Bacon, Delia Salter, 1811–1859.

LAC 12128

Castle Nowhere: lake-country sketches. Boston, J. R. Osgood and company, 1875.
Woolson, Constance Fenimore, 1840–1894.

LAC 14168

The casual laborer, and other essays, by Carleton H. Parker. With introduction by Cornelia Stratton Parker. New York, Harcourt, Brace and Howe, 1920.
Parker, Carleton Hubbell, 1879–1918.

LAC 10346

Catalogue of the library of the American philosophical society, held at Philadelphia, for promoting useful knowledge. Pub. by order of the society. Philadelphia, Printed by J. R. A. Skerrett, 1824.
American Philosophical Society, *Philadelphia. Library.*

LAC 14016

Catalogus plantarum Americae Septentrionalis, huc usque cognitarum indigenarum et cicurum: or, A catalogue of the hitherto known native and naturalized plants of North America, arranged according to the sexual system of Linnaeus. Lancaster [Pa.] Printed by W. Hamilton, 1813.
Muhlenberg, Henry, 1753–1815.

LAC 14020

The catastrophe of the Presbyterian church, in 1837, including a full view of the recent theological controversies in New England. New Haven, B. & W. Noyes, 1838.
Crocker, Zebulon.

LAC 40081

Catechism for social observation. An analysis of social phenomena. Boston, D. C. Heath & co., 1894.
Henderson, Charles Richmond, 1848–1915.

LAC 14870

Catholic church in Boston.
The story of the Irish in Boston: together with biographical sketches of representative men and noted women, ed. and comp. by James Bernard Cullen. Boston, J. B. Cullen & company, 1889.
Cullen, James Bernard, 1857–   *ed.*

LAC 13862

The Catholic history of North America. Five discourses. To which are added two discourses on the relations of Ireland and America. Boston, P. Donahoe, 1855.
McGee, Thomas D'Arcy, 1825–1868.

LAC 15735

Catholic immigrant colonization projects in the United States, 1815–1860. New York, The United States Catholic historical society, 1939.
Kelly, Mary Gilbert, *sister,* 1894–

LAC 16665

The Catholic question in America: whether a Roman Catholic clergyman be in any case compellable to disclose the secrets of auricular confession. Decided at the Court of General Sessions, in the City of New York. With the arguments of counsel, and the unanimous opinion of the Court, delivered by the mayor, with his reasons in support of that opinion. Reported by William Sampson. New York, Edward Gillespy, 1813.
New York *(County) Court of General Sessions.*

LAC 30411–90

The Catholic world. A monthly magazine of general literature and science. v. 1–80. Apr. 1865–Mar. 1905. New York, 1865–1905.

LAC 14230

Catholicity in the Carolinas and Georgia: leaves of its history. By Rev. Dr. J. J. O'Connell ... A. D. 1820 — A. D. 1878. New York, Montreal, D. & J. Sadlier & co. [1879]
O'Connell, Jeremiah Joseph, 1821–1894.

LAC 22239

Catlin's notes of eight years' travels and residence in Europe, with his North American Indian collection: with anecdotes and incidents of the travels and adventures of three different parties of American Indians whom he introduced to the courts of England, France, and Belgium... London, The author, 1848.
Catlin, George, 1796–1872.

LAC 22754–55

Cato's letters: or, Essays on liberty, civil and religious, and other important subjects. In four volumes. 3d ed., carefully cor. London, Printed for W. Wilkins, T. Woodward, J. Walthoe, and J. Peele, 1733.
Trenchard, John, 1662–1723.

LAC 16071

Cattle-raising on the plains of North America. New York, D. Appleton and company, 1885.
Richthofen, Walter, *baron* von, 1848–1898.

LAC 15211

Cattle; their breeds, management, and diseases; with an index. Pub. under the superintendence of the Society for the diffusion of useful knowledge. Philadelphia, Grigg & Elliot, 1836.
Youatt, William, 1776–1847.

LAC 16284

The cattlemen's invasion of Wyoming in 1892.
The banditti of the plains; or, The cattlemen's invasion of Wyoming in 1892... [n.p., c1894]
Mercer, Asa Shinn, 1839–1917.

LAC 40132
A caution to Great Britain and her colonies, in a short representation of the calamitous state of the enslaved negroes in the British dominions. Philadelphia printed, London reprinted, 1767.
Benezet, Anthony, 1713–1784.

LAC 11702
The Cavaliers & Roundheads of Barbados, 1650–1652; with some account of the early history of Barbados. Georgetown, British Guiana, "Argosy" press, 1887.
Davis, Nicholas Darnell, 1846–1915.

LAC 23356
The cavaliers of Virginia, or, The recluse of Jamestown. An historical romance of the Old Dominion. By the author of "The Kentuckian in New-York"... New-York, Harper & brothers, 1834–35.
Caruthers, William Alexander, 1800 (ca.)–1846.

LAC 16835
Cavalry studies from two great wars, comprising the French cavalry in 1870, by Lieutenant-Colonel Bonie. The German cavalry in the battle of Vionville–Mars-la-Tour, by Major Kaehler. The operations of the cavalry in the Gettysburg campaign, by Lieutenant-Colonel George B. Davis. Kansas City, Mo., Hudson-Kimberly publishing company, 1896.

LAC 14497
Cavalry tactics; or, Regulations for the instruction, formations, and movements of the cavalry of the Army and volunteers of the United States. Washington, Govt. print. off., 1862.
Cooke, Philip St. George, 1809–1895.

LAC 15732
The Cechs (Bohemians) in America; a study of their national, cultural, political, social, economic and religious life. Boston and New York, Houghton Mifflin company, 1920.
Capek, Thomas, 1861–1950.

LAC 12121
Cecil Dreeme. New York, Dodd, Mead and company [c1861]
Winthrop, Theodore, 1828–1861.

LAC 14579
The celebrity, an episode. New York, London, The Macmillan co., 1899, [c1897]
Churchill, Winston, 1871–1947.

LAC 12702
The cell doctrine: its history and present state. For the use of students in medicine and dentistry. Also, a copious bibliography of the subject. Philadelphia, Lindsay & Blakiston, 1870.
Tyson, James, 1841–1919.

LAC 12707
The cell in development and inheritance. 2d ed., rev. & enl. ... New York, The Macmillan company; London, Macmillan & co., ltd., 1906, [c1900]
Wilson, Edmund Beecher, 1856–

LAC 14284
A census of pensioners for revolutionary or military services, with their names, ages, and places of residence, as returned by the marshals of the several judicial districts, under the act for taking the sixth census. Washington, Printed by Blair and Rives, 1841; Baltimore, Reprinted Southern book company, 1954.
U.S. *Census Office. 6th Census*, 1840.

LAC 14716
Census of the city of Charleston, South Carolina, for the year 1848, exhibiting the condition and prospects of the city, illustrated by many statistical details, prepared under the authority of the City council. By J. L. Dawson, M. D., and H. W. De Saussure, M. D. Charleston, S. C., J. B. Nixon, printer, 1849.
Charleston, *S. C. City Council.*

LAC 23560–65
The centennial edition of the works of Sidney Lanier. [Baltimore, The Johns Hopkins press, 1945]
Lanier, Sidney, 1842–1881.

LAC 15650
The Centennial exposition, described and illustrated, being a concise and graphic description of this grand enterprise, commemorative of the first centenary [!] of American independence... Philadelphia, Hubbard bros.; [etc., etc., c1876]
Ingram, J   S.

LAC 12264
Centennial history of American Methodism, inclusive of its ecclesiastical organization in 1784 and its subsequent development under the superintendency of Francis Asbury. With sketches of the character and history of all the preachers known to have been members of the Christmas conference; also, an appendix, showing the numerical position of the Methodist Episcopal church as compared with the other leading evangelical denominations in the cities of the United States; and the condition of the educational work of the church. New York, Phillips & Hunt; Cincinnati, Cranston & Stowe, 1884.
Atkinson, John, 1835–1897.

LAC 11652
Central electric light and power stations, 1902. Prepared under the supervision of William M. Steuart. Washington, Govt. print. off., 1905.
U.S. *Bureau of the Census.*

LAC 16907
The Central water-line from the Ohio River to the Virginia capes, connecting the Kanawha and James rivers, affording the shortest outlet of navigation from the Mississippi basin to the Atlantic. 2d ed. Richmond, Va., Gary, Clemmitt & Jones, printers, 1869.
James River and Kanawha Company, *Richmond.*

LAC 30930–77
The Century illustrated monthly magazine. v. 23–70 (new ser., v. 1–48); Nov. 1881–Oct. 1905. New York, The Century co.

LAC 12655
A century of dishonor; a sketch of the United States government's dealings with some of the Indian tribes; New York, Harper & brothers, 1881.
Jackson, Helen Maria Hunt, 1831–1885.

LAC 11183
A century of drink reform in the United States. Cincinnati, Jennings and Graham; New York, Eaton and Mains [1904]
Fehlandt, August F.

LAC 12664
A century of electricity. Boston and New York, Houghton, Mifflin and company, 1887.
Mendenhall, Thomas Corwin, 1841–1924.

LAC 16095
A century of finance. Martin's history of the Boston stock and money markets, one hundred years, from January, 1798, to January, 1898, comprising the annual fluctuations of all public stocks and investment securities ... also a review of the Boston money market, 1831 to 1898... Boston, The author, 1898.
Martin, Joseph Gregory.

LAC 16232
A century of population growth from the first census of the United States to the twelfth, 1790–1900. Washington, Govt. print. off., 1909.
U.S. *Bureau of the Census.*

LAC 20258
A century of printing. The issues of the press in Pennsylvania, 1685–1784. Philadelphia [Press of Matlack & Harvey] 1885–86.
Hildeburn, Charles Swift Riche, 1855–1901.

LAC 11282
A century of town life; a history of Charlestown, Massachusetts, 1775–1887. With surveys, records and twenty-eight pages of plans and views. Boston, Little, Brown and company, 1888.
Hunnewell, James Frothingham, 1832–1910.

LAC 11019
A century's change in religion. Boston and New York, Houghton Mifflin company, 1914.
Harris, George, 1844–1922.

LAC 40097
The century's great men in science. [Washington, Govt. print. off., 1901]
Peirce, Charles Santiago Sanders, 1839–1914.

LAC 15135
The ceramic art; a compendium of the history and manufacture of pottery and porcelain. With 464 illustrations... New York, Harper & brothers, 1878.
Young, Jennie J.

LAC 10114
The cereals in America. New York, Orange Judd company; [etc., etc.] 1904.
Hunt, Thomas Forsyth, 1862–1927.

LAC 13641
Certain dangerous tendencies in American life, and other papers. Boston, Houghton, Osgood and company, 1880.
Harrison, Jonathan Baxter, 1835–1907.

LAC 40045
Certain inducements to well minded people who are here straitned in their estates or otherwise: or, such as are willing, out of noble and publike principles, to transport themselves or some servants, or agents for them into the West Indies, for the propagating of the gospel and increase of trade... New York, Reprinted for J. Sabin [by Munsell] 1865.

LAC 16712
A certain rich man. New York, The Macmillan company, 1909.
White, William Allen, 1868–1944.

LAC 10550
The challenge of facts, and other essays, by William Graham Sumner, ed. by Albert Galloway Keller. New Haven, Yale university press; [etc., etc.] 1914.
Sumner, William Graham, 1840–1910.

LAC 11155
The challenge of the future; a study in American foreign policy. Boston and New York, Houghton Miflin company, 1916.
Usher, Roland Greene, 1880–

LAC 11972
A chance acquaintance, by William D. Howells; illustrated by William L. Sheppard. Boston and New York, Houghton, Mifflin and company [c1901]
Howells, William Dean, 1837–1920.

LAC 11024
The chaplains and clergy of the revolution. New York, C. Scribner, 1864, [c1861]
Headley, Joel Tyler, 1813–1897.

LAC 40035
A chaplain's campaign with Gen. Butler. New York, Printed for the author, 1865.
Hudson, Henry Norman, 1814–1886.

LAC 13728
A chapter of sketches on finance; with an appendix, showing the train of insidious causes by which the removal of the deposites was effected; being detached from a book now in preparation for the press, entitled, Sketches of eight years in Washington, &c., &c. Baltimore, F. Lucas, jr.; Boston, Hilliard, Gray & co.; [etc., etc.] 1837.
Mayo, Robert, 1784–1864.

LAC 16867
Chapters of opera; being historical and critical observations and records concerning the lyric drama in New York from its earliest days down to the present time. With over seventy illustrations. 3d ed., rev., with an appendix containing tables of the opera seasons, 1908–1911, etc. New York, H. Holt and company, 1911.
Krehbiel, Henry Edward, 1854–1923.

LAC 11362
Chapters on banking. Cambridge [Mass.] 1885.
Dunbar, Charles Franklin, 1830–1900.

LAC 40076

The character and influence of abolitionism. A sermon preached in the First Presbyterian church, Brooklyn, on Sabbath evening, Dec. 9th, 1860. New York, G. F. Nesbit & co., printers, 1860.
Van Dyke, Henry Jackson, 1822–1891.

LAC 16319

Character & opinion in the United States, with reminiscences of William James and Josiah Royce and academic life in America. New York, C. Scribner's sons, 1920.
Santayana, George, 1863–1952.

LAC 11306

A character of the province of Maryland. Reprinted from the original edition of 1666. With introduction and notes by Newton D. Mereness. Cleveland, The Burrows brothers company, 1902.
Alsop, George, *b.* 1638.

LAC 11456

The character of Thomas Jefferson, as exhibited in his own writings. Boston, Weeks, Jordan & company, 1839.
Dwight, Theodore, 1764–1846.

LAC 12098

Characteristics of literature, illustrated by the genius of distinguished writers. 2d series. Philadelphia, Lindsay and Blakiston, 1851.
Tuckerman, Henry Theodore, 1813–1871.

LAC 12879

Characteristics of the southern negro. New York and Washington, The Neale publishing company, 1910.
Randle, Edwin Henderson, 1830–

LAC 12621

Characteristics of volcanoes, with contributions of facts and principles from the Hawaiian islands, including a historical review of Hawaiian volcanic action for the past sixty-seven years, a discussion of the relations of volcanic islands to deep-sea topography, and a chapter on volcanic-island denudation. New York, Dodd, Mead, and company, 1890.
Dana, James Dwight, 1813–1895.

LAC 12037

Charcoal sketches; or, Scenes in a metropolis. By Joseph C. Neal. With illustrations by David C. Johnston. Philadelphia, E. L. Carey and A. Hart, 1838.
Neal, Joseph Clay, 1807–1847.

LAC 13719

The charities of Springfield, Illinois; a survey under the direction of the American association of societies for organizing charity [by] Francis H. McLean; the Springfield survey, Charities section. New York city, Department of surveys and exhibits, Russell Sage foundation, 1915.
McLean, Francis Herbert, 1869–

LAC 40123

The charity school movement in colonial Pennsylvania... Philadelphia, Press of G. F. Lasher [pref. 1905]
Weber, Samuel Edwin, 1875–

LAC 16967

Charlemont; or, The pride of the village, a tale of Kentucky. New and rev. ed. Chicago, Belford, Clarke, & co., 1889.
Simms, William Gilmore, 1806–1870.

LAC 13840

Charles Francis Adams, by his son, Charles Francis Adams. Boston and New York, Houghton, Mifflin and company, 1900.
Adams, Charles Francis, 1835–1915.

LAC 10486

Charles Francis Adams, 1835–1915; an autobiography; with a Memorial address delivered November 17, 1915, by Henry Cabot Lodge. Boston & New York, Houghton Mifflin company, 1916.
Adams, Charles Francis, 1835–1915.

LAC 13654

Charles Jewett: life and recollections. Boston, J. H. Earle, 1880.
Thayer, William Makepeace, 1820–1898.

LAC 40054

Charles the Second; or, The merry monarch: a comedy, in two acts, by John Howard Payne. Printed from the acting copy, with remarks, biographical and critical, by D.—G. As performed at the Theatres Royal. London, Davidson [n.d.]
Payne, John Howard, 1791–1852.

LAC 16180

Charlotte Temple, a tale of truth, by Susanna Haswell Rowson; reprinted from the rare first American edition (1794), over twelve hundred errors in later editions being corrected, and the preface restored; with an historical and biographical introduction, bibliography, etc., by Francis W. Halsey. New York and London, Funk & Wagnalls company, 1905.
Rowson, Susanna, 1762–1824.

LAC 40023

A chart and description of the Boston and Worcester and Western railroads; in which is noted the towns, villages, stations, bridges, viaducts, tunnels, cuttings, embankments, gradients, &c., the scenery and its natural history, and other objects passed by this line of railway. With numerous illustrations. Constituting a novel and complete companion for the railway carriage. Boston, Bradbury & Guild, 1847.
Guild, William.

LAC 13441

Charters of the old English colonies in America. With an introduction and notes. Pub. for the Society for the reform of colonial government. London, J. W. Parker, 1850.
Lucas, Samuel, 1818–1868.

LAC 11933

The Chatelaine of La Trinite. New York, The Century co., 1892.
Fuller, Henry Blake, 1857–1929.

LAC 11580

The Chautauqua movement. By John H. Vincent. With an introduction by President Lewis Miller. Boston, Chautauqua press, 1886, [c1885]
Vincent, John Heyl, *bp.*, 1832–1920.

LAC 40019
Cheap cotton by free labor: by a cotton manufacturer.
Boston, A. Williams & co., 1861.
Atkinson, Edward, 1827–1905.

LAC 14272
A check list of American eighteenth century newspapers in the Library of Congress, originally compiled by John Van Ness Ingram. New ed., rev. and enl. under the direction of Henry S. Parsons, chief, Periodical division. Washington, U.S. Govt. print. off., 1936.
U.S. *Library of Congress. Periodicals Division.*

LAC 15451
Check-list of session laws, compiled by Grace E. Macdonald for the Public document clearing house committee of the National association of state libraries. New York, The H. W. Wilson company, 1936.
National Association of State Libraries. *Public Document Clearing House Committee.*

LAC 13767
Check-list of statutes of states of the United States of America including revisions, compilations, digests, codes and indexes, compiled by Grace E. MacDonald for the Public document clearing house committee of the National association of state libraries... Providence, The Oxford press, 1937.
National Association of State Libraries. *Public Document Clearing House Committee.*

LAC 10136
The chemistry of dairying; an outline of the chemical and allied changes which take place in milk, and in the manufacture of butter and cheese; and the rational feeding of dairy stock. Easton, Pa., Chemical publishing co., 1897.
Snyder, Harry, 1867–1927.

LAC 14082
Cherokee Bible.
Story of the Cherokee Bible. An address, with additional ... notes, delivered before the meeting of the Ladies' missionary society of the First Congregational church, Ithaca, N. Y., Feb. 5, 1897. 2d ed., enl. Ithaca, N. Y., Democrat press, 1899.
Foster, George Everett, 1849–

LAC 11934
The Chevalier of Pensieri Vani. [4th ed., rev.] New York, The Century co., 1892.
Fuller, Henry Blake, 1857–1929.

LAC 12015
Chicago and the great conflagration. By Elias Colbert and Everett Chamberlin. With numerous illustrations by Chapin & Gulick, from photographic views taken on the spot. Cincinnati and New York, C. F. Vent; Chicago, J. S. Goodman & co.; [etc., etc.] 1871.
Colbert, Elias, *b.* 1831.

LAC 16750
Chicago and the Old Northwest, 1673–1835; a study of the evolution of the northwestern frontier, together with a history of Fort Dearborn. Chicago, The University of Chicago press [c1913]
Quaife, Milo Milton, 1880–1959.

LAC 11292
Chicago, as it was, and as it is
The lost city! drama of the fire fiend! or Chicago, as it was and as it is! and its glorious future! a vivid and truthful picture of all of interest connected with the destruction of Chicago and the terrible fires of the great North-west... By Frank Luzerne. Ed. by John G. Wells. Profusely illustrated with maps and engravings from photographs taken on the spot. New York, Wells & company; [etc., etc.] 1872.
Luzerne, Frank.

LAC 16837
Chicago commons through forty years. Chicago, Ill., Chicago commons association [1936]
Taylor, Graham, 1851–1938.

LAC 16400
The Chicago martyrs; the famous speeches of the eight anarchists in Judge Gary's court, October 7, 8, 9, 1886, and reasons for pardoning Fielden, Neebe and Schwab... San Francisco, Free society, 1899.
Altgeld, John Peter, 1847–1902.

LAC 40009
Chicago relief. First special report of the Chicago relief and aid society. Chicago, Culver, Page, Hoyne & co., 1871.
Chicago Relief and Aid Society.

LAC 12894
Chicago sewerage. Report of the results of examinations made in relation to sewerage in several European cities, in the winter of 1856-7, by the chief engineer of the Board of sewerage commissioners. Chicago, The Board, 1858.
Chicago. *Board of Sewerage Commissioners.*

LAC 12835
Chicora.
The hireling and the slave, Chicora, and other poems. Charleston, S. C., McCarter, 1856.
Grayson, William John, 1788–1863.

LAC 40014
The child and the curriculum. Chicago, The University of Chicago press [c1902]
Dewey, John, 1859–1952.

LAC 13100
The child in the city; a series of papers presented at the conferences held during the Chicago Child Welfare exhibit. Published by the Department of social investigation, Chicago school of civics and philanthropy. [Chicago, Manz engraving company, The Hollister press] 1912.
Chicago. Child Welfare Exhibit, *1911.*

LAC 40136
Child-labor bill. Hearings before the Committee on labor, House of representatives, Sixty-third Congress, second session, on H. R. 12292, a bill to prevent interstate commerce in the products of child labor, and for other purposes. February 27 [and March 9] 1914. Washington, Govt. print. off., 1914.
U.S. *Congress. House. Committee on Labor.*

LAC 40136

Child-labor bill. Statement before the Committee on labor, House of representatives, Sixty-fourth Congress, first session, on H. R. 8234, a bill to prevent interstate commerce in the products of child labor, and for other purposes, by Hon. W. W. Kitchin, of Raleigh, N. C. January 11, 1916. Washington, Govt. print. off., 1916.
U.S. *Congress. House. Committee on Labor.*

LAC 11274

Child labor in city streets. New York, The Macmillan company, 1912.
Clopper, Edward Nicholas, 1879–1953.

LAC 12183

Child life in colonial days, written by Alice Morse Earle, with many illustrations from photographs. New York, The Macmillan company; London, Macmillan & co., ltd., 1899.
Earle, Alice, 1851–1911.

LAC 40123

The children at the phalanstery. A familiar dialogue on education. By F. Cantagrel. Tr. by Francis Geo Shaw. New York, W. H. Graham, 1848.
Cantagrel, Felix Francois Jean, 1810–1887.

LAC 12055

The children of the night; a book of poems. Boston, R. G. Badger & company, 1897.
Robinson, Edwin Arlington, 1869–1935.

LAC 13647

The children of the poor. New York, C. Scribner's sons, 1892.
Riis, Jacob August, 1849–1914.

LAC 40083

The Children's aid society of New York. Its history, plan and results. Comp. from the writings and reports of the late Charles Loring Brace, the founder of the society, and from the records of the secretary's office. New York [Children's aid society] 1893.
Children's Aid Society, *New York.*

LAC 21333

China and her people; being the observations, reminiscences, and conclusions of an American diplomat, by the Hon. Charles Denby. Profusely illustrated with reproductions of photographs collected by the author. Boston, L. C. Page & company, 1906.
Denby, Charles, 1830–1904.

LAC 16423

China and the Chinese; a general description of the country and its inhabitants; its civilization and form of government; its religious and social institutions; its intercourse with other nations, and its present condition and prospects. By the Rev. John L. Nevius. New York, Harper & brothers, 1869.
Nevius, John Livingston, 1829–1893.

LAC 11138

China and the Far East. New York, T. Y. Crowell & co. [1910]
Blakeslee, George Hubbard, 1871–1 *ed.*

LAC 12245

China collecting in America. New York, Charles Scribner's sons, 1892.
Earle, Alice, 1851–1911.

LAC 16303

The Chinese, and the Chinese question. 2d ed. New York, Tibbals book company, 1888.
Whitney, James Amaziah, 1839–

LAC 14868

Chinese immigration, by Mary Roberts Coolidge. New York, H. Holt and company, 1909.
Coolidge, Mary Elizabeth Burroughs Smith, 1860–

LAC 40141

Chinese immigration. Washington, Govt. print. off., 1878.
Sargent, Aaron Augustus, 1827–1887.

LAC 40141

Chinese immigration. A paper read before the Social science association at Saratoga, September 10, 1879. New York, C. Scribner's sons, 1879.
Williams, Samuel Wells, 1812–1884.

LAC 15551

Chinese immigration in its social and economical aspects. New York, C. Scribner's sons, 1881.
Seward, George Frederick, 1840–1910.

LAC 15730

Chinese immigration; its social, moral, and political effect. Report to the California state Senate of its special committee on Chinese immigration. Sacramento, F. P. Thompson, supt. state printing, 1878.
California. *Legislature. Senate. Special Committee on Chinese Immigration.*

LAC 14862

The Chinese in America. By Rev. O. Gibson. Cincinnati, Hitchcock & Walden, 1877.
Gibson, Otis.

LAC 15532

The Chinese: their education, philosophy, and letters. New York, Harper & brothers, 1881.
Martin, William Alexander Parsons, 1827–1916.

LAC 12395

The Chisolm massacre: a picture of "home rule" in Mississippi. 3rd. ed. Washington, D. C., Chisolm Monument association, 1878.
Wells, James Monroe, *b.* 1838.

LAC 16581

Chita: a memory of Last Island. New York, Harper & brothers [c1889]
Hearn, Lafcadio, 1850–1904.

LAC 16672

A choice selection of hymns and spiritual songs, designed to aid in the devotions of prayer, conference and camp meetings. Concord [N. H.?] 1828.

LAC 11814
The choir invisible. New York, The Macmillan company; London, Macmillan & co., ltd., 1897.
Allen, James Lane, 1849–1925.

LAC 16679
Christ in the army; a selection of sketches of the work of the U.S. Christian commission, by various writers. Printed for the Ladies' Christian commission. [Philadelphia, J. B. Rodgers, pr.] 1865.

LAC 15257
Christ in the camp; or, Religion in Lee's army. Supplemented by a sketch of the work in the other Confederate armies. [By] Rev. J. Wm. Jones. With an introduction by Rev. J. C. Granberry, bishop of the Methodist Episcopal church, South. Richmond, Va., B. F. Johnson & co., 1888.
Jones, John William, 1836–1909.

LAC 12266
The Christ of to-day. Boston and New York, Houghton, Mifflin and company, 1895.
Gordon, George Angier, 1853–1929.

LAC 10791
Christian Ballads... New York, Wiley and Putnam, 1840.
Coxe, Arthur Cleveland, *bp.* 1818–1896.

LAC 40083
The Christian church and social reform, a discourse delivered before the Religious Union of Associationists. Boston, Wm. Crosby and H. R. Nichols, 1848.
Channing, William Henry, 1810–1884.

LAC 40044
The Christian commonwealth: or, The civil policy of the rising kingdom of Jesus Christ. Written before the interruption of the government, by Mr. John Eliot, teacher of the church of Christ at Roxbury in New-England. And now published (after his consent given) by a server of the season. London, Printed for Livewell Chapman, at the Crown in Popes-Head-alley [1659]
Eliot, John, 1604–1690.

LAC 12789
The Christian doctrine of slavery. By G. D. Armstrong, D. D., pastor of the Presbyterian church of Norfolk, Va. New York, C. Scribner; Richmond, Va., P. B. Price, 1857.
Armstrong, George Dodd, 1813–1899.

LAC 31319–66
The Christian examiner. v. 1–5, v. 6–18 (new ser., v. 1–13), v. 19–35 (3d ser., v. 1–17), v. 36–62 (4th ser., v. 1–27), v. 63–79 (5th ser., v. 1–17), v. 80–87 (6th ser., v. 1–8); Jan. 1824–Nov. 1869. Boston, O. Everett; New York, C. S. Francis; etc. etc.

LAC 20084
The Christian history, containing accounts of the revival and propagation of religion in Great-Britain & America... No. 1–104, Mar. 5, 1743–Feb. 23, 1744, 5. Boston, N. E., Printed by S. Kneeland and T. Green, for T. Prince, junr., 1744–45.

LAC 11011
The Christian league of Connecticut. New-York, The Century co. [c1883]
Gladden, Washington, 1836–1918.

LAC 20349–51
Christian missions and social progress; a sociological study of foreign missions, by the Rev. James S. Dennis. New York, Chicago [etc.] Fleming H. Revell company [c1897] 1906.
Dennis, James Shepard, 1842–1914.

LAC 13510
Christian non-resistance, in all its important bearings, illustrated and defended. Philadelphia, J. M. M'Kim, 1846.
Ballou, Adin, 1803–1890.

LAC 15723
The Christian philosopher: a collection of the best discoveries in nature, with religious improvements. London, E. Matthews, 1721.
Mather, Cotton, 1663–1728.

LAC 16397
The Christian psalmist, a collection of tunes and hymns, original and selected, for the use of worshiping assemblies, singing and Sunday schools. Compiled from many authors by Silas W. Leonard and A. D. Fillmore. Rev. and greatly enl. by S. W. Leonard. Louisville, Ky., S. W. Leonard [1854, c1850]
Leonard, Silas W.

LAC 10645
Christian reconstruction in the South. Boston, New York [etc.] The Pilgrim press [c1909]
Douglass, Harlan Paul, 1871–

LAC 11027
The Christian society. Chicago, New York [etc.] Fleming H. Revell company, 1894.
Herron, George Davis, 1862–1925.

LAC 11028
The Christian state; a political vision of Christ. A course of six lectures delivered in churches in various American cities. New York, Boston, T. Y. Crowell & co. [c1895]
Herron, George Davis, 1862–1925.

LAC 15407
The Christian system, in reference to the union of Christians, and a restoration of primitive Christianity, as plead in the current reformation. [2d ed.] Cincinnati, Standard publishing co. [1839?]
Campbell, Alexander, 1788–1866.

LAC 15406
The Christian unity of capital and labor... Philadelphia, New York, American Sunday-school union [1888]
Cadman, Harry W.

LAC 13623
Christianity and modern thought. Boston, American Unitarian association, 1872.

LAC 11057
Christianity and positivism: a series of lectures to the times on natural theology and apologetics, delivered in New York, Jan. 16 to March 20, 1871, on the "Ely foundation" of the Union theological seminary. New York, Robert Carter and brothers, 1871.
McCosh, James, 1811–1894.

LAC 11081
Christianity and science. A series of lectures delivered in New York, in 1874, on the Ely foundation of the Union theological seminary. New York, R. Carter and brothers, 1875, [c1874]
Peabody, Andrew Preston, 1811–1893.

LAC 10916
Christianity and social problems. Boston and New York, Houghton, Mifflin and company, 1896.
Abbott, Lyman, 1835–1922.

LAC 10977
Christianity and social questions. New York, Charles Scribner's sons, 1910.
Cunningham, William, 1849–1919.

LAC 11012
Christianity and socialism. New York, Eaton & Mains; Cincinnati, Jennings & Graham [c1905]
Gladden, Washington, 1836–1918.

LAC 10926
Christianity and the labor movement. Boston, Sherman, French & company, 1912.
Balch, William Monroe.

LAC 16702
Christianity and the social crisis. New York, The Macmillan company; London, Macmillan & co., ltd., 1908, [c1907]
Rauschenbusch, Walter, 1861–1918.

LAC 11053
Christianity and the social state. Philadelphia, A. F. Rowland [c1898]
Lorimer, George Claude, 1838–1904.

LAC 10986
Christianity in the United States from the first settlement down to the present time. New York, Hunt & Eaton; Cincinnati, Cranston & Stowe, 1890.
Dorchester, Daniel, 1827–1907.

LAC 23700–1
Christianity practically applied. The discussions of the International Christian conference held in Chicago, October 8–14, 1893, in connection with the World's Congress Auxiliary of the World's Columbian Exposition and under the auspices and direction of the Evangelical Alliance for the United States. New York, Baker and Taylor [c1894]
Evangelical Alliance for the United States of America. *Conference, Chicago,* 1893.

LAC 11082
Christianity the religion of nature. Lectures delivered before the Lowell institute. Boston, Gould and Lincoln; New York, Sheldon and company; [etc., etc.] 1864, [c1863]
Peabody, Andrew Preston, 1811–1893.

LAC 16707
Christianizing the social order. New York, The Macmillan co., 1912.
Rauschenbusch, Walter, 1861–1918.

LAC 14755
Christoph von Graffenried's account of the founding of New Bern, ed. with an historical introduction and an English translation, by Vincent H. Todd, in cooperation with Julius Goebel. Raleigh, Edwards & Broughton printing co., state printers, 1920.
Graffenried, Christoph von, *baron,* 1661–1743.

LAC 16861
Christophe Colomb devant l'histoire. Paris, H. Welter, 1892.
Harrisse, Henry, 1830–1910.

LAC 20723–25
Christopher Columbus: his life, his work, his remains, as revealed by original printed and manuscript records, together with an essay on Peter Martyr of Anghera and Bartolome de las Casas, the first historians of America. New York and London, G. P. Putnam's sons, 1903–04.
Thacher, John Boyd, 1847–

LAC 13607
Christopher Columbus, his own book of privileges, 1502. Photographic facsimile of the manuscript in the archives of the Foreign office in Paris, now for the first time published, with expanded text, translation into English, and an historical introduction; the transliteration and translation by George F. Barwick, the introduction by Henry Harrisse; the whole comp. and ed. with preface, by Benjamin Franklin Stevens. London, B. F. Stevens, 1893.
Colombo, Cristoforo.

LAC 11521
Christopher Gist's journals, with historical, geographical and ethnological notes and biographies of his contemporaries, by William M. Darlington. Pittsburgh, J. R. Weldin & co., 1893.
Gist, Christopher, *d.* 1759.

LAC 40047
Christy's new songster and black joker, containing all the most popular and original songs, choruses, stump speeches, witticisms, jokes, conundrums, etc., etc., as sung and delivered by the world-renowned Christy's minstrels at their opera houses. Compiled and arranged by E. Byron Christy and William E. Christy. New York, Dick and Fitzgerald [c1863]
Christy, E   Byron, *comp.*

LAC 13524
The chronicles of Baltimore; being a complete history of "Baltimore town" and Baltimore city from the earliest period to the present time. Baltimore, Turnbull brothers, 1874.
Scharf, John Thomas, 1843–1898.

LAC 15054
Chronicles of border warfare; or, A history of the settlement by the whites, of northwestern Virginia, and of the Indian wars and massacres, in that section of the state with reflections, anecdotes, &c., by Alexander Scott Withers. A new ed., edited and annotated by R. G. Thwaites with the addition of a memoir of the author, and several illustrative notes by L. C. Draper. Cincinnati, The R. Clarke company, 1903, [c1895]
Withers, Alexander Scott, 1792–1865.

LAC 20388–89
Chronicles of Pennsylvania from the English revolution to the peace of Aix-la-Chapelle, 1688–1748. Philadelphia [Patterson & White co.] 1917.
Keith, Charles Penrose, 1854–

LAC 12260
Chronicles of Pineville: embracing sketches of Georgia scenes, incidents, and characters. By the author of "Major Jones's courtship." With twelve original engravings by Darley. Philadelphia, Carey and Hart, 1845.
Thompson, William Tappan, 1812–1882.

LAC 15342
Chronicles of the Cape Fear river, 1660–1916. 2d ed. Raleigh, Edwards & Broughton printing co., 1916.
Sprunt, James, 1846–1924.

LAC 12321
Chronicles of the first planters of the colony of Massachusetts Bay, from 1623–1636. Now first collected from original records and contemporaneous manuscripts... Boston, C. C. Little and J. Brown, 1846.
Young, Alexander, 1800–1854.

LAC 23248–50
Chronicles of the Scotch-Irish settlement in Virginia; extracted from the original court records of Augusta County, 1745–1800, by Lyman Chalkley; pub. by Mary S. Lockwood. Rosslyn, Va., Printers: The Commonwealth printing co. [c1912–13]
Augusta Co., *Va.*

LAC 11048
Chronicon ephratense; a history of the community of Seventh day Baptists at Ephrata, Lancaster county, Penn'a, by "Lamech and Agrippa." Translated from the original German by J. Max Hark. Lancaster, Pa., S. H. Zahm, 1889.
Lamech, *brother,* d. 1763.

LAC 10577
A chronological history of New-England, in the form of annals: being a summary and exact account of the most material transactions and occurrences relating to this country, in the order of time wherein they happened, from the discovery of Capt. Gosnold, in 1602, to the arrival of Governor Belcher, in 1730. With an introduction containing a brief epitome of the most considerable transactions and events abroad. From the creation... A new ed. [Boston] Cummings, Hilliard, 1826.
Prince, Thomas, 1687–1758.

LAC 13523
A chronological history of the Boston watch and police, from 1631–1865; together with the Recollections of a Boston police office, or, Boston by daylight and gaslight, from the diary of an officer fifteen years in the service. 2d ed., rev. Boston, The author, 1865.
Savage, Edward Hartwell, 1812–1893.

LAC 23236–37
Chronological history of the West Indies. London, Longman, Rees, Orme, Brown, and Green, 1827.
Southey, Thomas.

LAC 12670
A chronology of paper and paper-making. 4th ed. Albany, J. Munsell, 1870.
Munsell, Joel, 1808–1880.

LAC 13955
The church and labor. Boston and New York, Houghton Mifflin company, 1910.
Stelzle, Charles, 1869–

LAC 15397
The church and modern life. Boston and New York, Houghton, Mifflin and company, 1908.
Gladden, Washington, 1836–1918.

LAC 11040
The church and modern society; lectures and addresses. Chicago and New York, D. H. McBride & co., 1897, [c1896]
Ireland, John, *abp.,* 1838–1918.

LAC 14966
The church and slavery. With an appendix. New York, Negro Universities Press [1969]
Barnes, Albert, 1798–1870.

LAC 11732
Church and state in Massachusetts, 1691–1740, by Susan Martha Reed. Urbana, University of Illinois, 1914.
Stifler, Susan Reed, 1884–

LAC 11122
Church and state in the United States; with an appendix on the German population. Boston, James R. Osgood, 1873.
Thompson, Joseph Parrish, 1819–1879.

LAC 14959
The church and the age; an exposition of the Catholic church in view of the needs and aspirations of the present age. By Very Rev. I. T. Hecker. New York, Office of the Catholic World, 1887.
Hecker, Isaac Thomas, 1819–1888.

LAC 15027
The church and the rebellion: a consideration of the rebellion against the government of the United States; and the agency of the church, north and south, in relation thereto. New York, Derby & Miller, 1864.
Stanton, Robert Livingston, 1810–1885.

LAC 40144
The church as it is: or, The forlorn hope of slavery. 2d ed.–rev. and improved. Concord, N. H., Printed by the Republican press association, 1885.
Pillsbury, Parker, 1809–1898.

LAC 10976
Church building; a study of the principles of architecture in their relation to the church. Boston, Small, Maynard & company, 1901.
Cram, Ralph Adams, 1863–1942.

LAC 16456
The church-idea; an essay towards unity. 4th ed. New York, C. Scribner's sons, 1899.
Huntington, William Reed, 1838–1909.

LAC 13516
Church life in colonial Maryland, by Rev. Theodore C. Gambrall, A. M. Baltimore, G. Lycett, 1885.
Gambrall, Theodore Charles.

LAC 10642
Church music in America, comprising its history and its peculiarities at different periods, with cursory remarks on its legitimate use and its abuse; with notices of the schools, composers, teachers, and societies. Boston, A. N. Johnson, 1853.
Gould, Nathaniel Duren, 1781–1864.

LAC 10647
The church praise book, a selection of hymns and tunes for Christian worship. Edited by Melancthon Woolsey Stryker, and Herbert Platt Main. Tonic sol-fa edition, edited by Theodore F. Seward. New York, Biglow & Main, 1888, [c1887]
Seward, Theodore Frelinghuysen, 1835–1902, ed.

LAC 16880
Church unity; studies of its most important problems. New York, C. Scribner's sons, 1909.
Briggs, Charles Augustus, 1841–1913.

LAC 14961
The churches and educated men; a study of the relation of the church to makers and leaders of public opinion. Boston, New York [etc.] The Pilgrim press [1904]
Hardy, Edwin Noah, 1861–

LAC 40146
The churches and the peace movement. [Washington, The American peace society, 190–?]
Tryon, James Libby, 1864–

LAC 15596
The churches quarrel espoused.
A vindication of the government of New England churches. Boston, John Boyles, 1772.
Wise, John, 1652–1725.

LAC 11539
Circassia; or, A tour to the Caucasus. New York, Stringer & Townsend; [etc., etc.] 1850.
Ditson, George Leighton, 1812–1894.

LAC 40072
A circuit of the continent: account of a tour through the West and South. By Henry Ward Beecher. (With portrait.) Being his Thanksgiving day discourse at Plymouth church, Brooklyn, Nov. 29th, 1883, describing his trip through thirty states and territories... New York, Fords, Howard, & Hulbert, 1884.
Beecher, Henry Ward, 1813–1887.

LAC 11904
The circuit rider: a tale of the heroic age. New York, C. Scribner's sons, 1901, [c1878]
Eggleston, Edward, 1837–1902.

LAC 40124
Circular of information; instructions for volunteer field workers; the Museum of ethnology, natural history and commerce. Manila, 1901.
Philippine Islands. *Bureau of Non-Christian Tribes.*

LAC 15353
The circus; its origin and growth prior to 1835. New York, The Dunlap society, 1898.
Greenwood, Isaac John, 1833–1911.

LAC 15158
The citizen-soldier; or, Memoirs of a volunteer. Cincinnati, Wilstach, Baldwin & co., 1879.
Beatty, John, 1828–1914.

LAC 12519
The citizen's part in government. New Haven, Yale University Press; [etc., etc.] 1911, [c1907]
Root, Elihu, 1845–1937.

LAC 40088
City architecture; or, Designs for dwelling houses, stores, hotels, etc. In 20 plates. With descriptions and an essay on the principles of design. New-York, Appleton, 1854.
Field, Marriott, b. 1803?

LAC 11227
The city for the people; or, The municipalization of the city government and of local franchises. Revision August, 1901... Philadelphia, C. F. Taylor [1901]
Parsons, Frank, 1854–1908.

LAC 10735
City government in the United States; with a chapter on the Greater New York charter of 1897. 4th ed., rev. New York, D. Appleton and company, 1899.
Conkling, Alfred Ronald, 1850–1917.

LAC 15449
The city government of Boston. By Nathan Matthews, jr. A valedictory address to the members of the City council, January 5, 1895. Boston, Rockwell and Churchill, city printers, 1895.
Matthews, Nathan, 1854–1927.

LAC 14568
The city of the dinner-pail. Boston and New York, Houghton Mifflin company, 1909.
Lincoln, Jonathan Thayer, 1869–1942.

LAC 40082
The city of the Mormons; or, Three days at Nauvoo, in 1842. By the Rev. Henry Caswall. London, Printed for J. G. F. & J. Rivington, 1842.
Caswall, Henry, 1810–1870.

LAC 13162
The city of the saints, and across the Rocky mountains to California. London, Longman, Green, Longman and Roberts, 1861.
Burton, *Sir* Richard Francis, 1821–1890.

LAC 40041
City planning; an introductory address delivered by Frederick Law Olmsted at the second National conference on city planning and congestion of population, at Rochester, New York, May 2, 1910. Department of city making, Frederick L. Ford, chairman, Hartford, Conn. Washington, D. C., American civic association [1910]
Olmsted, Frederick Law, 1870–1957.

LAC 40041
City subways for pipes and wires. New York, J. B. Walker, 1899.
Bryant, Henry F.

LAC 15880
The city that was, by Stephen Smith, commissioner of the Metropolitan board of health, 1868–1870; commissioner of the Board of health of New York, 1870–1875. New York, F. Allaben [c1911]
Smith, Stephen, 1823–1922.

LAC 10883
The city, the hope of democracy. New York, C. Scribner's sons, 1914, [c1905]
Howe, Frederic Clemson, 1867–1940.

LÁC 11251
The city wilderness; a settlement study by residents and associates of the South End house ... South End Boston. Boston and New York, Houghton, Mifflin and company [c1898]
Woods, Robert Archey, 1865–1925, ed.

LAC 13384
A city's danger and defense. Or, Issues and results of the strikes of 1877, containing the origin and history of the Scranton city guard. By Samuel C. Logan, D. D. Scranton, Pa. [Philadelphia, Press of the J. B. Rodgers printing co.] 1887.
Logan, Samuel Crothers, 1823–1907.

LAC 40104
Civic centers. [New York, Reform club, Committee on civic affairs, 1902]
Warner, John DeWitt, 1851–

LAC 16153
Civil and military list of Rhode Island, 1647–1800. A list of all officers elected by the General assembly from the organization of the legislative government of the colony to 1800. Comp. from the records by Joseph Jencks Smith. Providence, R. I., Preston and Rounds co., 1900.
Smith, Joseph Jencks, d. 1907, comp.

LAC 12333
The civil and political history of the state of Tennessee from its earliest settlement up to the year 1796, including the boundaries of the state. By John Haywood. Exact reprint of the edition of 1823, pub. by W. H. Haywood, great-grandson of the author; with a biographical sketch of Judge John Haywood, by Col. A. S. Colyar. Nashville, Tenn. [etc.] Publishing house of the Methodist Episcopal church, South, 1915, [c1891]
Haywood, John, 1753?–1826.

LAC 12405
Civil history of the government of the Confederate States, with some personal reminiscences. Richmond, Va., B. F. Johnson publishing company [c1900]
Curry, Jabez Lamar Monroe, 1825–1903.

LAC 23238–39
The civil, political, professional and ecclesiastical history, and commercial and industrial record of the county of Kings and the city of Brooklyn, N. Y. from 1683 to 1884, by Henry R. Stiles, assisted by L. B. Proctor and L. P. Brockett. New York, W. W. Munsell & co. [c1884]
Stiles, Henry Reed, 1832–1909, ed.

LAC 13640
The civil service and the patronage. Cambridge, Harvard university press; [etc., etc., c1904]
Fish, Carl Russell, 1876–1932.

LAC 13111
Civil service in Great Britain; a history of abuses and reforms and their bearing upon American politics. New York, Harper & brothers, 1880.
Eaton, Dorman Bridgman, 1823–1899.

LAC 10265
Civil war and reconstruction in Alabama. New York, The Columbia university press, The Macmillan company, agents; [etc., etc.] 1905.
Fleming, Walter Lynwood, 1874–1932.

LAC 10258
The civil war and reconstruction in Florida. New York, Columbia university; [etc., etc.] 1913.
Davis, William Watson, 1884–1960.

LAC 20042
The Civil War and the Constitution, 1859–1865. New York, C. Scribner's sons, 1901.
Burgess, John William, 1844–1931.

LAC 15166
The civil war by campaigns. Topeka, Kan., Crane & company, 1899.
Foster, Eli Greenawalt.

LAC 40035
The civil war in America: an address read at the last meeting of the Manchester Union and emancipation society. London, Simpkin, Marshall & co.; [etc., etc.] 1866.
Smith, Goldwin, 1823–1910.

LAC 22641–42
The civil war on the border... New York and London, G. P. Putnam's sons, 1899–1904.
Britton, Wiley.

LAC 11413
Civilization in the United States; first and last impressions of America. Boston, Cupples and Hurd, 1889, [c1888]
Arnold, Matthew, 1822–1888.

LAC 12194–95
Civilized America. 2d ed. London, Bradbury and Evans, 1859.
Grattan, Thomas Colley, 1792–1864.

LAC 11471
The claim of the American loyalists reviewed and maintained upon incontrovertible principles of law and justice... London, Printed for G. and T. Wilkie, 1788.
Galloway, Joseph, 1731–1803.

LAC 40057
The claims of the Jews to an equality of rights. Illustrated in a series of letters to the editor of the Philadelphia gazette. Philadelphia, C. Sherman [1841]
Leeser, Isaac, 1806–1868, ed.

LAC 11899

The clansman; an historical romance of the Ku Klux klan, by Thomas Dixon, jr., illustrated by Arthur I. Keller. New York, Doubleday, Page & company, 1905.
Dixon, Thomas, 1864–1946.

LAC 13364

Clarence King memoirs. The helmet of Mambrino. New York and London, Pub. for the King memorial committee of the Century association by G. P. Putnam's sons, 1904.
The Century Association, *New York. King Memorial Committee.*

LAC 15529

A class-book of botany, designed for colleges, academies, and other seminaries. Part I. The elements of botanical science. Part II. The natural orders. Illustrated by a flora of the northern, middle, and western states; particularly of the United States north of the Capitol, lat. 38 3 4 deg. 23d ed., rev. and enl. Claremont, N. H., Manufacturing Co., 1851.
Wood, Alphonso, 1810–1881.

LAC 16815

Class struggles in America. 3d ed., rev. and enl., with notes and references. Chicago, C. H. Kerr & company [c1906]
Simons, Algie Martin, 1870–1950.

LAC 12954

The Clayton-Bulwer treaty and the Monroe doctrine. A letter from the secretary of state to the minister of the United States at London dated May 8, 1882, with sundry papers and documents explanatory of the same, selected from the archives of the Department of state. Washington, Govt. print. off., 1882.
U. S. *Dept. of State.*

LAC 11935

The cliff-dwellers, a novel, by Henry B. Fuller; illustrated by T. De Thulstrup. New York, Harper & brothers, 1893.
Fuller, Henry Blake, 1857–1929.

LAC 40032

The climate, soil, physical resources, and agricultural capabilites of the state of Maine, with special reference to the occupation of its new lands. Washington, Govt. print. off., 1884.
Boardman, Samuel Lane, 1836–1914.

LAC 16498

Clotelle; or, The colored heroine. A tale of the southern states. Miami, Mnemosyne publishing inc., 1969.
Brown, William Wells, 1815–1884.

LAC 10226

The clothing industry in New York. [Columbia, Mo.] University of Missouri, 1905.
Pope, Jesse Eliphalet, 1869–

LAC 21111

Clovernook; or, Recollections of our neighborhood in the West. [1st–]2d series. By Alice Carey [!] New York, Redfield, 1852, 1853.
Cary, Alice, 1820–1871.

LAC 10330

Coal, iron, and oil; or, The practical American miner. A plain and popular work on our mines and mineral resources, and text-book or guide to their economical development... By Samuel Harries Daddow and Benjamin Bannan. Pottsville, Pa., B. Bannan; Philadelphia, J. B. Lippincott & co.; [etc., etc.] 1866.
Daddow, Samuel Harries.

LAC 13412

The coal-mine workers; a study in labor organizations. New York [etc.] Longmans, Green and co., 1905.
Warne, Frank Julian, 1874–

LAC 16610

The coal mines; containing a description of the various systems of working and ventilating mines, together with a sketch of the principal coal regions of the globe, including statistics of the coal production. Cleveland, O., Robison, Savage & co., 1876.
Roy, Andrew.

LAC 14729

The coal-regions of America: their topography, geology, and development... 3d ed. with a supplement for the year 1874. New York, D. Appleton and company, 1875.
Macfarlane, James, 1819–1885.

LAC 40129

The coal regions of Pennsylvania, being a general, geological, historical & statistical review of the anthracite coal districts. Illustrated with ... maps and engravings, and ... containing ... statistical tables. Ed. by Ele [!] Bowen. Pottsville, Pa., E. N. Carvalho & co., 1848.
Bowen, Eli, *b.* 1824, *ed.*

LAC 11973

The coast of Bohemia. Biographical ed. New York and London, Harper & brothers, 1899.
Howells, William Dean, 1837–1920.

LAC 16932

The coast of Bohemia. New York, C. Scribner's sons, 1906.
Page, Thomas Nelson, 1853–1922.

LAC 40027

The code of honor, or, Rules for the government of principals and seconds in duelling. Charleston, S. C., Printed by J. Phinney, 1858.
Wilson, John Lyde, 1784–1849.

LAC 15655

The code of 1650, being a compilation of the earliest laws and orders of the General court of Connecticut: also, the constitution, or civil compact, entered into and adopted by the towns of Windsor, Hartford, and Wethersfield, in 1638-9. To which is added, some extracts from the laws and judicial proceedings of New-Haven colony, commonly called Blue laws. Hartford, S. Andrus [1822]
Connecticut *(Colony) Laws, statutes, etc.*

LAC 13607

Codex diplomaticus of Christopher Columbus.
Christopher Columbus, his own book of privileges, 1502. Photographic facsimile of the manuscript in the archives of the Foreign office in Paris, now for the first time

published, with expanded text, translation into English, and an historical introduction; the transliteration and translation by George F. Barwick, the introduction by Henry Harrisse; the whole comp. and ed. with preface, by Benjamin Franklin Stevens. London, B. F. Stevens, 1893.
Colombo, Cristoforo.

LAC 15646
Coin on money, trusts, and imperialism. Chicago, Ill., Coin publishing company [c1899]
Harvey, William Hope, 1851–1936.

LAC 13934
Coin's financial school. Chicago, Coin publishing company [1894]
Harvey, William Hope, 1851–1936.

LAC 11337
Colbert's West India policy. New Haven, Yale university press; [etc., etc.] 1912.
Mims, Stewart Lea, 1880–

LAC 12113
Collect.
Specimen days & Collect. Philadelphia, R. Welsh & co., 1882–83.
Whitman, Walt, 1819–1892.

LAC 13954
Collected essays and reviews. New York [etc.] Longmans, Green and co., 1920.
James, William, 1842–1910.

LAC 16889
Collected essays in political and social science. New York, H. Holt and company, 1885.
Sumner, William Graham, 1840–1910.

LAC 16338
Collected papers of Herbert D. Foster, professor of history at Dartmouth college, 1893–1927; historical and biographical studies. [New York] Priv. print., 1929.
Foster, Herbert Darling, 1863–1927.

LAC 23349–54
Collected works. New York, Gordian press [etc.] 1909–66.
Bierce, Ambrose, 1842–1914?

LAC 23379–85
The collected works (1871–1872) Hildesheim, G. Olms, 1969.
Kennedy, John Pendleton, 1795–1870.

LAC 10909
The collection and disposal of municipal waste. 1st ed. New York, The Municipal journal and engineer [c1908]
Morse, William Francis, 1841–

LAC 13610
A collection of documents on Spitzbergen and Greenland, comprising a translation from F. Martens' voyage to Spitzbergen; a translation from Isaac de La Peyrere's Histoire du Groenland; and God's power and providence in the preservation of eight men in Greenland nine moneths and twelve dayes. London, Printed for the Hakluyt society, 1855.
White, Adam, 1817–1879, *ed.*

LAC 15981
A collection of interesting, authentic papers, relative to the dispute between Great Britain and America; shewing the causes and progress of that misunderstanding, from 1764 to 1775. London, Printed for J. Almon, 1777.
Almon, John, 1737–1805, *comp.*

LAC 16505
A collection of millenial hymns, adapted to the present order of the church... Canterbury, N. H., Printed in the United society, 1847.
Shakers.

LAC 11716
A collection of original papers relative to the History of the colony of Massachusetts-bay. Boston, New England: Printed by Thomas and John Fleet, 1769.
Hutchinson, Thomas, 1711–1780, *comp.*

LAC 10068
Collection of plays and poems. Petersburg, Va., 1798.
Munford, Robert, *d.* 1784.

LAC 14468
A collection of some of the most interesting narratives of Indian warfare in the West, containing an account of the adventures of Colonel Daniel Boone, one of the first settlers of Kentucky, comprehending the most important occurrences relative to its early history—also, an account of the manners, and customs of the Indians, their traditions and religious sentiments, their police or civil government, their discipline and method of war: to which is added, an account of the expeditions of Genl's. Harmer, Scott, Wilkinson, St. Clair, & Wayne. The whole compiled from the best authorities, by Samuel L. Metcalf. Lexington, Ky., Printed by William G. Hunt, 1821. New York, Reprinted W. Abbatt, 1913.
Metcalfe, Samuel L   1798–1856.

LAC 16475
A collection of the facts and documents, relative to the death of Major-General Alexander Hamilton; with comments: together with the various orations, sermons, and eulogies, that have been published or written on his life and character... By the editor of the Evening post. New York, I. Riley and co., 1804.
Coleman, William, 1766–1829.

LAC 12346
Collection of the official accounts, in detail, of all the battles fought by sea and land, between the navy and army of the United States and the navy and army of Great Britain, during the years 1812, 13, 14, & 15. New-York, Printed by E. Conrad, 1817.
Fay, Heman Allen, 1799–1865, *ed.*

LAC 20065
A collection of the political writings of William Leggett selected and arranged with a preface by Theodore Sedgwick jr. New-York, Taylor & Dodd, 1840.
Leggett, William, 1801–1839.

LAC 21079–80
A collection of the sufferings of the people called Quakers for the testimony of a good conscience from the time of their being first distinguished by that name in the year 1650 to the time of the act commonly called the Act of toleration granted to Protestant dissenters in the first year of the reign of King William the Third and Queen Mary in the year 1689. Taken from original records and other authentick accounts. London, L. Hinde, 1753.
Besse, Joseph, 1683?–1757.

LAC 15781
A collection of the works of that ancient, faithful servant of Jesus Christ, Thomas Chalkley, who departed this life in the island of Tortola, the fourth day of the ninth month, 1741. To which is prefixed, A journal of his life, travels, and Christian experiences, written by himself. 5th ed. London, J. Phillips, 1791.
Chalkley, Thomas, 1675–1741.

LAC 20940–41
A collection of the works of William Penn. In two volumes. To which is prefixed a journal of his life. With many original letters and papers not before published. London, J. Sowle, 1726.
Penn, William, 1644–1718.

LAC 15266
A collection of the writings of John James Ingalls; essays, addresses, and orations... Kansas City, Mo., Hudson-Kimberly publishing co., 1902.
Ingalls, John James, 1833–1900.

LAC 22833–38
A collection of voyages and travels, some now first printed from original manuscripts, others now first published in English. To which is prefixed, an introductory discourse (supposed to be written by the celebrated Mr. Locke) intitled, The whole history of navigation from its original to this time. Illustrated with maps and cuts, curiously engraved. 3d ed. ... London, Printed by assignment from Messrs. Churchill, for H. Lintot [etc.] 1744–46.
Churchill, Awnsham, d. 1728, comp.

LAC 24080–84
Collections. v. 1–9. Savannah, Ga., The Georgia historical society, 1840–1916.
Georgia Historical Society.

LAC 23621–57
Collections, v. 1–70. [Cambridge, Mass., The Massachusetts historical society; etc., etc.] 1792–1915.
Massachusetts Historical Society, *Boston*.

LAC 21244–50
Collections. v. 1–14, 1824–1931. Concord [etc.]
New Hampshire Historical Society, *Concord*.

LAC 23705–12
Collections. v. 1–34; [1827]–Oct. 1941. Providence.
Rhode Island Historical Society.

LAC 12597
Collections for an essay towards a materia medica of the United States. Philadelphia, 1798 & 1804. With biography and portrait. [Cincinnati, Lloyd library, 1900]
Barton, Benjamin Smith, 1766–1815.

LAC 23223–24
Collections, historical and miscellaneous, and monthly literary journal. v. 1–3; Apr. 1822–Nov.–Dec. 1824. Concord, N. H., Hill and Moore.

LAC 23542–49
Collections of the Connecticut historical society. v. 1–14. Hartford, The society, 1860–1912.
Connecticut Historical Society, *Hartford*.

LAC 21491–504
Collections of the Maine historical society. [1st ser.] v. 1–10; 2d ser., v. 1–10; 3d ser., v. 1–2. Portland, The Society, 1831–1906.
Maine Historical Society.

LAC 23933–72
Collections of the New York historical society. v. 1–4, 4–5; 2d series, v. 1–4; publication fund series, v. 1–56. New York, 1811–1923.
New York Historical Society.

LAC 22891–92
Collections of the Vermont historical society, prepared and published by the printing and publishing committee in pursuance of a vote of the society. Montpelier, Printed for the Society, 1870–71.
Vermont Historical Society.

LAC 23801–6
Collections of the Virginia historical society, new series, v. 1–11. [Richmond, The Society, 1833–92]
Virginia Historical Society, *Richmond*.

LAC 23223–24
Collections, topographical, historical & biographical. Collections, historical and miscellaneous, and monthly literary journal. v. 1–3; Apr. 1822–Nov.–Dec. 1824. Concord, N. H., Hill and Moore.

LAC 15998
The college-bred Negro; report of a social study made under the direction of Atlanta university; together with the Proceedings of the fifth Conference for the study of the Negro problems, held at Atlanta university, May 29–30, 1900. Atlanta, Ga., Atlanta university press, 1900.
Du Bois, William Edward Burghardt, 1868–1963, *ed.*

LAC 15223
The college curriculum in the United States. New York, Teachers college, Columbia university, 1907.
Snow, Louis Franklin, 1862–

LAC 40101
College libraries in the United States. Boston, W. Kellogg, 1897.
Willard, Ashton Rollins, 1858–1918.

LAC 40033
The college of William and Mary: a contribution to the history of higher education, with suggestions for its national promotion. Washington, Govt. print. off., 1887.
Adams, Herbert Baxter, 1850–1901.

LAC 40101
The College settlements association. [New York, 1890]

LAC 13639
The college, the market, and the court; or, Woman's relation to education, labor, and law. Boston, Lee and Shepard, 1867.
Dall, Caroline Wells, 1822–1912.

LAC 40011
Colleges, a power in civilization to be used for Christ. A discourse before the Society for the promotion of collegiate and theological education at the West, delivered in High street church, Providence, R. I., October 30, 1855. New York, N. A. Calkins, 1856.
Storrs, Richard Salter, 1821–1900.

LAC 14676
The colleges and the courts; judicial decisions regarding institutions of higher education in the United States, by Edward C. Elliott and M. M. Chambers. New York city [Boston, D. B. Updike, The Merrymount press] 1936.
Elliott, Edward Charles, 1874–1960.

LAC 12981
Colleges in America. By John Marshall Barker, with an introduction by Rev. Sylvester F. Scovel. Cleveland, O., Cleveland Printing and Publishing, 1894.
Barker, John Marshall, 1849–

LAC 12073
Colonel Carter of Cartersville. With illustrations by E. W. Kemble and the author. Boston and New York, Houghton, Mifflin and company, 1896, [c1891]
Smith, Francis Hopkinson, 1838–1915.

LAC 11884
Col. Crockett's exploits and adventures in Texas: wherein is contained a full account of his journey from Tennessee to the Red river and Natchitoches, and thence across Texas to San Antonio; including his many hairbreadth escapes; together with a topographical, historical, and political view of Texas... Written by himself. [Philadelphia, J. E. Potter, 1865]
Smith, Richard Penn, 1799–1854, *supposed author.*

LAC 11862
The colonel's dream. Upper Saddle River, N.J., Gregg press [1968]
Chesnutt, Charles Waddell, 1858–1932.

LAC 14140
Colonial Amherst; the early history, customs and homes; geography and geology, of Amherst, life and character of General and Lord Jeffery Amherst, reminiscences of "Cricket Corner" and "Pond Parish" districts, by Prof. Warren Upham. Comp. by Emma P. Boylston Locke. [Milford, N. H., Printed by W. B. & A. B. Rotch] 1916.
Locke, Emma P   Boylston, *comp.*

LAC 13900
Colonial architecture of Cape Cod, Nantucket and Martha's Vineyard. New York, W. Helburn, inc., 1932.
Poor, Alfred Easton, 1899–

LAC 15599
Colonial children; selected and annotated by Albert Bushnell Hart, with the collaboration of Blanche E. Hazard. New York, The Macmillan company; [etc., etc.] 1901.
Hart, Albert Bushnell, 1854–1943.

LAC 23492–95
Colonial currency reprints, 1682–1751, with an introduction and notes, by Andrew McFarland Davis. Boston, Prince society, 1910–11.
Davis, Andrew McFarland, 1833–1920, *ed.*

LAC 13563
Colonial dames and good wives, written by Alice Morse Earle. Boston and New York, Houghton, Mifflin & company, 1895.
Earle, Alice, 1851–1911.

LAC 12230
Colonial days & ways as gathered from family papers, by Helen Evertson Smith, with decorations by T. Guernsey Moore. New York, The Century co., 1901, [c1900]
Smith, Helen Evertson.

LAC 10372
Colonial days in old New York. New York, C. Scribner's sons, 1896.
Earle, Alice, 1851–1911.

LAC 20698–99
Colonial families of Philadelphia. New York, Chicago, The Lewis publishing company, 1911.
Jordan, John Woolf, 1840–1921, *ed.*

LAC 13892
Colonial furniture in America. New York, C. Scribner's sons, 1901.
Lockwood, Luke Vincent, 1872–1951.

LAC 11291
The colonial history of Hartford, gathered from the original records ... by Rev. William De Loss Love PH. D. Hartford, Conn., The author, 1914.
Love, William De Loss, 1851–1918.

LAC 13885
The colonial homes of Philadelphia and its neighbourhood, by Harold Donaldson Eberlein and Horace Mather Lippincott; with 72 illustrations. Philadelphia and London, J. B. Lippincott company, 1912.
Eberlein, Harold Donaldson.

LAC 40090
Colonial immigration laws; a study of the regulation of immigration by the English colonies in America. New York, 1900.
Proper, Emberson Edward, 1864–

LAC 13820
Colonial justice in Virginia; the development of a judicial system, typical laws, and cases of the period. Richmond, The Dietz press, 1938.
Chumbley, George Lewis.

LAC 14744
The colonial laws of Massachusetts. Reprinted from the edition of 1672, with the supplements through 1686. Published by order of the City council of Boston, under the supervision of William H. Whitmore, record commissioner. Containing a new and complete index. Boston, 1887.
Massachusetts *(Colony) Laws, Statutes, etc.*

LAC 23339–44
The colonial laws of New York from the year 1664 to the revolution, including the charters to the Duke of York, the commissions and instructions to colonial governors, the Duke's laws, the laws of the Dongan and Leisler assemblies, the charters of Albany and New York and the acts of the colonial legislatures from 1691

to 1775 inclusive... Transmitted to the Legislature by the Commissioners of statutory revision, pursuant to chapter 125 of the laws of 1891. Albany, J. B. Lyon, state printer, 1894–96 [v. 1, '96]
New York (Colony) Laws, statutes, etc.

LAC 12248
Colonial life in New Hampshire. Boston, Ginn & company, 1899.
Fassett, James Hiram.

LAC 14071
Colonial Mobile. An historical study, largely from original sources, of the Alabama-Tombigbee basin from the discovery of Mobile bay in 1519 until the demolition of Fort Charlotte in 1821. Boston and New York, Houghton Mifflin and company, 1897.
Hamilton, Peter Joseph, 1859–1927.

LAC 20835–36
Colonial New York; Philip Schuyler and his family. New York, C. Scribner's sons, 1885.
Schuyler, George Washington, 1810–1888.

LAC 16530
Colonial precedents of our national land system as it existed in 1800... [Madison] The University of Wisconsin, 1910.
Ford, Amelia Clewley.

LAC 21577–91
[Colonial records of Pennsylvania] Harrisburg, Printed by T. Fenn & co., 1851–53.

LAC 20726
Colonial records of Spanish Florida; letters and reports of governors and secular persons... translated and edited by Jeannette Thurber Connor. Deland, The Florida state historical society, 1925–1930.
Connor, Jeannette M., d. 1927, ed. and tr.

LAC 22973–97
The colonial records of the state of Georgia, comp. and published under authority of the legislature by Allen D. Candler... v. 1–26. Atlanta, Ga., The Franklin printing and publishing co., Geo. W. Harrison, state printer, 1904–1916.

LAC 14104
Colonial self-government, 1652–1689. New York and London, Harper & brothers, 1904.
Andrews, Charles McLean, 1863–1943.

LAC 12249
The colonial tavern; A glimpse of New England town life in the seventeenth and eighteenth centuries. Providence, R. I., Preston and Rounds, 1897.
Field, Edward, 1858–

LAC 12148
Colonial times on Buzzard's bay. [2nd ed., enlarged] Boston and New York, Houghton, Mifflin and company, 1888.
Bliss, William Root, 1825–1906.

LAC 40127
The colonial trade of Connecticut. [New Haven] Published for the Tercentenary commission by the Yale university press, 1936.
Hooker, Roland Mather, 1900–

LAC 15861
The colonial Virginia register. A list of governors, councillors and other higher officials, and also of members of the House of burgesses, and the revolutionary conventions of the colony of Virginia. Comp. by William G. and Mary Newton Stanard. Albany, N. Y., J. Munsell's sons, 1902.
Stanard, William Glover, 1858–1933, comp.

LAC 16329
Colonial women of affairs; women in business and the professions in America before 1776, by Elisabeth Anthony Dexter, PH. D. 2d ed., rev. Boston and New York, Houghton Mifflin company, 1931.
Dexter, Elisabeth Williams, 1887–

LAC 16734
The color line; a brief in behalf of the unborn. New York, McClure, Phillips & co., 1905.
Smith, William Benjamin, 1850–1934.

LAC 14533
Colorado: a summer trip. New York, G. P. Putnam, and son, 1867.
Taylor, Bayard, 1825–1878.

LAC 10125
Colorado as an agricultural state. Its farms, fields, and garden lands. New York, Orange Judd co., 1883, [c1882]
Pabor, William Edgar, 1834–

LAC 13213
Colorado gold rush; contemporary letters and reports, 1858–1859. Glendale, Calif., The Arthur H. Clark company, 1941.
Hafen, Le Roy Reuben, 1893–   ed.

LAC 13197
Colorado; its gold and silver mines, farms and stock ranges, and health and pleasure resort. Tourist's guide to the Rocky mountains. New York, C. G. Crawford, printer, 1879.
Fossett, Frank.

LAC 16687
The colored American from slavery to honorable citizenship, by Prof. J. W. Gibson and Prof. W. H. Crogman. Special features: National negro business league and introduction by Prof. Booker T. Washington. Club movement among negro women by Fannie Barrier Williams. Atlanta, Ga., Naperville, Ill. [etc.] J. L. Nichols & co., 1903, [c1902]
Gibson, John William, 1841–

LAC 16478
The colored cadet at West Point; autobiography of Lieut. Henry Ossian Flipper, U.S.A., first graduate of color from the U.S. Military Academy. New York, H. Lee, 1878; New York, Johnson Reprint Corp. [1968]
Flipper, Henry Ossian, 1856–1940.

LAC 16615
A colored man round the world. By a quadroon. [Cleveland? O.] Printed for the author, 1858.
Dorr, David F

LAC 40092
A colored man's reminiscences of James Madison. Brooklyn, G. C. Beadle, 1865.
Jennings, Paul, *b.* 1799.

LAC 12868
The colored patriots of the American revolution, with sketches of several distinguished colored persons: to which is added a brief survey of the condition and prospects of colored Americans. By William C. Nell. With an introduction by Harriet Beecher Stowe. Boston, R. F. Wallcut, 1855.
Nell, William Cooper, 1816–1874.

LAC 15644
The colored regulars in the United States army, with a sketch of the history of the colored American, and an account of his services in the wars of the country, from the period of the revolutionary war to 1899. Introductory letter from Lieutenant-General Nelson A. Miles. By Chaplain T. G. Steward. Philadelphia, A. M. E. book concern, 1904.
Steward, Theophilus Gould, 1843–

LAC 15834
Colored school children in New York, by Frances Blascoer. Ed. by Eleanor Hope Johnson. [New York] Public education association of the city of New York, 1915.
Blascoer, Frances.

LAC 13171
Colton's traveler and tourist's guide-book through the western states and territories, containing brief descriptions of each, with the routes and distances on the great lines of travel. Accompanied by a map, exhibiting the township lines of the U. S. surveys, the boundaries of counties, position of cities, villages, settlements, etc. New York, J. H. Colton and company, 1855.
Colton, Joseph Hutchins, 1800–1893.

LAC 10606
Columbia. New York, Oxford university press, American branch; [etc., etc.] 1914.
Keppel, Frederick Paul, 1875–1943.

LAC 11823
The Columbiad, a poem. Printed by Fry and Kammerer for C. and A. Conrad and co. Philadelphia; Conrad, Lucas and co. Baltimore, 1807.
Barlow, Joel, 1754–1812.

LAC 16565
The Columbian history of education in Wisconsin. [Milwaukee] State committee on educational exhibit for Wisconsin, 1893.
Stearns, John William, 1839–1909, *ed.*

LAC 11873
The Columbian muse. A Selection of American poetry, from various authors of established reputation. New-York: Printed by J. Carey, 1794.

LAC 15377
The Columbian orator: containing a variety of original and selected pieces; together with rules; calculated to improve youth and others in the ornamental and useful art of eloquence. Stereotype edition. Boston: Printed for Caleb Bingham and co. and sold at their bookstore, no. 45 Cornhill, 1817.
Bingham, Caleb, 1757–1817.

LAC 14215
Combination, consolidation and succession of corporations. Principles, rules and leading cases collated, classified, abridged and annotated. Chicago, Callaghan & company, 1896.
Hirschl, Andrew Jackson, 1852–1908.

LAC 10181
Combination in the mining industry: a study of concentration in lake Superior iron ore production. New York, The Columbia university press, the Macmillan company, agents; [etc., etc.] 1905.
Mussey, Henry Raymond, 1875–1940.

LAC 40098
Combinations: their uses and abuses, with a history of the Standard oil trust. An argument relative to bills pending before the New York legislature, based upon testimony given before the Senate committee on general laws. New York, G. F. Nesbitt & co., 1888.
Dodd, Samuel Calvin Tait, 1836–1907.

LAC 15712
The coming climax in the destinies of America... Chicago, C. H. Kerr & company, 1891.
Hubbard, Lester Coe, 1843?–

LAC 13257
The coming empire; or, Two thousand miles in Texas on horseback. By H. F. McDaniel and N. A. Taylor. New York, Chicago [etc.] A. S. Barnes & company [c1877]
McDanield, H   F.

LAC 21841–44
Commentaries on American law. 4th ed. New-York, The author, 1840.
Kent, James, 1763–1847.

LAC 12554
Commentaries on law, embracing chapters on the nature, the source, and the history of law; on international law, public and private; and on constitutional and statutory law. Philadelphia, Kay & brother, 1884.
Wharton, Francis, 1820–1889.

LAC 12760–61
Commentaries on statute and constitutional law and statutory and constitutional construction, containing an examination of adjudged cases on constitutional law under the Constitution of the United States, and the constitution of the respective states concerning legislative power, and also the consideration of the rules of law in the construction of statutes and constitutional provisions. Albany, Gould, Banks & Gould; New York, Banks, Gould & co., 1848.
Smith, E   Fitch.

LAC 15282

Commentaries on the conflict of laws, foreign and domestic, in regard to contracts, rights, and remedies, and especially in regard to marriages, divorces, wills, successions, and judgments. By Joseph Story. 6th ed., carefully rev. and considerably enl., by Isaac F. Redfield. Boston, Little, Brown, and company, 1865.
Story, Joseph, 1779–1845.

LAC 15689

Commentaries on the Constitution of the United States, historical and juridical, with observations upon the ordinary provisions of state constitutions and a comparison with the constitutions of other countries. Volume I. Boston, The Boston book company, 1895.
Foster, Roger, 1857–1924.

LAC 15281

Commentaries on the Constitution of the United States; with a preliminary review of the constitutional history of the colonies and states, before the adoption of the Constitution. Abridged by the author, for the use of colleges and high schools... Boston, Hilliard, Gray, and company; Cambridge [Mass.] Brown, Shattuck, and co., 1833.
Story, Joseph, 1779–1845.

LAC 11145

Commentaries on the jurisdiction, practice, and peculiar jurisprudence of the courts of the United States. Vol. I, containing a view of the judicial power, and the jurisdiction and practice of the Supreme court of the United States. Philadelphia, T. & J. W. Johnson, 1854.
Curtis, George Ticknor, 1812–1894.

LAC 40039

The Commerce and navigation of the valley of the Mississippi; and also that appertaining to the city of St. Louis: considered, with reference to the improvement, by the general government, of the Mississippi River and its principal tributaries; being a report, prepared by authority of the delegates from the city of St. Louis, for the use of the Chicago convention of July 5, 1847. St. Louis, Mo., Printed by Chambers & Knapp [1847]

LAC 10324

The commerce of America with Europe; particularly with France and Great Britain... Shewing the importance of the American revolution to the interests of France... By J. P. Brissot de Warville, and Etienne Claviere. Tr. from the last French edition, rev. by Brissot, and called the 2d volume of his View of America. With the life of Brissot, and an appendix, by the translator. London, J. S. Jordan, 1794.
Brissot de Warville, Jacques Pierre, 1754–1793.

LAC 40106

The commercial and financial strength of the United States, as shown in the balances of foreign trade and the increased production of staple articles. Philadelphia, King & Baird, printers, 1864.
Blodget, Lorin, 1823–1901.

LAC 40039

Commercial associations; their uses and opportunities. Boston, J. H. Eastburn's press, 1869.
Hill, Hamilton Andrews, 1827–1895.

LAC 10823

Commercial directory; containing, a topographical description, extent and productions of different sections of the Union, statistical information relative to manufactures, commercial and port regulations, a list of the principal commercial houses, tables of imports and exports, foreign and domestic; tables of foreign coins, weights and measures, tariff of duties. Philadelphia, J. C. Kayser & co., 1823.

LAC 16362

The commercial policy of England toward the American colonies. New York, Columbia college, 1893.
Beer, George Louis, 1872–1920.

LAC 31367–71

The Commercial review of the South and West. v. 1–8; Jan. 1846–June 1850. New Orleans.

LAC 10407

Commercial trusts, the growth and rights of aggregated capital; an argument delivered before the Industrial commission at Washington, D. C., December 12, 1899, cor. and rev. New York & London, G. P. Putnam's sons, 1901.
Dos Passos, John Randolph, 1844–1917.

LAC 16920

Commissions and instructions from the lords proprietors of Carolina to public officials of South Carolina, 1685–1715. Ed. by A. S. Salley, jr., secretary of the Historical commission of South Carolina. Columbia, S. C., Printed for the Historical commission of South Carolina by the State co., 1916.
Carolina. *Proprietors.*

LAC 14483

Commodore Hull; papers of Isaac Hull, commodore, United States navy; edited by Gardner Weld Allen. [Boston] The Boston athenaeum, 1929.
Hull, Isaac, 1773–1843.

LAC 15019

Commodore John Rodgers, captain, commodore, and senior officer of the American navy, 1773–1838; a biography. Cleveland, O., The Arthur H. Clark company, 1910, [c1909]
Paullin, Charles Oscar, 1868 *or* 9–1944.

LAC 11965

The common lot. New York, The Macmillan company; London, Macmillan & co., ltd., 1919, [c1904]
Herrick, Robert, 1868–1938.

LAC 30504–8

The Common school journal. v. 1–10, Nov. 1838–Dec. 1848. Boston, Marsh, Capen, Lyon, and Webb [etc.] 1839–48.

LAC 13582

Common school law. A digest of the provisions of statute and common law as to the relations of the teacher to the pupil, the parent, and the district. With four hundred references to legal decisions in twenty-one different states; to which are added the eight hundred questions given at the first five New York examinations for state certificates. 4th ed. entirely rewritten. Syracuse, N. Y., Davis, Bardeen & co.; New York, Baker, Pratt & co., c1878.
Bardeen, Charles William, 1847–1924.

LAC 40090

Common sense applied to the immigrant question: showing why the "California immigrant union" was founded and what it expects to do. [San Francisco, Turnbull & Smith, printers, 1869]
Hopkins, Caspar Thomas, 1826–1893.

LAC 10482

Communication from the secretary of the Treasury transmitting ... the report of Israel D. Andrews ... on the trade and commerce of the British North American colonies, and upon the trade of the Great Lakes and rivers; also, notices of the internal improvements in each state, of the Gulf of Mexico and straits of Florida, and a paper on the cotton crop of the United States. Washington, R. Armstrong, 1853.
U.S. *Treasury Dept.*

LAC 10572

Communism and socialism in their history and theory, a sketch. New York, C. Scribner's sons, 1880.
Woolsey, Theodore Dwight, 1801–1889.

LAC 40073

Communism in America. New York, H. Holt and company, 1879.
James, Henry Ammon, 1854–1929.

LAC 11221

The communistic societies of the United States; from personal visit and observation: including detailed accounts of the Economists, Zoarites, Shakers, the Amana, Oneida, Bethel, Aurora, Icarian and other existing societies; their religious creeds, social practices, numbers, industries, and present condition. New York, Harper & brothers, 1875.
Nordhoff, Charles, 1830–1901.

LAC 16280

The compact with the charter and laws of the colony of New Plymouth: together with the charter of the Council at Plymouth, and an appendix, containing the Articles of confederation of the United colonies of New England, and other valuable documents. Published agreeably to a resolve, passed April 5, 1836. Under the supervision of William Brigham. Boston, Dutton and Wentworth, printers to the state, 1836.
New Plymouth Colony. *Laws, statutes, etc.*

LAC 15477

A comparison of the institutions of Moses with those of the Hindoos and other ancient nations; with remarks on Mr. Dupuis's origin of all religions, the laws and institutions of Moses methodized, and an address to the Jews on the present state of the world and the prophecies relating to it. Northumberland [Pa.] A. Kennedy, 1799.
Priestley, Joseph, 1733–1804.

LAC 40103

A compassionate address to the Christian Negroes in Virginia. With an appendix, containing some account of the rise and progress of Christianity among that poor people... Salop, Printed by F. Eddowes and F. Cotton, 1756.
Fawcett, Benjamin, 1715–1780.

LAC 40135

A compendious account of the whole art of breeding, nursing, and the right ordering of the silk-worm. Illustrated with figures engraven on copper: whereon is curiously exhibited the whole management of this profitable insect. London, Printed for J. Worrall [etc.] 1733.

LAC 11111

A compendious history of American Methodism. Abridged from the author's "History of the Methodist Episcopal church." New York, Hunt & Eaton, 1889, [c1867]
Stevens, Abel, 1815–1897.

LAC 10098

Compendium of agriculture; or, The farmer's guide, in the most essential parts of husbandry and gardening; compiled from the best American and European publications, and the unwritten opinions of experienced cultivators... By William Drown, with the aid and inspection of Solomon Drown, M. D. Providence, Printed by Field & Maxcy, 1824.
Drowne, William, 1793–1874.

LAC 11612

Compendium of transportation theories... A compilation of essays upon transportation subjects by eminent experts. Publication of series under direction of C. C. McCain. Washington, Kensington pub. co., 1893.
McCain, Charles Curtice, 1856–1942, *comp.*

LAC 14520

Compensation for injuries to employees of the United States arising from accidents occurring between August 1, 1908, and June 30, 1911. Report of operations under the act of May 30, 1908. Washington, Govt. print. off., 1913.
U.S. *Dept. of Commerce and Labor.*

LAC 15145–46

A compilation of all the treaties between the United States and the Indian tribes, now in force as laws. Prepared under the provisions of the act of Congress, approved March 3, 1873... Washington, Govt. print. off., 1873.
U.S. *Treaties, etc.*

LAC 21399–401

Compilation of executive documents and diplomatic correspondence relative to a trans-isthmian canal in Central America. With specific reference to the treaty of 1846 between the United States and New Granada (U.S. of Colombia) and the "Clayton-Bulwer" treaty of 1850 between the United States and Great Britain... [New York, The Evening post job printing house, 1905]
Sullivan and Cromwell, *New York.*

LAC 23166–70

Compilation of reports of Committee ... 1789–1901, First Congress, first session, to Fifty-sixth Congress, second session... Washington, Govt. print. off., 1901.
U.S. *Congress. Senate. Committee on Foreign Relations.*

LAC 20043–44

A compilation of the messages and papers of the confederacy, including the diplomatic correspondence, 1861–1865; published by permission of Congress by James D. Richardson. Nashville, United States publishing company, 1905.
Confederate States of America. *President.*

LAC 20814–23

A compilation of the messages and papers of the presidents, 1789–1897. Published, by authority of Congress, by James D. Richardson. Washington, Govt. print. off., 1896–99.
U.S. *President.*

LAC 16023
Complete both early and late history of the Ottawa and Chippewa Indians of Michigan, a grammar of their language, personal and family history of the author. Harbor Springs, Mich., Babcock & Darling, 1897.
Blackbird, Andrew J.

LAC 10105
The complete farmer and rural economist; containing a compendious epitome of the most important branches of agriculture and rural economy. 10th ed. rev. New York, C. M. Saxton, Agricultural book publisher, 1852.
Fessenden, Thomas Green, 1771–1837.

LAC 20160–61
A complete history of Connecticut, civil and ecclesiastical, from the emigration of its first planters, from England, in the year 1630, to the year 1764; and to the close of the Indian wars. With an appendix containing the original patent of New England. New London, H. D. Utley, 1898.
Trumbull, Benjamin, 1735–1820.

LAC 15001
A complete history of the late war, or, Annual register, of its rise, progress, and events, in Europe, Asia, Africa, and America... With ... additions ... taken from Capt. John Knox's Historical journal of the war in America. 6th ed. ... Dublin, J. Exshaw, 1774.
The Annual Register of World Events.

LAC 13553
The complete journal of Townsend Harris, first American consul and minister to Japan. Introduction and notes by Mario Emilio Cosenza. With a pref. by Douglas MacArthur, II. Rev. [i. e. 2d] ed. Rutland, Vt., C. E. Tuttle Co. [1959]
Harris, Townsend, 1804–1878.

LAC 13681
The complete manual for young sportsmen: with directions for handling the gun, the rifle, and the rod; the art of shooting on the wing; the breaking, management, and hunting of the dog; the varieties and habits of game; river, lake, and sea fishing, etc. ... By Frank Forester [pseud.] Rev. ed. New York, Excelsior publishing house [c1873]
Herbert, Henry William, 1807–1858.

LAC 12583
The complete poetical works of Joaquin Miller. Rev. ed. San Francisco, The Whitaker & Ray co., 1902.
Miller, Joaquin, 1841–1913.

LAC 13566
A complete practical guide to the art of dancing. Containing descriptions of all fashionable and approved dances, full directions for calling the figures, the amount of music required; hints on etiquette, the toilet, etc. New York, Dick & Fitzgerald, 1868, [c1863]
Hillgrove, Thomas.

LAC 23034–36
The complete prose works of Walt Whitman. New York, G. P. Putnam's sons, 1902.
Whitman, Walt, 1819–1892.

LAC 23056–61
Complete works of Abraham Lincoln, ed. by John G. Nicolay and John Hay; with a general introduction by Richard Watson Gilder, and special articles by other eminent persons. New and enl. ed. New York, Francis D. Tandy company [c1905]
Lincoln, Abraham, pres. U.S., 1809–1865.

LAC 21414–16
The complete works of Count Rumford. Published by the American academy of arts and sciences. Boston [1870–75]
Rumford, Sir Benjamin Thompson, count, 1753–1814.

LAC 21379–86
The complete works of Edgar Allan Poe; ed. by James A. Harrison. [Virginia ed.] New York, A M S Press [1965]
Poe, Edgar Allan, 1809–1849.

LAC 23009–13
The complete works of Henry George. New York, Doubleday, Page & company, 1904.
George, Henry, 1839–1897.

LAC 23357–77
The complete works of J. Fenimore Cooper. Leather stocking edition in thirty-two volumes... [New York, G. P. Putnam's sons, 1893?]
Cooper, James Fenimore, 1789–1851.

LAC 16684
The complete works of Josh Billings, (Henry W. Shaw) With one hundred illustrations by Thomas Nast and others, and a biographical introduction. Rev. ed. Chicago, New York, M. A. Donohue [c1876]
Shaw, Henry Wheeler, 1818–1885.

LAC 22503–11
The complete works of Nathaniel Hawthorne, with introductory notes by George Parsons Lathrop and illustrated with etchings by Blum, Church, Dielman, Gifford, Shirlaw, and Turner... [Boston, Houghton Mifflin, 1882–99]
Hawthorne, Nathaniel, 1804–1864.

LAC 20612–23
The complete works of Ralph Waldo Emerson, with a biographical introduction and notes by Edward Waldo Emerson, and a general index. [Centenary ed.] [Boston and New York, Houghton, Mifflin and company, 1903–04]
Emerson, Ralph Waldo, 1803–1882.

LAC 15831
The complete writings of Constantine Smaltz Rafinesque, on recent & fossil conchology. Ed. by Wm. G. Binney and George W. Tryon, jr. New York, Bailliere brothers; [etc., etc.] 1864.
Rafinesque, Constantine Samuel, 1783–1840.

LAC 21003–10
The complete writings of James Russell Lowell. Ed. de luxe. [Cambridge, Printed at the Riverside press, 1904]
Lowell, James Russell, 1819–1891.

LAC 23874-78

The complete writings of O. Henry [*pseud.*]... Garden City, N. Y., Doubleday, Page and company, 1917.
Porter, William Sydney, 1862–1910.

LAC 40057

A comprehensive immigration policy and program; a step towards peace. Boston, American Unitarian association [1916]
Gulick, Sidney Lewis, 1860–

LAC 40098

Concentrated wealth. Madison, Wis., 1910.
Edwards, Richard Henry, 1877–1954, *ed.*

LAC 10215

Concentration and control; a solution of the trust problem in the United States. New York, The Macmillan company, 1912.
Van Hise, Charles Richard, 1857–1918.

LAC 11090

The conception of God. A philosophical discussion concerning the nature of the divine idea as a demonstrable reality, by Josiah Royce, Joseph Le Conte and G. H. Howison, and Sidney Edward Mezes. New York, The Macmillan company; London, Macmillan & co., ltd., 1897.
Royce, Josiah, 1855–1918.

LAC 20828

A concise and impartial history of the American revolution. To which is prefixed, a general history of North and South America. Together with an account of the discovery and settlement of North America... Printed at Boston, By I. Thomas and E. T. Andrews, (proprietors of the work) Faust's statue, No. 45, Newbury street, 1795.
Lendrum, John.

LAC 40073

A concise exposition of the doctrine of association. Or, Plan for a re-organization of society, which will secure to the human race, individually and collectively, their happiness and elevation. (Based on Fourier's theory of domestic and industrial association.) 7th ed. New York, J. S. Redfield, 1844.
Brisbane, Albert, 1809–1890.

LAC 16088

A concise history of the iron manufacture of the American colonies up to the revolution, and of Pennsylvania until the present time. Philadelphia, Allen, Lane & Scott, 1876.
Pearse, John Barnard, 1842–1914.

LAC 10935

A concise history of the Methodist Protestant Church, from its origin: with biographical sketches of several leading ministers of the denomination, and also a sketch of the author's life. With an introduction by William Collier. 3d ed. rev. and enl. Pittsburg, W. M. McCracken; Baltimore, W. J. C. Dulary, 1887.
Bassett, Ancel Henry.

LAC 14889

A concise history of the Mormon battalion in the Mexican War, 1846–1847. Chicago, Rio Grande Press [1964]
Tyler, Daniel, *b.* 1816.

LAC 40102

A concise refutation of the claims of New-Hampshire and Massachusetts-Bay, to the territory of Vermont: with occasional remarks on the long disputed claim of New-York to the same. Written by Ethan Allen and Jonas Fay, esq'rs. and pub. by order of the governor and Council of Vermont. Bennington, the first day of January, 1780. Joseph Fay, sec'ry. Hartford, Printed by Hudson and Goodwin [1780]
Allen, Ethan, 1738–1789.

LAC 15427

Conclin's new river guide, or A gazetteer of all the towns on the western waters: containing sketches of the cities, towns and countries ... on the Ohio and Mississippi rivers, and their principal tributaries ... with their population ... commerce, &c., &c., in 1848... With forty-four maps. Cincinnati, G. Conclin, 1849, [c1848]
Conclin, George.

LAC 11808

Concord days. Boston, Roberts brothers, 1872.
Alcott, Amos Bronson, 1799–1888.

LAC 40036

A condensed anti-slavery Bible argument; by a citizen of Virginia. New York, Printed by S. W. Benedict, 1845.
Bourne, George, 1780–1845.

LAC 22672-73

A condensed geography and history of the western states, or the Mississippi valley. Cincinnati, E. H. Flint, 1828.
Flint, Timothy, 1780–1840.

LAC 40059

Condensed proceedings of the Southern convention, held at Nashville, Tennessee, June, 1850. Published by authority. Jackson, Miss., Fall & Marshall, printers, 1850.
Southern Convention. *Nashville*, 1850.

LAC 16709

The condition, elevation, emigration, and destiny of the colored people of the United States. Politically considered, by Martin Robison Delany. Philadelphia, The author, 1852.
Delany, Martin Robison, 1812–1885.

LAC 40107

The condition of the Mission Indians of Southern California. Philadelphia, Office of the Indian rights association, 1901.
Du Bois, Constance Goddard.

LAC 13067

Condition of the Negro in various cities. Washington, Govt. print. off., 1897.
U.S. *Bureau of Labor.*

LAC 13560

The condition of woman in the United States. A traveller's notes. By Madame Blanc. (Th. Bentzon) Tr. by Abby Langdon Alger. Boston, Roberts brothers, 1895.
Blanc, Marie Therese, 1840–1907.

LAC 40067

Conditions in the Philippines... Editorial correspondence of the Evening Star, Washington, D. C., by Theodore W. Noyes, relative to conditions in the Philippines. [Washington, U.S. Govt. print. off., 1900]
U.S. *Congress. Senate. Committee on Territories and Insular Affairs.*

LAC 13117

Conditions of living among the poor. By S. E. Forman. Washington, Govt. print. off., 1906.
U.S. *Bureau of Labor.*

LAC 12474

Conditions of progress in democratic government. New Haven, Yale university press; [etc., etc.] 1910.
Hughes, Charles Evans, 1862–1948.

LAC 40085

The conduct of a noble commander in America, impartially reviewed. With the genuine causes of the discontents at New-York and Hallifax. And the true occasion of the delays in that important expedition. Including a regular account of all the proceedings and incidents in the order of time wherein they happened. London, Printed for R. Baldwin, 1758.

LAC 15395

The conduct of Major Gen. Shirley, late general and commander in chief of His Majesty's forces in North America. Briefly stated. London, Printed for R. & J. Dodsley [etc.] 1758.
Alexander, William, 1726–1783.

LAC 40065

The conduct of the administration... Boston, Stimpson & Clapp, 1832.
Everett, Alexander Hill, 1790–1847.

LAC 12567

Conductor Generalis: or, the Office, Duty and Authority of Justices of the Peace, High-Sheriffs, Under-Sheriffs, Coroners, Constables, Goalers [!] Jury-Men, and Overseers of the Poor. As also, the Office of Clerks of Assize and of the Peace, &c. To which are added, Several Choice Maxims in Law, &c. Compiled chiefly from Burn's Justice, and the several other Books on those Subjects. By James Parker, Esquire, late Justice of the Peace in Middlesex County, in New Jersey. Adapted to these United States. The whole Alphabetically digested under the several Titles; with a Table directing to the ready finding out the proper Matter under those Titles. New-York: Printed by John Patterson, for Robert Hodge, 1788.

LAC 16356

A Confederate girl's diary, by Sarah Morgan Dawson; with an introduction by Warrington Dawson and with illustrations. Boston and New York, Houghton Mifflin company, 1913.
Dawson, Sarah, 1842–1909.

LAC 22773–81

Confederate military history; a library of Confederate states history ... written by distinguished men of the South, and ed. by Gen. Clement A. Evans. Atlanta, Ga., Confederate publishing company, 1899.
Evans, Clement Anselm, 1833–1911, *ed.*

LAC 16856

The Confederate soldier in the civil war, 1861–1865. Prefaced by a eulogy by Major-General Fitzhugh Lee. The foundation and formation of the Confederacy and the secession of the southern states and the prominent parts taken by Hon. Jefferson Davis, Hon. Alexander H. Stephens and others. Campaigns, battles, sieges, charges, skirmishes, etc. By General Robert E. Lee, Generals Albert Sidney Johnston, Joseph E. Johnston and others. The Confederate states navy, from its first organization to the end of the war. Naval engagements, blockade running, operations of cruisers, torpedo service, etc. By Admiral Franklin Buchanan, Rear Admiral Raphael Semmes, etc. Edited by Ben La Bree... Louisville, Ky. The Prentice press (The Courier-journal job printing company) 1897.
La Bree, Benjamin, *ed.*

LAC 14159

The Confederate States of America, 1861–1865; a financial and industrial history of the South during the civil war. New York, C. Scribner's sons; London, E. Arnold, 1901.
Schwab, John Christopher, 1865–1916.

LAC 16109

Confederate war papers. Fairfax Court House, New Orleans, Seven Pines, Richmond and North Carolina. 2d ed. New York, Atlantic pub. and engraving co., 1884.
Smith, Gustavus Woodson, 1822–1896.

LAC 13444

The confederation and the constitution, 1783–1789. New York and London, Harper & brothers [c1905]
McLaughlin, Andrew Cunningham, 1861–1947.

LAC 10840

Confession; or, The blind heart; a domestic story. New and rev. ed. New York, Redfield, 1856.
Simms, William Gilmore, 1806–1870.

LAC 13554

Confessions and criticisms. Boston, Ticknor and company, 1887, [c1886]
Hawthorne, Julian, 1846–1934.

LAC 14116

The confessions of a reformer. New York, C. Scribner's sons, 1925.
Howe, Frederic Clemson, 1867–1940.

LAC 10651

The confessions of Nat Turner, leader of the late insurrection in Southampton, Va. ... made to Thos. C. Gray ... and acknowledged by him ... when read before the court of Southampton, convened at Jerusalem, November 5, 1831, for his trial [n. p., n. d.]
Turner, Nat, 1800?–1831.

LAC 16409

The confidence-man: his masquerade. New York, Dix, Edwards & co., 1857.
Melville, Herman, 1819–1891.

LAC 22392–93

Confidential correspondence of Gustavus Vasa Fox, assistant secretary of the navy, 1861–1865, edited by Robert Means Thompson and Richard Wainwright. New York, Printed for the Naval history society by the De Vinne press, 1918–19, [c1920]
Fox, Gustavus Vasa, 1821–1883.

LAC 13056

The confidential correspondence of Robert Morris, the great financier of the revolution and signer of the Declaration of independence, embracing letters of the most vital historical importance from signers of the Declaration of independence (many of them written in 1776) members of the Continental congress, generals, commodores, other officers and patriots in the revolution ... to be sold Tuesday afternoon and evening, Jan. 16th, 1917... Philadelphia, Pa., S. V. Henkels [1917?]
Morris, Robert, 1734–1806.

LAC 12738

The confiscation of John Chandler's estate. Boston and New York, Houghton, Mifflin and company, 1903.
Davis, Andrew McFarland, 1833–1920.

LAC 16869

The conflict and commingling of the races; a plea not for the heathens by a heathen to them that are not heathens. New York, Broadway publishing company, 1913.
Taylor, Caesar Andrew Augustus P.

LAC 14244

The conflict over judicial powers in the United States to 1870. New York, Columbia university, Longmans, Green & co., agent; [etc., etc.] 1909.
Haines, Charles Grove, 1879–1948.

LAC 16591

The Congo, and other poems; by Vachel Lindsay, with an introduction by Harriet Monroe. New York, The Macmillan company, 1919, [c1914]
Lindsay, Nicholas Vachel, 1879–1931.

LAC 13630–31

The Congregationalism of the last three hundred years, as seen in its literature: with special reference to certain recondite, neglected, or disputed passages. In twelve lectures, delivered on the Southworth foundation in the Theological seminary at Andover, Mass., 1876–1879. With a bibliographical appendix. New York, Harper & brothers, 1880.
Dexter, Henry Martyn, 1821–1890.

LAC 40028

A congress of nations. Addresses at the International peace congresses at Brussells (1848), Paris (1849), and Frankfort (1850). [Boston, Directors of the Old South work, 1904]
Burritt, Elihu, 1810–1879.

LAC 12562

Congressional government: a study in American politics. Boston, New York, Houghton, Mifflin and company, 1885.
Wilson, Woodrow, *pres. U.S.*, 1856–1924.

LAC 13485

Congressional grants of land in aid of railways. Madison, Wis., 1899.
Sanborn, John Bell, 1876–

LAC 14208

A Congressional history of railways in the United States to 1850. Madison, Wis., 1908.
Haney, Lewis Henry, 1882–

LAC 15526

Congressional policy of Chinese immigration; or, Legislation relating to Chinese immigration to the United States. Nashville, Tenn., Printed for the author, Publishing house of the Methodist Episcopal church, South, 1916.
Li, Tien Lu.

LAC 14519

Congressional reminiscences. Adams, Benton, Calhoun, Clay, and Webster. An address: delivered at Central music hall ... March 16, 1882, before the Chicago historical society; with notes and an appendix. Chicago, Fergus printing company, 1882.
Wentworth, John, 1815–1888.

LAC 15927

Congressman Swanson. Chicago, C. H. Sergel & company [c1891]
Post, Charles Cyrel, 1846–

LAC 14580

Coniston, by Winston Churchill. With illustrations by Florence Scovel Shinn. New York, The Macmillan company; London, Macmillan & co., ltd., 1906.
Churchill, Winston, 1871–1947.

LAC 11863

The conjure woman. Boston and New York, Houghton, Mifflin and company, 1900, [c1899]
Chesnutt, Charles Waddell, 1858–1932.

LAC 10160

A connected view of the whole internal navigation of the United States, natural and artificial; present and prospective. With maps. Philadelphia, H. C. Carey & I. Lea, 1826.
Armroyd, George.

LAC 11721

Connecticut; a study of a commonwealth-democracy. Boston, Houghton, Mifflin, 1888, [c1887]
Johnston, Alexander, 1849–1889.

LAC 15894

Connecticut as a corporate colony... Lancaster, Pa., The New era printing company, 1906.
Mead, Nelson Prentiss, 1878–

LAC 11817

The conqueror; being the true and romantic story of Alexander Hamilton. New York, The Macmillan company; London, Macmillan & co., ltd., 1914, [c1902]
Atherton, Gertrude Franklin, 1857–1948.

LAC 10135

The conquest of arid America. New and rev. ed. New York and London, Macmillan company, 1905.
Smythe, William Ellsworth, 1861–1922.

LAC 14178

The conquest of Kansas, by Missouri and her allies. A history of the troubles in Kansas, from the passage of the organic act until the close of July, 1856. Boston, Phillips, Sampson and company, 1856.
Phillips, William Addison, 1824–1893.

LAC 13158

The conquest of mount McKinley: the story of three expeditions through the Alaskan wilderness to mount McKinley, North America's highest and most inaccessible mountain, by Belmore Browne; appendix by Herschel C. Parker: with 100 illustrations from original drawings by the author and from photographs and maps. New York and London, G. P. Putnam's sons, 1913.
Browne, Belmore, 1880–

LAC 22670-71

Conquest of the country northwest of the river Ohio 1778-1783; and life of Gen. George Rogers Clark. Over one hundred and twenty-five illustrations. With numerous sketches of men who served under Clark... Indianapolis, Ind., and Kansas City, Mo., The Bowen-Merrill company, 1896.
English, William Hayden, 1822-1896.

LAC 16527

The conquest of the old Southwest; the romantic story of the early pioneers into Virginia, the Carolinas, Tennessee, and Kentucky, 1740-1790. New York, The Century co. [c1920]
Henderson, Archibald, 1877-1963.

LAC 14302

Conrad Weiser and the Indian policy of colonial Pennsylvania. Philadelphia, G. W. Jacobs & co. [c1900]
Walton, Joseph Solomon, d. 1912.

LAC 40087

Conrad Weiser's journal of a tour to the Ohio, August 11-October 2, 1748... [Cleveland, Arthur H. Clark, 1904]
Weiser, Conrad, 1696-1760.

LAC 16656

Consciousness in Concord; the text of Thoreau's hitherto "lost journal," 1840-1841, together with notes and a commentary by Perry Miller. Boston, Houghton Mifflin, 1958.
Thoreau, Henry David, 1817-1862.

LAC 11046

The conservative reformation and its theology: as represented in the Augsburg confession, and in the history and literature of the Evangelical Lutheran church. Philadelphia, J. B. Lippincott company, 1888, [c1871]
Krauth, Charles Porterfield, 1823-1883.

LAC 14557

Considerations on painting; lectures given in the year 1893 at the Metropolitan museum of New York. New York and London, Macmillan and co., 1896, [c1895]
La Farge, John, 1835-1910.

LAC 15816

Considerations on some of the elements and conditions of social welfare and human progress. Being academic and occasional discourses and other pieces, by C. S. Henry, D. D. New York [etc.] D. Appleton and company, 1861.
Henry, Caleb Sprague, 1804-1884.

LAC 15715

Considerations on some recent social theories. Boston, Little, Brown, and co., 1853.
Norton, Charles Eliot, 1827-1908.

LAC 40126

Considerations, on the approaching dissolution, of the United States bank. In a series of numbers. New-Haven, Sidney's press, 1810.
Atwater, Jesse.

LAC 40016

Considerations on the great western canal, from the Hudson to lake Erie: with a view of its expence, advantages, and progress. Re-published by order of the New-York corresponding association, for the promotion of internal improvements. Spooner & Worthington, printers, Brooklyn. 1818.
Haines, Charles Glidden, 1792-1825.

LAC 40028

Considerations on the injustice and impolicy of punishing murder by death. Extracted from the American museum. With additions. Philadelphia, M. Carey, 1792.
Rush, Benjamin, 1745-1813.

LAC 14701

Considerations on the measures carrying on with respect to the British colonies in North America. The 2d ed. With additions and an appendix relative to the present state of affairs on that continent... London, Printed for R. Baldwin [etc., 1774]
Rokeby, Matthew Robinson-Morris, 2d baron, 1713-1800.

LAC 40004

Considerations on the necessity of establishing an agricultural college, and having more of the children of wealthy citizens educated for the profession of farming. Albany, Printed by Websters & Skinners, 1819.
De Witt, Simeon, 1756-1834.

LAC 40091

Considerations on the practicability and utility of immediately constructing a central railway, from Pottsville to Sunbury and Danville, through the coal region of Mahanoy and Shamokin, with the proceedings of a meeting at Sunbury, Dec. 1830. Republished with additions by the Philadelphia committee... [Philadelphia] 1830.

LAC 40147

Considerations on the present state of Virginia; attributed to John Randolph, attorney general; and Considerations on the present state of Virginia examined, by Robert Carter Nicholas; edited by Earl Gregg Swem. New York city, C. F. Heartman, 1919.
Randolph, John, 1727-1784, supposed author.

LAC 40115

Considerations on the Society or order of Cincinnati; lately instituted by the major-generals, brigadier-generals, and other officers of the American army. Proving that it creates a race of hereditary patricians, or nobility. Interspersed with remarks on its consequences to the freedom and happiness of the republic. Addressed to the people of South-Carolina, and their representatives. By Cassius. Supposed to be written by Aedanus Burke. Philadelphia, Robert Bell. M.DCC.LXXXIII.
Burke, Aedanus, 1743?-1802?

LAC 12578

Considerations on the trade and finances of this kingdom, and on the measures of administration, with respect to those great national objects since the conclusion of the peace. London, Printed for J. Wilkie, 1766.
Whately, Thomas, *d.* 1772.

LAC 40129

Considerations upon the art of mining. To which are added, reflections on its actual state in Europe, and the advantages which would result from an introduction of this art into the United States. Philadelphia, M. Carey and sons, 1821.
Keating, William Hypolitus, 1799–1840.

LAC 14243

Considerations upon the nature and tendency of free institutions. Cincinnati, H. W. Derby & co.; [etc., etc.] 1848.
Grimke, Frederick, 1791–1863.

LAC 12343

The conspiracy unveiled. The South sacrificed; or, The horrors of secession. By Rev. James W. Hunnicutt, editor of the Fredericksburg (Va.) Christian banner. Philadelphia, J. B. Lippincott & co., 1863.
Hunnicutt, James W., 1814–

LAC 20083

Constantinople and its environs. In a series of letters, exhibiting the actual state of the manners, customs, and habits of the Turks, Armenians, Jews, and Greeks... By an American, long resident at Constantinople. New-York, Harper & brothers, 1835.
Porter, David, 1780–1843.

LAC 16726

Constitution and digest of the laws and enactments of the order of Patrons of husbandry; including the decisions of the masters, executive committees, and court of appeals of the National grange, from the organization of the order to April 1, 1907, in which is included declaration of purposes, the parliamentary guide, rules and regulations for grange trials, etc. Issued by authority of the National grange. Rev. ed. St. Johnsbury, Vt., The Republican company, 1907.
Patrons of Husbandry. *National Grange.*

LAC 16000

Constitution and laws of the Cherokee nation. Published by authority of the National council. St. Louis, R. & T. A. Ennis, printers, 1875.
Cherokee Nation. *Constitution.*

LAC 40049

The constitution of the state of New Mexico, adopted by the Constitutional convention, held at Santa Fe, N. M., September 3–21, 1889; amended August 18–20, 1890; and Address to the people by a Committee of the convention. [Santa Fe? 1890?]
New Mexico *(Ter.) Constitutional Convention,* 1889.

LAC 21397–98

The Constitution of the United States. A critical discussion of its genesis, development, and interpretation. By John Randolph Tucker. Ed. by Henry St. George Tucker. Chicago, Callaghan & co., 1899.
Tucker, John Randolph, 1823–1897.

LAC 10556–57

The Constitution of the United States of America; analysis and interpretation. Annotations of cases decided by the Supreme Court of the United States to June 30, 1952. Prepared by the Legislative Reference Service, Library of Congress, Edward S. Corwin, editor. Washington, U.S. Govt. Print. Off., 1953.
U. S. *Constitution.*

LAC 14952

The constitution of the United States, with notes of the decisions of the Supreme Court thereon, from the organization of the court till October, 1900. Madison, Wis., The Democrat printing company, 1901.
Bryant, Edwin Eustace, 1835–1903.

LAC 22601–06

The constitutional and political history of the United States. By Dr. H. von Holst. Chicago, Callaghan, 1881–92.
Holst, Hermann Eduard von, 1841–1904.

LAC 13455

Constitutional conflict in provincial Massachusetts; a study of some phases of the opposition between the Massachusetts governor and General court in the early eighteenth century... Columbus, Ohio, Fred. J. Heer, 1905.
Spencer, Henry Russell, 1879–

LAC 14856

The constitutional convention; its history, powers, and modes of proceeding. New York, C. Scribner and company; Chicago, Callaghan and Cutler, 1867.
Jameson, John Alexander, 1824–1890.

LAC 13969

Constitutional equality a right of woman: or, A consideration of the various relations which she sustains as a necessary part of the body of society and humanity; with her duties to herself–together with a review of the Constitution of the United States, showing that the right to vote is guaranteed to all citizens. Also a review of the rights of children. By Tennie C. Claflin. New York, Woodhull, Claflin & co., 1871.
Cook, Tennessee Celeste, *Lady,* 1845–1923.

LAC 16824

Constitutional government in the United States. New York, The Columbia university press, 1921, [c1908]
Wilson, Woodrow, *pres. U.S.,* 1856–

LAC 13699

Constitutional history and political development of the United States. New York [etc.] Cassell, Petter, Galpin & co. [1882]
Sterne, Simon, 1839–1901.

LAC 21166–70

The constitutional history of New York from the beginning of the colonial period to the year 1905, showing the origin, development, and judicial construction of the constitution. Rochester, N. Y., The Lawyers co-operative publishing company, 1906.
Lincoln, Charles Zebina, 1848–

LAC 20366

The constitutional history of the Presbyterian church in the United States of America. Philadelphia, William S. Martien, 1839–40.
Hodge, Charles, 1797–1878.

LAC 12750
Constitutional history of the United States as seen in the development of American law; a course of lectures before the Political science association of the University of Michigan... New York & London, G. P. Putnam's sons, 1889.
Michigan. University. *Political Science Association.*

LAC 21184-86
The constitutional history of the United States, 1765–1895... Chicago, Callaghan & company, 1901.
Thorpe, Francis Newton, 1857–1926.

LAC 12759
Constitutional law. Being a collection of points arising upon the Constitution and jurisprudence of the United States, which have been settled, by judicial decision and practice. Philadelphia, A. Small, 1822.
Sergeant, Thomas, 1782–1860.

LAC 16281
Constitutional legislation in the United States; its origin, and application to the relative powers of Congress, and of state legislatures. Philadelphia, T. & J. W. Johnson & co., 1891.
Ordronaux, John, 1830–1908.

LAC 16602
The constitutional power of Congress over the territory of the United States. [Philadelphia, Avil printing co., 1901]
Bikle, Henry Wolf, 1877–

LAC 10595
Constitutional provisions in regard to education in the several states of the American union. Washington, Govt. print. off., 1875.
Hough, Franklin Benjamin, 1822–1885.

LAC 11379
Constitutional republicanism, in opposition to fallacious federalism; as published occasionally in the Independent chronicle, under the signature of Old-South. To which is added, a prefatory address to the citizens of the United States, never before published. Boston: Printed for Adams & Rhoades, editors of the Independent Chronicle, 1803.
Austin, Benjamin, 1752–1820.

LAC 12756
Constitutional studies, state and federal. New York, Dodd, Mead and company, 1897.
Schouler, James, 1839–1920.

LAC 22730-31
A constitutional view of the late war between the states; its causes, character, conduct and results. Presented in a series of colloquies at Liberty hall. Philadelphia, Pa. [etc.] National publishing company; Chicago, Ill. [etc.] Zeigler, McCurdy & co. [c1868–70]
Stephens, Alexander Hamilton, 1812–1883.

LAC 15928
Construction construed, and constitutions vindicated. Richmond, Printed by Shepherd & Pollard, 1820.
Taylor, John, 1753–1824.

LAC 10890
Constructive and preventive philanthropy, by Joseph Lee, with an introduction by Jacob A. Riis. New York, The Macmillan company; London, Macmillan & co., ltd., 1902.
Lee, Joseph, 1862–

LAC 40039
The "constructive and reconstructive forces that are essential to maintain American international commercial supremacy" and that "universal commercial reciprocity treaties and tariff revision are premature." [3d ed.] New York [1902]
Seabury, George J   1844–

LAC 13715
Consular courts of the United States in
Outline lectures on the history, organization, jurisdiction, and practice of the ministerial and consular courts of the United States of America in Japan, by G. H. Scidmore, LL. B. Tokio, Igirisu horitsu gakko, 1887.
Scidmore, George Hawthorne, 1854–1922.

LAC 14842
The consular service of the United States, its history and activities. Philadelphia, Published for the University, 1906.
Jones, Chester Lloyd, 1881–1941.

LAC 40128
Consumption and how to prevent its spread in Colorado. [Circular no. 9, Denver(?), 1896(?)]
Colorado. *State Board of Health.*

LAC 10745
Contemporaries. Boston and New York, Houghton, Mifflin and company [c1899]
Higginson, Thomas Wentworth, 1823–1911.

LAC 40017
The contemporary American conception of equality among men as a social and political ideal; oration delivered by President Charles William Eliot of Harvard university, June 2, 1909, before the Alpha of Missouri. [Columbia? Mo., 1909?]
Eliot, Charles William, 1834–

LAC 16483
Contending forces; a romance illustrative of Negro life north and south, by Pauline E. Hopkins. With illustrations and cover design by R. Emmett Owen. Boston, The colored co-operative publishing co., 1900.
Hopkins, Pauline Elizabeth.

LAC 40050
The contents of children's minds on entering school. New York and Chicago, E. L. Kellogg & co. [c1893]
Hall, Granville Stanley, 1844–1924.

LAC 15015
The contest in America between Great Britain and France, with its consequences and importance; giving an account of the views and designs of the French, with the interests of Great Britain, and the situation of the British and French colonies, in all parts of America: in which a proper barrier between the two nations in North America is pointed out, with a method to prosecute the war, so as to obtain that necessary security for our colonies. By an impartial hand. London, Printed for A. Millar, 1757.
Mitchell, John, *d.* 1768.

LAC 14505
The contest over the ratification of the Federal constitution in the state of Massachusetts. New York, London [etc.] Longmans, Green and co., 1896.
Harding, Samuel Bannister, 1866–1927.

LAC 11338
Continuation of the history of the province of Massachusetts bay, from the year 1748 [to 1765] With an introductory sketch of events from its original settlement. Boston, Printed by Manning & Loring, Feb., 1798–June, 1803.
Minot, George Richards, 1758–1802.

LAC 12102
The Contrast, a Comedy; in five acts: written by a Citizen of the United States; performed with Applause at the Theatres in New-York, Philadelphia, and Maryland; and published (under an Assignment of the CopyRight) by Thomas Wignell. Philadelphia: From the press of Prichard & Hall, 1790.
Tyler, Royall, 1757?–1826.

LAC 14361
A contrast between Calvinism and Hopkinsianism. New-York: Published by S. Whiting and co. theological and classical booksellers, 96 Broadway. Paul & Thomas, printers, 1811.
Ely, Ezra Stiles, 1786–1861.

LAC 13019
The contribution of the Oswego normal school to educational progress in the United States. Boston, D. C. Heath & co., 1898.
Hollis, Andrew Phillip.

LAC 40089
Contribution to the physical anthropology of California, based on collections in the Department of anthropology of the University of California and in the U.S. National museum. Berkeley, The University press, 1906.
Hrdlicka, Ales, 1869–1943.

LAC 23098–103
Contributions to North American ethnology. Vol. I–VII, IX. [Ed. by J. W. Powell] Washington, Govt. print. off., 1877–93.

LAC 12665
Contributions to the history of American geology. [Washington, Govt. print. off., 1906]
Merrill, George Perkins, 1854–1929.

LAC 20938–39
Contributions to the natural history of the United States of America. Boston, Little, Brown and company; London, Trubner & co., 1857–62.
Agassiz, Louis, 1807–1873.

LAC 11375
Control of municipal public service corporations. Philadelphia, American academy of political and social science, 1908
American Academy of Political and Social Science, *Philadelphia*.

LAC 14873
The control of strikes in American trade unoins [!] Baltimore, 1916.
Janes, George Milton, 1869–

LAC 40023
Controversy between John C. Calhoun and Robt. Y. Hayne as to the proper route of a railroad from South Carolina to the West. [Spartanburg, 1913]
Cleveland, John Bomar.

LAC 13080
Controversy between Rev. Messrs. Hughes and Breckenridge, on the subject "Is the Protestant religion the religion of Christ?" 5th ed. Philadelphia, E. Cummiskey, 1862.
Hughes, John, *abp.*, 1797–1864.

LAC 14395
Convenient houses, with fifty plans for the housekeeper, Architect and housewife; a journey through the house; fifty convenient house plans; practical house building for the owner; business points in building; how to pay for a home. New York, T. Y. Crowell & co. [1889]
Gibson, Louis Henry, 1854–

LAC 22444
Conversations in a studio. Boston and New York, Houghton, Mifflin and company [c1890]
Story, William Wetmore, 1819–1895.

LAC 13992
Conversations on the principal subjects of political economy. Philadelphia, H. C. Baird & co., 1882.
Elder, William, 1806–1885.

LAC 13994
Conversations on the science of the human mind. By Ezra Stiles Ely, D. D. pastor of the Third Presbyterian church in the city of Philadelphia. Philadelphia, Printed for the author. Sold by A. Finley, corner of Chestnut and Fourth streets. William Fry, printer, 1819.
Ely, Ezra Stiles, 1786–1861.

LAC 16115
Conversations, principally on the aborigines of North America... Salem [Mass.] W. and S. B. Ives, 1828.
Sanders, Elizabeth, 1762–1851.

LAC 40083
The convict. His punishment; what it should be; and how applied. Philadelphia, Allen, Lane & Scott's printing house, 1884.
Vaux, Richard, 1816–1895.

LAC 40096
The convict lease system in the Southern states. [New York, C. Scribner's sons, 1885]
Cable, George Washington, 1844–1925.

LAC 40040
Cool thoughts on the consequences to Great Britain of American independence. On the expence of Great Britain in the settlement and defence of the American colonies. On the value and importance of the American colonies and the West Indies to the British empire. London, Printed for J. Wilkie, 1780.
Galloway, Joseph, 1731–1803.

LAC 14780

The co-operative commonwealth; an exposition of modern socialism. Authorized and copyright English ed., with a new preface by the author... London, S. Sonnenschein & co., ltd., 1896.
Gronlund, Laurence, 1846–1899.

LAC 40146

Cooperative communities in the United States. [Washington, Govt. print. off., 1901]
Kent, Alexander, 1837–1908.

LAC 40035

The Copperhead catechism. For the instruction of such politicians as are of tender years. Carefully comp. by divers learned and designing men. Authorized and with admonitions by Fernando the Gothamite, high priest of the order of Copperheads. New York, For the compilers by S. Tousey, 1864.

LAC 40064

The Copperhead; or, The secret political history of our Civil War unveiled; showing the falsity of New England... How Abraham Lincoln came to be President... To be delivered and published in a series of four illustrated lectures. New Haven, 1902.
Hall, Fayette.

LAC 40062

Copy of letters sent to Great-Britain, by His Excellency Thomas Hutchinson, the Hon. Andrew Oliver, and several other persons, born and educated among us. Which original letters have been returned to America, and laid before the Honorable House of representatives of this province. In which (notwithstanding His Excellency's declaration to the House, that the tendency and design of them was not to subvert the constitution, but rather to preserve it entire) the judicious reader will discover the fatal source of the confusion and bloodshed in which this province especially has been involved, and which threatened total destruction to the liberties of all America. Boston, Printed by Edes and Gill, 1773.
Hutchinson, Thomas, 1711–1780.

LAC 11916

The coquette; or, The history of Eliza Wharton; a novel; founded on fact. By a lady of Massachusetts. Charlestown, Mass., Printed by Samuel Etheridge, for E. Larkin, no. 47, Cornhill, 1802.
Foster, Hannah, 1759–1840.

LAC 11848

The cords of vanity; a comedy of shirking. New York, R. M. McBride, 1929.
Cabell, James Branch, 1879–1958.

LAC 40110

Corduroy Charlie, the boy bravo; or, Deadwood Dick's last act. New York, Beadle & Adams, 1885.
Wheeler, Edward L.

LAC 40008

Corn yields per acre and prices, by states, 50 years, 1866–1915. Washington [Govt. print. off.] 1917.

LAC 10147

Corporate promotions and reorganizations. Cambridge, Harvard university press; [etc., etc.] 1914.
Dewing, Arthur Stone, 1880–

LAC 10189

The corporation problem; the public phases of corporations, their uses, abuses... New York, G.P. Putnam's sons, 1891.
Cook, William Wilson, 1858–1930.

LAC 20021

Corporations; a study of the origin and development of great business combinations and of their relation to the authority of the state. New York and London, G. P. Putnam's sons, 1905.
Davis, John Patterson, 1862–1903.

LAC 12907

A correct history of the John Brown invasion at Harper's Ferry, West Va., Oct. 17, 1859. Compiled by the late Capt. John H. Zittle who was an eye-witness to many of the occurrences, and edited and published by his widow. Hagerstown, Md., Mail publishing company, 1905.
Zittle, John Henry, 1830–1901.

LAC 20418–19

Correction and prevention ... prepared for the Eighth international prison congress, ed. by Charles Richmond Henderson. New York, Charities publication committee, 1910.
Henderson, Charles Richmond, 1848–1915, *ed.*

LAC 12711

The correlation and conservation of forces: a series of expositions, by Prof. Grove, Prof. Helmholtz, Dr. Mayer, Dr. Faraday, Prof. Liebig and Dr. Carpenter. With an introduction and brief biographical notices of the chief promoters of the new views. By Edward L. Youmans. New York, D. Appleton and company, 1865.
Youmans, Edward Livingston, 1821–1887.

LAC 13712

Correspondence and documents relative to the attempt to negotiate for the release of the American captives at Algiers; including remarks on our relations with that regency. Washington City: Printed, 1816.
Noah, Mordecai Manuel, 1785–1851.

LAC 21023–25

The correspondence and public papers of John Jay... Ed. by Henry P. Johnston. New York, London, G. P. Putnam's sons [1890–93]
Jay, John, 1745–1829.

LAC 12460

The correspondence between Benjamin Harrison and James G. Blaine, 1882–1893; collected and edited by Albert T. Volwiler. Philadelphia, The American philosophical society, 1940.
Harrison, Benjamin, *pres. U.S.*, 1833–1901.

LAC 40056

The correspondence between Citizen Genet, Minister of the French Republic, to the United States of North America, and the officers of the Federal Government; to which are prefixed the instructions from the constituted authorities of France to the said minister. All from authentic documents. Philadelphia, Printed and sold by B. F. Bache, 1793.
France. *Legation. U.S.*

LAC 40065

Correspondence between Gen. Andrew Jackson and John C. Calhoun, president and vice-president of the U. States, on the subject of the course of the latter, in the deliberations of the cabinet of Mr. Munroe, on the occurrences in the Seminole war. Washington, Printed by D. Green, 1831.
Calhoun, John Caldwell, 1782–1850.

LAC 40065

Correspondence between John Quincy Adams, president of the United States, and several citizens of Massachusetts concerning the charge of a design to dissolve the union alleged to have existed in that state. Boston, Press of the Boston daily advertiser, 1829.
Adams, John Quincy, *pres. U.S.*, 1767–1848.

LAC 40124

Correspondence between the United States government and Spain in relation to the island of Cuba. Message from the President of the United States, transmitting in response to resolution of the House of representatives of the 17th instant, a report from the secretary of state, with accompanying documents. January 21, 1876.–Referred to the Committee on foreign affairs and ordered to be printed. [Washington, Gov't print. off., 1876]
U.S. *Dept. of State.*

LAC 23128–34

Correspondence concerning claims against Great Britain, transmitted to the Senate of the United States in answer to the resolutions of December 4 and 10, 1867, and of May 27, 1868... Washington, Govt. print. off., 1869–71.
U.S. *Dept. of State.*

LAC 16901

Correspondence in relation to the boundary controversy between Great Britain and Venezuela, being a reprint of Senate executive document no. 226, Fiftieth Congress, first session, and Senate document no. 31, Fifty-fourth Congress, first session. Washington, Govt. print. off., 1896.
U.S. *Dept. of State.*

LAC 22329–33

Correspondence of Andrew Jackson, edited by John Spencer Bassett. Washington, D. C., Carnegie institution of Washington, 1926–35.
Jackson, Andrew, *pres. U.S.*, 1767–1845.

LAC 16093

Correspondence of Henry Laurens, of South Carolina. [New York, Printed for the Zenger club, 1861]
Laurens, Henry, 1724–1792.

LAC 40070

Correspondence of John Quincy Adams, 1811–1814, ed. by Charles Francis Adams. Worcester, Mass., The American antiquarian society, 1913.
Adams, John Quincy, *pres. U.S.*, 1767–1848.

LAC 20798

Correspondence of John Sedgwick, major-general. [New York] Printed for C. and E. B. Stoeckel [by the De Vinne press] 1902–03.
Sedgwick, John, 1813–1864.

LAC 22243–44

The correspondence of Jonathan Worth, collected and ed. by J. G. de Roulhac Hamilton. Raleigh, Edwards & Broughton printing company, 1909.
Worth, Jonathan, 1802–1869.

LAC 13595

Correspondence of Mr. Ralph Izard, of South Carolina, from the year 1774 to 1804; with a short memoir. Vol. I. New-York, C. S. Francis & co., 1844.
Izard, Ralph, 1742–1804.

LAC 10279

The correspondence of Nicholas Biddle dealing with national affairs, 1807–1844, ed. by Reginald C. McGrane. Boston & New York, Houghton Mifflin company, 1919.
Biddle, Nicholas, 1786–1844.

LAC 12477

Correspondence of Robert M. T. Hunter, 1826–1876; ed. by Charles Henry Ambler. Washington [Govt. print. off.] 1918.
Hunter, Robert Mercer Taliaferro, 1809–1887.

LAC 20845–47

Correspondence of the American revolution; being letters of eminent men to George Washington, from the time of his taking command of the army to the end of his presidency. Edited from the original manuscripts. Boston, Little, Brown and company, 1853.
Sparks, Jared, 1789–1866, *ed.*

LAC 21955–56

The correspondence of the colonial governors of Rhode Island, 1723–1775; published by the National society of the colonial dames of America in the state of Rhode Island and Providence plantations; edited by Gertrude Selwyn Kimball. Boston and New York, Houghton, Mifflin and company, 1902–03.
Rhode Island *(Colony) Governors.*

LAC 11560–61

Correspondence of the French ministers to the United States, 1791–1797. Edited by Prof. Frederick J. Turner. [Washington, Govt. print. off., 1904]
Turner, Frederick Jackson, 1861–1932, *ed.*

LAC 21330

The correspondence of Thomas Carlyle and Ralph Waldo Emerson, 1834–1872... Boston, J. R. Osgood and company, 1883.
Carlyle, Thomas, 1795–1881.

LAC 40149

Correspondence of Thomas Jefferson, 1788–1826. [St. Louis, Jefferson memorial, 1936]
Jefferson, Thomas, *pres. U.S.*, 1743–1826.

LAC 20263–64

Correspondence of William Shirley, governor of Massachusetts and military commander in America, 1731–1760, ed. under the auspices of the National society of the colonial dames of America, by Charles Henry Lincoln. New York, The Macmillan company, 1912.
Shirley, William, 1694–1771.

LAC 13705
Correspondence on the present relations between Great Britain and the United States of America. Boston, Little, Brown, and company, 1862.
Field, Edwin Wilkins.

LAC 16652
Correspondence relating to the Fenian invasion, and the rebellion of the southern states. Printed by order of Parliament. Ottawa, Printed by Hunter, Rose & company, 1869.
Canada. *Dept. of the Secretary of State.*

LAC 40097
Correspondence relating to the invention of the Jacquard brussels carpet power loom. Boston, A. Mudge & son, printers, 1868.
Wood, William, 1816–1871.

LAC 22689-90
Correspondence relating to the war with Spain and conditions growing out of the same, including the insurrection in the Philippine Islands and the China relief expedition, between the adjutant-general of the army and military commanders in the United States, Cuba, Porto Rico, China, and the Philippine Islands, from April 15, 1898, to July 30, 1902. With an appendix giving the organization of army corps and a brief history of the volunteer organizations in the service of the United States during the war with Spain. Washington, Gov't print. off., 1902.
U.S. *Adjutant-general's Office.*

LAC 15025
The cosmic God. A fundamental philosophy in popular lectures. Cincinnati, Office American Israelite and Deborah, 1876.
Wise, Isaac Mayer, 1819–1900.

LAC 12314
The Cosmographiae introductio of Martin Waldseemuller in facsimilie, followed by the Four voyages of Amerigo Vespucci, with their translation into English; to which are added Waldseemuller's two world maps of 1507, with an introduction by Joseph Fischer and Franz von Wieser; ed. by Charles George Herbermann. New York, The United States Catholic Historical Society, 1907.
Waldseemuller, Martin, 1470–1521?

LAC 10871
The Cosmopolis city club. New York, The Century company, 1893.
Gladden, Washington, 1836–1918.

LAC 12722
The cost, by David Graham Phillips, illustrated by Harrison Fisher. Indianapolis, The Bobbs-Merrill company [1904]
Phillips, David Graham, 1867–1911.

LAC 11641
The cost of competition; an effort at the understanding of familiar facts. Illustrated with diagrams and photographs. New York, McClure, Phillips & co., 1906.
Reeve, Sidney Armor, 1866–

LAC 13762
Cost of living in American towns. Report of an inquiry by the Board of trade of London into working class rents, housing, and retail prices, together with rates of wages in certain occupations in the principal industrial towns of the United States of America as presented to the British parliament by command of his majesty... Washington [Govt. print. off.] 1911.
Gt. Brit. *Board of Trade.*

LAC 40067
I. The cost of national crime. II. The hell of war and its penalties. Two treatises suggested by the appointment of a day of national thanksgiving by the President of the United States. [Boston, Rockwell & Churchill press, 1898]
Atkinson, Edward, 1827–1905.

LAC 40117
Cost of railroad transportation, railroad accounts, and governmental regulation of railroad tariffs. Extract from the annual report of the Louisville & Nashville railroad co. Louisville, Printed by J. P. Morton and company, 1875.
Fink, Albert, 1827–1897.

LAC 40024
Cost of transportation on railroads. By Charles Ellet, jr. Philadelphia, 1844.
Ellet, Charles, 1810–1862.

LAC 12184
Costume of colonial times. New York, C. Scribner's sons, 1894.
Earle, Alice, 1851–1911.

LAC 14398
Cottage residences; or, A series of designs for rural cottages and cottage villas, and their gardens and grounds. Adapted to North America. Part I. Illustrated by numerous engravings. 2d ed. New-York and London, Wiley and Putnam, 1844.
Downing, Andrew Jackson, 1815–1852.

LAC 10040
Cotton culture and the South considered with reference to emigration. By F. W. Loring and C. F. Atkinson. Boston, A. Williams & co., 1869.
Loring, Francis William.

LAC 10262
Cotton is king, and pro-slavery arguments: comprising the writings of Hammond, Harper, Christy, Stringfellow, Hodge, Bledsoe, and Cartwright, on this important subject. With an essay on slavery in the light of international law, by the editor. Augusta, Ga., Pritchard, Abbott & Loomis, 1860.
Elliott, E   N   *ed.*

LAC 10249
Cotton is king: or, The culture of cotton, and its relation to agriculture, manufactures and commerce; to the free colored people; and to those who hold that slavery is in itself sinful; by an American. Cincinnati, Moore, Wilstach, Keys & co., 1855.
Christy, David, *b.* 1802.

LAC 10085

Cotton, its cultivation, marketing, manufacture, and the problems of the cotton world, by Charles William Burkett and Clarence Hamilton Poe. New York, Doubleday, Page & company, 1908, [c1906]
Burkett, Charles William, 1873–

LAC 13092

Cotton Mather, the Puritan priest. New York, Dodd, Mead and company [c1891]
Wendell, Barrett, 1855–1921.

LAC 40020

Cotton Mather's scientific communications to the Royal society. Worcester, Mass., American antiquarian society, 1916.
Kittredge, George Lyman, 1860–1941.

LAC 10403

The cotton mills of South Carolina. Columbia, S. C., 1907.
Kohn, August, 1868–1930.

LAC 16924

The cotton planter's manual: being a compilation of facts from the best authorities on the culture of cotton; its natural history, chemical analysis, trade, and consumption; and embracing a history of cotton and the cotton gin. New York, Orange Judd, 1865, [c1857]
Turner, Joseph Addison, 1826–1868.

LAC 15946

The cotton question. The production, export, manufacture, and consumption of cotton. A condensed treatise on cotton in all its aspects: agricultural, commercial, and political. Illustrated with engravings. New York, Metropolitan record office, 1866.
Barbee, William J   1816–1892.

LAC 12368

The cotton states in the spring and summer of 1875. New York, B. Franklin, 1876.
Nordhoff, Charles, 1830–1901.

LAC 40019

Cotton tables: exhibiting at a glance the cost of cotton, with all charges, at Liverpool or Havre, from New Orleans, Mobile, Charleston, and New York, at all prices, rates of freight, and exchange... Likewise, exchange tables. New York, E. B. Clayton's sons [1853]
Entz, John F.

LAC 10690

The cotton trade: its bearing upon the prosperity of Great Britain and commerce of the American republics, considered in connection with the system of negro slavery in the Confederate States. London, Saunders, Otley & co., 1863.
McHenry, George, of Philadelphia.

LAC 13488

The Council of Revision of the state of New York; its history, a history of the courts with which its members were connected, biographical sketches of its members, and its vetoes. Albany, W. Gould, 1859.
Street, Alfred Billings, 1811?–1881.

LAC 14582

Council records of Massachusetts under the administration of President Joseph Dudley [by] Robert N. Toppan. Boston, Massachusetts Historical Society, 1900.
Massachusetts (Colony) Council.

LAC 14869

Counsel for emigrants, and interesting information from numerous sources concerning British America, the United States, and New South Wales... 3d ed., with a supplement. Aberdeen, J. Mathison [pref. 1838]

LAC 40066

Count the cost. An address to the people of Connecticut, on sundry political subjects, and particularly on the proposition for a new constitution. By Jonathan Steadfast [pseud.] Hartford: Printed by Hudson and Goodwin, 1804.
Daggett, David, 1764–1851.

LAC 15472

The counties of Maryland, their origin, boundaries and election districts. Baltimore, The Johns Hopkins press, 1907.
Mathews, Edward Bennett, 1869–

LAC 11784

The country home. New York, McClure, Phillips & co., 1905, [c1904]
Powell, Edward Payson, 1833–1915.

LAC 10070

The country-life movement in the United States. New York, The Macmillan company, 1911.
Bailey, Liberty Hyde, 1858–1954.

LAC 14515

The country school. With illustrations by the author. New York, T. Y. Crowell & co. [1907]
Johnson, Clifton, 1865–1910.

LAC 13382

A country without strikes; a visit to the compulsory arbitration court of New Zealand, by Henry Demarest Lloyd, with introduction by William Pember Reeves. New York, Doubleday, Page & co., 1900.
Lloyd, Henry Demarest, 1847–1903.

LAC 11374

County government... Philadelphia, American academy of political and social science, 1913.
American Academy of Political and Social Science, Philadelphia.

LAC 15277

A course of lectures on the constitutional jurisprudence of the United States: delivered annually in Columbia college, New York. The 2d ed., rev., enl., and adapted to professional as well as general use... Boston, Little, Brown and company, 1856.
Duer, William Alexander, 1780–1858.

LAC 20153

A course of legal study, addressed to students and the profession generally. 2d ed., rewritten and much enl. ... Baltimore, J. Neal, 1836.
Hoffman, David, 1784–1854.

LAC 12997
Course of popular lectures, as delivered by Frances Wright in New York, Philadelphia ... and other cities ... of the United States. With all her addresses on various public occasions, and a reply to the charges against the French Reformers of 1789. 6th ed. New York, G. W. & A. J. Matsell, 1836, [c1829]
D'Arusmont, Frances, 1795–1852.

LAC 14014
The courses of the Ohio river taken by Lt. T. Hutchins, anno 1766, and two accompanying maps, edited by Beverly W. Bond, jr. Cincinnati, Historical and philosophical society of Ohio, 1942.
Hutchins, Thomas, 1730–1789.

LAC 16630
Court of inquiry–operations in Florida, &c. Letter from the secretary of war, transmitting copies of the proceedings of a Court of inquiry, convened at Fredericktown, in relation to the operations against the Seminole and Creek Indians, &c. ... [Washington, 1838]
U.S. *War Dept.*

LAC 13445
The courts, the Constitution and parties; studies in constitutional history and politics. Chicago, Ill., The University of Chicago press [c1912]
McLaughlin, Andrew Cunningham, 1861–1947.

LAC 12338
The cradle of the Confederacy; or, The times of Troup, Quitman, and Yancey. A sketch of southwestern political history from the formation of the federal government to A. D. 1861. Mobile, Printed at the Register publishing office, 1876.
Hodgson, Joseph, 1838–

LAC 14015
Crania americana; or, A comparative view of the skulls of various aboriginal nations of North and South America. To which is prefixed an essay on the varieties of the human species. Illustrated by seventy-eight plates and a colored map. Philadelphia, J. Dobson, 1839.
Morton, Samuel George, 1799–1851.

LAC 14672
Creation myths of primitive America in relation to the religious history and mental development of mankind. Boston, Little, Brown & Co., 1898.
Curtin, Jeremiah, 1835–1906.

LAC 40048
The Credit mobilier of America, a paper read before the Rhode Island historical society, Tuesday evening, February 22, 1881. Providence, S. S. Rider, 1881.
Hazard, Rowland.

LAC 10191
The Credit mobilier of America; its origin and history, its work of constructing the Union Pacific railroad and the relation of members of Congress therewith. Boston, C. W. Calkins & co., 1880.
Crawford, Jay Boyd.

LAC 40096
The credit of the South: viewed from a state, municipal and general standpoint. Address delivered before the Commercial club of Nashville, Tenn., May 24th, 1892. Richmond, Va., W. E. Jones, printer, 1892.
Williams, John Skelton, 1865–1926.

LAC 40017
The credit system and the public domain. Nashville, Tenn., Cumberland Presbyterian publishing house, 1899.
Emerick, C   F.

LAC 11411
The credit system in France, Great Britain, and the United States. London, J. Miller; Philadelphia, Carey, Lea & Blanchard, 1838.
Carey, Henry Charles, 1793–1879.

LAC 10919
Creed and deed; a series of discourses. New York, Pub. for the Society for ethical culture, by G. P. Putnam's sons, 1877.
Adler, Felix, 1851–1933.

LAC 13568
The creeds and platforms of Congregationalism. New York, C. Scribner's sons, 1893.
Walker, Williston, 1860–1922, *ed.*

LAC 40048
Creeds of great business men. [Chicago, Printed by the I H C service bureau of the International harvester company of America, c1913]
Barker, Edwin Lincoln, 1868–

LAC 16847
The Creek war of 1813 and 1814. By H. S. Halbert and T. H. Ball. Chicago, Ill., Donohue & Henneberry; Montgomery, Ala., White, Woodruff, & Fowler, 1895.
Halbert, Henry Sale, 1837–1916.

LAC 11853
Creole life, A story of.
The Grandissimes, a story of Creole life. New York, C. Scribner's sons, 1880.
Cable, George Washington, 1844–1925.

LAC 40139
Creole songs from New Orleans in the negro-dialect, set to music by Clara Gottschalk Peterson. New Orleans, L. Grunewald co. l'td., c1902.
Peterson, Clara.

LAC 11851
The Creoles of Louisiana. New York, C. Scribner's sons, 1884.
Cable, George Washington, 1844–1925.

LAC 16601
Creoles of St. Louis. St. Louis, Nixon-Jones printing co., 1893.
Beckwith, Paul Edmond, 1848–1907.

LAC 13233
The crest of the continent: a record of a summer's ramble in the Rocky mountains and beyond. Chicago, R. R. Donnelley & sons, 1885.
Ingersoll, Ernest, 1852–1946.

LAC 11230
Crime and criminals. Los Angeles, Cal., Prison reform league publishing company [c1910]
Prison Reform League.

LAC 11194
Crime: its nature, causes, treatment, and prevention.
Philadelphia, J. B. Lippincott company, 1889.
Green, Sanford Moon, 1807–1901.

LAC 40031
Criminal aggression: by whom committed? An inquiry. A sequel to I. The cost of a national crime. II. The hell of war and its penalties. 1st ed. Boston, Mass., 1899.
Atkinson, Edward, 1827–1905.

LAC 40021
Criminal record of the Western federation of miners, Coeur d'Alene to Cripple Creek. 1894–1904. Compiled by the Colorado mine operators' association, Colorado Springs, Colorado. [Denver, Smith Brooks ptg. co., 1904]
Mine Owners' Association, (Colorado)

LAC 23320
Criminal trials.
American criminal trials. Boston, T. H. Carter, 1844.
Chandler, Peleg Whitman, 1816–1889.

LAC 11869
The crisis. With illustrations from the scenes of the play. New York, The Macmillan company; London, Macmillan & co., ltd., 1902.
Churchill, Winston, 1871–1947.

LAC 40065
The crisis... [n.p., 1832]
Pendleton, Edmund.

LAC 40075
A crisis chapter on government. [New York, 1865?]
Blanchard, Calvin.

LAC 15686
The crisis: or, Essays on the usurpations of the federal government. By Brutus [pseud.] Charleston, Printed by A. E. Miller, 1827.
Turnbull, Robert James, 1775–1833.

LAC 15524
The crisis; or The enemies of America unmasked.
Philadelphia, G. D. Miller, 1855.
Laurens, J   Wayne.

LAC 16663
Critical essays on a few subjects connected with the history and present condition of speculative philosophy.
Boston, H. B. Williams, 1842.
Bowen, Francis, 1811–1890.

LAC 11115
Critical history and defence of the Old Testament canon. Andover [Mass.] Allen, Morrill and Wardwell; New York, M. H. Newman, 1845.
Stuart, Moses, 1780–1852.

LAC 12340
A critical study of nullification in South Carolina.
Cambridge, Harvard university press; [etc., etc., 1896]
Houston, David Franklin, 1866–1940.

LAC 11974
Criticism and fiction. New York, Harper and brothers, 1891.
Howells, William Dean, 1837–1920.

LAC 11900
The Croakers, by Joseph Rodman Drake and Fitz Greene Halleck. 1st complete ed. New York, 1860.
Drake, Joseph Rodman, 1795–1820.

LAC 16828
Crofutt's grip-sack guide of Colorado. A complete encyclopedia of the state: resources and condensed authentic descriptions of every city, town, village, station, post office and important mining camp in the state ... 1881.
Omaha, Neb., The Overland publishing co.; Denver, Alvord & co. [1881]
Crofutt, George A.

LAC 11870
The crossing, with illustrations by Sydney Adamson and Lilian Bayliss. New York, The Macmillan company; London, Macmillan & co., ltd., 1904.
Churchill, Winston, 1871–1947.

LAC 16503
Crotchets and quavers; or, Revelations of an opera manager in America. New York, S. French, 1855.
Maretzek, Max, 1821–1897.

LAC 12111
Crucial instances. New York, C. Scribner's sons, 1901.
Wharton, Edith Newbold, 1862–1937.

LAC 16511
Cruise of the United States frigate Potomac round the world, during the years 1831–34. Embracing the attack on Quallah-Battoo... New York, Leavitt, Lord & co.; Boston, Crocker & Brewster, 1835.
Warriner, Francis, 1805–1866.

LAC 11941
Crumbling idols: twelve essays on art, dealing chiefly with literature, painting and the drama. Chicago and Cambridge [Mass.] Stone and Kimball, 1894.
Garland, Hamlin, 1860–1940.

LAC 12692
Crusoe's island: a ramble in the footsteps of Alexander Selkirk. With sketches of adventure in California and Washoe. New York, Harper & brothers, 1864.
Browne, John Ross, 1821–1875.

LAC 11149
Cuba and the intervention. New York [etc.] Longmans, Green, and co., 1905.
Robinson, Albert Gardner, 1855–1932.

LAC 14500

The Cuban and Porto Rican campaigns. New York, C. Scribner's sons, 1898.
Davis, Richard Harding, 1864–1916.

LAC 15487

The cultural heritage of the Swedish immigrant; selected references. [Rock Island, Ill., Augustana College Library, 1956]
Ander, Oscar Fritiof, 1903–

LAC 40019

Culture of Carolina rice. [n.p. 185–?]
Russell, Robert, d. 1871.

LAC 13008

The culture of justice; a mode of moral education and of social reform. New York, Dodd, Mead and company, 1907.
Du Bois, Patterson, 1847–1917.

LAC 13810

Culture, The key to.
The key to culture; customs, manners and niceties of society. Chicago, The Geographical publishing co. [c1921]
Gilbert, Paul Thomas, 1876–

LAC 11910

Culture's garland; being memoranda of the gradual rise of literature, art, music and society in Chicago, and other western ganglia, by Eugene Field; with an introduction by Julian Hawthorne. Boston, Ticknor and company, 1887.
Field, Eugene, 1850–1895.

LAC 15122

Curiosities of the American stage. New York, Harper & brothers, 1891.
Hutton, Laurence, 1843–1904.

LAC 13959

Curious punishments of bygone days, by Alice Morse Earle. Chicago, Printed for H. S. Stone, 1896. Detroit, Singing Tree Press, 1968.
Earle, Alice, 1851–1911.

LAC 20088–89

Currency and banking in the province of the Massachusetts-bay. New York, Pub. for the American economic association by the Macmillan company [c1901]
Davis, Andrew McFarland, 1833–1920.

LAC 40001

Currency: the evil and the remedy. By Godek Goodwell [pseud.] 6th ed. New York, W. H. Graham, 1846.
Kellogg, Edward, 1790–1858.

LAC 12242

Current superstitions: collected from the oral tradition or English speaking folk, edited by Fanny D. Bergen; with notes, and an introduction by William Wells Newell. Boston and New York Pub. for the American folklore society by Houghton, Mifflin and company; [etc., etc.] 1896.
Bergen, Fanny, 1846–   comp.

LAC 15764

The curse of Clifton. Chicago, W. B. Conkley [18–?]
Southworth, Emma Dorothy Eliza, 1819–1899.

LAC 40045

A cursory view of Spanish America, particularly the neighbouring vice-royalties of Mexico and New-Grenada, chiefly intended to elucidate the policy of an early connection between the United States and those countries. Georgetown, D. C., Published by Richards and Mallory, 1815. [Tarrytown, N. Y., Reprinted, W. Abbatt, 1928]
Robinson, William Davis.

LAC 16592

The custom of the country. New York, C. Scribner's sons, 1913.
Wharton, Edith Newbold, 1862–1937.

LAC 12190

The customs of New England. Boston, Press of T. R. Marvin, 1853.
Felt, Joseph Barlow, 1789–1869.

LAC 23930–32

Cyclopedia of American government, ed. by Andrew C. McLaughlin and Albert Bushnell Hart. New York and London, D. Appleton and company, 1914.

LAC 22123–26

Cyclopedia of American horticulture, comprising suggestions for cultivation of horticultural plants, descriptions of the species of fruits, vegetables, flowers and ornamental plants sold in the United States and Canada, together with geographical and biographical sketches, by L. H. Bailey. Assisted by Wilhelm Miller and many expert cultivators and botanists. Illustrated with over two thousand original engravings. New York [etc.] The Macmillan company, 1900–02.
Bailey, Liberty Hyde, 1858–1954, ed.

LAC 20609–11

Cyclopaedia of American literature: embracing personal and critical notices of authors, and selections from their writings, from the earliest period to the present day; with portraits, autographs, and other illustrations. By Evert A. Duyckinck and George L. Duyckinck. Edited to date by M. Laird Simons. Philadelphia, Rutter, 1877.
Duyckinck, Evert Augustus, 1816–1878.

LAC 11356–57

Cyclopaedia of Methodism. Embracing sketches of its rise, progress and present condition, with biographical notices and numerous illustrations. Edited by Matthew Simpson. 5th rev. ed. Philadelphia, L. H. Everts, 1882.
Simpson, Matthew, bp., 1811–1884.

LAC 20803–07

Cyclopaedia of political science, political economy, and of the political history of the United States. By the best American and European writers. Ed. by John J. Lalor. Chicago, Rand, McNally & company, 1882–1884.
Lalor, John Joseph, d. 1899, ed.

LAC 13977

The cyclopedia of temperance, prohibition and public morals. (1917 ed.) By Deets Pickett, editor, Clarence True Wilson, supervising editor, Ernest Dailey Smith, assistant editor. New York, Cincinnati, The Methodist book concern [1917]

LAC 15490

The Cymry of '76; or, Welshmen and their descendants of the American revolution. An address with an appendix, containing notes, sketches, and nomenclature of the Cymbri; by Alexander Jones. To which is added a letter on eminent Welshmen. By Samuel Jenkins, esq. and a brief sketch of St. David's benevolent society. 2d ed. New York, Sheldon, Lamport & co., 1855.
Jones, Alexander, 1802–1863.

LAC 40020

Cyrus Hall McCormick and the reaper. (From the Proceedings of the State historical society of Wisconsin for 1908...) Madison, The Society, 1909.
Thwaites, Reuben Gold, 1853–1913.

LAC 12617

Cyrus Hall McCormick, his life and work. Chicago, A. C. McClurg & co., 1909.
Casson, Herbert Newton, 1869–

LAC 10467

Cyrus W. Field, his life and work [1819–1892] New York, Harper & brothers, 1896.
Judson, Isabella, 1846–   *ed.*

LAC 13942

Dahcotah; or, Life and legends of the Sioux around Fort Snelling. By Mrs. Mary Eastman, with preface by Mrs. C. M. Kirkland. Illustrated from drawings by Captain Eastman. New York, J. Wiley, 1849.
Eastman, Mary, 1818–1890.

LAC 40032

Dairying for profit: or, The poor man's cow. New York, Charles H. Nicoll, 1896.
Jones, Eliza Maria.

LAC 11919

The damnation of Theron Ware; or, Illumination. New York, Stone & Kimball, 1896.
Frederic, Harold, 1856–1898.

LAC 10007

Danger signals. The enemies of youth, from the businessman's standpoint... Boston, Lee & Shepard; New York, C. T. Dillingham, 1885.
Clark, Francis Edward, 1851–1927.

LAC 10845

The dangerous classes of New York and twenty years' work among them. 3rd ed.–with addenda. New York, Wynkoop & Hallenbeck, 1880, [c1872]
Brace, Charles Loring, 1826–1890.

LAC 12297

The dangerous voyage of Capt. Thomas James, in his intended discovery of a north west passage into the South Sea... To which is added, a map for sailing in those seas; also divers tables of the author's of the variation of the compass, &c. With an appendix concerning the longitude, by Master Gellibrand. 2d ed., rev. and cor. London, Printed in 1633, and now reprinted for O. Payne, 1740.
James, Thomas, 1593?–1635?

LAC 14219

Daniel Boone. New York and London, D. Appleton & company, 1913, [c1902]
Thwaites, Reuben Gold, 1853–1913.

LAC 14818

Daniel Falckner's Curieuse nachricht from Pennsylvania, the book that stimulated the great German immigration to Pennsylvaina [!] in the early years of the XVIII century; tr. and annotated by Julius Friedrich Sachse. Prepared at the request of the Pennsylvania-German society. Lancaster, Pa. [The Society] 1905.
Falckner, Daniel, *b.* 1666.

LAC 14286

Daniel Gookin, 1612–1687, assistant and major general of the Massachusetts bay colony; his life and letters and some account of his ancestry. Chicago, Priv. print. [R. R. Donnelley & sons co.] 1912.
Gookin, Frederick William, 1853–

LAC 21426

Daniel H. Burnham, architect, planner of cities. Boston and New York, Houghton Mifflin company, 1921.
Moore, Charles, 1855–1942.

LAC 15684

Daniel Webster. New York, The Century co., 1902.
McMaster, John Bach, 1852–1932.

LAC 20745

Danish Arctic expeditions, 1605 to 1620. In two books. Ed., with notes and introductions, by C. C. A. Gosch. London, Printed for the Hakluyt society, 1897.
Gosch, Christian Carl August, 1832–1913, *ed.*

LAC 40054

Darby's return. A comic sketch. As performed at the New-York theatre, November 24, 1789, for the benefit of Mr. Wignell. New-York, Printed by Hodge, Allen, and Campbell, and sold at their respective bookstores, and by Berry and Rogers, 1789.
Dunlap, William, 1766–1839.

LAC 16189

The daring adventures of Kit Carson and Fremont, among buffaloes, grizzlies and Indians, being a spirited diary of the most difficult and wonderful explorations ever made, opening ... the great pathway to the Pacific. New York, J. W. Lovell [c1885]

LAC 14646

Daring and suffering: a history of the great railroad adventure. By Lieut. William Pittenger, one of the adventurers. With an introduction by Rev. Alexander Clark. Philadelphia, J. W. Daughaday, 1863.
Pittenger, William, 1840–1904.

LAC 14216

The dark side of the beef trust; a treatise concerning the "canner" cow, the cold-storage fowl, the diseased meats, the dopes and preservatives, and what takes place on the other side of the partitions of the packing houses... by a practical butcher. [Jamestown, N. Y., Printed for T. Z. Root] 1905.
Hirschauer, Herman.

LAC 13924
Darkness and daylight; or, Lights and shadows of New York life. A pictorial record of personal experiences by day and night in the great metropolis ... by Mrs. Helen Campbell, Col. Thomas W. Knox and Supt. Thomas Byrnes, with an introduction by Rev. Lyman Abbott. Superbly illustrated with two hundred and fifty engravings from photographs... Hartford, Conn., The Hartford publishing company, 1895.
Campbell, Helen, 1839–1918.

LAC 13824
The Dartmouth college causes and the Supreme court of the United States. St. Louis, G. I. Jones and company, 1895, [c1879]
Shirley, John Major, 1831–1887.

LAC 10516
Darwiniana: essays and reviews pertaining to Darwinism. New York, D. Appleton and company, 1876.
Gray, Asa, 1810–1888.

LAC 40089
David Cusick's sketches of ancient history of the Six nations, comprising first–a tale of the foundation of the Great island, (now North America,) the two infants born, and the creation of the universe. Second–a real account of the early settlers of North America, and their dissensions. Third–origin of the kingdom of the Five nations, which was called a Long House: the wars, fierce animals, &c. Lockport, N. Y., Turner & McCollum, printers, 1848.
Cusick, David, d. ca. 1840.

LAC 15638
David Zeisberger's history of the northern American Indians, ed. by Archer Butler Hulbert and William Nathaniel Schwarze. [Columbus, O., Press of F. J. Heer, 1910]
Zeisberger, David, 1721–1808.

LAC 14550
Day before yesterday; reminiscences of a varied life, by Maitland Armstrong, 1836–1918, ed. by his daughter Margaret Armstrong. New York, C. Scribner's sons, 1920.
Armstrong, David Maitland, 1836–1918.

LAC 40107
The day breaking if not the sun rising of the gospel with the Indians in New England. New York, Reprinted for J. Sabin, 1865.
Wilson, John, 1588–1667, *supposed author.*

LAC 12115
The day of doom; or, A poetical description of the great and last judgment: with other poems. By Michael Wigglesworth. Also a memoir of the author, autobiography, and sketch of his funeral sermon by Rev. Cotton Mather. From the 6th ed., 1715. New York, American news company, 1867.
Wigglesworth, Michael, 1631–1705.

LAC 10535
The day of the Saxon. New York and London, Harper & brothers, 1912.
Lea, Homer, 1876–1912.

LAC 16343
Days on the road; crossing the plains in 1865, by Sarah Raymond Herndon. New York, Burr printing house, 1902.
Herndon, Sarah.

LAC 16150
Days with Walt Whitman, with some notes on his life and work. New York, The Macmillan company; [etc., etc.] 1906.
Carpenter, Edward, 1844–1929.

LAC 11123
De civitate Dei. The divine order of human society; being the L. P. Stone lectures for 1891, delivered in Princeton theological seminary. Philadelphia, J. D. Wattles, 1891.
Thompson, Robert Ellis, 1844–1924.

LAC 13154
De la France et des Etats-Unis; ou, De l'importance de la revolution de l'Amerique pour le bonheur de la France, des rapports de ce royaume & des Etats-Unis, des avantages reciproques qu'il peuvent retirer de leurs liaisons de commerce, & enfin de la situation actuelle des Etats-Unis. Par Etienne Claviere et J. P. Brissot de Warville. Londres, 1787.
Brissot de Warville, Jacques Pierre, 1754–1793.

LAC 16315
De la litterature et des hommes de lettres des Etats Unis d'Amerique. Paris, C. Gosselin, 1841.
Vail, Eugene A.

LAC 12803
De l'esclavage dans ses rapports avec l'union americaine. Paris, Michel Levy freres, 1862.
Carlier, Auguste, 1803–1890.

LAC 16531
A deal in wheat and other stories of the new and old West, by Frank Norris; illustrated by Remington, Leyendecker, Hitchcock and Hooper. New York, Doubleday, Page & company, 1903.
Norris, Frank, 1870–1902.

LAC 40035
The death of slavery. Letter from Peter Cooper to Governor Seymour. New York, 1863.
Cooper, Peter, 1791–1883.

LAC 13366
The debatable land.
Arredondo's historical proof of Spain's title to Georgia; a contribution to the history of one of the Spanish borderlands, edited by Herbert E. Bolton. Berkeley, Calif., University of California press, 1925.
Arredondo, Antonio de.

LAC 12781
A debate on slavery, held on the first, second, third and sixth days on October, 1845, in the city of Cincinnati, between Rev. J. Blanchard and N. L. Rice. Fourth thousand. Cincinnati, W. H. Moore & co.; New York, M. H. Newman, 1846.
Blanchard, Jonathan, 1811–1892.

LAC 11077

Debate on the evidences of Christianity, containing an examination of the social system, and of all the systems of scepticism of ancient and modern times, held in the city of Cincinnati ... between Robert Owen, of New Lanark, Scotland, and Alexander Campbell, of Bethany, Virginia. With an appendix by the parties. London, R. Groombridge, 1839.
Owen, Robert, 1771–1858.

LAC 21603–45

The debates and proceedings in the Congress of the United States; with an appendix, containing important state papers and public documents, and all the laws of a public nature; with a copious index... [First to] Eighteenth Congress.–first session: comprising the period from [March 3, 1789] to May 27, 1824, inclusive. Comp. from authentic materials. Washington, Gales and Seaton, 1834–56.
U.S. *Congress.*

LAC 14359

Debates and proceedings in the New-York state convention, for the revision of the Constitution. By S. Croswell and R. Sutton, reporters for the Argus. Albany, Printed at the office of the Albany Argus, 1846.
New York *(State) Constitutional Convention,* 1846.

LAC 23093–95

Debates and proceedings of the Constitutional convention of the state of Illinois, convened at the city of Springfield, Tuesday, December 13, 1869. Ely, Burnham & Bartlett, official stenographers. Springfield, E. L. Merritt & brother, printers to the Convention, 1870.
Illinois. *Constitutional Convention,* 1869–1870.

LAC 16463

The debates and proceedings of the constitutional convention of the state of New York assembled at Poughkeepsie on the 17th June, 1788. A fac-simile reprint of an original copy in the Adriance memorial library. Poughkeepsie, N. Y., Vassar brothers institute, 1905.
New York *(State) Convention,* 1788.

LAC 15079

Debates and proceedings of the convention which assembled at Little Rock, January 7th, 1868 ... to form a constitution for the state of Arkansas. Official: J. G. Price, secretary. Little Rock, J. G. Price, printer to the convention, 1868.
Arkansas. *Constitutional Convention,* 1868.

LAC 20945–48

Debates and proceedings of the first Constitutional convention of West Virginia (1861–1863) Edited by Charles H. Ambler, Frances Haney Atwood and William B. Mathews, under direction of the Supreme court of appeals of West Virginia. Huntington, W. Va., Gentry brothers, printers [1939?]
West Virginia. *Constitutional Convention,* 1861–1863.

LAC 22127–28

Debates and proceedings of the Maryland reform convention to revise the state constitution... Published by order of the convention... Annapolis, W. M'Neir, official printer, 1851.
Maryland. *Constitutional Convention,* 1850–1851.

LAC 20214–17

The debates in the several state conventions, on the adoption of the federal Constitution, as recommended by the general convention at Philadelphia, in 1787. Together with the Journal of the federal convention, Luther Martin's letter, Yates's minutes, Congressional opinions, Virginia and Kentucky resolutions of '98–'99, and other illustrations of the Constitution... 2d ed., with considerable additions. Collected and rev. from contemporary publications, by Jonathan Elliot. Published under the sanction of Congress. Philadelphia, J. B. Lippincott, 1863–1891.
Elliot, Jonathan, 1784–1846, *ed.*

LAC 21171–72

The debates of the Constitutional convention; of the state of Iowa, assembled at Iowa City, Monday, January 19, 1857. Being a full ... report of the debates and proceedings, by authority of the Convention; accompanied ... by a copious index of subjects, and remarks of members thereon. Official. W. Blair Lord, reporter. Davenport, Luse, Lane & co., 1857.
Iowa. *Constitutional Convention,* 1857.

LAC 21359–61

The debates of the Constitutional convention of the state of Maryland, assembled at the city of Annapolis, Wednesday, April 27, 1864; being a full and complete report of the debates and proceedings of the Convention, together with the old constitution, the law under which the Convention assembled, and the new constitution. Official: Wm. Blair Lord, reporter–Henry M. Parkhurst, assistant. Annapolis, Printed by R. P. Bayly, 1864.
Maryland. *Constitutional Convention,* 1864.

LAC 15075

Debates of the Maryland constitutional convention of 1867 (as reprinted from articles reported in the Baltimore sun.) Compiled by Philip B. Perlman. Baltimore, Hepbron & Haydon [c1923]
Maryland. *Constitutional Convention,* 1867.

LAC 22763–70

Debates of the Missouri Constitutional convention of 1875, edited by Isidor Loeb, and Floyd C. Shoemaker. Columbia, Mo., The State historical society of Missouri, 1930–44.
Missouri. *Constitutional Convention,* 1875–

LAC 31372–93

De Bow's review and industrial resources, statistics, etc. v. 9–30; July 1850–June 1861. New Orleans [etc.]

LAC 12955

Debs; his life, writings and speeches, with a department of appreciations... Girard, Kan., The Appeal to reason, 1908.
Debs, Eugene Victor, 1855–1926.

LAC 40150

Debt and resources of the United States: and the effect of secession upon the trade and industry of the loyal states. Philadelphia, Ringwalt & Brown, printers, 1863.
Elder, William, 1806–1885.

LAC 10368

A decade of civic development. Chicago, The University of Chicago press, 1905.
Zueblin, Charles, 1866–1924.

LAC 12287

The Decades of the newe worlde or west India, conteynyng the nauigations and conquestes of the Spanyardes, with the particular description of the moste ryche and large landes and Ilandes lately founde in the west Ocean perteynyng to the inheritaunce of the kinges of Spayne. In the which the diligent reader may not only consyder what commoditie may hereby chaunce to the hole christian world in tyme to come, but also learne many secreates touchynge the lande, the sea, and the starres, very necessarie to be knowe to al such as shal attempte any nauigations, or otherwise haue delite to beholde the strange and woonderfull woorks of God and nature. Wrytten in the Latine tounge by Peter Martyr of Angleria, and translated into Englysshe by Rycharde Eden. Londini, In aedibus Guilhelmi Powell, Anno. 1555.
Eden, Richard, 1521?–1576, *ed. and tr.*

LAC 40012

A declaration and remonstrance of the distressed and bleeding frontier inhabitants of the province of Pennsylvania, presented by them to the Honourable the governor and Assembly of the province, shewing the causes of their late discontent and uneasiness and the grievances under which they have laboured, and which they humbly pray to have redress'd. [Philadelphia] Printed [by W. Bradford?] in the year M,DCC,LXIV.
Smith, Matthew.

LAC 11468

The Declaration of independence, an interpretation and an analysis. New York, The Macmillan company; London, Macmillan & co., ltd., 1904.
Friedenwald, Herbert, 1870–1944.

LAC 40025

The declaration of the American citizens, on the Mobile, with relation to British aggressions. September, 1807 [Tarrytown, N. Y., 1925]
Washington Co., Ala. Citizens.

LAC 40093

A declaration of the Lord Baltemore's plantation in Maryland; wherein is set forth how Englishmen may become angels, the King's dominions be extended and the adventurers attain land and gear; together with other advantages of that sweet land. A facsimile of the original tract of 1633 made, by permission, from the only known copy in the possession of his Eminence the Cardinal Archbishop of Westminster. Baltimore [The Lord Baltimore press] 1929.

LAC 40044

A declaration of the sad and great persecution and martyrdom of the people of God, called Quakers, in New-England for the worshipping of God... Also, some considerations, presented to the King, which is in answer to a petition and address, which was presented unto him by the General court at Boston: subscribed by J. Endicot, the chief persecutor there; thinking thereby to cover themselves from the blood of the innocent... London, Printed for Robert Wilson, in Martins le grand [1660]
Burrough, Edward, 1634–1662.

LAC 14315

The decoration of houses, by Edith Wharton and Ogden Codman, jr. New York, C. Scribner's sons, 1897.
Wharton, Edith Newbold, 1862–1937.

LAC 12229

Decorum, a practical treatise on etiquette and dress of the best American society... Chicago, J. A. Ruth & co., 1879, [c1877]
Ruth, John A   *comp.*

LAC 20730–35

Decouvertes et etablissements des francais dans l'ouest et dans le sud de l'Amerique Septentrionale (1614–1754) Memoires et documents originaux recueillis et pub. [Paris, Impr. D. Jouaust. 1876–86]
Margry, Pierre, 1818–1894, *ed.*

LAC 40059

A defence for fugitive slaves, against the acts of Congress of February 12, 1793, and September 18, 1850. Boston, B. Marsh, 1850.
Spooner, Lysander, 1808–1887.

LAC 14484

Defence of Brigadier General W. Hull. Delivered before the general court martial, of which Major General Dearborn was president, at Albany, March, 1814. With an Address to the citizens of the United States. Written by himself. Copied from the original manuscript, and published by his authority. To which are prefixed, the charges against Brigadier General Hull, as specified by the government. Boston: Published by Wells and Lilly, Court-street, 1814.
Hull, William, 1753–1825.

LAC 15140

A defence of capital punishment, by Rev. George B. Cheever, D. D., and An essay on the ground and reason of punishment, with special reference to the penalty of death; by Tayler Lewis, esq. With an appendix, containing a review of Burleigh on the death penalty. New York, Wiley and Putnam, 1846.
Cheever, George Barrell, 1807–1890.

LAC 12824

A defence of Negro slavery, as it exists in the United States. Montgomery, Press of the "Alabama journal", 1846.
Estes, Matthew.

LAC 10944

The defence of Professor Briggs before the Presbytery of New York, December 13, 14, 15, 19, and 22, 1892. New York, C. Scribner's sons, 1893.
Briggs, Charles Augustus, 1841–1913.

LAC 11160

A defence of the American policy, as opposed to the encroachments of foreign influence, and especially to the interference of the papacy in the political interests and affairs of the United States. New York, De Witt & Davenport [1856]
Whitney, Thomas Richard, 1804–1858.

LAC 40062

A defence of the Letter from a gentleman at Halifax, to his friend in Rhode-Island... Newport, Printed and sold by S. Hall, 1765.
Howard, Martin, 1730 (*ca.*)–1781.

LAC 15467

A defence of the measures of the administration of Thomas Jefferson. By Curtius [*pseud.*] Taken from the National intelligencer. Washington, Printed by S. H. Smith, 1804.
Taylor, John, 1753–1824, *supposed author.*

LAC 13791

A defence of the Observations on the charter and conduct of the Society for the propagation of the gospel in foreign parts against an anonymous pamphlet falsly [!] intitled, A candid examination of Dr. Mayhew's Observations, &c. and also against the Letter to a friend annexed thereto, said to contain a short vindication of said society. By one of its members. By Jonathan Mayhew, D. D., pastor of the West church in Boston. Boston, Printed and sold by R. and S. Draper, in Newbury-street; Edes and Gill, in Queen-street; and T. & J. Fleet, in Cornhill, 1763.
Mayhew, Jonathan, 1720–1766.

LAC 15177

A defence of Virginia, (and through her, of the South) in recent and pending contests against the sectional party. New York, E. J. Hale & son, 1867.
Dabney, Robert Lewis, 1820–1898.

LAC 40092

A definition of parties; or, The political effects of the paper system considered. Philadelphia, April 5th, 1794. Philadelphia, Printed by Francis Bailey, No. 116, High-street, 1794.
Taylor, John, 1753–1824.

LAC 14475

Deh-he-wa-mis: or, A narrative of the life of Mary Jemison: otherwise called the White woman, who was taken captive by the Indians in MDCCLV; and who continued with them seventy eight years. Containing an account of the murder of her father and his family; her marriages and sufferings; Indian barbarities, customs and traditions. Carefully taken from her own words, by James E. Seaver. Also the life of Hiokatoo, and Ebenezer Allen: a sketch of General Sullivan's campaign; tragedy of the "Devils Hole," etc. The whole revised, corrected and enlarged: with descriptive and historical sketches of the Six Nations, the Genesee country, and other interesting facts connected with the narrative: by Ebenezer Mix. 2d ed. Batavia, N. Y., W. Seaver and son, 1842.
Seaver, James Everett, 1787–1827.

LAC 21332

Delaplaine's repository of the lives and portraits of distinguished American characters. Philadelphia, 1815–[16]
Delaplaine, Joseph, 1777–1824.

LAC 20524–26

Delaware archives... Published by the Public archives commission of Delaware by authority. v. 1–5. Wilmington, Del., 1911–16.
Delaware. *Public Archives Commission.*

LAC 40006

De Leon-Carmody debate. Individualism vs. socialism. Daniel De Leon and Thomas F. Carmody, under the auspices of the People's forum, stenographically reported by Mr. Emmet W. Connors, delivered at Proctor's theatre, Troy, N. Y., April 14, 1912; issued by the National executive committee, Socialist labor party. 4th ed. New York, The Franklin press [c1912]
De Leon, Daniel, 1852–1914.

LAC 15083

The delight makers. New York, Dodd, Mead and company [c1890]
Bandelier, Adolph Francis Alphonse, 1840–1914.

LAC 12719

Delineations of American scenery and character, by John James Audubon, with an introduction by Francis Hobart Herrick. London, Simpkin, Marshall, Hamilton, Kent, & co., ltd., 1926.
Audubon, John James, 1785–1851.

LAC 12723

The deluge, by David Graham Phillips, with illustrations by George Gibbs. New York, Grosset & Dunlap [c1905]
Phillips, David Graham, 1867–1911.

LAC 11410

Democracy ... New-York, Harper and brothers, 1841.
Camp, George Sidney.

LAC 11802

Democracy, an American novel. New York, H. Holt and company, 1880.
Adams, Henry, 1838–1918.

LAC 15505

Democracy and assimilation; the blending of immigrant heritages in America. New York, The Macmillan company, 1920.
Drachsler, Julius, 1889–

LAC 12922

Democracy and empire; with studies of their psychological, economic, and moral foundations. New York, The Macmillan company; London, Macmillan & co., ltd., 1900.
Giddings, Franklin Henry, 1855–1931.

LAC 15291

Democracy and social ethics. New York, The Macmillan company; [etc., etc.] 1902.
Addams, Jane, 1860–1935.

LAC 10540

Democracy and social growth in America; four lectures. New York & London, G. P. Putnam's sons, 1898.
Moses, Bernard, 1846–1930.

LAC 20826–27

Democracy and the organization of political parties, by M. Ostrogorski, translated from the French by Frederick Clarke, with a preface by the Right Hon. James Bryce. New York, The Macmillan company; London, Macmillan & co., ltd., 1902.
Ostrogorskii, Moisei IAkovlevich, 1854–1919.

LAC 40006

Democracy, constructive and pacific. New York, J. Winchester, 1844.
Godwin, Parke, 1816–1904.

LAC 21002

Democracy in America, by Alexis de Tocqueville (tr. by Henry Reeve) with special introductions by Hon. John T. Morgan ... and Hon. John J. Ingalls. Rev. ed. New York, The Colonial press [c1900]
Tocqueville, Alexis Charles Henri Maurice Clerel de, 1805–1859.

LAC 11475

Democracy in the United States. What it has done, what it is doing, and what it will do. New York, D. Appleton and company, 1868.
Gillet, Ransom Hooker, 1800–1876.

LAC 20219

Democracy unveiled, or, Tyranny stripped of the garb of patriotism. By Christopher Caustic [*pseud.*] 3d ed., with large additions. New-York: Printed for I. Riley & co., 1806.
Fessenden, Thomas Green, 1771–1837.

LAC 13692

Democracy vindicated and Dorrism unveiled. Providence, Printed by H. H. Brown, 1846.
Randall, Dexter.

LAC 40150

The Democratic hand-book, compiled by Mich. W. Cluskey of Washington City, D. C. Recommended by the Democratic National Committee. Washington, Printed by R. A. Waters, 1856.
Cluskey, Michael W.

LAC 10726

The democratic judge: or, The equal liberty of the press, as exhibited, explained, and exposed, in the prosecution of William Cobbett, for a pretended libel against the King of Spain and his Embassador, before Thomas M'Kean, chief justice of the state of Pennsylvania. By Peter Porcupine [*pseud.*] Philadelphia: Published by William Cobbett, opposite christ church March, 1798.
Cobbett, William, 1763–1835.

LAC 20809–10

The Democratic party of the state of New York; a history of the origin, growth and achievements of the Democratic party of the state of New York, including a history of Tammany Hall in its relation to state politics; ed. by James K. McGuire. An historical chapter on Kings county Democracy by Martin W. Littleton. Biographical sketches of the leading Democratic politicians in the state of New York... [New York] United States history company, 1905.
McGuire, James K.   1868–1923, *ed.*

LAC 12178

The Department of state of the United States. Its history and functions. Washington, Department of state, 1893.
U.S. *Dept. of State.*

LAC 11154

El derecho de intervencion y la doctrina de Monroe (antecedentes historicos) Buenos Aires, Impr. J. Peuser, 1898.
Urien, Carlos Maria, 1855–1921.

LAC 40129

The derrick. [Jersey City, Press of A. J. Doan, c1911]
Ryan, William.

LAC 22342–43

The Derrick's hand-book of petroleum; a complete chronological and statistical review of petroleum developments from 1859 to [1899]... Oil City, Pa., Derrick company, 1898–1900.

LAC 11948

The descendant. New York and London, Harper & brothers, 1900, [c1897]
Glasgow, Ellen Anderson Gholson, 1873–1945.

LAC 13341

A description of East-Florida, with a Journal, kept by John Bartram of Philadelphia, botanist to His Majesty for the Floridas; upon a journey from St. Augustine up the river St. John's as far as the lakes. With explanatory botanical notes... 3d ed., much enlarged and improved...
London, Sold by W. Nicoll [etc.] 1769.
Stork, William.

LAC 40088

A description of Ithiel Town's improvement in the construction of wood and iron bridges; intended as a general system of bridge building. New Haven, Printed by S. Converse [1821]
Town, Ithiel, 1784–1844.

LAC 14095

A description of Louisiana, by Father Louis Hennepin, Recollect missionary. Tr. from the edition of 1683, and compared with the Nouvelle decouverte, the La Salle documents and other contemporaneous papers. By John Gilmary Shea. New York, J. G. Shea, 1880.
Hennepin, Louis, *17th cent.*

LAC 40020

Description of the American electro magnetic telegraph: now in operation between the cities of Washington and Baltimore. Illustrated by fourteen wood engravings. Washington, Printed by J. & G. S. Gideon, 1845.
Vail, Alfred, 1807–1859.

LAC 40072

A description of the bounty lands in the state of Illinois: also, the principal roads and routes, by land and water, through the territory of the United States; extending from the province of New-Brunswic, in Nova Scotia, to the Pacific Ocean... Cincinnati, Looker, Reynolds & co., printers, 1819.
Dana, Edmund.

LAC 12545

A description of the canals and rail roads of the United States, comprehending notices of all the works of internal improvement throughout the several states. New York, T. R. Tanner & J. Disturnell, 1840.
Tanner, Henry Schenck, 1786–1858.

LAC 15176

A description of the English province of Carolana. By the Spaniards call'd Florida, and by the French, La Louisiane... To which is added a large and accurate map of Carolana, and of the river Meschacebe. [London] Printed for and sold by O. Payne, 1741.
Coxe, Daniel, 1673–1739.

LAC 40122

Description of the iron bridge over the Connecticut River, on the Hartford & New Haven R. R.; with a brief history of iron bridges... Hartford, Conn., Brown & Gross, 1866.
Ellis, Theodore Gunville, 1829–1883.

LAC 40129

Description of the principles and plan of proposed establishments of salt works; for the purpose of supplying the United States with home made salt. Philadelphia: Printed by John Bioren, M.DCC.XCVIII.
Fennell, James, 1766–1816.

LAC 40060

A description of the roads in the United States. Comp. from the most authentic materials. Philadelphia, Printed by G. Palmer, 201 Chesnut street, 1814.
Melish, John, 1771–1822.

LAC 14189

A descriptive and historical account of hydraulic and other machines for raising water, ancient and modern: with observations on various subjects connected with the mechanic arts: including the progressive development of the steam engine... In five books. Illustrated by nearly three hundred engravings. New York, D. Appleton and company, 1842.
Ewbank, Thomas, 1792–1870.

LAC 22487–89

A descriptive catalogue of Friends' books, or books written by members of the Society of Friends, commonly called Quakers, from their first rise to the present time, interspersed with critical remarks and ... biographical notices... London, J. Smith, 1867.
Smith, Joseph, *bookseller*.

LAC 13209

A descriptive sketch of the present state of Vermont. One of the United States of America. London, Printed and sold for the author, by H. Fry, 1797.
Graham, John Andrew, 1764–1841.

LAC 11920

The deserter, and other stories. A book of two wars. Boston, Lothrop publishing company [c1898]
Frederic, Harold, 1856–1898.

LAC 14643

Desertion during the civil war. New York, London, The Century co. [c1928]
Lonn, Ella, 1879–1962.

LAC 12284

The despatches of Hernando Cortes, the conqueror of Mexico, addresssed to the emperor Charles V, written during the conquest, and containing a narrative of its events. Now first translated into English from the original Spanish, with an introduction and notes, by G. Folsom. New York [etc.] Wiley & Putnam, 1843.
Cortes, Hernando, 1485–1547.

LAC 10691

The despatches of Molyneux Shuldham, vice-admiral of the Blue and commander-in-chief of His Britannic Majesty's ships in North America, January–July, 1776; ed. by Robert Wilden Neeser. New York, Printed for the Naval history society by the De Vinne press, 1913.
Shuldham, Molyneux Shuldham, *baron*, 1717?–1798.

LAC 12849

Despotism in America; an inquiry into the nature, results and legal basis of the slave-holding system in the United States. Boston, J. P. Jewett and company; New York, Sheldon, Lamport & Blakeman; [etc., etc.] 1854.
Hildreth, Richard, 1807–1865.

LAC 40063

The destiny of America. The inevitable political union of the United States and Canada... Washington, D. C., W. H. Lowdermilk & co., 1889.
Sutherland, Edwin.

LAC 10512

The destiny of man viewed in the light of his origin. Boston and New York, Houghton, Mifflin and company [1884]
Fiske, John, 1842–1901.

LAC 40138

The destiny of the races of this continent. An address delivered before the Mercantile library association of Boston, Massachusetts. On the 26th of January, 1859. By Frank P. Blair, jr., of Missouri. Washington, D. C., Buell & Blanchard, printers, 1859.
Blair, Francis Preston, 1821–1875.

LAC 12391

Destruction and reconstruction: personal experiences of the late war. New York, D. Appleton and company, 1879.
Taylor, Richard, 1826–1879.

LAC 40064

Destruction of Republicanism the object of the rebellion! The testimony of southern witnesses. [Boston] Published by the Emancipation league [186–]
Moody, Loring.

LAC 11643

The destructive influence of the tariff upon manufacture and commerce and the figures and facts relating thereto. 2d ed. New York, Pub. for the New York free trade club, by G. P. Putnam's sons, 1884.
Schoenhof, Jacob, 1839–1903.

LAC 15737

Das deutsche element in den Vereinigten Staaten von Nordamerika, 1818–1848. Cincinnati, A. E. Wilde & co., 1880.
Korner, Gustav Philipp, 1809–1896.

LAC 16004

Die Deutschen von Iowa und deren errungenschaften. Eine geschichte des staates, dessen deutscher pioniere und ihrer nachkommen. Des Moines, Ia., Druck und verlag des "Iowa staats-anzeiger", 1900.
Eiboeck, Joseph, 1838–1913.

LAC 15968

The development of agriculture in New Jersey, 1640–1880, a monographic study in agricultural history. New Brunswick, N. J., New Jersey agricultural experiment station, Rutgers university, 1927.
Woodward, Carl Raymond, 1890–

LAC 14666

Development of American architecture, 1783–1830. Philadelphia, David McKay co. [c1926]
Jackson, Joseph, 1867–

LAC 10195

The development of banking in Illinois, 1817–1863. Urbana, The University of Illinois, 1913.
Dowrie, George William, 1880–

LAC 13548

The development of Chicago and vicinity as a manufacturing center prior to 1880... [Chicago, McElroy pub. co.] 1911.
Riley, Elmer Author.

LAC 12740

The development of freedom of the press in Massachusetts. New York, London [etc.] Longmans, Green, and co., 1906.
Duniway, Clyde Augustus, 1866–1944.

LAC 10517

The development of religious liberty in Connecticut. Boston and New York, Houghton, Mifflin and company, 1905.
Greene, Maria Louise.

LAC 40029

The development of school support in colonial Massachusetts. New York, 1909.
Jackson, George Leroy, 1876–

LAC 13660

The development of sentiment on negro suffrage to 1860. [Madison, Wis.] The University of Wisconsin, 1912.
Olbrich, Emil, *d.* 1906.

LAC 15422

The development of the organisation of Anglo-American trade, 1800–1850. New Haven, Yale university press; [etc., etc.] 1925.
Buck, Norman Sydney, 1892–

LAC 40131

The development of the resources of the southern states. An address to the Atlanta chamber of commerce. April fourteenth, 1898. [Boston? 1898]
Atkinson, Edward, 1827–1905.

LAC 16457

The development of the Sunday-school, 1780–1905. The offical report of the eleventh International Sunday-school convention, Toronto, Canada, June 23–27, 1905. Boston, Mass., Executive committee of the International Sunday-school association, 1905.
International Sunday-School Convention of the United States and British American provinces. *11th, Toronto,* 1905.

LAC 10415

Development of transportation systems in the United States; comprising a comprehensive description of the leading features of advancement, from the colonial era to the present time, in water channels, roads, turnpikes, canals, railways, vessels, vehicles, cars and locomotives... With illustrations of hundreds of typical objects. Philadelphia, Pub. by the author, Railway world office, 1888.
Ringwalt, John Luther.

LAC 11493

De Witt Clinton and the origin of the spoils system in New York. New York, Columbia university press, the Macmillan company, agents; [etc., etc.] 1907.
McBain, Howard Lee, 1880–

LAC 30234–36

The Dial: a magazine for literature, philosophy, and religion. v. 1–4; July 1840–Apr. 1844. Boston, Weeks, Jordan, and company [etc.]; London, Wiley and Putnam [etc.] 1841–44.

LAC 40133

A dialogue concerning the slavery of the Africans; shewing it to be the duty and interest of the American states to emancipate all their African slaves. With an address to the owners of such slaves. Dedicated to the honourable the Continental congress. To which is prefixed, the institution of the Society, in New-York, for promoting the manumission of slaves, and protecting such of them as have been, or may be, liberated... Norwich [Conn.]: Printed by Judah P. Spooner, 1776. New-York: Re-printed for Robert Hodge, 1785.
Hopkins, Samuel, 1721–1803.

LAC 20689–92

Diaries and correspondence of James Harris, first earl of Malmesbury; containing an account of his missions to the courts of Madrid, Frederick the Great, Catherine the Second, and the Hague; and his special missions to Berlin, Brunswick, and the French republic. Ed. by his grandson, the third earl. London, R. Bentley, 1844.
Malmesbury, James Harris, *1st earl of*, 1746–1820.

LAC 15361

The diaries of Benjamin Lynde and of Benjamin Lynde, jr.; with an appendix. Boston, Priv. print. [Cambridge, Riverside press] 1880.
Lynde, Benjamin, 1666–1745.

LAC 22658–59

The diaries of George Washington, 1748–1799, edited by John C. Fitzpatrick. Published for the Mount Vernon ladies' association of the Union. Boston and New York, Houghton Mifflin company [1925]
Washington, George, *pres. U.S.*, 1732–1799.

LAC 23915–17

Diary; edited by Allan Nevins and Milton Halsey Thomas. New York, Macmillan, 1952.
Strong, George Templeton, 1820–1875.

LAC 23240–41

The diary and letters of Gouverneur Morris. Edited by Anne Cary Morris. New York, Da Capo Press, 1970.
Morris, Gouverneur, 1752–1816.

LAC 22721–24

Diary and letters of Rutherford Birchard Hayes, nineteenth president of the United States, edited by Charles Richard Williams. [Columbus, O.] The Ohio state archaeological and historical society, 1922–26.
Hayes, Rutherford Birchard, *pres. U.S.*, 1822–1893.

LAC 10248

A diary from Dixie, as written by Mary Boykin Chesnut, wife of James Chesnut, jr., United States senator from South Carolina, 1859–1861, and afterward an aide to Jefferson Davis and a brigadier-general in the Confederate army; ed. by Isabella D. Martin and Myrta Lockett Avary. New York, D. Appleton and company, 1905.
Chesnut, Mary Boykin, 1823–1886.

LAC 20693–94
A diary in America, with remarks on its institutions. By Capt. Marryat. London, Longman, Orme, Brown, Green & Longmans, 1839.
Marryat, Frederick, 1792–1848.

LAC 15562
The diary of a forty-niner, edited by Chauncey L. Canfield. New York, San Francisco, M. Shepard company, 1906.
Canfield, Chauncey de Leon, 1843–1909.

LAC 21141
Diary of a journey from the Mississippi to the coasts of the Pacific with a United States government expedition. By Baldwin Mollhausen. With an introduction by Alexander von Humboldt. Tr. by Mrs. Percy Sinnett. London, Longman, Brown, Green, Longmans, & Roberts, 1858.
Mollhausen, Balduin, 1825–1905.

LAC 40064
Diary of a soldier, and prisoner of war in the Rebel prisons. Trenton [N. J.] Murphy & Bechtel, printers, 1865.
Forbes, Eugene, d. 1865.

LAC 14409
The diary of a young officer serving with the armies of the United States during the war of the rebellion, by Josiah Marshall Favill, adjutant, captain, and brevet major 57th New York infantry, brevet lieutenant-colonel, and colonel U.S. volunteers. Chicago, R. R. Donnelley & sons company, 1909.
Favill, Josiah Marshall.

LAC 15985
Diary of Colonel Israel Angell, commanding the Second Rhode Island continental regiment during the American revolution, 1778–1781; transcribed from the original manuscript, together with a biographical sketch of the author and illustrative notes by Edward Field. Providence, R. I., Preston and Rounds company, 1899.
Angell, Israel, 1740–1832.

LAC 40125
Diary of David How, a private in Colonel Paul Dudley Sargent's regiment of the Massachusetts line, in the army of the American revolution. From the original manuscript. With a biographical sketch of the author by George Wingate Chase, and illustrative notes by Henry B. Dawson, Morrisania, N. Y. [Cambridge, Mass., Printed by H. O. Houghton and company] 1865.
How, David, 1758–1842.

LAC 22904–5
Diary of David Zeisberger, a Moravian missionary among the Indians of Ohio; tr. from the original German manuscript and ed. by Eugene F. Bliss. Cincinnati, R. Clarke & co., 1885.
Zeisberger, David, 1721–1808.

LAC 13434
Diary of George Mifflin Dallas, while United States minister to Russia 1837 to 1839, and to England 1856 to 1861, ed. by Susan Dallas. Philadelphia, J. B. Lippincott company, 1892.
Dallas, George Mifflin, 1792–1864.

LAC 22406–8
Diary of Gideon Welles, secretary of the navy under Lincoln and Johnson, with an introduction by John T. Morse, jr. ... Boston and New York, Houghton Mifflin company, 1911.
Welles, Gideon, 1802–1878.

LAC 23321–22
The diary of James A. Garfield. Edited with an introd. by Harry James Brown [and] Frederick D. Williams. [East Lansing] Michigan State University, 1967.
Garfield, James Abram, *pres. U.S.*, 1831–1881.

LAC 22654–57
The diary of James K. Polk during his presidency, 1845 to 1849, now first printed from the original manuscript in the collections of the Chicago historical society; ed. and annotated by Milo Milton Quaife. With an introduction by Andrew Cunningham McLaughlin. Chicago, A. C. McClurg & co., 1910.
Polk, James Knox, *pres. U.S.*, 1795–1849.

LAC 11711
Diary of Joshua Hempstead of New London, Connecticut, covering a period of forty-seven years, from September, 1711, to November, 1758; containing valuable genealogical data relating to many New London families, references to the colonial wars, to the shipping and other matters of interest pertaining to the town and the times, with an account of a journey made by the writer from New London to Maryland. New London, Conn., The New London county historical society, 1901.
Hempstead, Joshua, 1678–1758.

LAC 10781
The diary of Matthew Patten of Bedford, N. H. From Seventeen hundred fifty-four to Seventeen hundred eighty-eight. Pub. by the town. Concord, N. H., The Rumford printing company, 1903.
Patten, Matthew, 1719–1795.

LAC 10375
The diary of Michael Floy, jr., Bowery village, 1833–1837. Edited by Richard Albert Edward Brooks, with an introductory note, annotations, and postscript by Margaret Floy Washburn. New Haven, Yale university press; London, H. Milford, Oxford university press, 1941.
Floy, Michael, 1808–1837.

LAC 21315
The diary of Philip Hone, 1828–1851. Ed., with an introduction, by Bayard Tuckerman. New York, Dodd, Mead and company, 1889.
Hone, Philip, 1780–1851.

LAC 15944
The diary of Rev. Ebenezer Parkman, of Westborough, Mass., for the months of February, March, April, October, and November, 1737, November and December of 1778 and the years of 1779 and 1780... Ed. by Harriette M. Forbes. [Westborough, Mass.] The Westborough historical society, 1899.
Parkman, Ebenezer, 1703–1782.

LAC 20225–26
Diary of the American revolution. From newspapers and original documents. New York, C. T. Evans, 1863.
Moore, Frank, 1828–1904.

LAC 15727

Diary of the siege of Detroit in the war with Pontiac, Also a narrative of the principal events of the siege, by Major Robert Rogers; a plan for conducting Indian affairs, by Colonel Bradstreet: and other authentick documents, never before printed. Ed. with notes by Franklin B. Hough. Albany, J. Munsell, 1860.
Hough, Franklin Benjamin, 1822–1885, *ed.*

LAC 13248

Diary of the Washburn expedition to the Yellowstone and Firehole rivers in the year 1870. [St. Paul? Minn., c1905]
Langford, Nathaniel Pitt, 1832–1911.

LAC 22685–88

The diary of William Bentley, D. D., pastor of the East church, Salem, Massachusetts... Salem, Mass., The Essex institute, 1905–14.
Bentley, William, 1759–1819.

LAC 22627–28

Diary of William Dunlap (1766–1839) the memoirs of a dramatist, theatrical manager, painter, critic, novelist, and historian... New York, Printed for the New York historical society, 1930.
Dunlap, William, 1766–1839.

LAC 10364

The diary of William Pynchon of Salem. A picture of Salem life, social and political, a century ago. Ed. by Fitch Edward Oliver. Boston and New York, Houghton, Mifflin and company, 1890.
Pynchon, William, 1723–1789.

LAC 10918

A dictionary of all religions and religious denominations, Jewish, heathen, Mahometan and Christian, ancient and modern. With an appendix, containing a sketch of the present state of the world, as to population, religion, toleration, missions, etc., and the articles in which all Christian denominations agree. Fourth ed., with corrections and large additions. Published by James Eastburn and company, at the Literary rooms, corner of Broadway and Pine street, N. York; and by Cummings and Hilliard, no. 1, Cornhill, Boston. 1817.
Adams, Hannah, 1755–1832.

LAC 11400

A dictionary of American politics: comprising accounts of political parties, measures and men... By Everit Brown and Albert Strauss. New York, A. L. Burt, 1892.
Brown, Everit.

LAC 12141

Dictionary of Americanisms. A glossary of words and phrases, usually regarded as peculiar to the United States. New York, Bartlett and Welford, 1848.
Bartlett, John Russell, 1805–1886.

LAC 20923–25

A dictionary of arts, manufactures and mines; containing a clear exposition of their principles and practice. Illustrated with nearly sixteen hundred engravings on wood. Reprinted entire from the last corrected and greatly enlarged English ed. New York, D. Appleton, 1860.
Ure, Andrew, 1778–1857.

LAC 11086

A dictionary of the Book of Mormon, comprising its biographical, geographical and other proper names, by Elder George Reynolds. Salt Lake City, Utah, J. H. Parry, 1891.
Reynolds, George.

LAC 20032–33

A dictionary, practical, theoretical, and historical, of commerce and commercial navigation. By J. R. M'Culloch, esq. Ed. by Henry Vethake. With an appendix, containing the new tariff of 1846, together with the tariff of 1842 ... also, the sub-treasury, warehousing, and the Canadian transit bills, of 1846. Likewise, the new British tariff... Philadelphia, A. Hart, 1852.
McCulloch, John Ramsay, 1789–1864.

LAC 20133

Didactics: social, literary, and political. Philadelphia, Carey, Lea & Blanchard, 1836.
Walsh, Robert, 1784–1859.

LAC 40073

The differences between the Socialist party and the Socialist labor party, also between socialism, anarchism and anti-political industrialism. [Brooklyn, N. Y., Linotype and print of Grayzel & co., c1908]
Rosenthal, Alter, 1875–

LAC 15470–71

Digest of decisions and precedents of the Senate and House of representatives of the United States, relating to their powers and privileges respecting their members and officers, and to investigations, contempts, libels, contumacious witnesses, expulsions, writs of habeas corpus, etc., with decisions of the U.S. Supreme court and other courts relating thereto. Comp., ed., and indexed by Henry H. Smith, clerk to the Senate Special committee to investigate attempts at bribery, etc., under the resolutions of May 17, 19, and 28, and August 16, 1894... Washington, Govt. print off., 1894.
U.S. *Congress. Senate. Special Committee to Investigate Attempts at Bribery, etc.*

LAC 11630–31

Digest of decisions of the courts and Interstate commerce commission under the act to regulate commerce from 1887 to 1908. With copy of Act to regulate commerce as amended to date, the original act and amendments, the Elkins act, the Expedition act, the Act in relation to testimony, etc. Chicago, 1908.
Peirce, Edward Beauchamp, 1868–1912.

LAC 10093

Digest of manufactures.
A statement of the arts and manufactures of the United States of America, for the year 1810: digested and prepared by Tench Coxe, esquire, of Philadelphia. Philadelphia, Printed by A. Cornman, junr. 1814.
U.S. *Treasury Dept.*

LAC 11726

A digest of the early Connecticut probate records. Vol. I, Hartford district, 1635–1700. Hartford, Conn., R. S. Peck & co., 1904, [c1902]
Manwaring, Charles William, 1829–1905, *comp.*

LAC 11760

Digest of the laws and enactments of the National grange, including the decisions of the masters, executive committees, and court of appeals. From the organization of the order to March 30, 1896. In which is included declaration of purposes, the parliamentary guide, rules and regulations for grange trials, &c. Issued by authority of the National grange. Rev. ed. Philadelphia, G. S. Ferguson co., 1900.
Patrons of Husbandry. *National Grange.*

LAC 16141

Digest of the laws of the state of Georgia, from its settlement as a British province, in 1755, to the session of the General assembly in 1800, inclusive. Comprehending all the laws passed within the above periods, and now in force, alphabetically arranged under their respective titles: also the state constitutions of 1777 and 1789, with the additions and amendments in 1795, and the constitution of 1798. To which is added, an appendix: comprising the Declaration of American independence; the Articles of confederation and perpetual union; the federal Constitution, with the amendments thereto: all the treaties between the United States and foreign nations; the treaties between the United States and the different tribes of Indians; and those between the state of Georgia and the southern and western Indians. With a copious index to the whole. Comp., arranged and digested from the original records, and under the special authority of the state. By Horatio Marbury & William H. Crawford, esqrs. Savannah: Printed by Seymour, Woolhopter & Stebbins, 1802.
Georgia. *Laws, statutes, etc.*

LAC 15128

The digressions of V., written for his own fun and that of his friends, by Elihu Vedder; containing the quaint legends of his infancy, an account of his stay in Florence, the garden of lost opportunities, return home on the track of Columbus, his struggle in New York in war-time coinciding with that of the nation, his prolonged stay in Rome, and likewise his prattlings upon art, tamperings with literature, struggles with verse, and many other things, being a portrait of himself from youth to age. With many illustrations by the author. Boston and New York, Houghton Mifflin company, 1910.
Vedder, Elihu, 1836–1923.

LAC 15097

The diplomacy of the revolution: an historical study. New York, D. Appleton & co., 1852.
Trescot, William Henry, 1822–1898.

LAC 40058

Diplomatic audiences at the court of China. London, Luzac & co., 1905.
Rockhill, William Woodville, 1854–1914.

LAC 13704

Diplomatic code of the United States of America: embracing a collection of treaties and conventions between the United States and foreign powers, from the year 1778 to 1827. With an index to the principal cases decided in the courts of the United States, upon points connected with their foreign relations; and various official acts, papers, and useful information, for public ministers and consuls. To which is annexed, extracts from treaties and conventions, at present subsisting between Great Britain, France, Spain, &c., chiefly intended to elucidate the policy pursued towards America, about the period of the late general pacification in Europe. Washington, Printed by J. Elliot, junior, 1827.
Elliot, Jonathan, 1784–1846, *comp.*

LAC 21034–41

The diplomatic correspondence of the American revolution; being the letters of Benjamin Franklin, Silas Deane, John Adams, John Jay, Arthur Lee, William Lee, Ralph Izard, Francis Dana, William Carmichael, Henry Laurens, John Laurens, M. de Lafayette, M. Dumas, and others, concerning the foreign relations of the United States during the whole revolution; together with the letters in reply from the secret committee of Congress, and the secretary of foreign affairs. Also the entire correspondence of the French ministers, Genard and Luzerne, with Congress. Pub. under the direction of the President of the United States, from the original manuscripts in the Department of State, conformably to a resolution of Congress, of March 27th, 1818. Ed. by Jared Sparks. Boston, N. Hale and Gray & Bowen; New York, G. & C. & H. Carvill; [etc., etc.] 1829–30.
U.S. *Dept. of State.*

LAC 23702–4

Diplomatic correspondence of the republic of Texas. Edited by George P. Garrison. [Washington, Govt. print. off., 1908–11]
Texas *(Republic) Dept. of State.*

LAC 22111–13

Diplomatic correspondence of the United States concerning the independence of the Latin-American nations; selected and arranged by William R. Manning. New York [etc.] Oxford university press, 1925.
Manning, William Ray, 1871–1942, *ed.*

LAC 21015–17

The diplomatic correspondence of the United States of America, from the signing of the definitive treaty of peace, 10th September, 1783, to the adoption of the Constitution, March 4, 1789. Being the letters of the presidents of Congress, the secretary for foreign affairs–American ministers at foreign courts, foreign ministers near Congress–reports of committees of Congress, and reports of the secretary for foreign affairs on various letters and communications; together with letters from individuals on public affairs. Published under direction of the secretary of state, from the original manuscripts in the Department of State, conformably to an act of Congress, approved May 5, 1832... Washington, Printed by Blair and Rives, 1837 [Washington, J. C. Rives, 1855]
U.S. *Dept. of State.*

LAC 15098

The diplomatic history of the administrations of Washington and Adams, 1789–1801. Boston, Little, Brown and company, 1857.
Trescot, William Henry, 1822–1898.

LAC 13832

Diplomatic history of the Panama canal. Correspondence relating to the negotiation and application of certain treaties on the subject of the construction of an interoceanic canal, and accompanying papers. Washington, Govt. print. off., 1914.
U.S. *Dept. of State.*

LAC 11577

Diplomatic history of the southern confederacy. New York, F. Ungar [1964]
Callahan, James Morton, 1864–1956.

LAC 20799
Diplomatic memoirs. Boston and New York, Houghton Mifflin company, 1909.
Foster, John Watson, 1836–1917.

LAC 14491
Diplomatic negotiations of American naval officers, 1778–1883. Baltimore, The Johns Hopkins press, 1912.
Paullin, Charles Oscar, 1868 or 9–1944.

LAC 12927
The diplomatic relations of the United States and Spanish America. Baltimore, The Johns Hopkins press, 1900.
Latane, John Holladay, 1869–1932.

LAC 40124
The diplomatic service of the United States, with some hints toward its reform. Washington, Smithsonian institution, 1905.
White, Andrew Dickson, 1832–1918.

LAC 10677
La diplomatie francaise et la Ligue des neutres de 1780 (1776–1783) par Paul Fauchille. Paris, G. Pedone-Lauriel, 1893.
Fauchille, Paul, 1858–1926.

LAC 15709
Direct legislation by the people. Chicago, A. C. McClurg and company, 1892.
Cree, Nathan.

LAC 15303
Directions for a candididate of the ministry.
Manuductio ad ministerium; directions for a candidate of the ministry, by Cotton Mather. Reproduced from the original edition, Boston, 1726, with a bibliographical note by Thomas J. Holmes and Kenneth B. Murdock. New York, Pub. for the Facsimile text society by Columbia university press, 1938.
Mather, Cotton, 1663–1728.

LAC 40132
Disclosures and confessions of Frank. A. Wilmot, the slave thief and negro runner. With an accurate account of the Under-ground railroad! What it is, and where located! By a late conductor on the same. Also–full particulars of the plans adopted for running off slaves from the Southern states to the Canadas. Added to which is a history of the abduction of Miss Lucille Hamet, the planter's daughter, and a true description of slave life on a plantation. Philadelphia, Barclay [1860]
Wilmot, Franklin A.

LAC 40012
A discourse and view of Virginia. By Sir William Berkeley (governor of Virginia) London, 1663 [reprinted, Norwalk, Conn., W. H. Smith, jr., 1914]
Berkeley, *Sir* William, 1608?–1677.

LAC 11452
A discourse concerning the currencies of the British plantations in America, &c. By William Douglass. Ed. by Charles J. Bullock. New York, Pub. for the American economic association by the Macmillan company; [etc., etc.] 1897.
Douglass, William, 1691–1732.

LAC 40034
A discourse concerning the influence of America on the mind: being the annual oration delivered before the American philosophical society, at the University in Philadelphia, on the 18th October, 1823... Philadelphia, A. Small, 1823.
Ingersoll, Charles Jared, 1782–1862.

LAC 40085
A discourse concerning unlimited submission and non-resistance to the higher powers: with some reflections on the resistance made to King Charles I. and on the anniversary of his death: in which the mysterious doctrine of that Prince's saintship and martyrdom is unriddled: the substance of which was delivered in a sermon preached in the West meeting-house in Boston the Lords-day after the 30th of January, 1749-50... Boston, Printed and sold by D. Fowle, in Queen-street, and by D. Gookin over against the South-meeting-house, 1750. [Boston, D. Lothrop, 1876]
Mayhew, Jonathan, 1720–1766.

LAC 40061
A discourse on medical education, delivered at the medical commencement of the College of physicians and surgeons of the University of the state of New-York, on the sixth of April, 1819. By Samuel Bard, M. D., LL. D., president of the college. New-York: Printed by C. S. Van Winkle, printer to the university, no. 101 Greenwich street, 1819.
Bard, Samuel, 1742–1821.

LAC 40046
A discourse on natural religion, delivered in the chapel of the University in Cambridge, September 3, 1795, at the lecture founded by the Honorable Paul Dudley. Boston, S. Hall, 1795.
Barnard, Thomas, 1748–1814.

LAC 13027
A discourse on popular education; delivered in the church at Princeton, the evening before the annual commencement of the College of New Jersey, September 26, 1826. Pub. at the request of the American Whig and Cliosophic societies. Princeton, Printed for the societies, by D. A. Borrenstein, 1826.
Mercer, Charles Fenton, 1778–1858.

LAC 40061
A discourse on self-limited diseases. Delivered before the Massachusetts medical society, at their annual meeting, May 27, 1835. Boston, N. Hale, 1835.
Bigelow, Jacob, 1787–1879.

LAC 40051
A discourse on the aborigines of the Ohio valley, in which the opinions of its conquest in the seventeenth century by the Iroquois or Six Nations, supported by Cadwallader Colden, Gov. Thomas Pownall, Dr. Benjamin Franklin, Hon. De Witt Clinton, and Judge John Haywood are examined and contested; to which are prefixed some remarks on the study of history. Prepared at the request of the Historical society of Ohio. With notes and an appendix. Chicago, Fergus printing company, 1883.
Harrison, William Henry, *pres. U.S.*, 1773–1841.

LAC 40032
A discourse on the agriculture of the state of Connecticut, and the means of making it more beneficial to the state: delivered at New-Haven, on Thursday, 12th September, 1816. New-Haven, Printed by T. G. Woodward, 1816.
Humphreys, David, 1752–1818.

LAC 10583
A discourse on the genius and character of the Rev. Horace Holley, LL. D., late president of Transylvania university. With an appendix, containing copious notes biographical and illustrative. Boston, Hilliard, Gray, Little and Wilkins, 1828.
Caldwell, Charles, 1772–1853.

LAC 40148
Discourse on the history, character, and prospects of the West: delivered to the Union literary society of Miami university, Oxford, Ohio, at their ninth anniversary, September 23, 1834. Cincinnati, Truman and Smith, 1834.
Drake, Daniel, 1785–1852.

LAC 40144
A discourse on the latest form of infidelity; delivered at the request of the "Association of the alumni of the Cambridge theological school," on the 19th of July, 1839. With notes. Cambridge, J. Owen, 1839.
Norton, Andrews, 1786–1853.

LAC 40111
A discourse, on the moral, legal and domestic condition of our colored population, preached before the Vermont colonization society, at Montpelier, October 17, 1832. Burlington [Vt.] E. Smith, 1832.
Converse, John Kendrick, 1801–1880.

LAC 40081
A discourse on the progress and limits of social improvement; including a general survey of the history of civilization. Addressed to the literary societies of Amherst college, at their public anniversary meeting, August 27, 1833. Boston, C. Bowen, 1834.
Everett, Alexander Hill, 1790–1847.

LAC 40054
A discourse on the prospects of letters and taste in Virginia, pronounced before the Literary and philosophical society of Hampden-Sydney college, at their fourth anniversary, in September, 1827. Cambridge [Mass.] Hilliard and Brown, 1828.
Harrison, Jesse Burton, 1805–1841.

LAC 40144
A discourse on the social influence of Christianity, delivered at Providence, R. I., Sept. 1838, at the instance of the Phi beta kappa society of Brown university. Andover, Printed by Gould and Newman, 1839.
Cushing, Caleb, 1800–1879.

LAC 40095
Discourse on woman, delivered at the Assembly buildings, December 17, 1849. Philadelphia, W. P. Kildare, 1869.
Mott, Lucretia, 1793–1880.

LAC 16454
A discourse upon the institution of medical schools in America; delivered at a public anniversary commencement, held in the College of Philadelphia, May 30 and 31, 1765. With a preface containing, amongst other things, the author's apology for attempting to introduce the regular mode of practising physic in Philadelphia. Philadelphia, W. Bradford, 1765.
Morgan, John, 1735–1789.

LAC 10445
Discourses and essays. 2d ed. Andover [Mass.] W. F. Draper, 1862.
Shedd, William Greenough Thayer, 1820–1894.

LAC 15047
Discourses of Brigham Young ... selected and arranged by John A. Widtsoe. Salt Lake City, Utah, Deseret book company [c1925]
Young, Brigham, 1801–1877.

LAC 14312
Discourses on architecture, by Eugene Emmanuel Viollet-Le-Duc. Tr., with an introductory essay, by Henry Van Brunt. Illustrated with plates and woodcuts. Boston, J. R. Osgood and company, 1875.
Viollet-Le-Duc, Eugene Emmanuel, 1814–1879.

LAC 10933
Discourses on the Christian spirit and life. 2d ed., rev., with an introduction. Boston, W. Crosby and H. P. Nichols, 1850.
Bartol, Cyrus Augustus, 1813–1900.

LAC 22824
Discourses on various subjects, by Jacob Duche, M. A., rector of Christ-church and St. Peter's, in Philadelphia. London, Printed by J. Phillips and sold by T. Cadell [etc.] M.DCC.LXXIX.
Duche, Jacob, 1738–1798.

LAC 13790
Discourses on war, by William Ellery Channing, with an introduction by Edwin D. Mead. Boston, For the International union [by] Ginn & company, 1903.
Channing, William Ellery, 1780–1842.

LAC 40012
The discoveries of John Lederer, in three several marches from Virginia to the West of Carolina, and other parts of the continent: in the years 1669 and 1670. With an explanatory introduction, by H. A. Rattermann. Cincinnati, O. H. Harpel, 1879.
Lederer, John.

LAC 12323
The discoveries of the world from their first original unto the year of Our Lord 1555, by Antonio Galvano, governor of Ternate. Corrected, quoted, and published in England, by Richard Hakluyt, (1601). Now reprinted, with the original Portuguese text: and ed. by the Vice Admiral Bethune, C. B. London, Printed for the Hakluyt society, 1862.
Galvao, Antonio, d. 1557.

LAC 40045
The discovery and colonization of America, and immigration to the United States. A lecture delivered before the New York historical society, in Metropolitan hall, on the 1st of June, 1853. Boston, Little, Brown, and company, 1853.
Everett, Edward, 1794–1865.

LAC 13180
The discovery and conquest of Terra Florida, by Don Ferdinando de Soto. Written by a gentleman of Elvas and tr. out of Portuguese, by Richard Hakluyt. Reprinted from the ed. of 1611. Ed. with notes and an introduction, and a translation of a narrative of the expedition by Luis Hernandez de Biedma, factor to the same, by William B. Rye. London, Printed for the Hakluyt society, 1851.

LAC 13146
Discovery and conquests of the North-west, with the history of Chicago. Wheaton [Ill.] R. Blanchard & company, 1881, [c1879]
Blanchard, Rufus, 1821–1904.

LAC 13361
Discovery and exploration of the Mississippi Valley: with the original narratives of Marquette, Allouez, Membre, Hennepin, and Anastase Douay. With a facsimile of the newly-discovered map of Marquette. New York, Redfield, 1852.
Shea, John Dawson Gilmary, 1824–1892.

LAC 13226
Discovery of America by Northmen; address at the unveiling of the statue of Leif Eriksen, delivered in Faneuil hall, Oct. 29, 1887. Boston and New York, Houghton, Mifflin and company, 1888.
Horsford, Eben Norton, 1818–1893.

LAC 16952
The discovery of America by the Northmen, in the tenth century, with notices of the early settlements of the Irish in the western hemisphere. London, T. and W. Boone, 1841.
Beamish, North Ludlow, 1797–1872.

LAC 12714
The discovery of North America; a critical, documentary, and historic investigation, with an essay on the early cartography of the New World, including descriptions of two hundred and fifty maps or globes existing or lost, constructed before the year 1536; to which are added a chronology of one hundred voyages westward, projected, attempted, or accomplished between 1431 and 1504; biographical accounts of the three hundred pilots who first crossed the Atlantic; and a copious list of the original names of American regions, caciqueships, mountains, islands, capes, gulfs, rivers, towns, and harbours. Amsterdam, N. Israel, 1961.
Harrisse, Henry, 1829–1910.

LAC 12311
The discovery of the large, rich, and beautiful empire of Guiana, with a relation of the great and golden city of Manoa ... etc. performed in the year 1595, by Sir W. Ralegh, knt. Reprinted from the edition of 1596, with some unpublished documents relative to that country. Ed., with copious explanatory notes and a biographical memoir, by Sir Robert H. Schomburgk. London, Printed for the Hakluyt society, 1848.
Raleigh, *Sir* Walter, 1552?–1618.

LAC 14297
Discovery of the Yosemite and the Indian war of 1851 which led to that event. 4th ed., reprinted from 3d ed. with new map and illustrations. Los Angeles, G. W. Gerlicher, 1911.
Bunnell, Lafayette Houghton, 1824–1903.

LAC 15520
Discrimination against the Japanese in California; a review of the real situation. Berkeley, Cal., Press of the Courier publishing company, 1907.
Johnson, Herbert Buell, 1858–

LAC 15039
A discussion of the question, is the Roman Catholic religion, in any or in all its principles or doctrines, inimical to civil or religious liberty? And of the question, is the Presbyterian religion, in any or in all its principles or doctrines, inimical to civil or religious liberty? By the Rev. John Hughes and the Rev. John Breckinridge. Philadelphia, Carey, Lea, and Blanchard, 1836.
Hughes, John, *abp.*, 1797–1864.

LAC 20132
Discussions in economics and statistics, by Francis A. Walker. Ed. by Davis R. Dewey. New York, H. Holt and company, 1899.
Walker, Francis Amasa, 1840–1897.

LAC 13793
A display of God's special grace. In a familiar dialogue between a minister & a gentleman of his congregation, about the work of God, in the conviction and conversion of sinners, so remarkably of late begun and going on in these American parts. Wherein the objections against some uncommon appearances amongst us are distinctly consider'd, mistakes rectify'd, and the work itself particularly prov'd to be from the Holy Spirit. With an addition, in a second conference, relating to sundry antinomian principles, beginning to obtain in some places. To which is prefixed an attestation, by several ministers of Boston. Boston, N. E. Printed by Rogers and Fowle, for S. Eliot in Cornhill, 1742.
Dickinson, Jonathan, 1688–1747.

LAC 40069
The disproportion of taxation in Pittsburgh. [n.p., n.d.]
Harrison, Shelby Millard, 1881–

LAC 13985
A disquisition on faith. Washington, A. Way, 1822.
Brown, Paul.

LAC 11072
The disruption of the Methodist Episcopal church, 1844–1846: comprising a thirty years' history of the relations of the two methodisms. By Edward H. Myers, D.D. With an introduction by T. O. Summers, D.D. Nashville, Tenn., A. H. Redford; [etc., etc.] 1875.
Myers, Edward Howell, 1816–1876.

LAC 10799
Dissertation on musical taste. New York, Mason brothers, 1853.
Hastings, Thomas, 1784–1872.

LAC 16606
A dissertation on slavery; with a proposal for the gradual abolition of it, in the state of Virginia. Philadelphia, Printed for M. Carey, 1796.
Tucker, St. George, 1752–1828.

LAC 13433
A dissertation on the freedom of navigation and maritime commerce, and such rights of states, relative thereto, as are founded on the law of nations: adapted more particularly to the United States; and interspersed with moral and political reflections, and historical facts. With an appendix, containing sundry state papers. Philadelphia, J. Conrad, 1802.
Barton, William, 1754–1817.

LAC 15803
A dissertation on the nature and extent of the jurisdiction of the courts of the United States, being a valedictory address delivered to the students of the Law academy of Philadelphia ... on the 22d April, 1824. By Peter S. Du Ponceau. To which are added, A brief sketch of the national judiciary powers exercised in the United States prior to the adoption of the present federal Constitution, by Thomas Sergeant, and the author's discourse on legal education, delivered at the opening of the Law academy, in February, 1821. With an appendix and notes. Philadelphia, A. Small, 1824.
Du Ponceau, Peter Stephen, 1760–1844.

LAC 12109
Dissertations on the English language; with notes, historical and critical. To which is added, by way of appendix An essay on a reformed mode of spelling, with Dr. Franklin's arguments on that subject. Boston, Printed for the author, by I. Thomas and company, 1789.
Webster, Noah, 1758–1843.

LAC 10301
The distribution of incomes in the United States. New York, Columbia university; [etc., etc.] 1912.
Streightoff, Frank Hatch, 1886–

LAC 10703
The distribution of products; or, The mechanism and the metaphysics of exchange. Three essays: What makes the rate of wages? What is a bank? The railway, the farmer, and the public. New York & London, G. P. Putnam's sons, 1885.
Atkinson, Edward, 1827–1905.

LAC 10730
The distribution of wealth. New York and London, Macmillan and co., 1893.
Commons, John Rogers, 1862–

LAC 10502
The distribution of wealth; a theory of wages, interest and profits. New York, The Macmillan company; London, Macmillan & co., ltd., 1924, [c1899]
Clark, John Bates, 1847–1938.

LAC 11574
The district school as it was. By one who went to it. Edited by Clifton Johnson. Boston, Lee and Shepard, 1897.
Burton, Warren, 1800–1866.

LAC 12292
Divers voyages touching the discovery of America and the islands adjacent. Collected and published by Richard Hakluyt in the year 1582. Edited, with notes and an introduction, by John Winter Jones. London, Printed for the Hakluyt society, 1850.
Hakluyt, Richard, 1552?–1616, *comp.*

LAC 14330
A dividend to labor; a study of employers' welfare institutions. Boston and New York, Houghton, Mifflin and company, 1899.
Gilman, Nicholas Paine, 1849–1912.

LAC 40092
The divine goodness to the United States of America, particularly in the course of the last year. A thanksgiving sermon, preached in New-York, February 19, 1795. By John M'Knight. New-York, Printed by T. Greenleaf, 1795.
McKnight, John, 1754–1823.

LAC 11123
The divine order of human society.
De civitate Dei. The divine order of human society; being the L. P. Stone lectures for 1891, delivered in Princeton theological seminary. Philadelphia, J. D. Wattles, 1891.
Thompson, Robert Ellis, 1844–1924.

LAC 12563
Division and reunion, 1829–1889. New York and London, Longmans, Green, and co., 1895, [c1893]
Wilson, Woodrow, *pres. U.S.*, 1856–1924.

LAC 11104
Divisions in the Society of Friends. 3d ed., enlarged. Philadelphia, Lippincott, 1896.
Speakman, Thomas Henry.

LAC 10233
Dixie after the war; an exposition of social conditions existing in the South, during the twelve years succeeding the fall of Richmond. By Myrta Lockett Avary. With an introduction by General Clement A. Evans; illustrated from old paintings, daguerreotypes and rare photographs. New York, Doubleday, Page & company, 1906.
Avary, Myrta.

LAC 14158
Dixie; or, Southern scenes and sketches. New York, Harper & brothers, 1896.
Ralph, Julian, 1853–1903.

LAC 40073
Dixon and his copyists. A criticism of the accounts of the Oneida community in "New America," "Spiritual wives," and kindred publications. 2d ed. [Wallingford, Conn.] The Oneida community, 1874.
Noyes, John Humphrey, 1811–1886.

LAC 11975
Dr. Breen's practice, a novel. Boston and New York, Houghton Mifflin company [c1881]
Howells, William Dean, 1837–1920.

LAC 13904
Dr. Chase's recipes; or, Information for everybody: An invaluable collection of about eight hundred practical recipes... Stereotyped. Carefully revised, illustrated, and much enlarged, with remarks and full explanations... Ann Arbor, Mich., The author, 1864.
Chase, Alvin Wood, 1817–1885.

LAC 11828
Dr. Heidenhoff's process. London, F. Warne and co. [1890?]
Bellamy, Edward, 1850–1898.

LAC 13933

Doctor Quintard, chaplain C. S. A. and second bishop of Tennessee; being his story of the war (1861–1865) ed. and extended by the Rev. Arthur Howard Noll. Sewanee, Tenn., The University press, 1905.
Quintard, Charles Todd, *bp.*, 1824–1898.

LAC 13650

Dr. S. G. Howe, the philanthropist. New York [etc.] Funk & Wagnalls, 1891.
Sanborn, Franklin Benjamin, 1831–1917.

LAC 11852

Dr. Sevier. Boston, J. R. Osgood and company, 1885.
Cable, George Washington, 1844–1925.

LAC 15631

Doctor Tucker, priest-musician; a sketch which concerns the doings and thinkings of the Rev. John Ireland Tucker, S. T. D., including a brief converse about the rise and progress of church music in America. New York, A. D. F. Randolph company, 1897.
Knauff, Christopher Wilkinson, 1838–1911.

LAC 10570

The doctrine of evolution: its data, its principles, its speculations, and its theistic bearings. New York, Harper & brothers, 1874.
Winchell, Alexander, 1824–1891.

LAC 14524

The doctrine of judicial review, its legal and historical basis, and other essays. Gloucester, Mass., Peter Smith, 1963.
Corwin, Edward Samuel, 1878–1963.

LAC 13781

The doctrine of the unity of the human race examined on the principles of science. Charleston, S. C., C. Canning, 1850.
Bachman, John, 1790–1874.

LAC 15787

Doctrine of the will. By Rev. A. Mahan. New York, M. H. Newman; Oberlin, O., R. E. Gillet, 1845.
Mahan, Asa, 1800–1889.

LAC 23809–13

A documentary history of American industrial society; ed. by John R. Commons, Ulrich B. Phillips, Eugene A. Gilmore, Helen L. Sumner, and John B. Andrews. Prepared under the auspices of the American bureau of industrial research, with the co-operation of the Carnegie institution of Washington. With preface by Richard T. Ely and introduction by John B. Clark. Cleveland, The A. H. Clark company, 1910–11.

LAC 20516–17

A documentary history of Chelsea, including the Boston precincts of Winnisimmet, Rumney Marsh, and Pullen Point, 1624–1824; collected and arranged, with notes, by Mellen Chamberlain. Boston, Printed for the Massachusetts historical society, 1908.
Chamberlain, Mellen, 1821–1900, *ed.*

LAC 23135–38

A documentary history of education in the South before 1860. Chapel Hill, University of North Carolina Press [c1949–53]
Knight, Edgar Wallace, 1885–1953, *ed.*

LAC 20518

Documentary history of Rhode Island. Providence, Preston and Rounds co., 1916–1919.
Chapin, Howard Millar, 1887–1940.

LAC 14098

Documentary history of the Amalgamated clothing workers of America, 1914–1916. [New York, N. Y., 1920]
Amalgamated Clothing Workers of America.

LAC 23024–25

Documentary history of the American revolution: consisting of letters and papers relating to the contest for liberty, chiefly in South Carolina from originals in the possession of the editor, and other sources. New York, D. Appleton & co. [etc.] 1853–57.
Gibbes, Robert Wilson, 1809–1866.

LAC 23870–73

The documentary history of the campaign upon the Niagara frontier... Collected and ed. for the Lundy's Lane historical society by Major E. Cruikshank. Welland, Printed at the Tribune [1896–1908]
Lundy's Lane Historical Society, *Welland, Ont.*

LAC 40063

Documentary history of the cession of Louisiana to the United States till it became an American province. With an appendix. Chicago, R. Blanchard, 1903.
Blanchard, Rufus, 1821–1904.

LAC 21392–96

Documentary history of the Constitution of the United States of America, 1786–1870. Derived from the records, manuscripts, and rolls deposited in the Bureau of rolls and library of the Department of State. Washington, Department of state, 1894–1905; New York, Johnson reprint co. [1965]
U.S. *Bureau of Rolls and Library.*

LAC 16653–54

Documentary history of the construction and development of the United States Capitol building and grounds... Washington, Govt. print. off., 1904.

LAC 40125

The documentary history of the destruction of the Gaspee. Comp. for the Providence journal. Providence, Knowles, Vose, & Anthony, 1845.
Staples, William Read, 1798–1868, *comp.*

LAC 10995

Documentary history of the Evangelical Lutheran ministerium of Pennsylvania and adjacent states. Proceedings of the annual conventions from 1748 to 1821. Compiled and translated from records in the archives and from the written protocols. Philadelphia, Board of publication of the General council of the Evangelical Lutheran church in North America, 1898.
Evangelical Lutheran Ministerium of Pennsylvania and Adjacent States.

LAC 21030

Documentary history of the Protestant Episcopal church in the United States of America. Containing numerous hitherto unpublished documents concerning the church in Connecticut... Francis L. Hawks and William Stevens Perry, editors. New-York, J. Pott, 1863–64.
Hawks, Francis Lister, 1798–1866, *ed.*

LAC 14231

Documentary history of the struggle for religious liberty in Virginia. Lynchburg, Va., J. P. Bell company, 1900.
James, Charles Fenton, 1844–1902.

LAC 14973

Documentary history of Yale university, under the original charter of the Collegiate school of Connecticut, 1701–1745, ed. by Franklin Bowditch Dexter, LITT. D. New Haven, Yale university press; [etc., etc.] 1916.
Dexter, Franklin Bowditch, 1842–1920, *ed.*

LAC 13609

Documentos historicos de la Florida y la Luisiana, siglos XVI al XVIII. Madrid, V. Suarez, 1912.
Serrano y Sanz, Manuel, 1866–1932, *ed.*

LAC 40058

Documents and facts illustrating the origin of the mission to Japan, authorized by government of the United States, May 10, 1851; and which finally resulted in the treaty concluded by Commodore M. C. Perry, U.S. navy, with the Japanese commissioners at Kanagawa, bay of Yedo, on the 31st March, 1854... Washington, H. Polkinhorn, 1857.
Palmer, Aaron Haight.

LAC 40070

Documents and facts, relative to military events, during the late war. [n.p., 1816]
Boyd, John Parker, 1764–1830.

LAC 16381

Documents and letters intended to illustrate the revolutionary incidents of Queens county; with connecting narratives, explanatory notes, and additions. By Henry Onderdonk, jr. New-York, Leavitt, Trow and company, 1846.
Onderdonk, Henry, 1804–1886.

LAC 14366

Documents, chiefly unpublished, relating to the Huguenot emigration to Virginia and to the settlement at Manakin-Town, with an appendix of genealogies, presenting data of the Fontaine, Maury, Dupuy, Trabue, Marye, Chastain, Cocke, and other families, edited and compiled for the Virginia Historical Society by R. A. Brock. Richmond, Va., 1886.
Virginia Historical Society, *Richmond.*

LAC 16056

Documents connected with the history of South Carolina... Printed for private distribution only. London, 1856.
Weston, Plowden Charles Jennett, *ed.*

LAC 10588

Documents illustrative of American educational history. Compiled and annotated by B. A. Hinsdale. Wash., Govt. print. off., 1895.
U. S. *Office of Education.*

LAC 13492–93

Documents illustrative of the formation of the union of the American states. Washington, Govt. print. off., 1927.
U.S. *Library of Congress. Legislative Reference Service.*

LAC 20972–75

Documents illustrative of the history of the slave trade to America. Washington, D. C., Carnegie institution of Washington, 1930–35.
Donnan, Elizabeth, 1883–1955, *ed.*

LAC 20436

Documents officiels recueillis dans la secretairerie privee de Maximilien. Histoire de l'intervention francaise au Mexique. Bruxelles & Londres [Impr. de Ve Pairt et fils] 1869.
Lefevre, Eugene.

LAC 40092

Documents on the Blount conspiracy, 1795–1797. New York, The Macmillan co., 1905.
Turner, Frederick Jackson, 1861–1932, *ed.*

LAC 14523

Documents on the state-wide initiative, referendum and recall, by Charles A. Beard and Birl E. Schultz. New York, The Macmillan company, 1912.
Beard, Charles Austin, 1874–1948, *comp.*

LAC 40023

Documents referring to the controversy between the Canal commissioners of the state of Pennsylvania and the Harrisburg and Lancaster and the Pennsylvania railroad companies. With remarks upon the relative position of the state improvements and the Pennsylvania railroad. Philadelphia, T. K. and P. G. Collins, printers, 1852.
Haupt, Herman, 1817–1905, *comp.*

LAC 10633

Documents relating to American economic history, 1651–1820, arranged by Felix Flugel. [Berkeley, Calif., University of California press, 1927]
Flugel, Felix, 1892–   *comp.*

LAC 11367

Documents relating to New-England Federalism. 1800 –1815. Boston, Little, Brown, and company, 1877.
Adams, Henry, 1838–   *ed.*

LAC 23658–82

Documents relating to the colonial history of the State of New Jersey. ser. 1, v. 1–31. Bayonne [etc.] 1880–1923.

LAC 12389

Documents relating to the history of South Carolina during the revolutionary war, ed. by A. S. Salley, jr., secretary of the Historical commission of South Carolina. Columbia, S. C., Printed for the Historical commission of South Carolina by the State company, 1908.
South Carolina. *Archives Dept.*

LAC 10260

Documents relating to the history of the Dutch and Swedish settlements on the Delaware river, tr. and comp. from original manuscripts in the office of the secretary of state at Albany, and in the Royal archives, at Stockholm, by B. Fernow. Albany, The Argus company, printers, 1877.

LAC 10660

Documents relating to the invasion of Canada and the surrender of Detroit, 1812. Selected and ed. by E. A. Cruikshank, lieut.-colonel. Pub. by authority of the Honourable the secretary of state, under the direction of the archivist. Ottawa, Government printing bureau, 1912. Canada. *Public Archives.*

LAC 40024

Documents relating to the organization of the Illinois central rail-road company. (3d ed.) New-York, G. S. Roe, printer, 1855. Illinois Central Railroad Company.

LAC 40116

Documents relating to the presidential election in the year 1804: containing a refutation of two passages in the writings of Thomas Jefferson, aspersing the character of the late James A. Bayard, of Delaware. Philadelphia, Mifflin and Parry, printers, 1831. Bayard, Richard Henry, 1796–1868, *comp.*

LAC 16120

Documents relating to the purchase & exploration of Louisiana. I. The limits and bounds of Louisiana. By Thomas Jefferson. II. The exploration of the Red, the Black, and the Washita rivers. By William Dunbar. Printed from the original manuscripts in the library of the American philosophical society and by direction of the society's Committee on historical documents. Boston and New York, Houghton, Mifflin & company, 1904.

LAC 20155–57

Documents relative to the manufactures in the United States, collected and transmitted to the House of Representatives, in compliance with a resolution of Jan. 19, 1832, by the Secretary of the Treasury, in two volumes... Washington, Printed by D. Green, 1833. U.S. *Treasury Dept.*

LAC 40023

Documents tending to prove the superior advantages of rail-ways and steam-carriages over canal navigation... New-York, Printed by T. and J. Swords, 1812. Tarrytown, N. Y., Reprinted, W. Abbatt, 1917. Stevens, John, 1749–1838.

LAC 10367

Dodge City, the cowboy capital, and the great Southwest in the days of the wild Indian, the buffalo, the cowboy; dance halls, gambling halls and bad men. [Wichita, Kan., Wichita eagle press, c1913] Wright, Robert Marr, 1840–

LAC 13816

Does protection protect? An examination of the effect of different forms of tariff upon American industry. New York, D. Appleton and company, 1871. Grosvenor, William Mason, 1835–1900.

LAC 12919

Dollars and democracy. With numerous illustrations from original drawings by the author. New York, D. Appleton and company, 1904. Burne-Jones, *Sir* Philip, *2d bart.,* 1861–

LAC 14549

The domestic and artistic life of John Singleton Copley, R. A. With notices of his works, and reminiscences of his son, Lord Lyndhurst, lord high chancellor of Great Britain. By his granddaughter, Martha Babcock Amory. Boston, New York, Houghton, Mifflin and company, 1882. Amory, Martha Babcock, 1812–1880.

LAC 40122

Domestic architecture in Massachusetts. An architectural monograph on domestic architecture in Massachusetts, 1750–1800, with text by Julian A. Buckly, prepared for publication by Russell F. Whitehead. [Saint Paul, White pine bureau] 1916. Buckly, Julian A 1872–1918.

LAC 16915

Domestic architecture of the American colonies and of the early republic. New York, C. Scribner's sons, 1922. Kimball, Sidney Fiske, 1888–1955.

LAC 12188

Domestic history of the American revolution. New York, Baker and Scribner, 1850. Ellet, Elizabeth Fries, 1818–1877.

LAC 40027

Domestic life in New England in the seventeenth century; a discourse delivered in the lecture hall of the Metropolitan museum of art in New York city, it being one of a series designed to mark the opening of the American wing. Topsfield, Mass., Printed for the author at the Perkins press, 1925. Dow, George Francis, 1868–1936.

LAC 12235

Domestic manners of the Americans. By Mrs. Trollope. London, Printed for Whittaker, Treacher & co.; New York, Reprinted for the booksellers, 1832. Trollope, Frances, 1780–1863.

LAC 15420

The domestic manufacturer's assistant, and family directory, in the arts of weaving and dyeing: comprehending a plain system of directions, applying to those arts and other branches nearly connected with them in the manufacture of cotton and woolen goods... By J. & R. Bronson. Utica, Printed by W. Williams, 1817. Bronson, J.

LAC 15582

A domestic narrative of the life of Samuel Bard, M. D., LL. D., late president of the College of physicians and surgeons of the University of the state of New York, &c. By the Rev. John M'Vickar. New York, literary rooms [Columbia college] A. Paul, printer, 1822. McVickar, John, 1787–1868.

LAC 12912

Domestic slavery considered as a Scriptural institution: in a correspondence between the Rev. Richard Fuller and the Rev. Francis Wayland. Rev. and cor. by the authors. 5th ed. New York, Sheldon Lamport & Blakeman, 1856. Fuller, Richard, 1804–1876.

LAC 40124
Dominican Republic. Message from the President of the United States in answer to a resolution of the House of 5th instant, transmitting report of Captain George B. McClellan upon the Dominican Republic, in the year 1854. [Washington, Govt. print. off., 1871]
U.S. *Congress. House. Committee on Foreign Affairs.*

LAC 40080
The dominion of Providence over the passions of men. A sermon preached at Princeton, on the 17th of May, 1776. Being the general fast appointed by the Congress through the United Colonies. To which is added, An address to the natives of Scotland residing in America. The second edition, with elucidating remarks. Philadelphia printed: Glasglow reprinted; Sold by booksellers in town and country, 1777.
Witherspoon, John, 1723–1794.

LAC 23339–44
Dongan and Leisler assemblies.
The colonial laws of New York from the year 1664 to the revolution, including the charters to the Duke of York, the commissions and instructions to colonial governors, the Duke's laws, the laws of the Dongan and Leisler assemblies, the charters of Albany and New York and the acts of the colonial legislatures from 1691 to 1775 inclusive... Transmitted to the Legislature by the Commissioners of statutory revision, pursuant to chapter 125 of the laws of 1891. Albany, J. B. Lyon, state printer, 1894–96 [v. 1, '96]
New York *(Colony) Laws, statutes, etc.*

LAC 14482
Doniphan's expedition. Account of the conquest of New Mexico, General Kearney's overland expedition to California; Doniphan's campaign against the Navajos; his unparalleled march upon Chihuahua and Durango; and the operations of General Price at Santa Fe... Washington, Govt. print. off., 1914.
Hughes, John Taylor, 1817–1862.

LAC 11907
Dorothy South; a love story of Virginia just before the war, by George Cary Eggleston; illustrated by C. D. Williams. Boston, Lothrop pub. co. [1902]
Eggleston, George Cary, 1839–1911.

LAC 13372
The double edge of labor's sword. Discussion and testimony on socialism and trade-unionism before the Commission on industrial relations, by Morris Hillquit, Samuel Gompers and Max J. Hayes. Chicago, Socialist party, National office [1914]
U.S. *Commission on Industrial Relations.*

LAC 12407
Down in Tennessee, and back by way of Richmond.
By Edmund Kirke [*pseud.*] New York, Carleton, 1864.
Gilmore, James Roberts, 1822–1903.

LAC 20520
Down South; or, An Englishman's experience at the seat of the American war. By Samuel Phillips Day, special correspondent of the Morning herald. London, Hurst and Blackett, 1862.
Day, Samuel Phillips.

LAC 10842
The draft riots in New York. July, 1863. The metropolitan police: their services during riot week. Their honorable record. New York, Baker & Godwin, 1863.
Barnes, David M.

LAC 20629
Dramas, discourses, and other pieces. Boston, C. C. Little and J. Brown, 1839.
Hillhouse, James Abraham, 1789–1841.

LAC 14562
Dramatic life as I found it: a record of personal experience with an account of the rise and progress of the drama in the West and South, with anecdotes and biographical sketches of the principal actors and actresses who have at times appeared upon the stage in the Mississippi valley. St. Louis, G. I. Jones and company, 1880.
Ludlow, Noah Miller, 1795–1886.

LAC 12083
The dramatic works of Bayard Taylor; with notes by Marie Hansen-Taylor. Boston and New York, Houghton, Mifflin and company [c1880]
Taylor, Bayard, 1825–1878.

LAC 40072
The dreadful sufferings and thrilling adventures of an overland party of emigrants to California, their terrible conflicts with savage tribes of Indians!! Compiled from the journal of Mr. George Adam, one of the adventurers, by Prof. Wm. Beschke. St. Louis, Mo., Barclay & co., 1850; New Orleans, Republished by Paul Veith and Carleton King, 1946.
Adam, George, *fl.* 1850.

LAC 12721
The dream of a day, and other poems. New Haven, S. Babcock, 1843.
Percival, James Gates, 1795–1856.

LAC 40054
The Dreiser bugaboo. New York, The Seven arts pub. co., 1917.
Mencken, Henry Louis, 1880–1956.

LAC 12240
Dress-reform: a series of lectures delivered in Boston, on dress as it affects the health of women; ed. by Abba Goold Woolson. Boston, Roberts brothers, 1874.
Woolson, Abba, 1838–1921, *ed.*

LAC 11212
Drift and mastery; an attempt to diagnose the current unrest. New York, M. Kennerley, 1914.
Lippmann, Walter, 1889–

LAC 12032
The drift of romanticism; Shelburne essays, eighth series. Boston and New York, Houghton Mifflin company, 1913.
More, Paul Elmer, 1864–1937.

LAC 40063
Drifting together. Will the United States and Canada unite? [New York, The World's work press, 1904?]
Carnegie, Andrew, 1835–1919.

LAC 11229

Driven from sea to sea; or, Just a campin'. Chicago, J. E. Downey & co., 1884.
Post, Charles Cyrel, 1846–

LAC 40110

Drummers' yarns; or, Fun on the "road"... New York, Excelsior publishing house, c1886.
Carey, Thomas Joseph, 1853–   *comp.*

LAC 10689

Dry-farming: its principles and practice. New York, The Century co., 1909.
Macdonald, William, 1875–1935.

LAC 11762

Dry land farming. St. Paul, Minn., The Pioneer company, 1911.
Shaw, Thomas, 1843–1918.

LAC 14582

Dudley records.
Council records of Massachusetts under the administration of President Joseph Dudley [by] Robert N. Toppan. Boston, Massachusetts Historical Society, 1900.
Massachusetts *(Colony) Council.*

LAC 14996–97

Due process of law and the equal protection of the laws; a treatise based, in the main, on the cases in which the Supreme court of the United States has granted or denied relief upon the one ground or the other. Chicago, Callaghan and company, 1917.
Taylor, Hannis, 1851–1922.

LAC 14857

Due process of law under the federal Constitution. Northport, Long Island, N. Y., Edward Thompson company, 1906.
McGehee, Lucius Polk, 1868–1923.

LAC 13132

Due west; or, Round the world in ten months. Boston, New York, Houghton, Mifflin and company, 1884.
Ballou, Maturin Murray, 1820–1895.

LAC 12923

Duff Green's "England and the United States" : with an introductory study of American opposition to the Quintuple treaty of 1841, by St. George L. Sioussat. [Worcester, Mass., American Antiquarian Society, 1931]
Green, Duff, 1791–1875.

LAC 11827

The Duke of Stockbridge; a romance of Shay's rebellion. New York, Boston [etc.] Silver, Burdett and company, 1900.
Bellamy, Edward, 1850–1898.

LAC 23339–44

Duke of York, Charters to the.
The colonial laws of New York from the year 1664 to the revolution, including the charters to the Duke of York, the commissions and instructions to colonial governors, the Duke's laws, the laws of the Dongan and Leisler assemblies, the charters of Albany and New York and the acts of the colonial legislatures from 1691 to 1775 inclusive... Transmitted to the Legislature by the Commissioners of statutory revision, pursuant to chapter 125 of the laws of 1891. Albany, J. B. Lyon, state printer, 1894–96 [v. 1, '96]
New York *(Colony) Laws, statutes, etc.*

LAC 23339–44

The Duke's laws.
The colonial laws of New York from the year 1664 to the revolution, including the charters to the Duke of York, the commissions and instructions to colonial governors, the Duke's laws, the laws of the Dongan and Leisler assemblies, the charters of Albany and New York and the acts of the colonial legislatures from 1691 to 1775 inclusive... Transmitted to the Legislature by the Commissioners of statutory revision, pursuant to chapter 125 of the laws of 1891. Albany, J. B. Lyon, state printer, 1894–96 [v. 1, '96]
New York *(Colony) Laws, statutes, etc.*

LAC 11363

Duncombe's free banking: an essay on banking, currency, finance, exchanges, and political economy. Cleveland [O.] Printed by Sanford & co., 1841.
Duncombe, Charles.

LAC 14760

Duplicate copy of the souvenir from the Afro-American league of Tennessee to Hon. James M. Ashley of Ohio... Ed. by Benjamin W. Arnett. Philadelphia, Publishing house of the A. M. E. church, 1894.
Ashley, James Monroe, 1824–1896.

LAC 10650

The duplicate letters, the fisheries and the Mississippi. Documents relating to transactions at the negotiation of Ghent. Collected and pub. by John Quincy Adams, one of the commissioners of the United States at that negotiation. Washington, Printed by Davis and Force, 1822.
Adams, John Quincy, *pres. U.-S.,* 1767–1848.

LAC 13887

The Dutch colonial house; its origin, design, modern plan and construction; illustrated with photographs of old examples and American adaptations of the style, by Aymar Embury, II. New York, McBride, Nast & company, 1913.
Embury, Aymar, 1880–

LAC 14054

Dutch houses and families.
Pre-revolutionary Dutch houses and families in northern New Jersey and southern New York, by Rosalie Fellows Bailey, A. B.; with an introduction by Franklin D. Roosevelt; photography by Margaret De M. Brown; prepared under the auspices of the Holland society of New York. New York, W. Morrow & company, 1936.
Bailey, Rosalie Fellows, 1908–

LAC 14391

Dutch houses in the Hudson valley before 1776, by Helen Wilkinson Reynolds; with an introduction by Franklin D. Roosevelt, photography by Margaret De M. Brown; prepared under the auspices of the Holland society of New York. New York, Payson and Clarke, ltd., 1929.
Reynolds, Helen Wilkinson.

LAC 11575

The Dutch schools of New Netherland and colonial New York. Washington, Govt. print. off., 1912.
Kilpatrick, William Heard, 1871–

LAC 16488
Duties of masters to servants: three premium essays. I.
By the Rev. H. N. McTyeire. II. By the Rev. C. F.
Sturgis. III. By the Rev. A. T. Holmes. Charleston, S. C.,
Southern Baptist publication society, 1851.
McTyeire, Holland Nimmons, *bp.*, 1824–1889.

LAC 15708
The duty of American women to their country. New-
York, Harper & brothers, 1845.
Beecher, Catharine Esther, 1800–1878.

LAC 40101
The duty of Columbia college to the community, and
its right to exclude Unitarians from its professorships of
physical science, considered by one of its trustees. New-
York, J. F. Trow, printer, 1854.
Ruggles, Samuel Bulkley, 1800–1881.

LAC 40059
The duty of disobedience to the Fugitive Slave Act: an
appeal to the legislators of Massachusetts. Boston, Published by the American Anti-slavery Society, 1860.
Child, Lydia Maria, 1802–1880.

LAC 40059
The duty of disobedience to wicked laws. A sermon on
the fugitive slave law. New-York, J. A. Gray, printer,
1851.
Beecher, Charles, 1815–1900.

LAC 40125
The duty of standing fast in our spiritual and temporal
liberties, a sermon, preached in Christ-church, July 7th,
1775. Before the First battalion of the city and liberties
of Philadelphia; and now published at their request. By
the Reverend Jacob Duche, M.A. Philadelphia, Printed
and sold by J. Humphreys, junior, 1775.
Duche, Jacob, 1737–1798.

LAC 40017
The duty of the American scholar to politics and the
times. An oration, delivered on Tuesday, August 5, 1856,
before the literary societies of Wesleyan university, Middletown, Conn. New York, Dix, Edwards & co., 1856.
Curtis, George William, 1824–1892.

LAC 40036
The duty of the free states. Second part. 2d ed. Boston,
W. Crosby & company, 1842.
Channing, William Ellery, 1780–1842.

LAC 20134–35
Dynamic sociology, or Applied social science, as
based upon statical sociology and the less complex
sciences. New York, D. Appleton and company, 1883.
Ward, Lester Frank, 1841–1913.

LAC 13888
Early American churches, by Aymar Embury II. Gar-
den City, N. Y., Doubleday, Page & company, 1914.
Embury, Aymar, 1880–

LAC 16230
Early American folk pottery, including the history of
the Bennington pottery. Hartford, Conn. [The Case,
Lockwood & Brainard co.] 1918.
Pitkin, Albert Hastings, 1852–1917.

LAC 16417
Early American houses. [Boston] The Walpole society,
1928.
Isham, Norman Morrison, 1864–1943.

LAC 15679
The early and later history of petroleum, with authen-
tic facts in regard to its development in western Pennsyl-
vania. The oil fields of Europe and America. Gas wells.
Spiritual wells. Oil well shafts. Petroleum products...
The Parkers' and Butler County oil fields. Also, life
sketches of pioneer and prominent operators, with the
refining capacity of the United States. New York,
B. Franklin [1965]
Henry, J   T.

LAC 40009
Early-Chicago reminiscences. (Rev. from the Chicago
tribune) Chicago, Fergus printing company, 1882.
Cleaver, Charles, 1814–1893.

LAC 10194
The early coins of America; and the laws governing
their issue. Comprising also descriptions of the Washington pieces, the Anglo-American tokens, many pieces
of unknown origin, of the seventeenth and eighteenth
centuries, and the first patterns of the United States
mint. By Sylvester S. Crosby. Boston, The author, 1875.
Crosby, Sylvester Sage, *d.* 1914.

LAC 16543
Early concert-life in America. (1731–1800) O. G. Son-
neck. Wiesbaden, M. Sandig [1969]
Sonneck, Oscar George Theodore, 1873–1928.

LAC 16705
Early Connecticut houses; an historical and architec-
tural study, by Norman M. Isham [and] Albert F. Brown.
Providence, R. I., The Preston and Rounds company,
1900.
Isham, Norman Morrison, 1864–1943.

LAC 16812
Early days in Arkansas; being for the most part the
personal recollections of an old settler. By Judge William
F. Pope. Arranged and ed. by his son Dunbar H. Pope.
With an introduction by Hon. Sam W. Williams. Little
Rock, Ark., F. W. Allsopp, 1895.
Pope, William F   1814–1895.

LAC 10664–65
Early days in Detroit; papers written by General
Friend Palmer, of Detroit; being his personal reminiscences of important events and descriptions of the city
for over eighty years. Detroit, Mich., Hunt & June
[c1906]
Palmer, Friend, 1820–1906.

LAC 13365
The early empire builders of the great West. Comp.
and enl. from the author's Early history of Dakota Territory in 1866. St. Paul, Minn., E. W. Porter, 1901.
Armstrong, Moses Kimball, 1832–1906.

LAC 16796
Early English and French voyages, chiefly from Hak-
luyt, 1534–1608. With maps and a facsimile reproduction.
New York, C. Scribner's sons, 1906.
Burrage, Henry Sweetser, 1837–1926, *ed.*

LAC 40018

Early factory labor in New England. Prepared under the direction of Carroll D. Wright. By Harriet H. Robinson. Reprinted in accordance with the provisions of chap. 7, Resolves of 1888. Boston, Wright & Potter printing co., 1889.
Robinson, Harriet Jane, 1825–1911.

LAC 40082

The early fathers of the Reformed church in the United States. By Rev. James I. Good. Reading, Pa., Daniel Miller [c1897]
Good, James Isaac, 1850–1924.

LAC 14829

The early Germans of New Jersey: their history, churches and genealogies. [Dover, N. J., Dover printing company, 1895]
Chambers, Theodore Frelinghuysen, 1849–1916.

LAC 13538

Early history of Cleveland, Ohio, including original papers and other matter relating to the adjacent country. With biographical notices of the pioneers and surveyors. Cleveland, O. [Fairbanks, Benedict & co., printer] 1867.
Whittlesey, Charles, 1808–1886.

LAC 13256

Early history of Idaho, by W. J. McConnell, ex-U. S. senator and -governor, who was present and cognizant of the events narrated; published by authority of the Idaho state legislature. Caldwell, Id., The Caxton printers, 1913.
McConnell, William John, 1839–1925.

LAC 11281

The early history of Southampton, L. I., New York, with genealogies. Rev., cor. and enl. 2d ed. Albany, Weed, Parsons and company, 1887.
Howell, George Rogers, 1833–1899.

LAC 11085

The early history of the Church of the United Brethren (Unitas Fratrum) commonly called Moravians, in North America, A. D. 1734–1748. By the Rev. Levin Theodore Reichel. Nazareth, Pa., Moravian historical society, 1888.
Reichel, Levin Theodore, 1812–1878.

LAC 14599

Early history of the Cleveland public schools. Pub. by order of the Board of education. Cleveland, O., Robison, Savage & co., book printers, 1876.
Freese, Andrew.

LAC 10628

Early history of the University of Pennsylvania from its origin to the year 1827, by George B. Wood. 3d ed. With supplementary chapters by Frederick D. Stone. Philadelphia, 1896.
Wood, George Bacon, 1797–1879.

LAC 14806

Early history of the University of Virginia, as contained in the letters of Thomas Jefferson and Joseph C. Cabell, hitherto unpublished; with an appendix, consisting of Mr. Jefferson's bill for a complete system of education, and other illustrative documents; and an introduction, comprising a brief historical sketch of the university, and a biographical notice of Joseph C. Cabell. Richmond, Va., J. W. Randolph, 1856.
Cabell, Nathaniel Francis, 1807–1891, *ed.*

LAC 11044

The early Jesuit missions in North America; comp. and tr. from the letters of the French Jesuits, with notes. By the Rev. William Ingraham Kip. New York, Wiley and Putnam, 1846.
Kip, William Ingraham, 1811–1893.

LAC 10734

Early letters of George Wm. Curtis to John S. Dwight; Brook Farm and Concord. Ed. by George Willis Cooke. New York and London, Harper & brothers, 1898.
Curtis, George William, 1824–1892.

LAC 20259

The early Massachusetts press, 1638–1711. Boston, Mass., The Club of odd volumes, 1907.
Littlefield, George Emery, 1844–

LAC 40077

The early negro convention movement. Washington, D. C., The Academy, 1904.
Cromwell, John Wesley, 1846–

LAC 16664

Early New England schools. Boston and London, Ginn and company, 1914.
Small, Walter Herbert, 1856–1909.

LAC 16506

Early opera in America. New York [etc.] G. Schirmer; Boston, The Boston music co. [c1915]
Sonneck, Oscar George Theodore, 1873–1928.

LAC 11491

Early political machinery in the United States... Philadelphia, 1903.
Luetscher, George Daniel.

LAC 16639

Early proceedings of the American philosophical society for the promotion of useful knowledge, compiled by one of the secretaries from the manuscript minutes of its meetings from 1744 to 1838. Philadelphia, Press of McCalla & Stavely, 1884.
American Philosophical Society, *Philadelphia.*

LAC 10856

Early recollections of Newport, R. I., from the year 1793 to 1811. Newport, R. I., A. J. Ward, C. E. Hammett, jr.; Boston, Mass., Nichols and Noyes, 1868.
Channing, George Gibbs.

LAC 11708

The early records of Groton, Massachusetts. 1662–1707. Ed. by Samuel A. Green, M. D. Groton, 1880.
Groton, *Mass.*

LAC 20069-70

Early records of the city and county of Albany, and colony of Rensselaerswyck. Translated from the original Dutch by Jonathan Pearson. Rev. and edited by A. J. F. Van Laer. Albany, The University of the state of New York, 1869–1919.
Albany Co., *N. Y.*

LAC 21942–43
The early records of the town... Dedham, Mass., Dedham transcript press, 1886–99.
Dedham, *Mass.*

LAC 15654
The early records of the town of Portsmouth; ed., in accordance with a resolution of the general assembly, by the librarian of the Rhode Island historical society. Providence, R. I., E. L. Freeman & sons, state printers, 1901.
Portsmouth, *R. I.*

LAC 11737
Early Rhode Island; a social history of the people. New York, The Grafton press [c1910]
Weeden, William Babcock, 1834–1912.

LAC 10609
Early schools and school-books of New England. Boston, Mass., The Club of odd volumes, 1904.
Littlefield, George Emery, 1844–

LAC 16107
The early schools of Methodism. New York, Phillips & Hunt, 1886.
Cummings, A   W.

LAC 40145
Early Spanish cartography of the New World. With special reference to the Wolfenbuttel-Spanish map and the work of Diego Ribero. [Worcester, Mass., American antiquarian society, 1909]
Stevenson, Edward Luther, 1860–1944.

LAC 13137
Early times in Southern California.
Reminiscences of a ranger; or, Early times in Southern California. Los Angeles, Yarnell, Caystile & Mathes, printers, 1881.
Bell, Horace, 1830–1918.

LAC 10138
The early trading companies of New France. A contribution to the history of commerce and discovery in North America. [Toronto] University of Toronto library, 1901.
Biggar, Henry Percival, 1872–

LAC 15863
Early travels in the Tennessee country, 1540–1800; with introductions, annotations and index by Samuel Cole Williams. Johnson City, Tenn., The Watauga press, 1928.
Williams, Samuel Cole, 1864–1947, *ed.*

LAC 15450
Early voyages up and down the Mississippi, by Cavelier, St. Cosme, Le Sueur, Gravier, and Guignas. With an introduction, notes, and an index. Albany, J. Munsell, 1861.
Shea, John Dawson Gilmary, 1824–1892, *ed.*

LAC 23409–25
Early western travels, 1748–1846; a series of annotated reprints of some of the best and rarest contemporary volumes of travel, descriptive of the aborigines and social and economic conditions in the middle and far West, during the period of early American settlement, ed. with notes, introduction, index, etc. Cleveland, O., The A. H. Clark company, 1904–07.
Thwaites, Reuben Gold, 1853–1913, *ed.*

LAC 40122
Early wood built houses of central New York.
An architectural monograph on early wood built houses of central New York, with text by Carl C. Tallman; prepared for publication by Russell F. Whitehead. [Saint Paul, White pine bureau] 1918.
Tallman, Carl Cornwell, 1884–

LAC 11260
Earnings of factory workers, 1899 to 1927. An analysis of pay-roll statistics. Washington, U. S. Govt. print. off., 1929.
Brissenden, Paul Frederick, 1885–

LAC 13058
The earth and man; lectures on comparative physical geography, in its relation to the history of mankind. By Arnold Guyot. Tr. from the French, by C. C. Felton. Boston, Gould, Kendall, and Lincoln, 1849.
Guyot, Arnold Henry, 1807–1884.

LAC 12661
The earth as modified by human action; a last revision of "Man and nature". New York, C. Scribner's sons, 1885.
Marsh, George Perkins, 1801–1882.

LAC 16947
Earthquake in California, April 18, 1906. Special report of Maj. Gen. Adolphus W. Greely, U.S.A., commanding the Pacific division, on the relief operations conducted by the military authorities of the United States at San Francisco and other points, with accompanying documents. Washington, Govt. print. off., 1906.
U.S. *Army. Pacific Division.*

LAC 11736
East Jersey under the proprietary governments: a narrative of events connected with the settlement and progress of the province, until the surrender of the government to the crown in 1702 [*i.e.* 1703] Drawn principally from original sources. By William A. Whitehead. With an appendix, containing "The model of the government of East New-Jersey, in America", by George Scot, of Pitlochie. Now first reprinted from the original edition of 1685. [New York] New-Jersey historical society, 1846.
Whitehead, William Adee, 1810–1884.

LAC 21428–29
The eastern and western states of America. London, Paris, Fisher, son, & co. [1842]
Buckingham, James Silk, 1786–1855.

LAC 40051
Eastern band of Cherokees of North Carolina. By Thomas Donaldson. Washington, D. C., United States census printing office, 1892.
U.S. *Census Office. 11th Census,* 1890.

LAC 40024
The Eastern railroad of Massachusetts; its blunders, mismanagement & corruption. Liverpool, Miss J. Green, printer, 1873.
Felt, Charles Wilson.

LAC 11246
Ecce femina: an attempt to solve the woman question. Being an examination of arguments in favor of female suffrage by John Stuart Mill and others, and a presentation of arguments against the proposed change in the constitution of society. Hanover, N. H., The author; Boston, Lee & Shepard, 1870.
White, Carlos, 1842–

LAC 23032–33

The ecclesiastical history of New England; comprising not only religious, but also moral, and other relations. Boston, Congregational library association, 1855–62.
Felt, Joseph Barlow, 1789–1869.

LAC 21813–19

Ecclesiastical records, state of New York. Pub. by the state under the supervision of Hugh Hastings, state historian. Albany, J. B. Lyon, state printer, 1901–16.
New York *(State) State Historian.*

LAC 40082

An ecclesiastical register of New-Hampshire, containing a succinct account of the different religious denominations, their origin and progress and present numbers, with a catalogue of the ministers of the several churches, from 1638 to 1822, the date of their settlement, removal or death, and the number of communicants in 1821. Concord, Hill and Moore, 1821.
Farmer, John, 1789–1838.

LAC 16063

Echoes from Niagara: historical, political, personal. By Mrs. Richard Crowley. Buffalo, C. W. Moulton, 1890.
Crowley, Julia M.

LAC 13166

Echoes from the Rocky Mountains; reminiscences and thrilling incidents of the romantic and golden age of the great West, with a graphic account of its discovery, settlement, and grand development. Chicago, New York [etc.] Belford, Clarke & co., 1889.
Clampitt, John Wesley, 1839–

LAC 12883

Echoes of Harper's Ferry... Boston, Thayer and Eldridge, 1860.
Redpath, James, 1833–1891, *ed.*

LAC 21424–25

Economic and social history of New England, 1620–1789. Boston and New York, Houghton, Mifflin and company [c1890]
Weeden, William Babcock, 1834–1912.

LAC 10211

Economic aspects of railroad receiverships. New York, Pub. for the American economic association by the Macmillan company; [etc., etc.] 1898.
Swain, Henry Huntington, 1863–

LAC 13975

Economic aspects of the liquor problem, by John Koren. An investigation made for the Committee of fifty under the direction of Henry W. Farnam. Boston and New York, Houghton, Mifflin and company [c1899]
Koren, John, 1861–1923.

LAC 10541

The economic basis of protection. 2d ed. Philadelphia, J. B. Lippincott company, 1895, [c1890]
Patten, Simon Nelson, 1852–1922.

LAC 16603

Economic co-operation among Negro Americans. Report of a social study made by Atlanta university under the patronage of the Carnegie institution of Washington,

D. C., together with the Proceedings of the 12th conference for the study of the Negro problems, held at Atlanta university, on Tuesday, May the 28th, 1907. Atlanta, Ga., The Atlanta university press, 1907.
Du Bois, William Edward Burghardt, 1868–1963, *ed.*

LAC 40017

Economic crumbs, or Plain talks for the people about labor, capital, money, tariff, etc. Hampton, Va., Normal school steam press, 1879.
Bryce, T   T.

LAC 11569

Economic cycles: their law and cause. New York, The Macmillan company, 1914.
Moore, Henry Ludwell, 1869–1958.

LAC 40073

Economic discontent and its remedy. Terre Haute, Ind., Standard publishing company, 1902.
Hagerty, Thomas Joseph.

LAC 10150

Economic essays by Charles Franklin Dunbar. Ed. by O. M. W. Sprague with an introduction [biographical sketch] by F. W. Taussig. New York, The Macmillan company; London, Macmillan & co., ltd., 1904.
Dunbar, Charles Franklin, 1830–1900.

LAC 14138

Economic history of a factory town; a study of Chicopee, Massachusetts. Northampton, Mass., The Department of history of Smith college [1935]
Shlakman, Vera, 1909–

LAC 20058–59

Economic history of Virginia in the seventeenth century. An inquiry into the material condition of the people, based upon original and contemporaneous records. New York and London, Macmillan and co., 1896.
Bruce, Philip Alexander, 1856–1933.

LAC 10617

Economic influences upon educational progress in the United States, 1820–1850. Madison, Wis., 1908.
Carlton, Frank Tracy, 1873–

LAC 10443

The economic interpretation of history. 2d ed. rev. New York, The Columbia university press, 1922, [c1902]
Seligman, Edwin Robert Anderson, 1861–1939.

LAC 10320

The economic theory of risk and insurance. New York, The Columbia university press; [etc., etc.] 1901.
Willett, Allan Herbert, 1865–

LAC 11395

Economica: a statistical manual for the United States of America... Washington, Printed for the author, 1806.
Blodget, Samuel, 1757–1814.

LAC 14786

Economics and politics; a series of papers upon public questions written on various occasions from 1840 to 1885, by Rowland Gibson Hazard, LL.D.; ed. by his granddaughter Caroline Hazard. Boston and New York, Houghton, Mifflin and company, 1889.
Hazard, Rowland Gibson, 1801–1888.

LAC 10277
Economics of forestry; a reference book for students of political economy and professional and lay students of forestry. New York, T. Y. Crowell & co. [1902]
Fernow, Bernhard Eduard, 1851–1923.

LAC 10340
Economics of interurban railways. 1st ed. New York [etc.] McGraw-Hill book company, inc., 1914.
Fischer, Louis Engelmann. 1876–

LAC 10071
The economics of land tenure in Georgia... [New York?] Columbia university, 1905.
Banks, Enoch Marvin, 1877–

LAC 14199
The economics of railroad construction. 2d ed., thoroughly rev. 1st thousand. New York, J. Wiley & sons; [etc., etc.] 1912.
Webb, Walter Loring, 1863–1941.

LAC 14712
Economics of the Iroquois. Bryn Mawr, Pa., 1905.
Stites, Sara Henry, 1877–

LAC 15874
The economy of high wages. An inquiry into the cause of high wages and their effect on methods and cost of production. By J. Schoenhof. With an introduction by Thomas F. Bayard. New York [etc.] G. P. Putnam's sons, 1893, [c1892]
Schoenhof, Jacob, 1839–1903.

LAC 10989
The ecumenical councils, by William P. Du Bose with an introduction by the Rt. Rev. Thomas F. Gailor. 2d ed. New York, The Christian literature co., 1896.
Du Bose, William Porcher, 1836–1918.

LAC 13809
Ed. Geers' experience with the trotters and pacers. Embracing a brief history of his early life in Tennessee, with descriptions of some of the customs peculiar to that state, and a general description of the most noted horses he has driven, together with a list of the horses he has given fast records; also instructions about conditioning and caring for the horse before and during racing. Buffalo, N. Y. [The Matthews-Northrup co.] 1901.
Geers, Edward Franklin, b. 1851.

LAC 12125
Edgar Allan Poe. Boston, New York, Houghton, Mifflin and company [c1885]
Woodberry, George Edward, 1855–1930.

LAC 11994
Edgar Allan Poe; his life, letters, and opinions. London, New York, Ward, Lock, Bowden, 1891.
Ingram, John Henry, 1842–1916.

LAC 10618
Education and industrial evolution. New York, The Macmillan company, 1908.
Carlton, Frank Tracy, 1873–

LAC 11565
Education and the higher life. Chicago, A. C. McClurg and company, 1916, [c1890]
Spalding, John Lancaster, abp., 1840–1916.

LAC 40014
Education for life, by Samuel Chapman Armstrong, founder of Hampton institute, with an introduction by Francis Greenwood Peabody and a biographical note by Helen W. Ludlow. [Hampton, Va., Press of the Hampton normal and agricultural institute, 1913]
Armstrong, Samuel Chapman, 1839–1893.

LAC 40081
Education for social work. Wash., Govt. print. off., 1915.
Abbott, Edith, 1876–1957.

LAC 10601
Education in Georgia. Washington, Govt. print. off., 1889.
Jones, Charles Edgeworth, 1867–1931.

LAC 40031
Education in the Philippines, Cuba, Porto Rico, Hawaii, and Samoa. Washington, Govt. print. off., 1901.
Packard, Robert Lawrence.

LAC 20138–39
Education in the United States; a series of monographs prepared for the United States exhibit at the Paris exposition, 1900. Albany, N. Y., J. B. Lyon company, 1900.
Butler, Nicholas Murray, 1862–1947, ed.

LAC 10579
Education in the United States; its history from the earliest settlements. New York, D. Appleton and company, 1915, [c1889]
Boone, Richard Gause, 1849–1923.

LAC 15619
The education of American girls. Considered in a series of essays. New York, G. P. Putnam's sons, 1874.
Brackett, Anna Callender, 1836–1911, ed.

LAC 16696
The education of girls in the United States. London, S. Sonnenschein; New York, Macmillan, 1894.
Burstall, Sara Annie, 1859–1939.

LAC 40078
The education of the negro; its rise, progress and present status: being an address delivered before the National educational association at its late meeting at Chautauqua, N. Y. Atlanta, Ga., J. P. Harrison & co., 1880.
Orr, Gustavus J.

LAC 10629
The education of the negro prior to 1861; a history of the education of the colored people of the United States from the beginning of slavery to the civil war. New York and London, G. P. Putnam's sons, 1915.
Woodson, Carter Godwin, 1875–1950.

LAC 40108
Education of the negroes since 1860. Baltimore, The Trustees, 1894.
Curry, Jabez Lamar Monroe, 1825–1903.

LAC 14102
The education of the wage-earners; a contribution toward the solution of the educational problem of democracy, by Thomas Davidson, ed. with an introductory chapter by Charles M. Bakewell. Boston, London [etc.] Ginn & company [c1904]
Davidson, Thomas, 1840–1900.

LAC 40094
Education; or, The coming man. An essay involving the basic truths, that underlie the universal church. Boston, Colby & Rich [c1884]
Edson, Jacob.

LAC 40094
Education: to whom does it belong? A rejoinder to the Civilta cattolica. By the Rev. Thomas Bouquillon. Baltimore, J. Murphy & co., 1892.
Bouquillon, Thomas Joseph, 1842–1902.

LAC 13583
Educational biography. Memoirs of teachers, educators, and promoters and benefactors of education, literature, and science, reprinted from the American journal of education. Part I. Teachers and educators. Volume 1. United States. New York, F. C. Brownell, 1859.
Barnard, Henry, 1811–1900, *ed.*

LAC 14596
Educational history of Illinois; growth and progress in educational affairs of the state from the earliest day to the present, with portraits and biographies. Chicago, Ill., The Henry O. Shepard company, 1912.
Cook, John Williston, 1844–

LAC 12990
Educational history of Ohio: a history of its progress since the formation of the state, together with the portraits and biographies of past and present state officials. Columbus, O., Historical publishing co., 1905.
Burns, James Jesse, 1838–1911.

LAC 13328
Educational issues in the kindergarten. New York, D. Appleton and company, 1908.
Blow, Susan Elizabeth, 1843–1916.

LAC 40014
The educational labors of Henry Barnard; a study in the history of American pedagogy. Syracuse, N. Y., C. W. Bardeen, 1893.
Monroe, Will Seymour, 1863–1939.

LAC 13036
Educational legislation and administration of the colonial governments. New York, The Macmillan co.; [etc., etc.] 1899.
Parsons, Elsie Worthington, 1875–1941.

LAC 13000
Educational periodicals during the nineteenth century. Washington, Govt. print. off., 1919.
Davis, Sheldon Emmor, 1876–

LAC 13010
Educational reform: essays and addresses. New York, The Century co., 1909, [c1898]
Eliot, Charles William, 1834–1926.

LAC 14968
The educational situation. Chicago, The University of Chicago press, 1902.
Dewey, John, 1859–1952.

LAC 40011
The educational systems of the Puritans and Jesuits compared. A premium essay, written for "The Society for the promotion of collegiate and theological education at the West." New York, M. W. Dodd, 1851.
Porter, Noah, 1811–1892.

LAC 11680
The educational views and influence of De Witt Clinton. New York city, Teachers college, Columbia university, 1911.
Fitzpatrick, Edward Augustus, 1884–

LAC 15105
Edwin Booth; recollections by his daughter Edwina Booth Grossmann, and letters to her and to his friends. New York, The Century co., 1902, [c1894]
Booth, Edwin, 1833–1893.

LAC 40043
The effect of immigration on municipal politics, by Hon. William S. Bennet. Philadelphia, National Municipal League, 1909.
Bennet, William Stiles, 1870–

LAC 40039
The effect of secession upon the commercial relations between the North and South, and upon each section. New York, New York times, 1861.
Lord, Daniel, 1795–1868.

LAC 40041
An effective exhibition of a community survey; a brief description of the Springfield survey exhibition... New York city, Dept. of surveys and exhibits, Russell Sage foundation [1915]
Russell Sage Foundation, *New York. Dept. of Surveys and Exhibits.*

LAC 40140
Effects of the stage on the manners of a people: and the propriety of encouraging and establishing a virtuous theatre. By a Bostonian. Boston: Printed by Young and Etheridge, Market-Square, sold by them and the several booksellers, 1792.
Haliburton, William.

LAC 14060
Efficiency in city government... Philadelphia, American academy of political and social science, 1912.
American Academy of Political and Social Science, *Philadelphia.*

LAC 40013
The eight hour movement. A reduction of hours is an increase of wages. An extract from a lecture delivered by Ira Steward. Boston, Boston labor reform association, 1865.
Steward, Ira, 1831–1883.

LAC 14521
Eight hours for laborers on government work. Report by the Hon. Victor H. Metcalf, secretary Department of commerce and labor, on H. R. 4064 (Eight-hour bill), submitted by resolution by the Committee on labor of the House of representatives, April 13, 1904. Washington, Govt. print. off., 1905.
U.S. *Dept. of Commerce and Labor.*

LAC 40078
1862-emancipation day-1884. The negro as a political problem. Oration, by the Hon. George W. Williams at the Asbury church, Washington, D. C., April 16, 1884...
Boston, A. Mudge & son, printers, 1884.
Williams, George Washington, 1849-1891.

LAC 15695
1812; the war, and its moral: a Canadian chronicle.
Montreal, Printed by J. Lovell, 1864.
Coffin, William Foster, 1808-1878.

LAC 11269
Eighth annual report of the Bureau of statistics of labor. March, 1877. Boston, A. J. Wright, 1877.
Massachusetts. *Dept. of Labor and Industries. Division of Statistics.*

LAC 11241
Eighty years and more (1815-1897). Reminiscences of Elizabeth Cady Stanton ... New York, European publishing company, 1898.
Stanton, Elizabeth, 1815-1902.

LAC 20090
Eighty years progress of the United States: showing the various channels of industry and education through which the people of the United States have arisen from a British colony to their present national importance... By eminent literary men. With over two hundred and twenty engravings. New York, Worcester, Mass., L. Stebbins, 1861.

LAC 11958
Elder Conklin, and other stories. [2d ed.] London, W. Heinemann, [1895]
Harris, Frank, 1855-1931.

LAC 13327
Eldorado, or, Adventures in the path of empire; comprising a voyage to California, via Panama; life in San Francisco and Monterey; pictures of the gold region, and experiences of Mexican travel. 7th ed. New York, G. P. Putnam; London, R. Bentley, 1855 [c1850]
Taylor, Bayard, 1825-1878.

LAC 10382
The election frauds of New York city and their prevention. In two volumes. Vol. I. Eleven years of fraud—1860-70. New York, The author, 1881.
Davenport, John Isaacs, 1843-

LAC 13850
Electricity one hundred years ago and to-day. With copious notes and extracts. New York, McGraw Publishing company, 1894.
Houston, Edwin James, 1847-1914.

LAC 13858
Electrotype manipulation... London, G. Knight and sons, 1841.
Walker, Charles Vincent, 1812-1882.

LAC 12706
An elementary and practical treatise on bridge building, an enl. and improved edition of the author's original work. New York, D. Van Nostrand, 1872.
Whipple, Squire.

LAC 12660
An elementary course of civil engineering, for the use of cadets of the United States' military academy. New ed., with large addenda and many new cuts. New York, J. Wiley & son, 1868.
Mahan, Dennis Hart, 1802-1871.

LAC 40050
Elementary education. [Albany, N. Y., J. B. Lyon company, 1900]
Harris, William Torrey, 1835-1909.

LAC 40014
Elementary instruction. An address delivered before the schools and the citizens, of the town of Quincy, July 4, 1837. Quincy, Printed by J. A. Green, 1837.
Brooks, Charles, 1795-1872.

LAC 13845
Elementary principles in statistical mechanics, developed with especial reference to the rational foundation of thermodynamics. New York, C. Scribner's sons; [etc., etc.] 1902.
Gibbs, Josiah Willard, 1839-1903.

LAC 16380
An elementary treatise on advanced-guard, out-post, and detachment service of troops, and the manner of posting and handling them in presence of an enemy. With a historical sketch of the rise and progress of tactics, &c., &c., intended as a supplement to the system of tactics adopted for the military service of the United States, and especially for the use of officers of militia and volunteers. New York, J. Wiley, 1853.
Mahan, Dennis Hart, 1802-1871.

LAC 10699
The elements of agriculture: a book for young farmers. 2d rev. ed. New York, The Tribune association, 1870, [c1868]
Waring, George Edwin, 1833-1898.

LAC 40061
Elements of animal magnetism; or, Process and application for relieving human suffering. Stereotype ed. New York, Fowlers and Wells [185-?]
Morley, Charles.

LAC 13847
The elements of botany for beginners and for schools. New York and Chicago, Ivison, Blakeman and company, 1887.
Gray, Asa, 1810-1888.

LAC 14610
The elements of constitutional law and political economy. 4th ed. Baltimore, Cushing & brother, 1840.
Raymond, Daniel, 1786-1849.

LAC 20130-31
Elements of mental philosophy. Portland, S. Colman; Boston, Hilliard, Gray & co. [etc.] 1831.
Upham, Thomas Cogswell, 1799-1872.

LAC 14347
Elements of military art and science; or, Course of instruction in strategy, fortification, tactics of battles, &c., embracing the duties of staff, infantry, cavalry, artillery, and engineers; adapted to the use of volunteers and militia. Third ed., with critical notes on the Mexican and Crimean wars. New York, London, D. Appleton & company, 1863.
Halleck, Henry Wager, 1815-1872.

LAC 10534
Elements of modern materialism: inculcating the idea of a future state, in which all will be more happy, under whatever circumstances they may be placed than if they experienced no misery in this life. Adams, Mass., Printed for the author, by A. Oakey, 1829.
Knowlton, Charles, 1800-1850.

LAC 12525
The elements of moral science. 16th thousand. Rev. and stereotyped. Boston, Gould, Kendall, and Lincoln, 1841.
Wayland, Francis, 1796-1865.

LAC 10452
The elements of moral science, theoretical and practical. New York, C. Scribner's sons, 1885, [c1884]
Porter, Noah, 1811-1892.

LAC 13856
Elements of physics, by Henry A. Rowland and Joseph S. Ames. New York, Cincinnati [etc.] American book company [1900]
Rowland, Henry Augustus, 1848-1901.

LAC 16851
Elements of political economy. Andover, Gould and Newman; New York, H. Griffin and company, 1835.
Newman, Samuel Phillips, 1797-1842.

LAC 10546
Elements of political economy. New York, C. Scribner and company, 1866.
Perry, Arthur Latham, 1830-1905.

LAC 20066
The elements of political economy. In two parts. 2d ed. In two volumes. Baltimore, F. Lucas jun. and E. J. Coale, 1823.
Raymond, Daniel, 1786-1849.

LAC 11587
The elements of political economy. New York, Leavitt, Lord & co., 1837.
Wayland, Francis, 1796-1865.

LAC 10122
Elements of scientific agriculture; or, The connection between science and the art of practical farming... New York, C. M. Saxton & co., 1855.
Norton, John Pitkin, 1822-1852.

LAC 10435
The elements of sociology; a text-book for colleges and schools. New York, The Macmillan company; London, Macmillan & co., ltd., 1907, [c1898]
Giddings, Franklin Henry, 1855-1931.

LAC 40048
Elements of success. An address delivered at the first annual meeting of the Alumni association of Columbian college, Washington, D. C. Washington, Printed by R. A. Waters, 1848.
Cushman, Robert Woodward, 1800-1868.

LAC 20898
Elements of surgery: for the use of students... 2d ed., with additions... Philadelphia, B. Warner [etc.] 1818.
Dorsey, John Syng, 1783-1818.

LAC 14612
Elements of the philosophy of mind, applied to the development of thought and feeling. Geneva [N. Y.] J. N. Bogert; New York, Collins, Keese and co., 1840.
Ricord, Elizabeth, 1788-1865.

LAC 15436
Elements of transportation; a discussion of steam railroad, electric railway, and ocean and inland water transportation. New York and London, D. Appleton and company, 1909.
Johnson, Emory Richard, 1864–

LAC 21421
Elements of useful knowledge ... for the use of schools. Hartford, Hudson & Goodwin, 1802-1812.
Webster, Noah, 1758-1843.

LAC 11180
Elihu Burritt: a memorial volume containing a sketch of his life and labors, with selections from his writings and lectures, and extracts from his private journals in Europe and America. Ed. by Chas. Northend, A. M. New York, D. Appleton & company [1879]
Burritt, Elihu, 1810-1879.

LAC 10018
Elijah Cobb, 1768-1848; a Cape Cod skipper, with a foreword by Ralph D. Paine. New Haven, Yale university press: [etc., etc.] 1925.
Cobb, Elijah, 1768-1848.

LAC 40080
Elijah Fisher's journal while in the war for independence, and continued two years after he came to Maine. 1775-1784. Augusta [Me.] Press of Badger & Manley, 1880.
Fisher, Elijah, b. 1758.

LAC 20415
Elizabeth Cady Stanton as revealed in her letters, diary and reminiscences, ed. by Theodore Stanton and Harriot Stanton Blatch, illustrated from photographs. New York and London, Harper & brothers [c1922]
Stanton, Elizabeth, 1815-1902.

LAC 40076

Emancipation. [n.p., 1840]
Channing, William Ellery, 1780–1842.

LAC 40121

Emancipation and the war. Compensation essential to peace and civilization... [Washington? D. C., 1861]
Goodloe, Daniel Reaves, 1814–1902.

LAC 40138

Emancipation in Louisiana; speech of Alfred C. Hills, (of Orleans Parish,) in the Constitutional Convention of Louisiana, May 4th and 5th, 1864. New Orleans, Printed at the Era Book and Job Office, 1864.
Hills, Alfred C.

LAC 13066

Emancipation in the West Indies. A six months' tour in Antigua, Barbadoes, and Jamaica, in the year 1837. By Jas. A. Thome, and J. Horace Kimball. New York, The American anti-slavery society, 1838.
Thome, James A.

LAC 16919

Emancipation: its course and progress from 1481 B. C. to A. D. 1875, with a review of President Lincoln's proclamations, the XIII amendment, and the progress of the freed people since emancipation; with a history of the emancipation monument. New York, Negro Universities Press [1969]
Wilson, Joseph Thomas, 1836–1891.

LAC 11742

The emancipation of Massachusetts. Boston and New York, Houghton, Mifflin and company, 1887, [c1886]
Adams, Brooks, 1848–1927.

LAC 10361

The emancipation of the American city. New York, Duffield and company, 1917.
Arndt, Walter Tallmadge, 1873–

LAC 40103

The emancipation problem in Maryland... [Baltimore, 1862]
Mayer, Brantz, 1809–1879.

LAC 12823

The Emancipator (complete) published by Elihu Embree, Jonesborough, Tennessee, 1820; a reprint of the Emancipator, to which are added a biographical sketch of Elihu Embree, author and publisher of the Emancipator, and two hitherto unpublished anti-slavery memorials bearing the signature of Elihu Embree. Nashville, Tenn., B. H. Murphy, 1932.

LAC 40118

The embargo; or, Sketches of the times. A satire. The second edition, corrected and enlarged. Together with the Spanish revolution, and other poems. Boston, Printed for the author by E. G. House, no. 5, Court street, 1809.
Bryant, William Cullen, 1794–1878.

LAC 14932

Embassy to the eastern courts of Cochin-China, Siam, and Muscat; in the U.S. sloop-of-war Peacock ... during the years 1832-3-4. New-York, Harper & brothers, 1837.
Roberts, Edmund, 1784–1836.

LAC 11861

Emerson. New York, C. Scribner's sons, 1898.
Chapman, John Jay, 1862–1933.

LAC 11874

Emerson at home and abroad. London, Trubner & co., 1883.
Conway, Moncure Daniel, 1832–1907.

LAC 11908

Emerson in Concord: a memoir, written for the "Social circle" in Concord, Massachusetts. Boston and New York, Houghton, Mifflin and company, 1889.
Emerson, Edward Waldo, 1844–1930.

LAC 14814

The emigrant to North America, from memoranda of a settler in Canada being a compendium of useful practical hints to emigrants with an account of every day's doings upon a farm for a year. By an emigrant farmer [*pseud.*] [3d ed.] Edinburgh and London, W. Blackwood & sons, 1844.
Abbott, Joseph, 1789–1863.

LAC 16078

The emigrants, by Johan Bojer; translated from the Norwegian by A. G. Jayne. New York & London, The Century co. [c1925]
Bojer, Johan, 1872–

LAC 15514

An emigrant's five years in the free states of America. London, T. C. Newby, 1860.
Hancock, William, *emigrant.*

LAC 16905

Emigrant's guide. Comprising advice and instruction in every stage of the voyage to America... Also, information which the emigrant needs on arrival... London, Wiley & Putnam, 1845.

LAC 15854

The emigrant's guide; in ten letters, addressed to the taxpayers of England; containing information of every kind, necessary to persons who are about to emigrate; including several authentic and most interesting letters from English emigrants, now in America, to their relations in England. London, The author, 1829.
Cobbett, William, 1763–1835.

LAC 14802

The emigrants' guide to California, by Joseph E. Ware. Reprinted from the 1849 edition, with introduction and notes by John Caughey. Princeton, Princeton university press, 1932.
Ware, Joseph E.

LAC 40022

The emigrant's guide to the gold mines. Three weeks in the gold mines, or Adventures with the gold diggers of California. New York, Joyce and co., 1848. [Tarrytown, N. Y., Reprinted W. Abbatt, 1932]
Simpson, Henry I.

LAC 13242
The emigrant's guide to the United States of America; containing the best advice and directions respecting the voyage,—preservation of health,—choice of settlement, &c. Also the latest information concerning the climate, productions ... and other subjects, economical and political, affecting the welfare of persons about to emigrate to the United States and British America. London, W. Hone, 1818.
Holditch, Robert.

LAC 16258
The emigrant's guide to the western and southwestern states and territories: comprising a geographical and statistical description of the states... Accompanied by a map of the United States... New York, Kirk & Mercein, 1818.
Darby, William, 1775–1854.

LAC 15856
The emigrant's hand-book; or, A directory and guide for persons emigrating to the United States of America... Also, a concise description of the states of Ohio, Indiana, Illinois, Michigan, Wisconsin, Missouri and Iowa, and the western territories; and including a statement of the modes and expenses of travelling from New York to the interior... New York, J. H. Colton, 1848.

LAC 15745
The emigrant's note book and guide; with recollections of Upper and Lower Canada, during the late war... London, Longman, Hurst, Rees, Orme, and Brown, 1824.
Morgan, *Lieut.* J   C.

LAC 15746
The emigrant's pocket companion; containing, what emigration is, who should be emigrants, where emigrants should go; a description of British North America, especially the Canadas; and full instructions to intending emigrants. London, J. Cochrane and co., 1832.
Mudie, Robert, 1777–1842.

LAC 40142
Emigrating Indians. Letter from the Secretary of War, transmitting information of the inadequacy of the fund for defraying the expenses attending the emigration of the Creek Indians. Washington, Printed by Gales & Seaton, 1828.
U.S. *War Dept.*

LAC 15534
Emigration and immigration; a study in social science. New York, C. Scribner's sons, 1890.
Mayo-Smith, Richmond, 1854–1901.

LAC 12300
Emigration and immigration; reports of the consular officers of the United States. Washington, Govt. print. off., 1887.
U.S. *Bureau of Foreign Commerce* (1854–1903)

LAC 16076
Emigration fields. North America, the Cape, Australia, and New Zealand; describing these countries, and giving a comparative view of the advantages they present to British settlers. Edinburgh, A. and C. Black; [etc., etc.] 1839.
Matthew, Patrick.

LAC 10501
The empire of business. New York, Doubleday, Page & co., 1902.
Carnegie, Andrew, 1835–1919.

LAC 40086
Employers' welfare work. May 15, 1913. Washington, Govt. print. off., 1913.
Otey, Elizabeth Dabney Langhorne, 1880–

LAC 40074
Employment of Pinkerton detectives. Washington, Govt. print. off., 1893.
U.S. *Congress. House. Committee on the Judiciary.*

LAC 15797
The employments of women: A cyclopaedia of woman's work. Boston, Walker, Wise, 1863.
Penny, Virginia, *b.* 1826.

LAC 13993
The enchanted beauty, and other tales, essays, and sketches. By William Elder, M. D. Philadelphia, J. W. Bradley, 1859.
Elder, William, 1806–1885.

LAC 14473
The enchanted moccasins and other legends of the American Indians, compiled from original sources, by Cornelius Matthews [!] New York, G. P. Putnam's sons, 1877.
Mathews, Cornelius, 1817–1889, *comp.*

LAC 22303
An encyclopaedia of freemasonry and its kindred sciences, comprising the whole range of arts, sciences and literature as connected with the institution, by Albert G. Mackey. This new and rev. ed. prepared under the direction, and with the assistance, of the late William J. Hughan, by Edward L. Hawkins. Chicago, New York [etc.] The Masonic history company [c1927]
Mackey, Albert Gallatin, 1807–1881.

LAC 23139–40
The Encyclopaedia of missions. Descriptive, historical, biographical, statistical. With a full assortment of maps, a complete bibliography, and lists of Bible versions... Edited by Rev. Edwin Munsell Bliss. New York, London [etc.] Funk & Wagnalls, 1891.

LAC 10796
The Encyclopaedia of popular songs: a choice collection of sentimental, patriotic, Irish, Ethiopian, and comic songs. Embracing several hundred of the newest and most fashionable lyrics of the day. New York, Dick & Fitzgerald [1864]

LAC 11074–75
Encyclopaedia of the Presbyterian church in the United States of America: including the northern and southern assemblies. Alfred Nevin, editor, assisted by B. M. Smith, W. E. Schenck and other eminent ministers of the church. Including a description of the historic decorations of the Pan Presbyterian Council of 1880 by Rev. Henry C. McCook. Philadelphia, Presbyterian encyclopaedia publishing co. [c1884]
Nevin, Alfred, 1816–1890, *ed.*

LAC 15889
The encyclopedia of ceramics, compiled by W. P. Jervis, with much original matter now first published. New York [c1902]
Jervis, William Percival, 1850–   *comp.*

LAC 23430–32
Encyclopedia of Mississippi history; comprising sketches of counties, towns, events, institutions and persons, planned and ed. by Dunbar Rowland. Madison, Wis., S. A. Brant, 1907.
Rowland, Dunbar, 1864–   *ed.*

LAC 16352
Encyclopedia of rural sports: comprising shooting, hunting, coursing, fishing, boating, racing, pedestrianism, cricket, base ball, &c. and the various rural games and amusements of Great Britain and America ... illustrated by numerous engravings on wood, from drawings by Wells, Harvey, Hind, &c., &c. First American from the eighth English ed., revised, with additions. Philadelphia, Porter and Coates [n.d.]
Walsh, John Henry, 1810–1888.

LAC 13919–20
The encyclopedia of social reform; including political economy, political science, sociology and statistics... Edited by William D. P. Bliss, with the co-operation of many specialists. 2d ed. New York and London, Funk & Wagnalls company, 1898, [c1897]
Bliss, William Dwight Porter, 1856–1926, *ed.*

LAC 12403
The end of an era. Boston and New York, Houghton, Mifflin and company, 1899.
Wise, John Sergeant, 1846–1913.

LAC 40094
The ends and means of a liberal education, an inaugural address, delivered July 11, 1854, by M. B. Anderson, president of the University of Rochester. Rochester, N. Y., William N. Sage, 1854.
Anderson, Martin Brewer, 1815–1890.

LAC 12874
Enfranchisement and citizenship: Addresses and papers, by Edward L. Pierce. Ed. by A. W. Stevens. Boston, Roberts brothers, 1896.
Pierce, Edward Lillie, 1829–1897.

LAC 12923
England and the United States.
Duff Green's "England and the United States" : with an introductory study of American opposition to the Quintuple treaty of 1841, by St. George L. Sioussat. [Worcester, Mass., American Antiquarian Society, 1931]
Green, Duff, 1791–1875.

LAC 16474
England in America, 1580–1652. New York and London, Harper & brothers, 1904.
Tyler, Lyon Gardiner, 1853–1935.

LAC 10154
England's treasure by forraign trade, 1664. New York and London, Macmillan and co., 1895.
Mun, Thomas, 1571–1641.

LAC 11604
English and American railroads compared. By Edward Bates Dorsey. With discussion by W. W. Evans, Thomas C. Clarke, Edward P. North. New York, J. Wiley & sons, 1887.
Dorsey, Edward Bates.

LAC 22874–77
English colonies in America... New York, H. Holt and company, 1889–1907.
Doyle, John Andrew, 1844–1907.

LAC 12753
The English colonization of America during the seventeenth century. London, Strahan & co., 1871.
Neill, Edward Duffield, 1823–1893.

LAC 11674
English democratic ideas in the seventeenth century, by G. P. Gooch. 2d ed., with supplementary notes and appendices by Professor H. J. Laski. Cambridge [Eng.] The University press, 1927.
Gooch, George Peabody, 1873–1968.

LAC 40025
English neutrality. Is the Alabama a British pirate? New York, A. D. F. Randolph, 1863.
Lowrey, Grosvenor Porter.

LAC 16580
The English notebooks, by Nathaniel Hawthorne, based upon the original manuscripts in the Pierpont Morgan library and edited by Randall Stewart. New York, Modern language association of America; London, Oxford university press, 1941.
Hawthorne, Nathaniel, 1804–1864.

LAC 40130
English policy toward America in 1790–1791 [pts. I, II] New York, London, Macmillan, 1902.
Turner, Frederick Jackson, 1861–1932.

LAC 16260
The English settlement in the Illinois. Reprints of three rare tracts on the Illinois country. With map and a view of a British colony house at Albion. Ed., with introduction and notes, by Edwin Erle Sparks. London, The Museum book store; Cedar Rapids, Ia., The Torch press, 1907.
Sparks, Edwin Erle, 1860–1924, *ed.*

LAC 14460
An English settler in pioneer Wisconsin; the letters of Edwin Bottomley, 1842–1850; ed. with introduction and notes by Milo M. Quaife. Madison, The Society, 1918.
Bottomley, Edwin, 1809–1850.

LAC 13138
The English sportsman in the western prairies. By the Hon. Grantley F. Berkeley. London, Hurst & Blackett, 1861.
Berkeley, George Charles Grantley Fitzhardinge, 1800–1881.

LAC 12379
The Englishman in Kansas: or, Squatter life and border warfare. By T. H. Gladstone. With an introduction by Fred. Law Olmsted. New York. Miller & company, 1857.
Gladstone, Thomas H.

LAC 16145
An Englishman's travels in America: his observations of life and manners in the free and slave states. London, Binns and Goodwin; [etc., etc., 1853?]
Benwell, J.

LAC 12147
The Englishwoman in America. London, J. Murray, 1856.
Bishop, Isabella Lucy, 1831–1904.

LAC 15996
An Englishwoman in Utah: the story of a life's experience in Mormonism. An autobiography: by Mrs. T. B. H. Stenhouse. With introductory preface by Mrs. Harriet Beecher Stowe. Including a full account of the Mountain Meadows massacre, and of the life, confession and execution of Bishop John D. Lee. Fully illustrated. New and cheaper ed. London, S. Low, Marston, Searle & Rivington, 1882.
Stenhouse, Fanny, 1829–

LAC 14820
An Englishwoman's experience in America. London, R. Bentley, 1853.
Finch, Marianne.

LAC 16224
The engraved portraits of Washington, with notices of the originals and brief biographical sketches of the painters. Philadelphia, Lindsay & Baker, 1880.
Baker, William Spohn, 1824–1897.

LAC 12839
An enquiry concerning the intellectual and moral faculties, and literature of negroes; followed with an account of the life and works of fifteen negroes & mulattoes, distinguished in science, literature and the arts. Tr. by D. B. Warden. Brooklyn: Printed by Thomas Kirk, Mainstreet, 1810.
Gregoire, Henri, *constitutional bp. of Blois*, 1750–1831.

LAC 15815
An enquiry how far the punishment of death is necessary in Pennsylvania. With notes and illustrations. By William Bradford, esq. To which is added, An account of the gaol and penitentiary house of Philadelphia, and of the interior management thereof. By Caleb Lownes. Philadelphia printed: London, Re-printed for J. Johnson, 1795.
Bradford, William, 1755–1795.

LAC 40126
An enquiry into the principles and tendency of certain public measures. Philadelphia, Printed by T. Dobson, 1794.
Taylor, John, 1753–1824.

LAC 40106
An enquiry into the principles on which a commercial system for the United States of America should be founded; to which are added some political observations connected with the subject. Read before the Society for political enquiries, convened at the house of His Excellency Benjamin Franklin, esquire, in Philadelphia May 11th, 1787. [Philadelphia] Printed and sold by Robert Aitken, at Pope's head, in Market street, M.DCC.LXXXVII.
Coxe, Tench, 1755–1824.

LAC 14927
Enquiry into the validity of the British claim to a right of visitation and search of American vessels suspected to be engaged in the African slave-trade. Philadelphia, Lea & Blanchard, 1842.
Wheaton, Henry, 1785–1848.

LAC 40079
An entire new plan for a national currency... To which is added, a plan for a real national bank. Philadelphia, Printed for the author, by J. Rakestraw, 1834.
Mendenhall, Thomas.

LAC 23307
Episodes of my second life, by Antonio Gallenga (L. Mariotti) London. Chapman and Hall, limited, 1884.
Gallenga, Antonio Carlo Napoleone, 1810–1895.

LAC 40036
An epistle to the clergy of the southern states. New-York, 1836.
Grimke, Sarah Moore, 1792–1873.

LAC 10507
An epitome of chymical philosophy; being an extended syllabus of the lectures on that subject, delivered at Dartmouth college; and intended as a text-book for students. Concord, N. H., Printed by I. Hill, 1825.
Dana, James Freeman, 1793–1827.

LAC 40010
An epitome of historical events and of official and other correspondence connected with the acquisition and other dealings of the United States with the Philippine Islands. Prepared by Erving Winslow. May 29, 1902.- Ordered to be printed as a document. Washington, Govt. print. off., 1902.
Winslow, Erving, 1839–1922.

LAC 40050
Epitome of some of the chief events and transactions in the life of Joseph Lancaster, containing an account of the rise and progress of the Lancasterian system of education; and the author's future prospects of usefulness to mankind; written by himself and published to promote the education of his family... New Haven, Printed for the author by Baldwin & Peck; New York, Carvill & co. [etc.] 1833.
Lancaster, Joseph, 1778–1838.

LAC 10496
Equality. New York, D. Appleton and company, 1897.
Bellamy, Edward, 1850–1898.

LAC 40126
Equality... West Brookfield, Mass., O. S. Cooke & co., 1849.
Greene, William Batchelder, 1819–1878.

LAC 40133
The equality of mankind and the evils of slavery, illustrated: a sermon, delivered on the day of the annual fast, April 6, 1820. Boston: Printed for Samuel T. Armstrong, by Crocker & Brewster, no. 50, Cornhill, 1820.
Wheaton, Josephus, 1788–1825.

LAC 11245

Equitable commerce: a new development of principles as substitutes for laws and governments... Proposed as elements of new society. New York, Fowlers and Wells, 1852.
Warren, Josiah, 1798–1874.

LAC 16715

The Erie railway; its history and management, from April 24, 1832, to July 13, 1875... Together with complete lists, containing the names of holders of all the common and preference shares... Being a report to the bond and shareholders. New York, J. Polhemus, printer, 1875.
Livingston, John.

LAC 16590

An errand to the South in the summer of 1862. By the Rev. William Wyndham Malet. London, R. Bentley, 1863.
Malet, William Wyndham, 1804–1885.

LAC 12717

The escape of William and Ellen Craft from slavery.
Running a thousand miles for freedom; or, The escape of William and Ellen Craft from slavery. London, W. Tweedie, 1860.
Craft, William.

LAC 14418

L'Espagne, Cuba et les Etats-Unis. Paris, Perrin et cie, 1898.
Benoist, Charles, 1861–1936.

LAC 11780

An essay on calcareous manures. 2d ed. Shellbanks, Va., Farmers' register, 1835.
Ruffin, Edmund, 1794–1865.

LAC 13853

An essay on comets, in two parts. Part I. Containing an attempt to explain the phaenomena of the tails of comets, and to account for their perpetual opposition to the sun, upon philosophical principles. Part II. Pointing out some important ends for which these tails were probably designed: wherein it is shewn, that, in consequence of these curious appendages, comets may be inhabited worlds, and even comfortable habitations: notwithstanding the vast excentricities of their orbits the whole interspersed with observations and reflections on the sun and primary planets. By Andrew Oliver, jun. Salem, New England: Printed and sold by Samuel Hall, near the Exchange MDCCLXXII.
Oliver, Andrew, 1731–1799.

LAC 40073

An essay on common wealths. Part I. The evils of exclusive and the benefits of inclusive wealth. Part II. Extracts from Robert Owen's "New view of society." Part III. Melish's account of the Harmonists... New-York, The New-York society for promoting communities, 1822.

LAC 11121

An essay on demonology, ghosts and apparitions, and popular superstitions. Also, an account of the witchcraft delusion at Salem, in 1692. Boston, Carter and Hendee, 1831.
Thacher, James, 1754–1844.

LAC 12737

An essay on judicial power and unconstitutional legislation, being a commentary on parts of the Constitution of the United States. Philadelphia, Kay and brother, 1893.
Coxe, Brinton, 1833–1892.

LAC 13060

An essay on Junius and his letters; embracing a sketch of the life and character of William Pitt, earl of Chatham, and memoirs of certain other distinguished individuals; with reflections historical, personal, and political, relating to the affairs of Great Britain and America from 1763 to 1785. Boston, Gray and Bowen, 1831.
Waterhouse, Benjamin, 1754–1846.

LAC 12782

An essay on liberty and slavery. By Albert Taylor Bledsoe, LL. D., professor of mathematics in the University of Virginia. Philadelphia, J. B. Lippincott & co., 1856.
Bledsoe, Albert Taylor, 1809–1877.

LAC 40097

Essay on scientific propagation. Oneida, N. Y., Oneida community [1875?]
Noyes, John Humphrey, 1811–1886.

LAC 40032

Essay on sea coast crops; read before the Agricultural association of the planting states, on occasion of the annual meeting, held at Columbia, the capital of South-Carolina, December 3d, 1853. Charleston, A. E. Miller, 1854.
Allston, Robert Francis Withers, 1801–1864.

LAC 11172

An essay on slavery and abolitionism, with reference to the duty of American females. Philadelphia, H. Perkins; Boston, Perkins & Marvin, 1837.
Beecher, Catharine Esther, 1800–1878.

LAC 40068

An essay on the African slave trade. London, G. G. and J. Robinson, 1799.
Belsham, William, 1752–1827.

LAC 40088

An essay on the beauties and excellencies of painting, music and poetry, pronounced at the anniversary commencement at Dartmouth college ... 1774. Hartford, Printed by Eben. Watson [n.d.]
Wheelock, John, 1754–1817.

LAC 15681

An essay on the causes of the decline of the foreign trade, consequently of the value of the lands of Britain, and on the means to restore both. Begun in the year 1739. 4th ed. Dublin, G. Faulkner, 1751.
Decker, *Sir* Matthew, *bart.*, 1679–1749.

LAC 12694

An essay on the causes of the variety of complexion and figure in the human species. To which are added strictures on Lord Kaims's [!] discourse, on the original diversity of mankind. By the Reverend Samuel Stanhope Smith. Philadelphia: Printed and sold by Robert Aitken, at Pope's head, Market street, M.DCC.LXXXVII.
Smith, Samuel Stanhope, 1750–1819.

LAC 40019
An essay on the improvement in the manufacture of sugar, adapted for Louisiana. Boston, Tuttle, Weeks & Dennett, printers, 1836.
Judd, Thomas.

LAC 12634
An essay on the law of patents for new inventions. With an appendix, containing the French patent law, forms, &c. Published by D. Mallory, & co. Boston; Lyman, Hall, & co. Portland; Swift & Chipman, Middlebury, Vt.; S. Gould, New York; D. W. Farrand & Green, Albany; Farrand & Nicholas, Philadelphia; P. H. Nicklin & co. Baltimore, S. T. Armstrong, printer, 1810.
Fessenden, Thomas Green, 1771–1837.

LAC 10023
An essay on the laws of trade, in reference to the works of internal improvement in the United States. Richmond, P.D. Bernard, 1839.
Ellet, Charles, 1810–1862.

LAC 40109
An essay on the liberty of the press, shewing, that the requisition of security for good behaviour from libellers is perfectly compatible with the constitution and laws of Virginia. Richmond: Printed by Samuel Pleasants, Junior, 1803.
Hay, George, 1765–1830.

LAC 10153
An essay on the life, character and writings of John B. Gibson, LL. D., lately chief justice of the Supreme court of Pennsylvania. Philadelphia, T. & J. W. Johnson, 1855.
Porter, William Augustus, 1821–1886.

LAC 14630
An essay on the life of the Honourable Major-General Israel Putnam. Addressed to the state Society of the Cincinnati in Connecticut, and first published by their order. By Col. David Humphreys. With notes and additions. With an appendix, containing an Historical and topographical sketch of Bunker Hill battle. By S. Swett. Boston, Published by Samuel Avery, No. 89 Court Street, 1818.
Humphreys, David, 1752–1818.

LAC 40111
An essay on the natural history of mankind, viewed in connection with Negro slavery, delivered before the Southern Rights association, 14th December, 1850. Mobile [Ala.] Dade, Thompson & co., 1851.
Nott, Josiah Clark, 1804–1873.

LAC 40034
An essay on the nature and foundation of moral virtue and obligation; being a short introduction to the study of ethics; for the use of the students of Yale-college. New-Haven: Printed by B. Mecom, 1765.
Clap, Thomas, 1703–1767.

LAC 14887
Essay on the necessity of improving our national forces. New York, Kirk and Mercein, 1819.
Tone, William Theobald Wolfe, 1791–1828.

LAC 16825
An essay on the philosophy of medical science... Philadelphia, Lea & Blanchard, 1844.
Bartlett, Elisha, 1804–1855.

LAC 40027
An essay on the practice of duelling, as it exists in modern society. Occasioned by the late lamentable occurrence near Philadelphia. By James Sega, LL. D. Tr. from the Italian, by the author. Philadelphia, 1830.
Sega, Giacomo.

LAC 10281
An essay on the present distribution of wealth in the United States. 2d ed. New York, Boston, T. Y. Crowell & company [c1896]
Spahr, Charles Barzillai, 1860–1904.

LAC 13733
Essay on the rate of wages: with an examination of the causes of the differences in the condition of the labouring population throughout the world... Philadelphia, Carey, Lea & Blanchard, 1835.
Carey, Henry Charles, 1793–1879.

LAC 40056
An essay on the rights and duties of nations, relative to fugitives from justice; considered with reference to the affair of the Chesapeake. By an American. Boston, Printed by D. Carlisle, 1807.
Everett, David, 1770–1813.

LAC 40106
An essay on the trade of the northern colonies of Great Britain in North America. Printed at Philadelphia. London, Reprinted for T. Becket & P. A. De Hondt, 1764.

LAC 15618
An essay on the trial by jury. Boston, J. P. Jewett and company; Cleveland, O., Jewett, Proctor & Worthington, 1852.
Spooner, Lysander, 1808–1887.

LAC 40061
An essay on the veterinary art; setting forth its great usefulness, giving an account of the veterinary colleges in France and England, and exhibiting the facility and utility of instituting similar schools in the United States. To which is added, a few hints upon the propriety of connecting therewith an insurance upon the lives of horses. Philadelphia, Printed by J. Thompson, 1837.
Browne, Peter Arrell, 1782–1860.

LAC 10398
An essay on trade and commerce: containing observations on taxes, as they are supposed to affect the price of labour in our manufactories: with some interesting reflections on the importance of our trade to America... By the author of Considerations on taxes, &c. London, S. Hooper, 1770.
Cunningham, J   *supposed author.*

LAC 14593
An essay on transcendentalism, 1842. With an introd. by Walter Harding. Gainesville, Fla., Scholars' Facsimiles & Reprints, 1954.
Ellis, Charles Mayo, 1818–1878, *supposed author.*

LAC 13866
An essay towards an Indian bibliography. Being a catalogue of books, relating to the history, antiquities, languages, customs, religion, wars, literature, and origin of the American Indians, in the library of Thomas W. Field. With bibliographical and historical notes, and synopses of the contents of some of the works least known. New York, Scribner, Armstrong, and co., 1873.
Field, Thomas Warren, 1820–1881.

LAC 40119
An essay towards the present and future peace of Europe, by the establishment of an European dyet, parliament or estates. [Boston, Directors of the Old South work, 1912]
Penn, William, 1644–1718.

LAC 40019
An essay upon the curing, management, and cultivation of tobacco. Washington, Printed by Gales & Seaton, 1832.
Tuck, David G.

LAC 13625
Essays and addresses, religious, literary and social, by Phillips Brooks. Ed. by the Rev. John Cotton Brooks. New York, E. P. Dutton and company, 1894.
Brooks, Phillips, *bp.*, 1835–1893.

LAC 10080
Essays and notes on husbandry and rural affairs. 2d ed. with additions. Philadelphia: Printed by Budd and Bartram, for Thomas Dobson, at the Stone house, no. 41, South second street, 1801. (Copy-right secured according to law.)
Bordley, John Beale, 1727–1804.

LAC 14588
Essays and poems. Boston, C. C. Little and J. Brown, 1839.
Very, Jones, 1813–1880.

LAC 22386
Essays and reviews... 7th ed. Boston, J. R. Osgood and Co., 1878.
Whipple, Edwin Percy, 1819–1886.

LAC 13952
Essays designed to elucidate the science of political economy, while serving to explain and defend the policy of protection to home industry, as a system of national cooperation for the elevation of labor. Philadelphia, Porter & Coates [c1869]
Greeley, Horace, 1811–1872.

LAC 12054
Essays in miniature. New York, C. L. Webster & co., 1892.
Repplier, Agnes, 1855–1950.

LAC 14148
Essays in radical empiricism. New York [etc.] Longmans, Green, and co., 1912.
James, William, 1842–1910.

LAC 13961
Essays in the constitutional history of the United States in the formative period, 1775–1789, by graduates and former members of the Johns Hopkins university; ed. by J. Franklin Jameson. Boston and New York, Houghton, Mifflin and company, 1889.
Jameson, John Franklin, 1859–   *ed.*

LAC 20011–12
Essays in the earlier history of American corporations... Cambridge, Harvard university press; [etc., etc.] 1917.
Davis, Joseph Stancliffe, 1885–

LAC 11119
Essays, lectures, etc. upon select topics in revealed theology. New York, Clark, Austin & Smith, 1859.
Taylor, Nathaniel William, 1786–1858.

LAC 15425
Essays on banking... Philadelphia; Published by The Author, June 1, 1816.
Carey, Mathew, 1760–1839.

LAC 11658
Essays on banking reform in the United States. New York, The Academy of political science, 1914.
Warburg, Paul Moritz, 1868–1932.

LAC 16357
Essays on domestic industry; an inquiry into the expediency of establishing cotton manufactures in South Carolina. Graniteville, S. C., Graniteville co., 1941.
Gregg, William, 1800–1867.

LAC 40034
Essays on liberty and necessity; in which the true nature of liberty is stated and defended; and the principal arguments used by Mr. Edwards and others, for necessity, are considered. Boston: Printed by Samuel Hall, in Cornhill, MDCCXCIII.
West, Samuel, 1731–1807.

LAC 10087
Essays on peat, muck, and commercial manures. Hartford, Brown & Gross, 1859.
Johnson, Samuel William, 1830–1909.

LAC 20936–37
Essays on physiognomy; for the promotion of the knowledge and the love of mankind. Written in the German language by J. C. Lavater, and translated into English by Thomas Holcroft. Illustrated by three hundred and sixty engravings. London, G. G. J. and J. Robinson, 1789.
Lavater, Johann Caspar, 1741–1801.

LAC 10074
Essays on practical agriculture; including his prize essays, carefully revised. Maysville, Ky., Collins & Brown, 1844.
Beatty, Adam, 1776?–1858.

LAC 10498
Essays on some of the first principles of metaphysyicks, ethicks, and theology. Portland [Me.] Printed by A. Shirley, 1824.
Burton, Asa, 1752–1836.

LAC 13823

Essays on the civil war and reconstruction and related topics. New York, The Macmillan company; London, Macmillan & co., ltd., 1898.
Dunning, William Archibald, 1857–1922.

LAC 10012

Essays on the monetary history of the United States. New York, The Macmillan company; London, Macmillan and co., ltd., 1900.
Bullock, Charles Jesse, 1869–1941.

LAC 15149

Essays on the present crisis in the condition of the American Indians; first published in the National intelligencer, under the signature of William Penn [*pseud.*] Boston, Perkins & Marvin, 1829.
Evarts, Jeremiah, 1781–1831.

LAC 11239

Essays on the punishment of death. 4th ed. Boston, The author; [etc., etc.] 1844.
Spear, Charles, 1801–1863.

LAC 16529

Essays upon field husbandry in New England, and other papers, 1748–1762, by Jared Eliot; edited by Harry J. Carman and Rexford G. Tugwell, with a biographical sketch by Rodney H. True. New York, Columbia university press, 1934.
Eliot, Jared, 1685–1763.

LAC 40029

Essays upon popular education, containing a particular examination of the schools of Massachusetts, and an outline of an institution for the education of teachers. Boston, Bowles & Dearborn, 1826.
Carter, James Gordon, 1795–1849.

LAC 40034

The essence of science; or, The catechism of positive sociology, and physical mentality. By a student of Auguste Comte. New-York, C. Blanchard, 1859.
Blanchard, Calvin.

LAC 13001

The essentials of method. A discussion of the essential form of right methods in teaching. Observation, generalization, application. Rev. ed. Boston, New York, etc., D. C. Heath & company [c1892]
De Garmo, Charles, 1849–1934.

LAC 11803

Esther, a novel, by Frances Snow Compton [*pseud.*] New York, H. Holt and company, 1884.
Adams, Henry, 1838–1918.

LAC 16694

Les Etats Confederes d'Amerique visites en 1863. Memoire adresse a S. M. Napoleon III. Paris, E. Dentu, 1864.
Girard, Charles Frederic, 1822–1895.

LAC 15354

Etching in America; with lists of American etchers and notable collections of prints, by J. R. W. Hitchcock. New York, White, Stokes, & Allen, 1886.
Hitchcock, Ripley, 1857–1918.

LAC 16593

Ethan Frome. New York, C. Scribner's sons, 1911.
Wharton, Edith Newbold, 1862–1937.

LAC 14267

The ethical import of Darwinism. New York, C. Scribner's sons, 1887.
Schurman, Jacob Gould, 1854–1942.

LAC 40123

Ethical principles underlying education. Chicago, The University of Chicago press, [1916]
Dewey, John, 1859–1952.

LAC 14775

Ethical religion. Boston, Little, Brown, and company, 1899, [c1889]
Salter, William Mackintire, 1853–1931.

LAC 40034

Ethices elementa. Or, The first principles of moral philosophy. And especially that part of it which is called Ethics. In a chain of necessary consequences from certain facts. [*Quotation: Isai. XLVI. 8. 1. line; Rom. XII. 1. 1 line; Cic. Tusc. Disp. 3 lines; Pers. Sat. 3. 5 lines*] By Aristocles [*pseud..* Boston: Printed and sold by Rogers and Fowle in Queen street, next to the prison, MDCCXLVI.
Johnson, Samuel, 1696–1772.

LAC 40034

Ethics. New York, The Columbia university press, 1908.
Dewey, John, 1859–1952.

LAC 16265

Ethics of democracy, a series of optimistic essays on the natural laws of human society. New York, Chicago, Moody publishing company [1903]
Post, Louis Freeland, 1849–1928.

LAC 16773

Ethics or science of duty. New York, G. P. Putnam's sons [c1879]
Bascom, John, 1827–1911.

LAC 15843

Ethiopia: her gloom and glory, as illustrated in the history of the slave trade and slavery, the rise of the Republic of Liberia, and the progress of African missions. With an introd. by W. P. Strickland. New York, Negro Universities Press [1969]
Christy, David, *b.* 1802.

LAC 15504

Ethnic factors in the population of Boston. New York, Pub. for the American economic association by the Macmillan company; London, S. Sonnenschein & co., 1903.
Bushee, Frederick Alexander, 1872–

LAC 14033

Ethnography and philology of the Hidatsa Indians. Washington, Govt. print. off., 1877.
Matthews, Washington, 1843–1905.

LAC 14425
Ethnology of the Gros Ventre. New York, The Trustees, 1908.
Kroeber, Alfred Louis, 1876–1960.

LAC 12682
An eulogium upon Benjamin Rush, M. D., professor of the institutes and practice of medicine and of clinical practice in the University of Pennsylvania. Who departed this life April 19, 1813, in the sixty-ninth year of his age. Written at the request of the Medical society of South Carolina, and delivered before them and others, in the Circular church of Charleston, on the 10th of June, 1813, and pub. at their request. Philadelphia, Bradford and Inskeep [etc.] 1813.
Ramsay, David, 1749–1815.

LAC 11457
Europe: or, A general survey of the present situation of the principal powers; with conjectures on their future prospects. By a citizen of the United States. Boston, O. Everett [etc.] 1822.
Everett, Alexander Hill, 1790–1847.

LAC 40141
European emigration to the United States. A paper read before the American social science association at New York, October 27, 1869. New York, Nation press, 1869.
Kapp, Friedrich, 1824–1884.

LAC 20431–32
European treaties bearing on the history of the United States and its dependencies... Washington, D. C., Carnegie institution of Washington, 1917–37.
Davenport, Frances Gardiner, 1870–1927, *ed.*

LAC 16962
Eutaw, a sequel to The forayers; or, The raid of the dog-days; a tale of the revolution. New York, W. J. Widdleton [1856]
Simms, William Gilmore, 1806–1870.

LAC 11065
The evangelization of the world in this generation. New York, Student volunteer movement for foreign missions, 1901, [c1900]
Mott, John Raleigh, 1865–1955.

LAC 13185
Evans's Pedestrious tour of four thousand miles–1818. Reprint of the original edition: Concord, New Hampshire, 1819. [Cleveland, Arthur H. Clark, 1904]
Evans, Estwick, 1787–1866.

LAC 15995
Every man a king; or, Might in mind-mastery, by Orison Swett Marden. With the assistance of Ernest Raymond Holmes. New York, T. Y. Crowell & co. [c1906]
Marden, Orison Swett, 1848–1924.

LAC 11584
Every-day topics; a book of briefs. New York, Scribner, Armstrong and company, 1876.
Holland, Josiah Gilbert, 1819–1881.

LAC 13778
Everything about our new possessions. Being a handy book on Cuba, Porto Rico, Hawaii, and the Philippines. By Thomas J. Vivian and Ruel P. Smith. New York, Fenno, 1899.
Vivian, Thomas Jondrie, 1855–1925.

LAC 11062
Evidence from Scripture and history of the second coming of Christ, about the year 1843; exhibited in a course of lectures. Troy, N. Y., E. Gates, 1838.
Miller, William, 1782–1849.

LAC 11136
Evidences of progress among colored people. 10th ed. Philadelphia, G. S. Ferguson co., 1903.
Richings, G   F.

LAC 10921
Evidences of the authenticity, inspiration, and canonical authority of the Holy Scriptures. By the Rev. Archibald Alexander. 6th ed. Philadelphia, Presbyterian board of publication [c1836]
Alexander, Archibald, 1772–1851.

LAC 22184–85
The evidences of the genuineness of the gospels... Boston, J. B. Russell [Cambridge, J. Owen] 1837–44.
Norton, Andrews, 1786–1853.

LAC 40095
The evils suffered by American women and American children: the causes and the remedy. Presented in an address prepared by Miss C. E. Beecher, and delivered by her brother to meetings of ladies in New York, and other cities. Also, An address to the Protestant clergy of the United States. New York, Harper & brothers, 1847.
Beecher, Catharine Esther, 1800–1878.

LAC 22115
Evolution and religion. New York, Fords, Howard & Hulbert, 1885.
Beecher, Henry Ward, 1813–1887.

LAC 10491
Evolution and religion; or, Faith as a part of a complete cosmic system. New York [etc.] G. P. Putnam's sons, 1897.
Bascom, John, 1827–1911.

LAC 14005
Evolution; its nature, its evidences, and its relation to religious thought. 2d ed., rev. New York, D. Appleton and company, 1891.
Le Conte, Joseph, 1823–1901.

LAC 14793
The evolution of modern capitalism; a study of machine production. New ed. London, The Walter Scott publishing co., ltd.; New York, C. Scribner's sons, 1917.
Hobson, John Atkinson, 1858–1940.

LAC 40128
The evolution of reaping machines. Washington, Govt. print. off., 1902.
Miller, Merritt Finley, 1875–

LAC 40033

The evolution of the American college, by John Bodine Thompson, D. D. An address before the alumni of Rutgers college, June 19, 1894. [Newark? N. J.] For the College, 1894.
Thompson, John Bodine, 1830–1907.

LAC 12744

The evolution of the Constitution of the United States, showing that it is a development of progressive history and not an isolated document struck off at a given time or an imitation of English or Dutch forms of government. Philadelphia, J. B. Lippincott company, 1897.
Fisher, Sydney George, 1856–1927.

LAC 12430

Evolution of the Ordinance of 1787; with an account of the earlier plans for the government of the Northwest territory. April, 1891. New York [etc.] G. P. Putnam's sons, 1891.
Barrett, Jay Amos, 1865–

LAC 14342

The evolution of the Sunday school. Boston, New York [etc.] The Pilgrim press [c1911]
Cope, Henry Frederick, 1870–1923.

LAC 12712

Evolution of the thermometer, 1592–1743. Easton, Pa., The Chemical publishing co., 1900.
Bolton, Henry Carrington, 1843–1903.

LAC 14006

Evolution social and organic. 4th ed. ... Chicago, C. H. Kerr & company, 1908.
Lewis, Arthur Morrow, 1873–

LAC 40038

The examination of Joseph Galloway, esq; late speaker of the House of assembly of Pennsylvania. Before the House of commons, in a committee on the American papers. With explanatory notes. London, Printed for J. Wilkie, 1779.
Gt. Brit. *Parliament, 1779. House of Commons.*

LAC 16673

An examination of President Edwards' inquiry into the freedom of the will. Philadelphia, H. Hooker, 1845.
Bledsoe, Albert Taylor, 1809–1877.

LAC 40026

An examination of the banking system of Massachusetts, in reference to the renewal of the bank charters. Boston, Stimpsen and Clapp, 1831.
Appleton, Nathan, 1779–1861.

LAC 14845

An examination of the Chilean incident, by a member of the bar. Boston, G. H. Ellis, 1896.
Gillis, James Andrew, 1829–1914.

LAC 40099

Examination of the decision of the Supreme court of the United States, in the case of Strader, Gorman and Armstrong *vs.* Christopher Graham, delivered at its December term, 1850: concluding with an address to the free colored people, advising them to remove to Liberia. Cincinnati, Truman & Spofford, 1852.
Birney, James Gillespie, 1792–1857.

LAC 10928

An examination of the doctrine of future retribution, on the principles of morals, analogy and the Scriptures. Boston, The Trumpet office, 1834.
Ballou, Hosea, 1771–1852.

LAC 11181

An examination of the new tariff proposed by the Hon. Henry Baldwin ...   By one of the people. New York, Gould & Banks, 1821.
Cambreleng, Churchill Caldom, 1786–1862.

LAC 14262

An examination of the principles contained in the Age of reason. In ten discourses. By James Muir, D. D., minister of the Presbyterian church, Alexandria. Baltimore: Printed by S. & J. Adams, for the Author; and sold by Clarke and Keddie, booksellers, in Market Street, 1795.
Muir, James, 1757–1820.

LAC 40056

An examination of the question, now in discussion, between the American and British governments, concerning the right of search. By an American. Baltimore, N. Hickman, 1842.
Cass, Lewis, 1782–1866.

LAC 40001

An examination of the theory and the effect of laws regulating the amount of specie in banks. Boston, Little, Brown and company, 1860.
Hooper, Samuel, 1808–1875.

LAC 14390

Examples of American domestic architecture, by John Calvin Stevens and Albert Winslow Cobb, architects, Portland, Maine... New York, W. T. Comstock, 1889.
Stevens, John Calvin.

LAC 13751

Examples of colonial architecture in South Carolina and Georgia, by Edward A. Crane and E. E. Soderholtz. New York, Bruno Hessling co. [1898?]
Crane, Edward Andrew, 1867–

LAC 14017

Examples of household taste. New York, R. Worthington [1880]
Smith, Walter.

LAC 40019

Exchange and cotton trade between England and the United States... New York, E. B. Clayton; Charleston, S. Babcock & co., 1840.
Entz, John F.

LAC 40030

"The ex-Confederate, and what he has done in peace." An address delivered before the Association of the Army of northern Virginia at the meeting held in Richmond, Va., October 26, 1892. Printed by order of the association. Richmond, J. L. Hill printing company, 1892.
Breckinridge, William Campbell Preston, 1837–1904.

LAC 16814

Excursion through the slave states, from Washington on the Potomac to the frontier of Mexico; with sketches of popular manners and geological notices. New York, Harper & brothers, 1844.
Featherstonhaugh, George William, 1780–1866.

LAC 16636

An excursion through the United States and Canada during the years 1822-23. By an English gentleman. London, Printed for Baldwin, Cradock, and Joy, 1824.
Blane, William Newnham, 1800-1825.

LAC 16846

Executive influence in determining military policy in the United States. Urbana, The University of Illinois [c1925]
White, Howard, 1893-

LAC 16102

Executive journal of Indiana Territory, 1800-1816, ed. and annotated by William Wesley Woollen, Daniel Wait Howe, and Jacob Piatt Dunn. Indianapolis [The Bowen-Merrill company] 1900.
Indiana *Ter.*

LAC 14154

Executive journals of Governor Winthrop Sargent and Governor William Charles Cole Claiborne, compiled and edited by Dunbar Rowland. Nashville, Tenn., Brandon Printing Co., 1905.
Mississippi. *Dept. of Archives and History.*

LAC 22381-82

Executive journals of the Council of colonial Virginia... Richmond, D. Bottom, superintendent of public printing, 1925-1928.
Virginia *(Colony) Council.*

LAC 12952

The executive proceedings of the Senate of the United States, on the subject of the mission to the Congress at Panama, together with the messages and documents relating thereto... Washington, Printed by Gales & Seaton, 1826.
U. S. *19th Cong., 1st Sess., 1825-1826. Senate.*

LAC 10576

Executive register of the United States, 1789-1902; a list of the presidents and their cabinets, to which have been added the laws governing their election, appointment, qualification, and term of office, the electoral and popular vote at each election, and, as an appendix, literal copies of the Declaration of independence, the Articles of confederation, and the Constitution. Baltimore, Md., The Friedenwald company [1903]
Mosher, Robert Brent, 1856-   *comp.*

LAC 12428

An exhibit of the losses sustained at the office of discount and deposit, Baltimore, under the administration of James A. Buchanan, president, and James W. McCulloh, cashier; comp. by the president and directors of the office at Baltimore, in pursuance of an order from the president and directors of the Bank of the United States: to which is appended a Report of the conspiracy cases tried at Harford County court in Maryland. Baltimore, Printed by T. Murphy, 1823.

LAC 23849-57

Exhibits presented by the Brotherhood of locomotive engineers and the Brotherhood of locomotive firemen and enginemen [in the Western railroads arbitration, 1914-1915] no. 1-5, 8-10, 15, 20-47, 50-89. [Chicago, 1915]
Brotherhood of Locomotive Engineers.

LAC 13084

Exiles in Virginia: with observations on the conduct of the Society of Friends during the revolutionary war, comprising the offical papers of the government relating to that period. 1777-1778. Philadelphia, Pub. for the subscribers [C. Sherman, printer] 1848.
Gilpin, Thomas, 1776-1853, *ed.*

LAC 13694

The existing conflict between republican government and southern oligarchy. Washington, D. C. [New York, Printed by The Charles M. Green printing company] 1884.
Raum, Green Berry, 1829-1909.

LAC 16277

Exotics and retrospectives. Boston, Little, Brown and company, 1898.
Hearn, Lafcadio, 1850-1904.

LAC 40031

Expansion. Reprinted from the American. Baltimore, New York, John Murphy company, 1900.
Marburg, Theodore, 1862-1946.

LAC 40137

Experience and personal narrative of Uncle Tom Jones: who was for forty years a slave. Also the surprising adventures of Wild Tom, of the island retreat, a fugitive negro from South Carolina. Boston, Sold at Skinner's rooms [185-?]
Jones, Thomas H.

LAC 10790

The experience of Thomas H. Jones, who was a slave for forty-three years, written by a friend as related to him by Brother Jones. New Bedford, E. Anthony, 1868.
Jones, Thomas H.

LAC 13188

The experiences of a Forty-niner during thirty-four years' residence in California and Australia, by Charles D. Ferguson, ed. by Frederick T. Wallace. Cleveland, O., The Williams publishing company, 1888.
Ferguson, Charles D   1832 *or* 3-

LAC 16345

Experiences of pioneer life in the early settlements and cities of the West. Chicago, Sumner & co., 1881.
Walker, James Barr, 1805-1887.

LAC 23070-71

Experimental psychology; a manual of laboratory practice. New York, The Macmillan company; London, Macmillan & co., ltd., 1901-05.
Titchener, Edward Bradford, 1867-1927.

LAC 11209

Experimental sociology. Descriptive and analytical. Delinquents. New York, The Macmillan company; London, Macmillan & co., ltd., 1901.
Kellor, Frances Alice, 1873-1952.

LAC 40129

Experiments and observations on American potashes. With an easy method of determining their respective qualities. Made at the request of the Society for the encouragement of arts, manufactures, and commerce, in consequence of an application from the House of representatives of Massachusets Bay. London, Printed by order of the Society, 1767.
Lewis, William, 1714-1781.

LAC 12638
Experiments and observations on electricity, made at Philadelphia in America. To which are added, letters and papers on philosophical subjects. The whole corrected, methodized, improved, and now first collected into one volume. London, Printed for David Henry, 1769.
Franklin, Benjamin, 1706-1790.

LAC 12601
Experiments and observations on the gastric juice, and the physiology of digestion. Plattsburgh, Printed by F. P. Allen, 1833.
Beaumont, William, 1785-1853.

LAC 12656
Experiments in aerodynamics. Washington, Smithsonian institution, 1891.
Langley, Samuel Pierpont, 1834-1906.

LAC 15758
Experiments in Colorado colonization, 1869-1872; selected contemporary records relating to the German colonization company and the Chicago-Colorado, St. Louis-western and Southwestern colonies, edited by James F. Willard and Colin B. Goodykoontz. Boulder, 1926.
Willard, James Field, 1876-1935, ed.

LAC 40017
Experiments in government and the essentials of the Constitution. Princeton, Princeton university press; [etc., etc.] 1913.
Root, Elihu, 1845-1937.

LAC 14010
Experiments to determine the comparative value of the principal varieties of fuel used in the United States, and also in Europe; and on the ordinary apparatus used for their combustion. Philadelphia, J. Dobson; New York, G. & C. Carvill; [etc., etc.] 1827.
Bull, Marcus.

LAC 20908-9
Explanations and sailing directions to accompany the Wind and current charts, approved by Captain D. N. Ingraham, chief of the Bureau of ordnance and hydrography, and pub. by authority of Hon. Isaac Toucey, secretary of the navy. 8th ed.-enl. and improved. Washington, W. A. Harris, printer, 1858-59.
Maury, Matthew Fontaine, 1806-1873.

LAC 13340
Exploration and survey of the valley of the Great salt lake of Utah, including a reconnoissance of a new route through the Rocky mountains. By Howard Stansbury, captain, Corps topographical engineers. Printed by order of the Senate of the United States. Philadelphia, Lippincott, Grambo & co., 1852.
U.S. *Army. Corps of Topographical Engineers.*

LAC 21254
Exploration of the valley of the Amazon, made under direction of the Navy department, by Wm. Lewis Herndon and Lardner Gibbon. Washington, R. Armstrong [etc.] public printer, 1853-54.
Herndon, William Lewis, 1813-1857.

LAC 40087
An exploration to Mount McKinley, America's highest mountain. Washington, Govt. print. off., 1904.
Brooks, Alfred Hulse, 1871-1924.

LAC 14190
Exploring expedition. Correspondence between J. N. Reynolds and the Hon. Mahlon Dickerson, under the respective signatures of "Citizen" and "Friend to the navy," touching the South Sea surveying and exploring expedition. [New York, 1838?]
Reynolds, Jeremiah N   1799-1858.

LAC 15887
Expose of the conditions and progress of the North American Phalanx; in reply to the inquiries of Horace Greeley ... intended to set forth the principles, aims, and character of the phalanx in its relations to ... social reform. New York, De Witt and Davenport, 1853.

LAC 16648
An expose of the Grangers. Containing the opening and closing ceremonies of a Grangers' lodge; the ceremonies of initiation, and the eight degrees of the order...
Dayton, O., Christian publishing association, 1875.
Gustin, M   E.

LAC 40053
An exposition of official tyranny in the United States navy. New-York, 1841.
Sanborn, Solomon Hewes, b. 1802.

LAC 40024
An exposition of the character and management of the New Jersey joint monopolies, the Camden and Amboy railroad and transportation company: the Delaware and Raritan canal company, and their appendages. Philadelphia, King & Baird, printers, 1852.
Tatham, George N.

LAC 40033
Exposition of the system of instruction and discipline pursued in the University of Vermont. By the faculty. Burlington, 1829.
Vermont. University.

LAC 14008
An exposition upon the thirteenth chapter of the Revelation. By that reverend and eminent servant of the Lord, Mr. John Cotton. Taken from his mouth in short-writing, and some part of it corrected by himselfe, and all of it since viewed over by a friend to him, and to the truth. London, Printed for Livewel Chapman, 1655.
Cotton, John, 1584-1652.

LAC 40075
An exposure of the malversations and corruptions of the executive government and of Congress. Washington, 1872.
National Democratic Executive Resident Committee, *Washington, D. C.*

LAC 13735
The extension of university teaching in England and America. A study in practical pedagogics... Leipzig, 1895.
Russell, James Earl, 1864-1945.

LAC 40055
Extracts from a supplementary letter from the Illinois; an address to British emigrants; and a reply to the remarks of William Cobbett, esq. London, Printed for J. Ridgway, 1819.
Birkbeck, Morris, 1764–1825.

LAC 40056
Extracts from official papers relating to the Bering Sea controversy, 1790–1892. New York, A. Lovell & co., 1892.
Hart, Albert Bushnell, 1854–1943, *ed.*

LAC 15151
Extracts from the diary of Christopher Marshall, kept in Philadelphia and Lancaster, during the American revolution, 1774–1781. Ed. by William Duane. Albany, J. Munsell, 1877.
Marshall, Christopher, 1709–1797.

LAC 10379
Extracts from the diary of Jacob Hiltzheimer, of Philadelphia. 1765–1798. Ed. by his great-grandson, Jacob Cox Parsons. Philadelphia, Press of W. F. Fell & co., 1893.
Hiltzheimer, Jacob, 1729?–1798.

LAC 10626
Extracts from the itineraries and other miscellanies of Ezra Stiles, D. D., LL. D., 1755–1794, with a selection from his correspondence; ed. under the authority of the corporation of Yale university, by Franklin Bowditch Dexter, LITT. D. New Haven, Conn., Yale university press, 1916.
Stiles, Ezra, 1727–1795.

LAC 40052
Extracts of letters from poor persons who emigrated last year to Canada and the United States. Printed for the information of the labouring poor, and their friends in this country. 2d ed., with additions. London, J. Ridgway, 1832.
Scrope, George Julius Duncombe Poulet, 1797–1876.

LAC 40053
Extracts relating to the origin of the American navy. Boston, The New England historic genealogical society, 1890.
Waite, Henry Edward, *comp.*

LAC 40015
Exultations. [Poems] London, E. Mathews, 1909.
Pound, Ezra Loomis, 1885–

LAC 10837
Ezekiel Cheever, schoolmaster; introduction by Edward Everett Hale. By Elizabeth Porter Gould. Boston, The Palmer company [1904]
Gould, Elizabeth Porter, 1848–1906.

LAC 15997
Ezra Stiles and the Jews; selected passages from his Literary diary concerning Jews and Judaism, with critical and explantory notes by George Alexander Kohut. New York, P. Cowen, 1902.
Stiles, Ezra, 1727–1795.

LAC 11008
Ezra Stiles Gannett. Unitarian minister in Boston, 1824–1871. A memoir. By his son, William C. Gannett. Boston, Roberts brothers, 1875.
Gannett, William Channing, 1840–1923.

LAC 11805
Fables in slang, by George Ade. Illustrated by Clyde J. Newman. Chicago & New York, H. S. Stone and company, 1900, [c1899]
Ade, George, 1866–

LAC 12975
Fables of Aesop and others. Translated into English with instructive applications, and one hundred and ninety-eight illustrations, by Samuel Croxall. Boston, Burnham, 1863.
Aesopus.

LAC 15696
Fabricius; or, Letters to the people of Great Britain; on the absurdity and mischiefs of defensive operations only in the American war; and on the causes of the failure in the southern operations. London, G. Wilkie, 1782.
Galloway, Joseph, 1731–1803.

LAC 14257
Facing the twentieth century; our country: its power and peril... New York, American union league society, 1899.
King, James Marcus, 1839–1907.

LAC 13802
Factory people and their employers, how their relations are made pleasant and profitable; a handbook of practical methods of improving factory conditions and the relations of employer and employe. New York, Lentilhon & company [c1900]
Shuey, Edwin Longstreet, 1857–1924.

LAC 13859
Facts about southern educational progress. Prepared under the direction of the Campaign committee of the Southern education board... [Durham, N. C., The Seeman printery, 1905]
Coon, Charles Lee, 1868–

LAC 40031
Facts about the Philippines. San Francisco, Cunningham, Curtiss & Welch, 1899.
Taylor, John W.

LAC 40030
Facts about the South... Baltimore [Manufacturers' record pub. co.] 1895.
Edmonds, Richard Hathaway, 1857–1930.

LAC 15507
Facts about Welsh factors... Welshmen as factors. The successful prize essay at the international Eisteddfod of the World's Columbia [!] exposition, Chicago, 1893. By "William Penn" [*pseud.*] [Utica, N. Y., Press of T. J. Griffiths, 1899]
Edwards, Ebenezer.

LAC 40023

Facts and arguments in favour of adopting railways in preference to canals, in the state of Pennsylvania. To which are added, a few remarks on the subject of internal improvements. 3d ed. Philadelphia, W. Fry, 1825.

LAC 10704

Facts and figures the basis of economic science... Boston and New York, Houghton, Mifflin and company, 1904.
Atkinson, Edward, 1827–1905.

LAC 40068

Facts and observations relative to the participation of American citizens in the African slave trade... Philadelphia, J. & W. Kite, 1841.
Friends, Society of. *Pennsylvania and New Jersey Yearly Meeting.*

LAC 16874

Facts and opinions; or, Dangers that beset us. Detroit, Mich., F. B. Dickerson Co., 1895.
Pingree, Hazen S., 1840–1901.

LAC 16494

Facts and opinions touching the real origin, character, and influence of the American Colonization Society; views of Wilberforce, Clarkson, and others, and opinions of the free people of color of the United States. Pref. by William Jay. New York, Negro Universities Press [1969]
Stebbins, Giles Badger, 1817–1900.

LAC 10278

Facts and suggestions, biographical, historical, financial and political, addressed to the people of the United States. New York, C. S. Westcott & co.'s Union Printing office, 1866.
Green, Duff, 1791–1875.

LAC 20598–99

Facts for farmers; also for the family circle. A compost of rich materials for all landowners, about domestic animals and domestic economy... New York, A. J. Johnson; Cleveland, F. G. and A. C. Rowe, 1866.
Robinson, Solon, 1803–1880, *ed.*

LAC 40112

Facts for the people of the South. Abolition intolerance and religious intolerance united. Know-nothingism exposed. Washington, Printed at the Union office, 1855.

LAC 12861

The facts of reconstruction. New York, The Neale publishing company, 1914, [c1913]
Lynch, John Roy, 1847–1939.

LAC 40057

Facts upon the other side of the Chinese question: with a memorial to the President of the U.S. from representative Chinamen in America. [San Francisco?] 1876.
Layres, Augustus.

LAC 11822

The fair Pilgrim.
Tales of the Puritans. The regicides.–The fair Pilgrim.–Castine. New-Haven, A. H. Maltby; New-York, G. and C. and H. Carvill, and J. Leavitt; [etc., etc.] 1831.
Bacon, Delia Salter, 1811–1859.

LAC 14964

Faith-healing, Christian science and kindred phenomena. New York, The Century co., 1900, [c1892]
Buckley, James Monroe, 1836–1920.

LAC 13517

The faith of our fathers: being a plain exposition and vindication of the church founded by our Lord Jesus Christ. By James, Cardinal Gibbons. 69th carefully rev. and enl. ed. 700th thousand. Baltimore, J. Murphy company; [etc., etc.] 1907.
Gibbons, James, *cardinal*, 1834–1921.

LAC 11833

Falconberg. New York, C. Scribner's sons, 1889, [c1879]
Boyesen, Hjalmar Hjorth, 1848–1895.

LAC 14384

The fall of bossism. A history of the Committee of one hundred and the reform movement in Philadelphia and Pennsylvania. Philadelphia, A. C. Bryson, printer, 1883.
Vickers, George Edward.

LAC 40140

The fall of British tyranny: or, American liberty triumphant. The first campaign. A tragi-comedy of five acts, as lately planned at the Royal theatrum pandemonium, at St. James's. The principal place of action in America. Pub. according to act of Parliament. Philadelphia: Printed by Styner and Cist, in Second-street, near Arch-street, 1776.
Leacock, John.

LAC 20604

The fall of Mexico.
The infidel; or, The fall of Mexico. A romance, by the author of "Calavar." Philadelphia, Carey, Lea & Blanchard, 1835.
Bird, Robert Montgomery, 1806–1854.

LAC 40035

The fallacy of neutrality. An address by the Hon. Joseph Holt, to the people of Kentucky, delivered at Louisville, July 13th, 1861; also his letter to J. F. Speed, esq. New York, J. G. Gregory, 1861.
Holt, Joseph, 1807–1894.

LAC 11369

Familiar letters of John Adams and his wife Abigail Adams, during the revolution. With a memoir of Mrs. Adams. By Charles Francis Adams. Boston, Houghton, Mifflin and company [c1875]
Adams, John, *pres. U.S.*, 1735–1826.

LAC 12540

Familiar letters on public characters, and public events; from the peace of 1783, to the peace of 1815... Boston, Russell, Odiorne, and Metcalf, 1834.
Sullivan, William, 1774–1839.

LAC 11340

Familiar letters to a gentleman, upon a variety of seasonable and important subjects in religion. By Jonathan Dickinson, A. M., minister of the gospel at Elizabethtown, New Jersey. Boston: Printed and sold by Rogers and Fowle in Queen-street, next to the prison: and by J. Blanchard at the Bible and Crown in Docksquare. 1745.
Dickinson, Jonathan, 1688–1747.

LAC 14951
The family and the state, select documents. Chicago, Ill., The University of Chicago press [c1934]
Breckinridge, Sophonisba Preston, 1866–1948.

LAC 15584
Family living on $500 a year; a daily reference-book for young and inexperienced housewives. New York, Harper & brothers, 1888.
Corson, Juliet, 1842–1897.

LAC 15602
The family monitor, or, A help to domestic happiness. 5th ed. London, F. Westley, and A. H. Davis. Birmingham, B. Hudson; [etc., etc.] 1833.
James, John Angell, 1785–1859.

LAC 10078
A family-text book for the country; or, The farmer at home: being a cyclopaedia of the more important topics in modern agriculture, and in natural history and domestic economy, adapted to rural life. New York, C.M. Saxton, 1856, [c1852]
Blake, John Lauris, 1788–1857.

LAC 15814
Family welfare work in a metropolitan community; selected case records. Chicago, Ill., The University of Chicago press [c1924]
Breckinridge, Sophonisba Preston, 1866–1948.

LAC 16803
Famous adventures and prison escapes of the civil war. New York, The Century co., 1893.

LAC 14686
Famous American fortunes and the men who have made them. A series of sketches of many of the notable merchants, manufacturers, capitalists, railroad presidents, bonanza and cattle kings of the country, by Laura C. Holloway. Philadelphia, Garretson, 1885.
Langford, Laura Holloway, 1848–

LAC 12221
Famous Americans of recent times. Boston, Ticknor and Fields, 1867.
Parton, James, 1822–1891.

LAC 15555
The 'fan kwae' at Canton before treaty days, 1825–1844. Taipei, Ch'eng-wen publishing co., 1965.
Hunter, William C.

LAC 21118
The far West: or, A tour beyond the mountains. Embracing outlines of western life and scenery; sketches of the prairies, rivers, ancient mounds, early settlements of the French, etc. ... New-York, Harper & brothers, 1838.
Flagg, Edmund, 1815–1890.

LAC 16124
Far-West sketches, by Jessie Benton Fremont. Boston, D. Lothrop [c1890]
Fremont, Jessie, 1824–1902.

LAC 10079
The farm and the fireside; or, The romance of agriculture. Being half hour sketches of life in the country. Detroit, Kerr, Doughty & Lapham, 1853.
Blake, John Lauris, 1788–1857.

LAC 11764
The farm and the fireside: sketches of domestic life in war and in peace... By Chas. H. Smith (Bill Arp) Atlanta, Ga., The Constitution publishing company, 1892.
Smith, Charles Henry, 1826–1903.

LAC 16008
Farm festivals. New York, Harper & brothers, 1881.
Carleton, Will, 1845–1912.

LAC 10694
Farm implements and farm machinery, and the principles of their construction and use: with simple and practical explanations of the laws of motion and force as applied on the farm. New York, O. Judd [c1869]
Thomas, John Jacob, 1810–1895.

LAC 10092
Farm machinery and farm motors, by J. Brownlee Davidson [and] Leon Wilson Chase. New York, Orange Judd company, 1908.
Davidson, Jay Brownlee, 1880–1957.

LAC 16007
The farmer and the new day. New York, The Macmillan company, 1920, [c1919]
Butterfield, Kenyon Leech, 1868–1935.

LAC 10078
The farmer at home.
A family-text book for the country; or, The farmer at home: being a cyclopaedia of the more important topics in modern agriculture, and in natural history and domestic economy, adapted to rural life. New York, C. M. Saxton, 1856, [c1852]
Blake, John Lauris, 1788–1857.

LAC 15954
The farmer of to-morrow. New York, The Macmillan company, 1913.
Anderson, Frederick Irving, 1877–

LAC 14731
The Farmers' alliance history and agricultural digest. Written by a board of editors. Editor-in-chief, N. A. Dunning. Washington, D. C., Alliance publishing company, 1891.
Dunning, Nelson A   ed.

LAC 11745
The farmers' alliance: its origin, progress and purposes. Fayetteville, Ark., 1891.
Bryan, J   E.

LAC 40120
The Farmers' alliance, what it aims to accomplish... New York, The Minerva publishing company, 1891.
Chamberlain, Henry Richardson, 1859–1911.

LAC 16788

The farmer's and emigrant's hand-book; being a full and complete guide for the farmer and the emigrant. Comprising the clearing of forest and prairie land–gardening–farming generally–farriery–cookery–and the prevention and cure of diseases. With copious hints, recipes, and tables. Hartford, O. D. Case & co., 1851.
Marshall, Josiah T.

LAC 10084

The farmer's companion; or, Essays on the principles and practice of American husbandry. With the address, prepared to be delivered before the agricultural and horticultural societies of New Haven County, Connecticut, and an appendix, containing tables and other matter useful to the farmer. Boston, Marsh, Capen, Lyon, and Webb, 1839.
Buel, Jesse, 1778–1839.

LAC 40117

The farmers' fight against the railroads. An impartial review of the merits of the quarrel. Facts and figures for the calm consideration of honest men. 1874. Indianapolis, J. Q. Thompson, c1874.
Thompson, J   Q.

LAC 11776

The farmer's library; or, Essays designed to encourage the pursuits, and promote the science of agriculture. 2d ed., cor. and enl. Windsor [Vt.] Printed by W. Spooner, 1826.
Lathrop, Leonard E.

LAC 11751

The farmer's mine, or source of wealth, being a compilation, with the addition of new and important information on the subject of manure, together with the most approved methods for the manufacture of vegetable manure, by which the farmer can obtain in the shortest possible time, as much manure of the richest quality as he pleases. To which is added, Productive farming, by Joseph A. Smith. By Henry Heermance. Rev. and cor. by A. B. Allen. New York, H. Heermance, 1843.
Heermance, Henry.

LAC 11781

The farmer's scientific manual. Prepared under the direction of Thomas P. Janes. Atlanta, Dept. of agriculture, 1878.
Georgia. *Dept. of Agriculture.*

LAC 15950

The farmer's side: his troubles and their remedy. New York, D. Appleton and company, 1891.
Peffer, William Alfred, 1831–1912.

LAC 10120

Farming, by Richard Kendall Munkittrick. Illustrated by Arthur Burdett Frost. New York, Harper & brothers, 1891.
Munkittrick, Richard Kendall, 1853–1911.

LAC 22266–68

Farrow's military encyclopedia; a dictionary of military knowledge, illustrated with maps and about three thousand wood engravings. New York, The author, 1885.
Farrow, Edward Samuel, 1855–1926.

LAC 12208

The fast and thanksgiving days of New England. Boston and New York, Houghton, Mifflin and company, 1895.
Love, William De Loss, 1851–1918.

LAC 16445

The fat knight. His complete career with conquests and collapse and final, marvelous triumph. Written in the light of current history and state papers on file in various castles in Columbia. His aids and his actions and the magic scup. In three cantos. [n.p.] 1896.

LAC 14741

The fat of the land: the story of an American farm. New York, The Macmillan company; London, Macmillan & co., ltd., 1904.
Streeter, John Williams, 1841–1905.

LAC 40040

The fate of blood-thirsty oppressors, and God's care of his distressed people. Tarrytown, N. Y., 1930.
Clark, Jonas, 1730–1805.

LAC 11010

Father Gavazzi's lectures in New York, reported in full by T. C. Leland, phonographer; also, the life of Father Gavazzi, corrected and authorized by himself. Together with reports of his addresses in Italian, to his countrymen in New York. Translated and revised by Madame Julie de Marguerittes. 3d ed. New York, De Witt and Davenport [c1853]
Gavazzi, Alessandro, 1809–1889.

LAC 15482

Father Marquette. New York, D. Appleton & company, 1902.
Thwaites, Reuben Gold, 1853–1913.

LAC 40054

The father; or, American Shandyism, a comedy, by William Dunlap. With an introduction by Thomas J. McKee. New-York, The Dunlap society, 1887.
Dunlap, William, 1766–1839.

LAC 11976

A fearful responsibility, and other stories. Boston and New York, Houghton, Mifflin company, 1895, [c1881]
Howells, William Dean, 1837–1920.

LAC 14002

Fears for democracy regarded from the American point of view. Philadelphia, J. B. Lippincott & co., 1875.
Ingersoll, Charles, 1805–1882.

LAC 13436

Federal aid in domestic disturbances. 1787–1903... Prepared under the direction of Major-General Henry O. Corbin, adjutant-general U. S. army, by Frederick T. Wilson, chief of division, Adjutant-general's office. March 2, 1903.–Ordered to be printed. Washington, Govt. print. off., 1903.
U. S. *Adjutant-General's Office.*

LAC 22756–62
The federal and state constitutions, colonial charters, and other organic laws of the state, territories, and colonies now or heretofore forming the United States of America. Comp. and ed. under the act of Congress of June 30, 1906. Washington, Govt. print. off., 1909.
Thorpe, Francis Newton, 1857–1926, *comp.*

LAC 20958–60
The federal and state constitutions, colonial charters, and other organic laws of the United States... Comp. under an order of the United States Senate by Ben: Perley Poore. Washington, Govt. print. off., 1877.
Poore, Benjamin Perley, 1820–1887, *comp.*

LAC 21187–88
Federal control of persons and property.
A treatise on state and federal control of persons and property in the United States, considered from both a civil and criminal standpoint. [2d ed.] St. Louis, The F. H. Thomas law book co., 1900.
Tiedeman, Christopher Gustavus, 1857–1903.

LAC 11476
The federal government; its officers and their duties. New-York and Chicago, Woolworth, Ainsworth & company, 1871.
Gillet, Ransom Hooker, 1800–1876.

LAC 12454
The federal income tax explained. With the regulations of the Treasury department. By John M. Gould and George F. Tucker. 2d ed. Boston, Little, Brown, and company, 1895.
Gould, John Melville, 1848–1909.

LAC 15440
The federal power over commerce and its effect on state action. Philadelphia, University of Pennsylvania press, 1892.
Lewis, William Draper, 1867–

LAC 16353
Federal regulation of railway rates. Boston and New York, Houghton, Mifflin and company, 1907.
Merritt, Albert Newton, 1878–

LAC 10035
The Federalist, on the new Constitution, written in 1788. By Mr. Hamilton, Mr. Madison, and Mr. Jay: with an appendix, containing the letters of Pacificus and Helvidius on the proclamation of neutrality of 1793; also, the original Articles of confederation, and the Constitution of the United States. New ed.: the numbers written by Mr. Madison corrected by himself. Hallowell [Me.] Masters, Smith & co., 1857.
The Federalist.

LAC 15269
The Federalist party in Massachusetts to the year 1800. Princeton, University library, 1909.
Morse, Anson Ely, 1879–

LAC 11388
The federalist system, 1789–1801. New York and London, Harper & brothers [c1906]
Bassett, John Spencer, 1867–1928.

LAC 13656
The federation of the world. Boston and New York, Houghton, Mifflin and company, 1899.
Trueblood, Benjamin Franklin, 1847–1916.

LAC 16200
Feeds and feeding, a hand-book for the student and stockman. 5th ed. Madison, Wis., The author, 1903, [c1898]
Henry, William Arnon, 1850–1932.

LAC 11087
Female convents. Secrets of nunneries disclosed. Compiled from the autograph manuscripts of Scipio de Ricci, by Mr. De Potter. Edited by Thomas Roscoe. With an introductory essay and appendix. New York, D. Appleton & co., 1834.
Ricci, Scipione de, *bp.*, 1741–1810.

LAC 11951
The female poets of America. Philadelphia, Carey and Hart, 1849.
Griswold, Rufus Wilmot, 1815–1857, *ed.*

LAC 21144
Female quixotism: exhibited in the romantic opinions and extravagant adventures of Dorcasina Sheldon. Boston, G. Clark, 1841.
Tenney, Tabitha, 1762–1837.

LAC 40150
The female warrior. An interesting narrative of the sufferings, and singular and surprising adventures of Miss Leonora Siddons... Written by herself. New York, E. E. Barclay, 1844, [c1843]
Siddons, Leonora, *b.* 1822.

LAC 13758
Females and their diseases; a series of letters to his class. Philadelphia, Lea and Blanchard, 1848.
Meigs, Charles Delucena, 1792–1869.

LAC 12045
Fern leaves from Fanny's port-folio. 2d series. With original designs by Fred M. Coffin. Auburn and Buffalo, Miller, Orton & Mulligan; London, S. Low, son & co., 1854.
Parton, Sara Payson, 1811–1872.

LAC 23213
Fernando Cortes: his five letters of relation to the Emperor Charles V, translated and edited, with a biographical introduction and notes compiled from original sources, by Francis Augustus MacNutt. Cleveland, Arthur H. Clark Co., 1908.
Cortes, Hernando, 1485–1547.

LAC 12057
The feud of Oakfield Creek; a novel of California life. Boston and New York, Houghton, Mifflin and company, 1887.
Royce, Josiah, 1855–1916.

LAC 40048
A few thoughts for a young man; a lecture, delivered before the Boston mercantile library association, on its 29th anniversary. Boston, Ticknor, Reed and Fields, 1850.
Mann, Horace, 1796–1859.

LAC 40124
A few thoughts on the foreign policy of the United States. Charleston [S. C.] J. Russell, 1849.
Trescot, William Henry, 1822-1898.

LAC 11599
The field and garden vegetables of America: containing full descriptions of nearly eleven hundred species and varieties; with directions for propagation, culture, and use. Boston, J. E. Tilton and company, 1865.
Burr, Fearing.

LAC 16529
Field husbandry in New England.
Essays upon field husbandry in New England, and other papers, 1748-1762, by Jared Eliot; edited by Harry J. Carman and Rexford G. Tugwell, with a biographical sketch by Rodney H. True. New York, Columbia university press, 1934.
Eliot, Jared, 1685-1763.

LAC 14688
Fifty years as a presiding elder. By Rev. Peter Cartwright. Ed. by Rev. W. S. Hooper. Cincinnati, Hitchcock and Walden; New York, Nelson and Phillips [c1871]
Cartwright, Peter, 1785-1872.

LAC 14404
Fifty years in camp and field, diary of Major-General Ethan Allen Hitchcock, U.S.A.; ed. by W. A. Croffut, PH. D. New York and London, G. P. Putnam's sons, 1909.
Hitchcock, Ethan Allen, 1798-1870.

LAC 10966
Fifty years in the Church of Rome. By Father Chiniquy. 3rd ed. Montreal, W. Drysdale co., 1886.
Chiniquy, Charles Paschal Telesphore, 1809-1899.

LAC 13195
Fifty years in the Northwest. With an introduction and appendix containing reminiscences, incidents and notes. By W. H. C. Folsom. Ed. by E. E. Edwards. [St. Paul] Pioneer press company, 1888.
Folsom, William Henry Carman, 1817-1900.

LAC 12170-71
Fifty years in Wall street. "Twenty-eight years in Wall street," revised and enlarged by a resume of the past twenty-two years, making a record of fifty years in Wall street. New York city, Irving publishing company [c1908]
Clews, Henry, 1836-1923.

LAC 11486
Fifty years' observations of men and events, civil and military. New York, C. Scribner's sons, 1884.
Keyes, Erasmus Darwin, 1810-1895.

LAC 22872-73
Fifty years of new Japan (Kaikoku gojunen shi) comp. by Count Shigenobu Okuma. English version ed. by Marcus B. Huish. London, Smith, Elder, & co., 1909.
Okuma, Shigenobu, 1838-1922, *comp.*

LAC 11671
Fifty years of public life. The life and times of Lewis Cass. New York, Derby & Jackson, 1856, [c1855]
Smith, William L   G   1814-1878.

LAC 11437
Fifty years of public service; personal recollections of Shelby M. Cullom, senior United States senator from Illinois. With portraits. 2d ed. Chicago, A. C. McClurg & co., 1911.
Cullom, Shelby Moore, 1829-1914.

LAC 16948
Fifty years of rapid transit, 1864-1917. New York city, The Law printing company, 1918.
Walker, James Blaine, 1864-

LAC 10341
Fifty years on the Mississippi; or, Gould's history of river navigation. Containing a history of the introduction of steam as a propelling power on ocean, lakes and rivers–the first steamboats on the Hudson, the Delaware, and the Ohio rivers–navigation of western rivers before the introduction of steam–character of the early navigators–description of first steamboats–steamboat New Orleans in 1811, and sixty consecutive boats, when and where built–their effect upon the settlement of the valley of the Mississippi–character and speed of boats at different periods–appropriations by Congress for the improvement of western water ways–floods in the Mississippi Valley for 150 years–Mississippi River commission and its work. Rapid increase and decline of river transportation. Causes of the decline–destruction of steamboats on western waters–biographies of prominent steamboatmen... Saint Louis, Nixon-Jones printing co., 1889.
Gould, Emerson W   1811-

LAC 13124
Fifty years on the road; the autobiography of a traveling salesman. Philadelphia, Printed by Lyon & Armor, 1911.
Briggs, Edward Page, 1839-

LAC 10950
Fifty years with the Sabbath schools. By Rev. Asa Bullard. Boston, Lockwood, Brooks and company, 1876.
Bullard, Asa, 1804-1888.

LAC 16286
The fight for Missouri, from the election of Lincoln to the death of Lyon. New York, C. Scribner's sons, 1886.
Snead, Thomas Lowndes, 1828-1890.

LAC 10881
A fight for the city. New York, The Macmillan company; London, Macmillan & co., ltd., 1903.
Hodder, Alfred, 1866-1907.

LAC 16848
"The fighting editor; or, Warren and the Appeal"; a word picture of the Appeal to reason office. Biography of Fred D. Warren. 2d ed.–rev. and enl. Girard, Kan., G. D. Brewer, 1910.
Brewer, George D.

LAC 16728
Fighting Phil; the life and military career of Philip Henry Sheridan, general of the army of the United States. New ed. Boston, Lee and Shepard; New York, C. T. Dillingham, 1889.
Headley, Phineas Camp, 1819-1903.

LAC 13114
Fighting the spoilsmen; reminiscences of the civil service reform movement. New York and London, G. P. Putnam's sons, 1919.
Foulke, William Dudley, 1848–1935.

LAC 11526
Figures of the past from the leaves of old journals. Boston, Roberts brothers, 1883.
Quincy, Josiah, 1802–1882.

LAC 21864
Final report of investigations among the Indians of the southwestern United States, carried on mainly in the years from 1880 to 1885... Cambridge [Mass.] Printed by J. Wilson and son, 1890–92.
Bandelier, Adolph Francis Alphonse, 1840–1914.

LAC 40088
Final report, of John A. Roebling, civil engineer, to the presidents and directors of the Niagara Falls suspension and Niagara Falls international bridge companies, May 1, 1855. Rochester, N. Y., Steam press of Lee, Mann & co., 1855.
Roebling, John Augustus, 1806–1869.

LAC 10370
The finances of New York city. New York, The Macmillan company; London, Macmillan & co., ltd., 1898.
Durand, Edward Dana, 1871–

LAC 10013
The finances of the United States from 1775 to 1789, with especial reference to the budget. Madison, Wis., The University, 1895.
Bullock, Charles Jesse, 1869–1941.

LAC 11450
The financial history of Massachusetts, from the organization of the Massachusetts Bay colony to the American revolution. New York, Columbia university, 1897.
Douglas, Charles Henry James, 1856–

LAC 10334
Financial history of the United States. New York [etc.] Longmans, Green, and co., 1903, [c1902]
Dewey, Davis Rich, 1858–1942.

LAC 10142
The financial history of the United States, from 1774 to 1789: embracing the period of the American revolution. 2d ed. New York, D. Appleton and company, 1884.
Bolles, Albert Sidney, 1846–1939.

LAC 10046
The financial history of the United States, from 1789 to 1860. 2d ed. New York, D. Appleton and company, 1885.
Bolles, Albert Sidney, 1846–1939.

LAC 10619
The financial status of the professor in America and in Germany... New York city [The Knickerbocker press (G. P. Putnam's sons) 1908]
Carnegie Foundation for the Advancement of Teaching.

LAC 20870
The financier and the finances of the American Revolution. New York, A. M. Kelley, 1968.
Sumner, William Graham, 1840–1910.

LAC 14112
Finding a way out; an autobiography. Garden City, New York, Doubleday, Page & company, 1921, [c1920]
Moton, Robert Russa, 1867–

LAC 15191
The finding of Wineland the good: the history of the Icelandic discovery of America; ed. and tr. from the earliest records by Arthur Middleton Reeves. London H. Frowde, 1890.
Reeves, Arthur Middleton, 1856–1891, *ed. and tr.*

LAC 40088
Fine arts. A reply to article X, no. LVIII, in the North American review, entitled "Academies of arts," &c. New York, G. & C. Carvill, 1828.
Morse, Samuel Finley Breese, 1791–1872.

LAC 15961
Fine wool, sheep husbandry. Read before the New York state agricultural society, February 12th, 1862. With an appendix, containing valuable statistics in reference to wool culture, imports, prices of fine wool from 1840 to August 1st, 1863, etc. New York, O. Judd company [c1863]
Randall, Henry Stephens, 1811–1876.

LAC 10381
The fireman: the fire departments of the United States, with a full account of all large fires, statistics of losses and expenses, theatres destroyed by fire... Boston, J. French and company, 1858.
Dana, David D.

LAC 13329
Fireside education. London, W. Smith, 1839.
Goodrich, Samuel Griswold, 1793–1860.

LAC 22391
The first American civil war; first period, 1775–1778, with chapters on the continental or revolutionary army and on the forces of the crown. London, Macmillan and co., limited, 1911.
Belcher, Henry, 1846–1916.

LAC 14217
The first and second banks of the United States, by John Thom Holdsworth and Davis R. Dewey. Washington, Govt. print. off., 1910.
Holdsworth, John Thom, 1873–

LAC 40030
First annual report of the Educational commission for freedmen. May, 1863. Boston, Prentiss & Deland, 1863.
New England Freedmen's Aid Society.

LAC 11403
The first battle. A story of the campaign of 1896, by William J. Bryan, together with a collection of his speeches and a biographical sketch by his wife... Chicago, W. B. Conkey company [c1896]
Bryan, William Jennings, 1860–1925.

LAC 14739
First book of forestry. Boston and London, Ginn & company, 1902.
Roth, Filibert, 1858–1925.

LAC 23893–94
The first century of the history of Springfield; the official records from 1636 to 1736, with an historical review and biographical mention of the founders, by Henry M. Burt. Springfield, Mass., H. M. Burt, 1898–99.
Springfield, *Mass.*

LAC 15488
The first chapter of Norwegian immigration, (1821–1840) its causes and results. With an introduction on the services rendered by the Scandinavians to the world and to America. 2d ed. Madison, Wis., The author, 1896, [c1895]
Anderson, Rasmus Bjorn, 1846–1936.

LAC 14597
The first colored Baptist church in North America. Constituted at Savannah, Georgia, January 20, A. D. 1788. With biographical sketches of the pastors. Written for the church by Rev. James M. Simms. Philadelphia, J. B. Lippincott company, 1888.
Simms, James Meriles.

LAC 12783
First days amongst the contrabands. Boston, Lee and Shepard, 1893.
Botume, Elizabeth Hyde.

LAC 13359
First explorations of Kentucky: Doctor Thomas Walker's journal of an exploration of Kentucky in 1750, being the first record of a white man's visit to the interior of that territory, now first published entire, with notes and biographical sketch; also Colonel Christopher Gist's journal of a tour through Ohio and Kentucky in 1751, with notes and sketch, by J. Stoddard Johnston. Louisville, Ky., J. P. Morton and company, 1898.
Johnston, Josiah Stoddard, 1833–1913.

LAC 11542
The first forty years of Washington society, portrayed by the family letters of Mrs. Samuel Harrison Smith (Margaret Bayard) from the collection of her grandson, J. Henley Smith; ed. by Gaillard Hunt. London, T. Fisher Unwin, 1906.
Smith, Margaret, 1778–1844.

LAC 13814
First impressions of the New world on two travellers from the Old, in the autumn of 1858. London, Longman, Brown, Green, Longmans, & Roberts, 1859.
Trotter, Isabella, 1816–1878.

LAC 10225
The first international railway and the colonization of New England. Life and writings of John Alfred Poor. Edited by Laura Elizabeth Poor. New York, London, G. P. Putnam's sons, 1892, [c1889]
Poor, John Alfred, 1808–1871.

LAC 40029
The first lines of English grammar, being a brief abstract of the author's larger work. Designed for young learners. New York, The author, 1823.
Brown, Goold, 1791–1857.

LAC 40055
The first map and description of Ohio, 1787, by Manasseh Cutler. A bibliographical account, with reprint of the "Explanation," by P. Lee Phillips. Washington, W. H. Lowdermilk & company, 1918.
Phillips, Philip Lee.

LAC 40052
The first Norwegian settlements in America, within the present century. Madison, State historical society of Wisconsin, 1899.
Anderson, Rasmus Bjorn, 1846–1936.

LAC 40147
The first presses of South Carolina. New York, Bibliographical society of America, 1908.
Salley, Alexander Samuel, 1871–

LAC 16799
First report to the Cotton planters' convention of Georgia, on the agricultural resources of Georgia. Augusta, Ga., Chronicle & sentinel, 1860.
Jones, Joseph, 1833–1896.

LAC 10238
The first republic in America; an account of the origin of this nation, written from the records then (1624) concealed by the Council, rather than from the histories then licensed by the Crown. Boston and New York, Houghton, Mifflin and company, 1898.
Brown, Alexander, 1843–1906.

LAC 40097
The first scientist of the Mississippi valley; a memoir of the life and work of Doctor Antoine Francois Saugrain. St. Louis, B. Von Phul [190–]
Byars, William Vincent, 1857–1938.

LAC 40149
The first state constitutions. Philadelphia, American academy of political and social science, 1893.
Morey, William Carey, 1843–1925.

LAC 12134
The first three English books on America. (?1511) –1555 A. D. Being chiefly translations, compilations, &c., by Richard Eden, from the writings, maps, &c., of Pietro Martire, of Anghiera (1455–1526) ... Sebastian Munster, the cosmographer (1489–1552) ... Sebastian Cabot, of Bristol (1474–1557) ... with extracts, &c., from the works of other Spanish, Italian, and German writers of the time. Ed. by Edward Arber. Birmingham [Printed by Turnbull & Spears, Edinburgh] 1885.
Arber, Edward, 1836–1912, *ed.*

LAC 16394
The first white man of the West; or, The life and exploits of Col. Dan'l Boone, the first settler of Kentucky, interspersed with incidents in the early annals of the country. Cincinnati, Applegate & company, 1856.
Flint, Timothy, 1780–1840.

LAC 12453
The fiscal history of Texas. Embracing an account of its revenues, debts, and currency, from the commencement of the revolution in 1834 to 1851–52. With remarks on American debts. Philadelphia, Lippincott, Grambo, and co., 1852.
Gouge, William M   1796–1863.

LAC 20013-19
The fisheries and fishery industries of the United States. Prepared through the co-operation of the commissioner of fisheries and the superintendent of the tenth census by George Brown Goode, and a staff of associates. Washington, Govt. print. off., 1884–87.
Goode, George Brown, 1851-1896.

LAC 12259
Fisher's river (North Carolina) scenes and characters, by "Skitt" [*pseud.*] "who was raised thar." Illustrated by John M'Lenan. New York, Harper & brothers, 1859.
Taliaferro, Harden E., 1818?-1875.

LAC 40037
The fishery question; or, American rights in Canadian waters. Montreal, Printed by D. Rose, 1868.
Kerr, William Warren Hastings, 1826-1888.

LAC 10130
Five acres too much. A truthful elucidation of the attractions of the country, and a careful consideration of the question of profit and loss as involved in amateur farming, with much valuable advice and instruction to those about purchasing large or small places in the rural districts. New York, Harper & brothers, 1869.
Roosevelt, Robert Barnwell, 1829-1906.

LAC 40051
The five civilized tribes in Indian territory: the Cherokee, Chickasaw, Choctaw, Creek, and Seminole nations. Washington, United States census printing office, 1894.
U.S. *Census Office. 11th Census,* 1890.

LAC 40059
The five cotton states and New York; or, Remarks upon the social and economical aspects of the southern political crisis. [Philadelphia?] 1861.
Colwell, Stephen, 1800-1871.

LAC 11778
Five hundred points of good husbandry, as well for the champion or open country, as for the woodland or several; together with A book of huswifery. Being a calendar of rural and domestic economy, for every month in the year; and exhibiting a picture of the agriculture, customs, and manners of England, in the sixteenth century. By Thomas Tusser. A new ed., with notes ... a glossary, and other improvements. By William Mavor. London, Lackington, Allen and co., 1812.
Tusser, Thomas, 1524?-1580.

LAC 14360
Five little Peppers and how they grew, by Margaret Sidney [*pseud.*] Boston, D. Lothrop and company [c1880]
Lothrop, Harriet Mulford, 1844-1924.

LAC 40035
Five months in rebeldom; or, Notes from the diary of a Bull Run prisoner, at Richmond. By Corporal W. H. Merrell. Rochester, N. Y., Adams and Dabney, 1862.
Merrell, William Howard, *d.* 1897.

LAC 14654
Five years of the War department following the war with Spain, 1899-1903, as shown in the Annual reports of the secretary of war. [Washington, Govt. print. off., 1904]
U.S. *War Dept.*

LAC 10701
Flax culture: an outline of the history and present condition of the flax industry in the United States, and a consideration of the influence exerted on it by legislation. By Edmund A. Whitman. With an introduction by J. R. Leeson. Boston, Rand Avery company, 1888.
Whitman, Edmund Allen, 1860–

LAC 12193
Flint's Letters from America, 1818-1820. Cleveland, O., The A. H. Clark company, 1904.
Flint, James (*Scotchman*)

LAC 12713
Flora virginica, exhibens plantas, quas ... d.d. Johannes Claytonus ... in Virginia crescentes observavit, collegit & obtulit d. Joh. Fred. Gronovio, cujus studio & opera descriptae & in ordinem sexualem systematicum redactae sistuntur. Lugduni Batavorum, 1762.
Gronovius, Joannes Fredericus, 1690–1760.

LAC 10235
The flush times of Alabama and Mississippi. A series of sketches. 9th thousand, New York [etc.] D. Appleton & co., 1854.
Baldwin, Joseph Glover, 1815-1864.

LAC 40123
A foe to American schools, a vacation study. Minneapolis, The Kingdom publishing company, 1897.
Gates, George Augustus, 1851-1912.

LAC 16876
Folkways; a study of the sociological importance of usages, manners, customs, mores and morals. Boston, New York [etc.] Ginn and company [1911?]
Sumner, William Graham, 1840–1910.

LAC 10049
Food from the far West; or, American agriculture, with special reference to beef production and importation of dead meat from America to Great Britain. London and Edinburgh, W. P. Nimmo, 1878.
Macdonald, James, 1852-1913.

LAC 40089
The food of certain American Indians and their methods of preparing it. Worcester, Mass., C. Hamilton, printer, 1895.
Carr, Lucien, 1829-1915.

LAC 12093
A fool's errand. By one of the fools. New York, Fords, Howard, & Hulbert, 1880, [c1879]
Tourgee, Albion Winegar, 1838-1905.

LAC 12177
Football, the American intercollegiate game. New York, C. Scribner's sons, 1911.
Davis, Parke Hill, 1871–

LAC 12950
A footnote to history; eight years of trouble in Samoa. London, Paris [etc.] Cassell & company, ltd., 1892.
Stevenson, Robert Louis, 1850-1894.

LAC 16955
The forayers; or, The raid of the dog-days. New and rev. ed. Chicago, Donohue, Henneberry, 1890.
Simms, William Gilmore, 1806–1870.

LAC 10161
Ford methods and the Ford shops, by Horace Lucien Arnold and Fay Leone Faurote. New York, The Engineering magazine company, 1915.
Arnold, Horace Lucian, *d,* 1915.

LAC 11977
A foregone conclusion. Boston and New York, Houghton, Mifflin and company, 1899, [c1874]
Howells, William Dean, 1837–1920.

LAC 14538
Foreign conspiracy against the liberties of the United States. The numbers of Brutus, originally published in the New-York observer, revised and corrected, with notes, by the author. New York, Leavitt, Lord, & co.; Boston, Crocker & Brewster, 1835.
Morse, Samuel Finley Breese, 1791–1872.

LAC 16541
Foreign parts. Authorized ed. Leipzig, B. Tauchnitz, 1883.
James, Henry, 1843–1916.

LAC 12914
The foreign policy of the United States, political and commercial. Addresses and discussion at the annual meeting of the American academy of political and social science, April 7–8, 1899. Philadelphia, American academy of political and social science, 1899.
American Academy of Political and Social Science, *Philadelphia.*

LAC 40090
Foreign settlements in Kansas. A contribution to dialect study in the state. [Lawrence, Kan., 1893]
Carruth, William Herbert, 1895–1924.

LAC 22578
Forerunners and competitors of the Pilgrims and Puritans; or, Narratives of voyages made by persons other than the Pilgrims and Puritans of the Bay colony to the shores of New England during the first quarter of the seventeenth century, 1601–1625, with especial reference to the labors of Captain John Smith in behalf of the settlement of New England. Ed. for the New England society of Brooklyn by Charles Herbert Levermore. Brooklyn, N. Y., Pub. for the Society, 1912.
Levermore, Charles Herbert, 1856–1927, *ed.*

LAC 20684
Forest life. By the author of "A new home." New York, C. S. Francis & co.; Boston, J. H. Francis, 1842.
Kirkland, Caroline Matilda, 1801–1864.

LAC 10418
Forest life and forest trees: comprising winter camplife among the loggers, and wild-wood adventure. With descriptions of lumbering operations on the various rivers of Maine and New Brunswick. New York, Harper & brothers, 1856, [c1851]
Springer, John S.

LAC 16766
Forest physiography; physiography of the United States and principles of soils in relation to forestry. 1st ed., 1st thousand. New York, J. Wiley & sons; [etc., etc.] 1911.
Bowman, Isaiah, 1878–1950.

LAC 11794
Forestry in Minnesota. [2d ed.] Published by the Geological and natural history survey of Minnesota. 1902. St. Paul, Minn., Pioneer press company, 1902.
Green, Samuel Bowdlear, 1859–1910.

LAC 40022
Forestry problems in the United States. Hendersonville, N. C., 1906.
Ivy, Thomas Parker, 1855–1926.

LAC 15913
The formation of the state of West Virginia, and other incidents of the late civil war; with remarks on subjects of public interest, arising since the war closed. Wellsburg, W. Va., Glass & son, 1875.
Parker, Granville.

LAC 15366
Formation of the Union, 1750–1829. With 5 maps. New York, Longmans, Green and co., 1902 [c1897]
Hart, Albert Bushnell, 1854–1943.

LAC 13492–93
Formation of the United States.
Documents illustrative of the formation of the union of the American states. Washington, Govt. print. off., 1927.
U.S. *Library of Congress. Legislative Reference Service.*

LAC 14126
The Fort Dearborn massacre, written in 1814 by Lieutenant Linai T. Helm, one of the survivors, with letters and narratives of contemporary interest, ed. by Nelly Kinzie Gordon. Chicago, New York, Rand, McNally & company [c1912]
Helm, Linai Taliaferro, *d.* 1838.

LAC 13875
"Fort Frick"; or, The siege of Homestead... A history of the famous struggle between the Amalgamated association of iron and steel workers and the Carnegie steel company (limited) of Pittsburg, Pa. Pittsburg, Pa., Pittsburg printing co., 1893.
Stowell, Myron R.

LAC 16414
The fortunes of Oliver Horn, by F. Hopkinson Smith; illustrated by Walter Appleton Clark. New York, C. Scribner's sons, 1902.
Smith, Francis Hopkinson, 1838–1915.

LAC 16282
Forty-five years under the flag. New York, D. Appleton and company, 1904.
Schley, Winfield Scott, 1839–1911.

LAC 14577
Forty modern fables. New York, R. H. Russell, 1901.
Ade, George, 1866–1944.

LAC 16283
Forty-six years in the army, by Lieutenant-General John M. Schofield. New York, The Century co., 1897.
Schofield, John McAllister, 1831–1906.

LAC 13178
Forty years a gambler on the Mississippi. 1st ed. Cincinnati, Devol & Haines, 1887.
Devol, George H., 1829–

LAC 15085
Forty years among the Indians. A true yet thrilling narrative of the author's experiences among the natives. Salt Lake City, Utah, Juvenile instructor office, 1890.
Jones, Daniel Webster.

LAC 15871
Forty years an advertising agent, 1865–1905. New York, Printers' ink publishing co., 1906.
Rowell, George Presbury, 1838–1908.

LAC 13935
A forty years' fight with the drink demon, or A history of the temperance reform as I have seen it, and of my labor in connection therewith. New York, National temperance society and publishing house, 1872.
Jewett, Charles, 1807–1879.

LAC 14173
Forty years in Washington. Boston, Little, Brown, and company, 1924.
Barry, David Sheldon, 1859–1936.

LAC 22889
Forty years of American life. New York, Negro Universities Press [1968]
Nichols, Thomas Low, 1815–1901.

LAC 21149
Forty years on the frontier as seen in the journals and reminiscences of Granville Stuart, gold-miner, trader, merchant, rancher and politician; edited by Paul C. Phillips. Cleveland, The Arthur H. Clark company, 1925.
Stuart, Granville, 1834–1918.

LAC 30606–25
Forum. v. 1–20, no. 1; Mar. 1886–Feb. 1896. New York.

LAC 10683
The foundations of American foreign policy, with a working bibliography. New York, The Macmillan company; London, Macmillan & co., ltd., 1901.
Hart, Albert Bushnell, 1854–1943.

LAC 11466
The Foundations of national prosperity; studies in the conservation of permanent national resources, by Richard T. Ely, Ralph H. Hess, Charles K. Leith [and] Thomas Nixon Carver. New York, The Macmillan company, 1917.

LAC 10352
Foundations of sociology. 5th ed. New York, The Macmillan company; London, Macmillan and co., 1919, [c1905]
Ross, Edward Alsworth, 1866–1951.

LAC 12613
The foundations of zoology. New York, The Macmillan company; London, Macmillan & co., ltd., 1899.
Brooks, William Keith, 1848–1908.

LAC 14567
The founders of Maryland as portrayed in manuscripts, provincial records and early documents. Albany, J. Munsell, 1876.
Neill, Edward Duffield, 1823–1893.

LAC 13668
Four days at the National Republican convention, St. Louis, June, 1896, and other political occasions. Speeches and addresses of Hon. Chauncey M. Depew, LL.D. [New York? 1898]
Depew, Chauncey Mitchell, 1834–1928.

LAC 14607–8
400 years of freethought. New York, The Truth seeker company, 1894.
Putnam, Samuel Porter, 1838–1896.

LAC 40086
Four letters respectfully dedicated to the workingmen of America. [n.p., 1840]
Democratic Party.

LAC 40070
The four principal battles of the late war, being a full detailed account of the battle of Chippeway, fall and destruction of the city of Washington, battles of Baltimore, and New-Orleans. By Adjutant P. M. Davis. Harrisburg, Printed by J. Baab, 1832. Tarrytown, N. Y., Reprinted, W. Abbatt, 1917.
Davis, Paris M.

LAC 14144
Four years in Rebel capitals: an inside view of life in the southern confederacy, from birth to death. From original notes, collated in the years 1861 to 1865, by T. C. De Leon. Mobile, Ala., The Gossip printing co., 1890.
De Leon, Thomas Cooper, 1839–1914.

LAC 14664
Four years in Secessia: adventures within and beyond the Union lines: embracing a great variety of facts, incidents, and romance of the war.... Hartford, O. D. Case and company; [etc., etc.] 1865.
Browne, Junius Henri, 1833–1902.

LAC 15004
Four years under Marse Robert. New York & Washington, The Neale publishing company, 1903.
Stiles, Robert, 1836–

LAC 14888
Four years with the Army of the Potomac. By Regis de Trobriand. Translated by George K. Dauchy. Boston, Ticknor and company, 1889.
Trobriand, Philippe Regis Denis de Keredern, *comte* de, 1816–1897.

LAC 40008
Fourteen agricultural experiments, to ascertain the best rotation of crops: addressed to the "Philadelphia agricultural society." By George Logan, M.D. Philadelphia, Printed by Francis and Robert Bailey, at Yorick's-head no. 116 High-street, 1797.
Logan, George, 1753–1821.

LAC 13821

The Fourteenth amendment and the states: a study of the operation of the restraint clauses of section one of the Fourteenth amendment to the Constitution of the United States. Boston, Little, Brown, and company, 1912.
Collins, Charles Wallace, 1879–

LAC 15429-30

Fowler's publicity. An encyclopedia of advertising and printing, and all that pertains to the public-seeing side of business. By Nath'l C. Fowler, jr. New York, Publicity publishing company, 1897.
Fowler, Nathaniel Clark, 1858–1918.

LAC 15086

Fox texts. Leyden, Late E. J. Brill, 1907.
Jones, William, 1871–1909.

LAC 10446

Fragments in philosophy and science; being collected essays and addresses. New York, C. Scribner's sons, 1902.
Baldwin, James Mark, 1861–1934.

LAC 15494

Les Francais en Amerique pendant la guerre de l'independance des Etats-Unis 1777–1783. Paris, A. Sauton; Philadelphia, J.-B. Lippincott; [etc., etc.] 1872.
Balch, Thomas, 1821–1877.

LAC 16929

Un Francais en Virginie; Voyages d'un Francois exile pour la religion, avec une description de la Virgine & Marilan dans l'Amerique, d'apres l'edition originale de 1687; avec une introduction et des notes par Gilbert Chinard. Paris, E. Droz; Baltimore, The Johns Hopkins press; [etc., etc.] 1932.
Durand,   of Dauphine, fl. 1685–1687.

LAC 11135

France and the Confederate navy, 1862–1868. An international episode. New York, Harper & brothers, 1888.
Bigelow, John, 1817–1911.

LAC 12312

France in America, 1497–1763. New York and London, Harper & brothers, 1905.
Thwaites, Reuben Gold, 1853–1913.

LAC 40056

France, Mexico, and the Confederate States. By M. M. Chevalier. Tr. by Wm. Henry Hurlbut [!] New York, C. B. Richardson, 1863.

LAC 13199

Franchere's narrative of a voyage to the northwest coast, 1811–1814; reprint of J. V. Huntington's English translation (New York, 1854) [Cleveland, Arthur H. Clark, 1904]
Franchere, Gabriel, 1786–1863.

LAC 15023

Francis Asbury: the prophet of the long road. New York, The Methodist book company [c1916]
Tipple, Ezra Squier, 1861–1936.

LAC 11103

Francis Hopkinson, the first American poet-composer (1737–1791) and James Lyon, patriot, preacher, psalmodist (1735–1794); two studies in early American music. Washington, D. C., Printed for the author by H. L. McQueen, 1905.
Sonneck, Oscar George Theodore, 1873–1928.

LAC 20680

Frank Forester's Field sports of the United States, and British provinces of North America. New York, Stringer & Townsend, 1849.
Herbert, Henry William, 1807–1858.

LAC 12198

Frank Forester's fish and fishing of the United States and British provinces of North America. Illustrated from nature by the author. New York, Stringer & Townsend, 1850.
Herbert, Henry William, 1807–1858.

LAC 23603

Franklin in France. From original documents, most of which are now published for the first time. By Edward E. Hale and Edward E. Hale, jr. Boston, Roberts brothers, 1887–1888.
Hale, Edward Everett, 1822–1909.

LAC 11407

Frauds and falsehoods of the Republican party...
Chicago and Philadelphia, H. J. Smith & co., 1892.
Buck, A.

LAC 13968

Frauds exposed; or, How the people are deceived and robbed, and youth corrupted. Being a full exposure of various schemes operated through the mails, and unearthed by the author in a seven years' service as a special agent of the Post office department and secretary and chief agent of the New York society for the suppression of vice. New York, J. H. Brown [c1880]
Comstock, Anthony, 1844–1915.

LAC 12897

Frederick Douglass. Philadelphia, G. W. Jacobs & company [1907]
Washington, Booker Taliaferro, 1859?–1915.

LAC 12853

Frederick Douglass: the colored orator. New York [etc.] Funk & Wagnalls, 1891.
Holland, Frederic May, 1836–1908.

LAC 14285

The free school system of the United States. London, Chapman and Hall, 1875.
Adams, Francis.

LAC 16518

Free schools; a documentary history of the free school movement in New York state. Albany, The University of the state of New York, 1921.
Finegan, Thomas Edward, 1866–

LAC 40152

Free thoughts, on the proceedings of the Continental Congress, held at Philadelphia Sept. 5, 1774, wherein their errors are exhibited, their reasonings confuted, and

the fatal tendency of their non-importation, non-exportation, and non-consumption measures, are laid open to the plainest understandings; and the only means pointed out for preserving and securing our present happy constitution: in a letter to the farmers, and other inhabitants of North America in general, and to those of the province of New-York in particular. By a farmer. [New York] Printed in the year M.DCC.LXXIV.
Seabury, Samuel, *bp.*, 1729–1796.

LAC 40002
Free trade vs. protection; or, A tariff for revenue only vs. a tariff for spoils only. A manual of facts and figures. Des Moines, State leader company, 1881.
Philpott, Henry J.

LAC 40096
The freedmen of South Carolina. An address delivered by J. Miller M'Kim, in Sansom hall, July 9th, 1862. Together with a letter from the same to Stephen Colwell, esq., chairman of the Port Royal relief committee. Philadelphia, W. P. Hazard, 1862.
McKim, James Miller, 1810–1874.

LAC 16770
The freedmen of the South. Cincinnati, Elm street printing company, 1869; New York, Kraus Reprint Co., 1969.
Slaughter, Linda Warfel, 1850–1920.

LAC 12809
The freedmen's book. Boston, Ticknor and Fields, 1865.
Child, Lydia Maria, 1802–1880.

LAC 12871
The freedmen's bureau; a chapter in the history of reconstruction. Iowa City, Ia., The University, 1904.
Pierce, Paul Skeels, 1874–

LAC 15934
Freedom and fellowship in religion. A collection of essays and addresses, edited by a committee of the Free religious association. Boston, Roberts brothers, 1875.
Free Religious Association, *Boston.*

LAC 11174
Freedom and war. Discourses on topics suggested by the times. Boston, Ticknor and Fields, 1863.
Beecher, Henry Ward, 1813–1887.

LAC 11067
The freedom of faith. Boston, New York, Houghton, Mifflin and company, 1883.
Munger, Theodore Thornton, 1830–1910.

LAC 13091
The freedom of the will, as a basis of human responsibility and a divine government elucidated and maintained in its issue with the necessitarian theories of Hobbes, Edwards, the Princeton essayists, and other leading advocates. New York, Carlton & Lanahan [c1864]
Whedon, Daniel Denison, 1808–1885.

LAC 15106
French art; classic and contemporary painting and sculpture. New and enl. ed. New York, C. Scribner's sons, 1905.
Brownell, William Crary, 1851–1928.

LAC 14830
The French in the Allegheny valley. Cleveland, O., W. W. Williams [c1887]
Chapman, Thomas Jefferson, 1836–1905.

LAC 16442
French poets and novelists. London, Macmillan, 1884.
James, Henry, 1843–1916.

LAC 40093
French Protestant refugee.
Report of a French Protestant refugee, in Boston, 1687: translated from the French by E. T. Fisher. Brooklyn, N. Y. [Albany, J. Munsell, printer] 1868.

LAC 12243
French traits; an essay in comparative criticism. New York, C. Scribner's sons, 1889.
Brownell, William Crary, 1851–1928.

LAC 14625
A French volunteer of the war of independence (the Chevalier de Pontgibaud) tr. and ed. by Robert B. Douglas. New York, D. Appleton, 1898.
More, Charles Albert, *chevalier de Pontgibaud [comte de]* 1758–1837.

LAC 12149
A Frenchman in America. Recollections of men and things. By Max O'Rell [*pseud.* With over one hundred and thirty illustrations by E. W. Kemble. New York, Cassell publishing company [c1891]
Blouet, Paul, 1848–1903.

LAC 10174
Frenzied finance. Volume I, The crime of Amalgamated. New York, The Ridgway-Thayer company, 1905.
Lawson, Thomas William, 1857–1925.

LAC 10911
Fresh air charity in the United States... New York, 1897.
Ufford, Walter Shepard, 1859–1940.

LAC 40040
A friendly address to all reasonable Americans, on the subject of our political confusions: in which the necessary consequences of violently opposing the king's troops, and of a general non-importation are fairly stated... New York, Printed [by James Rivington] 1774.
Chandler, Thomas Bradbury, 1726–1790.

LAC 14467
Friends and the Indians, 1655–1917. Philadelphia, The Associated executive committee of Friends on Indian affairs, 1917.
Kelsey, Rayner, Wickersham, 1879–1934.

LAC 23918–24
The Friends' Library: comprising journals, doctrinal treatises, and other writings of members of the religious society of friends. Ed. by William Evans and Thomas Evans. Philadelphia, J. Rakestraw, 1837–1850.
Philadelphia. Friends' Library.

LAC 12447
The Fries rebellion, 1798–99; an armed resistance to the House tax law, passed by Congress, July 9, 1798, in Bucks and Northampton counties, Pennsylvania. Doylestown, Pa. [Doylestown pub. co. printers] 1899.
Davis, William Watts Hart, 1820–1910.

LAC 16686
Froissart ballads, and other poems. Philadelphia, Carey and Hart, 1847.
Cooke, Philip Pendleton, 1816–1850.

LAC 10877
From a forest to a city. Personal reminiscences of Syracuse, N. Y. Syracuse, Masters & Stone, printers, 1889.
Hand, Marcus Christian.

LAC 16669
From a New England woman's diary in Dixie in 1865. Springfield [Mass., The Plimpton press, Norwood, Mass.] 1906.
Ames, Mary, 1831–

LAC 16285
From Chattanooga to Petersburg under Generals Grant and Butler; a contribution to the history of the war, and a personal vindication. Boston and New York, Houghton, Mifflin and co., 1893.
Smith, William Farrar, 1824–1903.

LAC 14485
From Gettysburg to the Rapidan. The Army of the Potomac, July, 1863, to April, 1864. New York, C. Scribner's sons, 1883.
Humphreys, Andrew Atkinson, 1810–1883.

LAC 16062
From Glasgow to Missouri and back. Glasgow, T. D. Morison [etc.] 1878.
Ferguson, Fergus, 1824–1897.

LAC 20213
From Harrison to Harding, a personal narrative, covering a third of a century, 1888–1921. New York and London, G. P. Putnam's sons, 1922.
Dunn, Arthur Wallace, 1859–1926.

LAC 16650
From immigrant to inventor. New York, London, C. Scribner's sons, 1926, [c1923]
Pupin, Michael Idvorsky, 1858–1935.

LAC 14642
From Manassas to Appomattox; memoirs of the civil war in America. Dallas, The Dallas publishing co., 1896.
Longstreet, James, 1821–1904.

LAC 14913
From sail to steam; recollections of naval life, by Capt. A. T. Mahan, U. S. N. (retired). New York and London, Harper & brothers, 1907.
Mahan, Alfred Thayer, 1840–1914.

LAC 16863
From servitude to service; being the Old South lectures on the history and work of southern institutions for the education of the negro. Boston, American Unitarian association, 1905.

LAC 13134
From the Atlantic to the Pacific, overland. A series of letters by Demas Barnes, describing a trip from New York ... to San Francisco, thence home, by Acapulco, and the isthmus of Panama. New York, D. Van Nostrand, 1866.
Barnes, Demas, 1827–1888.

LAC 11650
From the cotton field to the cotton mill; a study of the industrial transition in North Carolina. New York, The Macmillan company; London, Macmillan & co., ltd., 1906.
Thompson, Holland, 1873–1940.

LAC 16607
From the deep woods to civilization; chapters in the auto-biography of an Indian, by Charles A. Eastman (Ohiyesa) Boston, Little, Brown, and company, 1920.
Eastman, Charles Alexander, 1858–

LAC 40098
From the directors of the Standard oil company to its employees and stockholders, August, 1907. [New York, Wynkoop, Hallenbeck, Crawford, co.] 1907.
Standard Oil Company.

LAC 10479
From the forecastle to the cabin. New York [etc.] Harper & brothers, 1887.
Samuels, Samuel, 1823–1908.

LAC 40030
From the old South to the new... Harriman, Tenn., Progress printing co., 1895.
Droke, Jacobus D.

LAC 40041
From the stage coach to the railroad train and the street car. An outline review written with special reference to public conveyances in and around Boston in the nineteenth century. Boston, W. B. Clarke co., 1900.
Crocker, George Glover, 1843–1913.

LAC 16252
From the Virginia plantation to the national capitol; or, The first and only Negro representative in Congress from the Old Dominion. Hartford, Conn., American publishing company, 1894; New York, Johnson reprint corp. [1968]
Langston, John Mercer, 1829–1897.

LAC 15383

From Yorktown to Santiago with the sixth U.S. cavalry. Baltimore, The Friedenwald co., 1900.
Carter, William Giles Harding, 1851–1925.

LAC 13240

Frontier advance on the upper Ohio, 1778–1779, ed. with introduction and notes by Louise Phelps Kellogg. Madison, The Society, 1916.
Kellogg, Louise Phelps, *d.* 1942, *ed.*

LAC 12167

The frugal housewife.
The American frugal housewife, dedicated to those who are not ashamed of economy. 30th ed., enl. and cor. by the author. New-York, Samuel S. & William Wood, 1844, [c1835]
Child, Lydia Maria, 1802–1880.

LAC 10072

The fruit garden; a treatise intended to explain and illustrate the physiology of fruit trees, the theory and practice of all operations connected with the propagation, transplanting, pruning and training of orchard and garden trees ... the laying out and arranging different kinds of orchards and gardens... Illustrated with upwards of 150 figures... New York, C. Scribner, 1851.
Barry, Patrick, 1816–1890.

LAC 10096

The fruits and fruit trees of America; or, The culture, propagation, and management, in the garden and orchard, of fruit trees generally; with descriptions of all the finest varieties of fruit, native and foreign, cultivated in this country. New York & London, Wiley and Putnam, 1847, [c1845]
Downing, Andrew Jackson, 1815–1852.

LAC 14222

Fruits of philosophy, or the private companion of adult people. 4th ed., with additions. Philadelphia, F. P. Rogers, 1839.
Knowlton, Charles, 1800–1850.

LAC 40133

The Fugitive slave bill; or, God's laws paramount to the laws of men. A sermon, preached on Sunday, October 20, 1850, by Rev. Nathaniel Colver, pastor of the Tremont st. church. Pub. by request of the church. Boston, J. M. Hewes & co., 1850.
Colver, Nathaniel, 1794–1870.

LAC 12862

The fugitive slave law, and its victims. Rev. and enl. ed. ... New York, American anti-slavery society, 1861.
May, Samuel, 1810–1899.

LAC 40128

A full and clear reply to Doct. Thomas Dale. Wherein the real impropriety of blistering with cantharides in the first fever of the small-pox is plainly demonstrated. With some diverting remarks on the doctor's great consistence, and exquisite attainments in physick and philology... By Ja: Killpatrick. Charles-town, Printed by Peter Timothy, 1739. [Ann Arbor, Mich., Edwards brothers, 1938]
Kirkpatrick, James, 1696 (ca.)–1770.

LAC 14904

A full and correct account of the chief naval occurrences of the late war between Great Britain and the United States of America; preceded by a cursory examination of the American accounts of their naval actions fought previous to that period: to which is added an appendix; with plates. London, Printed for T. Egerton, 1817.
James, William, *d.* 1827.

LAC 40045

A full and impartial account of the Company of Mississipi [!] otherwise call'd the French East-India-company, projected and settled by Mr. Law. Wherein the nature of that establishment and the almost incredible advantages thereby accruing to the French king, and a great number of his subjects, are clearly explain'd and made out. With an account of the establishment of the Bank of Paris, by the said Mr. Law. To which are added, a description of the country of Mississippi, and a relation of the first discovery of it: in two letters from a gentleman to his friend. In French and English. London, R. Francklin, 1720.

LAC 13346

A full description of the soil, water, timber, and prairies of each lot, or quarter section of the military lands between the Mississippi and Illinois rivers. Washington city, Printed by P. Force, 1818.
Van Zandt, Nicholas Biddle.

LAC 40110

Fun on the "road."
Drummers' yarns; or, Fun on the "road"... New York, Excelsior publishing house, c1886.
Carey, Thomas Joseph, 1853–   *comp.*

LAC 12023

The function of the poet, and other essays, by James Russell Lowell; collected and ed. by Albert Mordell. Boston and New York, Houghton Mifflin company, 1920.
Lowell, James Russell, 1819–1891.

LAC 21457–62

Fund publication, no. 1–7; 7(supplement) 8–37. Baltimore [Printed by J. Murphy & co., 1867]–1901.
Maryland Historical Society.

LAC 10949

The fundamentals and their contrasts. Nashville, Tenn., Dallas, Tex., Publishing house of the Methodist Episcopal church, South, Smith & Lamar, agents, 1906.
Buckley, James Monroe, 1836–1920.

LAC 10459-60

The funding system of the United States and of Great Britain, with some tabular facts of other nations touching the same subject. Prepared under a resolution of the House of representatives of the United States, by Jonathan Elliot. Washington, Blair and Rives, printers, 1845.
Elliot, Jonathan, 1784–1846.

LAC 40088

A funeral oration, occasioned by the death of Thomas Cole, delivered before the National academy of design, New-York, May 4, 1848. Pub. by order of the Council of the academy. New York, D. Appleton & company; Philadelphia, G. S. Appleton, 1848.
Bryant, William Cullen, 1794–1878.

LAC 20702–03

The furniture of our forefathers, by Esther Singleton, with critical descriptions of plates by Russell Sturgis. New York, Doubleday, Page and company, 1901.
Singleton, Esther, d. 1930.

LAC 40044

Further notes on the history of witchcraft in Massachusetts, containing additional evidence of the passage of the Act of 1711, for reversing the attainders of the witches; also, affirming the legality of the Special court of oyer and terminer of 1692. With ... an appendix of documents, etc. Cambridge, J. Wilson and son, 1884.
Goodell, Abner Cheney, 1831–1914.

LAC 12332

Fusang; or, The discovery of America by Chinese Buddhist priests in the fifth century. London, Trubner, 1875.
Leland, Charles Godfrey, 1824–1903.

LAC 12898

The future of the American Negro. Boston, Small, Maynard & company, 1902, [c1899]
Washington, Booker Taliaferro, 1859?–1915.

LAC 40111

The future of the colored race in America: being an article in the Presbyterian quarterly review, of July, 1862. Philadelphia, W. S. Young, printer, 1862.
Aikman, William, 1824–1909.

LAC 40022

The future situs of the principal iron production of the world. Where is it? Baltimore, Manufacturers' record co., 1890.
Atkinson, Edward, 1827–1905.

LAC 13546

Gabriel Collins' Louisville and New Albany directory, and annual advertiser, for 1848... Louisville, Ky., G. H. Monsarrat [1848]
Collins, Gabriel.

LAC 30689–712

The Galaxy; a magazine of entertaining reading. v. 1–23; May 1866–June 1877. New York, Sheldon [etc.]

LAC 40055

Galland's Iowa emigrant: containing a map, and general descriptions of Iowa Territory. Chillicothe [O.] W. C. Jones, 1840.
Galland, Isaac, 1790–1858.

LAC 11849

Gallantry; dizain des fetes galantes. New York, R. M. McBride, 1928.
Cabell, James Branch, 1879–1958.

LAC 10875

Galveston: the horrors of a stricken city. Portraying by pen and picture the awful calamity that befell the Queen city on the Gulf and the terrible scenes that followed the disaster... [Chicago] American publishers' association [c1900]
Halstead, Murat, 1829–1908.

LAC 11351

Games and songs of American children. Collected and compared by William Wells Newell. New York, Harper & brothers, 1883.
Newell, William Wells, 1839–1907.

LAC 15036

Garden cities of to-morrow (being the second edition of "To-morrow: a peaceful path to real reform") London, S. Sonnenschein & co., ltd., 1902.
Howard, Sir Ebenezer, 1850–1928.

LAC 13177

The garden of the world, or, The great West; its history, its wealth, its natural advantages, and its future. Also comprising a complete guide to emigrants, with a full description of the different routes westward. By an old settler. With statistics and facts, from Hon. Thomas H. Benton, Hon. Sam Houston, Col. John C. Fremont, and other "old settlers." Boston, Wentworth, 1856.
Dana, C   W.

LAC 10700

Gardening for the South; or, How to grow vegetables and fruits. By the late William N. White with additions by Mr. J. Van Buren, and Dr. Jas. Camak. Rev. and newly stereotyped. New York, O. Judd and company [c1868]
White, William N   1819–1867.

LAC 16597

Garrulities of an octogenarian editor, with other essays somewhat biographical and autobiographical. Boston and New York, Houghton Mifflin company, 1923.
Holt, Henry, 1840–1926.

LAC 16525

Gass's journal of the Lewis and Clark expedition, by Sergeant Patrick Gass, one of the persons employed in the expedition. Reprinted from the edition of 1811, with facsimiles of the original title-page and the five original illustrations, a reproduction of a rare portrait of Gass, and a map of the Lewis and Clark route. With an analytical index, and an introduction by James Kendall Hosmer. Chicago, A. C. McClurg & co., 1904.
Gass, Patrick, 1771–1870.

LAC 12105

The gates ajar. By Elizabeth Stuart Phelps. Boston, Fields, Osgood, & co., 1869.
Ward, Elizabeth Stuart, 1844–1911.

LAC 11698

Gathered sketches from the early history of New Hampshire and Vermont; containing vivid and interesting account of a great variety of the adventures of our forefathers, and of other incidents of olden time. Original and selected. Ed. by Francis Chase, M. A. Claremont, N. H., Tracy, Kenney & co., 1856.
Chase, Francis.

LAC 20666

The gathering of the forces, by Walt Whitman; editorials, essays, literary and dramatic reviews and other material written by Walt Whitman as editor of the Brooklyn daily eagle in 1846 and 1847, ed. by Cleveland Rodgers and John Black; with a foreword and sketch of Whitman's life and work during two unknown years ... illustrations in photogravure. New York and London, G. P. Putnam's sons, 1920.
Whitman, Walt, 1819–1892.

LAC 16943

A gazetteer of Georgia; containing a particular description of the state; its resources, counties, towns, villages, and whatever is usual in statistical works. 4th ed. rev. and cor. Macon, Ga., S. Boykin; Atlanta, J. Richards; [etc., etc.] 1860.
Sherwood, Adiel, 1791–1879.

LAC 11694

Gazetteer of the state of Michigan, in three parts ... with a succinct history of the state, from the earliest period to the present time ... with an appendix, containing the usual statistical tables and a directory for emigrants, &c. Detroit, S. L. Rood & co.; New York, Robinson, Pratt & co., 1840, [c1838]
Blois, John T.

LAC 13350

Gazetteer of the state of Missouri. With a map of the state... To which is added an appendix, containing frontier sketches, and illustrations of Indian character. With a frontispiece, engraved on steel. St. Louis, C. Keemle, 1837.
Wetmore, Alphonso, comp.

LAC 13206

Geary and Kansas. Governor Geary's administration in Kansas: with a complete history of the territory until July 1857: embracing a full account of its discovery, geography, soil, rivers, climate, products; its organization as a territory. All fully authenticated. Philadelphia, J. H. C. Whiting, 1857.
Gihon, John H.

LAC 22478–79

Genealogical gleanings in England. Boston, New-England historic genealogical society, 1901.
Waters, Henry Fitz-Gilbert, 1833–1913.

LAC 20930–31

The genealogies and estates of Charlestown, in the county of Middlesex and commonwealth of Massachusetts, 1629–1818. Boston, D. Clapp and son, 1879.
Wyman, Thomas Bellows, 1817–1878.

LAC 14090

The genealogies of the families of Cohasset, Massachusetts, comp. under the direction of the Committee on town history, by George Lyman Davenport and Elizabeth Osgood Davenport, with chapters on town history written by members of the Committee and others, supplementary to the narrative history of Cohasset, by Rev. E. Victor Bigelow, published in 1898. [Cohasset, Mass.] Pub. under the auspices of the Committee on town history, 1909.
Davenport, George Lyman, 1852–   comp.

LAC 20912

The genera of North American plants, and a catalogue of the species, to the year 1817. Philadelphia, Printed for the author by D. Heartt, 1818.
Nuttall, Thomas, 1786–1859.

LAC 22348–56

A general abridgment and digest of American law, with occasional notes and comments. Boston, Cummings, Hilliard & co., 1823–29.
Dane, Nathan, 1752–1835.

LAC 40072

A general circular to all persons of good character, who wish to emigrate to the Oregon territory, embracing some account of the character and advantages of the country; the right and the means and operations by which it is to be settled;–and all necessary directions for becoming an emigrant. [By] Hall J. Kelley, general agent. By order of the American society for encouraging the settlement of the Oregon territory. Instituted in Boston, A.D. 1829. Charlestown, Printed by W. W. Wheildon; Boston, R. P. & C. Williams, 1831. Tarrytown, N. Y., Reprinted, W. Abbatt, 1918.
Kelley, Hall Jackson, 1790–1874.

LAC 21437–53

A general collection of the best and most interesting voyages and travels in all parts of the world; many of which are now first translated into English. Digested on a new plan. London, Longman, Hurst, Rees, and Orme [etc.] 1808–14.
Pinkerton, John, 1758–1826, ed.

LAC 15622

The General education board; an account of its activities, 1902–1914. With 32 full page illustrations and 31 maps. New York, General education board, 1915.
General Education Board.

LAC 15808

General evidences of catholicity: being the substance of a course of lectures, lately delivered in the cathedral of St. Louis, Louisville. Louisville [Ky.] B. J. Webb & brother, 1847.
Spalding, Martin John, abp., 1810–1872.

LAC 23903–14

A general history and collection of voyages and travels, arranged in systematic order: forming a complete history of the origin and progress of navigation, discovery, and commerce, by sea and land, from the earliest ages to the present time. Edinburgh, W. Blackwood; [etc., etc.] 1824.
Kerr, Robert, 1755–1813, ed.

LAC 13230

A general history of New England, from the discovery to MDCLXXX. By the Rev. William Hubbard. Second ed., collated with the original ms. ... Boston, Charles C. Little and James Brown, 1848.
Hubbard, William, 1621–1704.

LAC 13075

A general history of the Baptist denomination in America and other parts of the world. 3d thousand. New York, Lewis Colby and company, 1848.
Benedict, David, 1779–1874.

LAC 20841–42

A general history of the British empire in America: containing an historical political, and commercial view of the English settlements; including all the countries in North-America, and the West-Indies, ceded by the peace of Paris... London, W. Richardson and L. Urquhart, 1770.
Wynne, John Huddlestone, 1743–1788.

LAC 22271–74

The general history of the late war: containing it's rise, progress, and event, in Europe, Asia, Africa, and America... By the Rev. John Entick and other gentlemen. London, E. Dilly [etc.] 1763–64.
Entick, John, 1703?–1773.

LAC 14084
A general history of the pyrates, from their first rise and settlement in the island of providence, to the present time. With the remarkable actions and adventures of the two female pyrates Mary Read and Anne Bonny... To which is added a short abstract of the statute and civil law, in relation to pyracy. 2d ed., with considerable additions. By Captain Charles Johnson. London, T. Warner, 1724.
Defoe, Daniel, 1661?–1731, *supposed author.*

LAC 10514
A general history of the United States of America; from the discovery in 1492, to 1792: or, Sketches of the divine agency, in their settlement, growth, and protection; and especially in the late memorable revolution. In three volumes. Vol. I. Exhibiting a general view of the principal events, from the discovery of North America, to the year 1765. Boston, Farrand, Mallory, 1810.
Trumbull, Benjamin, 1735–1820.

LAC 14503
General Lee. By Fitzhugh Lee, his nephew. New York, D. Appleton and company, 1894.
Lee, Fitzhugh, 1835–1905.

LAC 15703
General McClellan, by General Peter S. Michie. New York, D. Appleton and company, 1901.
Michie, Peter Smith, 1839–1901.

LAC 10201
The general manager's story; old-time reminiscences of railroading in the United States. New York [etc.] Macmillan company, 1898.
Hamblen, Herbert Elliott, 1849–

LAC 13822
The general principles of constitutional law in the United States of America. By Thomas M. Cooley. 3d ed., by Andrew C. McLaughlin. Boston, Little, Brown and company, 1898.
Cooley, Thomas McIntyre, 1824–1898.

LAC 15056
General Scott. New York, D. Appleton and company, 1912, [c1893]
Wright, Marcus Joseph, 1831–1922.

LAC 10354
General sociology; an exposition of the main development in sociological theory from Spencer to Ratzenhofer. Chicago, The University of Chicago press; [etc., etc.] 1905.
Small, Albion Woodbury, 1854–1926.

LAC 12648
General theory of bridge construction: containing demonstrations of the principles of the art and their application to practice. New York, D. Appleton & company; 1853, [c1851]
Haupt, Herman, 1817–1905.

LAC 16213
A general view of the fine arts, critical and historical. With an introduction by D. Huntington. New York, G. P. Putnam, 1851.
Ludlow, *Miss*

LAC 40137
General Washington and General Jackson, on Negro soldiers... Philadelphia, H. C. Baird, 1863.
Baird, Henry Carey, 1825–1912.

LAC 12014
General William Booth enters into Heaven, and other poems. New York, Mitchell Kennerley, 1915, [c1913]
Lindsay, Nicholas Vachel, 1879–1931.

LAC 10922
The genesis of the New England churches. New York, Harper & brothers, 1874.
Bacon, Leonard, 1802–1881.

LAC 11003
A genetic history of the New England theology. Chicago, The University of Chicago press, 1907.
Foster, Frank Hugh, 1851–1935.

LAC 10447
Genetic theory of reality, being the outcome of genetic logic as issuing in the aesthetic theory of reality called pancalism, with an extended glossary of terms. New York and London, G. P. Putnam's sons, 1915.
Baldwin, James Mark, 1861–1934.

LAC 16510
The genius of Italy: being sketches of Italian life, literature, and religion. By Rev. Robert Turnbull. New-York, G. P. Putnam; [etc., etc.] 1849.
Turnbull, Robert, 1809–1877.

LAC 15337
The gentle art of making enemies, as pleasingly exemplified in many instances, wherein the serious ones of this earth, carefully exasperated, have been prettily spurred on to unseemliness and indiscretion, while overcome by an undue sense of right. New York, John W. Lovell co., 1890.
Whistler, James Abbott McNeill, 1834–1903.

LAC 12082
The gentleman from Indiana. New York, Doubleday & McClure co., 1900, [c1899]
Tarkington, Booth, 1869–1946.

LAC 13680
The gentlemen's book of etiquette, and manual of politeness; being a complete guide for a gentleman's conduct in all his relations towards society... From the best French, English, and American authorities. Boston, G. W. Cottrell [c1860]
Hartley, Cecil B.

LAC 40007
A geographical and statistical view of Massachusetts proper. Greenfield, Printed by Denio and Phelps, 1813.
Dickinson, Rodolphus, 1787–1863.

LAC 13307
The geographical catechism of Pennsylvania, and the western states; designed as a guide and pocket companion, for travellers and emigrants, to Pennsylvania, Ohio, Indiana, Illinois, Michigan and Missouri; containing a geographical and early historical account of these several states, from their first settlement up to the present time. Harrisburg, Pa., J. Winebrenner, 1836.
Rupp, Israel Daniel, 1803–1878.

LAC 12748
The geographical distribution of the vote of the thirteen states on the Federal constitution, 1787-8. Madison, Wis., The University, 1894.
Libby, Orin Grant, 1864–

LAC 15199
Geographical sketches on the western country: designed for emigrants and settlers: being the result of extensive researches and remarks. To which is added, A summary of all the most interesting matters on the subject, including a particular description of all the unsold public lands, collected from a variety of authentic sources. Also, a list of the principal roads. Cincinnati: Looker, Reynolds & co. printers, 1819.
Dana, Edmund.

LAC 12322
The geography of Hudson's bay: being the remarks of Captain W. Coats, in many voyages to that locality, between the years 1727 and 1751. With an appendix, containing extracts from the log of Capt. Middleton on his voyage for the discovery of the North-west passage, in H. M. S. "Furnace," in 1741-2. Ed. by John Barrow. London, Printed for the Hakluyt society, 1852.
Coats, William.

LAC 13757
Geology of North America; with two reports on the prairies of Arkansas and Texas, the Rocky mountains of New Mexico, and the Sierra Nevada of California, originally made for the United States government. Zurich, Zurcher and Furrer; New York, Wiley and Halsted; [etc., etc.] 1858.
Marcou, Jules, 1824–1898.

LAC 12603
Geology of the Comstock lode and the Washoe district, with atlas. Washington, Govt. print. off., 1882.
Becker, George Ferdinand, 1847–1919.

LAC 12587
George Bernard Shaw; his plays. Boston and London, J. W. Luce & co., 1905.
Mencken, Henry Louis, 1880–

LAC 11688
George Cleeve of Casco bay, 1630-1667, with collateral documents... Portland, Me., Printed for the Gorges society, 1885.
Baxter, James Phinney, 1831–1921.

LAC 16226
George Fuller, his life and works; with illustrations. Boston and New York, Houghton, Mifflin and company, 1886.
Millet, Josiah B   *ed.*

LAC 15692
George Hamilton Perkins, commodore, U.S.N.; his life and letters. With portraits and other illustrations. Boston and New York, Houghton Mifflin company, 1914.
Alden, Carroll Storrs, 1876–

LAC 13192
George Mason, the young backwoodsman; or, 'Don't give up the ship'. A story of the Mississippi. By the author of 'Francis Berrian.' Boston, Hilliard, Gray, Little and Wilkins, 1829.
Flint, Timothy, 1780–1840.

LAC 10741
George Ripley. 6th ed. Boston, New York, Houghton, Mifflin and company, 1888, [c1882]
Frothingham, Octavius Brooks, 1822–1895.

LAC 20220
George Washington. [Ed. de bibliophile] Paris, Goupil & co.; New York, Manzi, Joyant & co., succ. [etc.] 1900.
Ford, Worthington Chauncey, 1858–1941.

LAC 10941
George Whitefield: a biography, with special reference to his labors in America. New York, American tract society [pref. 1857]
Belcher, Joseph, 1794–1859, *comp.*

LAC 11182
George William Curtis. Boston and New York, Houghton, Mifflin and company, 1894.
Cary, Edward, 1840–1917.

LAC 15830
George's mother. London, New York, E. Arnold, 1896.
Crane, Stephen, 1871–1900.

LAC 12356
Georgia as a proprietary province; the execution of a trust. Boston, R. G. Badger; [etc., etc., c1917]
McCain, James Ross, 1881–

LAC 40055
Georgia: from the immigrant settler's stand-point. Giving the results of the experience of actual settlers from other states and countries, prefaced with an account of the natural resources of Georgia, and the inducements to immigrants and capitalists. Prepared under the direction of Thomas P. James, commissioner of agriculture of Georgia. Atlanta, Ga., 1879.
Georgia. *Dept. of Agriculture.*

LAC 10205
Georgia, historical and industrial. By the Department of agriculture. Illustrated. O. B. Stevens, commissioner, R. F. Wright, asst. commissioner. Atlanta, Ga., G. W. Harrison, state printer, 1901.
Georgia. *Dept. of Agriculture.*

LAC 12355
Georgia scenes, characters, incidents, &c., in the first half century of the republic. By a native Georgian. Augusta, Ga., Printed at the S. R. sentinel office, 1835.
Longstreet, Augustus Baldwin, 1790–1870.

LAC 14394
The Georgian period; a collection of carefully selected details illuminating "colonial" or XVIII-century architecture in the United States, illustrated with 100 full-page reproductions of measured drawings and photographic views, together with miscellaneous illustrations in the text; ed. by William Rotch Ware. [Students' ed.] Boston, American architect company, 1904.

LAC 15247
Georgical dictionary.
The New-England farmer: or, Georgical dictionary: containing a compendious account of the ways and meth-

ods in which the most important art of husbandry, in all its various branches, is, or may be, practised to the greatest advantage in this country. By Samuel Deane, A. M. Fellow of the American academy of arts and sciences. Printed at Worcester, Mass. By Isaiah Thomas...1790.
Deane, Samuel, 1733–1814.

LAC 14412
The German allied troops in the North American war of independence, 1776–1783. Translated and abridged from the German of Max von Eelking. By J. G. Rosengarten. Albany, J. Munsell's sons, 1893.
Eelking, Max von, 1813–1873.

LAC 15624
German-Americans and the world war (with special emphasis on Ohio's German-language press) Columbus, O., The Ohio state archaeological and historical society, 1936.
Wittke, Carl Frederick, 1892–

LAC 14832
The German-Americans in politics, 1914–1917. Madison, The University of Wisconsin press [c1939]
Child, Clifton James.

LAC 15738
The German and Swiss settlements of colonial Pennsylvania: a study of the so-called Pennsylvania Dutch. New York, H. Holt and company, 1901.
Kuhns, Levi Oscar, 1856–1929.

LAC 15540
German culture in America; philosophical and literary influences, 1600–1900 [by] Henry A. Pochmann. With the assistance of Arthur R. Schultz and others. Madison, University of Wisconsin Press, 1957.
Pochmann, Henry August, 1901–

LAC 22532–33
The German element in the United States with special reference to its political, moral, social, and educational influence. Boston and New York, Houghton Mifflin company, 1909.
Faust, Albert Bernhardt, 1870–1951.

LAC 16951
German ideals of to-day, and other essays on German culture. Boston and New York, Houghton, Mifflin and company, 1907.
Francke, Kuno, 1855–

LAC 15734
The German immigration into Pennsylvania through the port of Philadelphia from 1700 to 1775. Part II. The redemptioners... Prepared at the request of the Pennsylvania-German society. Lancaster, Pa. [The Society] 1900.
Diffenderffer, Frank Ried, 1833–1921.

LAC 14877
The German in America, or Advice and instruction for German emigrants in the United States of America. Also, a reader for beginners in the English and German languages. 3d ed. Boston, B. H. Greene, 1852.
Bogen, Frederick W.

LAC 15067
The German settlement society of Philadelphia and its colony, Hermann, Missouri. Philadelphia, Americana Germanica press, 1907.
Bek, William Godfrey, 1873–

LAC 15496
The German settlements in Texas.
The history of the German settlements in Texas, 1831–1861. Austin, Tex., Press of Von Boeckmann-Jones co. [c1930]
Biesele, Rudolph Leopold, 1886–1960.

LAC 14980
German socialism and Ferdinand Lassalle; a biographical history of German socialistic movements during this century. London, S. Sonnenschein & co., lim.; New York, C. Scribner's sons, 1899.
Dawson, William Harbutt, 1860–1948.

LAC 14702
The German soldier in the wars of the United States. 2d ed., rev. and enl. Philadelphia, J. B. Lippincott company, 1890.
Rosengarten, Joseph George, 1835–1921.

LAC 15588
The Germans in colonial times. New York, Russell & Russell [1968]
Bittinger, Lucy Forney, 1859–1907.

LAC 15552
The Germans in Texas; a study in immigration. Philadelphia [Publications of the University of Pennsylvania; New York, D. Appleton & company, publishing agents] 1909, [c1910]
Benjamin, Gilbert Giddings, 1874–1941.

LAC 16435
Germany seen without spectacles; or, Random sketches of various subjects, penned from different standpoints in the empire. Boston, Lee & Shepard; New York, C. T. Dillingham, 1883.
Ruggles, Henry.

LAC 10742
Gerrit Smith; a biography. New York, G. P. Putnam's sons, 1878.
Frothingham, Octavius Brooks, 1822–1895.

LAC 13078
Gesta Christi: or, A history of humane progress under Christianity. 4th ed., with new preface and supplementary chapter. New York, A. C. Armstrong & son, 1885.
Brace, Charles Loring, 1826–1890.

LAC 11261
Getting a living; the problem of wealth and poverty–of profits, wages and trade unionism. New York, The Macmillan company; London: Macmillan & co., ltd., 1903.
Bolen, George Lewis, 1861–

LAC 13572
Getting on in the world; or, Hints on success in life. Chicago, S. C. Griggs and company, 1873.
Mathews, William, 1818–1909.

LAC 12152

A girl's life eighty years ago; selections from the letters of Eliza Southgate Bowne; with an introduction by Clarence Cook; illustrated with portraits and views. New York, C. Scribner's sons, 1888, [c1887]
Bowne, Eliza, 1783–1809.

LAC 14142

A girl's life in Virginia before the war, by Letitia M. Burwell; with sixteen full-page illustrations by William A. McCullough and Jules Turcas. New York, F. A. Stokes company [c1895]
Burwell, Letitia M.

LAC 15537

Gleanings from a gathered harvest. New-York, C. Wells, 1845.
Noah, Mordecai Manuel, 1785–1851.

LAC 11772

Gleanings from the most celebrated books on husbandry, gardening, and rural affairs... From the London 2d ed. of 1803. Interspersed with remarks and observations by a gentleman of Philadelphia. Philadelphia: Printed and sold by James Humphreys, at the N. W. corner of Walnut and Dock-Streets, 1803.

LAC 16582

Gleanings in Buddha-fields. Studies of hand and soul in the Far East. Boston and New York, Houghton, Mifflin and company, 1897.
Hearn, Lafcadio, 1850–1904.

LAC 12222

Glimpses of colonial society and the life at Princeton college, 1766–1773, by one of the class of 1763; ed. by W. Jay Mills. Philadelphia & London, J. B. Lippincott company, 1903.
Paterson, William, 1745–1806.

LAC 10768

Glimpses of fifty years; the autobiography of an American woman, by Frances E. Willard. Written by order of the National woman's Christian temperance union. Introduction by Hannah Whitall Smith. Chicago, Woman's Temperance publication association [c1889]
Willard, Frances Elizabeth, 1839–1898.

LAC 13598

Glimpses of the Orient; or, The manners, customs, life, and history of the people of China, Japan, and Corea, the Philippine, Caroline, and Ladrone islands... With illustrations by Teitoku Morimoto, J. C. Fireman, and others. [Philadelphia, Franklin bk. co., 1898]
White, Trumbull, 1868–1941.

LAC 11997

Glimpses of three coasts. By Helen Jackson (H. H.) Boston, Roberts brothers, 1886.
Jackson, Helen Maria Hunt, 1831–1885.

LAC 11921

Gloria mundi. Chicago & New York, H. S. Stone & company, 1898.
Frederic, Harold, 1856–1898.

LAC 12807

God against slavery: and the freedom and duty of the pulpit to rebuke it, as a sin against God. Cincinnati, Am. Reform Tract and Book Society [n.d.]
Cheever, George Barrell, 1807–1890.

LAC 14196

God in Christ. Three discourses, delivered at New Haven, Cambridge, and Andover, with a preliminary dissertation on language. Hartford, Brown and Parsons, 1849.
Bushnell, Horace, 1802–1876.

LAC 16700

God's hand in America. By the Rev. George B. Cheever. With an essay, by the Rev. Dr. Skinner. New-York, M. W. Dodd; London, Wiley & Putnam, 1841.
Cheever, George Barrell, 1807–1890.

LAC 11879

God's mercie mixed with His justice; or, His peoples deliverance in times of danger (1641) By John Cotton. A facsimile reproduction with an introduction by Everett H. Emerson. Gainesville, Fla., Scholars' facsimiles & reprints, 1958.
Cotton, John, 1584–1652.

LAC 40012

Gods promise to His plantations: 2 Sam. 7.10. *Moreover I will appoint a place for my people Israell, and I will plant them, that they may dwell in a place of their owne, and move no more.* As it was delivered in a sermon. By John Cotton. London, Printed by William Jones for John Bellamy, and are to be sold at the three Golden lyons by the Royall exchange. 1630. [Boston, Directors of the Old South work, 1896]
Cotton, John, 1584–1652.

LAC 15232

Gods way and course.
The way of life; or, Gods way and course, in bringing the soule into, keeping it in, and carrying it on, in the wayes of life and peace. Laid downe in foure severall treatises on foure texts of Scripture... London, Printed by M. F. for L. Fawne and S. Gellibrand, 1641.
Cotton, John, 1584–1652.

LAC 12256

The goede vrouw of Mana-ha-ta at home and in society, 1609–1760, by Mrs. John King Van Rensselaer. New York, C. Scribner's sons, 1898.
Van Rensselaer, May, 1848–1925.

LAC 10393

Gold and silver; comprising an economic history of mining in the United States, the geographical and geological occurrence of the precious metals, with their mineralogical associations, history and description of methods of mining and extraction of values, and a detailed discussion of the production of gold and silver in the world and the United States. 1st ed. 1st thousand. New York, J. Wiley & sons; [etc., etc.] 1908.
Crane, Walter Richard, 1870–

LAC 10747

Gold bricks of speculation. A study of speculation and its counterfeits, and an expose of the methods of bucketshop and "get-rich-quick" swindles. Chicago, Lincoln book concern, 1904.
Hill, John, jr.

LAC 14899
The gold diggings of Cape Horn. A study of life in Tierra del Fuego and Patagonia. New York [etc.] G. P. Putnam's sons, 1895.
Spears, John Randolph, 1850–1936.

LAC 13234
Gold fields of the Klondike and the wonders of Alaska. A ... description of the newly-discovered gold mines. How they were found. How worked... Carefully prepared by Ernest Ingersoll. With an introduction by Hon. Henry W. Elliott. n.p. [c1897]
Ingersoll, Ernest, 1852–1946.

LAC 40022
Gold hunting in Alaska as told by Joseph Grinnell. Ed. by Elizabeth Grinnell. Elgin, Ill., Chicago, David C. Cook publishing company [c1901]
Grinnell, Joseph, 1877–1939.

LAC 10220
Gold, prices, and wages under the greenback standard. Berkeley, The University press, 1908.
Mitchell, Wesley Clair, 1874–1948.

LAC 12303
The golden age of Prince Henry the Navigator, by J. P. Oliveira Martins; tr., with additions and annotations, by Jas. Johnston Abraham and Wm. Edward Reynolds, with twelve illustrations. London, Chapman and Hall, ltd., 1914.
Oliveira Martins, Joaquim Pedro, 1845–1894.

LAC 20396
Golden book of the Wanamaker stores... Jubilee year, 1861–1911. Philadelphia [c1911–13]
Wanamaker, John, *firm, Philadelphia.*

LAC 12586
The golden fleece diuided into three parts, under which are discouered the errours of religion, the vices and decayes of the kingdome, and lastly the wayes to get wealth, and to restore trading so much complayned of. Transported from Cambrioll Colchos, out of the southermost part of the iland, commonly called the Newfovndland, By Orpheus, iunior, for the generall and perpeutall good of Great Britaine. London, Printed for F. Williams, 1626.
Vaughan, William, 1577–1641.

LAC 40043
Golden Rule Jones, mayor of Toledo. Chicago, The Public publishing company [c1906]
Crosby, Ernest Howard, 1856–

LAC 16912
Gondola days. With illustrations by the author. Boston and New York, Houghton, Mifflin and company, 1898, [c1897]
Smith, Francis Hopkinson, 1838–1915.

LAC 40012
Good newes from Virginia. 1613... [New York, 1936]
Whitaker, Alexander, 1585–1617?

LAC 15138
The Good news of Our Lord Jesus, the Anointed; from the critical Greek text of Tittmann... Boston, J. V. Himes, 1849.
Bible. *N.T. English. 1849. Whiting.*

LAC 15271
Good order established in Pennsylvania and New Jersey, in America, being a true account of the country; with its produce and commodities there made in the year 1685. By Thomas Budd. A new ed., with an introduction and notes. By Edward Armstrong. New York, W. Gowans, 1865.
Budd, Thomas, *d.* 1698.

LAC 40127
A good speed to Virginia (1609) [by] Robert Gray. Newes from Virginia (1610) [by] R. Rich. [New York, 1937]
Gray, Robert, *fl.* 1609.

LAC 14037
The gospel among the Dakotas.
Tah-koo wah-kan; or, The gospel among the Dakotas. By Stephen R. Riggs. With an introduction, by S. B. Treat. Boston, Congregational publishing society [c1869]
Riggs, Stephen Return, 1812–1883.

LAC 12336
The gospel among the slaves. A short account of missionary operations among the African slaves of the southern states. Compiled from original sources and edited by W. P. Harrison. Nashville, Tenn., Publishing house of the M. E. church, South, 1893.
Harrison, William Pope, 1830–1895.

LAC 14965
The gospel-covenant; or, The covenant of grace opened. Wherein are explained; 1. The difference betwixt the covenant of grace and covenant of workes. 2. The different administration of the covenant before and since Christ. 3. The benefits and blessings of it. 4. The condition. 5. The properties of it. Preached in Concord in New-England. The 2d ed., much enlarged, and corrected by the author... London, Printed by M. Simmons, 1651.
Bulkeley, Peter, 1583–1659.

LAC 16316
Gospel hymns and sacred songs. By P. P. Bliss and Ira D. Sankey, as used by them in gospel meetings... New York, Biglow & Main; Cincinnati, J. Church & co.; [etc., etc., c1875]
Bliss, Philip Paul, 1838–1876, *ed.*

LAC 10395
The gospel of wealth, and other timely essays. New York, The Century co., 1900.
Carnegie, Andrew, 1835–1919.

LAC 15621
The gossip's manual.
Lectures on female education, comprising the first and second series of a course delivered to Mrs. Garnett's pupils, at Elm-Wood, Essex county, Virginia. By James M. Garnett. To which is annexed, The gossip's manual. 3d ed., with corrections and additions by the author. Richmond, T. W. White, 1825.
Garnett, James Mercer, 1770–1843.

LAC 13880
The Gothic quest. New York, The Baker and Taylor company, 1907.
Cram, Ralph Adams, 1863–

LAC 12215
Gottlieb Mittelberger's journey to Pennsylvania in the year 1750 and return to Germany in the year 1754, containing not only a description of the country according to its present condition, but also a detailed account of the sad and unfortunate circumstances of most of the Germans that have emigrated, or are emigrating to that country. Tr. from the German by Carl Theo. Eben. Philadelphia, J. J. McVey, 1898.
Mittelberger, Gottlieb.

LAC 11376
Gouldtown, a very remarkable settlement of ancient date; studies of some sturdy examples of the simple life, together with sketches of early colonial history of Cumberland County and southern New Jersey and some early genealogical records, by William Steward and Rev. Theophilus G. Steward. Philadelphia, Press of J. B. Lippincott company, 1913.
Steward, William, 1840–

LAC 11619
The government and the currency. New ed., with alterations. New York, C. B. Norton, 1850.
Middleton, Henry, 1797–1876.

LAC 40084
Government assistance to export trade. Philadelphia, The American academy of political and social science [1909]
Donaldson, Charles S.

LAC 10767
Government by all the people; or, The initiative, the referendum and the recall as instruments of democracy. New York, The Macmillan company, 1912.
Wilcox, Delos Franklin, 1873–1928.

LAC 10876
Government by commission; or, The dethronement of the city boss; being a study of the commission plan as begun in Galveston, developed and extended in Des Moines, and already taken up by many other cities, east and west. 3d ed. New York and London, Funk & Wagnalls company, 1911, [c1910]
Hamilton, John Judson, 1854–

LAC 10385
The government of American cities; a program of democracy; a study of municipal organization and of the relation of the city to the state. Also a reprint of the municipal program of the National municipal league. New York and London, G. P. Putnam's sons, 1909.
Deming, Horace Edward, 1850–

LAC 10373
The government of municipalities. New York, Pub. for the Columbia university press by the Macmillan company; London, Macmillan & co., ltd., 1899.
Eaton, Dorman Bridgman, 1823–1899.

LAC 11499
Government of the colony of South Carolina. Baltimore, The Johns Hopkins press, 1895.
Whitney, Edson Leone, 1861–

LAC 10473
Government regulation of railway rates, a study of the experience of the United States, Germany, France, Austria-Hungary, Russia, and Australia. New York, The Macmillan company; London, Macmillan & co., ltd., 1905.
Meyer, Hugo Richard, 1866–1923.

LAC 10206
Government revenue, especially the American system. An argument for industrial freedom against the fallacies of free trade. Boston, New York, Houghton, Mifflin and company, 1884.
Roberts, Ellis Henry, 1827–1918.

LAC 10229
Governor Chamberlain's administration in South Carolina; a chapter of reconstruction in the southern states. New York and London, G. P. Putnam's sons, 1888.
Allen, Walter, 1840–1907.

LAC 15155
Grace Barclay's diary; or, Personal recollections of the American revolution. Ed. by Sidney Barclay [*pseud.*] 2d ed. New York, A. D. F. Randolph, 1866.
Post, Lydia.

LAC 10081
Grace defended, in a modest plea for an important truth; namely, that the offer of salvation made to sinners in the gospel, comprises in it an offer of the grace given in regeneration. And shewing the consistency of this truth with the free and sovereign grace of God, in the whole work of man's salvation. In which the doctrine of original sin and humane impotence, the object and extent of redemption, the nature of regeneration, the difference between common and special grace, the nature of justifying faith, and other important points, are considered and cleared. Boston: Printed by B. Green, and company, for D. Henchman, in Cornhil, 1744.
Mayhew, Experience, 1673–1758.

LAC 40003
Graduate courses. A handbook for graduate students. With a list of advanced courses announced by eleven universities of the United States for the year 1893–94. Compiled by a Committee of the Graduate club of Harvard in co-operation with committees of similar clubs at Cornell, John Hopkins, and Yale. Boston, Ginn & co., 1893.

LAC 31030–37
Graham's American monthly magazine of literature and art. v. 19–33; July 1841–Dec. 1948. Philadelphia, G. R. Graham [etc.]

LAC 31030–37
Graham's lady's and gentleman's magazine.
Graham's American monthly magazine of literature and art. v. 19–33; July 1841–Dec. 1948. Philadelphia, G. R. Graham [etc.]

LAC 10134

Grains for the grangers, discussing all points bearing upon the farmers' movement for the emancipation of white slaves from the slave-power of monopoly. New York, United States book company [c1873]
Smith, Stephe R.

LAC 10413-14

The grammar of English grammars, with an introduction, historical and critical; the whole methodically arranged and amply illustrated ... and a key to the oral exercises: to which are added four appendixes, pertaining separately to the four parts of grammar. 10th ed.–rev. and improved. Enl. by the addition of a copious index of matters. By Samuel U. Berrian, A.M. New York, W. Wood, 1878.
Brown, Goold, 1791-1857.

LAC 23574

A grammatical institute of the English language. Menston, (Yorks.) Scolar Press, 1968.
Webster, Noah, 1758-1843.

LAC 16502

Grand opera in America. Boston, L. C. Page & company [c1901]
Lahee, Henry Charles, 1856–

LAC 15593

Grand transformation scenes in the United States; or, Glimpses of home after thirteen years abroad. New York [etc.] G. W. Carleton & co., 1875.
Fuller, Hiram, 1814-1880.

LAC 11853

The Grandissimes, a story of Creole life. New York, C. Scribner's sons, 1880.
Cable, George Washington, 1844-1925.

LAC 15820

The Grange illustrated; or, Patron's hand-book, in the interests of the order of Patrons of husbandry. Embracing the origin and history of the order, constitutions, by-laws... Together with invaluable suggestions ... for farmers' everyday wants. By John G. Wells. Approved by William Saunders, T. A. Thompson. New York, Grange publishing co., 1874.
Wells, John G.

LAC 40004

The grange. Its advantages. What it has accomplished. What it hopes to accomplish. Organization of granges. Declaration of purposes. [Washington, D.C.? Nat. grange] executive committee [1895?]
Messer, Alpha.

LAC 11179

The Granger movement; a study of agricultural organization and its political, economic and social manifestations, 1870-1880. Cambridge, Harvard university press; [etc., etc.] 1933, [c1913]
Buck, Solon Justus, 1884-1962.

LAC 40004

The granger movement in Illinois. Urbana, University press, 1904.
Paine, Arthur Elijah, 1876–

LAC 14498

Grant and his campaigns: a military biography. New York, C. B. Richardson; Cincinnati, C. F. Vent & co.; [etc., etc.] 1866.
Coppee, Henry, 1821-1895.

LAC 14420

Grant as a soldier. St. Louis, The author, 1887.
Alexander, Augustus Washington, 1832–

LAC 11381

Grant in peace. From Appomattox to Mount McGregor. A personal memoir. Hartford, S. S. Scranton & co.; [etc., etc.] 1887.
Badeau, Adam, 1831-1895.

LAC 12821

Grant, Lincoln and the freedmen; reminiscences of the civil war with special reference to the work for the contrabands and freedmen of the Mississippi valley, by John Eaton in collaboration with Ethel Osgood Mason. New York [etc.] Longmans, Green, and co., 1907.
Eaton, John, 1829-1906.

LAC 15986

Grant's campaigns of 1864 and 1865. The Wilderness and Cold harbor (May 3–June 3, 1864) London, H. Rees, ltd., 1908.
Atkinson, Charles Francis, 1880–

LAC 12754

The grants, concessions, and original constitutions of the province of New Jersey. The acts passed during the proprietary governments, and other material transactions before the surrender thereof to Queen Anne. The instrument of surrender, and her formal acceptance thereof. Lord Cornbury's commission and instructions consequent thereon. Collected by some gentlemen employed by the General assembly. And afterwards published by virtue of an act of the Legislature of the said province, with proper tables alphabetically digested, containing the principal matters in the book. By Aaron Leaming and Jacob Spicer. Philadelphia, Printed by W. Bradford, printer to the king's most excellent majesty for the province of New Jersey [ca. 1752] [Somerville, N. J., Honeyman & company, 1881]
New Jersey *(Colony)*

LAC 12902

A graphic analysis of the census of manufactures of the United States, 1849 to 1919. New York, National industrial conference board [c1923]
National Industrial Conference Board.

LAC 15325

Graphics; a manual of drawing and writing, for the use of schools and families. 2d ed. improved. New York, B. & S. Collins, 1835.
Peale, Rembrandt, 1778-1860.

LAC 10089

Graphics, the art of accurate delineation; a system of school exercise, for the education of the eye and the training of the hand, as auxiliary to writing, geography, and drawing. Philadelphia, E. C. & J. Biddle, 1854, [c1845]
Peale, Rembrandt, 1778-1860.

LAC 16515
Gray days and gold. New York, Macmillan & co., 1892, [c1890]
Winter, William, 1836–1917.

LAC 10957
The great American battle; or, The contest between Christianity and political Romanism. New York, Miller, Orton & Mulligan, 1856.
Carroll, Anna Ella, 1815–1894.

LAC 12459
Great American sculptures, by William J. Clark, jr.; with twelve superb steel engravings, India proofs. New York, R. Worthington, 1878.
Clark, William J   1840–1889.

LAC 11126
The great awakening. A history of the revival of religion in the time of Edwards and Whitefield. Boston, Tappan and Dennet; New York, J. Adams, 1842.
Tracy, Joseph, 1793?–1874.

LAC 16275
Great battles of the world. London, New York [etc.] Hodder and Stoughton, 1914.
Crane, Stephen, 1871–1900.

LAC 20182
Great Britain and the American Civil War. New York, Russell & Russell [1958?]
Adams, Ephraim Douglass, 1865–1930.

LAC 11321
The great Centennial exhibition, critically described and illustrated by Phillip T. Sandhurst and others. Philadelphia and Chicago, P. W. Ziegler & co. [c1876]
Sandhurst, Phillip T.

LAC 40023
The great central railroad from Philadelphia to St. Louis. Read before the Pittsburgh "Board of trade." [Philadelphia, 1847]
Roebling, John Augustus, 1806–1869.

LAC 13539
Great cities in America, their problems and their government. New York, The Macmillan company, 1910.
Wilcox, Delos Franklin, 1873–1928.

LAC 40064
The great civil war in America. Speech of Hon. Clement Laird Vallandigham, of Ohio. New York, J. Walter, 1864.
Vallandigham, Clement Laird, 1820–1871.

LAC 40008
The great error of American agriculture exposed: and hints for improvement suggested. Baltimore, The author, 1801.
Moore, Thomas, 1760–1822.

LAC 16575
The great flood of 1884 in the Ohio valley. The rise and fall of the waters from Pittsburgh to Cairo ... together with useful and important information and statistics. Also, the work of the Gallipolis relief committee. Gallipolis, O., The Bulletin office, 1884.
Vance, John L   1839–   ed.

LAC 21873
Great Georgian houses of America, published for the benefit of the Architects emergency committee by the Editorial committee, Dwight James Baum, Richard H. Dana, William Emerson [and others]... William Lawrence Bottomley, chairman. New York, Printed by the Kalkhoff press, inc., 1933–37.
Architects' Emergency Committee.

LAC 23396–97
The great harmonia; being a philosophical revelation of the natural, spiritual, and celestial universe. Boston, B. Marsh, 1852–66.
Davis, Andrew Jackson, 1826–1910.

LAC 15432–33
The Great industries of the United States: being an historical summary of the origin, growth, and perfection of the chief industrial arts of this country: by Horace Greeley, Leon Case [and others] Hartford, J. B. Burr & Hyde; Chicago [etc.] J. B. Burr, Hyde & co., 1872, [c1871]

LAC 12270
The great iron wheel; or, Republicanism backwards and Christianity reversed. In a series of letters addressed to J. Soule... 30th ed. Nashville, South western publishing house; New York, Sheldon and company, 1860.
Graves, James Robinson, 1820–1896.

LAC 16171
The great issue: or, The three presidential candidates; being a brief historical sketch of the free soil question in the United States from the Congresses of 1774 and '87 to the present time. New-York, W. C. Bryant & co.; Boston, B. B. Mussey & co., 1848.
Gardiner, Oliver Cromwell.

LAC 10851
The great metropolis; a mirror of New York. A complete history of metropolitan life and society, with sketches of prominent places, persons, and things in the city, as they actually exist. Hartford, American publishing company; San Francisco, Cal., H. H. Bancroft & co.; [etc., etc.] 1869.
Browne, Junius Henri, 1833–1902.

LAC 15553
The great migration; the Atlantic crossing by sailing-ship since 1770. Toronto, New York [etc.] T. Nelson and sons, 1937.
Guillet, Edwin Clarence, 1898–

LAC 11469
A great peace maker; the diary of James Gallatin, secretary to Albert Gallatin, 1813–1827. With an introduction by Viscount Bryce. New York, C. Scribner's sons, 1914.
Gallatin, James, 1796–1876.

LAC 13286
The great plains; the romance of western American exploration, warfare, and settlement, 1527–1870. Chicago, A. C. McClurg & co., 1907.
Parrish, Randall, 1858–1923.

LAC 40121
The great questions of the times, exemplified in the antagonistic principles involved in the slaveholders' rebellion against democratic institutions as well as against the national Union; as set forth in the speech of the Hon. Lorenzo Sherwood ... delivered at Champlain, in northern N. Y., Oct. 1862; and also in the 1. resolutions of the Democratic league; 2. in an economic view of the present contest, by S. Dewitt Bloodgood; 3. in the views of the loyal press of the North; 4. and in an incipient chapter of the rebellion, concerning "the Texan secessionists, versus, Lorenzo Sherwood in 1856." Arranged for Publication ... by Henry O'Rielly. New York, C. S. Westcott & co., printers, 1862.
O'Rielly, Henry, 1806–1886.

LAC 40091
The great railroad route to the Pacific, and its connections; showing the relation of the Alabama and Chattanooga railroad to the proposed southern line to the Pacific. Boston, A. Mudge & son, printers, 1870.
Alabama and Chattanooga Railroad Company.

LAC 14160
The great rebellion: its secret history, rise, progress, and disastrous failure. By John Minor Botts, of Virginia. The political life of the author vindicated. New York, Harper & brothers, 1866.
Botts, John Minor, 1802–1869.

LAC 15595
The great republic. New York, Scribner and Welford, 1884.
Griffin, *Sir* Lepel Henry, 1840–1908.

LAC 11105
The great revival of 1800. Philadelphia, Presbyterian board of publication [c1872]
Speer, William, 1822–1904.

LAC 10956
Great revivals and the great republic. Nashville, Tenn., Dallas, Tex., Publishing house of the M. E. church, South; Smith & Lamar, agents, 1904.
Candler, Warren Akin, *bp.*, 1857–1941.

LAC 11166
The great revolution, a history of the rise and progress of the People's party in the city of Chicago and county of Cook, with sketches of the elect in office. Chicago, Lakeside publishing and printing company, 1874.
Ahern, M   L.

LAC 11515
The great revolution of 1840. Reminiscences of the log cabin and hard cider campaign. Mount Vernon, O., and Dallas, Tex., A. B. Norton & co., 1888.
Norton, Anthony Banning.

LAC 14072
The great riots of New York, 1712 to 1873. Including a full and complete account of the four days' draft riot of 1863. By Hon. J. T. Headley. New York, E. B. Treat, 1873.
Headley, Joel Tyler, 1813–1897.

LAC 14528
The Great Salt lake trail, by Colonel Henry Inman and Colonel William F. Cody. New York, The Macmillan company; London, Macmillan & co., ltd., 1898.
Inman, Henry, 1837–1899.

LAC 12351
The great South; a record of journeys in Louisiana, Texas, the Indian territory, Missouri, Arkansas, Mississippi, Alabama, Georgia, Florida, South Carolina, North Carolina, Kentucky, Tennessee, Virginia, West Virginia, and Maryland. By Edward King. Profusely illustrated from original sketches by J. Wells Champney. Hartford, Conn., American publishing company, 1875.
King, Edward, 1848–1896.

LAC 11380
The great treason plot in the North during the war...
Chicago, U. S. publishing co. [c1895]
Ayer, I   Winslow.

LAC 14478
The great trial; or The genius of civilization brought to judgment. [Philadelphia] 1873.
Harness, A   C.

LAC 13177
The great West.
The garden of the world, or, The great West; its history, its wealth, its natural advantages, and its future. Also comprising a complete guide to emigrants, with a full description of the different routes westward. By an old settler. With statistics and facts, from Hon. Thomas H. Benton, Hon. Sam Houston, Col. John C. Fremont, and other "old settlers." Boston, Wentworth, 1856.
Dana, C   W.

LAC 16129
The great West: travellers', miners', and emigrants' guide and hand-book to the western, north-western, and Pacific states and territories. With a map of the best routes to the gold and silver mines, and complete tables of distances: also the United States homestead law, mining laws of the respective states, etc., etc. New York, D. Appleton and company, 1865.
Hall, Edward Hepple.

LAC 40100
The greatest of grains. Rice. Hints as to its culture. Also, a brief account of its earlier history, together with facts and figures regarding the cereal at the present time in China, Japan and the United States. New York, Charleston [etc.] Dan Talmage's sons, 1892.
Talmage, Dan, sons.

LAC 13483
The greatest trust in the world. New York, The Ridgway-Thayer company, 1905.
Russell, Charles Edward, 1860–

LAC 15612
The Greeks in America, by J. P. Xenides. With an introduction by Charles Hatch Sears. New York, George H. Doran company [c1922]
Xenides, J   P.

LAC 15501
Greeks in America; an account of their coming, progress, customs, living, and aspirations; with an historical introduction and the stories of some famous American-Greeks. Boston, Sherman, French & company, 1913.
Burgess, Thomas, 1880–

LAC 12089
The Green mountain boys. New York, Boston, H. M. Caldwell [1839]
Thompson, Daniel Pierce, 1795–1868.

LAC 40112
The greenback movement of 1875–1884 and Wisconsin's part in it. Milwaukee, E. B. Usher, 1911.
Usher, Ellis Baker, 1852–1931.

LAC 15315
Greenfield Hill: a poem, in seven parts. I. The prospect. II. The flourishing village. III. The burning of Fairfield. IV. The destruction of the Pequods. V. The clergyman's advice to the villagers. VI. The farmer's advice to the villagers. VII. The vision, or Prospect of the future happiness of America. By Timothy Dwight, D. D. New-York:–Printed by Childs and Swaine, 1794.
Dwight, Timothy, 1752–1817.

LAC 14064
Greenwich Village, by Anna Alice Chapin, with illustrations by Alan Gilbert Cram. New York, Dodd, Mead and company, 1917.
Chapin, Anna Alice, 1880–1920.

LAC 20630
Greyslaer: a romance of the Mohawk. By the author of "A winter in the West," and "Wild scenes in the forest and prairie". New York, Harper & brothers, 1840.
Hoffman, Charles Fenno, 1806–1884.

LAC 40062
The grievances of the American colonies candidly examined... Printed by authority, at Providence, in Rhode-Island. London, Reprinted for J. Almon, 1766.
Hopkins, Stephen, 1707–1785.

LAC 10772
The Grimke sisters. Sarah and Angelina Grimke, the first American women advocates of abolition and woman's rights. Boston, Lee and Shepard; New York, C. T. Dillingham, 1885.
Birney, Catherine H.

LAC 12720
The grocery man and Peck's bad boy.
Peck's bad boy, no. 2. The grocery man and Peck's bad boy. Being a continuation of Peck's bad boy and his pa. Chicago and New York, Belford, Clarke & co., 1883.
Peck, George Wilbur, 1840–1916.

LAC 10128
The groundswell. A history of the origin, aims, and progress of the farmers' movement: embracing an authoritative account of farmers' clubs, granges, etc. ... together with sketches of the lives of prominent leaders, etc. Over one hundred illustrations. Cincinnati, E. Hannaford & company; Chicago, Hannaford & Thompson; [etc., etc.] 1874.
Periam, Jonathan.

LAC 40054
The Group, 1779. Ann Arbor, University of Michigan, 1953.
Warren, Mercy, 1728–1814.

LAC 11473
Grover Cleveland: a record of friendship. New York, The Century co., 1910.
Gilder, Richard Watson, 1844–1909.

LAC 40131
The growing South: an address delivered before the Civic forum ... New York city, March 22, 1908. With portrait. New York, The Civic forum, 1908.
Alderman, Edwin Anderson, 1861–1931.

LAC 12989
The growth and development of the Catholic school system in the United States. New York, Arno Press, 1969.
Burns, James Aloysius, 1867–1940.

LAC 13531
The growth of cities in the nineteenth century. A study in statistics. New York, Pub. for Columbia university by the Macmillan company; [etc., etc.] 1899.
Weber, Adna Ferrin, 1870–1968.

LAC 12439
The growth of democracy in the United States; or, the evolution of popular co-operation in government and its results. Chicago, The Quadrangle press, 1898.
Cleveland, Frederick Albert, 1865–1946.

LAC 10310
The growth of large fortunes; a study of economic causes affecting the acquisition and distribution of property. [New York, American economic association, c1907]
Watkins, George Pendleton, 1876–1933.

LAC 15921
Growth of nationality in the United States; a social study. New York & London, G. P. Putnam's sons, 1899.
Bascom, John, 1827–1911.

LAC 12749
The growth of the Constitution in the Federal convention of 1787; an effort to trace the origin and development of each separate clause from its first suggestion in that body to the form finally approved. Containing also a fac-simile of a heretofore unpublished manuscript of the first draft of the instrument made for use in the Committee of detail. Philadelphia, J. B. Lippincott company, 1900.
Meigs, William Montgomery, 1852–1929.

LAC 16169
Guarding a great city. New York, Harper and brothers, 1906.
McAdoo, William Gibbs.

LAC 11550
Guarding the mails; or, The secret service of the Post office department. Illustrative sketches. Hartford, Chicago [etc.] Dustin, Gilman & co., 1876
Woodward, Patrick Henry, 1833–

LAC 40055
A guide in the wilderness; or, The history of the first settlements in the western counties of New York with useful instructions to future settlers in a series of letters addressed by Judge Cooper, of Cooperstown, to William Sampson, Barrister, of New York. Dublin, Gilbert & Hodges, 1810. [Rochester, N. Y., G. P. Humphrey, 1897.]
Cooper, William, 1754–1809.

LAC 10573
Guide to British West Indian archive materials, in London and in the islands, for the history of the United States. By Herbert C. Bell, David W. Parker, and others. Washington, D.C., Carnegie institution of Washington, 1926.
Bell, Herbert Clifford Francis, 1881–

LAC 16223
Guide to church furnishing and decoration. Chicago: A. H. Andrews & co. ... 1876-7. [Chicago] Chicago legal news co., printers, 1876.
Andrews, A. H., & Company, *Chicago.*

LAC 40091
Guide to the lands of the Northern Pacific railroad in Minnesota. New York, Land department, Northern Pacific railroad company, 1872.
Northern Pacific Railroad Company.

LAC 12427
Guide to the manuscript materials for the history of the United States to 1783, in the British museum, in minor London archives, and in the libraries of Oxford and Cambridge, by Charles M. Andrews and Frances G. Davenport. Washington, D. C., The Carnegie institution of Washington, 1908.
Andrews, Charles McLean, 1863–1943, *comp.*

LAC 40052
Guide to the material on Swedish history in the Augustana college library, prepared by O. Fritiof Ander. Rock Island, Ill., Augustana college library and Augustana historical society, 1934.
Augustana College and Theological Seminary, *Rock Island. Ill. Denkmann Memorial Library.*

LAC 20779
Guide to the materials for American history, to 1783, in the Public record office of Great Britain. Washington, D. C., Carnegie institution of Washington, 1912–14.
Andrews, Charles McLean, 1863–1943.

LAC 16361
Guide to the materials for the history of the United States in Spanish archives (Simancas, the Archivo historico nacional, and Seville) Washington, D. C., Carnegie institution of Washington, 1907.
Shepherd, William Robert, 1871–1934.

LAC 40091
Guide to the Union Pacific railroad lands. 12,000,000 acres best farming and mineral lands in America, for sale by the Union Pacific railroad company, in tracts to suit purchasers and at low prices, Omaha, Nebraska. [Omaha] Land department, Union Pacific railroad building, 1870.
Union Pacific Railroad Company.

LAC 10925
A guide-book in the administration of the discipline of the Methodist Episcopal church. New York, Carlton & Phillips, 1855.
Baker, Osmon Cleander, 1812–1871.

LAC 12808
The guilt of slavery and the crime of slaveholding, demonstrated from the Hebrew and Greek scriptures. By Rev. George B. Cheever. Boston, J. P. Jewett & company, 1860.
Cheever, George Barrell, 1807–1890.

LAC 14747
Guiteau trial. Closing speech to the jury of John K. Porter, of New York, in the case of Charles J. Guiteau, the assassin of President Garfield, Washington, January 23, 1882. New York, J. Polhemus, printer, 1882.
Porter, John Kilham, 1819–1892.

LAC 14914
The gulf and inland waters. New York, C. Scribner's sons, 1883.
Mahan, Alfred Thayer, 1840–1914.

LAC 40022
Gunnison and San Juan. A late and reliable description of the wonderful gold and silver belts and iron and coal fields of that newest and best land for prospector and capitalist, southwestern Colorado ... as presented in a series of letters written to the "New York world" by its special correspondent, "R. E. S." Also, containing a valuable appendix on mining laws. Omaha, The New West publishing company, 1881.
Strahorn, Robert Edmund, 1852–

LAC 10146
Gustav Korner, deutsch-amerikanischer jurist, staatsmann, diplomat und geschichtschreiber. Ein lebensbild, nach seiner unveroffentlichten autobiographie, seinen schriften und briefen, bearbeitet und dem andenken des verstorbenen freundes in dankbarer erinnerung gewidmet. Separatdruck aus dem 11. band der Gesammelten werke. Cincinnati, O., Verlag des verfassers, 1902.
Rattermann, Heinrich Armin, 1832–1923.

LAC 12911
Gustavus Vassa, the African.
The life of Olaudah Equiano, or Gustavus Vassa, the African. Written by himself. Two volumes in one. Boston, I. Knapp, 1837.
Equiano, Olaudah.

LAC 16963
Guy Rivers; a tale of Georgia. New and rev. ed. Chicago, Donohue, Henneberry, 1890.
Simms, William Gilmore, 1806–1870.

LAC 11750
Haaff's practical dehorner; or, Every man his own dehorner... Chicago, The Clark & Longley company, 1888.
Haaff, H   H.

LAC 40071
Habeas corpus, and martial law. A review of the opinion of Chief Justice Taney in the case of John Merryman. Cambridge [Mass.] Welch, Bigelow, and company, printers to the University, 1861.
Parker, Joel, 1795–1875.

LAC 21335-36
The Hague peace conferences of 1899 and 1907; a series of lectures delivered before the Johns Hopkins university in the year 1908. Baltimore, The Johns Hopkins press, 1909.
Scott, James Brown, 1866-1943.

LAC 15575
A hairdresser's experience in high life. Cincinnati, The author, 1859.
Potter, Eliza.

LAC 13063
Half a century. 2d ed. Chicago, Jansen, McClurg & company, 1880.
Swisshelm, Jane Grey, 1815-1884.

LAC 40018
Half a century of rope making, 1857-1907. St. Louis, Mo., New York [etc.] A. Leschen & sons rope company [c1907]
Leschen, A., & Sons Rope Co., *St. Louis, Mo.*

LAC 16489
Half a man; the status of the Negro in New York, by Mary White Ovington; with a foreword by Dr. Franz Boas. New York [etc.] Longmans, Green, and co., 1911.
Ovington, Mary White, 1865-1951.

LAC 14594
A half-century of the Unitarian controversy, with particular reference to its origin, its course, and its prominent subjects among the Congregationalists of Massachusetts. With an appendix. Boston, Crosby, Nichols, and company, 1857.
Ellis, George Edward, 1814-1894.

LAC 11441
The half century; or, A history of the changes that have taken place, and events that have transpired, chiefly in the United States, between 1800 and 1850. With an introduction by Mark Hopkins, D. D. Boston, Tappan & Whittemore, 1851.
Davis, Emerson, 1798-1866.

LAC 13978
A half century with juvenile delinquents; or, The New York house of refuge and its times. New York, D. Appleton and company, 1869.
Peirce, Bradford Kinney, 1819-1889.

LAC 16225
Hamilton, the young artist. By Augusta Browne. With an Essay on sculpture and painting, by Hamilton A. C. Browne. Philadelphia, Lippincott, Grambo & co., 1852.
Browne, Augusta.

LAC 15855
The Hamiltoniad. By John Williams, (Anthony Pasquin.) New York, Printed for the Hamilton club, 1865.
Williams, John, 1761-1818.

LAC 12978
Hampton and its students. By two of its teachers, Mrs. M. F. Armstrong and Helen W. Ludlow. With fifty cabin and plantation songs, arranged by Thomas F. [!] Fenner, New York, G. P. Putnam's sons, 1874.
Armstrong, Mary Frances, d. 1903.

LAC 15022
The hand of God in American history: a study of national politics. New York, T. Y. Crowell & co. [1902]
Thompson, Robert Ellis, 1844-1924.

LAC 40120
Hand book and history of the National farmers' alliance and industrial union. Washington, D. C., 1893.
Blood, F   G   *ed.*

LAC 15967
A handbook for farmers and dairymen. By F. W. Woll. With the assistance of well-known specialists. 1st ed. 1st thousand. New York, J. Wiley & sons; [etc., etc.] 1898, [c1897]
Woll, Fritz Wilhelm, 1865-

LAC 11496
Handbook for immigrants to the United States. Prepared by the American social science association. New York, For the Association, by Hurd and Houghton, 1871.
American Social Science Association.

LAC 23464-66
Handbook of American Indian languages, by Franz Boas. With illustrative sketches by Roland B. Dixon, P. E. Goddard, William Jones and Truman Michelson, John R. Swanton, and William Thalbitzer. Washington, Govt. print. off., 1911-38.
Boas, Franz, 1858-1942.

LAC 23689-91
Handbook of American Indians north of Mexico. Washington, Govt. print. off., 1910-12 [v. 1, 1912]
Hodge, Frederick Webb, 1864-1956, *ed.*

LAC 40018
Hand book of gasoline automobiles. For the information of the public who are interested in their manufacture and use. New York city, Association of licensed automobile manufacturers [c1904]

LAC 13147
Hand-book of Iowa; describing its agricultural, commercial and manufacturing resources, and other capabilities of producing wealth, also, its physical geography and geology. Chicago, Blanchard & Cram, 1867.
Blanchard, Rufus, 1821-1904.

LAC 15926
A hand-book of politics for 1894: being a record of important political action, legislative and executive, national and state, from July 31, 1892, to August 15, 1894. Washington, R. Beall, 1894.
McPherson, Edward, 1830-1895.

LAC 15680
Handbook of railroad construction; for the use of American engineers. Containing the necessary rules, tables, and formula for the location, construction, equipment, and management of railroads, as built in the United States... Boston, J. Monroe, 1857.
Vose, George Leonard, 1831-

LAC 40152

A hand-book of requirements for admission to the colleges of the United States, with miscellaneous addenda, for the use of high schools, academies, and other college-preparatory institutions. Comp. and arranged by A. F. Nightingale. New York, D. Appleton and company, 1879.
Nightingale, Augustus Frederick, 1843–1925, comp.

LAC 14374

Handbook of settlements, ed. by Robert A. Woods and Albert J. Kennedy. New York, Charities publication committee, 1911.
Woods, Robert Archey, 1865–1925, ed.

LAC 13098

A handbook of socialism; a statement of socialism in its various aspects, and a history of socialism in all countries... London, S. Sonnenschein & co.; New York, C. Scribner's sons, 1895.
Bliss, William Dwight Porter, 1856–1926.

LAC 14960

A Hand-book of the church's mission to the Indians; in memory of William Hobart Hare, an apostle to the Indians. Hartford, Conn., Church missions publishing company [c1914]

LAC 40073

Hand-book of the Oneida community; with a sketch of its founder, and an outline of its constitution and doctrines. Wallingford, Conn., Office of the Circular, Wallingford community, 1867.
Oneida Community.

LAC 15717

Hand-book of the useful arts; including agriculture, architecture, domestic economy, engineering, machinery; manufactures, mining, photogenic and telegraphic art: being an exposition of their principles and practice and a compend of American and European invention. New-York, G. P. Putnam, 1852.
Antisell, Thomas, 1817–1893.

LAC 12034

Handkerchiefs from Paul, being pious and consolatory verses of Puritan Massachusetts, including unpublished poems by Benjamin Tompson, John Wilson and Anna Hayden, together with other poems by Samuel Torrey and Samuel Danforth and John Wilson, reprinted from rare originals, edited with introduction and notes by Kenneth B. Murdock. Cambridge, Harvard university press, 1927.
Murdock, Kenneth Ballard, 1895–   ed.

LAC 11746

Handy farm devices and how to make them. New York, Orange Judd company, 1910.
Cobleigh, Rolfe.

LAC 20652

Hannah Thurston: a story of American life. London, S. Low, son, and co., 1863.
Taylor, Bayard, 1825–1878.

LAC 40116

The happiness of a people in the wisdome of their rulers directing and in the obedience of their brethren attending unto what Israel ougho [!] to do: recommended in a sermon before the Honourable Governour and Council, and the respected Deputies of the Mattachusets [!] colony in New-England. Preached at Boston, May 3d, 1676, being the day of election there. By William Hubbard minister of Ipswich. Boston, Printed by John Foster, 1676.
Hubbard, William, 1621?–1704.

LAC 16937

The harbor. New York, The Macmillan company, 1915.
Poole, Ernest, 1880–1950.

LAC 40001

Hard cash; an essay to show that financial monopolies hinder enterprise and defraud both labor and capital; that panics and business revulsions, caused by arbitrary interference with production and exchange, will be effectually prevented only through free money. Twentieth thousand. Princeton, Mass., Co-operative publishing co., 1875.
Heywood, Ezra Hervey, 1829–1893.

LAC 14419

Hardtack and coffee; or, The unwritten story of army life, including chapters on enlisting, life in tents and log huts, Jonahs and beats, offences and punishments, raw recruits, foraging, corps and corps badges, the wagon trains, the army mule, the engineer corps, the signal corps, etc. Illustrated with six color plates; and over two hundred original sketches by Charles W. Reed. Philadelphia, Thompson pub. co., 1888, [c1887]
Billings, John Davis, b. 1842.

LAC 16339

Harlem (city of New York): its origin and early annals. Prefaced by home scenes in the fatherlands; or, notices of its founders before emigration. Also, sketches of numerous families, and the recovered history of the land-titles... New York, Printed for the author, 1881.
Riker, James, 1822–1889.

LAC 40151

The Harlem Republican Club; organized November 26, 1887, incorporated January 25, 1888. Club house, 145–147 West 125th Street. New York City, F. S. & C. B. Bartram, printers, 1892.

LAC 40089

The harmonic structure of Indian music. New York, G. P. Putnam's, 1899.
Fillmore, John Comfort, 1843–1898.

LAC 16678

The Harmony Society at Economy, Penn'a, founded by George Rapp, A. D. 1805. With an appendix. Pittsburgh, Pa., W. S. Haven, 1866.
Williams, Aaron.

LAC 30102–218

Harper's monthly magazine. v. 1–110; June 1850–May 1905. New York, Harper & brothers.

LAC 30984

Harper's monthly magazine. Index ... alphabetical, analytical and classified. Volumes I. to LXXXV. inclusive, from June 1850, to November 1892. New York, Harper & brothers, 1893.

LAC 23994

Harper's pictorial history of the Civil war. By Alfred H. Guernsey and Henry M. Alden. Chicago, Ill., McDonnell bros. [c1866–68]
Guernsey, Alfred Hudson, 1824–1902.

LAC 11955

The Harpe's head; a legend of Kentucky. Philadelphia, Key & Biddle, 1833.
Hall, James, 1793–1868.

LAC 12785

Harriet, the Moses of her people. New York, For the author by G. R. Lockwood & son, 1886.
Bradford, Sarah Elizabeth, *b.* 1818.

LAC 20213

Harrison to Harding.
From Harrison to Harding, a personal narrative, covering a third of a century, 1888–1921. New York and London, G. P. Putnam's sons, 1922.
Dunn, Arthur Wallace, 1859–1926.

LAC 20488–89

Harvard college records ... corporation records, 1636–1750... [Boston, The Society, 1925]
Harvard University.

LAC 22893–94

The Harvard medical school; a history, narrative and documentary. 1782–1905. By Thomas Francis Harrington, M. D., class of 1888; ed. by James Gregory Mumford, M. D., class of 1888. New York, Chicago, Lewis publishing company, 1905.
Harrington, Thomas Francis, 1866–

LAC 40072

Harvey's illustrations of our country, with an outline of its social progress, political development, and material resources, being an epitome of a part of eight lectures ... before ... the Royal institution of Great Britain, in 1849 ... entitled the Discovery, resources, and progress of North America, north of Virginia... Boston, Printed by Dutton & Wentworth, 1851.
Harvey, George, *A.N.A.*

LAC 40136

Has the non-unionist a right to work how, when, and where he pleases? Washington, D. C., The American federation of labor, 1904.
Foster, Frank Keyes, 1854–1909.

LAC 40118

Hasty-pudding: a poem, in three cantos. Written at Chamrery [!] in Savoy, January, 1793, by Joel Barlow... Together with, The ruling passion. By Robert T. Paine, jr., esq. Exeter, N. H., A. Brown [182-?]
Barlow, Joel, 1754–1812.

LAC 40025

Hasty recognition of rebel belligerency, and our right to complain of it. Boston, A. Williams & co. [c1865]
Bemis, George, 1816–1878.

LAC 13711

Hawaii. Our new possessions. An account of travels and adventure, with ... an appendix containing the treaty of annexation to the United States. By John R. Musick. Illustrated by Philip E. Flintoff and Freeland A. Carter. New York and London, Funk & Wagnalls company, 1898.
Musick, John Roy, 1849–1901.

LAC 14846

The Hawaiian incident; an examination of Mr. Cleveland's attitude toward the revolution of 1893. Boston, Lee and Shepard, 1897.
Gillis, James Andrew, 1829–1914.

LAC 16545

Hawaiian life: being lazy letters from low latitudes. Chicago, New York, F. T. Neely, 1894.
Stoddard, Charles Warren, 1843–1909.

LAC 14979

Hawaii's story by Hawaii's queen, Liliuokalani. Boston, Lee and Shepard, 1898.
Liliuokalani, *Queen of the Hawaiian Islands,* 1838–1917.

LAC 12325

The Hawkins' voyages during the reigns of Henry VIII, Queen Elizabeth, and James I. Ed., with an introduction. London, Printed for the Hakluyt society, 1878.
Markham, *Sir* Clements Robert, 1830–1916, *ed.*

LAC 14722

Hawthorne, by Henry James, jun. London and New York, Macmillan and co., 1887.
James, Henry, 1843–1916.

LAC 13555

Hawthorne and his circle. New York and London, Harper & brothers, 1903.
Hawthorne, Julian, 1846–1934.

LAC 40110

Hawthorne and his friends; reminiscence and tribute. Cedar Rapids, Ia., The Torch press, 1908.
Sanborn, Franklin Benjamin, 1831–1917.

LAC 12462

The Hayes-Tilden disputed presidential election of 1876... Cleveland, Burrows brothers company, 1906.
Haworth, Paul Leland, 1876–1938.

LAC 11978

A hazard of new fortunes, by William Dean Howells; introduction by Alexander Harvey. New York, Boni and Liveright, inc. [1917]
Howells, William Dean, 1837–1920.

LAC 20408–10

Hazard's United States commercial and statistical register, containing documents, facts, and other useful information, illustrative of the history and resources of the American Union and of each state... Ed. by Samuel Hazard. v. 1–6; Feb. 13, 1839–June 29, 1842. Philadelphia, Printed by W. F. Geddes, 1840–42.

LAC 11068

Health and the inner life; an analytical and historical study of spiritual healing theories, with an account of the life and teachings of P. P. Quimby. New York and London, G. P. Putnam's sons, 1907, [c1906]
Dresser, Horatio Willis, 1866–

LAC 15824

The heart of Happy Hollow, by Paul Laurence Dunbar. Illustrated by E. W. Kemble. New York, Dodd, Mead and company, 1904.
Dunbar, Paul Laurence, 1872–1906.

LAC 12088

Helen of Troy, and other poems. New York and London, G. P. Putnam's sons, 1911.
Teasdale, Sara, 1884–1933.

LAC 40067

The hell of war and its penalties.
I. The cost of national crime. II. The hell of war and its penalties. Two treatises suggested by the appointment of a day of national thanksgiving by the President of the United States. [Boston, Rockwell & Churchill press, 1898]
Atkinson, Edward, 1827–1905.

LAC 12569

Helper's Impending crisis dissected. Philadelphia, J. T. Lloyd, 1860.
Wolfe, Samuel M.

LAC 10581

Helps to education in the homes of our country. Boston, Crosby and Nichols, 1863.
Burton, Warren, 1800–1866.

LAC 20416

Henry Demarest Lloyd, 1847–1903, a biography by Caro Lloyd, with an introduction by Charles Edward Russell. New York and London, G. P. Putnam's sons, 1912.
Lloyd, Caroline Augusta, 1859–

LAC 15663

Henry Dexter, sculptor; a memorial. [Cambridge, Mass.] Priv. print., 1898.
Albee, John, 1833–1915.

LAC 40074

Henry George, traitor. New York, B. R. Tucker, 1896.
Tucker, Benjamin Ricketson, 1854–1939.

LAC 15625

Henry Hill Goodell; the story of his life, with letters and a few of his addresses, by Calvin Stebbins. Cambridge, Printed at the Riverside press, 1911.
Goodell, Henry Hill, 1839–1905.

LAC 10471

Henry J. Raymond and the New York press, for thirty years. Progress of American journalism from 1840 to 1870. With portrait, illustrations and appendix. Published by subscription only. Hartford, Conn., A. S. Hale and company, 1870.
Maverick, Augustus.

LAC 11914

Henry James, a critical study, by Ford Madox Hueffer. London, M. Secker, 1913.
Ford, Ford Madox, 1873–

LAC 12003

Henry W. Longfellow. Biography, anecdote, letters, criticism. Cambridge, Mass., M. King, 1882.
Kennedy, William Sloane, 1850–1929.

LAC 10917

Henry Ward Beecher. Boston and New York, Houghton, Mifflin and company, 1904, [c1903]
Abbott, Lyman, 1835–1922.

LAC 15341

Heraldry in America. 2d ed. With over nine hundred and fifty illustrations. Philadelphia, The Department of heraldry of the Bailey, Banks & Biddle company, 1909.
Zieber, Eugene.

LAC 13541

The Herald's history of Los Angeles city. Los Angeles, Cal., Kingsley-Barnes & Neuner co., 1901.
Willard, Charles Dwight, 1866–1914.

LAC 40055

Herbert Spencer on the Americans and the Americans on Herbert Spencer. Being a full report of his interview, and of the proceedings of the farewell banquet of Nov. 11, 1882. New York, D. Appleton and company, 1883, [c1882]
Youmans, Edward Livingston, 1821–1887.

LAC 12063

A hermit of Carmel, and other poems. London, T. Fisher Unwin [1907]
Santayana, George, 1863–1952.

LAC 23457

Herndon's Lincoln; the true story of a great life... The history and personal recollections of Abraham Lincoln, by William H. Herndon, and Jesse William Weik. Chicago, New York [etc.] Belford, Clarke & company; [etc., etc., c1889]
Herndon, William Henry, 1818–1891.

LAC 13514

Heroes of insurgency. Boston, Human life publishing company [c1910]
Dreier, Thomas, 1884–

LAC 11942

Hesper; a novel. New York and London, Harper & brothers, 1903.
Garland, Hamlin, 1860–1940.

LAC 21131

Hesperos: or, Travels in the West. London, J. W. Parker, 1850.
Houstoun, Matilda Charlotte Fraser, 1815?–1892.

LAC 14920

The Hessians and the other German auxiliaries of Great Britain in the revolutionary war. Port Washington, N. Y., Kennikat press [1965]
Lowell, Edward Jackson, 1845–1894.

LAC 15765
The hidden hand; or, Capitola the mad-cap. New York, G. W. Dillingham, 1888.
Southworth, Emma Dorothy Eliza, 1819–1899.

LAC 15538
A hidden phase of American history; Ireland's part in America's struggle for liberty, by Michael J. O'Brien. Illustrated by portraits from the Emmet collection, facsimiles of documents in English archives, reproduced by Anna Frances Levins. New York, The Devin-Adair company [c1919]
O'Brien, Michael Joseph, 1870–

LAC 40101
Higher education in Wisconsin, by William F. Allen and David E. Spencer... Washington, Govt. print. off., 1889.
Allen, William Francis, 1830–1889.

LAC 40003
The higher education of the people. Madison, State historical society, 1891.
Adams, Herbert Baxter, 1850–1901.

LAC 13972
The higher law, in its relations to civil government: with particular reference to slavery, and the fugitive slave law. Auburn [N. Y.] Derby & Miller, 1852.
Hosmer, William.

LAC 11564
The higher learning in America; a memorandum on the conduct of universities by business men, by Thorstein Veblen; introduction by David Riesman. Stanford, Academic reprints, 1954.
Veblen, Thorstein, 1857–1929.

LAC 15915
Highways of progress. New York, Doubleday, Page & company, 1910.
Hill, James Jerome, 1838–1916.

LAC 12199
Hill's manual of social and business forms: a guide to correct writing... [300th thousand] Chicago, Hill standard book co., 1886.
Hill, Thomas Edie, 1832–1915.

LAC 16922
The hindered hand; or, The reign of the repressionist. 3d ed. rev. New York, AMS Press [1969]
Griggs, Sutton Elbert, 1872–

LAC 14681
Hints on a system of popular education: addressed to R. S. Field ... chairman of the Committee on education in the Legislature of New Jersey; and to the Rev. A. B. Dod, professor of mathematics in the College of New Jersey. Philadelphia, Hogan and Thompson, 1838.
Wines, Enoch Cobb, 1806–1879.

LAC 13883
Hints on household taste in furniture, upholstery, and other details. By Charles L. Eastlake. Ed., with notes by Charles C. Perkins. 1st American, from the rev. London ed. Boston, J. R. Osgood and company, 1872.
Eastlake, Charles Locke, 1833–1906.

LAC 14135
Hints to young architects, calculated to facilitate their practical operations. By George Wightwick. With additional notes, and hints to persons about building in the country. By A. J. Downing. 1st American ed. New York & London, Wiley and Putnam, 1847.
Wightwick, George, 1802–1872.

LAC 16049
Hints toward reforms, in lectures, addresses, and other writings. New-York, Harper & brothers, 1850.
Greeley, Horace, 1811–1872.

LAC 12835
The hireling and the slave, Chicora, and other poems. Charleston, S. C., McCarter, 1856.
Grayson, William John, 1788–1863.

LAC 21018–22
Histoire de la participation de la France a l'etablissement des Etats-Unis d'Amerique. Correspondance diplomatique et documents. Paris, Imprimerie nationale, 1886–92.
Doniol, Henri, 1818–1906.

LAC 15068
Histoire de la presse franco-americaine: comprenant l'historique de l'emigration des Canadiens-Francais aux Etats-Unis, leur developpement, et leurs progres. Cet ouvrage contient aussi un historique des journaux publies depuis 1838 jusqu' a nos jours, les biographies des journalistes, defunts et vivants, et un supplement sur les journaux publies par des Francais a New-York, en Louisiane et ailleurs. Par Alexandre Belisle, avec un preface par J.-G. Le Boutillier. Worcester, Mass., Ateliers typographiques de "L'Opinion publique," 1911.
Belisle, Alexandre, 1856–

LAC 15423
Histoire et commerce des colonies angloises, dans l'Amerique Septentrionale, ou l'on trouve l'etat actuel de leur population, & des details curieux sur la constitution de leur gouvernement, principalement sur celui de la Nouvelle-Angleterre, de la Pensilvanie, de la Caroline & de la Georgie. A Londres, et se vend a Paris, chez Le Breton [etc.] M.DCC.LV.
Butel-Dumont, Georges Marie, 1725–1788.

LAC 22621–23
Histoire generale des Antilles habitees par les Francois... Par le R. P. dv Tertre. Paris, T. Iolly, 1667–71.
Dutertre, Jean Baptiste, 1610–1687.

LAC 23104–7
Historia general de los hechos de los castellanos en las islas i tierra firme del mar oceano. Escrita por Antonio de Herrera coronista mayor de Sv Md de las Indias y sv coronista de Castilla. En quatro decades desde al ano de 1492 hasta el de 1531. Decada primera al rey nuestro senor. En Madrid en la Imprento real de Nicolas Rodiquez [!] Franco, ano de 1726–28.
Herrera y Tordesillas, Antonio de, 1559–1625.

LAC 12725
Historic annals of the National academy of design, New-York drawing association, etc., with occasional dottings by the way-side, from 1825 to the present time. Philadelphia, G. W. Childs, 1865.
Cummings, Thomas Seir, 1804–1894.

LAC 40009

Historic buildings now standing in New York, which were erected prior to eighteen hundred. New York [1914] Chase Manhattan Bank, *New York*.

LAC 15569

Historic dress in America, 1607-1800; with an introductory chapter on dress in the Spanish and French settlements in Florida and Louisiana, by Elisabeth McClellan. Illustrations in colour, pen and ink, and halftone by Sophie B. Steel, together with reproductions from photographs of rare portraits, original garments, etc. Philadelphia, G. W. Jacobs & company [c1904] McClellan, Elisabeth, 1851-1920.

LAC 20180-81

Historic New York during two centuries. New York and London, G. P. Putnam's sons [c1898]

LAC 40031

The historic policy of the United States as to annexation. Boston, Ginn, 1893. Baldwin, Simeon Eben, 1840-1927.

LAC 10167

Historic silver of the colonies and its makers. New York, The Macmillan company, 1917. Bigelow, Francis Hill, 1859-

LAC 14377

Historic sketches of the cattle trade of the West and Southwest. Illustrated by Prof. Henry Worrall, engraved by Baker & co. ... electrotyped by J. T. Reton & co. ... Reprinted. Washington, D. C., The Rare book shop, 1932. McCoy, Joseph Geiting, 1837-1915.

LAC 13549

Historic towns of the middle states. New York & London, G. P. Putnam's sons, 1899. Powell, Lyman Pierson, 1866-1946, *ed.*

LAC 10638

Historic towns of the southern states. New York & London, G. P. Putnam's sons, 1904, [c1900] Powell, Lyman Pierson, 1866-   *ed.*

LAC 13550

Historic towns of the western states. New York & London, G. P. Putnam's sons, 1901. Powell, Lyman Pierson, 1866-1946, *ed.*

LAC 13890

Historic Virginia homes and churches, by Robert A. Lancaster, jr., with 316 illustrations. Philadelphia and London, J. B. Lippincott company, 1915. Lancaster, Robert Alexander, 1862-1940.

LAC 15058

Historical account of Bouquet's expedition against the Ohio Indians, in 1764. With preface by Francis Parkman ... and a translation of Dumas' biographical sketch of General Bouquet. Cincinnati, O., R. Clarke & co., 1907. Smith, William, 1727-1803.

LAC 13417

An historical account of Massachusetts currency. Boston, Printed by Perkins & Marvin, 1839. Felt, Joseph Barlow, 1789-1869.

LAC 14254

An historical account of the expedition against Sandusky under Col. William Crawford in 1782; with biographical sketches, personal reminiscences, and descriptions of interesting localities; including, also, details of the disastrous retreat, the barbarities of the savages, and the awful death of Crawford by torture. Cincinnati, R. Clarke & co., 1873. Butterfield, Consul Willshire, 1824-1899.

LAC 13930

An historical account of the incorporated Society for the propagation of the gospel in foreign parts. Containing their foundation, proceedings, and the success of their missionaries in the British colonies, to the year 1728. By David Humphreys, D. D., secretary to the honourable society. London, Printed by J. Downing, 1730. Humphreys, David, 1689-1740.

LAC 10658

A historical account of the neutrality of Great Britain during the American civil war. London, Longmans, Green, Reader, and Dyer, 1870. Bernard, Mountague, 1820-1882.

LAC 15782

An historical account of the Protestant Episcopal church, in South-Carolina, from the first settlement of the province, to the war of the revolution; with notices of the present state of the church in each parish: and some account of the early civil history of Carolina, never before published. To which are added; the laws relating to religious worship; the journals and rules of the convention of South-Carolina; the constitution and canons of the Protestant Episcopal church, and the course of ecclesiastical studies... Charleston, Published by E. Thayer, at his theological bookstore, Broad Street. Arch'd. E. Miller, Printer, 120 Broadstreet, 1820. Dalcho, Frederick, 1770?-1836.

LAC 15740

An historical account of the settlements of Scotch Highlanders in America prior to the peace of 1783; together with notices of Highland regiments and biographical sketches. Cleveland, The Helman-Taylor co.; [etc., etc.] 1900. MacLean, John Patterson, 1848-1939.

LAC 12988

A historical and critical discussion of college admission requirements... New York, The Macmillan co.; Berlin, Mayer and Maller, 1903. Broome, Edwin Cornelius, 1874-

LAC 22713-15

Historical and genealogical miscellany; data relating to the settlement and settlers of New York and New Jersey. New York, 1903-32. Stillwell, John Edwin, 1853-1930, *comp.*

LAC 16790

An historical and geographical account of the province and country of Pensilvania; and of West-New-Jersey in America. The richness of the soil... The strange crea-

tures... The natives ... the first planters, the Dutch, Sweeds and English, with the number of its inhabitants; as also a touch upon George Keith's new religion, in his second change since he left the Quakers. With a map of both countries. London, A. Baldwin, 1698. [New-York, Lithographed for H. A. Brady, 1848]
Thomas, Gabriel, *17th cent.*

LAC 12727
Historical and legal examination of that part of the decision of the Supreme court of the United States in the Dred Scott case, which declares the unconstitutionality of the Missouri compromise act and the self-extension of the Constitution to territories, carrying slavery along with it. With an appendix, containing: I. The debates in the Senate in March, 1849, between Mr. Webster and Mr. Calhoun, on the legislation extension of the Constitution to territories, as contained in vol. II. ch. CLXXXII. of the "Thirty years' view" II. The inside view of the southern sentiment, in relation to the Wilmot proviso, as seen in vol. II. ch. CLXVIII. of the "Thirty years' view". III. Review of President Pierce's annual message to Congress of December, 1856, so far as it relates to the abrogation of the Missouri compromise act and the classification of parties... By the author of the "Thirty years' view". New York, D. Appleton and company, 1860, [c1857]
Benton, Thomas Hart, 1782–1858.

LAC 12490
Historical and political essays. Boston and New York, Houghton, Mifflin and company [c1892]
Lodge, Henry Cabot, 1850–1924.

LAC 15262
Historical and political reflections on the rise and progress of the American rebellion. In which the causes of that rebellion are pointed out and the policy and necessity of offering to the Americans a system of government founded in the principles of the British constitution, are clearly demonstrated. By the author of Letters to a nobleman on the conduct of the American war. London, Printed for G. Wilkie, 1780.
Galloway, Joseph, 1731–1803.

LAC 10692
An historical and practical essay on the culture and commerce of tobacco. London, Printed for Vernor & Hood, 1800.
Tatham, William, 1752–1819.

LAC 13479
An historical and statistical account of the foreign commerce of the United States ... comp. by J. Smith Homans, junior. New York, G. P. Putnam & co. [etc.] 1857.
Homans, Isaac Smith.

LAC 14812
Historical aspects of the immigration problem; select documents. Chicago, Ill., The University of Chicago press [c1926]
Abbott, Edith, 1876–1957.

LAC 23453
Historical collections; consisting of state papers, and other authentic documents; intended as materials for an history of the United States of America. Philadelphia: Printed by T. Dobson, for the author, 1792–94.
Hazard, Ebenezer, 1744–1817.

LAC 16827
Historical collections of Georgia: containing the most interesting facts, traditions, biographical sketches, anecdotes, etc., relating to its history and antiquities, from its first settlement to the present time. Comp. from original records and official documents. Illustrated by nearly one hundred engravings. By the Rev. George White. New-York, Pudney & Russell, 1854.
White, George, 1802–1887.

LAC 10268
Historical collections of Louisiana and Florida, including translations of original manuscripts relating to their discovery and settlement, with numerous historical and biographical notes. New series. New York, J. Sabin & sons, 1869.
French, Benjamin Franklin, 1799–1877, ed.

LAC 20079–80
Historical collections of Louisiana, embracing translations of many rare and valuable documents relating to the natural, civil and political history of that state. Compiled with historical and biographical notes, and an introduction, by B. F. French. New York, Wiley and Putnam; [etc., etc.] 1846–53.
French, Benjamin Franklin, 1799–1877, *ed.*

LAC 16950
Historical collections of Ohio; containing a collection of the most interesting facts, traditions, biographical sketches, anecdotes, etc., relating to its general and local history: with descriptions of its counties, principal towns and villages. Illustrated by 177 engravings. Cincinnati, Derby, Bradley & co., 1847.
Howe, Henry, 1816–1893.

LAC 40051
Historical collections of the Indians in New England. Of their several nations, numbers, customs, manners, religion and government, before the English planted there. Also a true and faithful account of the present state and condition of the praying Indians (or those who have visibly received the gospel in New England) declaring the number of that people, the situation and place of their towns and churches, and their manner of worshipping God... Together with a brief mention of the instruments and means, that God hath been pleased to use for their civilizing and conversion, briefly declaring the prudent and faithful endeavours of the Right honourable the Corporation at London, for promoting that affair. Also suggesting some expedients for their further civilizing and propagating the Christian faith among them. First printed from the original manuscript. 1792. [Boston, Massachusetts historical society, printed 1792, re-printed 1859]
Gookin, Daniel, 1612?–1687.

LAC 15164
Historical collections of the state of New Jersey; containing a general collection of the most interesting facts, traditions, biographical sketches, anecdotes, etc. relating to its history and antiquities, with geographical descriptions of every township in the state. Illustrated by 120 engravings. By John W. Barber and Henry Howe. Newark, N. J., B. Olds [c1844]
Barber, John Warner, 1798–1885.

LAC 14876
Historical collections relating to Gwynedd, a township of Montgomery county, Pennsylvania, settled, 1698, by immigrants from Wales, with some data referring to the adjoining township of Montgomery, also settled by Welsh. 2d ed. Philadelphia, Pa., The author, 1897.
Jenkins, Howard Malcolm, 1842–1902.

LAC 20479-82
Historical collections relating to the American colonial church. [Hartford] Printed for the subscribers, 1870-78.
Perry, William Stevens, *ed.*

LAC 12731
The historical development of the poor law of Connecticut. New York, The Columbia university press, The Macmillan company, agents; London, P. S. King & son, 1905.
Capen, Edward Warren, 1870-

LAC 22831-32
Historical documents relating to New Mexico, Nueva Vizcaya and approaches thereto, to 1773, collected by Adolph F. A. Bandelier and Fanny R. Bandelier; Spanish texts and English translations, edited with introductions and annotations by Charles Wilson Hackett. Washington, D. C., The Carnegie institution of Washington, 1923-37.
Hackett, Charles Wilson, 1888-1951, *ed.*

LAC 10818
A historical geography of the British colonies. Vol. 2. Oxford, The Clarendon press, 1890.
Lucas, Charles Prestwood, 1853-1931.

LAC 15886
An historical inquiry concerning the attempt to raise a regiment of slaves by Rhode Island during the war of the revolution. By Sidney S. Rider. With several tables prepared by Lt.-Col. Jeremiah Olney, commandant. Providence, S. S. Rider, 1880.
Rider, Sidney Smith.

LAC 23348
An historical journal of the campaigns in North-America, for the years 1757, 1758, 1759, and 1760: containing the most remarkable occurrences of that period; particularly the two sieges of Quebec, &c., &c., the orders of the admirals and general officers; descriptions of the countries where the author has served, with their forts and garrisons; their climates, soil, produce; and a regular diary of the weather. As also several manifesto's, a mandate of the late bishop of Canada; the French orders and disposition for the defence of the colony, &c. &c. &c. London, Printed for the author; and sold by W. Johnston [etc.] 1769.
Knox, *Capt.* John, d. 1778.

LAC 31017-28
The Historical magazine, and notes and queries concerning the antiquities, history, and biography of America. v. 1-10, Jan. 1857-Dec. 1866; [v. 11-20] (2d ser. v. 1-10) Jan. 1867-Aug. 1871; v. 21-23 (3d ser. v. 1-3) Jan. 1872-Apr. 1875. Boston, C. B. Richardson; [etc., etc.]

LAC 12872
An historical memoir of the Pennsylvania society, for promoting the abolition of slavery; the relief of free negroes unlawfully held in bondage, and for improving the condition of the African race. Comp. from the minutes of the Society and other official documents, by Edward Needles, and pub. by authority of the Society. Philadelphia, Merrihew and Thompson, printers, 1848.
Pennsylvania Society for Promoting the Abolition of Slavery.

LAC 14694
Historical memoir of the war in West Florida and Louisiana in 1814-15. With an atlas. A facsim. reproduction of the 1816 ed., with an introduction by Jane Lucas de Grummond. Gainesville, University of Florida Press, 1964.
Latour, Arsene Lacarriere.

LAC 10140
Historical memoir of the Western railroad. Springfield, Mass., S. Bowles & company, printers, 1863.
Bliss, George, 1793-1873.

LAC 21142-43
Historical memoirs of New California, by Fray Francisco Palou, O. F. M., translated into English from the manuscript in the archives of Mexico; edited by Herbert Eugene Bolton. Berkeley, Calif., University of California press, 1926.
Palou, Francisco, 1723-1789.

LAC 40137
Historical notes on the employment of negroes in the American army of the revolution. New York, C. T. Evans, 1862.
Moore, George Henry, 1823-1892.

LAC 11022
Historical notices of the missions of the Church of England in the North American colonies, previous to the independence of the United States: chiefly from the ms. documents of the Society for the propagation of the gospel in foreign parts. London, B. Fellowes, 1845.
Hawkins, Ernest, 1802-1868.

LAC 40099
A historical outline of the American colonization society, and remarks on the advantages and practicability of colonizing in Africa the free people of color from the United States... Boston, O. Everett, 1824.
Sparks, Jared, 1789-1866.

LAC 10852
Historical record of Macon and central Georgia, containing many interesting and valuable reminiscences connected with the whole state, including numerous incidents and facts never before published and of great historic value. Macon, J. W. Burke & co., printers, 1879.
Butler, John Campbell, 1833-1911.

LAC 22564-65
Historical register and dictionary of the United States army, from its organization, September 29, 1789, to March 2, 1903. Pub. under act of Congress approved March 2, 1903. Washington, Govt. print. off., 1903.
Heitman, Francis Bernard, 1838-1926.

LAC 12858
An historical research respecting the opinions of the founders of the republic on negroes as slaves, as citizens and as soldiers. Read before the Massachusetts historical society, August 14, 1862. Boston, Printed by J. Wilson and son, 1862.
Livermore, George, 1809-1865.

LAC 40042
Historical sketch of Amherst, in the county of Hillsborough, in New-Hampshire. From the first settlement to the present period. Amherst, R. Boylston, 1820.
Farmer, John, 1789-1838.

LAC 14595
A historical sketch of Hamilton college, Clinton, New York. By the Rev. Charles Elmer Allison. Yonkers, N. Y., 1889.
Allison, Charles Elmer.

LAC 12699
An historical sketch of Henry's contribution to the electromagnetic telegraph: with an account of the origin and development of Prof. Morse's invention. (From the Smithsonian report for 1878.) Washington, Govt. print. off., 1879.
Taylor, William Bower, 1821–1895.

LAC 40060
An historical sketch of internal improvements in Michigan, 1836–1846. [Ann Arbor, 1900]
Keith, Hannah Emily.

LAC 13591
Historical sketch of normal instruction in Wisconsin. 1846–1876. Madison, Wis., Atwood & Culver, printers, 1876.
Salisbury, Albert, 1843–1911.

LAC 40042
An historical sketch of Sturbridge, Mass., from its settlement to the present time. Brookfield, E. and L. Merriam, printers, 1838.
Clark, Joseph Sylvester, 1800–1861.

LAC 40041
An historical sketch of the city of Brooklyn, and the surrounding neighborhood, including the village of Williamsburgh, and the towns of Bushwick, Flatbush, Flatlands, New Utrecht, and Gravesend. To which is added, an interesting account of the battle of Long Island. Comp. from the best authorities. Brooklyn, The author, 1840.
Bailey, J   T.

LAC 40068
An historical sketch of the early movement in Illinois for the legalization of slavery, read at the annual meeting of the Chicago historical society, December 5th, 1864. Chicago, Fergus printing company, 1876.
Brown, William H   1796–1867.

LAC 15829
Historical sketch of the electric telegraph: including its rise and progress in the United States. New York, G. P. Putnam, 1852.
Jones, Alexander, 1802–1863.

LAC 14761
Historical sketch of the finances and financial policy of Massachusetts from 1780 to 1905, by Charles J. Bullock, PH. D. May, 1907. New York, For the American economic association, by the Macmillan company; [etc., etc., c1907]
Bullock, Charles Jesse, 1869–1941.

LAC 13466
Historical sketch of the German-English independent school of Indianapolis, "our old school." [Indianapolis, The Cheltenham-Aetna press, c1913]
Stein, Theodore, 1858–

LAC 10635
Historical sketch of the Illinois-central railroad, together with a brief biographical record of its incorporators and some of its early officers. Chicago, Fergus printing company, 1890.
Ackerman, William K., b. 1832.

LAC 14850
Historical sketch of the organization, administration, materiel and tactics of the artillery, United States army. Washington, D. C., J. J. Chapman, agent, 1884.
Birkhimer, William Edward, 1848–

LAC 23264
Historical sketch of the second war between the United States of America, and Great Britain, declared by act of Congress, the 18th of June, 1812, and concluded by peace, the 15th of February, 1815. Philadelphia, Lea and Blanchard, 1845–49.
Ingersoll, Charles Jared, 1782–1862.

LAC 40061
An historical sketch of the state of medicine in the American colonies, from their first settlement to the period of the revolution. 2d ed. Albany, C. Van Benthuysen, printer, 1850.
Beck, John Brodhead, 1794–1851.

LAC 10423
An historical sketch of Troy [N. H.] and her inhabitants, from the first settlement of the town, in 1764, to 1855. Keene, N. H. sentinel office, 1859.
Caverly, Abiel Moore, 1817–1879.

LAC 13690
Historical view of the American revolution... Boston, Ticknor & Fields, 1865.
Greene, George Washington, 1811–1883.

LAC 12359
An historical view of the government of Maryland, from its colonization to the present day. v. 1. Baltimore, F. Lucas, jr., Cushing & sons, and W. & J. Neal, 1831.
McMahon, John Van Lear, 1800–1871.

LAC 23019–23
Histories of the several regiments and battalions from North Carolina, in the great war 1861–'65. Written by members of the respective commands. Ed. by Walter Clark. Pub. by the state. Raleigh, E. M. Uzzell, printer, 1901.
Clark, Walter, 1846–1924, ed.

LAC 11333
The history and antiquities of Boston ... from its settlement in 1630, to the year 1770. Also, an introductory history of the discovery and settlement of New England. With notes, critical and illustrative. Boston, L. Stevens, 1856.
Drake, Samuel Gardner, 1798–1875.

LAC 13627
History and character of American revivals of religion. By the Rev. Calvin Colton. London, F. Westley and A. H. Davis, 1832.
Colton, Calvin, 1789–1857.

LAC 16886

History and civics of Oklahoma. Boston, New York [etc.] Ginn and company [c1910]
Abbott, Luther Jewett, 1872–1914.

LAC 12933

The history and conquest of the Philippines and our other island possessions, embracing our war with the Filipinos in 1899 together with a complete history of those islands from the earliest times to the present; an authentic history of the Spanish war prepared from official government reports of our army and navy officers ... the history of Cuba, Porto Rico, the Ladrone and the Hawaiian islands ... with over one hundred full page half-tone and other engravings. Philadelphia, Chicago [etc.] J. C. Winston & co. [1899]
March, Alden, 1869–

LAC 10094

History and cultivation of cotton and tobacco. By Colonel Robert L. De Coin. London, Chapman and Hall, 1864.
De Coin, Robert L.

LAC 40032

The history and culture of the olive. The anniversary address of the State agricultural society of South Carolina, delivered in the hall of the House of representatives, November 26th, 1846. By the Hon. Mitchel [!] King. Pub. by the society. Columbia, S. C., I. C. Morgan, printer, 1846.
King, Mitchell, 1783–1862.

LAC 20720–22

History and general description of New France, by Rev. P. F. X. de Charlevoix, S. J. Tr. from the original edition and ed., with notes, by Dr. John Gilmary Shea; with a new memoir and bibliography of the translator by Noah Farnham Morrison. New York, F. P. Harper, 1900.
Charlevoix, Pierre Francois Xavier de, 1682–1761.

LAC 13193

The history and geography of the Mississippi valley. To which is appended a condensed physical geography of the Atlantic United States, and the whole American continent. 2d ed. Cincinnati, E. H. Flint and L. R. Lincoln, 1832.
Flint, Timothy, 1780–1840.

LAC 13438

The history and growth of the United States census, prepared for the Senate committee on the census, by C. D. Wright, assisted by W. C. Hunt. Washington, Govt. print. off., 1900.
U. S. *Bureau of Labor.*

LAC 11747

History and incidents of Indian corn, and its culture. Including statistical, analytical and other tables: also, illustrations and diagrams. Cincinnati, Wrightson & co., printers, 1878.
Emerson, William Dana, 1813–1891.

LAC 20896–97

History and pathology of vaccination. Philadelphia, P. Blackiston, Son, & co., 1889.
Crookshank, Edgar March.

LAC 40013

History and philosophy of the eight-hour movement. Publication of the American federation of labor. [Washington, D. C.] c1889.
Danryid, Lemuel.

LAC 16016

History and present condition of the newspaper and periodical press of the United States, with a catalogue of the publications of the census year. By S. N. D. North, special agent. [Washington, Govt. print. off., 1884]
North, Simon Newton Dexter, 1849–1924.

LAC 12681

The history and present state of electricity, with original experiments. 2d ed., cor. and enl. ... London, Printed for J. Dodsley [etc.] 1769.
Priestley, Joseph, 1733–1804.

LAC 15620

History and progress of education, from the earliest times to the present. Intended as a manual for teachers and students. By Philobiblius [*pseud.*] With an introduction by Henry Barnard. New York, A. S. Barnes & Burr, 1866, [c1859]
Brockett, Linus Pierpont, 1820–1893.

LAC 14585

History and reminiscences of lower Wall street and vicinity. New York, The Spice mill publishing co., 1914.
Wakeman, Abram.

LAC 16034

The history, botany, and agriculture of sugar cane. Issued by the State bureau of agriculture and immigration. [Baton Rouge, La., 1897]
Stubbs, William Carter, 1846–1924.

LAC 20590–91

The history, civil and commercial, of the British colonies in the West Indies... Philadelphia, J. Humphreys, 1805–06.
Edwards, Bryan, 1743–1800.

LAC 12595

The history, diagnosis, and treatment of typhoid and of typhus fever; with an essay on the diagnosis of bilious remittent and of yellow fever... Philadelphia, Lea and Blanchard, 1842.
Bartlett, Elisha, 1804–1855.

LAC 14578

History of a literary radical, and other essays; ed. with an introduction by Van Wyck Brooks. New York, B. W. Huebsch, inc., 1920.
Bourne, Randolph Silliman, 1886–1918.

LAC 16512

History of a voyage to the China Sea. 2d ed. Boston, Wells and Lilly, 1826, [c1823]
White, John, *U.S.N.*

LAC 10029

History of Aberdeen-Angus cattle, by James Macdonald and James Sinclair. Rev. ed. by James Sinclair. London, Vinton & company, ltd., 1910.
Macdonald, James, 1852–1913.

LAC 11377
The history of Abraham Lincoln, and the overthrow of slavery. Chicago, Clark & co., 1866.
Arnold, Isaac Newton, 1815–1884.

LAC 13049
A history of agricultural education in the United States, 1785–1925. Washington, U. S. Govt. print. off., 1929.
True, Alfred Charles, 1853–1929.

LAC 10695
A history of agricultural experimentation and research in the United States 1607–1925 including a history of the United States Department of 'agriculture. By Alfred Charles True, late specialist in States relations work, United States Department of agriculture. Washington, U.S. Govt. print. off., 1937.
True, Alfred Charles, 1853–1929.

LAC 11768
A history of agricultural extension work in the United States, 1785–1923. Washington, U.S. Govt. print. off., 1928.
True, Alfred Charles, 1853–1929.

LAC 10112
The history of agriculture in Dane county, Wisconsin. Madison, Wis., 1905.
Hibbard, Benjamin Horace, 1870–

LAC 15217
History of agriculture in the northern United States, 1620–1860, by Percy Wells Bidwell and John I. Falconer. Washington, The Carnegie institution of Washington, 1925.
Bidwell, Percy Wells, 1888–

LAC 23816–17
History of agriculture in the southern United States to 1860, by Lewis Cecil Gray, assisted by Esther Katherine Thompson, with an introductory note by Henry Charles Taylor. Washington, The Carnegie institution of Washington, 1933.
Gray, Lewis Cecil, 1881–

LAC 20749
History of Alabama, and incidentally of Georgia and Mississippi, from the earliest period. 2d ed. Charleston [S. C.] Walker and James, 1851.
Pickett, Albert James, 1810–1858.

LAC 20829–30
The history of America. London, W. Strahan [etc.] 1777.
Robertson, William, 1721–1793.

LAC 40077
History of American abolitionism; its four great epochs, embracing narratives of the ordinance of 1787, compromise of 1820, annexation of Texas, Mexican war, Wilmot proviso, negro insurrections, abolition riots, slave rescues, compromise of 1850, Kansas bill of 1854, John Brown insurrection, 1859, valuable statistics, &c., &c., &c., together with a history of the southern confederacy. (Originally published in the New York Herald) New York, D. Appleton & co., 1861.
De Fontaine, Felix Gregory, 1832–1896.

LAC 16351
A history of American amateur athletics and aquatics with the records. New York, Outing co. [c1887]
Janssen, Frederick William, *comp.*

LAC 14879
History of American conspiracies: a record of treason, insurrection, rebellion, &c., in the United States of America, from 1760 to 1860. New York, J. D. Torrey [1863]
Victor, Orville James, 1827–1910.

LAC 12580
A history of American currency, with chapters on the English bank restriction and Austrian paper money. To which is appended "The bullion report". New York, H. Holt and company, 1874.
Sumner, William Graham, 1840–1910.

LAC 20659
A history of American literature... New York, G. P. Putnam's sons, 1885, [c1878]
Tyler, Moses Coit, 1835–1900.

LAC 20025–27
A history of American manufactures from 1608 to 1860 ... comprising annals of the industry of the United States in machinery, manufactures and useful arts, with a notice of the important inventions, tariffs, and the results of each decennial census. By J. Leander Bishop. With an appendix, containing statistics of the principal maunufacturing centres, and descriptions of remarkable manufactories at the present time... 3d ed., rev. and enl. Philadelphia, E. Young & co.; London, S. Low, son & co., 1868.
Bishop, John Leander, 1820–1868.

LAC 10794
The history of American music. With twelve full-page photogravures and one hundred and two illustrations in the text. New York, The Macmillan company; [etc., etc.] 1904.
Elson, Louis Charles, 1848–1920.

LAC 15882
History of American music. With introductions by George W. Chadwick and Frank Damrosch. W. L. Hubbard, editor. Toledo, I. Squire [c1908]
Hubbard, William Lines, 1867–   *ed.*

LAC 16718
The history of American painting. With twelve full-page photogravures and one hundred and twenty-one illustrations in the text. New York, The Macmillan company; London, Macmillan & co., ltd., 1905.
Isham, Samuel, 1855–1914.

LAC 15822
A history of American political theories. New York, London, The Macmillan company, 1903.
Merriam, Charles Edward, 1874–1953.

LAC 12480
History of American politics. New York, H. Holt and company, 1881, [c1879]
Johnston, Alexander, 1849–1889.

LAC 16450
A history of American privateers. Freeport, N. Y., Books for Libraries Press [1970]
Maclay, Edgar Stanton, 1863–1919.

LAC 16875
The history of American sculpture. With twelve full-page photogravures and one hundred and four illustrations in the text. New York, London, The Macmillan company, 1903.
Taft, Lorado, 1860–1936.

LAC 16868
The history of American slavery and Methodism, from 1780 to 1849: and History of the Wesleyan Methodist connection of America; in two parts, with an appendix. New York, 1849.
Matlack, Lucius C.

LAC 10441
History of American socialisms. Philadelphia, J. B. Lippincott & co., 1870.
Noyes, John Humphrey, 1811–1886.

LAC 10179
History of American steam navigation. New York, W. F. Sametz & co., inc., 1903.
Morrison, John Harrison, 1841–1917.

LAC 10901
History of Amesbury, including the first seventeen years of Salisbury, to the separation in 1654; and Merrimac, from its incorporation in 1876. Haverhill [Mass.] Press of F. P. Stiles, 1880.
Merrill, Joseph, 1814–1898.

LAC 13051
A history of Amherst college during the administrations of its first five presidents, from 1821 to 1891. By William S. Tyler, with an introductory note by Richard Salter Storrs. New York, F. H. Hitchcock, 1895.
Tyler, William Seymour, 1810–1897.

LAC 21820–22
The history of ancient Wethersfield, Connecticut; comprising the present towns of Wethersfield, Rocky Hill, and Newington; and of Glastonbury prior to its incorporation in 1693, from date of earliest settlement until the present time... New York, The Grafton press, 1904.
Adams, Sherman Wolcott, 1836–1898.

LAC 16154
History of ancient Windham, Ct. Genealogy. Containing a genealogical record of all the early families of ancient Windham, embracing the present towns of Windham, Mansfield, Hampton, Chaplin and Scotland. Part I. A–Bil. Willimantic, Weaver & Curtiss, 1864.
Weaver, William Lawton, 1816–1867.

LAC 22468
History of Andrew Jackson, pioneer, patriot, soldier, politician, president. New York, C. Scribner's sons, 1904.
Buell, Augustus C., 1847–1904.

LAC 14274–75
History of Ashburnham, Massachusetts, from the grant of Dorchester Canada to the present time, 1734–1886; with a genealogical register of Ashburnham families. Ashburnham, Mass., Pub. by the town, 1887.
Stearns, Ezra Scollay, 1838–1915.

LAC 10874
The history of Auburn. Auburn [N. Y.] Dennis bros. & co., 1869.
Hall, Henry, 1845–

LAC 14378–79
History of Baltimore city and county, from the earliest period to the present day: including biographical sketches of their representative men. Philadelphia, L. H. Everts, 1881.
Scharf, John Thomas, 1843–1898.

LAC 40026
History of banking in Mississippi. Oxford, Miss., Mississippi historical society, 1900.
Brough, Charles Hillman, 1876–1935.

LAC 10402
A history of banking in the United States, by John Jay Knox, assisted by a corps of financial writers in the various states; the entire work revised and brought up to date by Bradford Rhodes and Elmer H. Youngman. New York, B. Rhodes & company, 1900.
Knox, John Jay, 1828–1892.

LAC 14031
History of Baptist Indian missions: embracing remarks on the former and present condition of the aboriginal tribes; their settlement within the Indian Territory, and their future prospects. Washington, W. M. Morrison; New-York, H. and S. Raynor; [etc., etc.] 1840.
McCoy, Isaac, 1784–1846.

LAC 16151
The history of Barbados; comprising a geographical and statistical description of the island; a sketch of the historical events since the settlement; and an account of its geology and natural productions. London, Longman, Brown, Green and Longmans, 1848.
Schomburgk, *Sir* Robert Hermann, 1804–1865.

LAC 11709
A history of Barbados 1625–1685. Oxford, Clarendon press, 1926.
Harlow, Vincent Todd.

LAC 11722
History of Barnstead [N. H.] from its first settlement in 1727 to 1872. By Jeremiah P. Jewett, M. D. Since his decease rev., enl. and pub. by Robert B. Caverly. Lowell, Mass., Marden & Rowell, printers, 1872.
Jewett, Jeremiah Peabody, *d.* 1870.

LAC 13907
A history of Barrington, Rhode Island. Providence, Snow & Farnham, printers, 1898.
Bicknell, Thomas Williams, 1834–1925.

LAC 14292
History of Bath and environs. Sagadahoc county, Maine. 1607–1894... Portland, Me., Lakeside press, printers, 1894.
Reed, Parker McCobb, b. 1813.

LAC 13910
History of Bergen and Passaic counties, New Jersey, with biographical sketches of many of its pioneers and prominent men. Comp. under the supervision of W. Woodford Clayton, assisted by William Nelson. Philadelphia, Everts & Peck, 1882.
Clayton, W   Woodford, comp.

LAC 15897–98
History of Berks county in Pennsylvania. Philadelphia, Everts, Peck & Richards, 1886.
Montgomery, Morton Luther, 1846–

LAC 10891
A history of Bethlehem, Pennsylvania, 1741–1892, with some account of its founders and their early activity in America. Bethlehem, Pa., Times publishing company, 1903.
Levering, Joseph Mortimer, 1849–1908.

LAC 10377
History of Billerica, Massachusetts, with a Genealogical register, by the Rev. Henry A. Hazen. Boston, A. Williams and co., 1883.
Hazen, Henry Allen, 1832–1900.

LAC 10173
The history of bimetallism in the United States. 4th ed., with new appendices, a study on the fall of silver since 1885, and the experience of the United States with silver since 1878. New York, D. Appleton and co., 1900, [c1896]
Laughlin, James Laurence, 1850–1933.

LAC 16354
A history of Block island from its discovery, in 1514, to the present time, 1876. Hartford, Conn., The Case, Lockwood & Brainard co., 1877.
Livermore, Samuel Truesdale, 1824–1892.

LAC 13545
The history of Boscawen and Webster [N. H.] from 1733 to 1878. Concord, N. H., Printed by the Republican press association, 1878.
Coffin, Charles Carleton, 1823–1896, comp.

LAC 15348
A history of Boston, the metropolis of Massachusetts, from its origin to the present period; with some account of the environs. Boston, A. Bowen, 1825.
Snow, Caleb Hopkins, 1796–1835.

LAC 15044
History of Bowdoin college. With biographical sketches of its graduates, from 1806 to 1879, inclusive. By Nehemiah Cleaveland. Edited and completed by Alpheus Spring Packard. Boston, J. R. Osgood & company, 1882.
Cleaveland, Nehemiah, 1796–1877.

LAC 13817
The history of Boxford, Essex county, Massachusetts, from the earliest settlement known to the present time: a period of about two hundred and thirty years. Boxford, Mass., The author, 1880.
Perley, Sidney, 1858–

LAC 13948
History of Braintree, Massachusetts (1639–1708) the north precinct of Braintree (1708–1792) and the town of Quincy (1792–1889). Cambridge, Printed at the Riverside press, 1891.
Adams, Charles Francis, 1835–1915.

LAC 15238–39
History of Bristol County, Massachusetts, with biographical sketches of many of its pioneers and prominent men. Comp. under the supervision of D. Hamilton Hurd. Philadelphia, J. W. Lewis & co., 1883.
Hurd, Duane Hamilton, ed.

LAC 10820
The history of Bristol, R. I. The story of the Mount Hope lands, from the visit of the Northmen to the present time. Containing accounts of the Indian wars, the character and lives of the early settlers in Bristol, the events of the revolution, the privateers of the war of 1812, details of the commerce of the port, and sketches of its distinguished men. Providence, J. A. & R. A. Reid, 1880.
Munro, Wilfred Harold, 1849–1934.

LAC 10411
The history of Brown university 1764–1914. Providence, The University, 1914.
Bronson, Walter Cochrane, 1862–1928.

LAC 10590
History of Brown university, with illustrative documents. Providence, R. I. [Providence press company, printers] 1867.
Guild, Reuben Aldridge, 1822–1899.

LAC 16207–08
History of Bucks County, Pennsylvania; including an account of its original exploration; its relation to the settlements of New Jersey and Delaware; its erection into a separate county, also its subsequent growth and development, with sketches of its historic and interesting localities, and biographies of many of its representative citizens. Philadelphia, Chicago, A. Warner & co., 1887.
Battle, J   H   ed.

LAC 16792–93
History of Burlington and Mercer counties, New Jersey, with biographical sketches of many of their pioneers and prominent men. By Major E. M. Woodward and John F. Hageman. Philadelphia, Everts & Peck, 1883.
Woodward, Evan Morrison.

LAC 16682
The history of California. San Francisco, H. H. Bancroft & company, 1866.
Tuthill, Franklin, 1822–1865.

LAC 14456
A history of California labor legislation, with an introductory sketch of the San Francisco labor movement. Berkeley, The University press [c1910]
Eaves, Lucile, 1869–

LAC 11591

History of Cambridge, Massachusetts. 1630–1877. With a genealogical register. Boston, H. O. Houghton and company; New York, Hurd and Houghton, 1877.
Paige, Lucius Robinson, 1802–1896.

LAC 20528–29

The history of Cape Cod: the annals of Barnstable County, including the district of Mashpee. Boston, Printed for the author, by Geo. C. Rand & Avery, 1860–1862.
Freeman, Frederick, 1799–1883.

LAC 14835

The history of Carleton college, its origin and growth, environment and builders, by Rev. Delavan L. Leonard. Introduction by President James W. Strong. Chicago, New York [etc.] F. H. Revell company [1904]
Leonard, Delavan Levant, 1834–1917.

LAC 11278

The history of Charlestown, Massachusetts. By Richard Frothingham, jr. Charlestown, C. P. Emmons; Boston, C. C. Little and J. Brown, 1845–49.
Frothingham, Richard, 1812–1880.

LAC 10376

History of Cincinnati, Ohio, with illustrations and biographical sketches. Comp. by Henry A. Ford, A. M., and Mrs. Kate B. Ford. Cleveland, O., L. A. Williams & co., 1881.
Ford, Henry Allen, *comp.*

LAC 11666

History of coinage and currency in the United States and the perennial contest for sound money. New York, The Macmillan company; London, Macmillan & co., ltd., 1903.
Hepburn, Alonzo Barton, 1846–1922.

LAC 40004

History of collegiate education in agriculture. Urbana, Ill., 1907.
Davenport, Eugene, 1856–1941.

LAC 22732–35

History of Colorado. Chicago, The S. J. Clarke publishing company, 1918–19.
Stone, Wilbur Fiske, 1833–1920, *ed.*

LAC 16209

History of Columbia county, New York. With illustrations and biographical sketches of some of its prominent men and pioneers. Philadelphia, Everts & Ensign, 1878.
Ellis, Franklin, 1828–1885.

LAC 13018

A history of Columbia university, 1754–1904; published in commemoration of the one hundred and fiftieth anniversary of the founding of King's college. New York, The Columbia university press, The Macmillan company, agents; London, Macmillan & co., ltd., 1904.

LAC 10844

The history of Concord, from its first grant in 1725, to the organization of the city government in 1853, with a history of the ancient Penacooks. The whole interspersed with numerous interesting incidents and anecdotes, down to the present period, 1855; embellished with maps; with portraits of distinguished citizens, and views of ancient and modern residences... Concord [N. H.] B. W. Sanborn, 1856.
Bouton, Nathaniel, 1799–1878.

LAC 14758

The history of Concord, Massachusetts. Vol. I, Colonial Concord. Concord, Mass., The Erudite press, 1904.
Hudson, Alfred Sereno.

LAC 20494–95

History of Concord, New Hampshire, from the original grant in seventeen hundred and twenty-five to the opening of the twentieth century; prepared under the supervision of the City history commission; James O. Lyford, editor. [Concord, N. H., The Rumford press, 1903]
Concord, *N. H. City History Commission.*

LAC 21603–45

History of Congress.
The debates and proceedings in the Congress of the United States; with an appendix, containing important state papers and public documents, and all the laws of a public nature; with a copious index... [First to] Eighteenth Congress.–first session: comprising the period from [March 3, 1789] to May 27, 1824, inclusive. Comp. from authentic materials. Washington, Gales and Seaton, 1834–56.
U.S. *Congress.*

LAC 10417

History of crises under the national banking system. Washington, Govt. print. off., 1910 [*i.e.* 1911]
Sprague, Oliver Mitchell Wentworth, 1873–1953.

LAC 13911

History of Cumberland Co., Maine. With illustrations and biographical sketches of its prominent men and pioneers. Philadelphia, Everts & Peck, 1880.
Clayton, W   Woodford.

LAC 16332

A history of currency in the United States, with a brief description of the currency systems of all commercial nations. New York, The Macmillan company, 1915.
Hepburn, Alonzo Barton, 1846–1922.

LAC 23895–902

History of Dakota Territory, by George W. Kingsbury. South Dakota; its history and its people, ed. by George Martin Smith. Chicago, The S. J. Clarke publishing company, 1915.
Kingsbury, George Washington, 1837–

LAC 21117

History of Dartmouth college. Hanover, N. H., Dartmouth college publications, 1932.
Richardson, Leon Burr, 1878–

LAC 21067–68

A history of Dartmouth college and the town of Hanover, New Hampshire, by Frederick Chase. Ed. by John K. Lord. Cambridge [Mass.] J. Wilson and son, 1891–1913.
Chase, Frederick, 1840–1890.

LAC 11741

The history of Dedham, from the beginning of its settlement, in September, 1635, to May, 1827. Boston, Dutton and Wentworth, printers, 1827.
Worthington, Erastus, 1779–1842.

LAC 21203–04

A history of Deerfield, Massachusetts: the times when and the people by whom it was settled, unsettled and resettled: with a special study of the Indian wars in the Connecticut valley. With genealogies. Deerfield, Mass. [Greenfield, Mass., Press of E. A. Hall & co.] 1895–96.
Sheldon, George, 1818–1916.

LAC 23251–52

History of Delaware. 1609–1888. By J. Thomas Scharf, assisted by a staff of able assistants... Philadelphia, L. J. Richards & co., 1888.
Scharf, John Thomas, 1843–1898.

LAC 16571

History of Denver, with outlines of the earlier history of the Rocky Mountain country; ed. for the Denver times by Jerome C. Smiley. Denver, The Denver times, The Times-Sun publishing company, 1901.
Smiley, Jerome Constant.

LAC 10386–87

The history of Detroit and Michigan; or, The metropolis illustrated; a chronological cyclopedia of the past and present, including a full record of territorial days in Michigan, and the annals of Wayne county. Detroit, S. Farmer & co., 1884.
Farmer, Silas, 1839–1902.

LAC 20269

History of domestic and foreign commerce of the United States, by Emory R. Johnson, T. W. Van Metre, G. G. Heubner, and D. S. Hanchett, with an introductory note by Henry W. Farnam. Washington, D. C., Carnegie institution of Washington, 1915.
Johnson, Emory Richard, 1864–1950.

LAC 16148

History of Dover, New Hampshire... (Tercentenary ed.) Containing historical, genealogical and industrial data of its early settlers, their struggles and triumphs. [Manchester, N. H.] Printed by authority of the City councils, 1923.
Scales, John, 1835–1928, *ed.*

LAC 20003

History of early steamboat navigation on the Missouri River; life and adventures of Joseph La Barge... New York, F. P. Harper, 1903.
Chittenden, Hiram Martin, 1858–1917.

LAC 16155

A history of East Boston; with biographical sketches of its early proprietors, and an appendix. Boston, J. E. Tilton, 1858.
Sumner, William Hyslop, 1780–1861.

LAC 11293

History of Easthampton: its settlement and growth; its material, educational, and religious interests, together with a genealogical record of its original families. Northampton [Mass.] Trumbull & Gere, 1866.
Lyman, Payson Williston, 1842–

LAC 12998

A history of education. New York, C. Scribner's sons, 1900.
Davidson, Thomas, 1840–1900.

LAC 40050

The history of education as a professional subject, by Professor William H. Burnham and Professor Henry Suzzallo. New York, Teachers college, Columbia university, 1908.
Burnham, William Henry, 1855–1941.

LAC 13053

History of education in Alabama, 1702–1889. Washington, Govt. print. off., 1889.
Clark, Willis G.

LAC 10630

The history of education in Connecticut. Washington, Govt. print. off., 1893.
Steiner, Bernard Christian, 1867–1926.

LAC 40029

History of education in Florida. Washington, Govt. print. off., 1889.
Bush, George Gary, 1843–1898.

LAC 10580

A history of education in Indiana. New York, D. Appleton and company, 1892.
Boone, Richard Gause, 1849–1923.

LAC 21062–64

History of education in Iowa. Iowa City, Ia., The State historical society of Iowa, 1914–20.
Aurner, Clarence Ray, 1863–

LAC 10787

The history of education in Louisiana. Washington, Govt. print. off., 1898.
Fay, Edwin Whitfield, 1865–1920.

LAC 10831

History of education in Mississippi. Washington, Govt. print. off., 1899.
Mayes, Edward, 1846–1917.

LAC 11576

A history of education in Pennsylvania, private and public, elementary and higher. From the time the Swedes settled on the Delaware to the present day. Pub. for the author. Lancaster, Pa., Inquirer publishing company, 1886.
Wickersham, James Pyle, 1825–1893.

LAC 15779

A history of education in the United States. New York, The Macmillan company; London, Macmillan & co., ltd., 1904.
Dexter, Edwin Grant, 1868–1938.

LAC 11392

History of elections in the American colonies. New York, Columbia college, 1893.
Bishop, Cortlandt Field, 1870–1935.

LAC 10879
History of Elizabeth, New Jersey; including the early history of Union county. By Rev. Edwin F. Hatfield. New York, Carlton & Lanahan, 1868.
Hatfield, Edwin Francis, 1807–1883.

LAC 21823–26
The history of Enfield, Connecticut... Compiled from all the public records of the town known to exist, covering from the beginning to 1850 ... with the graveyard inscriptions and those Hartford, Northampton and Springfield records which refer to the people of Enfield. Ed. and pub. by Francis Olcott Allen. Lancaster, Pa., The Wickersham printing co., 1900.
Allen, Francis Olcott, 1840–1909, *ed.*

LAC 40053
History of engineer troops in the United States army, 1775–1901. Prepared under the direction of Major Thomas H. Rees ... by First Lieutenant G. A. Youngberg. Washington barracks, D. C., Press of the Engineer school, 1910.
Youngberg, Gilbert Albin, 1875–

LAC 23255–56
History of Essex and Hudson counties, New Jersey. Comp. by William H. Shaw. Philadelphia, Everts & Peck, 1884.
Shaw, William H.

LAC 20237–39
History of Essex County, Massachusetts, with biographical sketches of many of its pioneers and prominent men. Comp. under the supervision of D. Hamilton Hurd. Philadelphia, J. W. Lewis & co., 1888.
Hurd, Duane Hamilton, *ed.*

LAC 15240–41
History of Fairfield county, Connecticut, with illustrations and biographical sketches of its prominent men and pioneers. Comp. under the supervision of D. Hamilton Hurd. Philadelphia, J. W. Lewis & co., 1881.
Hurd, Duane Hamilton, *comp.*

LAC 23253–54
The history of Fairfield, Fairfield County, Connecticut, from the settlement of the town in 1639 to 1818. New York, The author, 1889–1905.
Schenck, Elizabeth Hubbell, 1832–

LAC 10784
The history of federal and state aid to higher education in the United States. Washington, Govt. print. off., 1890.
Blackmar, Frank Wilson, 1854–1931.

LAC 10780
The history of Fitzwilliam, New Hampshire, from 1752–1887. By Rev. John F. Norton, A. M. With a genealogical record of many Fitzwillian families by Joel Whittemore. New York, Burr printing house, 1888.
Norton, John Foote, 1809–1892.

LAC 10848
History of Fort Wayne, from the earliest known accounts of this point, to the present period. Embracing an extended view of the aboriginal tribes of the Northwest, including, more especially, the Miamies ... with a sketch of the life of General Anthony Wayne; including also a lengthy biography of ... pioneer settlers of Fort Wayne. Also an account of the manufacturing, mercantile, and railroad interests of Fort Wayne and vicinity. Fort Wayne, Ind., D. W. Jones & son, printers, 1868.
Brice, Wallace A.

LAC 11788
History of Framingham, Massachusetts, early known as Danforth's Farms, 1640–1880; with a genealogical register. [Framingham] Pub. by the town of Framingham, 1887.
Temple, Josiah Howard, 1815–1893.

LAC 10843
A history of Framingham, Massachusetts, including the Plantation, from 1640 to the present time, with an appendix, containing a notice of Sudbury and its first proprietors; also, a register of the inhabitants of Framingham before 1800, with genealogical sketches: Boston, J. Munroe and company, 1847.
Barry, William, 1805–1885.

LAC 13007
History of Franklin and Marshall college; Franklin college, 1787–1853; Marshall college, 1836–1853; Franklin and Marshall college, 1853–1903. Lancaster, Pa., Franklin and Marshall College Alumni association, 1903.
Dubbs, Joseph Henry, 1838–1910.

LAC 20747
The history of Georgia, containing brief sketches of the most remarkable events, up to the present day. By Capt. Hugh M'Call. Savannah, Seymour & Williams [etc.] 1811–16.
McCall, Hugh.

LAC 20767–68
A history of Georgia, from its first discovery by Europeans to the adoption of the present constitution in MDCCXCVIII. By Rev. William Bacon Stevens. New York, D. Appleton and co.; Savannah, W. T. Williams, 1847.
Stevens, William Bacon, *bp.*, 1815–1887.

LAC 11787
History of Great Barrington, (Berkshire County,) Massachusetts. Great Barrington, Mass., C. W. Bryan & co., 1882.
Taylor, Charles James, 1824–1904.

LAC 14795
History of Hadley, including the early history of Hatfield, South Hadley, Amherst and Granby, Massachusetts, by Sylvester Judd, with family genealogies, by Lucius M. Boltwood. Northampton, Printed by Metcalf & company, 1863.
Judd, Sylvester, 1789–1860.

LAC 21830–31
History of Hampton Falls, N. H. ... by Hon. Warren Brown. Concord, N. H., The Rumford press, 1900–18.
Brown, Warren, 1836–

LAC 10388–89
The history of Hancock, New Hampshire, 1764–1889. Pub. by Orland Eaton, agent, Joshua Stanley Lakin, John Peabody Hills, town history committee. Lowell, Mass., Vox populi press, S. W. Huse & co., 1889.
Hayward, William Willis, 1834–

LAC 15473
History of Hardwick, Massachusetts. With a genealogical register. Boston, New York, Houghton, Mifflin and company, 1883.
Paige, Lucius Robinson, 1802–1896.

LAC 15628
History of Harford County, Maryland, from 1608 (the year of Smith's expedition) to the close of the war of 1812. Baltimore, Md., Press of Sun book office, 1901.
Preston, Walter Wilkes, 1863–

LAC 20335–36
The history of Harvard university. Cambridge, J. Owen, 1840.
Quincy, Josiah, 1772–1864.

LAC 13038
A history of Harvard university, from its foundation, in the year 1636, to the period of the American revolution. Cambridge, Brown, Shattuck, and company, 1833.
Peirce, Benjamin, 1778–1831.

LAC 10859
The history of Haverhill, Massachusetts, from its first settlement, in 1640, to the year 1860. Haverhill, Pub. by the author, 1861.
Chase, George Wingate, 1826–1867.

LAC 11693
History of Haverhill, N. H., by Rev. J. Q. Bittinger. Haverhill, N. H. [Cohos steam press] 1888.
Bittinger, John Quincy.

LAC 13530
History of Hennepin county and the city of Minneapolis, including the Explorers and pioneers of Minnesota, by Rev. Edward D. Neill, and Outlines of the history of Minnesota, by J. Fletcher Williams. Minneapolis, North star publishing company, 1881.
Warner, George E. 1826?–1917.

LAC 15071
A history of Herkimer County, including the upper Mohawk Valley, from the earliest period to the present time: with a brief notice of the Iroquois Indians, the early German tribes, the Palatine immigrations ... also biographical notices of the most prominent public men of the county: with important statistical information. Albany, J. Munsell, 1856.
Benton, Nathaniel Soley.

LAC 13050
A history of higher education in America. New York, D. Appleton and company, 1906.
Thwing, Charles Franklin, 1853–1937.

LAC 13023
History of higher education in Michigan. Washington, Govt. print. off., 1891.
McLaughlin, Andrew Cunningham, 1861–1941.

LAC 13054
The history of higher education in Ohio, by George W. Knight and John R. Commons. Washington, Govt. print. off., 1891.
Knight, George Wells, 1858–1932.

LAC 10592
A history of higher education in Pennsylvania, by Charles H. Haskins and William I. Hull. Washington, Gov't print. off., 1902.
Haskins, Charles Homer, 1870–1937.

LAC 15205
History of higher education in South Carolina, with a sketch of the free school system. Washington, Govt. print. off., 1889.
Meriwether, Colyer, d. 1920.

LAC 12985
History of higher education of women in the South prior to 1860. New York and Washington, The Neale publishing company, 1909.
Blandin, Isabella Margaret Elizabeth.

LAC 11563
History of Hillsborough County, New Hampshire. Comp. under the supervision of D. Hamilton Hurd. Philadelphia, J. W. Lewis & co., 1885.
Hurd, Duane Hamilton, ed.

LAC 14801
The history of Idaho. Boise, Id., Press of Syms-York company, inc., 1910.
Hailey, John, 1835–1921.

LAC 13155
The history of Illinois, from its first discovery and settlement to the present time. New-York, J. Winchester, 1844.
Brown, Henry, 1789–1849.

LAC 14463
History of immigration to the United States, exhibiting the number, sex, age, occupation, and country of birth, of passengers arriving ... by sea from foreign countries, from September 30, 1819 to December 31, 1855; compiled entirely from official data: with an introductory review of the progress and extent of immigration to the United States prior to 1819, and an appendix, containing the naturalization and passenger laws of the United States... New York, Redfield, 1856.
Bromwell, William Jeremy, 1834–1874.

LAC 15148
History of Indian missions on the Pacific coast. Oregon, Washington and Idaho. By Rev. Myron Eells. With an introduction by Rev. G. H. Atkinson, D. D. Philadelphia, New York, The American Sunday-school union [c1882]
Eells, Myron, 1843–1907.

LAC 13179
A history of Indiana, from its earliest exploration by Europeans to the close of the territorial government, in 1816: comprehending a history of the discovery, settlement, and civil and military affairs of the territory of the U.S. northwest of the river Ohio, and a general view of the progress of public affairs in Indiana, from 1816–1856. Indianapolis, Bingham & Doughty, 1859.
Dillon, John Brown, 1808?–1879.

LAC 10910
A history of industrial Paterson ... together with outlines of state, county and local history... Illustrated with views and portraits on steel, and including a map of the city, carefully revised and corrected to date. Paterson, N. J., C. M. Herrick, printer, 1882.
Trumbull, Levi R.

LAC 14211
History of insurance in Philadelphia for two centuries (1683-1882) Philadelphia, Review publishing and printing company, 1888.
Fowler, John A   *d.* 1911.

LAC 23554-56
History of Iowa from the earliest times to the beginning of the twentieth century... Illustrated with photographic views of the natural scenery of the state, public buildings, pioneer life, etc., with portraits and biographies of notable men and women of Iowa... New York, The Century history company [c1903]
Gue, Benjamin F   1828-1904.

LAC 22725-27
The history of Jamaica; or, General survey of the antient and modern state of that island: with reflections on its situation, settlements, inhabitants, climate, products, commerce, laws, and government... Illustrated with copper plates. London, T. Lowndes, 1774.
Long, Edward, 1734-1813.

LAC 16365
History of Jefferson college: including an account of the early "log-cabin" schools, and the Canonsburg academy: with biographical sketches of Rev. Matthew Brown, D. D., Rev. Samuel Ralston, D. D., Rev. Matthew Henderson, Rev. James Ramsey, D. D., Rev. John H. Kennedy, and Rev. Abrm. Anderson, D. D. Pittsburgh, J. T. Shryock, 1857.
Smith, Joseph, 1796-1868.

LAC 10903
The history of Kansas City, together with a sketch of the commercial resources of the country with which it is surrounded. Kansas City, Birdsall & Miller, 1881.
Miller, William H.

LAC 10825
History of Kansas newspapers; a history of the newspapers and magazines published in Kansas from the organization of Kansas territory, 1854, to January 1, 1916. Together with brief statistical information of the counties, cities and towns of the state. William E. Connelley, secretary. Topeka, Kansas state printing plant, 1916.
Kansas State Historical Society.

LAC 14388
A history of Kentucky. New York, Prentice-Hall, inc., 1937.
Clark, Thomas Dionysius, 1903-

LAC 23044-45
The history of Kentucky. Exhibiting an account of the modern discovery; settlement; progressive improvement; civil and military transactions; and the present state of the country. [2d ed.] Frankfort, G. S. Robinson, printer, 1824.
Marshall, Humphrey, 1760-1841.

LAC 14434
The history of Kentucky, from its earliest discovery and settlement to the present date... Louisville, Ky., The Prentice press, 1895.
Smith, Zachariah Frederick, 1827-1911.

LAC 16364
The history of King Philip's war, by Benjamin Church; with an introduction and notes by Henry Martyn Dexter. Boston, J. K. Wiggin, 1865.
Church, Benjamin, 1639-1718.

LAC 13636
The history of King Philip's war, by the Rev. Increase Mather, D. D. Also, a history of the same war, by the Rev. Cotton Mather, D. D. To which are added an introduction and notes by Samuel G. Drake. Albany, Printed for the editor, 1862.
Mather, Increase, 1639-1723.

LAC 16152
The history of Kingston, New York. From its early settlement to the year 1820. New York, Burr printing house, 1888.
Schoonmaker, Marius, 1811-1894.

LAC 16393
History of Labette county, Kansas, from the first settlement to the close of 1892. Topeka, Kan., Crane & company, 1893.
Case, Nelson, 1845-1921.

LAC 12458
The history of legislative methods in the period before 1825. New Haven, Yale university press; [etc., etc.] 1917.
Harlow, Ralph Volney, 1884-1956.

LAC 11739
The history of Leominster, or the northern half of the Lancaster new or additional grant, from June 26, 1701, the date of the deed from George Tahanto, Indian sagamore, to July 4, 1852. Fitchburg, Printed at the Reveille office, 1853.
Wilder, David, 1778-1866.

LAC 11275
History of Lexington, Kentucky; its early annals and recent progress, including biographical sketches and personal reminiscences of the pioneer settlers, notices of prominent citizens, etc., etc. Cincinnati, R. Clarke & co., 1872.
Ranck, George Washington, 1841-1900.

LAC 11358-59
History of Litchfield county, Connecticut, with illustrations and biographical sketches of its prominent men and pioneers. Philadelphia, J. W. Lewis & co., 1881.

LAC 23890-92
History of Louisiana... 2d ed. New York, W. J. Widdleton, 1867.
Gayarre, Charles Etienne Arthur, 1805-1895.

LAC 12360
The history of Louisiana, from the earliest period, by Francois Xavier Martin. With a memoir of the author, by Judge W. W. Howe. To which is appended Annals of Louisiana, from the close of Martin's history, 1815, to the commencement of the civil war, 1861, by John F. Condon. New Orleans, J. A. Gresham, 1882.
Martin, Francois Xavier, 1762-1846.

LAC 10652
The history of Louisiana, particularly of the cession of that colony to the United States of America; with an introductory essay on the Constitution and government of the United States. Tr. from the French by an American citizen. Philadelphia, Carey & Lea, 1830.
Barbe-Marbois, Francois, *marquis* de. 1745–1837.

LAC 15649
The history of Louisville, from its earliest settlement till the year 1852. Louisville, Ky., Hull and brother, 1852.
Casseday, Benjamin.

LAC 11295
The history of Ludlow, Massachusetts, with biographical sketches of leading citizens, reminiscences, genealogies, farm histories, and an account of the centennial celebration, June 17, 1874. 2d ed., rev. and enl. Printed by vote of the town. Springfield, Mass., Springfield printing and binding company, 1912.
Noon, Alfred, *comp.*

LAC 20177
History of Lynn, Essex County, Massachusetts, including Lynnfield, Saugus, Swampscott, and Nahant, 1629–[1890] Lynn, G. C. Herbert, 1890.
Lewis, Alonzo, 1794–1861.

LAC 10371
A history of Madison, the capital of Wisconsin; including the Four lake country; to July, 1874, with an appendix of notes on Dane county and its towns. Madison, Wis. [Atwood & Culver, printers] 1874.
Durrie, Daniel Steele, 1819–1892.

LAC 14205
A history of manufactures in the Ohio valley to the year 1860... [New York, The Knickerbocker press] 1914.
Lippincott, Isaac, 1879–

LAC 20782–83
History of manufactures in the United States ... by Victor S. Clark; with an introductory note by Henry W. Farnam. 1929 ed. New York [etc.] Published for the Carnegie institution of Washington by the McGraw-Hill book company, inc., 1929.
Clark, Victor Selden, 1868–

LAC 16348
A history of Marlboro county, with traditions and sketches of numerous families. Rev. J. A. W. Thomas, author. Atlanta, Ga., The Foote & Davies company, 1897.
Thomas, J   A   W   1822–1896.

LAC 20508–10
The history of Martha's Vineyard, Dukes County, Massachusetts... Boston, G. H. Dean, 1911–25.
Banks, Charles Edward, 1854–1931.

LAC 15759
A history of Maryland; from its settlement in 1634, to the year 1848, with an account of its first discovery, and the various explorations of the Chesapeake Bay, anterior to its settlement; to which is added, a copious appendix, containing the names of the officers of the old Maryland line; the lords proprietary of the province, and the governors of Maryland, from its settlement to the present time... For the use of schools. Baltimore, J. Murphy & co.; Cushings & Bailey, 1850.
McSherry, James, 1819–1869.

LAC 23859–60
History of Maryland, from the earliest period to the present day. Baltimore, J. B. Piet, 1879.
Scharf, John Thomas, 1843–1898.

LAC 20771–72
The history of Maryland; its first settlement, in 1633, to the restoration, in 1660; with a copious introduction, and notes and illustrations. Baltimore, J. Lucas & E. K. Deaver, 1837.
Bozman, John Leeds, 1757–1823.

LAC 40147
The history of Mason and Dixon's line; contained in an address delivered by John H. B. Latrobe ... before the Historical society of Pennsylvania, November 8, 1854. [Philadelphia] Press of the Society, 1855.
Latrobe, John Hazlehurst Boneval, 1803–1891.

LAC 21431–32
History of Massachusetts... Boston, Richardson and Lord [etc.] 1822–29.
Bradford, Alden, 1765–1843.

LAC 22556–57
A history of Massachusetts in the civil war. Boston, E. P. Dutton & co., 1868–71.
Schouler, William, 1814–1872.

LAC 21268–69
A history of matrimonial institutions chiefly in England and the United States, with an introductory analysis of the literature and the theories of primitive marriage and the family. Chicago, The University of Chicago press, Callaghan & company; [etc., etc.] 1904.
Howard, George Elliott, 1849–1928.

LAC 20448
History of Mecklenburg county and the city of Charlotte, from 1740 to 1903. Charlotte, N. C., Observer printing house, 1903.
Tompkins, Daniel Augustus, 1851–1914.

LAC 13844
History of medical education and institutions in the United States, from the first settlement of the British colonies to the year 1850; with a chapter on the present condition and wants of the profession, and the means necessary for supplying those wants, and elevating the character and extending the usefulness of the whole profession. Chicago, S. C. Griggs & co., 1851.
Davis, Nathan Smith, 1817–1904.

LAC 14306
History of medicine in New Jersey, and of its medical men, from the settlement of the province to A. D. 1800. Newark, N. J., M. R. Dennis & co., 1879.
Wickes, Stephen, 1813–1889.

LAC 16087
The history of medicine in the United States; a collection of facts and documents relating to the history of medical science in this country, from the earliest English colonization to the year 1800; with a supplemental chapter on the discovery of anaesthesia. Philadelphia and London, J. B. Lippincott company, 1901.
Packard, Francis Randolph, 1870–1950.

LAC 11717
The history of Medway, Mass. 1713 to 1885, ed. by Rev. E. O. Jameson. Illustrated by G. J. La Croix. Pub. by the town. [Providence, R. I., J. A. & R. A. Reid, printers, c1886]
Jameson, Ephraim Orcutt, 1832–1902.

LAC 11718–19
History of Merrimack and Belknap counties, New Hampshire. Ed. by D. Hamilton Hurd. Philadelphia, J. W. Lewis & co., 1885.
Hurd, Duane Hamilton, *ed.*

LAC 22584–85
History of Methodism in Tennessee. Nashville, Tenn., Publishing house of the M. E. church, South, 1886–95.
McFerrin, John Berry, 1807–1887.

LAC 15971
History of middle Tennessee; or, Life and times of Gen. James Robertson. Nashville, Tenn., Printed for the author, 1859.
Putnam, Albigence Waldo.

LAC 20543
History of Middlesex County, Massachusetts, with biographical sketches of many of its pioneers and prominent men. Comp. under the supervision of D. Hamilton Hurd. Philadelphia, J. W. Lewis & co., 1890.
Hurd, Duane Hamilton, *ed.*

LAC 14650
A history of military government in newly acquired territory of the United States... New York, Columbia university press, 1904.
Thomas, David Yancey, 1872–1943.

LAC 16798
History of military mobilization in the United States Army, 1775–1945, by Marvin A. Kreidberg, Lt. Col., Inf., U.S. Army, and Merton G. Henry, 1st Lt., AGC, U.S. Army. [Washington, 1955]
U.S. *Dept. of the Army. Office of Military History.*

LAC 15346
The history of Milton, Mass., 1640 to 1887... [Boston, Press of Rockwell and Churchill, 1887]
Teele, Albert Kendall, 1823–1901, *ed.*

LAC 12306
The history of Minnesota: from the earliest French explorations to the present time. By the Rev. Edward Duffield Neill. Philadelphia, J. B. Lippincott & co., 1858.
Neill, Edward Duffield, 1823–1893.

LAC 22137–38
A history of Missouri from the earliest explorations and settlements until the admission of the state into the union. Chicago, R. R. Donnelley & sons company, 1908.
Houck, Louis, 1840–1925.

LAC 13476
The history of money in America from the earliest times to the establishment of the constitution. New York, The Cambridge encyclopedia company, 1899.
Del Mar, Alexander, 1836–1926.

LAC 13338–39
History of Montana. 1739–1885. A history of its discovery and settlement, social and commercial progress, mines and miners, agriculture and stock-growing, churches, schools and societies, Indians and Indian wars, vigilantes, courts of justice, newspaper press, navigation, railroads and statistics, with histories of counties, cities, villages and mining camps... Chicago, Warner, Beers & company, 1885.
Leeson, Michael A *ed.*

LAC 14443
History of Montgomery county; embracing early discoveries; the advance of civilization; the labors and triumphs of Sir William Johnson; the inception and development of manufactures; with town and local records; and military achievements of Montgomery patriots. Rev. and ed. by Washington Frothingham. Syracuse, N. Y., D. Mason, 1892.
Frothingham, Washington, *b.* 1822.

LAC 21378
The history of moral science. London, J. Duncan; [etc., etc.] 1833.
Blakey, Robert, 1795–1878.

LAC 14692
History of Morgan's cavalry. Cincinnati, Miami printing and publishing company, 1867.
Duke, Basil Wilson, 1838–1916.

LAC 16594
A history of music in New England: with biographical sketches of reformers and psalmists. Boston, Wilkins, Carter & co., 1846.
Hood, George.

LAC 11614
The history of Nantucket; being a compendious account of the first settlement of the island by the English, together with the rise and progress of the whale fishery; and other historical facts relative to said island and its inhabitants. In two parts. Boston, Hilliard, Gray and co., 1835.
Macy, Obed.

LAC 13043
A history of Nazareth hall, from 1755 to 1855: and of the reunions of its former pupils, in 1854 and 1855. By Rev. Levin T. Reichel. Philadelphia, J. B. Lippincott & company, 1855.
Reichel, Levin Theodore, 1812–1878.

LAC 11700
History of Needham, Massachusetts, 1711–1911; including West Needham, now the town of Wellesley, to its separation from Needham in 1881, with some references to its affairs to 1911. [Cambridge] Priv. print. at the University press [c1912]
Clarke, George Kuhn, 1858–

LAC 12841
The history of Negro servitude in Illinois, and of the slavery agitation in that state, 1719–1864. Chicago, A. C. McClurg & co., 1904.
Harris, Norman Dwight, 1870–

LAC 16860
History of Nevada. With illustrations and biographical sketches of its prominent men and pioneers. Oakland, Cal., Thompson & West, 1881.
Angel, Myron, *ed.*

LAC 21310-14
History of New England. Boston, Little, Brown, and company, 1859–90.
Palfrey, John Gorham, 1796–1881.

LAC 20824
The history of New-England containing an impartial account of the civil and ecclesiastical affairs of the country to the year of Our Lord, 1700. To which is added the present state of New-England. With a new and accurate map of the country. And an appendix containing their present charter, their ecclesiastical discipline, and their municipal-laws. In two volumes. The 2d ed. with many additions by the author. London, Printed for A. Ward [etc.] 1747.
Neal, Daniel, 1678–1743.

LAC 22736-37
The history of New England from 1630 to 1649. By John Winthrop, esq. first governour of the colony of the Massachusetts bay. From his original manuscripts. With notes to illustrate the civil and ecclesiastical concerns, the geography, settlement, and institutions of the country, and the lives and manners of the principal planters. By James Savage. A new ed., with additions and corrections by the former editor. Boston, Little, Brown and company, 1853.
Winthrop, John, 1588–1649.

LAC 21376-77
A history of New England. With particular reference to the denomination of Christians called Baptists. By Isaac Backus. 2d ed., with notes. By David Weston. Newton, Mass., The Backus historical society, 1871.
Backus, Isaac, 1724–1806.

LAC 20669-70
The history of New-Hampshire. Comprehending the events of one complete century and seventy-five years from the discovery of the river Pascataqua to the year one thousand seven hundred and ninety. Containing also, a geographical description of the state, with sketches of its natural history, productions, improvements, and present state of society and manners, laws, and government. 2d ed., with large additions and improvements, published from the author's last manuscript. Illustrated by a map. Boston: Published by Bradford and Read, 1813.
Belknap, Jeremy, 1744–1798.

LAC 11706
The history of New Jersey, from its discovery by Europeans, to the adoption of the federal Constitution. Trenton, D. Fenton, 1834.
Gordon, Thomas Francis, 1787–1860.

LAC 14062
History of New London, Connecticut. From the first survey of the coast in 1612, to 1852. New London, The author [Hartford, Ct., Press of Case, Tiffany and company] 1852.
Caulkins, Frances Manwaring, 1795–1869.

LAC 15242
History of New London county, Connecticut, with biographical sketches of many of its pioneers and prominent men. Comp. under the supervision of D. Hamilton Hurd. Philadelphia, J. W. Lewis & co., 1882.
Hurd, Duane Hamilton, *ed.*

LAC 16569
History of New Mexico from the Spanish conquest to the present time, 1530–1890, with portraits and biographical sketches of its prominent people. New York, New Mexico historical publishing co., 1891.
Haines, Helen.

LAC 20736-37
History of New Netherland; or, New York under the Dutch. New York, D. Appleton & company; Philadelphia, G. S. Appleton, 1848.
O'Callaghan, Edmund Bailey, 1797–1880.

LAC 16222
History of New York city, embracing an outline sketch of events from 1609 to 1830, and a full account of its development from 1830 to 1884. By Benson J. Lossing. Illustrated with portraits, views of parks, buildings, etc., engraved on steel by Perine. New York, G. E. Perine [c1884]
Lossing, Benson John, 1813–1891.

LAC 10908
History of New York ship yards. New York, Press of W. F. Sametz & co. [c1909]
Morrison, John Harrison, 1841–1917.

LAC 14087
History of Newbury, Mass., 1635–1902. Boston, Damrell & Upham, 1902.
Currier, John James, 1834–1912.

LAC 21196-97
History of Newburyport, Mass., 1764–1909. Newburyport, Mass., The author, 1906–09.
Currier, John James, 1834–1912.

LAC 15984
A history of Newfoundland from the English, colonial, and foreign records. With numerous illustrations and maps. 2d ed., rev. and cor. London, Eyre and Spottiswoode, 1896.
Prowse, Daniel Woodley.

LAC 13676-77
History of Newport county, Rhode Island. From the year 1638 to the year 1887, including the settlement of its towns, and their subsequent progress... New York, L. E. Preston & co., 1888.
Bayles, Richard Mather, *ed.*

LAC 11302
History of Newton, Massachusetts. Town and city, from its earliest settlement to the present time. 1630–1880. By S. F. Smith, D. D. Boston, The American logotype company, 1880.
Smith, Samuel Francis, 1808–1895.

LAC 11714–15

History of Norfolk county, Massachusetts, with biographical sketches of many of its pioneers and prominent men. Comp. under the supervision of D. Hamilton Hurd. Philadelphia, J. W. Lewis & co., 1884.
Hurd, Duane Hamilton, *ed.*

LAC 14086

History of Norfolk, Litchfield county, Connecticut. Opening chapters by Rev. Joseph Eldridge, D. D. Comp. by Theron Wilmot Crissey, L. L. B. Everett, Mass., Massachusetts publishing company, 1900.
Crissey, Theron Wilmot, *comp.*

LAC 14213

The history of North Atlantic steam navigation with some account of early ships and shipowners. With over fifty illustrations of ships and portraits of owners. New York, C. Scribner's sons, 1896.
Fry, Henry.

LAC 11789

History of North Brookfield, Massachusetts. Preceded by an account of old Quabaug, Indian and English occupation, 1647–1676; Brookfield records, 1686–1783. By J. H. Temple. With a genealogical register. North Brookfield, Pub. by the town [Boston, printed] 1887.
Temple, Josiah Howard, 1815–1893.

LAC 20154

History of North Carolina. With maps and illustrations. Fayetteville, N. C., E. J. Hale & son, 1857–58.
Hawks, Francis Lister, 1798–1866.

LAC 20762

The history of North Carolina. Philadelphia: Published by Thomas Dobson, At the Stone House, no. 41, South Second street. Fry and Kammerer, printers, 1812.
Williamson, Hugh, 1735–1819.

LAC 14821

A history of Norwegian immigration to the United States from the earliest beginning down to the year 1848. Iowa City, Ia., Priv. print., 1909.
Flom, George Tobias, 1871–

LAC 14063

History of Norwich, Connecticut: from its settlement in 1660, to January 1845. Norwich, T. Robinson, 1845.
Caulkins, Frances Manwaring, 1795–1869.

LAC 23052–53

A history of Nova-Scotia, or Acadie. Halifax, N. S., J. Barnes, 1865–67.
Murdoch, Beamish, *b.* 1800.

LAC 16199

History of Ohio agriculture; a treatise on the development of the various lines and phases of farm life in Ohio. Concord, N. H., The Rumford press, 1900.
Burkett, Charles William, 1873–

LAC 10858

History of old Chester [N. H.] from 1719 to 1869. Auburn, N. H., The author, 1869.
Chase, Benjamin, 1799–1889.

LAC 16638

History of old Yarmouth: comprising the present towns of Yarmouth and Dennis. From the settlement to the division in 1794 with the history of both towns to these times. Yarmouth Port, The author, 1884.
Swift, Charles Francis.

LAC 15349

History of Omaha from the pioneer days to the present time. Omaha, Gibson, Miller & Richardson, printers, 1889.
Sorenson, Alfred Rasmus, 1850–

LAC 10778

The history of Orangeburg County, South Carolina, from its first settlement to the close of the revolutionary war, by A. S. Salley, jr. Orangeburg, S. C., R. L. Berry, printer, 1898.
Salley, Alexander Samuel, 1871–

LAC 16128

A history of Oregon, 1792–1849, drawn from personal observation and authentic information. Portland, Or., Harris & Holman; New York, The American news company; [etc., etc.] 1870.
Gray, William Henry, 1810–1889.

LAC 11438

The history of our customs, aids, subsidies, national debts, and taxes. From William the Conqueror, to the present year MDCCLXI... London, Printed for G. Kearsly, 1761.
Cunningham, Timothy, *d.* 1789.

LAC 11594

History of Pelham, Mass., from 1738 to 1898, including the early history of Prescott... Amherst, Mass., Press of Carpenter & Morehouse, 1898.
Parmenter, Charles Oscar, 1833–

LAC 20165

History of Pembroke, N. H. 1730–1895. In two volumes. By Rev. N. F. Carter, assisted by Hon. T. L. Fowler. Concord, N. H., Printed by Republican press association, 1895.
Carter, Nathan Franklin, 1830–1915.

LAC 13644

History of Pennsylvania hall, which was destroyed by a mob, on the 17th of May, 1838... Philadelphia, Printed by Merrihew and Gunn [1838]
Pennsylvania Hall Association, *Philadelphia.*

LAC 20556–57

The history of Pennsylvania, in North America, from the original institution and settlement of that province, under the first proprietor and governor, William Penn, in 1681, till after the year 1742; with an introduction, respecting, the life of W. Penn, prior to the grant of the province, and the religious society of the people called Quakers;–with the first rise of the neighbouring colonies, more particularly of West-New-Jersey, and the settlement of the Dutch and Swedes on Delaware. To which is added, a brief description of the said province, and of the general state, in which it flourished, principally between the years 1760 and 1770... With an appendix. Written principally between the years 1776 and 1780, by Robert Proud. Philadelphia: Printed and sold by Zachariah Poulson, junior, number eighty, Chesnut-street, 1797–98.
Proud, Robert, 1728–1813.

LAC 21200-2
History of Philadelphia. 1609-1884. By J. Thomas Scharf and Thompson Westcott. Philadelphia, L. H. Everts & co., 1884.
Scharf, John Thomas, 1843-1898.

LAC 16301
The history of Philip's war, commonly called the great Indian war, of 1675 and 1676. Also, of the French and Indian wars at the eastward, in 1689, 1690, 1692, 1696, and 1704. By Thomas Church, esq. With numerous notes to explain the situation of the places of battles, the particular geography of the ravaged country, and the lives of the principal persons engaged in those wars. Also, an appendix containing an account of the treatment of the natives by the early voyagers, the settlement of N. England by the forefathers, the Pequot war, narratives of persons carried into captivity, anecdotes of the Indians, and the most important late Indian wars to the time of the Creek war. By Samuel G. Drake. 2d ed. ... Exeter, N. H., J. & B. Williams, 1829.
Church, Benjamin, 1639-1718.

LAC 15439
The history of Pithole: by "Crocus" (Chas. C. Leonard) Pithole City, Pa., Morton, Longwell & co., 1867.
Leonard, Charles C   1843-1879.

LAC 10884
The history of Pittsburgh, its rise and progress. Pittsburgh, Pa., B. C. & Gordon Montgomery co., 1906.
Killikelly, Sarah Hutchins, 1840-1912.

LAC 15229
The history of Pittsburgh, with a brief notice of its facilities of communication, and other advantages for commercial and manufacturing purposes. With two maps. Pittsburgh, J. H. Mellor, 1851.
Craig, Neville B., 1787-1863.

LAC 20559-60
The history of Pittsfield, (Berkshire county,) Massachusetts... Comp. and written, under the general direction of a committee, by J. E. A. Smith. By authority of the town. Boston, Lee and Shepard, 1869-76.
Smith, Joseph Edward Adams, 1822-1896.

LAC 11390
The history of political parties in the province of New York, 1760-1776... Madison, Wis., 1909.
Becker, Carl Lotus, 1873-1945.

LAC 14794
History of political parties, in the state of New York. From the acknowledgment of the independence of the United States to the close of the presidential election in eighteen hundred forty-four... Auburn, N. Y., Alden & Markham, 1846.
Jenkins, John Stilwell, 1818-1852.

LAC 20795-97
The history of political parties in the state of New-York, from the ratification of the federal Constitution to December, 1840... Syracuse, Hall, Mills, 1852.
Hammond, Jabez Delano, 1778-1855.

LAC 11197
History of poor relief legislation in Pennsylvania, 1682-1913. Cleona, Pa., Holzapfel publishing company [c1913]
Heffner, William Clinton, 1865-1931.

LAC 14373
The history of Portland, from 1632 to 1864: with a notice of previous settlements, colonial grants, and changes of government in Maine. 2d ed.-rev. and enl. Portland, Bailey & Noyes, 1865.
Willis, William, 1794-1870.

LAC 20189
History of Princeton and its institutions: the town from its first settlement, through the revolutionary war, to the present time-its churches-schools-college-theological seminary-literature ... etc. Illustrated with steel and wood engravings. Philadelphia, J. B. Lippincott & co., 1879.
Hageman, John Frelinghuysen.

LAC 20054-55
The history of printing in America, with a biography of printers, and an account of newspapers... 2d ed. With the author's corrections and additions, and a catalogue of American publications previous to the revolution of 1776. Pub. under the supervision of a special committee of the American antiquarian society. Albany, N. Y., J. Munsell, printer, 1874.
Thomas, Isaiah, 1749-1831.

LAC 14730
History of propellers and steam navigation with biographical sketches of the early inventors. New-York, G. P. Putnam, 1851.
Macfarlane, Robert, 1815-1883.

LAC 11511
History of proprietary government in Pennsylvania. New York, Columbia university, 1896.
Shepherd, William Robert, 1871-1934.

LAC 20511-12
History of Providence County, Rhode Island. Edited by Richard M. Bayles, assisted by a corps of writers. New York, W. W. Preston & co., 1891.
Bayles, Richard Mather, *ed.*

LAC 13046
A history of public permanent common school funds in the United States, 1795-1905. New York, H. Holt and company, 1911.
Swift, Fletcher Harper, 1876-1947.

LAC 13974
The history of public poor relief in Massachusetts, 1620-1920. Boston and New York, Houghton Mifflin company, 1922.
Kelso, Robert Wilson, 1880-

LAC 13534
History of Ramsey county and the city of St. Paul, including the Explorers and pioneers of Minnesota, by Rev. Edward D. Neill. And Outlines of the history of Minnesota, by J. Fletcher Williams. Minneapolis, North star publishing co., 1881.
Warner, George E.

LAC 14141
History of Richmond, by John P. Little; reprinted from the Southern literary messenger. Introduction by Rev. A. A. Little, foreword by J. H. Whitty, woodblocks by Norma E. Dietz, index by George F. Scheer. Richmond, Va., The Dietz printing company, 1933.
Little, John Peyton, 1818-1873.

LAC 10323
History of road legislation in Iowa. Iowa City, Ia., State historical society of Iowa, 1912.
Brindley, John Edwin, 1878-

LAC 15243-44
History of Rockingham and Strafford counties, New Hampshire, with biographical sketches of many of its pioneers and prominent men. Compiled under the supervision of D. Hamilton Hurd. Philadelphia, J. W. Lewis & co., 1882.
Hurd, Duane Hamilton, ed.

LAC 10988
The history of Romanism: from the earliest corruptions of Christianity to the present time. With full chronological table, analytical and alphabetical indexes and glossary. Illustrated by numerous accurate and highly finished engravings of its ceremonies, superstitions, persecutions, and historical incidents. By Rev. John Dowling. 6th ed. New York, E. Walker, 1845.
Dowling, John, 1807-1878.

LAC 10866
The history of Saint Augustine, Florida, with an introductory account of the early Spanish and French attempts at exploration and settlement in the territory of Florida; together with sketches of events and objects of interest connected with the oldest town in the United States; to which is added a short description of the climate and advantages of Saint Augustine as a health resort. New York, G. P. Putnam's sons, 1881.
Dewhurst, William Whitwell, 1850-

LAC 14080-81
History of Salt Lake City... Edward W. Tullidge, publisher and proprietor. Salt Lake City, Star printing company, 1886.
Tullidge, Edward Wheelock.

LAC 21179
History of San Diego, 1542-1908; an account of the rise and progress of the pioneer settlement on the Pacific coast of the United States. Volume I: Old town. By William E. Smythe, author of "The conquest of arid America," "Constructive democracy" etc. San Diego, The History company, 1908.
Smythe, William Ellsworth, 1861-1922.

LAC 23483-84
History of Sanbornton, New Hampshire... By Rev. M. T. Runnels. Boston, Mass., A. Mudge & son, printers, 1882, '81.
Runnels, Moses Thurston, 1830-1902.

LAC 20166-67
A history of Savannah and South Georgia. Illustrated. Chicago, Lewis Publishing co., 1913.
Harden, William, 1844-1936.

LAC 20397-98
A history of savings banks in the United States from their inception in 1816 down to 1874. With discussions of their theory, practical workings and incidents, present condition and prospective development. New York, B. Rhodes, 1876-78.
Keyes, Emerson Willard, 1828-1897.

LAC 16031
History of Schoharie county, and border wars of New York; containing also a sketch of the causes which led to the American revolution; and interesting memoranda of the Mohawk valley... Illustrated with more than thirty engravings. Albany, Munsell & Tanner, printers, 1845.
Simms, Jeptha Root, 1807-1883.

LAC 11347
History of sculpture, painting, and architecture. Edinburgh, Constable and co.; [etc., etc.] 1829.
Memes, John Smythe.

LAC 13034
A history of secondary education in Pennsylvania. Philadelphia, The author, 1933.
Mulhern, James, 1890-

LAC 11763
History of Shorthorn cattle. London, Vinton & company, ltd., 1907.
Sinclair, James, 1853-1915, ed.

LAC 14735
The history of silk, cotton, linen, wool, and other fibrous substances; including observations on spinning, dyeing, and weaving. Also an account of the pastoral life of the ancients, their social state and attainments in the domestic arts. With appendices on Pliny's Natural history; on the origin and manufacture of linen and cotton paper; on felting, netting &c. ... New York, Harper & brothers, 1845.
Gilroy, Clinton G.

LAC 16278
A history of Simon Willard, inventor and clockmaker, together with some account of his sons–his apprentices–and the workmen associated with him, with brief notices of other clockmakers of the family name, by his great grandson, John Ware Willard. [Boston, Printed by E. O. Cockayne] 1911.
Willard, John Ware.

LAC 16754
The history of slavery and the slave trade, ancient and modern. The forms of slavery that prevailed in ancient nations, particularly in Greece and Rome. The African slave trade and the political history of slavery in the United States. Compiled from authentic materials by W. O. Blake. Columbus, O., H. Miller, 1860.
Blake, William O.

LAC 40068
History of slavery in Connecticut. Baltimore, The Johns Hopkins press, 1893.
Steiner, Bernard Christian, 1867-1926.

LAC 13373
History of socialism in the United States. New York and London, Funk & Wagnalls company, 1903.
Hillquit, Morris, 1869-1933.

LAC 12357
The history of South Carolina in the revolution, 1780–1783. New York, Macmillan, 1902.
McCrady, Edward, 1833–1903.

LAC 12358
The history of South Carolina under the proprietary government, 1670–1719. New York, Russell & Russell [1969]
McCrady, Edward, 1833–1903.

LAC 16306
The history of South Carolina under the royal government, 1719–1776. New York, The Macmillan company; London, Macmillan & co., ltd., 1899.
McCrady, Edward, 1833–1903.

LAC 23309–11
History of South Dakota, together with personal mention of citizens of South Dakota... [Logansport? Ind.] B. F. Bowen & co., 1904.
Robinson, Doane, 1856–

LAC 10369
History of Spencer, Massachusetts, from its earliest settlement to the year 1860: including a brief sketch of Leicester, to the year 1753. 2d ed., enl. and improved. Worcester, Printed by Henry J. Howland [1860?]
Draper, James, 1776–1868.

LAC 10817
History of Stamford, Connecticut, from its settlement in 1641, to the present time, including Darien, which was one of its parishes until 1820; Stamford, The author, 1868.
Huntington, Elijah Baldwin, 1816–1877.

LAC 40039
History of steam navigation between New York & Providence. Comp. by Chas. H. Dow under the direction of D. S. Babcock, esq., president of the Providence & Stonington steamship co. New York, W. Turner & co., printers, 1877.
Dow, Charles H   comp.

LAC 15236
The history of Sudbury, Massachusetts. 1638–1889. [Boston, Printed by R. H. Blodgett] 1889.
Hudson, Alfred Sereno, 1839–1907.

LAC 16721
History of Sussex and Warren Counties, New Jersey, with illustrations and biographical sketches of its prominent men and pioneers. Compiled by James P. Snell, assisted by W. W. Clayton and a numerous corps of writers. Philadelphia, Everts & Peck, 1881.
Snell, James P   comp.

LAC 20577–78
The history of Sutton, New Hampshire: consisting of the historical collections of Erastus Wadleigh, esq., and A. H. Worthen. Comp. and arranged by Mrs. Augusta Harvey Worthen. Concord, N. H., Printed by the Republican press association, 1890.
Worthen, Augusta, 1823–   comp.

LAC 13187
The history of Tammany hall. 2d ed., rev. and enl. New York, Boni & Liveright, inc., 1917.
Myers, Gustavus, 1872–1942.

LAC 40002
The history of tariff adminstration in the United States, from colonial times to the McKinley administrative bill. 2d ed. New York, 1897.
Goss, John Dean.

LAC 16210
History of Taunton, Massachusetts, from its settlement to the present time, by Samuel Hopkins Emery. With an introductory notice by Hon. Edmund Hatch Bennett. Syracuse, N. Y., D. Mason & co., 1893.
Emery, Samuel Hopkins, 1815–1901.

LAC 11695
The history of Temple, N. H. Boston, printed by G. C. Rand & Avery, 1860.
Blood, Henry Ames, 1838–

LAC 22369–70
History of Texas from its first settlement in 1685 to its annexation to the United States in 1846. Austin, Tex., The Steck co., 1935.
Yoakum, Henderson K   1810–1856.

LAC 16101
The history of the administration of John Adams, esq. late president of the United States. New-York printed: 1802.
Wood, John, 1775?–1822.

LAC 16764
History of the African Methodist Episcopal Church, by Daniel A. Payne. Edited by Rev. C. S. Smith. New York, Johnson Reprint Corp. [1968]
Payne, Daniel Alexander, bp., 1811–1893.

LAC 40004
History of the agricultural college land grant act of July 2, 1862. Devoted largely to the history of the "land scrip" which under that grant was allotted to the state of New York and afterwards given to Cornell university. Ithaca, N. Y., Ithaca Democrat press, 1905.
Halliday, Samuel Dumont, 1847–

LAC 40008
History of the agriculture of the United States. Washington, Govt. print. off., 1867.
Poore, Benjamin Perley.

LAC 16212
History of the Albany penitentiary. Albany, J. Munsell, 1867.
Dyer, David.

LAC 16717
A history of the American bar. New York, Howard Fertig, 1966, [c1939]
Warren, Charles, 1868–1954.

LAC 22446–48
History of the American Civil War. New York, Harper, 1868–70.
Draper, John William, 1811–1882.

LAC 11608
History of the American clock business for the past sixty years, and life of Chauncey Jerome, written by himself. Barnum's connection with the Yankee clock business. New Haven, F. C. Dayton, jr., 1860.
Jerome, Chauncey.

LAC 40099
History of the American colony in Liberia, from December 1821 to 1823. Comp. from the authentic records of the colony. Washington city, Printed by Way & Gideon, 1826.
Ashmun, Jehudi, 1794–1828.

LAC 11054
History of the American Episcopal church. 10th ed., rev. and enl. and continued to the year 1915. Milwaukee, The Young churchman co.; London, A. R. Mowbray & co., 1916.
McConnell, Samuel David, 1845–1939.

LAC 20483–84
The history of the American Episcopal church, 1587–1883. Projected by Clarence F. Jewett. Boston, J. R. Osgood & company, 1885.
Perry, William Stevens, *bp.*, 1832–1898.

LAC 14288
The history of the American Indians; particularly those nations adjoining to the Missisippi [!] East and West Florida, Georgia, South and North Carolina, and Virginia: containing an account of their origin, language, manners, religious and civil customs, laws, form of government, punishments, conduct in war and domestic life, their habits, diet, agriculture, manufactures, diseases and method of cure... With observations on former historians, the conduct of our colony governors, superintendents, missionaries, &c. Also an appendix, containing a description of the Floridas, and the Missisippi [!] lands, with their productions–the benefits of colonizing Georgiana, and civilizing the Indians–and the way to make all the colonies more valuable to the mother country... London, E. and C. Dilly, 1775.
Adair, James, *ca.* 1709–*ca.* 1783.

LAC 15399
History of the American medical association from its organization up to January, 1855. By N. S. Davis, M. D., to which is appended biographical notices. Ed. by S. W. Butler, M. D. Philadelphia, Lippincott, Grambo & co., 1855.
Davis, Nathan Smith, 1817–1904.

LAC 10416
History of the American pianoforte; its technical development, and the trade. Illustrated. New York, D. Spillane, 1890.
Spillane, Daniel, 1861–1893.

LAC 15000
History of the American privateers, and letters-of-marque, during our war with England in the years 1812, '13, and '14. Interspersed with several naval battles between American and British ships-of-war. New York, The author, 1856.
Coggeshall, George, 1784–1861.

LAC 20752
The history of the American revolution. New York, Russell & Russell [1968]
Ramsay, David, 1749–1815.

LAC 12181
History of the American theatre. New York, J. & J. Harper, 1832.
Dunlap, William, 1766–1839.

LAC 22630–31
History of the American theatre... Philadelphia, Globe printing house, 1888–91.
Seilhamer, George Overcash, 1839–1916.

LAC 11647
History of the American whale fishery from its earliest inception to the year 1876. [Washington, Govt. print. off., 1878.]
Starbuck, Alexander, 1841–1925.

LAC 14336
History of the Andover theological seminary, by the Rev. Leonard Woods. Boston, J. R. Osgood and company, 1885.
Woods, Leonard, 1774–1854.

LAC 12903
History of the antislavery measure of the Thirty-seventh and Thirty-eighth United States Congresses, 1861–64. Boston, Walker, Wise, and company, 1864.
Wilson, Henry, 1812–1875.

LAC 22549
History of the Army of the Cumberland; its organization, campaigns, and battles, written at the request of Major-General George H. Thomas chiefly from his private military journal and official and other documents furnished by him; by Thomas B. Van Horne. Illustrated with campaign and battle maps, compiled by Edward Ruger. Cincinnati, R. Clarke & co., 1875.
Van Horne, Thomas Budd, *d.* 1895.

LAC 40115
History of the Army service schools, Fort Leavenworth, Kansas, comp. by Henry Shindler from general orders of the War department, annual reports of commandants from 1881 to date, and other available data, under the direction of Captain E. E. Booth... [Fort Leavenworth, Kan.] Staff college press, 1908.
Shindler, Henry, 1854–   *comp.*

LAC 12636
History of the Atlantic telegraph. New-York, C. Scribner & co., 1866.
Field, Henry Martyn, 1822–1907.

LAC 15418
History of the Baldwin locomotive works, 1831–1923. [Philadelphia, 1923?]
Baldwin-Lima-Hamilton Corporation.

LAC 10951
A history of the Baptists in New England. Philadelphia, American Baptist publication society, 1894.
Burrage, Henry Sweetser, 1837–1926.

LAC 11127
A history of the Baptists in the middle states. Philadelphia, American Baptist publication society, 1898.
Vedder, Henry Clay, 1853–1935.

LAC 11088
A history of the Baptists in the southern states east of the Mississippi. Philadelphia, American Baptist publication society, 1898.
Riley, Benjamin Franklin, 1849–1925.

LAC 11101
A history of the Baptists in the western states east of the Mississippi. Philadelphia, American Baptist publication society, 1896.
Smith, Justin Almerin, 1819–1896.

LAC 15171
History of the battle of Lake Erie, and miscellaneous papers, by Hon. George Bancroft. Life and writings of George Bancroft, by Oliver Dyer. New York, R. Bonner's sons, 1891.
Bancroft, George, 1800–1891.

LAC 13358
The historye of the Bermudaes or Summer islands. Ed. from a ms. in the Sloane collection, British museum, by General Sir J. Henry Lefroy. London, Printed for the Hakluyt society, 1882.

LAC 16693
History of the big bonanza: an authentic account of the discovery, history, and working of the world renowned Comstock silver lode of Nevada; including the present condition of the various mines situated thereon; sketches of the most prominent men interested in them... By Dan De Quille (William Wright) Hartford, Conn., American publishing company; San Francisco, A. L. Bancroft & co., 1876.
Wright, William, 1829–1898.

LAC 13419
History of the Boston massacre, March 5, 1770; consisting of the narrative of the town, the trial of the soldiers: and a historical introduction, containing unpublished documents of John Adams, and explanatory notes, by Frederic Kidder. Albany, N. Y., J. Munsell, 1870.
Kidder, Frederic, 1804–1885.

LAC 15800
The history of the Boston theatre, 1854–1901, by Eugene Tompkins, manager from 1878 to 1901; compiled with the assistance of Quincy Kilby, treasurer from 1886 to 1901. Boston and New York, Houghton Mifflin company, 1908.
Tompkins, Eugene.

LAC 11595
The history of the British plantations in America. With a chronological account of the most remarkable things, which happen'd to the first adventurers in their several discoveries of that new world. Part I. Containing The history of Virginia; with remarks on the trade and commerce of that colony... London, Printed at the expence of the Society for the encouragement of learning, by S. Richardson, 1738.
Keith, Sir William, bart., 1680–1749.

LAC 13421
History of the Bureau of statistics of labor of Massachusetts, and of labor legislation in that state from 1833 to 1876. Prepared for the Bureau, as a contribution to the Centennial exhibition at Philadelphia in 1876. Boston, Wright & Potter, state printers, 1876.
Pidgin, Charles Felton, 1844–1923.

LAC 14637
A history of the campaigns of 1780 and 1781, in the southern provinces of North America. Dublin, Printed for Colles [etc.] 1787
Tarleton, Sir Banastre, bart., 1754–1833.

LAC 23879
History of the Catholic Church in the United States from the earliest period to the present time, with biographical sketches of the living bishops... Philadelphia, Gebbie, 1889–90.
Clarke, Richard Henry, 1827–1911, ed.

LAC 22839–41
A history of the Catholic church within the limits of the United States, from the first attempted colonization to the present time... New York, J. G. Shea, 1886–90.
Shea, John Dawson Gilmary, 1824–1892.

LAC 14476
History of the Catholic missions among the Indian tribes of the United States. 1529–1854. New York, E. Dunigan & brother, 1855.
Shea, John Dawson Gilmary, 1824–1892.

LAC 15447
History of the Chicago police from the settlement of the community to the present time, under authority of the mayor and superintendent of the force, by John J. Flinn, assisted by John E. Wilkie. Chicago, Under the auspices of the Police book fund, 1887.
Flinn, John Joseph, 1851–

LAC 11064
A history of the Christian denomination in America, 1794–1911 A. D. Dayton, O., The Christian publishing association, 1912.
Morrill, Milo True.

LAC 11016
A history of the church known as the Moravian church, or, The Unitas fratrum, or, The Unity of the brethren, during the eighteenth and nineteenth centuries. Bethlehem, Pa., Times publishing company, printers, 1900.
Hamilton, John Taylor, 1859–

LAC 10980
The history of the church known as the Unitas Fratrum, Or, The unity of the Brethren, founded by the followers of John Hus, The Bohemian reformer and martyr. 2d ed. Bethlehem, Pa., Moravian publication concern, 1901, [c1885]
De Schweinitz, Edmund Alexander, 1825–1887.

LAC 21362–64
The history of the Church of England, in the colonies and foreign dependencies of the British empire, by the Rev. James S. M. Anderson. London, F. & J. Rivington, 1845–1856.
Anderson, James Stuart Murray, 1800–1869.

LAC 16688
History of the church of the United brethren in Christ.
1st ed. Circleville, O., Conference office of the United
brethren in Christ, 1851.
Spayth, Henry G

LAC 11280
A history of the city government of Savannah, Ga.,
from 1790 to 1901. Compiled from official records by
Thomas Gamble, jr., under direction of the City Council,
1900. [Savannah, 1901]
Gamble, Thomas, 1868–

LAC 21338–40
A history of the city of Brooklyn. Including the old
town and village of Brooklyn, the town of Bushwick, and
the village and city of Williamsburgh. Brooklyn, N.Y.,
Pub. by subscription, 1867–70.
Stiles, Henry Reed, 1832–1909.

LAC 21205–06
History of the city of Buffalo and Erie county, with ...
biographical sketches of some of its prominent men and
pioneers... Syracuse, N. Y., D. Mason & co., 1884.
Smith, Henry Perry, 1839–1925.

LAC 11287
A history of the city of Cleveland; its settlement, rise
and progress. 1796–1896. Illustrated with maps, portraits
and views. Cleveland, The Imperial press, 1896.
Kennedy, James Henry, 1849–1934.

LAC 10380
History of the city of Denver, Arapahoe county, and
Colorado. Containing a history of the state of
Colorado ... a condensed sketch of Arapahoe county; a
history of the city of Denver ... biographical sketches
... &c., &c.... Chicago, O. L. Baskin & co., 1880

LAC 14383
History of the city of New-York. New York, G. P.
Putnam & company, 1853.
Valentine, David Thomas, 1801–1869.

LAC 22260–61
History of the city of New York in the seventeenth
century, by Mrs. Schuyler Van Rensselaer. New York,
The Macmillan company, 1909.
Van Rensselaer, Mariana, 1851–1934.

LAC 21944–45
History of the city of New York: its origin, rise, and
progress. New York and Chicago, A. S. Barnes and company, 1877–[96]
Lamb, Martha Joanna Reade, 1829–1893.

LAC 10880
A history of the city of San Francisco and incidentally
of the state of California. San Francisco, A. L. Bancroft
& company, 1878.
Hittell, John Shertzer, 1825–1901.

LAC 20073–75
History of the city of Spokane and Spokane country,
Washington, from its earliest settlement to the present
time. Spokane, Chicago [etc.] The S. J. Clarke publishing
company, 1912.
Durham, Nelson Wayne, 1859–1938.

LAC 11297
History of the city of Trenton, New Jersey, embracing
a period of nearly two hundred years, commencing in
1676, the first settlement of the town, and extending up
to the present time, with official records of the popula-
tion, extent of the town at different periods, its manufac-
tories, church history, and fire department. Trenton, N.
J., W. T. Nicholson & co., printers, 1871.
Raum, John O.

LAC 10855
A history of the city of Vincennes, Indiana, from 1702
to 1901. October 15, 1901. Cleveland, The Arthur H.
Clark company [c1902]
Cauthorn, Henry Sullivan, 1828–1905.

LAC 16111
A history of the civil war in the United States, 1861–5,
by W. Birkbeck Wood and Colonel J. E. Edmonds. With
an introduction by Spencer Wilkinson; with thirteen
maps and eleven plans. London, Methuen & co., ltd.
[c1905]
Wood, Walter Birkbeck, 1866–

LAC 10627
History of the College of California. San Francisco, S.
Carson & co., 1887.
Willey, Samuel Hopkins.

LAC 20140
History of the College of New Jersey, from its origin
in 1746 to the commencement of 1854. Philadelphia, J. B.
Lippincott & co., 1877.
Maclean, John, 1800–1886.

LAC 12622
History of the College of Physicians and Surgeons in
the city of New York; Medical department of Columbia
college. New York, Pub. by order of the college, 1888.
Dalton, John Call, 1825–1889.

LAC 11723
History of the colony of New Haven, before and after
the union with Connecticut. Containing a particular de-
scription of the towns which composed that government,
viz., New Haven, Milford, Guilford, Branford, Stam-
ford, & Southold, L. I. with a notice of the towns which
have been set off from "the original six"... New Haven,
Hitchcock & Stafford, 1838.
Lambert, Edward Rodolphus.

LAC 11687
History of the colony of New Haven to its absorption
into Connecticut. New Haven, Printed for the author,
1881.
Atwater, Edward Elias, 1816–1887.

LAC 12909
History of the colored race in America. Prepared and
arr. by Wm. T. Alexander. New York, Negro Universities press [1968]
Alexander, William T.

LAC 10030
The history of the commercial crisis, 1857–58, and the
stock exchange panic of 1859. London, Groombridge and
sons, 1859.
Evans, David Morier, 1819–1874.

LAC 15221
History of the common school system of the state of New York, from its origin in 1795, to the present time. Including the various city and other special organizations, and the religious controversies of 1821, 1832, and 1840. New York and Chicago, Ivison, Blakeman, Taylor and co., 1871.
Randall, Samuel Sidwell, 1809–1881.

LAC 10244
A history of the Commonwealth of Kentucky. Louisville, Ky., Wilcox, Dickerman, 1834.
Butler, Mann, 1784–1852.

LAC 14903
History of the Confederate States navy from its organization to the surrender of its last vessel. Its stupendous struggle with the great navy of the United States; the engagements fought in the rivers and harbors of the South, and upon the high seas; blockade-running, first use of iron-clads and torpedoes, and privateer history. New York, Rogers & Sherwood; San Francisco, A. L. Bancroft & co.; [etc., etc.] 1887.
Scharf, John Thomas, 1843–1898.

LAC 15152
History of the conflict between religion and science. 5th ed. New York, D. Appleton and company, 1875.
Draper, John William, 1811–1882.

LAC 20645–46
History of the conquest of Mexico, with a preliminary view of the ancient Mexican civilization, and the life of the conqueror, Hernando Cortes. London, R. Bentley, 1843.
Prescott, William Hickling, 1796–1859.

LAC 20647–48
History of the conquest of Peru, with a preliminary view of the civilization of the Incas. Paris, Baudry's European library, 1847.
Prescott, William Hickling, 1796–1859.

LAC 40003
History of the controversy in the University of the city of New-York; with original documents and an appendix. By the professors of the Faculty of science and letters. New York, J. S. Taylor, 1838.
New York University.

LAC 14088
History of the counties of Gloucester, Salem, and Cumberland, New Jersey, with biographical sketches of their prominent citizens. By Thos. Cushing, M. D., and Charles E. Sheppard, esq. Philadelphia, Everts & Peck, 1883.
Cushing, Thomas, b. 1821.

LAC 16015
History of the county of Schenectady, N. Y., from 1662 to 1886... [by] Howell [and] Munsell. Assisted by local writers. New York, W. W. Munsell & co., 1886.
Howell, George Rogers, 1833–1899, ed.

LAC 11058
History of the Cumberland Presbyterian church. 2d ed. Nashville, Tenn., Board of publication of Cumberland Presbyterian church, 1888.
McDonnold, Benjamin Wilburn, 1827–1889.

LAC 21157–58
History of the discovery and settlement of the valley of the Mississippi, by the three great European powers, Spain, France, and Great Britain, and the subsequent occupation, settlement, and extension of civil government by the United States until the year 1846. New-York, Harper & brothers, 1846.
Monette, John Wesley.

LAC 11734
The history of the district of Maine. Boston, Printed by I. Thomas and E. T. Andrews, 1795.
Sullivan, James, 1744-1808.

LAC 23355
History of the dividing line, and other tracts. From the papers of William Byrd, of Westover, in Virginia, esquire. Richmond, Va., 1866.
Byrd, William, 1674–1744.

LAC 13259
History of the Donner party; a tragedy of the Sierra. 14th ed. San Francisco, A. Carlisle, 1927, [c1880]
McGlashan, Charles Fayette, 1847–1931.

LAC 16732
History of the early settlement of the Juniata Valley: embracing an account of the early pioneers, and the trials and privations incident to the settlement of the valley, predatory incursions, massacres, and abductions by the Indians during the French and Indian wars, and the war of the revolution, &c. Philadelphia, H. B. Ashmead, 1856.
Jones, Uriah James, 1818–1864.

LAC 16631
The history of the eastern expeditions of 1689, 1690, 1692, 1696, and 1704, against the Indians and French, by Benjamin Church. With an introduction and notes by Henry Martyn Dexter. Boston, J. K. Wiggin and W. P. Lunt, 1867.
Church, Benjamin, 1639–1718.

LAC 13194
History of the English settlement in Edwards county, Illinois, founded in 1817 and 1818, by Morris Birkbeck and George Flower. By George Flower. With preface and footnotes by E. B. Washburne. 2d ed. Chicago, Fergus printing co., 1909.
Flower, George, 1790–1862.

LAC 21138–39
History of the expedition under the command of Captains Lewis and Clark, to the sources of the Missouri, thence across the Rocky Mountains and down the river Columbia to the Pacific Ocean. Performed during the years 1804-5-6. By order of the government of the United States. Prepared for the press by Paul Allen, esquire... Philadelphia, Pub. by Bradford and Inskeep; New York, Abm. H. Inskeep, J. Maxwell, printer, 1814.
Lewis, Meriwether, 1774–1809.

LAC 12571
History of the express companies: and the origin of American railroads. Together with some reminiscences of the latter days of the mail coach and baggage wagon business in the United States. (2d ed.) New York, 1858.
Stimson, Alexander Lovett, 1816–

LAC 14351
The history of the fall of Fort Sumter; being an inside history of the affairs in South Carolina and Washington, 1860-1, and the conditions and events in the South which brought on the rebellion; the genesis of the Civil War. New York, S. F. McLean, 1898.
Crawford, Samuel Wylie, 1829-1892.

LAC 15994
History of the First church in Boston, 1630-1880. By Arthur B. Ellis. With an introduction, by George E. Ellis. Boston, Hall & Whiting, 1881.
Ellis, Arthur Blake, 1854-

LAC 12390
The history of the first discovery and settlement of Virginia: being an essay towards a general history of this colony. With an appendix. Williamsburg [Va.] Printed by W. Parks, 1747.
Stith, William, 1707-1755.

LAC 13947
A history of the first half-century of the National academy of sciences, 1863-1913. Washington, 1913.
National Academy of Sciences, *Washington, D. C.*

LAC 14619
A history of the foundation of New Orleans (1717-1722) By Baron Marc de Villiers. Translated from the French by Warrington Dawson. [New Orleans, Louisiana Historical Society] 1920.
Villiers du Terrage, Marc, *baron* de, 1867-

LAC 15731
History of the Friendly sons of St. Patrick and of the Hibernian society for the relief of emigrants from Ireland. March 17, 1771-March 17, 1892. By John H. Campbell, historian of the Hibernian society. Philadelphia, The Hibernian society, 1892.
Campbell, John Hugh, 1847-

LAC 10948
A history of the German Baptist brethren in Europe and America. Elgin Ill., Brethren publishing house, 1899.
Brumbaugh, Martin Grove, 1862-1930.

LAC 11132
History of the German settlements and of the Lutheran church in North and South Carolina, from the earliest period of the colonization of the Dutch, German and Swiss settlers to the close of the first half of the present century. Philadelphia, The Lutheran book store, 1872.
Bernheim, Gotthardt Dellmann.

LAC 15496
The history of the German settlements in Texas, 1831-1861. Austin, Tex., Press of Von Boeckmann-Jones co. [c1930]
Biesele, Rudolph Leopold, 1886-1960.

LAC 10886
The history of the government of Denver with special reference to its relations with public service corporations. Denver, Col., The Fisher book company, 1911.
King, Clyde Lyndon, 1879-1937.

LAC 14238
History of the Government printing office, (at Washington, D.C.) with a brief record of the public printing for a century, 1789-1881. Lancaster, Pa., Inquirer printing and publishing co., 1881.
Kerr, Robert Washington, 1841-

LAC 14974
A history of the Grammar school, or, "The free schoole of 1645 in Roxburie." With biographical sketches of the ministers of the First church, and other trustees. Roxbury, J. Backup, 1860.
Dillaway, Charles Knapp, 1804-1889.

LAC 14615
History of the Grand army of the republic, by Robert B. Beath, with an introduction by General Lucius Fairchild. Illustrated. New York, Bryan, Taylor & co., 1889.
Beath, Robert Burns, 1839-1914.

LAC 11215
History of the Grange movement; or, The farmer's war against monopolies: being a full ... account of the struggles of the American farmers against the extortions of the railroad companies. With a history of the rise and progress of the order of Patrons of husbandry ... to which is added sketches of the leading Grangers. By Edward Winslow Martin [*pseud.*] With 60 fine engravings and portraits. Philadelphia, Pa., Chicago, Ill., National publishing company; [etc., etc., 1874]
McCabe, James Dabney, 1842-1883.

LAC 20085
History of the granite industry of New England. Boston, Mass., Pub. by authority of the National association of granite industries of the United States, 1913.
Brayley, Arthur Wellington, 1863-

LAC 22829-30
History of the great American fortunes. Chicago, C. H. Kerr & company, 1911-17
Myers, Gustavus, 1872-1942.

LAC 13386
The history of the great riots. Being a full and authentic account of the strikes and riots on the various railroads of the United States and in the mining regions. Embracing brilliant and graphic pen-pictures of the reign of terror in Pittsburgh, Baltimore, Chicago, and other cities. The conflicts between the troops and the mob. Terrible conflagrations and destruction of property. Thrilling scenes and incidents, etc., etc. Together with a full history of the Mollie Maguires. By Edward Winslow Martin [*pseud.*] Philadelphia [etc.] National publishing company [c1877]
McCabe, James Dabney, 1842-1883.

LAC 11624
A history of the greenbacks, with special reference to the economic consequences of their issue: 1862-65. Chicago, The University of Chicago press, 1903.
Mitchell, Wesley Clair, 1874-1948.

LAC 10285
A history of the growth of the steam-engine. New York, D. Appleton and company, 1878.
Thurston, Robert Henry, 1839-1903.

LAC 21356-58

History of the Harvard law school and of early legal conditions in America. New York, Lewis publishing company, 1908.
Warren, Charles, 1868-1954.

LAC 16006

The history of the hen fever. A humorous record. [2d. ed.] Boston, J. French and company; New York, J. C. Derby; [etc., etc., 1855]
Burnham, George Pickering, 1814-1902.

LAC 10717

History of the Hopedale community, from its inception to its virtual submergence in the Hopedale parish. By Adin Ballou. William S. Heywood, editor. Lowell, Mass., Thompson & Hill, 1897.
Ballou, Adin, 1803-1890.

LAC 22860

History of the Huguenot emigration to America. New York, Dodd, Mead & company [1885]
Baird, Charles Washington, 1828-1887.

LAC 21866-67

History of the Indian tribes of North America, with biographical sketches and anecdotes of the principal chiefs. Embellished with one hundred and twenty portraits, from the Indian gallery in the Department of war at Washington. By Thomas L. McKenney and James Hall. Philadelphia, J. T. Bowen, 1848-50.
McKenney, Thomas Lorraine, 1785-1859.

LAC 22288

The history of the Indian wars in New England from the first settlement to the termination of the war with King Philip, in 1677. From the original work, by the Rev. William Hubbard. Carefully rev., and accompanied with an historical preface, life and pedigree of the author, and extensive notes, by S. G. Drake. Roxbury,Mass., W. E. Woodward, 1865.
Hubbard, William, 1621-1704.

LAC 14673

History of the Indians of Connecticut from the earliest known period to 1850. Published with the sanction of the Connecticut historical society... Hartford, W. J. Hamersley, 1853, [c1850]
De Forest, John William, 1826-

LAC 10177

A history of the Insurance company of North America of Philadelphia: the oldest fire and marine insurance company in America. Began business as an association in 1792. Incorporated 1794. Philadelphia, Press of Review publishing and printing company, 1885.
Montgomery, Thomas Harrison, 1830-1905.

LAC 12505

The history of the insurrections in Massachusetts. In the year seventeen hundred and eighty six. And the rebellion consequent thereon. By George Richards Minot, A. M. 2d ed. Boston: Published by James W. Burditt & co. Franklin's head, Court street. J. Belcher, printer, 1810.
Minot, George Richards, 1758-1802.

LAC 10846

History of the introduction of pure water into the city of Boston, with a description of its Cochituate water works... Comp. by a member of the Water board. Boston, Mass., A. Mudge & son, city printers, 1868.
Bradlee, Nathaniel J

LAC 15988

History of the invasion and capture of Washington, and of the events which preceded and followed. New York, Harper & brothers, 1857.
Williams, John S.

LAC 15739

A history of the Irish settlers in North America, from the earliest period to the census of 1850. 6th ed. Boston, P. Donahoe, 1855, [c1850]
McGee, Thomas D'Arcy, 1825-1868.

LAC 40061

A history of the Jefferson medical college of Philadelphia. By James F. Gayley, M. D., with biographical sketches of the early professors. Philadelphia, J. M. Wilson, 1858.
Gayley, James Fyfe, 1818-1894.

LAC 22643

The history of the Jews from the destruction of Jerusalem to the nineteenth century. Boston, J. Eliot, jr., 1812.
Adams, Hannah, 1755-1832.

LAC 11284

History of the Johnstown flood ... With full accounts also of the destruction on the Susquehanna and Juniata rivers, and the Bald Eagle Creek. [Philadelphia] Edgewood publishing co., 1889.
Johnson, Willis Fletcher, 1857-1931.

LAC 15760

History of the kingdom of cotton and cotton statistics of the world. The earliest history of cotton production and manufacture [etc.]... New Orleans, Printed by W. B. Stansbury & co., 1884.
Chew, Morris R.

LAC 16405

A history of the labor movement in California. Berkeley, Calif., University of California press, 1935.
Cross, Ira Brown, 1880-

LAC 40058

The history of the late expedition to Cuba, by O. D. D. O., one of the participants, with an appendix, containing the last speech of the celebrated orator, S. S. Prentiss, in defence of Gen. Lopez. New Orleans, Printed at the job office of the Daily delta, 1850.
Davis, J   C

LAC 16318

History of the late war between the United States and Great Britain: comprising a minute account of the various military and naval operations. Philadelphia, J. Kay, jun. & brother; Pittsburgh, C. H. Kay & co., 1839.
Brackenridge, Henry Marie, 1786-1871.

LAC 16378

History of the late war in the western country, comprising a full account of all the transactions in that quarter, from the commencement of hostilities at Tippecanoe, to the termination of the contest at New Orleans on the return of peace. Lexington, K., Published by Worsley & Smith, 1816.
McAfee, Robert Breckinridge, 1784–1849.

LAC 14045

History of the League for industrial rights. New York city, League for industrial rights, 1925.
Merritt, Walter Gordon.

LAC 22482–84

History of the life and times of James Madison. Boston, Little, Brown and company, 1866–1870.
Rives, William Cabell, 1793–1868.

LAC 12274

The history of the life of Thomas Ellwood; or, An account of his birth, education, etc., with divers observations on his life and manners when a youth; and how he came to be convinced of the truth; with his many sufferings and services for the same; also several other remarkable passages and occurrences written by his own hand. Ed. by C. G. Crump. New York, G. P. Putnam's sons; [etc., etc.] 1900.
Ellwood, Thomas, 1639–1713.

LAC 11409

The history of the Loco-foco, or Equal Rights Party, its movements, conventions and proceedings, with short characteristic sketches of its prominent men. New York, Burt Franklin [1967]
Byrdsall, Fitzwilliam.

LAC 40029

A history of the McGuffey readers. With three portraits. New ed. Cleveland, The Burrows brothers co., 1911.
Vail, Henry Hobart, 1839–1925.

LAC 40053

History of the manufacture of armor plate for the United States navy. Comp. by the American iron and steel association. December 1, 1899. Philadelphia, Amer. iron and steel assoc., 1899.
American Iron and Steel Association, *comp.*

LAC 10212

History of the manufacture of iron in all ages, and particularly in the United States from colonial times to 1891. Also a short history of early coal mining in the United States... 2d ed., thoroughly rev. and greatly enl. Philadelphia, The American iron and steel association, 1892.
Swank, James Moore, 1832–1914.

LAC 12607

A history of the Massachusetts general hospital. To August 5, 1851. (Privately printed in 1851.) 2d ed., with a continuation to 1872. Prepared by request, in a vote of the trustees, chiefly from the records and annual reports. Boston, Printed by the trustees from the Bowditch fund, 1872.
Bowditch, Nathaniel Ingersoll, 1805–1861.

LAC 22579–81

A history of the Methodist Episcopal church... New-York, Pub. by T. Mason and G. Lane, for the Methodist Episcopal church, 1838–41.
Bangs, Nathan, 1778–1862.

LAC 15120

A history of the Metropolitan museum of art, with a chapter on the early institutions of art in New York. New York [Printed at the Gilliss press] 1913.
Howe, Winifred Eva, 1876–

LAC 14883

History of the Mexican war, by General Cadmus M. Wilcox. Ed. by his niece, Mary Rachel Wilcox. Washington, D. C., Church news publishing co., 1892.
Wilcox, Cadmus Marcellus, 1826–1890.

LAC 22663–65

History of the Military company of the Massachusetts, now called the Ancient and honorable artillery company of Massachusetts. 1637–1888. By Oliver Ayer Roberts, historian of the company. Boston, A. Mudge & son, printers, 1895–1901.
Roberts, Oliver Ayer.

LAC 11354

History of the Minnesota state agricultural society from its organization in 1854 to the annual meeting of 1910. Darwin S. Hall, supervisor, R. I. Holcombe, historian. St. Paul, The McGill-Warner company, 1910.
Hall, Darwin S.

LAC 14030

History of the mission of the United Brethren among the Indians in North America... By George Henry Loskiel. Tr. from the German by Christian Ignatius LaTrobe. London, The Brethren's society for the furtherance of the gospel, 1794.
Loskiel, George Henry, 1740–1814.

LAC 14263

A history of the Moravian seminary for young ladies, at Bethlehem, Pa. With a catalogue of its pupils, 1785–1870. By William C. Reichel and Wm. H. Bigler. With a sketch of the school from 1742 to 1785, by Bishop J. Mortimer Levering, and a continuation of the history and catalogue to the year 1900. 4th ed. Bethlehem, Pa., The Seminary, 1901.
Reichel, William Cornelius, 1824–1876.

LAC 20500–1

A history of the national capital from its foundation through the period of the adoption of the organic act. New York, The Macmillan company, 1914–16.
Bryan, Wilhelmus Bogart, 1854–1938.

LAC 15881

History of the National peace jubilee and great musical festival, held in the city of Boston, June, 1869, to commemorate the restoration of peace throughout the land. Illustrated with steel engravings. Published by the author, and for sale by Lee and Shepard, Boston; Lee, Shepard, and Dillingham, New York, 1871.
Gilmore, Patrick Sarsfield, 1829–1892.

LAC 40039
History of the navigation of the Great Lakes. Washington, Govt. print. off., 1911.
Plumb, Ralph Gordon.

LAC 22538-39
The history of the navy during the rebellion. New York, D. Appleton & co., 1867-68.
Boynton, Charles Brandon, 1806-1883.

LAC 22299
The history of the navy of the United States of America. Philadelphia, Lea & Blanchard, 1839.
Cooper, James Fenimore, 1789-1851.

LAC 20980-81
History of the Negro race in America from 1619 to 1880. Negroes as slaves, as soldiers, and as citizens; together with a preliminary consideration of the unity of the human family, an historical sketch of Africa, and an account of the Negro governments of Sierra Leone and Liberia. New York, G. P. Putnam's sons, 1883.
Williams, George Washington, 1849-1891.

LAC 12901
A history of the Negro troops in the war of the rebellion 1861-1865, preceded by a review of the military services of Negroes in ancient and modern times. New York, Harper & brothers, 1888.
Williams, George Washington, 1849-1891.

LAC 10202
A history of the New England fisheries, with maps. [Philadelphia] University of Pennsylvania; New York, D. Appleton and company, agents, 1911.
McFarland, Raymond, 1872–

LAC 16052
A history of the new school, and of the questions involved in the disruption of the Presbyterian church in 1838. By Samuel J. Baird, D. D. Philadelphia, Claxton, Remsen & Haffelfinger, 1868.
Baird, Samuel John, 1817-1893.

LAC 12279
History of the New world, by Girolamo Benzoni, of Milan. Shewing his travels in America, from A. D. 1541 to 1556: with some particulars of the island of Canary. Now first tr. and ed. by Rear-Admiral W. H. Smyth. London, Printed for the Hakluyt society, 1857.
Benzoni, Girolamo, b. 1519.

LAC 12786
The history of the New-York African free-schools, from their establishment in 1787, to the present time; embracing a period of more than forty years; also a brief account of the successful labors, of the New-York manumission society: with an appendix... New York, Negro Universities Press [1969]
Andrews, Charles C.

LAC 10603
History of the New York society library, with an introductory chapter on libraries in colonial New York, 1698-1776, comp. and written by Austin Baxter Keep, A. M. [New York] Printed for the trustees by the De Vinne press, 1908.
Keep, Austin Baxter, 1875–

LAC 22624-26
A history of the New York stage from the first performance in 1732 to 1901. New York, Dodd, Mead and company, 1903.
Brown, Thomas Allston, 1836-1918.

LAC 10184
History of the Northern Pacific railroad. New York, G. P. Putnam's sons, 1883.
Smalley, Eugene Virgil, 1841-1899, ed.

LAC 10217
A history of the Northern securities case. Madison, Wis., 1906.
Meyer, Balthasar Henry, 1866-1954.

LAC 11611
History of the Ohio canals, their construction, cost, use and partial abandonment [by C. P. McClelland and C. C. Huntington] Pub. by the Ohio state archaeological and historical society. Columbus, O., F. J. Heer, 1905.
McClelland, Cloys Peter, 1879–

LAC 20076-77
History of the Ohio falls cities and their counties, with illustrations and biographical sketches... Cleveland, O., L. A. Williams & co., 1882.

LAC 15094
History of the Ojebway Indians; with especial reference to their conversion to Christianity. By Rev. Peter Jones, (Kahkewaquonaby,) Indian missionary. With a brief memoir of the writer; and introductory notice by the Rev. G. Osborn. London, A. W. Bennett [186-?]
Jones, Peter, Chippewa Chief, 1802-1856.

LAC 20370-71
History of the Old South church (Third church) Boston, 1669-1884. Boston and New York, Houghton, Mifflin and company, 1890.
Hill, Hamilton Andrews, 1827-1895.

LAC 11590
The history of the old town of Derby, Connecticut, 1642-1880. With biographies and genealogies. By Samuel Orcutt and Ambrose Beardsley, M. D. Springfield, Mass., Press of Springfield printing company, 1880.
Orcutt, Samuel.

LAC 21884-85
A history of the old town of Stratford and the city of Bridgeport, Connecticut. By Rev. Samuel Orcutt. Pub. under the auspices of the Fairfield county historical society. [New Haven, Conn., Press of Tuttle, Morehouse & Taylor] 1886.
Orcutt, Samuel.

LAC 14121
History of the organization of the Methodist Episcopal church, South. Nashville, Tenn., A. H. Redford, 1875.
Redford, Albert H.

LAC 15789
History of the organization of the Methodist Episcopal church, South: comprehending all the official proceedings of the General conference; the southern annual

conferences, and the general convention; with such other matters as are necessary to a right understanding of the case. Nashville, Compiled and published by the editors and publishers of the Southwestern Christian advocate, for the Methodist Episcopal church, South. By order of the Louisville convention, 1845.
Methodist Episcopal Church, South.

LAC 22345-46
History of the origin, formation, and adoption of the Constitution of the United States; with notices of its principal framers. New York, Harper and brothers, 1854-59.
Curtis, George Ticknor, 1812-1894.

LAC 22619-20
The history of the origin, progress and termination of the American war. By C. Stedman, who served under Sir W. Howe, Sir H. Clinton, and the Marquis Cornwallis. Dublin, Printed for Messrs. P. Wogan, P. Byrne [etc.] 1794.
Stedman, Charles, 1753-1812.

LAC 16195
A history of the original settlements on the Delaware, from its discovery by Hudson to the colonization under William Penn. To which is added an account of the ecclesiastical affairs of the Swedish settlers, and a history of Wilmington, from its first settlement to the present time... Wilmington, Wilson & Heald, 1846.
Ferris, Benjamin, 1780-1867.

LAC 23405-6
History of the Pacific Northwest: Oregon and Washington; embracing an account of the original discoveries on the Pacific coast of North America, and a description of the conquest, settlement and subjugation of the ... original territory of Oregon; also interesting biographies of the earliest settlers and more prominent men and women of the Pacific Northwest, including a ... description of the climate, soil, productions ... of Oregon and Washington... Portland, Or., North Pacific history company [c1889]

LAC 23440
History of the Pennsylvania railroad company with plan of organization, portraits of officials, and biographical sketches. Philadelphia, H. T. Coates & company, 1899.
Wilson, William Bender, 1839-1919.

LAC 21958-65
A history of the people of the United States, from the revolution to the civil war. New York [etc.] D. Appleton-Century co., 1885-1938.
McMaster, John Bach, 1852-1932.

LAC 13030
History of the Pestalozzian movement in the United States; with nine portraits and a bibliography. Syracuse, N. Y., C. W. Bardeen, c1907.
Monroe, Will Seymour, 1863-1939.

LAC 16840
A history of the plantation of Menunkatuck and of the original town of Guilford, Connecticut, comprising the present towns of Guilford and Madison, written largely from the manuscripts of the Hon. Ralph Dunning Smyth. Baltimore, The author, 1897.
Steiner, Bernard Christian, 1867-1926.

LAC 13508
History of the Polk administration. New-York, G. P. Putnam, 1850.
Chase, Lucien Bonaparte, 1817-1864.

LAC 16671
A history of the Presbyterian church in America, from its origin until the year 1760. With biographical sketches of its early ministers. By the Rev. Richard Webster. With a memoir of the author, by the Rev. C. Van Rensselaer, and an historical introduction, by the Rev. William Blackwood. Philadelphia, J. M. Wilson, 1857.
Webster, Richard, 1811-

LAC 20364-65
History of the Presbyterian church in the United States of America. Philadelphia, Presbyterian publishing committee [c1864]
Gillett, Ezra Hall, 1823-1875.

LAC 12468
A history of the President's cabinet. Ann Arbor, Mich., G. Wahr, 1911.
Hinsdale, Mary Louise.

LAC 40102
A history of the private, political, and official villanies of Fernando Wood.
A biography of Fernando Wood. A history of the forgeries, perjuries, and other crimes of our "model" mayor. No. 1... [New York, 1856]
Ingraham, Abijah.

LAC 10316
History of the Prudential insurance company of America (industrial insurance) 1875-1900. [Newark, N. J.] Prudential press, 1900.
Hoffman, Frederick Ludwig, 1865-1946.

LAC 10819
History of the public domain of Georgia. Atlanta, Foote & Davies co. [1924]
McLendon, Samuel Guyton.

LAC 14324
A history of the public land policies. New York, The Macmillan company, 1924.
Hibbard, Benjamin Horace, 1870-

LAC 10410
History of the Public school society of the city of New York, with portraits of the presidents of the Society. New York, W. Wood & co.; [etc.,etc.] 1870.
Bourne, William Oland.

LAC 14601
History of the public school system of California. San Francisco, A. L. Bancroft and company, 1876.
Swett, John, 1830-1913.

LAC 11713
A history of the purchase and settlement of western New York, and of the rise, progress, and present state of the Presbyterian church in that section. By Rev. James H. Hotchkin. New York, Published by M. W. Dodd, 1848.
Hotchkin, James Harvey, 1781-1851.

LAC 16096
History of the railroads and canals of the United States... v. 1. New York, J. H. Schultz & co., 1860.
Poor, Henry Varnum, 1812–1905.

LAC 10821
A history of the railway mail service, together with a brief account of the origin and growth of the post office service and a sketch showing the daily life of a railway mail clerk. Washington, D.C., Columbian correspondence college [1903]
Columbian Correspondence College, *Washington*, D.C.

LAC 12560
History of the reconstruction measures of the Thirty-ninth and Fortieth Congresses. 1865–68. Hartford publishing company; Chicago, Ill., J. A. Stoddard; [etc., etc.] 1868.
Wilson, Henry, 1812–1875.

LAC 12265
History of the Reformed church in the United States. 1725–1792. Reading, Pa., D. Miller, 1899.
Good, James Isaac, 1850–1924.

LAC 12435
History of the Republican party in Illinois 1854–1912; with a review of the aggressions of the slavepower. Rockford, Ill., Press of Wilson brothers company, printers [c1912]
Church, Charles A., 1857–

LAC 21341–42
History of the Republican party in Ohio, ed. by Joseph P. Smith; and memoirs of its representative supporters. Chicago, The Lewis publishing company, 1898.
Smith, Joseph Patterson, 1856–1898, *ed.*

LAC 20753–54
The history of the revolution of South-Carolina, from a British province to an independent state. Trenton: Printed by Isaac Collins, M.DCC.LXXXV.
Ramsay, David, 1749–1815.

LAC 20982–84
History of the rise and fall of the slave power in America. Boston, J. R. Osgood and company, 1873–77.
Wilson, Henry, 1812–1875.

LAC 22629
The history of the rise and progress of the arts of design in the United States. New York, G. P. Scott and co., printers, 1834.
Dunlap, William, 1766–1839.

LAC 16055
A history of the rise and progress of the Baptists in Alabama: with a miniature history of the denomination from the aspostolic age down to the present time, interspersed with anecdotes original and selected, and concluded with an address to the Baptists of Alabama. Philadelphia, King and Baird, printers, 1840.
Holcombe, Hosea.

LAC 14212
History of the rise and progress of the iron trade of the United States, from 1621 to 1857. With numerous statistical tables, relating to the manufacture, importation, exportation, and prices of iron for more than a century. New York, Wiley & Halsted, 1858.
French, Benjamin Franklin, 1799–1877.

LAC 23038
The history of the rise, increase, and progress of the Christian people called Quakers, intermixed with several remarkable occurrences. By William [!] Sewel. Written originally in Low Dutch, and translated by himself into English. To which is prefixed, a short biographical notice of the author. Philadelphia, Friend's book store, 1856.
Sewel, Willem, 1653–1720.

LAC 20971
The history of the rise, progress, and accomplishment of the abolition of the African slave-trade, by the British parliament. New York, Taylor, 1836.
Clarkson, Thomas, 1760–1846.

LAC 10419
History of the rise, progress, and existing condition of the western canals in the state of New York, from September, 1788, to ... 1819. Together with the rise, progress, and existing state of modern agricultural societies, on the Berkshire system, from 1807, to the establishment of the Board of agriculture in the state of New-York, January 10, 1820. Albany, D. Steele, 1820.
Watson, Elkanah, 1758–1842.

LAC 11031
History of the rise, progress, genius, and character of American Presbyterianism: together with a review of "The constitutional history of the Presbyterian church in the United States of America, by Chas. Hodge..." By William Hill. Washington city, J. Gideon, jr., 1839.
Hill, William, 1769–1852.

LAC 20890–92
The history of the Royal society of London for improving of natural knowledge, from its first rise. In which the most considerable of those papers communicated to the society, which have hitherto not been published, are inserted in their proper order, as a supplement to the Philosophical transactions. London, Printed for A. Millar, 1756–57.
Birch, Thomas, 1705–1766.

LAC 13076
The history of the saints; or, An expose of Joe Smith and Mormonism. Boston, Leland & Whiting; New York, Bradbury, Soden, & co.; [etc., etc.] 1842.
Bennett, John C.

LAC 11664
History of the San Francisco stock and exchange board, by the chairman, Jos. L. King. San Francisco, J. L. King, 1910.
King, Joseph L.

LAC 23308
History of the Scandinavians and successful Scandinavians in the United States. Comp. and ed. by O. N. Nelson. 2d, rev. ed. Minneapolis, Minn., O. N. Nelson & company, 1900.
Nelson, Olof Nickolaus, *d.* 1917, *ed.*

LAC 13713
History of the second Pan-American congress, with notes on the republic of Mexico. Baltimore, Md., Guggenheimer, Weil & co., 1902.
Noel, John Vavasour.

LAC 14124
History of the Shawnee Indians, from the year 1681 to 1854, inclusive. Cincinnati, E. Morgan & sons, 1855.
Harvey, Henry, *missionary to the Shawnee Indians.*

LAC 10002
History of the short-horn cattle: their origin, progress and present condition. Buffalo, N. Y., Author, 1872.
Allen, Lewis Falley, 1800–1890.

LAC 14125
History of the Sioux war and massacres of 1862 and 1863. New York, Harper & brothers, 1865, [c1863]
Heard, Isaac V D b. 1834.

LAC 21081
The history of the Society of Friends in America. London, 1850–54.
Bowden, James.

LAC 14188
A history of the Spanish-American war of 1898. New York, D. Appleton and company, 1900.
Titherington, Richard Handfield, 1861–

LAC 20037
The history of the Standard oil company. New York, McClure, Phillips & co., 1904.
Tarbell, Ida Minerva, 1857–1944.

LAC 20052-53
History of the state of Delaware, from the earliest settlements to the year 1907... Wilmington, Del. The author, 1908.
Conrad, Henry Clay, 1852–

LAC 10234
The history of the state of Georgia from 1850 to 1881, embracing the three important epochs: the decade before the war of 1861–5; the war; the period of reconstruction ... New-York, Brown & Derby [c1881]
Avery, Isaac Wheeler, 1837–1897.

LAC 21146–47
The history of the state of Indiana, from the earliest explorations by the French to the present time. Containing an account of the principal civil, political, and military events, from 1763–1897. Indianapolis, The B. L. Blair company, 1897.
Smith, William Henry, 1839–

LAC 22912–3
History of the state of New York. New York, Harper & brothers, 1859–71.
Brodhead, John Romeyn, 1814–1873.

LAC 15772
History of the state of New-York, including its aboriginal and colonial annals. By John V. N. Yates and Joseph W. Moulton. New-York, A. T. Goodrich, 1824–26.
Moulton, Joseph White, 1789–1875.

LAC 11378
A history of the state of Ohio, natural and civil. 1st ed. Cincinnati, Stereotyped by Glezen & Shepard [c1838]
Atwater, Caleb, 1778–1867.

LAC 12836
A history of the struggle for slavery extension or restriction in the United States, from the Declaration of independence to the present day. Mainly compiled and condensed from the journals of Congress and other official records, and showing the vote by yeas and nays on the most important divisions in either House. New York, Dix, Edwards & co., 1856.
Greeley, Horace, 1811–1872.

LAC 22577
The history of the Supreme court of the United States; with biographies of all the chief and associate justices. By Hampton L. Carson. A. D. 1790–1902. With portraits of the 58 judges engraved by Max and Albert Rosenthal. Philadelphia, P. W. Ziegler and company, 1902.
Carson, Hampton Lawrence, 1852–1929.

LAC 10050
The history of the surplus revenue of 1837; being an account of its origin, its distribution among the states, and the uses to which it was applied. New York & London, G. P. Putnam's sons, 1885.
Bourne, Edward Gaylord, 1860–1908.

LAC 23756
History of the Swedes of Illinois... Chicago, The Engberg-Holmberg publishing company, 1908.
Olson, Ernst Wilhelm, 1870– *ed.*

LAC 13685
History of the Tammany society from its organization to the present time. By E. Vale Blake, published under the direction of Fred Feigl. New York, Souvenir publishing company [c1901]
Blake, Euphemia, 1817–1904.

LAC 12616
The history of the telephone. Chicago, A. C. McClurg & co., 1910.
Casson, Herbert Newton, 1869–

LAC 13513
History of the temperance reform in Massachusetts, 1813–1883. Boston, Clarke & Carruth, 1888.
Clark, George Faber, 1817–1899.

LAC 15941
A history of the theology of the Disciples of Christ... St. Louis, Christian publishing company, 1907.
Van Kirk, Hiram, 1868–1920.

LAC 14078–79
History of the town of Amherst, Hillsborough county, New Hampshire, (first known as Narragansett township number three, and subsequently as Souhegan West) from the grant of the township by the Great and General court of the province of Massachusetts bay, in June, 1728, to March, 1882, with genealogies of Amherst families ... and a sketch of the Narraganset fort fight, 19 December, 1675... Concord, N. H., Printed by Evans, Sleeper & Woodbury, 1883.
Secomb, Daniel Franklin, 1820–1895.

LAC 15648
The history of the town of Amherst, Massachusetts. Published in two parts. Part I.–General history of the town. Part II.–Town meeting records. Complete in one volume. Comp. and pub. by Carpenter & Morehouse. Amherst, Mass., Press of Carpenter & Morehouse, 1896.
Carpenter, Edward Wilton, 1856–

LAC 15474
History of the town of Bellingham, Massachusetts, 1719–1919. [Bellingham] Pub. by the town, 1919.
Partridge, George Fairbanks, 1863–

LAC 22752–53
History of the town of Canterbury, New Hampshire, 1727–1912. Concord, N. H., The Rumford press, 1912.
Lyford, James Otis, 1853–

LAC 20519
History of the town of Cornish, New Hampshire, with genealogical record, 1763–1910. Concord, N.H., The Rumford press [1911?]
Child, William Henry, 1832–

LAC 20571–72
History of the town of Durham, New Hampshire (Oyster River Plantation) with genealogical notes. By Everett S. Stackpole and Lucien Thompson. [Durham? N. H.] Pub. by vote of the town [1913]
Stackpole, Everett Schermerhorn, 1850–

LAC 15563
History of the town of Durham, N. C., embracing biographical sketches and engravings of leading business men, and a carefully compiled business directory of Durham, to which is annexed a compilation of useful information in relation to the cultivation, curing and manufacture of tobacco in North Carolina and Virginia. Raleigh, Edwards, Broughton & co., printers, 1884.
Paul, Hiram Voss, 1848–

LAC 14756
History of the town of East Greenwich and adjacent territory, from 1677 to 1877. Providence, J. A. & R. A. Reid, 1877.
Greene, Daniel Howland, 1807–1886.

LAC 11690
History of the town of Exeter, New Hampshire. Exeter [Press of J. E. Farwell & co., Boston] 1888.
Bell, Charles Henry, 1823–1893.

LAC 10378
History of the town of Goshen, Connecticut, with genealogies and biographies based upon the records of Deacon Lewis Mills Norton, 1897. Hartford, Conn., Press of the Case, Lockwood & Brainard company, 1897.
Hibbard, Augustine George, 1833–

LAC 10899
Ye historie of ye town of Greenwich, county of Fairfield and state of Connecticut, with genealogical notes... By Spencer P. Mead. Being a revision, amplification, and continuation of the History of the town of Greenwich published in 1857, by Daniel M. Mead. New York, The Knickerbocker press, 1911.
Mead, Spencer Percival, 1863–

LAC 20178–79
History of the town of Hampton, New Hampshire. From its settlement in 1638, to the autumn of 1892. By Joseph Dow. Ed. and pub. by his daughter. Salem, Mass., Printed by the Salem press publishing and printing co., 1893.
Dow, Joseph, 1807–1889.

LAC 11296
History of the town of Harvard, Massachusetts. 1732–1893. Harvard, W. Hapgood, 1894.
Nourse, Henry Stedman, 1831–1903.

LAC 15598
History of the town of Lancaster, Massachusetts: from the first settlement to the present time, 1643–1879. By Rev. Abijah P. Marvin. Lancaster, The town, 1879.
Marvin, Abijah Perkins.

LAC 21046–47
History of the town of Lexington, Middlesex county, Massachusetts, from its first settlement to 1868, by Charles Hudson; rev. and continued to 1912 by the Lexington historical society. [Bi-centenary ed.] Boston and New York, Houghton Mifflin company, 1913.
Hudson, Charles, 1795–1881.

LAC 15237
History of the town of Marlborough, Middlesex county, Massachusetts, from its first settlement in 1657 to 1861; with a brief sketch of the town of Northborough, a genealogy of the families in Marlborough to 1800, and an account of the celebration of the two hundredth anniversary of the incorporation of the town. Boston, Press of T. R. Marvin & son, 1862.
Hudson, Charles, 1795–1881.

LAC 16724
History of the town of Medfield, Massachusetts. 1650. 1886; with genealogies of the families that held real estate or made any considerable stay in the town during the first two centuries. Ed. by William S. Tilden. Illustrated with portraits and with engravings after drawings by John A. S. Monks. Boston, G. H. Ellis, 1887.
Tilden, William Smith, 1830–1912, *ed.*

LAC 13535
History of the town of Middleboro, Massachusetts. Boston and New York, Houghton, Mifflin and company, 1906.
Weston, Thomas, 1834–1920.

LAC 11790
A history of the town of Northfield, Massachusetts, for 150 years, with an account of the prior occupation of the territory by the Squakheags: and with family genealogies. By J. H. Temple and George Sheldon. Albany, N. Y., J. Munsell, 1875.
Temple, Josiah Howard, 1815–1893.

LAC 11791
History of the town of Palmer, Massachusetts, early known as the Elbow tract: including records of the plantation, district and town. 1716–1889. With a genealogical register. [Springfield] Pub. by the town of Palmer, 1889.
Temple, Josiah Howard.

LAC 21337
History of the town of Rochester, New Hampshire, from 1722 to 1890. By Franklin McDuffee, A. M.; ed. and rev. by Silvanus Hayward. Manchester, The J. B. Clarke co., printers, 1892.
McDuffee, Franklin, 1832–1880.

LAC 14569
History of the town of Rye, New Hampshire, from its discovery and settlement to December 31, 1903. Concord, N. H., Rumford printing company, 1905.
Parsons, Langdon Brown, 1844–

LAC 13536
History of the town of Stonington, county of New London, Connecticut, from its first settlement in 1649 to 1900, with a genealogical register of Stonington families. New London, Conn., Press of the Day publishing company, 1900.
Wheeler, Richard Anson, 1817–

LAC 10672–73
History of the town of Surry, Cheshire County, New Hampshire, from date of severance from Gilsum and Westmoreland, 1769–1922, with a genealogical register and map of the town. Surry, N. H., Pub. by the town, 1925.
Kingsbury, Frank Burnside, 1868–

LAC 11382
History of the town of Townsend, Middlesex County, Massachusetts, from the grant of Hathorn's farm, 1676–1878. Fitchburg, The author, 1878.
Sawtelle, Ithamar Bard.

LAC 11792
History of the town of Whately, Mass., including a narrative of leading events from the first planting of Hatfield: 1660–1871. With family genealogies. Boston, Printed for the town, by T. R. Marvin & son, 1872.
Temple, Josiah Howard, 1815–1893.

LAC 11724
History of the town of Wilton, Hillsborough County, New Hampshire, with a genealogical register by Abiel Abbot Livermore and Sewall Putnam. Lowell, Mass., Marden & Rowell, printers, 1888.
Livermore, Abiel Abbot, 1811–1892.

LAC 11725
History of the town of Winchendon (Worcester County, Mass.) from the grant of Ipswich Canada, in 1735, to the present time. By Rev. A. P. Marvin. Winchendon, The author, 1868.
Marvin, Abijah Perkins.

LAC 10898
A history of the townships of Byberry and Moreland, in Philadelphia, Pa., from their earliest settlement by the whites to the present time. Philadelphia, T. E. Zell, 1867.
Martindale, Joseph C.

LAC 13405–6
History of the Typographical union, its beginnings, progress and development, its beneficial and educational features, together with a chapter on the early organizations of printers. Comp. by authority of the Executive council of the International typographical union, by George A. Tracy. [Indianapolis] The International typographical union, 1913.
Tracy, George A   comp.

LAC 11237
History of the Underground railroad in Chester and the neighboring counties of Pennsylvania. Illustrated. New York, Negro universities press, 1968.
Smedley, Robert C   d. 1883.

LAC 10314
History of the Union Pacific railway. Chicago, The University of Chicago press, 1895.
White, Henry Kirke, 1865–

LAC 21109
History of the United States Capitol. Washington, Govt. print. off., 1900–03.
Brown, Glenn, 1854–

LAC 23204–6
History of the United States from the Compromise of 1850... Port Washington, N. Y., Kennikat Press [1967, c1892–1899]
Rhodes, James Ford, 1848–1927.

LAC 22291–93
A history of the United States navy from 1775 to 1901... New and enl. ed. ... New York, D. Appleton, 1906–1910.
Maclay, Edgar Stanton, 1863–1919.

LAC 15156
History of the United States navy-yard, Portsmouth, N. H. Prepared by order of the Hon. secretary of the navy, under the direction of the Bureau of yards and docks, by Geo. Henry Preble, rear-admiral, U.S.N. Washington, Govt. print. off., 1892.
Preble, George Henry, 1816–1885.

LAC 21409–13
History of the United States of America. New York, C. Scribner's sons, 1909–11.
Adams, Henry, 1838–1918.

LAC 11675
A history of the United States of America, by Rev. Charles A. Goodrich. With engravings. 3d ed. Hartford, Barber & Robinson, 1823.
Goodrich, Charles Augustus, 1790–1862.

LAC 40067
History of the United States of America. Constitution of the United States of America, with amendments. Declaration of independence... Pub. under the direction of Arthur MacArthur, major general, U.S.A., military governor of the Philippine islands... Historia de los Estados Unidos de America. Constituion de los Estados Unidos de America, con enmiendas. Declaracion de independencia... Pub. bajo la direccion de Arthur MacArthur. [Philadelphia, Ketterlinus lithographic manufacturing company, c1900]
Philippine Islands. *Military Governor, 1900–1901 (Arthur MacArthur)*

LAC 22534–37
History of the United States of America, from the discovery of the continent [to 1789] The author's last revision... New York, D. Appleton and company, 1883–85.
Bancroft, George, 1800–1891.

LAC 20243-44
The history of the United States of America, from the discovery of the continent to the organization of government under the federal constitution. In three volumes. New York, Harper & brothers, 1849, [c1848-49]
Hildreth, Richard, 1807-1865.

LAC 23485-89
History of the United States of America, under the Constitution. New York, Dodd, Mead & company [c1894-1913]
Schouler, James, 1839-1920.

LAC 12536
History of the United States sanitary commission, being the general report of its work during the war of the rebellion. By Charles J. Stille. Philadelphia, J. B. Lippincott & co., 1866.
United States Sanitary Commission.

LAC 14172
History of the United States secret service, by General L. C. Baker. Philadelphia, L. C. Baker, 1867.
Baker, La Fayette Charles, 1826-1868.

LAC 21065-66
History of the University of North Carolina... Raleigh, N. C., Printed for the author by Edwards & Broughton printing company, 1907-12.
Battle, Kemp Plummer, 1831-1919.

LAC 11567
A history of the University of Pennsylvania, from its foundation to A. D. 1770; including biographical sketches of the trustees, faculty, the first alumni and others. Philadelphia, G. W. Jacobs & co., 1900.
Montgomery, Thomas Harrison, 1830-1905.

LAC 16399
A history of the upper country of South Carolina, from the earliest periods to the close of the war of independence. Vol. I. Charleston, S. G. Courtenay & co.; Columbia, P. B. Glass, 1859.
Logan, John Henry.

LAC 12350
A history of the valley of Virginia. 3d ed. Rev. and extended by the author. Woodstock, Va., W. N. Grabill, 1902.
Kercheval, Samuel, 1786-1845.

LAC 40016
History of the various projects, reports, discussions and estimates for reaching the Great Lakes from tidewater. 1768-1901. [Oswego? N. Y., 1901]
Judson, William Pierson, 1849-

LAC 13276
History of the Virginia company of London, with letters to and from the first colony, never before printed. Albany, N. Y., J. Munsell, 1869.
Neill, Edward Duffield, 1823-1893.

LAC 16740
A history of the war between Great Britain and the United States of America. During the years 1812, 1813, and 1814. Toronto, Maclear & co., 1855.
Auchinleck, Gilbert.

LAC 14905
History of the war between the United States and Mexico, from the commencement of hostilities to the ratification of the treaty of peace. Auburn [N. Y.] Derby, Miller & co., 1849.
Jenkins, John Stilwell, 1818-1852.

LAC 14346
History of the war between the United States and the Sac and Fox nations of Indians, and parts of other disaffected tribes of Indians, in the years eighteen hundred and twenty-seven, thirty-one, and thirty-two. Jacksonville, Ill., Printed by C. Goudy, 1834.
Wakefield, John Allen, 1797-1873.

LAC 14631
A history of the War department of the United States. With biographical sketches of the secretaries. Washington, D. C., F. B. Mohun, 1880, [c1879]
Ingersoll, Lurton Dunham.

LAC 14627
History of the war of 1812 between Great Britain and the United States of America. Toronto, Morang & co., limited, 1905.
Hannay, James, 1842-1910.

LAC 21850-51
History of the war of the independence of the United States of America. Written by Charles Botta. Tr. from the Italian, by George Alexander Otis. Philadelphia: Printed for the translator, Lydia R. Bailey, printer, 1820-21.
Botta, Carlo Giuseppe Guglielmo, 1766-1837.

LAC 20505
A history of the warfare of science with theology in christendom. New York and London, D. Appleton & company, 1923, [c1896]
White, Andrew Dickson, 1832-1918.

LAC 14472
The history of the wars of New-England with the Eastern Indians; or, A narrative of their continued perfidy and cruelty, from the 10th of August, 1703, to the peace renewed 13th of July, 1713. And from the 25th of July, 1722, to their submission 15th December, 1725, which was ratified August 5th, 1726. Cincinnati, Reprinted ... for W. Dodge, by J. Harpel, 1859.
Penhallow, Samuel, 1665-1726.

LAC 14710
History of the West End street railway, in which is included sketches of the early street railways of Boston-consolidation of the various lines-foreign street railways-the Berlin viaduct-anecdotes, etc., together with speeches by President Henry M. Whitney, and others. Also, expert testimony as to the safety of electric currents... Boston, Ed. and pub. by L. P. Hager [1892]
Hager, Louis P.

LAC 13687
History of the western insurrection in western Pennsylvania, commonly called the whiskey insurrection. 1794. Pittsburgh, Printed by W. S. Haven, 1859.
Brackenridge, Henry Marie, 1786-1871.

LAC 10755
History of the Wheel and Alliance and the impending revolution. Hardy, Ark., Pub. by the author; Fort Scott, Kan., J. H. Rice & sons, printers and publishers, 1889.
Morgan, W   Scott.

LAC 12509
A history of the Whig party, or some of its main features; with a hurried glance at the formation of parties in the United States, and the outlines of the history of the principal parties of the country to the present time, etc., etc. Boston, Crosby, Nichols & company, 1859.
Ormsby, Robert McKinley, 1814–1881.

LAC 16005
History of the Zoar society, from its commencement to its conclusion; a sociological study in communism. 3d ed. Columbus, O., Press of F. J. Heer, 1904, [c1899]
Randall, Emilius Oviatt, 1850–1919.

LAC 15559
A history of three of the judges of King Charles I. Major-General Whalley, Major-General Goffe, and Colonel Dixwell: who, at the restoration, 1660, fled to America; and were secreted and concealed in Massachusetts and Connecticut, for near thirty years. With an account of Mr. Theophilus Whale, of Narragansett, supposed to have been also one of the judges. By President Stiles. Hartford: Printed by Elisha Babcock, 1794.
Stiles, Ezra, 1727–1795.

LAC 11331–32
History of Tolland county, Connecticut, including its early settlement and progress to the present time; a description of its historic and interesting localities; sketches of its towns and villages; portraits of some of its prominent men, and biographies of many of its representative citizens. New York, W. W. Preston & co., 1888.
Cole, J   R.

LAC 14076
History of Torrington, Connecticut, from its first settlement in 1737, with biographies and genealogies. By Rev. Samuel Orcutt. Albany, J. Munsell, printer, 1878.
Orcutt, Samuel.

LAC 15356
A history of transportation in the eastern cotton belt to 1860. New York, The Columbia university press, 1908.
Phillips, Ulrich Bonnell, 1877–1934.

LAC 22116–17
A history of travel in America... New York, Greenwood press, 1915–1968.
Dunbar, Seymour.

LAC 12328
The historie of travaile into Virginia Britannia; expressing the cosmographie and comodities of the country, togither with the manners and customes of the people. Gathered and observed as well by those who went first thither as collected by William Strachey. Now first ed. from the original manuscript, in the British museum, by R. H. Major. London, Printed for the Hakluyt society, 1849.
Strachey, William, 1572?–1621.

LAC 13922–23
History of Union and Middlesex counties, New Jersey, with biographical sketches of many of their pioneers and prominent men. Philadelphia, Everts & Peck, 1882.
Clayton, W   Woodford, ed.

LAC 22283–84
History of United mine workers of America... Indianapolis [1918?–20]
Evans, Chris, d. 1924.

LAC 40053
History of United States military policy on reserve forces, 1775–1957. Prepared at the request of Overton Brooks, chairman, Subcommittee No. 1, Committee on Armed Services, House of Representatives, by Eilene Galloway, national defense analyst. Washington, U.S. Govt. Print. Off., 1957.
U.S. *Library of Congress. Legislative Reference Service.*

LAC 11735
History of Vermont, natural, civil and statistical, in three parts, with a new map of the state, and 200 engravings. Burlington, C. Goodrich, 1842.
Thompson, Zadock, 1796–1856.

LAC 11689
The history of Vermont; with descriptions, physical and topographical. Brattleboro, G. H. Salisbury, 1846.
Beckley, Hosea.

LAC 12341
The history of Virgil A. Stewart, and his adventure in capturing and exposing the great "western land pirate" and his gang, in connexion with the evidence; also of the trials, confessions, and execution of a number of Murrell's associates in the state of Mississippi during the summer of 1835, and the execution of five professional gamblers by the citizens of Vicksburg, on the 6th July, 1835... New York, Harper & brothers, 1836.
Howard, H   R   *comp.*

LAC 23125–27
The history of Virginia, from its first settlement to the present day. Petersburg, Virginia, Printed for the author, by Dickson & Pescud, 1804–16.
Burk, John Daly, d. 1808.

LAC 13878
History of wages and prices in Massachusetts: 1752–1883. Including Comparative wages and prices in Massachusetts and Great Britain: 1860–1883. [Being parts III. and IV. of the Sixteenth annual report of the Massachusetts Bureau of statistics of labor.] By Carroll D. Wright, chief of the Bureau of statistics of labor. Boston, Wright & Potter printing co., state printers, 1885.
Massachusetts. *Bureau of Statistics of Labor.*

LAC 13427
History of wages in the United States from colonial times to 1928. Revision of Bulletin no. 499, with Supplement, 1929–1933 (page 523) Washington, U. S. Govt. print. off., 1934.
U. S. *Bureau of Labor Statistics.*

LAC 10383–84
History of Wallingford, Conn., from its settlement in 1670 to the present time, including Meriden, which was one of its parishes until 1806, and Cheshire, which was incorporated in 1780. Meriden, The author, 1870.
Davis, Charles Henry Stanley, 1840–1917.

LAC 10365
The history of Warren; a mountain hamlet, located among the White hills of New Hampshire. Manchester, N. H., W. E. Moore, printer, 1870.
Little, William, 1833–1893.

LAC 16025–26
History of Washington and Kent counties, Rhode Island, including their early settlement and progress to the present time; a description of their historic and interesting localities; sketches of their towns and villages; portraits of some of their prominent men, and biographies of many of their representative citizens. New York, W. W. Preston & co., 1889.
Cole, J   R.

LAC 15771
History of Washington Co., New York. With illustrations and biographical sketches of some of its prominent men and pioneers. Philadelphia, Everts & Ensign, 1878.
Johnson, Crisfield.

LAC 10893–94
The history of Weare, New Hampshire, 1735–1888. By William Little. David Cross, Abner P. Collins, Josiah G. Dearborn, Robert Peaslee, Sylvester C. Gould, town committee who furnished the material. Pub. by the town. Lowell, Mass., Printed by S. W. Huse & co., 1888.
Little, William, 1833–1893.

LAC 11696
The history of Wells and Kennebunk from the earliest settlement to the year 1820, at which time Kennebunk was set off, and incorporated. With biographical sketches. Portland, B. Thurston & company, 1875.
Bourne, Edward Emerson, 1797–1873.

LAC 14662
History of West Point, and its military importance during the American Revolution: and the origin and progress of the United States Military Academy. Freeport, N. Y., Books for Libraries Press [1970]
Boynton, Edward Carlisle, 1824–1893.

LAC 14136
The history of Westborough, Massachusetts. Part I. The early history. By Heman Packard De Forest. Part II. The later history. By Edward Craig Bates. Westborough, The town, 1891.
De Forest, Heman Packard.

LAC 20240–42
History of Westchester county, New York, including Morrisania, Kings Bridge, and West Farms, which have been annexed to New York city. Philadelphia, L. E. Preston & co., 1886.
Scharf, John Thomas, 1843–1898, ed.

LAC 20863–64
History of western Massachusetts. The counties of Hampden, Hampshire, Franklin, and Berkshire. Embracing an outline, or general history, of the section, an account of its scientific aspects and leading interests, and separate histories of its one hundred towns. Springfield, S. Bowles and company, 1855.
Holland, Josiah Gilbert, 1819–1881.

LAC 15248
A history of Western Reserve college, during its first half century, 1826–1876. Cleveland, Crocker's publishing house, 1876.
Cutler, Carroll, 1829–1894.

LAC 20158
History of Wichita and Sedgwick County, Kansas, past and present, including an account of the cities, towns and villages of the county, editor-in-chief, Hon. O. H. Bentley. Chicago, C. F. Cooper & co., 1910.
Bentley, Orsemus Hills, ed.

LAC 15475
The history of Wilbraham, Massachusetts; prepared in connection with the celebration of the one hundred and fiftieth anniversary of the incorporation of the town, June 15, 1913. [Wilbraham? Mass., pref. 1914]
Peck, Chauncey Edwin.

LAC 20547–48
History of Windham County, Connecticut. Published by the author. Worcester, Mass., Printed by C. Hamilton, 1874–80.
Larned, Ellen Douglas, 1825–1912.

LAC 21148
The history of Wisconsin. In three parts, historical, documentary, and descriptive. Comp. by direction of the Legislature of the state. By William R. Smith. v. 1, 3. Madison, B. Brown, 1854.
Smith, William Rudolph, 1787–1868.

LAC 23749–55
History of woman suffrage. Ed. by Elizabeth Cady Stanton, Susan B. Anthony, and Matilda Joslyn Gage. New York, Fowler & Wells, 1881–[1922]
Stanton, Elizabeth, 1815–1902, ed.

LAC 20141–42
A history of woman's education in the United States. New York, N. Y., and Lancaster, Pa., The Science press, 1929.
Woody, Thomas, 1891–

LAC 23000–2
History of Worcester County, Massachusetts, with biographical sketches of many of its pioneers and prominent men. Comp. under the supervision of D. Hamilton Hurd. Philadelphia, J. W. Lewis & co., 1889.
Hurd, Duane Hamilton, ed.

LAC 13270
History of Wyoming, in a series of letters, from Charles Miner, to his son William Penn Miner, esq. ... Philadelphia, J. Crissy, 1845.
Miner, Charles, 1780–1865.

LAC 13913
History of York County, Maine. With illustrations and biographical sketches of its prominent men and pioneers... Philadelphia, Everts & Peck, 1880.
Clayton, W   Woodford.

LAC 40016
History, structure, and statistics of plank roads, in the United States and Canada. By W. Kingsford. With remarks on roads in general, by F. G. Skinner; and a letter on plank roads, by the Hon. Charles E. Clarke. Philadelphia, A. Hart, 1851.
Kingsford, William, 1819–1898.

LAC 12680

History, theory, and practice of the electric telegraph.
3d ed., rev. and enl. Boston, Ticknor and Fields, 1866,
[c1860]
Prescott, George Bartlett, 1830–1894.

LAC 15902

Hits at American whims and hints for home use. Boston, Walker, Wise and co., 1860.
Sawyer, Frederick William, 1810–1875.

LAC 12091

The hive of "the bee-hunter," a repository of sketches, including peculiar American character, scenery, and rural sports. New-York [etc.] D. Appleton and company, 1854.
Thorpe, Thomas Bangs, 1815–1878.

LAC 15761

The hobo; the sociology of the homeless man. A study prepared for the Chicago council of social agencies under the direction of the Committee on homeless men.
Chicago, Ill., The University of Chicago press [1923]
Anderson, Nels, 1889–

LAC 15907

The holidays: Christmas, Easter, and Whitsuntide; together with May-day, Midsummer, and harvest-home festivals. By Nathan B. Warren. Illustrated by F. O. C. Darley. 3d ed. Troy, N. Y., H. B. Nims and company [1876]
Warren, Nathan Boughton, 1815–1898.

LAC 15756

The Hollanders of Iowa. Iowa City, Ia., The State historical society of Iowa, 1912.
Van der Zee, Jacob, 1884–

LAC 14131

Holly's country seats: containing lithographic designs for cottages, villas, mansions, etc., with their accompanying out-buildings; also, country churches, city buildings, railway stations, etc., etc. New York, D. Appleton and company, 1863.
Holly, Henry Hudson, 1834–1892.

LAC 11556–57

The Holy Bible containing the Old and New Testaments: translated out of the original tongues: and with the former translations diligently compared and revised.
Trenton, I. Collins, 1791.
Bible. *English. Authorized. 1791.*

LAC 22522–23

The Holy Bible, translated from the Latin vulgate: diligently compared with the Hebrew, Greek, and other editions in divers languages. The Old Testament, first published by the English college at Douay, A. D. 1609. And the New Testament, first published by the English college at Rheims, A. D. 1582. With useful notes, critical, historical, controversial, and explanatory, selected from the most eminent commentators ... by the Late Rev. Geo. Leo Haydock. The text carefully collated with that of the original edition, and the annotations abridged, by the Very Rev. F. C. Husenbeth. New York, G. Virtue [1850]
Bible. *English. Douai. 1850.*

LAC 13006

The Holyoke diaries, 1709–1856; Rev. Edward Holyoke, Marblehead and Cambridge, 1709–1768, Edward Augustus Holyoke, M. D., Cambridge, 1742–1747, John Holyoke, Cambridge, 1748, Mrs. Mary (Vial) Holyoke, Salem, 1760–1800, Margaret Holyoke, Salem, 1801–1823, Mrs. Susanna (Holyoke) Ward, Salem, 1793–1856; with an introduction and annotations by George Francis Dow. Salem, Mass., The Essex institute, 1911.
Dow, George Francis, 1868–1936, *ed.*

LAC 16746

A home for all; or, The gravel wall and octagon mode of building... New York, Fowler and Wells, 1854.
Fowler, Orson Squire, 1809–1887.

LAC 12185

Home life in colonial days, written by Alice Morse Earle in the year MDCCCXCVIII, illustrated by photographs, gathered by the author, of real things, works, and happenings of olden times. New York, The Macmillan company; London, Macmillan & co., ltd., 1898.
Earle, Alice, 1851–1911.

LAC 13976

Home-talks, by John Humphrey Noyes. Ed. by Alfred Barron and George Noyes Miller. v.1. Oneida, Pub. by the Community, 1875.
Noyes, John Humphrey, 1811–1886.

LAC 12289

Home-treatment for sexual abuses... By R. T. Trall, M.D. New York, Fowlers and Wells, 1853.
Trall, Russell Thacher, 1812–1877.

LAC 14316

Homes for the people in suburb and country; the villa, the mansion, and the cottage, adapted to American climate and wants. With examples showing how to alter and remodel old buildings. In a series of one hundred original designs. 6th thousand. Rev. ed. New York, G. E. Woodward, 1868.
Wheeler, Gervase.

LAC 14132

Homes of American authors; comprising anecdotical, personal, and descriptive sketches, by various writers. New-York, D. Appleton, 1857, [c1852]

LAC 20040–41

The homes of the New world; impressions of America.
By Fredrika Bremer. Tr. by Mary Howitt. New York, Harper & brothers, 1853.
Bremer, Fredrika, 1801–1865.

LAC 12401

The homes of the pilgrim fathers in England and America (1620–1685) by Martin S. Briggs, F. R. I. B. A. London and New York, Oxford university press, 1932.
Briggs, Martin Shaw, 1882–

LAC 13731

Homestead. A complete history of the struggle of July, 1892, between the Carnegie steel company, limited, and the Amalgamated association of iron and steel workers.
Pittsburgh, Pa. [Rawsthorne engraving and printing co.] 1893.
Burgoyne, Arthur Gordon, *d.* 1914.

LAC 11749
The Homestead manual of valuable information for the people relating principally to the farm, orchard, garden and household... Carefully prepared from the best authorities, by B. F. Gue. Des Moines, The Homestead company, 1881.
Gue, Benjamin, F   1828–1904, comp.

LAC 40001
An honest dollar. [Baltimore] American economic association, 1889.
Andrews, Elisha Benjamin, 1844–1917.

LAC 13113
The honorable Peter Stirling and what people thought of him. New York, Grosset & Dunlap [c1894]
Ford, Paul Leicester, 1865–1902.

LAC 10288
The Honorable Peter White, a biographical sketch of the Lake Superior iron country. Cleveland, The Penton publishing co. [c1907]
Williams, Ralph D.

LAC 16954
Hooper bill.
The origin of the national banking system. Washington, Govt. Print. Off., 1910.
Davis, Andrew McFarland, 1833–1920.

LAC 40016
The Hoosac tunnel: its condition and prospects. Boston, Wright & Potter, printers, 1865.
Bird, Francis William, 1809–1894.

LAC 16666
The Hoosier school-boy. New York, C. Scribner's sons, 1883.
Eggleston, Edward, 1837–1902.

LAC 11905
The Hoosier schoolmaster. A novel. New York, Orange Judd and company [c1871]
Eggleston, Edward, 1837–1902.

LAC 20558
Hope Leslie; or, Early times in the Massachusetts. By the author of Redwood... New York, White, Gallaher, and White, 1827.
Sedgwick, Catharine Maria, 1789–1867.

LAC 10547
The hope of the great community. New York, The Macmillan company, 1916.
Royce, Josiah, 1855–1916.

LAC 16114
Hopi songs. Boston and New York, Houghton Mifflin company, 1908.
Gilman, Benjamin Ives, 1852–1933.

LAC 14361
Hopkinsianism.
A contrast between Calvinism and Hopkinsianism. New-York: Published by S. Whiting and co. theological and classical booksellers, 96 Broadway. Paul & Thomas, printers, 1811.
Ely, Ezra Stiles, 1786–1861.

LAC 11070
Horace Bushnell, preacher and theologian. Boston and New York, Houghton, Mifflin and company, 1899.
Munger, Theodore Thornton, 1830–1910.

LAC 40030
Horace Greeley and the South. His advocacy of the Ku-Klux act and of the law to enforce the XVth amendment; of mixed schools and of equal civil rights. [Washington? 1872]
Greeley, Horace, 1811–1872.

LAC 40030
Horace Greeley's views on Virginia, and what he knows about the South–slave-breeding–mixed schools–miscegnation–making sectional war–Kansas and the South–favoring secession–letting "the erring sisters go"–confiscation, rapine, and ravage–slave insurrections–supporting General Butler's New Orleans order–the Ku-Klux trials, &c., &c., &c., Washington, Gibson Brothers, 1872.
Greeley, Horace, 1811–1872.

LAC 13017
Horace Mann and the common school revival in the United States. New York, C. Scribner's sons, 1898.
Hinsdale, Burke Aaron, 1837–1900.

LAC 40133
Horrors of slavery. In two parts. Part I. Containing observations, facts, and arguments, extracted from the speeches of Wilberforce, Grenville, Pitt, Burke, Fox, Martin, Whitehead, and other distinguished members of the British Parliament. Part II. Containing extracts, chiefly American, comp. from authentic sources; demonstrating that slavery is impolitic, antirepublican, unchristian, and highly criminal: and proposing measures for its complete abolition through the United States. Cambridge [Mass.]: Printed by Hilliard and Metcalf. 1817. Sold by Cummings & Hilliard, no. 1, and Lincoln & Edmands, no. 53, Cornhill, Boston.
Kenrick, John, 1755–1833.

LAC 11355
The horse. By William Youatt. With a treatise on draught. Rev. and enl. by Walker Watson. New York, D. Appleton & co., 1866.
Youatt, William, 1776–1847.

LAC 13576
The horse of America in his derivation, history, and development... New York, The author, 1897.
Wallace, John Hankins, 1822–1903.

LAC 10086
Horse, truck and tractor; the coming of cheaper power for city and farm, by Herbert N. Casson, Rollin W. Hutchinson, jr., L. W. Ellis. Chicago, F. G. Browne & co., 1913.
Casson, Herbert Newton, 1869–

LAC 12298
Horses, saddles and bridles. Leavenworth, Kan., Ketcheson & Reeves, printers, 1895.
Carter, William Giles Harding, 1851–1925.

LAC 30987-91

The Horticulturist and journal of rural art and rural taste... v. 1-7; July 1846-Dec. 1852. Albany, L. Tucker, 1847-1852.

LAC 40046

Hosea Ballou and the gospel renaissance of the nineteenth century; by Rev. John Coleman Adams, D. D. Boston and Chicago, Universalist publishing house, 1903.
Adams, John Coleman, 1849-1922.

LAC 15055

Hospital days. Printed for private use. New York, D. Van Nostrand, 1870.
Woolsey, Jane Stuart.

LAC 12684

Hospital life in the Army of the Potomac. Boston, W. V. Spencer, 1866.
Reed, William Howell, 1837-

LAC 11810

Hospital sketches. Boston, J. Redpath, 1863.
Alcott, Louisa May, 1832-1888.

LAC 13806

Hot plowshares. A novel. New York, Fords, Howard, & Hulbert, 1883.
Tourgee, Albion Winegar, 1838-1905.

LAC 15974

Hours with art and artists. New York, D. Appleton and company [c1882]
Sheldon, George William, 1843-1914.

LAC 13879

The house beautiful; essays on beds and tables, stools and candlesticks. New-York, Scribner, Armstrong and company, 1878.
Cook, Clarence Chatham, 1828-1900.

LAC 11864

The house behind the cedars. Boston and New York, Houghton, Mifflin and company, 1901, [c1900]
Chesnutt, Charles Waddell, 1858-1932.

LAC 16613

The house in good taste; illustrated with photographs in color and black and white. New York, The Century co., 1915.
De Wolfe, Elsie, 1865-1950.

LAC 11957

The house of Harper; a century of publishing in Franklin square. New York and London, Harper & brothers, 1912.
Harper, Joseph Henry, 1850-1938.

LAC 12112

The house of mirth, by Edith Wharton; with illustrations by A. B. Wenzell. New York, C. Scribner's sons, 1905.
Wharton, Edith Newbold, 1862-1937.

LAC 10762

The house on Henry street, by Lillian D. Wald; with illustrations from etchings and drawings by Abraham Phillips and from photographs. New York, H. Holt and company, 1915.
Wald, Lillian D   1867-1940.

LAC 16331

Household manufacturers in the United States, 1640-1860; a study in industrial history. Chicago, Ill., The University of Chicago press [c1917]
Tryon, Rolla Milton, 1875-

LAC 11298

The housing of the poor in American cities. The prize essay of the American economic association for 1892. [Baltimore] American economic association, 1893.
Reynolds, Marcus Tullius, 1869-

LAC 11250

The housing of the unskilled wage earner; America's next problem. New York, Macmillan, 1919.
Wood, Edith, 1871-1945.

LAC 13663

The housing of the working people. Prepared under the direction of Carroll D. Wright, commissioner of labor, by E. R. L. Gould, PH. D. Washington, Gov't print. off., 1895.
U. S. *Bureau of Labor.*

LAC 14583

Housing reform, a hand-book for practical use in American cities. New York, Charities publication committee, 1911, [c1910]
Veiller, Lawrence Turnure.

LAC 16122

Houston journal; adventures in North America and Texas, 1837-1841. Translated from a German ms. and edited by Max Freund. Austin, University of Texas Press, 1954.
Dresel, Gustav, 1818-1848.

LAC 11783

How crops feed. A treatise on the atmosphere and the soil as related to the nutrition of agricultural plants... New York, Orange Judd and company 1890, [c1870]
Johnson, Samuel William, 1830-1909.

LAC 11782

How crops grow. A treatise on the chemical composition, structure and life of the plant, for students of agriculture... Rev. and enl. ed. New York, Orange Judd company 1894, [c1890]
Johnson, Samuel William, 1830-1909.

LAC 14651

How George Rogers Clark won the Northwest, and other essays in western history. Chicago, A. C. McClurg & co., 1927, [c1903]
Thwaites, Reuben Gold, 1853-

LAC 16573

How I know, or Sixteen years' eventful experience. An authentic narrative, embracing a brief record of serious and severe service on the battle-fields of the South; a detailed account of hazardous enterprises ... on the western frontier... Cincinnati, O., The author, 1881.
Swisher, James, 1849-

LAC 13593

The "How I was educated" papers. From the Forum magazine. New York, D. Appleton and company, 1888.

LAC 40105

How many miles from St. Jo? The log of Sterling B. F. Clark, a forty-niner, with comments by Ella Sterling Mighels; together with a brief autobiography of James Phelan, 1819–1892, pioneer merchant. San Francisco, Priv. print., 1929.
Clark, Sterling B   F   1825–1852.

LAC 13277

How Marcus Whitman saved Oregon. A true romance of patriotic heroism, Christian devotion and final martyrdom with sketches of life on the plains and mountains in pioneer days, by Oliver W. Nixon. Introduction by Rev. Frank W. Gunsaulus. Chicago, Star publishing company, 1895.
Nixon, Oliver Woodson, 1825–1905.

LAC 40102

How New York is governed. Frauds of the Tammany Democrats. New York, New York Daily Times, 1871.

LAC 12641

How plants grow.
Botany for young people and common schools. How plants grow, a simple introduction to structural botany. With a popular flora, or an arrangement and description of common plants, both wild and cultivated. Illustrated by 500 wood engravings. New York, Ivison, Blakeman, Taylor, & co. [c1858]
Gray, Asa, 1810–1888.

LAC 11300

How the other half lives; studies among the tenements of New York. With illustrations chiefly from photographs taken by the author. New York, C. Scribner's sons, 1906, [c1890]
Riis, Jacob August, 1849–1914.

LAC 10743

How they lived in Hampton; a study of practical Christianity applied in the manufacture of woollens. Boston, J. S. Smith & co. [c1888]
Hale, Edward Everett, 1822–1909.

LAC 14790

How to cooperate. The full fruits of labor to producer, honest value to consumer, just return to capital, prosperity to all. A manual for cooperators. New York, Orange Judd company, 1891.
Myrick, Herbert, 1860–1927.

LAC 11613

How to do business; or, The secret of success in retail merchandizing. A book for every merchant, containing invaluable information for every business man, clerk or student. Chicago, Ill., J. Jackson, 1890.
McLean, George N.

LAC 11648

How to get rich in California. A history of the progress and present condition of the gold and silver mining and other industrial interests of the great Pacific state ... containing ... some brief notices of some of California's most successful business men. Philadelphia, McMorris & Gans, 1876.
Taylor, Burrell B   *comp.*

LAC 15444

How to get rich in the South. Telling what to do, how to do it, and the profits to be realized. Chicago, W. H. Harrison, jr., publishing co., 1888.
Harrison, William H   *jr.*

LAC 10336

How to make a living; suggestions upon the art of making, saving, and using money. New York, G. P. Putnam's sons, 1875.
Eggleston, George Cary, 1839–1911.

LAC 11779

How to make the farm pay; or, The farmer's book of practical information on agriculture, stock raising, fruit culture, special crops, domestic economy & family medicine. By Charles W. Dickerman. Assisted by Hon. Charles L. Flint. Illustrated with one hundred and forty engravings. Philadelphia, Zeigler, McCurdy [c1869]
Dickerman, Charles W.

LAC 12255

How to mix drinks; or, The bon-vivant's companion, containing ... directions for mixing all the beverages used in the United States, together with the most popular British, French, German, Italian, Russian, and Spanish recipes... by Jerry Thomas. To which is appended a manual for the manufacture of cordials, liquors, fancy syrups, by Christian Schultz. New York, Dick & Fitzgerald, 1862.
Thomas, Jerry.

LAC 11793

How to pay off the national debt, regulate the value of money, and maintain stability in the values of property and labor. Philadelphia, Claxton, Remsen & Haffelfinger, 1872.
Green, Duff, 1791–1875.

LAC 10055

How we built the Union Pacific railway, and other railway papers and addresses, by Major-General Grenville M. Dodge, chief engineer Union Pacific railway 1866–1870. Washington, Govt. print. off., 1910.
Dodge, Grenville Mellen, 1831–1916.

LAC 11448

How we elected Lincoln; personal recollections of Lincoln and men of his time, by Abram J. Dittenhoefer, a campaigner for Lincoln in 1860 and a Lincoln elector in 1864. New York and London, Harper & brothers [1916]
Dittenhoefer, Abram Jesse, 1836–1919.

LAC 12354

How West Virginia was made. Proceedings of the first Convention of the people of northwestern Virginia at Wheeling, May 13, 14 and 15, 1861, and the journal of the second Convention of the people of northwestern Virginia at Wheeling, which assembled, June 11th 1861, and continued in session until June 25th. Adjourned until August 6th, 1861. Reassembled on that date, and continued in session until August 21st, when it adjourned sine die. With appendixes and an introduction, annotations and addenda by Virgil A. Lewis. [Charleston, W. Va., News-mail company, public printer] 1909.
Lewis, Virgil Anson, 1848–1912, *ed.*

LAC 40052
How Wisconsin came by its large German element, by Kate Asaphine Everest. Madison, State historical society of Wisconsin, 1892.
Levi, Kate Asaphine.

LAC 15630
Howard university, the capstone of Negro education, a history: 1867-1940. Washington, D. C., The Graduate school, Howard university, 1941.
Dyson, Walter, 1882–

LAC 13469
Howdy, honey, howdy, by Paul Laurence Dunbar; illustrated with photographs by Leigh Richmond Miner, decorations by Will Jenkins. New York, Dodd, Mead and company, 1905.
Dunbar, Paul Laurence, 1872-1906.

LAC 11878
Huckleberries gathered from New England hills. By Rose Terry Cooke. Boston and New York, Houghton, Mifflin and company, 1891.
Cooke, Rose, 1827-1892.

LAC 40023
The Hudson river railroad. Observations on the western trade, and its influence upon the growth and prosperity of the cities of New York, Boston and Philadelphia, through the several competing lines of communication, and the Hudson river railroad. Poughkeepsie, Journal & Eagle printing establishment, 1846.
Grant, William H.

LAC 14366
Huguenot emigration to Virginia
Documents, chiefly unpublished, relating to the Huguenot emigration to Virginia and to the settlement at Manakin-Town, with an appendix of genealogies, presenting data of the Fontaine, Maury, Dupuy, Trabue, Marye, Chastain, Cocke, and other families, edited and compiled for the Virginia Historical Society by R. A. Brock. Richmond, Va., 1886.
Virginia Historical Society, *Richmond.*

LAC 16783
The Huguenots of colonial South Carolina. Durham, N. C., Duke university press, 1928.
Hirsch, Arthur Henry, 1878–

LAC 12679
The human intellect: with an introduction upon psychology and the soul. New York, C. Scribner & company, 1868.
Porter, Noah, 1811-1892.

LAC 14605
Human motives. Boston, Little, Brown, and company, 1915.
Putnam, James Jackson, 1846-1918.

LAC 16934
Human nature and the social order. New York [etc.] C. Scribner's sons [c1902]
Cooley, Charles Horton, 1864-1929.

LAC 11216
The humane movement; a descriptive survey, prepared on the Henry Bergh foundation for the promotion of humane education in Columbia university. New York, The Columbia university press, 1910.
McCrea, Roswell Cheney, 1876–

LAC 11029
Humanity immortal; or, Man tried, fallen, and redeemed. Boston, Lee and Shepard; New York, Lee, Shepard and Dillingham, 1872.
Hickok, Laurens Perseus, 1798-1888.

LAC 10857
Humanity in the city. By the Rev. E. H. Chapin. New York, De Witt & Davenport; Boston, A. Tompkins [1854]
Chapin, Edwin Hubbell, 1814-1880.

LAC 11927
A humble romance, and other stories, by Mary E. Wilkins. New York [etc.] Harper & brothers, 1887.
Freeman, Mary Eleanor, 1852-1930.

LAC 13634
A hundred years of Methodism. New York, Phillips & Hunt, 1881, [c1876]
Simpson, Matthew, *bp.,* 1811-1884.

LAC 16121
Hunting for gold: reminiscences [!] of personal experience and research in the early days of the Pacific coast from Alaska to Panama. By Major William Downie. San Francisco, Cal., Press of the California publishing co., 1893.
Downie, William, *b.* 1819.

LAC 22695-96
Huntington town records, including Babylon, Long Island, N. Y. ... With introduction, notes and index, by Charles R. Street. Transcribed, comp. and pub. by authority and at the expense of the two towns. [Huntington, L. I., The "Long Islander" print] 1887-89.
Huntington, *N. Y.*

LAC 30668-88
Hunt's merchants' magazine and commercial review. v. 23-43; July 1850–Dec. 1860. New York, F. Hunt [etc.]

LAC 12568
Hypocrisie unmasked; a true relation of the proceedings of the governor and company of the Massachusetts against Samuel Gorton of Rhode Island, by Edward Winslow, governor of Plymouth colony. Reprinted from the original edition issued at London in 1646; with an introduction by Howard Millar Chapin. Providence, The Club for colonial reprints, 1916.
Winslow, Edward, 1595-1655.

LAC 15454
The I. W. W.; a study of American syndicalism. New York, Columbia university; [etc., etc.] 1919.
Brissenden, Paul Frederick, 1885–

LAC 11235
Icaria, a chapter in the history of communism. New York & London, G. P. Putnam's sons, 1884.
Shaw, Albert, 1857-1947.

LAC 13207
Ice-pack and tundra; an account of the search for the Jeannette and a sledge journey through Siberia. New York, C. Scribner's sons, 1883.
Gilder, William Henry, 1838–1900.

LAC 22906–11
The iconography of Manhattan Island, 1498–1909. [Compiled from original sources and illustrated by photo-intaglio reproductions of important maps, plans, views, and documents in public and private collections. New York] Arno Press [1967]
Stokes, Isaac Newton Phelps, 1867–1944.

LAC 12875
Ida May; a story of things actual and possible. By Mary Langdon [*pseud.*] 45th thousand. Boston, Phillips, Sampson and company; New York, J. C. Derby, 1855.
Pike, Mary Hayden, 1825–1908.

LAC 14266
Ideals of the republic. Boston, Little, Brown, and company, 1908.
Schouler, James, 1839–1920.

LAC 10737
Ideas for a science of good government, in addresses, letters and articles on a strictly national currency, tariff and civil service. 2d ed. New York, Trow's printing and bookbinding company, 1883.
Cooper, Peter, 1791–1883.

LAC 11108
If Christ came to Chicago. A plea for the union of all who love in the service of all who suffer... Chicago, Laird & Lee, 1894.
Stead, William Thomas, 1849–1912.

LAC 40046
If Jesus came to Boston. Boston, J. Stillman Smith & co., 1895.
Hale, Edward Everett, 1822–1909.

LAC 15419
If not silver, what? Springfield, O. [New York, J. J. Little & co.] 1896.
Bookwalter, John Wesley, 1837–1915.

LAC 11953
If, yes, and perhaps. Four possibilities and six exagerations, with some bits of fact. Boston, Ticknor and Fields, 1868.
Hale, Edward Everett, 1822–1909.

LAC 16069
Illinois as it is; its history, geography, statistics, constitution, laws, government ... etc. With a prairie and wood map, a geological map, a population map, and other illustrations. Chicago, Ill., Keen and Lee; Philadelphia, C. Desilver, 1857.
Gerhard, Frederick.

LAC 40072
An Illinois gold hunter in the Black Hills; the diary of Jerry Bryan, March 13 to August 20, 1876. With an introduction and notes by Clyde C. Walton. Springfield, Illinois State Historical Society, 1960.
Bryan, Jerry.

LAC 16201
Illinois in 1837; a sketch descriptive of the situation, boundaries, face of the country, prominent districts, prairies, rivers, minerals, animals, agricultural productions, public lands, plans of internal improvement, manufactures, &c., of the state of Illinois: also, suggestions to emigrants, sketches of the counties, cities, and principal towns in the state: together with a letter on the cultivation of the prairies, by the Hon. H. L. Ellsworth. To which are annexed the letters from a rambler in the West... Philadelphia, S. A. Mitchell [etc.] 1837.

LAC 40055
Illinois in the eighteenth century. Kaskaskia and its parish records: Old Fort Chartres: and Col. John Todds recordbook. Chicago, Fergus printing company, 1881.
Mason, Edward Gay, 1839–1898.

LAC 40024
Illinois railway legislation and commission control since 1870, by Joseph Hinckley Gordon, with an introduction by M. B. Hammond. Urbana, University press [1904]
Gordon, Joseph Hinckley.

LAC 14155
The ills of the south; or, Related causes hostile to the general prosperity of the southern people. New York, London, G. P. Putnam's sons, 1894.
Otken, Charles H   *b.* 1839.

LAC 21159–61
Illustrated history of Nebraska; a history of Nebraska from the earliest explorations of the trans-Mississippi region. With steel engravings, photogravures, copper plates, maps and tables. By J. Sterling Morton, succeeded by Albert Watkins as editor-in-chief, Dr. George L. Miller, associate editor. Lincoln, J. North, 1907–13.
Morton, Julius Sterling, 1832–1902.

LAC 11360–61
An illustrated history of the commonwealth of Pennsylvania, civil, political and military, from its earliest settlement to the present time, including historical descriptions of each county in the state, their towns, and industrial resources. Harrisburg, De W. C. Goodrich & co., 1876.
Egle, William Henry, 1830–1901.

LAC 15662
Illustrated history of the University of California, 1868–1895. San Francisco, F. H. Dukesmith, 1895.
Jones, William Carey, 1854–1923.

LAC 13174
Illustrated lives and adventures of Frank and Jesse James and the Younger brothers, the noted western outlaws. New ed. New York, N. D. Thompson, 1882.
Dacus, Joseph A.

LAC 15583
Illustrated sketch book of Danville, Virginia; its manufactures and commerce. [Danville, E. R. Waddill & bro., printers] 1885.
Pollock, Edward.

LAC 13754

Illustrations of the birds of California, Texas, Oregon, British, and Russian America. Intended to contain descriptions and figures of all North-American birds not given by former American authors, and a general synopsis of North American ornithology. 1835 to 1855. Philadelphia, J. B. Lippincott & co., 1856.
Cassin, John, 1813–1869.

LAC 22409

Illustrations of the manners, customs, and condition of the North American Indians: in a series of letters and notes written during eight years of travel and adventure among the wildest and most remarkable tribes now existing. With three hundred and sixty engravings from the author's original paintings. 9th ed. London, H. G. Bohn, 1857.
Catlin, George, 1796–1872.

LAC 15517

The immigrant, an asset and a liability. New York, Chicago [etc.] Fleming H. Revell company [c1913]
Haskin, Frederic Jennings, 1872–1944.

LAC 14813

The immigrant and the community, by Grace Abbott. With an introduction by Judge Julian W. Mack. New York, The Century co., 1917.
Abbott, Grace, 1878–1939.

LAC 16680

The immigrant invasion. New York, Dodd, Mead and company, 1913.
Warne, Frank Julian, 1874–

LAC 40090

The immigrant population of Massachusetts. Boston, Wright & Potter printing company, state printers, 1913.
Massachusetts. *Bureau of Statistics.*

LAC 15539

The immigrant press and its control. New York and London, Harper & brothers, 1922.
Park, Robert Ezra, 1864–1944.

LAC 15547

Immigrant races in North America. New York, The Young men's Christian association press, 1910.
Roberts, Peter, 1859–

LAC 15608

The immigrant tide, its ebb and flow. New York, Chicago [etc.] F. H. Revell company [c1909]
Steiner, Edward Alfred, 1866–1956.

LAC 40052

The immigrants' trek; a detailed history of the Lake Hendricks colony in Brookings County, Dakota Territory, from 1873–1881. [Sioux Falls, S. D., Sessions printing co., c1929]
Sandro, Gustav O.

LAC 40057

Immigration. Madison, Wis., 1909.
Edwards, Richard Henry, 1877–1954, ed.

LAC 16467

Immigration, a world movement and its American significance. New York, The Macmillan company, 1913.
Fairchild, Henry Pratt, 1880–1956.

LAC 16730

Immigration and Americanization; selected readings, comp. and ed. by Philip Davis assisted by Bertha Schwartz. Boston, New York [etc.] Ginn and company [c1920]
Davis, Philip, 1876–   ed.

LAC 15512

Immigration and its effects upon the United States. New York, H. Holt and company, 1906.
Hall, Prescott Farnsworth, 1868–

LAC 16784

Immigration and labor; the economic aspects of European immigration to the United States. New York and London, G. P. Putnam's sons, 1912.
Hourwich, Isaac Aaronovich, 1860–1924.

LAC 15521

Immigration, and the Commissioners of emigration of the state of New York. New York, The Nation Press, 1870.
Kapp, Friedrich, 1824–1884.

LAC 14831

Immigration fallacies, by John Chetwood, jr. Boston, Arena publishing company, 1896.
Chetwood, John, 1859–

LAC 15642

Immigration into the United States. Boston, C. C. Little and J. Brown, 1848.
Chickering, Jesse, 1797–1855.

LAC 40052

The immigration into the United States of America, from a statistical and national-economical point of view. Washington, Printed at the Union office, 1856.
Schade, Louis, 1829–1903.

LAC 15503

Immigration, its evils and consequences. New York, De Witt & Davenport [c1856]
Busey, Samuel Clagett, 1828–1901.

LAC 15747

Immigration of the Irish Quakers into Pennsylvania, 1682–1750, with their early history in Ireland. Swarthmore, Pa., The author, 1902.
Myers, Albert Cook, 1874–1960.

LAC 16390

The immigration problem, by Jeremiah W. Jenks and W. Jett Lauck. New York and London, Funk & Wagnalls company, 1912, [1911]
Jenks, Jeremiah Whipple, 1856–1929.

LAC 14811

Immigration; select documents and case records. Chicago, Ill., The University of Chicago press [c1924]
Abbott, Edith, 1876–1957.

LAC 15546

Immigration, Selected articles on.
Selected articles on immigration. White Plains, N. Y., and New York city, The H. W. Wilson company, 1915.
Reely, Mary Katharine, 1881–   *comp.*

LAC 40052

Immigration to the southern states. Boston, Ginn & company, 1905.
Fleming, Walter Lynwood, 1874–1932.

LAC 40090

Imminent dangers to the free institutions of the United States through foreign immigration, and the present state of the naturalization laws. A series of numbers, originally published in the New-York journal of commerce. By an American. Rev. and cor., with additions. New-York, E. B. Clayton, printer, 1835.
Morse, Samuel Finley Breese, 1791–1872.

LAC 40045

An impartial enquiry into the right of the French king to the territory west of the great river Mississippi, in North America, not ceded by the preliminaries, including a summary account of that river, and the country adjacent... London, W. Nicoll [1762]

LAC 16870

An impartial history of the present war in America.
A philosophical and political history of the British settlements and trade in North America. From the French of Abbe Raynal. With an introductory preface, not in the first edition. To which is annexed, An impartial history of the present war in America: from its commencement, to the present time. Edinburgh, Printed by C. Denovan, 1779.
Raynal, Guillaume Thomas Francois, 1713–1796.

LAC 13669

The impeachment and trial of Andrew Johnson, seventeenth president of the United States; a history. New York, The Macmillan company; London, Macmillan & co., ltd., 1903.
Dewitt, David Miller, 1837–1912.

LAC 14240–41

Impeachment of the President. [Washington, Govt. print. off., 1868]
U.S. *Congress. House Committee on the Judiciary.*

LAC 10462

The impending crisis; conditions resulting from the concentration of wealth in the United States. Chicago, Midway press committee, 1900.
Bouroff, Basil A.

LAC 12334

The impending crisis of the South: how to meet it.
New-York, Burdick brothers, 1857.
Helper, Hinton Rowan, 1829–1909.

LAC 14843

Imperial democracy; a study of the relation of government by the people, equality before the law, and other tenets of democracy, to the demands of a vigorous foreign policy and other demands of imperial dominion. New York, D. Appleton and company, 1899.
Jordan, David Starr, 1851–1931.

LAC 40010

"Imperial democracy": Dutch colonizers in Malaysia, annexation of the Philippines. San Francisco, Cal., 1899.
Valentine, John Joseph, 1840–1901.

LAC 12060

Imperial purple. New York, Brentano's [c1906]
Saltus, Edgar Evertson, 1855–1921.

LAC 11152

Imperialism and liberty. Los Angeles, The Ronbroke press, 1899.
Swift, Morrison Isaac, 1856–

LAC 40031

Imperialism, our new national policy. An address delivered before the Monday evening club, January 9, 1899. St. Louis, Gottschalk printing co., 1899.
Blair, James Lawrence, 1854–1904.

LAC 40050

The importance of exalting the intellectual spirit of the nation; and need of a learned class. A discourse pronounced before the Phi Sigma Nu Society of the University of Vermont, August 3, 1836, by the Rev. C. S. Henry. Burlington, N. J. [!] J. L. Powell, 1836.
Henry, Caleb Sprague, 1804–1884.

LAC 10785

Importance of practical education and useful knowledge. Boston, Marsh, Capen, Lyon, and Webb, 1840.
Everett, Edward, 1794–1865.

LAC 14094

The importance of the British plantations in America to this kingdom; with the state of their trade, and methods for improving it; as also a description of the several colonies there. London, Printed for J. Peele, 1731.
Hall, F

LAC 40003

Importance of the study of political science, as a branch of academic education in the United States.
Philadelphia, Carey and Hart, 1845.
Tucker, Nathaniel Beverley, 1784–1851.

LAC 15414

Imported Americans; the story of the experiences of a disguised American and his wife studying the immigration question. With sixty-six illustrations from photographs by the author. New York, F. A. Stokes company [1904]
Brandenburg, Broughton.

LAC 11979

Impressions and experiences. New York, Harper & brothers [c1896]
Howells, William Dean, 1837–1920.

LAC 40007

Impressions of America. By Oscar Wilde. Ed., with an introduction, by Stuart Mason [*pseud.*] Sunderland, Keystone press, 1906.
Wilde, Oscar, 1854–1900.

LAC 21274
Impressions of America; during the years 1833, 1834, and 1835. London, R. Bentley, 1836.
Power, Tyrone, 1797–1841.

LAC 13575
Impressions. Sketches of American life as observed by a Russian. [By] Prince Serge Wolkonsky. Chicago, Unity publishing company, 1893.
Volkonskii, Sergei Mikhailovich, *kniaz*, 1860–1937.

LAC 14663
Impressment of American seamen. New York, Columbia university; [etc., etc.] 1925.
Zimmerman, James Fulton, 1887–1944.

LAC 13537
Improved dwellings for the working classes, 1877. 1879; Better homes for workingmen, 1885; Riverside buildings, 1890. [n.p., 1891?]
White, Alfred Tredway, 1846–1921.

LAC 11579
The improvement of the mind; or, A supplement to the Art of logic. In two parts. To which is added, a discourse on the education of children and youth. Boston, Printed for D. West, 1793.
Watts, Isaac, 1674–1748.

LAC 40039
The improvement of the Mississippi river. An address delivered at St. Louis, Mo., January 26, 1884, on the invitation of the Merchants' exchange, by Judge Robert S. Taylor, of Indiana, member of the Mississippi river commission. St. Louis, R. P. Studley & co., 1884.
Taylor, Robert Stewart, 1838–1918.

LAC 14955
The improvement of the park system of the District of Columbia. I.–Report of the Senate Committee on the District of Columbia. II.–Report of the Park commission. Ed. by Charles Moore. Washington, Govt. print. off., 1902.
U.S. *Congress. Senate. Committee on the District of Columbia.*

LAC 14572
The improvement of towns and cities; or, The practical basis of civic aesthetics. New York & London, G. P. Putnam's sons, 1901.
Robinson, Charles Mulford, 1869–1917.

LAC 15006
In and out of rebel prisons, by Lieut. A. Cooper. Oswego, N. Y., R. J. Oliphant, printer, 1888.
Cooper, Alonzo, 1830–1919.

LAC 12817
In freedom's birthplace: a study of the Boston Negroes. New York, Negro Universities Press [1968]
Daniels, John, 1881–

LAC 16583
In ghostly Japan. Boston, Little, Brown and company, 1903, [c1899]
Hearn, Lafcadio, 1850–1904.

LAC 14976
In his steps; "What would Jesus do?" Philadelphia, American Baptist publication society, 1898.
Sheldon, Charles Monroe, 1857–1946.

LAC 11999
In old New York. New York, Harper & brothers, 1894.
Janvier, Thomas Allibone, 1849–1913.

LAC 15095
In old plantation days. New York, Dodd, Mead and company, 1903.
Dunbar, Paul Laurence, 1872–1906.

LAC 12041
In ole Virginia; or, Marse Chan, and other stories. New York, C. Scribner's sons, 1890.
Page, Thomas Nelson, 1853–1922.

LAC 16309
In Palestine and other poems. New York, The Century co. [1898]
Gilder, Richard Watson, 1844–1909.

LAC 12095
In re Walt Whitman: ed. by his literary executors, Horace L. Traubel, Richard Maurice Bucke, Thomas B. Harned. Philadelphia, Pub. by the editors through D. McKay, 1893.
Traubel, Horace, 1858–1919, *ed.*

LAC 13231
In the heart of the Sierras; the Yo Semite valley, both historical and descriptive: and scenes by the way. Big tree groves ... and other objects of interest; with tables of distances and altitudes, maps, etc. ... Yo Semite valley, Pub. at the Old cabin; Oakland, Cal., Pacific press publishing house, 1886.
Hutchings, James Mason, 1820–1902.

LAC 12035
In the Tennessee mountains, by Charles Egbert Craddock [*pseud.*]. Boston, New York, Houghton, Mifflin and company, 1884.
Murfree, Mary Noailles, 1850–1922.

LAC 11923
In the valley. New York, C. Scribner's sons, 1902, [c1890]
Frederic, Harold, 1856–1898.

LAC 16426
In the wake of Columbus; adventures of the special commissioner sent by the World's Columbian exposition to the West Indies. With above two hundred illustrations from photographs by the author, and sketches by H. R. Blaney. Boston, D. Lothrop company, 1893.
Ober, Frederick Albion, 1849–1913.

LAC 15828
An inaugural discourse, delivered at the opening of Rutgers medical college, in the city of New-York, on Monday, the 6th day of November, 1826. New-York, Printed by J. Seymour, 1826.
Hosack, David, 1769–1835.

LAC 40020
An inaugural oration, on the progress and importance of the mathematical sciences. Delivered at Princeton on the evening preceding the annual commencement of 1788. Trenton, Printed by I. Collins, 1788.
Minto, Walter, 1753–1796.

LAC 40031
Inauguration of the American school system in Porto Rico. Washington, Govt. print. off., 1907.
Lindsay, Samuel McCune, 1869–1960.

LAC 40095
Inauguration of the Spartanburg female college, on the 22d August, 1855, with the address, on that occasion, by W. Gilmore Simms, esq. To which are prefixed an account of the institution, its faculty, course of study, and terms of instruction. Spartanburg, Pub. by the Trustees, 1855.
Spartanburg Female College, *Spartanburg, S. C.*

LAC 15786
Inchiquin, the Jesuit's letters, during a late residence in the United States of America: being a fragment of a private correspondence, accidentally discovered in Europe; containing a favourable view of the manners, literature, and state of society, of the United States, and a refutation of many of the aspersions cast upon this country, by former residents and tourists. By some unknown foreigner. New-York: Printed and published by I. Riley, 1810.
Ingersoll, Charles Jared, 1782–1862.

LAC 14647
Incidents and anecdotes of the civil war. By Admiral Porter. New York, D. Appleton and co., 1885.
Porter, David Dixon, 1813–1891.

LAC 14880
Incidents and anecdotes of the war; together with life sketches of eminent leaders, and narratives of the most memorable battles for the Union. New York, J. D. Torrey, [c1862]
Victor, Orville James, 1827–1910.

LAC 12855
Incidents in the life of a slave girl. Written by herself. Edited by L. Maria Child. Boston, Pub. for the author, 1861.
Jacobs, Harriet, 1818–1896.

LAC 16103
Incidents in the life of Arba Lankton, with sermons and lectures on religion, temperance and anti-tobacco. Also 136 selected songs and hymns as used at his meetings. Composed and comp. by Arba Lankton. Hartford, Conn., Arba Lankton's total abstinence and anti-tobacco society, 1891.
Lankton, Arba, *b.* 1835.

LAC 16428
Incidents of a whaling voyage. To which are added observations on the scenery, manners and customs, and missionary stations of the Sandwich and Society islands. New-York, D. Appleton and co., 1841.
Olmsted, Francis Allyn.

LAC 16806
Incidents of my life; professional–literary–social, with services in the cause of Ireland. With twenty-seven illustrations. New York and London, G. P. Putnam's sons, 1911.
Emmet, Thomas Addis, 1828–1919.

LAC 13163
Incidents of travel and adventure in the far West; with Col. Fremont's last expedition across the Rocky Mountains: including three months' residence in Utah, and a perilous trip across the great American desert to the Pacific. New York, Derby & Jackson, 1860.
Carvalho, Solomon Nunes, 1815–1897.

LAC 21001
Incidents of travel in Greece, Turkey, Russia, and Poland. By the author of "Incidents of travel in Egypt, Arabia Petraea, and the Holy Land." With a map and engravings... 7th ed. New York, Harper & brothers, 1854, [c1838]
Stephens, John Lloyd, 1805–1852.

LAC 21154–55
Incidents of travel in Yucatan. Illustrated by 120 engravings... New York, Harper & brothers, 1843.
Stephens, John Lloyd, 1805–1852.

LAC 13652
The income tax; a study of the history, theory and practice of income taxation at home and abroad. New York, The Macmillan company, 1911.
Seligman, Edwin Robert Anderson, 1861–1939.

LAC 40081
Increased mental activity of the age; its causes and demands. An address, delivered before the literary societies of the University of Michigan, June 26th, 1854. By Rev. E. O. Haven. Ann Arbor, Power press of E. B. Pond, 1854.
Haven, Erastus Otis, *bp.*, 1820–1881.

LAC 11665
The Independent treasury of the United States and its relations to the banks of the country. Washington, Govt. print. off., 1910.
Kinley, David, 1861–1944.

LAC 10815
Indian affairs in Georgia, 1732–1756... Philadelphia, 1936.
Corry, John Pitts, 1900–

LAC 22029–34
Indian affairs. Laws and treaties... Comp., annotated and ed. by Charles J. Kappler. Washington, U.S. Govt. print. off., 1903–1929.
U.S. *Laws, statutes, etc.*

LAC 14471
Indian and white in the Northwest; or, A history of Catholicity in Montana. By L. B. Palladino, S. J., with an introduction by Right Reverend John B. Brondel. Baltimore, J. Murphy & company, 1894.
Palladino, Lawrence Benedict, 1837–1927.

LAC 23200

Indian biography; or, An historical account of those individuals who have been distinguished among the North American natives as orators, warriors, statesmen, and other remarkable characters. New-York, Harper & brothers, 1840.
Thatcher, Benjamin Bussey, 1809–1840.

LAC 40089

The Indian captive, a narrative of the adventures and sufferings of Matthew Brayton, in his thirty-four years of captivity among the Indians of North-Western America. Cleveland, Fairbanks, Benedict & Co., Printers, 1860. [Tucson, Territorial Press, 1964]
Brayton, Matthew, 1818–1862.

LAC 16001

Indian captivities; or, Life in the wigwam; being true narratives of captives who have been carried away by the Indians, from the frontier settlements of the U.S., from the earliest period to the present time. Auburn, Derby, Miller & co., 1850.
Drake, Samuel Gardner, 1798–1875.

LAC 14040

The Indian captivity of O. M. Spencer. Edited by Milo Milton Quaife. Chicago, R. R. Donnelley, 1917.
Spencer, Oliver M   1781–1838.

LAC 15090

Indian converts: or, Some account of the lives and dying speeches of a considerable number of the Christianized Indians of Martha's Vineyard, in New-England... By Experience Mayhew. To which is added, Some account of those English ministers who have successively presided over the Indian work in that and the adjacent islands. By Mr. Prince. London, Printed for S. Gerrish, bookseller in Boston in New-England; and sold by J. Osborn [etc.] 1727.
Mayhew, Experience, 1673–1758.

LAC 16030

The Indian dispossessed. With 16 full-page illustrations from photographs. Rev. ed. New York, Young People's Missionary Movement of the United States and Canada [c1905]
Humphrey, Seth King, 1864–

LAC 13165

Indian education and civilization; a report prepared in answer to Senate resolution of February 23, 1885, by Alice C. Fletcher, under direction of the commissioner of education. Washington, Govt. print. off., 1888.
U.S. *Office of Education.*

LAC 40051

The Indian grammar begun; or, An essay to bring the Indian language into rules... Cambridge [Mass.] Printed by M. Johnson, 1666. [Boston, Directors of the Old South work, 1896]
Eliot, John, 1604–1690.

LAC 15091

The Indian in his wigwam, or Characteristics of the red race of America. From original notes and manuscripts. New York, W. H. Graham, 1848.
Schoolcraft, Henry Rowe, 1793–1864.

LAC 14495

Indian life and Indian history, by an Indian author. Embracing the traditions of the North American Indians regarding themselves, particularly of ... the Ojibways. By ... Kah-ge-ga-gah-bowh, chief of the Ojibway nation; known also by the English name of George Copway. Boston, A. Colby and company, 1860.
Copway, George, *Chippewa chief*, 1818?–1863.

LAC 14493

The Indian miscellany; containing papers on the history, antiquities, arts, languages, religions, traditions and superstitions of the American aborigines; with descriptions of their domestic life, manners, customs, traits, amusements and exploits; travels and adventures in the Indian country; incidents of border warfare; missionary relations, etc. Albany, J. Munsell, 1877.
Beach, William Wallace, *ed.*

LAC 40051

Indian myths of south central California. Berkeley, The University press, 1907.
Kroeber, Alfred Louis, 1876–1960.

LAC 15484

Indian nullification of the unconstitutional laws of Massachusetts, relative to the Marshpee tribe: or, The pretended riot explained. By William Apes, an Indian and preacher of the gospel. Boston, Press of J. Howe, 1835.
Apes, William, *b.* 1798.

LAC 40051

The Indian of New-England, and the north-eastern provinces; a sketch of the life of an Indian hunter, ancient traditions relating to the Etchemin tribe, their modes of life, fishing, hunting, &c.: with vocabularies in the Indian and English, giving the names of the animals, birds, and fish: the most complete that has been given for New-England, in the languages of the Etchemin and Micmacs... Derived from Nicola Tenesles. By a citizen of Middletown, Conn. Middletown, Conn., C. H. Pelton, printer, 1851.
Barratt, Joseph, *d.* 1882.

LAC 16002

The Indian question. By Francis A. Walker, late U.S. commissioner of Indian affairs. Boston, J. R. Osgood and company, 1874.
Walker, Francis Amasa, 1840–1897.

LAC 21941

Indian sketches, taken during an expedition to the Pawnee and other tribes of American Indians. By John T. Irving, junior. London, J. Murray, 1835.
Irving, John Treat, 1812–1906.

LAC 14426

Indian slavery in colonial times within the present limits of the United States. New York, Columbia university; [etc., etc.] 1913.
Lauber, Almon Wheeler, 1880–

LAC 13804

Indian summer. Boston, Ticknor and company, 1886.
Howells, William Dean, 1837–1920.

LAC 22903

The Indian tribes of the upper Mississippi Valley and region of the Great Lakes as described by Nicolas Perrot, French commandant in the Northwest; Bacqueville de la Potherie, French royal commissioner to Canada; Morrell Marston, American army officer; and Thomas Forsyth, United States agent at Fort Armstrong, tr., ed., annotated, and with bibliography and index by Emma Helen Blair. Cleveland, O., The Arthur H. Clark company, 1911–12.
Blair, Emma Helen, d. 1911, ed.

LAC 14303

The Indian war of 1864, being a fragment of the early history of Kansas, Nebraska, Colorado, and Wyoming. By Eugene F. Ware, formerly captain of Co. "F," Seventh Iowa cavalry, who took part in the Indian troubles of that time. Topeka, Kan., Crane & company, 1911.
Ware, Eugene Fitch, 1841–1911.

LAC 23187–88

Indian wars of New England. Boston, W. B. Clarke company, 1910.
Sylvester, Herbert Milton, 1849–

LAC 13148

Indian wars of the Northwest. A California sketch. San Francisco, Bacon & company, 1885.
Bledsoe, Anthony Jennings, 1858–

LAC 15726

Indian wars of the United States; from the earliest period to the present time. By John Frost, LL. D. With numerous engravings, from original designs by W. Croome and other artists. Auburn, Derby and Miller, 1852.
Frost, John, 1800–1859.

LAC 13868

Indian wars of the West; containing biographical sketches of those pioneers who headed the western settlers in repelling the attacks of the savages, together with a view of the character, manners, monuments, and antiquities of the western Indians. Cincinnati, E. H. Flint, 1833.
Flint, Timothy, 1780–1840.

LAC 40135

Indiana agriculture. Agricultural resources and development of the state. The struggles of pioneer life compared with present conditions. Indianapolis, W. B. Burford, 1893.
Conner, John B.

LAC 13252

Indiana as seen by early travelers; a collection of reprints from books of travel, letters and diaries prior to 1830, selected and edited by Harlow Lindley. Indianapolis, Indiana historical commission, 1916.
Indiana. *Historical Commission.*

LAC 13316

Indiana miscellany: consisting of sketches of Indian life, the early settlement, customs, and hardships of the people, and the introduction of the gospel and of schools. Together with biographical notices of the pioneer Methodist preachers of the state, by Rev. William C. Smith. Cincinnati, Pub. by Poe & Hitchcock for the author, 1867.
Smith, William C   1809–1886.

LAC 14026

The Indians of the Northwest, their maners [!], customs, &c. &c., or Remarks made on a tour to Prairie du Chien and thence to Washington city in 1829. Columbus [O.] 1850.
Atwater, Caleb, 1778–1867.

LAC 40107

Indians west of the Rocky Mountains. Statement of Major J. W. Powell, made before the Committee on Indian affairs, as to the condition of the Indian tribes west of the Rocky Mountains. [Washington, Govt. print. off., 1874]
U.S. *Congress. House. Committee on Indian Affairs.*

LAC 15802

Indices of public opinion. 1860–1870. New York, Printed for private circulation, 1871.
Tousey, Sinclair, 1818–1887.

LAC 10448

The individual and society; or, Psychology and sociology. Boston, R. G. Badger, 1911.
Baldwin, James Mark, 1861–1934.

LAC 10783

Individual training in our colleges. New York, The Macmillan company; London, Macmillan & co., ltd., 1907.
Birdseye, Clarence Frank, 1854–1927.

LAC 10515

Individualism; four lectures on the significance of consciousness for social relations. New York [etc.] Longmans, Green, and co., 1911.
Fite, Warner, 1867–1955.

LAC 10436

Inductive sociology; a syllabus of methods, analyses and classifications, and provisionally formulated laws. New York, The Macmillan company; London, Macmillan & co., ltd., 1901.
Giddings, Franklin Henry, 1855–1931.

LAC 13375

Industrial accident statistics. March, 1915. Washington, Govt. print. off., 1915.
Hoffman, Frederick Ludwig, 1865–1946.

LAC 14163

Industrial accidents in the United States to the end of 1927. Washington, Govt. print off., 1929.
U.S. *Bureau of Labor Statistics.*

LAC 13588–89

Industrial and technical training in schools of technology and in U.S. land grant colleges, by Isaac Edwards Clarke. Washington, Govt. print. off., 1898.
U.S. *Office of Education.*

LAC 13385

Industrial arbitration and conciliation; some chapters from the industrial history of the past thirty years. New York, London, G. P. Putnam's sons, 1893.
Lowell, Josephine, 1843–1905, *comp.*

LAC 10640
Industrial causes of congestion of population in New York city. New York, Columbia university, Longmans, Green & co., agents; [etc., etc.] 1911.
Pratt, Edward Ewing, 1886–

LAC 10042
Industrial competition and combination... Philadelphia, American academy of political and social science, 1912.
American Academy of Political and Social Science, *Philadelphia.*

LAC 40021
Industrial conciliation and arbitration in New York, Ohio, and Pennsylvania. By Joseph D. Weeks. From the Twelfth annual report of the Massachusetts Bureau of statistics of labor. With comments by Carroll D. Wright, chief. Boston, Rand, Avery, & co., printers, 1881.
Weeks, Joseph Dame, 1840–1896.

LAC 15845
Industrial conditions among negroes in St. Louis. St. Louis, Mo. [Press of Mendle printing co.] 1914.
Crossland, William August.

LAC 14320
Industrial conference, under the auspices of the National civic federation, held at rooms of Board of trade and transportation, New York, December 8, 9, 10, 1902. New York, The Winthrop press, 1903.
National Conference on Industrial Conciliation, *New York.* 1902.

LAC 12943
Industrial Cuba; being a study of present commercial and industrial conditions, with suggestions as to the opportunities presented in the island for American capital, enterprise, and labour. With maps and 62 illustrations. New York and London, G. P. Putnam's sons, 1899.
Porter, Robert Percival, 1852–1917.

LAC 13379
Industrial democracy.
Man to man; the story of industrial democracy. New York, B. C. Forbes company [c1919]
Leitch, John, 1868–

LAC 16622
Industrial depressions; their causes analysed and classified with a practical remedy for such as result from industrial derangements; or, Iron the barometer of trade. New York, Frederick A. Stokes company, 1911.
Hull, George Huntington.

LAC 23529
Industrial efficiency: a comparative study of industrial life in England, Germany and America. London, New York [etc.] Longmans, Green, and co., 1906.
Shadwell, Arthur, 1854–1936.

LAC 10290
The industrial evolution of the United States. Meadville, Pa., New York, Flood and Vincent, 1895.
Wright, Carroll Davidson, 1840–1909.

LAC 12295
The industrial history of the Negro race of the United States, [by] Giles B. Jackson and D. Webster Davis. Richmond, Va., The Virginia press [c1908]
Jackson, Giles B.

LAC 13474
Industrial history of the United States, from the earliest settlements to the present time: being a complete survey of American industries, embracing agriculture and horticulture; including the cultivation of cotton, tobacco, wheat; the raising of horses, meat-cattle, etc.; all the important manufactures, shipping and fisheries, railroads, mines and mining, and oil; also a history of the coal-miners and the Molly Maguires; banks, insurance, and commerce; trade-unions, strikes, and eight-hour movement; together with a description of Canadian industries. Norwich, Conn., The H. Bill publishing company, 1879.
Bolles, Albert Sidney, 1846–

LAC 11255
The industrial problem; being the William Levi Bull lectures for the year 1905. Philadelphia, G. W. Jacobs & co. [1905]
Abbott, Lyman, 1835–1922.

LAC 20985–99
Industrial relations. Final report and testimony, submitted to Congress by the Commission on industrial relations created by the act of August 23, 1912... Washington, Govt. print. off., 1916.
U.S. *Commission on Industrial Relations.*

LAC 10483
The industrial republic; a study of the America of ten years hence. London, W. Heinemann, 1907.
Sinclair, Upton Beall, 1878–1968.

LAC 20004–6
The industrial resources, etc., of the southern and western states: embracing a view of their commerce, agriculture, manufactures, internal improvements, slave and free labor, slavery institutions, products, etc., of the South, together with historical and statistical sketches of the different states and cities of the Union–statistics of the United States commerce and manufactures, from the earliest periods, compared with other leading powers–the results of the different census returns since 1790, and returns of the census of 1850, on population, agriculture and general industry, etc., With an appendix... New-Orleans, New York [etc.] Pub. at the office of Debow's review, 1853, [c1852]
De Bow, James Dunwoody Brownson, 1820–1867.

LAC 40152
Industrial unionism. An address delivered at Grand Central palace, New York, Sunday, December 10, 1905. New York, New York labor news company [1905?]
Debs, Eugene Victor, 1855–1926.

LAC 40030
The industry of the South: its immediate organization indispensable to the financial security of the country. A speech delivered before the Boston board of trade, Nov. 27, 1865. Boston, J. H. Eastburn's press, 1865.
Tobey, Edward S.

LAC 40116
Inequality of individual wealth the ordinance of Providence and essential to civilization. A sermon preached before His Excellency John Davis, governor, His Honor Samuel T. Armstrong, lieutenant governor, the honorable Council, and the legislature of Massachusetts, on the annual election, January 7, 1835. Boston, Dutton and Wentworth, printers to the state, 1835.
Wainwright, Jonathan Mayhew, *bp.*, 1792–1854.

LAC 20604
The infidel; or, The fall of Mexico. A romance, by the author of "Calavar." Philadelphia, Carey, Lea & Blanchard, 1835.
Bird, Robert Montgomery, 1806–1854.

LAC 11785
The influence of farm machinery on production and labor. New York, Pub. for the association by the Macmillan company, 1904.
Quaintance, Hadly Winfield, 1864–

LAC 10945
The influence of Jesus. Delivered in the Church of the Holy Trinity, Philadelphia, in February, 1879. New York, E. P. Dutton and company, 1880, [c1879]
Brooks, Phillips, *bp.*, 1835–1893.

LAC 13584
The influence of reconstruction on education in the South. New York, Arno Press, 1969.
Knight, Edgar Wallace, 1885–1933.

LAC 14915
The influence of sea power upon history, 1660–1783; by Captain A. T. Mahan. London, Sampson, Low, Marston & company [c1890]
Mahan, Alfred Thayer, 1840–1914.

LAC 40093
The influence of the English universities in the development of New England. Boston, Massachusetts Historical Society, 1880.
Dexter, Franklin Bowditch, 1842–1920.

LAC 40091
Influence of the railroads of the United States in the creation of its commerce and wealth. New York, Journeymen printers' co-operative association, 1869.
Poor, Henry Varnum, 1812–1905.

LAC 40045
The influence of the rise of the Ottoman Turks upon the routes of oriental trade. Washington, Govt. print. off., 1916.
Lybyer, Albert Howe, 1876–1949.

LAC 14439
Ingalls of Kansas; a character study. Topeka, Kan., The author, 1909.
Connelley, William Elsey, 1855–1930.

LAC 12313
An inglorious Columbus; or, Evidence that Hwui Shan and a party of Buddhist monks from Afghanistan discovered America in the fifth century, A. D. New York, D. Appleton and company, 1885.
Vining, Edward Payson, 1847–1920.

LAC 12915
An inquiry into the causes and consequences of the Orders in council; and an examination of the conduct of Great-Britain towards the neutral commerce of America. 2d American ed. By Alexander Baring. New-York, Reprinted, Hopkins & Bayard [etc.] 1808.
Ashburton, Alexander Baring, *1st baron*, 1774–1848.

LAC 40068
Inquiry into the causes which have retarded the accumulation of wealth and increase of population in the southern states; in which the question of slavery is considered in a politico-economical point of view. By a Carolinian. Washington, D. C., W. Blanchard, printer, 1846.
Goodloe, Daniel Reaves, 1814–1902.

LAC 40028
An inquiry into the effects of spirituous liquors on the human body. To which is added, A moral and physical thermometer. Boston, Thomas and Andrews, MDCCXC.
Rush, Benjamin, 1745–1813.

LAC 40126
An inquiry into the expediency of dispensing with bank agency and bank paper in the fiscal concerns of the United States. Philadelphia, Printed by W. Stavely, 1837.
Gouge, William M   1796–1863.

LAC 40053
An inquiry into the importance of the militia to a free commonwealth; in a letter from William H. Sumner to John Adams, late president of the United States; with his answer. Boston, Cummings and Hilliard, 1823.
Sumner, William Hyslop, 1780–1861.

LAC 12814
An inquiry into the law of Negro slavery in the United States of America. To which is prefixed, an historical sketch of slavery. Vol. I. Philadelphia, T. & J. W. Johnson & co., Savannah, W. T. Williams, 1858.
Cobb, Thomas Read Rootes, 1823–1862.

LAC 40077
An inquiry into the merits of the American colonization society: and a reply to the charges brought against it. With an account of the British African colonization society. London, J. & A. Arch [etc.] 1833.
Hodgkin, Thomas, 1798–1866.

LAC 11467
An inquiry into the moral and religious character of the American government... New-York, Wiley and Putnam, 1838.
Warner, Henry Whiting, 1787–1875.

LAC 40032
An inquiry into the nature and benefits of an agricultural survey of the state of South Carolina. Charleston, Miller & Browne, 1843.
Bachman, John, 1790–1874.

LAC 11500
Inquiry into the origin and course of political parties in the United States. New York, Augustus M. Kelley, 1967.
Van Buren, Martin, *pres. U.S.*, 1782–1862.

LAC 15443
An inquiry into the past and present relations of France and the United States of America... London, Printed for J. Hatchard, 1811.
Walsh, Robert, 1784–1859.

LAC 12548
An inquiry into the principles and policy of the government of the United States... Fredericksburg, Va., Green and Cady, 1814.
Taylor, John, 1753–1824.

LAC 40125
An inquiry into the rights of the British colonies, by Richard Bland, of Virginia, edited by Earl Gregg Swem. Williamsburg, 1766; Richmond, Reprinted by the Appeals press, inc., for the William Parks club, 1922.
Bland, Richard, 1710–1776.

LAC 12790
An inquiry into the Scriptural views of slavery. Philadelphia, Perkins & Purves; Boston, B. Perkins & co., 1846.
Barnes, Albert, 1798–1870.

LAC 13989
An inquiry respecting the self-determining power of the will; or, Contingent volition. New Haven, Herrick & Noyes, 1838.
Day, Jeremiah, 1773–1867.

LAC 12700
The insane in the United States and Canada. London, H. K. Lewis, 1885.
Tuke, Daniel Hack, 1827–1895.

LAC 14214
The inside history of the Carnegie steel company; a romance of millions. New York, The Aldine book company, 1903.
Bridge, James Howard, 1858–1939.

LAC 12537
Inside the White House in war times. By William O. Stoddard. Illustrated by Dan Beard. New York, C. L. Webster & co., 1890.
Stoddard, William Osborn, 1835–1925.

LAC 16864
Inside view of slavery; or, A tour among the planters. With an introductory note by Mrs. H. B. Stowe. [New York] Argosy-Antiquarian, 1969.
Parsons, Charles Grandison, 1808–1864.

LAC 12400
An inside view of the formation of the state of West Virginia. With character sketches of the pioneers in that movement. Wheeling, W. Va., The News pub. co., 1901.
Willey, William Patrick.

LAC 13115
Instead of a book, by a man too busy to write one; a fragmentary exposition of philosophical anarchism, culled from the writings of Benj. R. Tucker. New York, B. R. Tucker, 1897.
Tucker, Benjamin Ricketson, 1854–1939.

LAC 13789
Instinct: its office in the animal kingdom, and its relation to the higher powers in man. New York, G. P. Putnam & sons, 1872.
Chadbourne, Paul Ansel, 1823–1883.

LAC 16472
Instruction for field artillery. Prepared by a board of artillery officers. Philadelphia, J. B. Lippincott & co., 1863, [c1860]
U.S. *War Dept.*

LAC 12746
The Instruction for Johan Printz, governor of New Sweden, "the first constitution or supreme law of the states of Pennsylvania and Delaware"; translated from the Swedish, with introduction, notes and appendices, including letters from Governor John Winthrop, of Massachusetts, and minutes of courts, sitting in New Sweden, by Amandus Johnson; with a special introduction by John Frederick Lewis. Philadelphia, The Swedish colonial society, 1930.
Johnson, Amandus, 1877–   *ed. and tr.*

LAC 40136
Insufficiency of Henry George's theory. New York, New York labor news company, 1887.
Gronlund, Laurence, 1846–1899.

LAC 13494–95
The insular cases, comprising the records, briefs, and arguments of counsel in the insular cases of the October term, 1900, in the Supreme court of the United States, including the appendixes thereto. Comp. and pub. pursuant to H. R. Con. res. no. 72, Fifty-sixth Congress, second session. By Albert H. Howe. Washington, Govt. print. off., 1901.
U.S. *Supreme Court.*

LAC 12579
Insurance in Connecticut. Boston, D. H. Hurd & co., 1897.
Woodward, Patrick Henry, 1833–1917.

LAC 40111
The integrity of our national union, vs. abolitionism: an argument from the Bible, in proof of the position that believing masters ought to be honored and obeyed by their own servants, and tolerated in, not excommunicated from, the church of God: being part of a speech delivered before the synod of Cincinnati, on the subject of slavery, September 19th and 20th, 1843. Cincinnati, Printed by R. P. Donogh, 1843.
Junkin, George, 1790–1868.

LAC 40073
The intellectuals.
Socialism and the intellectuals. Brooklyn, New York labor news, 1967.
Lafargue, Paul, 1842–1911.

LAC 40076
The interest in slavery of the southern non-slaveholder. The right of peaceful secession. Slavery in the Bible. Charleston, Presses of Evans & Cogswell, 1860.
De Bow, James Dunwoody Brownson, 1820–1867.

LAC 14916

The interest of America in sea power, present and future. By Captain A. T. Mahan. Boston, Little, Brown and company, 1911, [c1897]
Mahan, Alfred Thayer, 1840–1914.

LAC 40025

Interesting correspondence between His Excellency Governour Sullivan and Col. Pickering; in which the latter vindicates himself against the groundless charges and insinuations made by the governour and others. Boston, Printed by Greenough and Stebbins, over the Palladium office, 1808.
Sullivan, James, 1744–1808.

LAC 15245

Interesting tracts, relating to the island of Jamaica, consisting of curious state-papers, councils of war, letters, petitions, narratives, &c. &c., which throw great light on the history of that island, from its conquest down to the year 1702. St. Jago de la Vega [Jamaica] Printed by Lewis, Lunan, and Jones, 1800.

LAC 40047

Interior decoration, by Arnold W. Brunner and Thomas Tryon. With 65 illustrations. New York, W. T. Comstock, 1887.
Brunner, Arnold William, 1857–1925.

LAC 10338

Internal improvements in early Indiana. Indianapolis, E. J. Hecker, printer, 1912.
Esarey, Logan, 1874–1942.

LAC 40019

International cotton exhibition.
Address of Edward Atkinson of Boston, Massachusetts, given in Atlanta, Georgia, in October, 1880, for the promotion of an international cotton exhibition. Boston, A. Williams and company, 1881.
Atkinson, Edward, 1827–1905.

LAC 11253

International courts of arbitration, by Thomas Balch, 1874. 6th ed., edited with an introduction and additional notes, by Thomas Willing Balch. Philadelphia, Allen, Lane and Scott, 1915.
Balch, Thomas, 1821–1877.

LAC 11653

The International harvester co. March 3, 1913. Washington, Govt. print. off., 1913.
U.S. *Bureau of Corporations.*

LAC 10656

International law and diplomacy of the Spanish-American war. Baltimore, The Johns Hopkins press, 1908.
Benton, Elbert Jay, 1871–1946.

LAC 15873

International monetary conferences, their purposes, character, and results, with a study of the conditions of currency and finance in Europe and America during intervening periods, and in their relations to international action. New York and London, Harper & brothers, 1898.
Russell, Henry Benajah, 1859–

LAC 13415

International seamen's union of America; a study of its history and problems. June, 1923. Washington, Govt. print. off., 1923.
Albrecht, Arthur Emil, 1894–

LAC 11161

The inter-oceanic canal and the Monroe doctrine ... New York, G. P. Putnam's sons, 1880.
Williams, Alfred.

LAC 40074

Interpretation by Conference committee of managers of the western arbitration award as applied to certain questions and answers of the Brotherhood of locomotive engineers and the Brotherhood of locomotive firemen and enginemen. Chicago, July 1st, 1915. [Chicago? 1915?]
Conference Committee of Managers *(Railroads of Western Territory)* 1914–1915.

LAC 14050

Interpretations of poetry and religion. New York, C. Scribner's sons, 1900.
Santayana, George, 1863–1952.

LAC 12577

Interstate commerce commission cases in the federal courts, 1887 to 1911. Index office. Washington, Govt. print. off., 1911.
U.S. *Interstate Commerce Commission.*

LAC 10777

The intimate life of Alexander Hamilton, based chiefly upon original family letters and other documents, many of which have never been published. New York, C. Scribner's sons, 1911, [c1910]
Hamilton, Allan McLane, 1848–1919.

LAC 16182

Intoxicants & opium in all lands and times, a twentieth-century survey of intemperance, based on a symposium of testimony from one hundred missionaries and travelers, by Dr. & Mrs. Wilbur F. Crafts and Misses Mary & Margaret W. Leitch. Rev. 6th ed., 1904, of "Protection of native races against intoxicants and opium"... Washington, D. C., The International reform bureau [1904]
Crafts, Wilbur Fisk, 1850–1922.

LAC 40104

Intramural interments in populous cities, and their influence upon health and epidemics. By John H. Rauch, M. D. Chicago, Tribune company, printers, 1866.
Rauch, John Henry, 1828–1894.

LAC 10187

Introduction and early progress of the cotton manufacture in the United States... Boston, Little, Brown and company, 1863.
Batchelder, Samuel, 1784–1879.

LAC 40100

Introduction of the power loom, and Origin of Lowell. Lowell, Mass., Printed by B. H. Penhallow, 1858.
Appleton, Nathan, 1779–1861.

LAC 40128
Introduction to a course of lectures on natural history. Delivered in the University of Pennsylvania, Nov. 16, 1799. Philadelphia, Printed by F. and R. Bailey, 1800.
Peale, Charles Willson, 1741–1827.

LAC 12697
Introduction to a history of ironmaking and coal mining in Pennsylvania. Contributed to the final report of the Pennsylvania Board of centennial managers. Philadelphia, Pub. by the author, 1878.
Swank, James Moore, 1832–1914.

LAC 13828
Introduction to American law, designed as a first book for students. Philadelphia, P. H. Nicklin & T. Johnson, 1837.
Walker, Thomas, 1806–1856.

LAC 10897
An introduction to city planning; democracy's challenge to the American city, by Benjamin Clarke Marsh; with a chapter on the technical phases of city planning, by George B. Ford. New York [c1909]
Marsh, Benjamin Clarke, 1877–1952.

LAC 10442
Introduction to economics. 2d ed. rev. New York, H. Holt and company, 1904.
Seager, Henry Rogers, 1870–1930.

LAC 10510
An introduction to political economy. New York, Chautauqua press, 1889.
Ely, Richard Theodore, 1854–1943.

LAC 16341
An introduction to political economy. New York, Scribner, Armstrong, & company, 1877.
Perry, Arthur Latham, 1830–1905.

LAC 16946
An introduction to social psychology. 4th ed., rev. Boston, J. W. Luce & co., 1911.
McDougall, William, 1871–1938.

LAC 14746
An introduction to the constitutional law of the United States. Especially designed for students, general and professional. By John Norton Pomeroy. 9th ed., rev. and enl., by Edmund H. Bennett. Boston and New York, Houghton, Mifflin and company, 1886.
Pomeroy, John Norton, 1828–1885.

LAC 10100
An introduction to the history of sugar as a commodity. Philadelphia, The John C. Winston co., 1905.
Ellis, Ellen Deborah, 1878–

LAC 20775
An introduction to the history of the revolt of the American colonies: being a comprehensive view of its origin, derived from the state papers contained in the public offices of Great Britain. Boston, J. Munroe and co., 1845.
Chalmers, George, 1742–1825.

LAC 12028
An introduction to the study of American literature. New York, Cincinnati [etc.] American book company [c1896]
Matthews, Brander, 1852–1929.

LAC 15402
Introduction to the study of Indian languages, with words, phrases and sentences to be collected. 2d ed.–with charts. Washington, Govt. print. off., 1880.
Powell, John Wesley, 1834–1902.

LAC 16500
Introduction to the study of mortuary customs among the North American Indians. By Dr. H. C. Yarrow. Washington, Govt. print. off., 1880.
Yarrow, Harry Crecy, 1840–1929.

LAC 40097
An introduction to the study of natural history, in a series of lectures delivered in the hall of the College of physicians and surgeons, New York. Also, a biographical notice of the author. New York, Greeley & McElrath, 1847.
Agassiz, Louis, 1807–1873.

LAC 13999
An introduction to the study of philosophy. With an outline treatise on logic. By Rev. E. V. Gerhart. Philadelphia, Lindsay & Blakiston, 1858.
Gerhart, Emanuel Vogel, 1817–1904.

LAC 40051
Introduction to the study of sign language among the North American Indians... Washington, Govt. print. off., 1880.
Mallery, Garrick, 1831–1894.

LAC 10484
An introduction to the study of society, by Albion W. Small and George E. Vincent. New York, Cincinnati [etc.] American book company [1894]
Small, Albion Woodbury, 1854–1926.

LAC 11196
An introduction to the study of the dependent, defective and delinquent classes and of their social treatment. 2d ed., enl. and rewritten. Boston, D. C. Heath and company, 1906, [c1901]
Henderson, Charles Richmond, 1848–1915.

LAC 13842
The introductory lecture of Thomas Cooper, esq., professor of chemistry at Carlisle college, Pennsylvania. Published at the request of the trustees. With notes and references. Carlisle [Pa.] Printed by A. Loudon, 1812.
Cooper, Thomas, 1759–1839.

LAC 40017
An introductory lecture on political economy, delivered at Clinton hall, before the New-York young men's society, December 22, 1832. New York, J. K. Moore, 1833.
Vethake, Henry, 1792–1866.

LAC 15988
Invasion and capture of Washington.
History of the invasion and capture of Washington, and of the events which preceded and followed. New York, Harper & brothers, 1857.
Williams, John S.

LAC 10304
Investigation into the causes of the gold panic. Report of the majority of the Committee on banking and currency. March 1, 1870. Washington, Govt. print. off., 1870.
U.S. *Congress. House. Committee on Banking and Currency.*

LAC 40024
An investigation into the cost of transportation on American railroads, with deductions for its cheapening. Louisville, Printed by J. P. Morton & company, 1874.
Fink, Albert, 1827–1897.

LAC 13467–68
Investigation of labor troubles in Missouri, Arkansas, Kansas, Texas, and Illinois. Washington, Govt. print. off., 1887.
U.S. *Congress. House. Select Committee on Existing Labor Troubles.*

LAC 23175–78
Investigation of Mexican affairs. Preliminary report and hearings of the Committee on foreign relations United States Senate pursuant to S. res. 106, directing the Committee on foreign relations to investigate the matter of outrages on citizens of the United States in Mexico... Washington, Govt. print. off., 1920.
U.S. *Congress. Senate. Committee on Foreign Relations.*

LAC 40018
Investigation of Taylor system of shop management. Hearings before the Committee on labor of the House of representatives. Sixty-second Congress, first session, on House resolution 90... Washington, 1911.
U.S. *Congress. House. Committee on Labor.*

LAC 10464
Investigation of telephone companies. Letter from the secretary of commerce and labor transmitting, in response to a Senate resolution of May 28, 1908, a report showing the results of an investigation made by the Bureau of labor into telephone companies engaged in the conduct of interstate business... Washington, Govt. print. off., 1910.
U.S. *Bureau of Labor.*

LAC 14166
Investigation of the employment of Pinkerton detectives in connection with the labor troubles at Homestead, Pa. Washington, Govt. print. off., 1892.
U.S. *Congress. House. Committee on the Judiciary.*

LAC 11259
Involuntary idleness. An exposition of the cause of the discrepancy existing between the supply of, and the demand for, labor and its products. Philadelphia, J. B. Lippincott company, 1889.
Bilgram, Hugo, *b.* 1847.

LAC 15212
Iowa as it is in 1855; a gazetteer for citizens, and a hand-book for immigrants, embracing a full description of the state of Iowa... Information for the immigrant respecting the selection, entry, and cultivation of prairie soil; a list of unentered lands in the state, &c. ... Chicago, Keen and Lee, 1855.
Parker, Nathan Howe.

LAC 14018
The Iowa band. Boston, Congregational publishing society, 1870.
Adams, Ephraim, 1818–1907.

LAC 13308
Iowa: the first free state in the Louisiana purchase, from its discovery to the admission of the state into the Union, 1673–1846. Chicago, A. C. McClurg & co., 1905.
Salter, William, 1821–1910.

LAC 14871
Iowa: the home for immigrants, being a treatise on the resources of Iowa, and giving useful information with regard to the state, for the benefit of immigrants and others. Pub. by order of the Iowa board of immigration. Des Moines, Mills & co., 1870.
Iowa. *Board of Immigration.*

LAC 23694–95
Ipswich in the Massachusetts Bay Colony. Ipswich, Mass., The Ipswich historical society, 1905–17.
Waters, Thomas Franklin, 1851–

LAC 22241–42
Ira Allen, founder of Vermont, 1751–1814. Boston and New York, Houghton Mifflin company, 1928.
Wilbur, James Benjamin, 1856–1929.

LAC 16424
Ireland's welcome to the stranger; or An excursion through Ireland, in 1844 & 1845, for the purpose of personally investigating the condition of the poor. New York, Baker and Scribner, 1847.
Nicholson, Asenath.

LAC 20159
Irish-American history of the United States. By the Very Rev. John canon O'Hanlon, M. R. I. A., with an introduction by the Very Rev. Thomas J. Shahan... New York, P. Murphy, 1907, [c1906]
O'Hanlon, John, 1821–1905.

LAC 14496
The Irish brigade and its campaigns: with some account of the Corcoran legion, and sketches of the principal officers. By Capt. D. P. Conyngham. New York, W. McSorley & co., 1861.
Conyngham, David Power, 1840–1883.

LAC 14819
The Irish confederates, and the rebellion of 1798. New York, Harper & brothers, 1851.
Field, Henry Martyn, 1822–1907.

LAC 15728
Irish emigration to the United States: what it has been, and what it is. Facts and reflections especially addressed to Irish people intending to emigrate from their

native land; and to those living in the large cities of Great Britain and of the United States. By the Rev. Stephen Byrne, O. S. D. New York, Catholic publication society, 1873.
Byrne, Stephen.

LAC 15741
The Irish in America. London, Longmans, Green and co., 1868.
Maguire, John Francis, 1815–1872.

LAC 40057
The Irish in America. A lecture by William R. Grace, at Boston theatre, February 21, 1886. Chicago, McDonnell bros., 1886.
Grace, William Russell, 1832–1904.

LAC 16523
The Irish in the revolution and the civil war, rev. and enl.; embracing the Spanish-American and Philippine wars and every walk of life, by Dr. J. C. O'Connell. Washington, D. C., The Trades unionist press [c1903]
O'Connell, J   C.

LAC 40057
The Irish position in British and in republican North America. A letter to the editors of the Irish press, irrespective of party. 2d ed. Montreal, M. Longmoore & co., 1866.
McGee, Thomas D'Arcy.

LAC 15543
The Irish race in California, and on the Pacific coast, with an introductory historical dissertation on the principal races of mankind, and a vocabulary of ancient and modern Irish family names, by Dr. Quigley. San Francisco, A. Roman & co., 1878.
Quigley, Hugh, 1819–1883.

LAC 12780
The iron furnace: or, Slavery and secession. By Rev. John H. Aughey, a refugee from Mississippi... Philadelphia, W. S. & A. Martien, 1863.
Aughey, John Hill, b. 1828.

LAC 10463
The iron manufacturer's guide to the furnaces, forges and rolling mills of the United States, with discussions of iron as a chemical element, an American ore, and a manufactured article, in commerce and in history. By J. P. Lesley, secretary of the American iron association, and published by authority of the same. With maps and plates. New York, J. Wiley; London, Trubner & co., 1859.
Lesley, J   Peter, 1819–1903.

LAC 10121
Irrigation in the United States. New York, T. Y. Crowell & co. [1902]
Newell, Frederick Haynes, 1862–1932.

LAC 10117
Irrigation institutions; a discussion of the economic and legal questions created by the growth of irrigated agriculture in the West. New York, The Macmillan company; London, Macmillan & co., ltd., 1903.
Mead, Elwood, 1858–1936.

LAC 40058
Is the Monroe doctrine involved in the controversy between Venezuela and Great Britain? [New York? 1896]
Daly, Charles Patrick, 1816–1899.

LAC 13460
Isaac T. Hopper: a true life. Boston, J. P. Jewett & co.; Cleveland, O., Jewett, Proctor & Worthington; [etc., etc.] 1853.
Child, Lydia Maria, 1802–1880.

LAC 14375
The Isles of Shoals. An historical sketch. New York, Hurd and Houghton; Cambridge, The Riverside press, 1873.
Jenness, John Scribner, 1827–1879.

LAC 40014
Isolation in the school... Chicago, The University of Chicago press, 1900.
Young, Ella, 1845–1918.

LAC 15743
The Italian contribution to American democracy, by John Horace Mariano. With an introduction by Hon. F. H. LaGuardia. Boston, The Christopher publishing house [c1921]
Mariano, John Horace, 1896–

LAC 14822
The Italian emigration of our times. Cambridge, Harvard university press; [etc., etc.] 1919.
Foerster, Robert Franz, 1883–1941.

LAC 13899
Italian gardens. New York, Harper & brothers, 1894.
Platt, Charles Adams, 1861–1933.

LAC 15210
Italian hours, by Henry James. With illustrations in color by Joseph Pennell. Boston and New York, Houghton Mifflin company, 1909.
James, Henry, 1843–1916.

LAC 14875
Italian sights and papal principles, seen through American spectacles. New York, Harper & brothers, 1856.
Jarves, James Jackson, 1818–1888.

LAC 14693
The Italians in Chicago. A social and economic study. Prepared under the direction of Carroll D. Wright, commissioner of labor. Washington, Govt. print. off., 1897.
U.S. *Bureau of Labor.*

LAC 16759
The ivory tower. New York, C. Scribner's sons, 1917.
James, Henry, 1843–1916.

LAC 11507
Jacobin and junto; or, Early American politics as viewed in the diary of Dr. Nathaniel Ames, 1758–1822. Cambridge, Mass., Harvard university press, 1931.
Warren, Charles, 1868–1954.

LAC 10744
James and Lucretia Mott. Life and letters. Ed. by their granddaughter, Anna Davis Hallowell. With portraits...[5th ed.] Boston, New York, Houghton, Mifflin and company, 1896, [c1884]
Hallowell, Anna, 1838– *ed.*

LAC 12463
James Baird Weaver. Iowa City, Ia., The State historical society of Iowa, 1919.
Haynes, Frederick Emory, 1868–

LAC 10724
James Freeman Clarke: autobiography, diary and correspondence, edited by Edward Everett Hale. Boston and New York, Houghton, Mifflin and company, 1891.
Clarke, James Freeman, 1810–1888.

LAC 13918
James G. Birney and his times; the genesis of the Republican party with some account of abolition movements in the South before 1828. New York, D. Appleton and company, 1890.
Birney, William, 1819–1907.

LAC 12535
James Gillespie Blaine. Boston and New York, Houghton, Mifflin and company [c1905]
Stanwood, Edward, 1841–1923.

LAC 14440
James Henry Lane, the "Grim chieftain of Kansas." Topeka, Kan., Crane & company, 1899.
Connelley, William Elsey, 1855–1930.

LAC 40062
James Otis, Samuel Adams, and John Hancock. John Adams's tributes to these as the three principal movers and agents of the American revolution. Boston, Directors of the Old South work, 1907.
Adams, John, *pres. U.S.,* 1735–1826.

LAC 15313
Janice Meredith; a story of the American revolution. New York, Dodd, Mead and company, 1899.
Ford, Paul Leicester, 1865–1902.

LAC 11139
Japan and Japanese-American relations... New York, G. E. Stechert and company, 1912.
Blakeslee, George Hubbard, 1871–1954, *ed.*

LAC 14872
Japan and the California problem, by T. Iyenaga and Kenoske Sato. New York and London, G. P. Putnam's sons, 1921.
Iyenaga, Toyokichi, 1862–1936.

LAC 15499
Japanese immigration. Boston, World peace foundation [1924]
Buell, Raymond Leslie, 1896–1946.

LAC 40052
Japanese immigration; its status in California. San Francisco, The Marshall press, 1915.
Ichihashi, Yamato.

LAC 40057
Japanese immigration, occupations, wages, etc. Comp. from U.S. government reports and reports of California Bureau of labor statistics. Pub. by Japanese and Korean exclusion league, January 1, 1907. [San Francisco, 1907]
Japanese and Korean Exclusion League, *San Francisco, pub.*

LAC 15523
The Japanese in America. Ed. by Charles Lanman. New York, University publishing company, 1872.
Lanman, Charles, 1819–1895.

LAC 13357
The Japanese invasion; a study in the psychology of interracial contacts, by Jesse Frederick Steiner, with an introduction by Robert E. Park. Chicago, A. C. McClurg & co., 1917.
Steiner, Jesse Frederick, 1880–

LAC 16269
A Japanese miscellany. Boston, Little, Brown, and company, 1901.
Hearn, Lafcadio, 1850–1904.

LAC 15536
The Japanese problem in the United States; an investigation for the Commission on relations with Japan appointed by the Federal council of the churches of Christ in America. New York, The Macmillan company, 1915.
Millis, Harry Alvin, 1873–1948.

LAC 11943
Jason Edwards, an average man. Boston, Arena Publishing company, 1892.
Garland, Hamlin, 1860–1940.

LAC 15978
Java, the garden of the East. New York, The Century co., 1897.
Scidmore, Eliza Ruhamah, 1856–1928.

LAC 20063–64
Jay Cooke, financier of the civil war. Philadelphia, G. W. Jacobs & co. [1907]
Oberholtzer, Ellis Paxson, 1868–1936.

LAC 12301
Jean Baptiste Le Moyne, sieur de Bienville. New York, Dodd, Mead and company, 1892.
King, Grace Elizabeth, 1852–

LAC 16042
Jeff Davis, governor and United States senator; his life and speeches, with personal reminiscences, by L. S. Dunaway; introduction by Judge J. V. Bourland. Little Rock, Democrat print. & litho. co., 1913.
Davis, Jeff, 1862–1913.

LAC 14146
Jefferson Davis. Philadelphia, G. W. Jacobs & company [1907]
Dodd, William Edward, 1869–1940.

LAC 40075

Jefferson Davis, and his complicity in the assassination of Abraham Lincoln ... and where the traitor shall be tried for treason. Philadelphia, Sherman, 1866.

LAC 22247-53

Jefferson Davis, constitutionalist, his letters, papers and speeches, collected and edited by Dunbar Rowland. Jackson, Miss., Printed for the Mississippi department of archives and history, 1923.
Davis, Jefferson, 1808-1889.

LAC 22245-46

Jefferson Davis, ex-president of the Confederate States of America; a memoir by his wife. New York, Belford company [c1890]
Davis, Varina, 1826-1906.

LAC 14433

Jefferson Davis, president of the South. New York, The Macmillan company, 1923.
Eckenrode, Hamilton James, 1881–

LAC 13688

Jefferson et les ideologues d'apres sa correspondance inedite avec Destutt de Tracy, Cabinis, J.-B. Say et Auguste Comte. Baltimore, Md., The Johns Hopkins press; Paris, Les Presses universitaires de France, 1925.
Chinard, Gilbert, 1881–

LAC 11416

The Jeffersonian system, 1801-1811. New York and London, Harper & brothers [c1906]
Channing, Edward, 1856-1931.

LAC 15250

Jefferson's Germantown letters, together with other papers relating to his stay in Germantown during the month of November, 1793, by Charles Francis Jenkins. Philadelphia, W. J. Campbell, 1906.
Jefferson, Thomas, *pres. U.S.*, 1743-1826.

LAC 10251

Jenny Lind in America. New York, Stringer & Townsend, 1851.
Rosenberg, Charles G.

LAC 10109

The Jersey, Alderney, and Guernsey cow: their history, nature and management. Showing how to choose a good cow; how to feed, to manage, to milk, and to breed to the most profit. Ed., from the writings of Edward P. P. Fowler and others. 10th ed. Philadelphia, Porter and Coates [c1872]
Hazard, Willis Pope, 1825-1913.

LAC 40032

The Jersey herd at the World's Columbian exposition, Chicago, 1893. New York, American Jersey cattle club, 1894.
Fuller, Valancey England.

LAC 21463-90

The Jesuit relations and allied documents: travels and explorations of the Jesuit missionaries in New France, 1610-1791. The original French, Latin, and Italian texts, with English trans. and notes. Ed. by Reuben Gold Thwaites. New York, Pageant Book Co., 1959.
Jesuits. Letters from Missions *(North America)*

LAC 15489

Jewish immigration to the United States from 1881 to 1910. New York, Columbia university; [etc., etc.] 1914.
Joseph, Samuel, 1881–

LAC 40057

"Jews in America." New York, Funk & Wagnalls, 1901.
Adler, Cyrus, 1863-1940.

LAC 14853

Jews in the diplomatic correspondence of the United States, being the address delivered by Cyrus Adler, PH. D., president of the American Jewish historical society, at the thirteenth annual meeting held in Cincinnati, Ohio, February 27th, 1905. [Baltimore, The Society] 1906.
Adler, Cyrus, 1863-1940.

LAC 11063

The Jews of Philadelphia. Their history from the earliest settlements to the present time. A record of events and institutions, and of leading members of the Jewish community in every sphere of activity. Philadelphia, The Levytype company, 1894.
Morais, Henry Samuel, 1860–

LAC 10408

The Jews of South Carolina from the earliest times to the present day. Philadelphia, Press of J. B. Lippincott company, 1905.
Elzas, Barnett Abraham 1867-1936.

LAC 14150

Joel Chandler Harris' life of Henry W. Grady including his writings and speeches. A memorial volume comp. by Mr. Henry W. Grady's co-workers on "The Constitution" and ed. by Joel Chandler Harris. New York, Cassell publishing company [c1890]
Harris, Joel Chandler, 1848-1908.

LAC 15736

Johann Conrad Beissel, mystic and martinet, 1690-1768. Philadelphia, University of Pennsylvania press, 1942.
Klein, Walter Conrad, *bp.*, 1904–

LAC 14235

John Adams, the statesman of the American revolution; with other essays and addresses, historical and literary. Boston and New York, Houghton, Mifflin and company, 1899, [c1898]
Chamberlain, Mellen, 1821-1900.

LAC 11018

John Alexander Dowie and the Christian Catholic apostolic church in Zion... Evansville, Wis., Press of R. M. Antes, 1906.
Harlan, Rolvix, 1876–

LAC 12278

John and Sebastian Cabot; the discovery of North America. London, T. Fisher Unwin, 1898.
Beazley, *Sir* Charles Raymond, 1868-1955.

LAC 11889
John Andross [a novel] By Rebecca Harding Davis.
New York, Orange Judd company [c1874]
Davis, Rebecca, 1831–1910.

LAC 20251–52
The John Askin papers ... edited by Milo M. Quaife.
[Detroit] Detroit library commission, 1928–1931.
Askin, John, 1739–1815.

LAC 10752
John B. Gough, the apostle of cold water. New York
[etc.] Funk & Wagnalls company, 1893.
Martyn Carlos, 1841–1917.

LAC 12851
John Brown and his men; with some account of the
roads they traveled to reach Harper's Ferry. Rev. ed.
New York and London, Funk & Wagnalls company
[c1894]
Hinton, Richard Josiah, 1830–1901.

LAC 12792
The John Brown invasion; an authentic history of the
Harper's Ferry tragedy, with full details of the capture,
trial, and execution of the invaders, and of all the inci-
dents connected therewith. With a lithographic portrait of
Capt. John Brown, from a photograph by Whipple. Bos-
ton, J. Campbell, 1860.
Drew, Thomas, *comp.*

LAC 12339
John C. Calhoun. Boston, New York, Houghton, Mif-
flin and company, 1882.
Holst, Hermann Eduard von, 1841–1904.

LAC 13220
John Cabot, the discoverer of North America, and
Sebastian, his son; a chapter of the maritime history of
England under the Tudors, 1496–1557. London, B. F.
Stevens, 1896.
Harrisse, Henry, 1830–1910.

LAC 13481
John D. Rockefeller and his career. New York, The
author, 1904.
Hubbard, Silas.

LAC 10293
John Foster, the earliest American engraver and the
first Boston printer. Pub. by the Massachusetts historical
society at the charge of the Waterston fund, no. 2. Boston,
1909.
Green, Samuel Abbott, 1830–1918.

LAC 12085
John Godfrey's fortunes; related by himself. A story of
American life. [1st ed.] New York, G. P. Putnam, Hurd
and Houghton, 1864.
Taylor, Bayard, 1825–1878.

LAC 16925
John Jasper, the unmatched negro philosopher and
preacher. New York, Chicago [etc.] F. H. Revell company [c1908]
Hatcher, William Eldridge, 1835–

LAC 40102
John Kinsey, speaker of the Pennsylvania assembly
and justice of the Supreme court of the province. Philadelphia, Friends' book association, 1900.
Walton, Joseph Solomon, *d.* 1912.

LAC 15129
John La Farge, artist and writer. London, Seeley and
co., limited; New York, Macmillan and co., 1896.
Waern, Cecilia, 1853–

LAC 11854
John March, southerner. New York, C. Scribner's
sons, 1894.
Cable, George Washington, 1844–1925.

LAC 40071
John Marshall. [Boston, 1901]
Thayer, James Bradley, 1831–1902.

LAC 13446
John Marshall, complete constitutional decisions, ed.
with annotations historical, critical and legal, by John M.
Dillon. Chicago, Callaghan & company, 1903.
Marshall, John, 1755–1835.

LAC 13501
John Peter Zenger, his press, his trial and a bibliography of Zenger imprints. Also a reprint of the first edition
of the trial. New York, Dodd, Mead & company, 1904.
Rutherfurd, Livingston.

LAC 10488
John Randolph. Boston, New York, Houghton, Mifflin
and company, 1882.
Adams, Henry, 1838–1918.

LAC 16360
John Wellborn Root; a study of his life and work, by
Harriet Monroe; with etchings and drawings by Charles
F. W. Mielatz and fac-similes of designs by Mr. Root.
Boston and New York, Houghton, Mifflin & company,
1896.
Monroe, Harriet, 1860–1936.

LAC 13909
Johnson's history of Nebraska. Omaha, Neb., H. Gib-
son, 1880.
Johnson, Harrison.

LAC 16972
Johnson's Wonder-working providence, 1628–1651;
ed. by J. Franklin Jameson. With a map and two facsimiles. New York, C. Scribner's sons [1910]
Johnson, Edward, 1599–1672.

LAC 12150
Jonathan and his continent. (Rambles through Ameri-
can society) By Max O'Rell [*pseud.*] and Jack Allyn.
Translated by Madame Paul Blouet. New York, Cassell
& company, limited [c1889]
Blouet, Paul, 1848–1903.

LAC 11184
Joseph Fels; his life-work. New York, B. W. Huebsch,
1916.
Fels, Mary, 1859–

LAC 40020
Joseph Henry and the magnetic telegraph. An address delivered at Princeton college, June 16, 1885. New York, C. Scribner's sons, 1885.
Dickerson, Edward Nicoll.

LAC 40144
Joseph Smith tells his own story. [Salt Lake City, Utah, The Church of Jesus Christ of latter-day saints, n.d.]
Smith, Joseph, 1805–1844.

LAC 16389
Josiah Warren, the first American anarchist; a sociological study. Boston, Small, Maynard & company, 1906.
Bailie, William.

LAC 40039
Josiah White's history, given by himself. [Philadelphia, Press of G. H. Buchanan company, 1909?]
White, Josiah, 1781–1850.

LAC 16844
Jottings of a year's sojourn in the South; or, First impressions of the country and its people; with a glimpse at school-teaching in that southern land, and reminiscences of distinguished men... Battle Creek, Mich., 1859.
Van Buren, A   De Puy.

LAC 20683
Journal [Aug. 1, 1832 to July 17, 1833] By Frances Anne Butler. Philadelphia, Carey, Lea & Blanchard, 1835.
Kemble, Frances Anne, 1809–1893.

LAC 22748
Journal and correspondence of Miss Adams, daughter of John Adams, second president of the United States. Written in France and England, in 1785. Ed. by her daughter. New-York [etc.] Wiley and Putnam, 1841–42.
Smith, Abigail, 1765–1813.

LAC 13264
Journal and letters of Col. John May, of Boston, relative to two journeys to the Ohio country in 1788 and '89. With a biographical sketch by Rev. Richard S. Edes, and illustrative notes by Wm. M. Darlington. Cincinnati, R. Clarke & co., for the Historical and philosophical society of Ohio, 1873.
May, John, 1748–1812.

LAC 12445
Journal and letters of the late Samuel Curwen, judge of Admiralty, etc., an American refugee in England, from 1775 to 1784, comprising remarks on the prominent men and measures of that period. To which are added, biographical notices of many American loyalists, and other eminent persons. By George Atkinson Ward. New-York, C. S. Francis and co.; Boston, J. H. Francis, 1842.
Curwen, Samuel, 1715–1802.

LAC 16942
Journal and votes of the House of Representatives of the province of Nova Cesarea, or New Jersey, in their first sessions of assembly, began at Perth Amboy, the 10th day of November, 1703. Jersey City, John H. Lyon, 1872.
New Jersey (Colony) General Assembly.

LAC 40025
A journal; containing an account of the wrongs, sufferings, and neglect, experienced by Americans in France. Tarrytown, N. Y., Reprinted, W. Abbatt, 1916.
Clubb, Stephen, b. 1762.

LAC 16845
Journal des campagnes au Canada de 1755 a 1760, par le comte de Maures de Malartic. Pub. par son arriere petit-neveu, le comte Gabriel de Maures de Malartic et par Paul Gaffarel. Paris, E. Plon, Nourrit et cie [1890]
Malartic, Anne Joseph Hippolyte de Maures, comte de, 1730–1800.

LAC 12207
A journal for the years 1739–1803, by Samuel Lane, of Stratham, New Hampshire; edited by Charles Lane Hanson. Concord, N. H., New Hampshire historical society, 1937.
Lane, Samuel, 1718–1806.

LAC 16321
Journal kept by Hugh Finlay, surveyor of the post roads on the continent of North America, during his survey of the post offices between Falmouth and Casco bay, in the province of Massachusetts, and Savannah, in Georgia; begun the 13th Septr., 1773 and ended 26th June 1774. Brooklyn, F. H. Norton, 1867.
Finlay, Hugh, 1732–1801.

LAC 16432
Journal of a cruise made to the Pacific ocean, by Captain David Porter, in the United States frigate Essex, in the years 1812, 1813, and 1814. Containing descriptions of the Cape de Verd islands, coasts of Brazil, Patagonia, Chile, and Peru, and of the Gallapagos islands... Philadelphia, Bradford and Inskeep; [etc., etc.] 1815.
Porter, David, 1780–1843.

LAC 13313
A journal of a missionary tour through Pennsylvania, Ohio, Indiana, Illinois, Iowa, Wiskonsin and Michigan; comprising a concise description of different sections of country; health of climate; inducements for emigration with the embarrassments; the religious condition of the people; meetings connected with the mission; and of the great western prairies. By Rev. James L. Scott. Providence, The author, 1843.
Scott, James Leander.

LAC 21264–65
Journal of a residence and tour in the United States of North America, from April, 1833, to October, 1834. London, J. Murray, 1835.
Abdy, Edward Strutt, 1791–1846.

LAC 12348
Journal of a residence on a Georgian plantation in 1838–1839. New York, Harper, 1863.
Kemble, Frances Anne, 1809–1893.

LAC 14408
Journal of a soldier under Kearny and Doniphan, 1846–1847. by George Rutledge Gibson, edited by Ralph P. Bieber. Glendale, Calif., The Arthur H. Clark company, 1935.
Gibson, George Rutledge, 1810(ca.)–1885.

LAC 13129
Journal of a tour in unsettled parts of North America, in 1796 & 1797. With a memoir of the author. London, Baily brothers, 1856.
Baily, Francis, 1774–1844.

LAC 16139
Journal of a tour into the interior of Missouri and Arkansaw, from Potosi, or Mine a Burton, in Missouri Territory, in a south-west direction, toward the Rocky Mountains; performed in the years 1818 and 1819. London, Printed for Sir R. Phillips and co., 1821.
Schoolcraft, Henry Rowe, 1793–1864.

LAC 13219
The journal of a tour into the territory northwest of the Alleghany mountains; made in the spring of the year 1803. With a geographical and historical account of the state of Ohio... Boston: Printed by Manning & Loring, no. 2, Cornhill. 1805.
Harris, Thaddeus Mason, 1768–1842.

LAC 15590
Journal of a tour through the State of New York in the year 1830, with remarks on agriculture in those parts most eligible for settlers. New York, A. M. Kelley, 1970.
Fowler, John.

LAC 13957
Journal of a tour through the United States, and in Canada, made during the years 1837–38. Oxford, Printed by T. Combe, 1843.
Daubeny, Charles Giles Bridle, 1795–1867.

LAC 40055
Journal of a trip to Michigan in 1841. Rochester, 1904.
Swan, Lansing B   1809–1861.

LAC 40042
A journal of a voyage from London to Savannah in Georgia... With a short preface, shewing the reasons of its publication. London, J. Hutton, 1738.
Whitefield, George, 1714–1770.

LAC 40105
Journal of a voyage from Savannah to Philadelphia, and from Philadelphia to England, M.DCC.XL. By William Seward, gent. companion in travel with the Reverend Mr. George Whitefield. London, J. Oswald; [etc., etc.] 1740.
Seward, William.

LAC 40045
A journal of a voyage made in the Hannibal of London, ann. 1693, 1694, from England, to Cape Monseradoe, in Africa; and thence along the coast of Guiney to Whidaw, the island of St. Thomas, and so forward to Barbadoes. With a cursory account of the country, the people, their manners, forts, trade, &c. By Thomas Phillips, commander of the said ship. [London, H. Lintot, 1746]
Phillips, Thomas, *fl.* 1693.

LAC 23202
Journal of a voyage to North America. Translated from the French of Pierre Francois Xavier de Charlevoix. Edited with historical introduction, notes and index, by Louise Phelps Kellogg. Chicago, The Caxton club, 1923.
Charlevoix, Pierre Francois Xavier de, 1682–1761.

LAC 13151
Journal of a voyage up the river Missouri; performed in eighteen hundred and eleven. 2d ed., rev. and enl. by the author. Baltimore, Pub. by Coale and Maxwell, Pomeroy & Toy, printers, 1816.
Brackenridge, Henry Marie, 1786–1871.

LAC 15008
Journal of Alfred Ely, a prisoner of war in Richmond. Edited by Charles Lanman. New York, D. Appleton and company, 1862.
Ely, Alfred, 1815–1892.

LAC 15198
The journal of Andrew Ellicott, late commissioner on behalf of the United States during part of the year 1796, the years 1797, 1798, 1799, and part of the year 1800: for determining the boundary between the United States and the possessions of His Catholic Majesty in America, containing occasional remarks on the situation, soil, rivers, natural productions, and diseases of the different countries on the Ohio, Mississippi, and gulf of Mexico, with six maps comprehending the Ohio, the Mississippi from the mouth of the Ohio to the gulf of Mexico, the whole of West Florida, and part of East Florida. To which is added an appendix, containing all the astronomical observations made use of for determining the boundary ... likewise a great number of thermometrical observations... Philadelphia, Printed by Budd & Bartram, for Thomas Dobson, at the stone house, no. 41, South second street, 1803.
Ellicott, Andrew, 1754–1820.

LAC 12070
The journal of Arthur Stirling ("The valley of the shadow") Revised and condensed, with an introductory sketch. New York, D. Appleton and company, 1903.
Sinclair, Upton Beall, 1878–1968.

LAC 16106
Journal of Captain Pausch, chief of the Hanau artillery during the Burgoyne campaign. Tr. and annotated by William L. Stone. Introduction by Edward J. Lowell. Albany, N. Y., J. Munsell's sons, 1886.
Pausch, Georg.

LAC 15018
The journal of Captain William Pote, jr. during his captivity in the French and Indian war from May, 1745, to August, 1747. New York, Dodd, Mead & co., 1896.
Pote, William, 1718–1755.

LAC 16624
Journal of Captain William Trent from Logstown to Pickawillany, A. D. 1752. Now published for the first time from a copy in the archives of the Western Reserve historical society, Cleveland, Ohio, together with letters of Governor Robert Dinwiddie; an historical notice of the Miami confederacy of Indians; a sketch of the English post at Pickawillany, with a short biography of Captain Trent, and other papers never before printed. Ed. by Alfred T. Goodman. Cincinnati, Printed by R. Clarke & co., for W. Dodge, 1871.
Trent, William, 1715–1778.

LAC 10246
Journal of Charles Carroll of Carrollton, during his visit to Canada, in 1776, as one of the commissioners from Congress; with a memoir and notes. By Brantz Mayer. Baltimore, Printed by John Murphy for the Maryland historical society, 1876.
Carroll, Charles, 1737–1832.

LAC 15652

The Journal of Charlotte L. Forten; with an introd. and notes by Ray Allen Billington. New York, Dryden Press [1953]
Forten, Charlotte L

LAC 12282

The journal of Christopher Columbus (during his first voyage, 1492–93) and documents relating the voyages of John Cabot and Gaspar Corte Real. Translated with notes and an introduction, by Clements R. Markham. London, Printed for the Hakluyt society, 1893.
Colombo, Cristoforo.

LAC 15078

Journal of Constitutional convention, assembled at Charleston, West Virginia, January 16, 1872... Charleston, H. S. Walker, convention printer, 1872.
West Virginia. *Constitutional Convention*, 1872.

LAC 40137

Journal of Daniel Coker, a descendant of Africa, from the time of leaving New York, in the ship Elizabeth, Capt. Sebor, on a voyage for Sherbro, in Africa, in company with three agents, and about ninety persons of colour... With an appendix. Baltimore: Published by Edward J. Coale, In aid of the funds of the Maryland auxiliary colonization society. 1820. John D. Toy, printer.
Coker, Daniel.

LAC 13750

Journal of debates and proceedings in the Convention of delegates, chosen to revise the constitution of Massachusetts, begun and holden at Boston, November 15, 1820, and continued by adjournment to January 9, 1821. Reported for the Boston daily advertiser. New ed., rev. and cor. Boston, Pub. at the office of the Daily advertiser, 1853.
Massachusetts. *Constitutional Convention*, 1820–1821.

LAC 40070

Journal of events principally on the Detroit and Niagara frontiers, during the war of 1812. By Capt. W. H. Merritt. St. Catharines, C. W., Historical society, B.N.A., 1863.
Merritt, William Hamilton, 1793–1862.

LAC 15157

Journal of Gen. Rufus Putnam kept in northern New York during four campaigns of the old French and Indian war 1757–1760. The whole copiously illustrated with notes and preceded by a biographical sketch of Gen. Putnam, by E. C. Dawes. Albany, N. Y., J. Munsell's sons, 1886.
Putnam, Rufus, 1738–1824.

LAC 15864

A journal of hospital life in the Confederate army of Tennessee, from the battle of Shiloh to the end of the war: with sketches of life and character, and brief notices of current events during that period. Louisville, J. P. Morgan & co.; New Orleans, W. Evelyn [c1866]
Cumming, Kate, 1835–1909.

LAC 40038

The journal of Isaac Senter, physician and surgeon to the troops detached from the American army encamped at Cambridge, Mass., on a secret expedition against Quebec, under the command of Col. Benedict Arnold, in September, 1775. Philadelphia, The Historical society of Pennsylvania, 1846. Tarrytown, N. Y., Reprinted, W. Abbatt, 1915.
Senter, Isaac, 1753?–1799.

LAC 13198

The journal of Jacob Fowler, narrating an adventure from Arkansas through the Indian territory, Oklahoma, Kansas, Colorado, and New Mexico, to the sources of Rio Grande del Norte, 1821–22. Ed. with notes, by Elliott Coues. New York, F. P. Harper, 1898.
Fowler, Jacob, 1765–1850.

LAC 16038

Journal of Jasper Danckaerts, 1679–1680; ed. by Bartlett Burleigh James and J. Franklin Jameson, with a facsimile and two maps. New York, C. Scribner's sons, 1913.
Danckaerts, Jasper, *b.* 1639.

LAC 13891

The journal of Latrobe; being the notes and sketches of an architect, naturalist and traveler in the United States from 1797 to 1820, by Benjamin Henry Latrobe, architect of the capitol at Washington; with an introduction by J. H. B. Latrobe. New York, D. Appleton and company, 1905.
Latrobe, Benjamin Henry, 1764–1820.

LAC 40080

The journal of Lieut. William Feltman, of the First Pennsylvania regiment, 1781–82. Including the march into Virginia and the siege of Yorktown. Philadelphia, Pub. for the Historical society of Pennsylvania, by H. C. Baird, 1853.
Feltman, William.

LAC 40007

The journal of Madam Knight, with an introductory note by George Parker Winship. New York, Peter Smith, 1935.
Knight, Sarah, 1666–1727.

LAC 40049

Journal of New Mexico convention of delegates to recommend a plan of civil government. September, 1849. Santa Fe, N. M., The New Mexican printing company, 1907.
New Mexico (Ter.) Convention, 1849.

LAC 14402

Journal of Pontiac's conspiracy. 1763. Published by Clarence Monroe Burton under the auspices of the Michigan Society of the colonial wars. Ed. by M. Agnes Burton. [Detroit, Speaker-Hines printing company, pref. 1912]

LAC 40114

Journal of the Commons house of assembly of South Carolina for the session beginning September 20, 1692, and ending October 15, 1692. Ed. by A. S. Salley, jr., secretary of the Historical commission of South Carolina. Columbia, S. C., Printed by the State company, 1907.
South Carolina (Colony) Assembly.

LAC 40114

Journal of the Commons house of assembly of South Carolina, for the session beginning January 30, 1696, and ending March 17, 1696. Ed. by A. S. Salley, jr., secretary of the Historical commission of South Carolina. Columbia, S. C., Printed for the Historical commission by the State company, 1908.
South Carolina (Colony) Assembly.

LAC 40114

Journal of the Commons house of assembly of South Carolina for the session beginning November 24, 1696, and ending December 5, 1696. Ed. by A. S. Salley, jr., secretary of the Historical commission of South Carolina. Columbia, S. C., Printed for the Historical commission of South Carolina by The state company, 1912.
South Carolina *(Colony) Assembly.*

LAC 40114

Journal of the Commons house of assembly of South Carolina for the session beginning October 30, 1700 and ending November 16, 1700. Edited by A. S. Salley, jr., secretary of the Historical commission of South Carolina. Columbia, S. C., Printed for the Historical commission of South Carolina by the State company, 1924.
South Carolina *(Colony) Assembly.*

LAC 40114

Journal of the Commons house of assembly of South Carolina for the session beginning February 4, 1701 and ending March 1, 1701. Ed. by A. S. Salley, jr., secretary of the Historical commission of South Carolina. Columbia, S. C., Printed for the Historical commission of South Carolina by the State company, 1925.
South Carolina *(Colony) Assembly.*

LAC 40114

Journal of the Commons house of assembly of South Carolina for the session beginning August 13, 1701 and ending August 28, 1701. Edited by A. S. Salley, jr., secretary of the Historical commission of South Carolina. Columbia, S. C., Printed for the Historical commission of South Carolina, 1926.
South Carolina *(Colony) Assembly.*

LAC 40114

Journal of the Commons house of assembly of South Carolina, March 6, 170(5)6–April 9, 1706. Edited by A. S. Salley, secretary of the Historical commission of South Carolina. Columbia, S. C., Printed for the Historical commission of South Carolina by the State company, 1937.
South Carolina *(Colony) Assembly.*

LAC 40114

Journal of the Commons house of assembly of South Carolina, November 20, 1706–February 8, 170(6)7. Edited by A. S. Salley, secretary of the Historical commission of South Carolina. Columbia, S. C., Printed for the Historical commission of South Carolina by the State company, 1939.
South Carolina *(Colony) Assembly.*

LAC 16521

Journal of the Commons house of assembly of South Carolina, June 5, 1707–July 19, 1707. Edited by A. S. Salley, secretary of the Historical commission of South Carolina. Columbia, S. C., Printed for the Historical commission of South Carolina by the State company, 1940.
South Carolina *(Colony) Assembly.*

LAC 40114

Journal of the Commons house of assembly of South Carolina, October 22, 1707–February 12, 170(7)8. Edited by A. S. Salley, secretary of the Historical commission of South Carolina. Columbia, S. C., Printed for the Historical commission of South Carolina by the State company, 1941.
South Carolina *(Colony) Assembly.*

LAC 20045–51

Journal of the Congress of the Confederate States of America, 1861–1865. Washington, Govt. print. off., 1904–05.
Confederate States of America. *Congress.*

LAC 12769

Journal of the Constitutional commission of Michigan. Printed by order of the Commission, under direction and supervision of Henry S. Clubb, clerk of the Constitutional commission. By authority. Lansing, W. S. George & co., state printers, 1873.
Michigan. *Constitutional Commission,* 1873.

LAC 13505

Journal of the Constitutional convention. Holden at Montpelier, on the second day of January, A. D. 1850, agreeable to the ordinance of the Council of censors: made on the twenty-eighth day of February, 1849, to consider certain amendments proposed to the constitution of the state of Vermont. Published by order of the Convention. Burlington, Sentinel office print., 1850.
Vermont. *Constitutional Convention,* 1850.

LAC 12767

Journal of the Constitutional convention of Connecticut, 1902. Printed by authority. Hartford, The Case, Lockwood & Brainard company, 1902.
Connecticut. *Constitutional Convention,* 1902.

LAC 13454

Journal of the Constitutional convention of South Dakota. July, 1889. Sioux Falls, S. D., Brown & Saenger, printers, 1889.
South Dakota. *Constitutional Convention,* 1889.

LAC 13449

Journal of the Constitutional convention of the people of Georgia, held in the city of Atlanta in the months of July and August, 1877. Atlanta, Ga., J. P. Harrison & co., state printers and publishers, 1877.
Georgia. *Constitutional Convention,* 1877.

LAC 12763

Journal of the Constitutional convention of the state of Alabama, assembled in the city of Montgomery September 6th, 1875. Montgomery, Ala., W. W. Screws, state printer, 1875.
Alabama. *Constitutional Convention,* 1875.

LAC 12768

Journal of the Constitutional convention of the state of Delaware, convened and held at Dover, on Tuesday, the first day of December, A. D. 1896. Georgetown, Del., Sussex journal print, 1897.
Delaware. *Constitutional Convention,* 1896–1897.

LAC 14325

Journal of the Constitutional convention of the state of Michigan. 1850. Printed by order of the Convention, under the supervision of John Swegles, jr., principal secretary of the Convention. Lansing, R. W. Ingals, state printer, 1850.
Michigan. *Constitutional Convention,* 1850.

LAC 14358

Journal of the Constitutional convention of the state of New Hampshire, January, 1889. Manchester, N. H., Printed by John B. Clarke, 1889.
New Hampshire. *Constitutional Convention,* 1889.

LAC 15673

Journal of the Constitutional convention of the state of North-Carolina, at its session 1868. Raleigh, J. W. Holden, convention printer, 1868.
North Carolina. *Constitutional Convention, 1868.*

LAC 13504

Journal of the Constitutional convention of the state of North Carolina, held in 1875. Raleigh, J. Turner, state printer, 1875.
North Carolina. *Constitutional Convention, 1875.*

LAC 13703

Journal of the Constitutional convention of the state of Oregon, held at Salem, commencing August 17, 1857, together with the constitution adopted by the people, November 9, 1857. Salem, W. H. Byars, state printer, 1882.
Oregon. *Constitutional Convention, 1857.*

LAC 13453

Journal of the Constitutional convention of the state of South Carolina. Begun to be holden at Columbia, S. C., on Tuesday, the tenth day of September, anno Domini eighteen hundred and ninety-five, and continued with divers adjournments until Wednesday, the fourth day of December, anno Domini eighteen hundred and ninety-five, when finally adjourned... Columbia, S. C., C. A. Calvo, jr., state printer, 1895.
South Carolina. *Constitutional Convention, 1895.*

LAC 15077

Journal of the Constitutional convention of the state of Virginia, convened in the city of Richmond December 3, 1867, by an order of General Schofield, dated November 2, 1867, in pursuance of the act of Congress of March 23, 1867. Richmond, Printed at the office of the New Nation, 1867, [1868]
Virginia. *Constitutional Convention, 1867–1868.*

LAC 40049

Journal of the Constitutional convention, which convened at Alexandria on the 13th day of February, 1864. Alexandria, D. Turner, printer to the state, 1864.
Virginia. *Constitutional Convention, Alexandria, 1864.*

LAC 40049

Journal of the Convention assembled to frame a constitution for the state of Rhode Island, at Newport, Sept. 12, 1842. Printed by order of the House of representatives, at its January session, 1859. Providence, Knowles, Anthony & co., state printers, 1859.
Rhode Island. *Constitutional Convention, 1842.*

LAC 40049

Journal of the Convention, holden at Montpelier, on the fourth day of January, A. D. 1843, agreeable to the ordinance of the Council of censors, made on the fourteenth day of February, 1842, to consider certain amendments proposed to the constitution of the state of Vermont. Published by order of the Convention. Montpelier, J. T. Marston, 1843.
Vermont. *Constitutional Convention, 1843.*

LAC 13506

Journal of the Convention holden at Montpelier, on the 6th day of January, A. D. 1836, agreeable to the ordinance of the Council of censors, made on the 16th day of January, 1835, together with the amendments of the constitution, as adopted by the Convention, and the whole of the constitution of the state of Vermont, as now in force. Published by order of the Convention. St. Albans [Vt.] J. Spooner, printer, 1836.
Vermont. *Constitutional Convention, 1836.*

LAC 15370

Journal of the Convention of the state of Missouri, assembled at ... Jefferson on Monday the seventeenth day of November, in the year ... one thousand eight hundred and forty-five, pursuant to an act of the General assembly of ... Missouri ... approved February 27, 1843. Printed by order of the Convention. Jefferson, J. Lusk, public printer, 1845.
Missouri. *Constitutional Convention, 1845–1846.*

LAC 21189

Journal of the Convention of the state of North-Carolina... Raleigh, Cannon & Holden, printers to the Convention, 1865–66.
North Carolina. *Constitutional Convention, 1865–1866.*

LAC 21810–12

Journal of the Convention of the state of Pennsylvania, to propose amendments to the constitution, commenced and held at the State capitol in Harrisburg, on the second day of May, 1837. Harrisburg, Printed by Thompson & Clark, 1837–38.
Pennsylvania. *Constitutional Convention, 1837–1838.*

LAC 40049

Journal of the Convention of Vermont, assembled at the state house, at Montpelier, on the 21st day of February, and dissolved on the 23d day of February, 1822. Published by order of Convention. Burlington [Vt.] J. Spooner, printer, 1822.
Vermont. *Constitutional Convention, 1822.*

LAC 40049

Journal of the Convention of Vermont, convened at the State house at Montpelier, June 26, A. D. 1828. Published by order of the Convention. Royalton [Vt.] Printed by W. Spooner [1828?]
Vermont. *Constitutional Convention, 1828.*

LAC 23007–8

Journal of the Convention to amend the constitution of Pennsylvania: convened at Harrisburg, November 12, 1872; adjourned November 27, to meet at Philadelphia, January 7, 1873... Harrisburg, B. Singerly, state printer, 1873.
Pennsylvania. *Constitutional Convention, 1872–1873.*

LAC 13457

Journal of the Convention to form a constitution for the state of Wisconsin, with a sketch of the debates, begun and held at Madison, on the fifteenth day of December, eighteen hundred and forty-seven. By authority of the Convention. Madison, W. T., Tenney, Smith & Holt, printers, 1848.
Wisconsin. *Constitutional Convention, 1847–1848.*

LAC 13502

Journal of the Convention which assembled in Concord, to revise the constitution of New Hampshire, 1791–1792... Ed. by Nathaniel Bouton, D. D. Concord, E. A. Jenks, state printer, 1876.
New Hampshire. *Constitutional Convention, 1791–1792.*

LAC 23016

The journal of the debates in the convention which framed the Constitution of the United States, May–September, 1787, as recorded by James Madison; ed. by Gaillard Hunt. New York and London, G. P. Putnam's sons, 1908.
U.S. *Constitutional Convention, 1787.*

LAC 40038
A journal of the expedition to Quebec, in the year 1775, under the command of Colonel Benedict Arnold. New York, 1857.
Melvin, James.

LAC 13962
The journal of the Joint committee of fifteen on reconstruction, 39th Congress, 1865–1867. New York, Columbia university; [etc., etc.] 1914.
Kendrick, Benjamin Burks, 1884–

LAC 20272–74
Journal of the Legislative council of the colony of New-York. Began the 9th day of April, 1691; and ended the [3d of April, 1775] Published by order of the Senate of the state of New York. Albany, Weed, Parsons & company, printers, 1861.
New York (Colony) Council.

LAC 21300
Journal of the life, labours, and travels of Thomas Shillitoe, in the service of the Gospel of Jesus Christ. London, Harvey and Darton, 1839.
Shillitoe, Thomas, 1754–1836.

LAC 13362
A journal of the life of Thomas Story, containing an account of his remarkable convincement of and embracing the principles of truth as held by the people called Quakers and also of his travels and labours in the service of the gospel, with many other occurrences and observations. Newcastle upon Tyne, Printed by I. Thompson, 1747.
Story, Thomas, 1662–1742.

LAC 16439
A journal of the life, travels, and religious labours, of William Savery, late of Philadelphia, a minister of the gospel of Christ, in the Society of Friends. Compiled from his original memoranda, by Jonathan Evans. London, C. Gilpin; [etc., etc.] 1844.
Savery, William, 1750–1804.

LAC 12772
Journal of the Missouri state convention, held at the city of St. Louis January 6–April 10, 1865. St. Louis, Missouri Democrat, print. 1865.
Missouri. Constitutional Convention, 1865.

LAC 40072
A journal of the overland route to California! And the gold mines. Lansingburgh, N. Y., A. Kirkpatrick, 1851.
Aldrich, Lorenzo D   1818 or 19–1851.

LAC 11513
The journall of the procedure of the governor and Councill of the province of East New Jersey from and after the first day of December anno Dmni–1682. Pub. by authority of the Legislature. Jersey City, Printed by J. H. Lyon, 1872.
New Jersey (Colony) Council.

LAC 15368
Journal of the proceedings and debates in the Constitutional convention of the state of Mississippi, August, 1865. By order of the Convention. Jackson, Miss., E. M. Yerger, state printer, 1865.
Mississippi. Constitutional Convention, 1865.

LAC 15369
Journal of the proceedings in the Constitutional convention of the state of Mississippi. 1868. Printed by order of the Convention. Jackson, E. Stafford, 1871.
Mississippi. Constitutional Convention, 1868.

LAC 10602
Journal of the proceedings of a convention of literary and scientific gentlemen, held in the Common council chamber of the city of New York, October, 1830. New York, J. Leavitt and G. & C. & H. Carvill, 1831.

LAC 40049
Journal of the proceedings of Convention of the state of Alabama, held in the city of Montgomery, on Tuesday, September 12, 1865. Benjamin Fitzpatrick, president of Convention... Montgomery, Gibson & Whitfield, state printers, 1865.
Alabama. Constitutional Convention, 1865.

LAC 40049
Journal of the proceedings of the Constitutional convention, assembled at Montpelier, on the first Wednesday of January, 1857. Burlington, G. J. Stacy, printer, 1856, [1857]
Vermont. Constitutional Convention, 1857.

LAC 15616
Journal of the proceedings of the Constitutional convention of the people of Georgia, held in the city of Atlanta in the months of December, 1867, and January, February, and March, 1868. And ordinances and resolutions adopted. Published by order of the Convention. Augusta, Ga., E. H. Pughe, printer, 1868.
Georgia. Constitutional Convention, 1867–1868.

LAC 40049
Journal of the proceedings of the Constitutional convention of the people of Vermont, begun and held at the state house in Montpelier, on the 8th of June, 1870. Printed by authority. Burlington, Free press print, 1870.
Vermont. Constitutional Convention, 1870.

LAC 13447
Journal of the proceedings of the Constitutional convention of the state of Florida, which convened at the Capitol, at Tallahassee, on Tuesday, June 9, 1885 ... Tallahassee, Fla., N. M. Bowen, state printer, 1885.
Florida. Constitutional Convention, 1885.

LAC 12771
Journal of the proceedings of the Constitutional convention, of the state of Mississippi, begun at the city of Jackson on August 12, 1890, and concluded November 1, 1890. Printed by authority. Jackson, Miss., E. L. Martin, printer to the Convention, 1890.
Mississippi. Constitutional Convention, 1890.

LAC 12766
Journal of the proceedings of the convention of delegates, convened at Hartford, August 26, 1818, for the purpose of forming a constitution of civil government for the people of the state of Connecticut ... Hartford, Conn., Printed by order of the comptroller [by the Case, Lockwood & Brainard co.] 1901.
Connecticut. Constitutional Convention, 1818.

LAC 13456

Journal of the proceedings of the convention of delegates elected by the people of Tennessee, to amend, revise, or form and make a new constitution, for the state. Assembled in the city of Nashville, January 10, 1870. Nashville, Jones, Purvis & co., printers to the state, 1870. Tennessee. *Constitutional Convention, 1870.*

LAC 13448

Journal of the proceedings of the Convention of the people of Georgia, held in Milledgeville in October and November, 1865; together with the ordinances and resolutions adopted. Pub. by order of the convention. Atlanta, Ga., 1910. Georgia. *Convention, 1865.*

LAC 13503

Journal of the proceedings of the Convention to form a constitution for the government of the state of New Jersey; begun at Trenton on the fourteenth day of May, A. D. 1844, and continued to the twenty-ninth day of June, A. D. 1844. Trenton, Printed by F. S. Mills, 1844. New Jersey. *Constitutional Convention, 1884.*

LAC 15076

Journal of the proceedings of the Convention to form a constitution for the state of Michigan; begun and held at the Capitol, in the city of Detroit, on Monday, the 11th day of May, A.D. 1835. Printed by order of the Convention. Detroit, Printed by S. M'Knight, 1835. Michigan. *Constitutional Convention, 1835.*

LAC 16646

Journal of the proceedings of the general council of the republic of Texas, held at San Felipe de Austin, November 14th, 1835[-March 11th, 1836] Houston, 1839. Texas *(Provisional Government)*

LAC 23096-97

Journal of the Reconstruction convention, which met at Austin, Texas... Austin, Tex., Tracy, Siemering & co., printers, 1870. Texas. *Constitutional Convention, 1868-1869.*

LAC 21365-66

The journal of the Rev. Francis Asbury, bishop of the Methodist Episcopal church, from August 7, 1771, to December 7, 1815... New York, N. Bangs and T. Mason, 1821. Asbury, Francis, 1745-1816.

LAC 15373

Journal of the Texas state convention, assembled at Austin, Feb. 7, 1866. Adjourned April 2, 1866. Austin, Printed at the Southern intelligencer office, 1866. Texas. *Constitutional Convention, 1866.*

LAC 15388

Journal of the Texian expedition against Mier; subsequent imprisonment of the author; his sufferings, and final escape from the castle of Perote. With reflections upon the present political and probable future relations of Texas, Mexico, and the United States. By Gen. Thomas J. Green. Illustrated by drawings taken from life by Charles M'Laughlin, a fellow-prisoner. New-York, Harper & brothers, 1845. Green, Thomas Jefferson, 1801-1863.

LAC 12290

A journal of the voyages and travels of a corps of discovery, under the command of Capt. Lewis and Capt. Clarke of the army of the United States, from the mouth of the river Missouri through the interior parts of North America to the Pacific Ocean, during the years 1804, 1805 & 1806. Containing an authentic relation of the most interesting transactions during the expedition,—a description of the country,—and an account of its inhabitants, soil, climate, curiosities and vegetable and animal productions. By Patrick Gass, one of the persons employed in the expedition. With geographical and explanatory notes by the publisher. Pittsburgh, Printed by Zadok Cramer, for David M'Keehan, publisher and proprietor. 1807. Gass, Patrick, 1771-1870.

LAC 40007

A journal of travels from New-Hampshire to Caratuck, on the continent of North America. London, Printed by J. Downing for B. Aylmer, 1706. Keith, George, 1639?-1716?

LAC 13302

Journal of travels from St. Josephs to Oregon, with observations of that country, together with some description of California, its agricultural interests, and a full description of its gold mines. Galesburg [Ill.] Gazetteer and Intelligencer Prints, 1850. Root, Riley.

LAC 22521

A journal of travels in England, Holland, and Scotland, and of two passages over the Atlantic, in the years 1805 and 1806... New York, Printed by D. & G. Bruce, for E. Sargeant, 1810. Silliman, Benjamin, 1779-1864.

LAC 13279

A journal of travels into the Arkansa territory, during the year 1819. With occasional observations on the manners of the aborigines. Illustrated by a map and other engravings. Philadelphia, T. H. Palmer, 1821. Nuttall, Thomas, 1786-1859.

LAC 14123

A journal of voyages and travels in the interiour of North America, between the 47th and 58th degrees of north latitude, extending from Montreal nearly to the Pacific ocean ... including an account of the principal occurrences, during a residence of nineteen years, in different parts of the country. To which are added, a concise description of the country, its inhabitants ... and considerable specimens of the two languages, most extensively spoken; together with an account of the principal animals, to be found in the forests and prairies of this extensive region... Andover: Printed by Flagg and Gould, 1820. Harmon, Daniel Williams, 1778-1845.

LAC 15685

The journal of William Maclay, United States senator from Pennsylvania, 1789-1791; introduction by Charles A. Beard. New York, A. & C. Boni, 1927. Maclay, William, 1734-1804.

LAC 13686

Journal or historical recollections of American events during the revolutionary war; by Elias Boudinot. Copied from his own original manuscript. Philadelphia, F. Bourquin, 1894. Boudinot, Elias, 1740-1821.

LAC 16410
Journal up the straits, October 11, 1856–May 5, 1857;
edited with an introduction by Raymond Weaver. New York, The Colophon, 1935.
Melville, Herman, 1819–1891.

LAC 10197
Journalism in the United States, from 1690 to 1872.
New York, Harper & brothers, 1873.
Hudson, Frederic, 1819–1875.

LAC 16971
Journals of Charles Beatty, 1762–1769. Edited with an introd. by Guy Soulliard Klett. University Park, Pennsylvania State University Press, 1962 [i.e. 1963]
Beatty, Charles, 1715?–1772.

LAC 11727
The journals of each Provincial congress of Massachusetts in 1774 and 1775, and of the Committee of safety, with an appendix, containing the proceedings of the county conventions–narratives of the events of the nineteenth of April, 1775–papers relating to Ticonderoga and Crown Point, and other documents, illustrative of the early history of the American revolution. Pub. agreeably to a resolve passed March 10, 1837, under the supervision of William Lincoln. Boston, Dutton and Wentworth, printers to the state, 1838.
Massachusetts (Colony) Provincial congress.

LAC 23683–85
The journals of Henry Melchior Muhlenberg, translated by Theodore G. Tappert and John W. Doberstein. Philadelphia, The Evangelical Lutheran ministerium of Pennsylvania and adjacent states and the Muhlenberg press, 1942–1958.
Muhlenberg, Henry Melchior, 1711–1787.

LAC 21331
The journals of Hugh Gaine, printer; ed. by Paul Leicester Ford. New York, Dodd, Mead & company, 1902.
Gaine, Hugh, 1726?–1807.

LAC 11151
The journals of Major Samuel Shaw, the first American consul at Canton. With a life of the author, by Josiah Quincy. Boston, W. Crosby and H. P. Nichols, 1847.
Shaw, Samuel, 1754–1794.

LAC 40114
Journals of the Commons house of assembly of South Carolina for the four sessions of 1693. Ed. by A. S. Salley, jr., secretary of the Historical commission of South Carolina. Columbia, S. C., Printed by the State company, 1907.
South Carolina (Colony) Assembly.

LAC 40114
Journals of the Commons house of assembly of South Carolina for the two sessions of 1697. Ed. by A. S. Salley, jr., secretary of the Historical commission of South Carolina. Columbia, S. C., Printed by the State company, 1913.
South Carolina (Colony) Assembly.

LAC 40114
Journals of the Commons house of assembly of South Carolina for the two sessions of 1698. Ed. by A. S. Salley, jr., secretary of the Historical commission of South Carolina. Columbia, S. C., Printed for the Historical commission by the State company, 1914.
South Carolina (Colony) Assembly.

LAC 16611
Journals of the Commons house of assembly of South Carolina for 1702. Edited by A. S. Salley, secretary of the Historical commission of South Carolina. Columbia, S. C., Printed for the Historical commission of South Carolina, 1932.
South Carolina (Colony) Assembly.

LAC 22383–84
Journals of the Council of colonial Virginia.
Legislative journals of the Council of colonial Virginia... ed. by H. R. McIlwaine. Richmond, Va. [The Colonial press, Everett Waddey co.] 1918–19.
Virginia (Colony) Council.

LAC 16156
Journals of the House of burgesses of Virginia, 1619 to 1658–59. Ed. by H. R. McIlwaine. Richmond, Va. [The Colonial press, E. Waddey co.] 1915.
Virginia (Colony) General Assembly. House of Burgesses.

LAC 16157
Journals of the House of burgesses of Virginia, 1659–60 to 1693. Ed. by H. R. McIlwaine. Richmond, Va. [The Colonial press, E. Waddey co.] 1914.
Virginia (Colony) General Assembly. House of Burgesses.

LAC 16158
Journals of the House of burgesses of Virginia, 1695–1696, 1696–1697, 1698, 1699, 1700–1702. Ed. by H. R. McIlwaine. Richmond, Va. [The Colonial press, E. Wadney co.] 1913.
Virginia (Colony) General Assembly. House of Burgesses.

LAC 16159
Journals of the House of burgesses of Virginia, 1702–3 to 1705, 1705 to 1706, 1710 to 1712. Ed. by H. R. McIlwaine. Richmond, Va. [The Colonial press, E. Waddey co.] 1912.
Virginia (Colony) General Assembly. House of Burgesses.

LAC 16160
Journals of the House of burgesses of Virginia, 1727–1734, 1736–1740. Ed. by H. R. McIlwaine. Richmond, Va. [The Colonial press, E. Waddey co.] 1910.
Virginia (Colony) General Assembly. House of Burgesses.

LAC 16161
Journals of the House of burgesses of Virginia, 1742–1747, 1748–1749. Ed. by H. R. McIlwaine. Richmond, Va. [The Colonial press, E. Waddey co.] 1909.
Virginia (Colony) General Assembly. House of Burgesses.

LAC 16162
Journals of the House of burgesses of Virginia, 1752–1755, 1756–1758. Ed. by H. R. McIlwaine. Richmond, Va. [The Colonial press, E. Waddey co.] 1909.
Virginia (Colony) General Assembly. House of Burgesses.

LAC 16163
Journals of the House of burgesses of Virginia, 1758–1761; ed. by H. R. McIlwaine. Richmond, Va. [The Colonial press, E. Waddey co.] 1908.
Virginia *(Colony) General Assembly. House of Burgesses.*

LAC 16164
Journals of the House of burgesses of Virginia, 1761–1765; edited by John Pendleton Kennedy. Richmond, Va. [The Colonial press, E. Waddey co.] 1907.
Virginia *(Colony) General Assembly. House of Burgesses.*

LAC 16165
Journals of the House of burgesses of Virginia, 1766–1769; edited by John Pendleton Kennedy. Richmond, Va. [The Colonial press, E. Waddey co.] 1906.
Virginia *(Colony) General Assembly. House of Burgesses.*

LAC 16166
Journals of the House of burgesses of Virginia, 1770–1772; ed. by John Pendleton Kennedy. Richmond, Va. [The Colonial press, E. Waddey co.] 1906.
Virginia *(Colony) General Assembly. House of Burgesses.*

LAC 16040
Journals of the House of burgesses of Virginia 1773–1776 including the records of the Committee of correspondence. Edited by John Pendleton Kennedy. Richmond, Va. [E. Waddey co.] 1905.
Virginia *(Colony) General Assembly. House of Burgesses.*

LAC 15347
Journals of the Rev. Thomas Smith, and the Rev. Samuel Deane, pastors of the First church in Portland: with notes and biographical notices: and a Summary history of Portland. By Wm. Willis. [2d ed.] Portland [Me.] J. S. Bailey, 1849.
Smith, Thomas, 1702–1795.

LAC 12294
A journey from the Prince of Wales's fort in Hudson's Bay, to the Northern Ocean. Undertaken by order of the Hudson's Bay company, for the discovery of copper mines, a northwest passage, &c., in the years 1769, 1770, 1771, & 1772. London, A. Strahan and T. Cadell, 1795.
Hearne, Samuel, 1745–1792.

LAC 20674
A journey in North America, containing a survey of the countries watered by the Mississippi, Ohio, Missouri, and other affluing rivers; with exact observations on the course and soundings of these rivers; and on the towns, villages, hamlets and farms of that part of the New-world; followed by philosophical, political, military and commercial remarks and by a projected line of frontiers and general limits, illustrated by 36 maps, plans, views and divers cuts, by Victor Collot. With an introduction and a critical index, also a translation of the appendix from the French edition, by J. Christian Bay. Firenze, O. Lange, 1924.
Collot, Georges Henri Victor, 1752?–1805.

LAC 15565
A journey in North America, described in familiar letters to Amelia Opie. Norwich [Eng.] Printed for private circulation, by J. Fletcher, 1841.
Gurney, Joseph John, 1788–1847.

LAC 12369
A journey in the back country. New York, Mason brothers, 1861, [c1860]
Olmsted, Frederick Law, 1822–1903.

LAC 12370
A journey in the seaboard slave states, with remarks on their economy. New York, Dix & Edwards; London, S. Low, son & co., 1856.
Olmsted, Frederick Law, 1822–1903.

LAC 14091
The journey of Alvar Nunez Cabeza de Vaca; translated from his own narrative by Fanny Bandelier. Chicago, Rio Grande Press [1964]
Nunez Cabeza de Vaca, Alvar, *16th cent.*

LAC 13281
A journey through Texas; or, A saddle-trip on the southwestern frontier; with a statistical appendix. New York, Dix, Edwards & co.; London, S. Low, son & co.; [etc., etc.] 1857.
Olmsted, Frederick Law, 1822–1903.

LAC 16508
A journey to central Africa; or, Life and landscapes from Egypt to the Negro kingdoms of the White Nile. [1852] 10th ed. New York, G. P. Putnam & co., 1856.
Taylor, Bayard, 1825–1878.

LAC 23243
The journeys of Rene Robert Cavelier, sieur de La Salle, as related by his faithful lieutenant, Henri de Tonty; his missionary colleagues, Fathers Zenobius Membre, Louis Hennepin, and Anastasius Douay; his early biographer, Father Christian Le Clercq; his trusted subordinate, Henri Joutel; and his brother, Jean Cavelier: together with memoirs, commissions, etc. Ed. with an introduction by Isaac Joslin Cox. New York, A. S. Barnes, 1905.
Cox, Isaac Joslin, 1873–   *ed.*

LAC 13238
Joutel's journal of La Salle's last voyage; a reprint (page for page and line for line) of the first English translation, London, 1714; with the map of the original French edition Paris, 1713, in facsimile; and notes by Melville B. Anderson. Chicago, The Caxton club, 1896.
Joutel, Henri, 1640?–1735.

LAC 23472
Joyfull newes out of the newe founde worlde, written in Spanish by Nicholas Monardes and Englished by John Frampton. With an introduction by Stephen Gaselee. London, Constable and co., ltd.; New York, A. A. Knopf, 1925.
Monardes, Nicolas, 1512 *(ca.)*–1588.

LAC 40005
The joyous miracle. New York, Doubleday, Page & company, 1906.
Norris, Frank, 1870–1902.

LAC 21296
Juan Diaz de Solis; estudio historico. Santiago de Chile, Impr. en casa del autor, 1897.
Medina, Jose Toribio, 1852–1930.

LAC 11372
The jubilee of the Constitution. A discourse delivered at the request of the New York historical society, in the city of New York, on Tuesday, the 30th of April, 1839; being the fiftieth anniversary of the inauguration of George Washington as president of the United States, on Thursday, the 30th of April, 1789... New York, S. Colman, 1839.
Adams, John Quincy, *pres. U.S.*, 1767–1848.

LAC 13707
Judah P. Benjamin. Philadelphia, G. W. Jacobs & company [1907]
Butler, Pierce, 1873–

LAC 20967–70
Judicial cases concerning American slavery and the Negro, edited by Helen Tunnicliff Catterall (Mrs. Ralph C. H. Catterall)... Washington, D. C., Carnegie institution of Washington, 1926–37.
Catterall, Helen Honor, 1870–1933, *ed.*

LAC 14524
Judicial review.
The doctrine of judicial review, its legal and historical basis, and other essays. Gloucester, Mass., Peter Smith, 1963.
Corwin, Edward Samuel, 1878–1963.

LAC 15275
The judicial veto. Boston and New York, Houghton Mifflin company, 1914.
Davis, Horace Andrew, 1870–

LAC 11837
Judith, Esther, and other poems. By a lover of the fine arts. Boston, Cummings & Hilliard, 1820.
Brooks, Maria, 1795–1845.

LAC 11204
Julia Ward Howe and the woman suffrage movement; a selection from her speeches and essays, with introduction and notes by her daughter, Florence Howe Hall. Boston, D. Estes & company [c1913]
Howe, Julia, 1819–1910.

LAC 16021
Julian M. Sturtevant. An autobiography. Ed. by J. M. Sturtevant, jr. New York, Chicago [etc.] F. H. Revell company [c1896]
Sturtevant, Julian Monson, 1805–1886.

LAC 12071
The jungle. New York, Doubleday, Page & company, 1906.
Sinclair, Upton Beall, 1878–1968.

LAC 12204
A juvenile guide; or, Manual of good manners. Consisting of counsels, instructions & rules of deportment, for the young. By lovers of youth. In two parts. Canterbury, N. H., Printed in the United society, 1844.

LAC 12030
Kaloolah, or, Journeyings to the Djebel Kumri: an autobiography of Jonathan Romer. Edited by W. S. Mayo, M.D. New-York, G. P. Putnam; London, D. Bogue, 1849.
Mayo, William Starbuck, 1812–1895.

LAC 15194
The Kansas & Nebraska hand-book. For 1857–8. With a new and accurate map. Boston, J. P. Jewett and company; Cleveland, O., H. P. B. Jewett, 1857.
Parker, Nathan Howe.

LAC 14718
Kansas Constitutional convention. A reprint of the proceedings and debates of the convention which framed the constitution of Kansas at Wyandotte in July, 1859. Also, the constitution annotated to date, historical sketches, etc. By authority of the state Legislature. Topeka, Printed by Kansas state printing plant, Imri Zumwalt, state printer, 1920.
Kansas. *(Ter.) Constitutional Convention*, 1859.

LAC 13299
Kansas; its interior and exterior life. Including a full view of its settlement, political history, social life, climate, soil, productions, scenery, etc. Boston, Crosby, Nichols and company; Cincinnati, G. S. Blanchard; [etc., etc.] 1856.
Robinson, Sara Tappan Doolittle, 1827–1911.

LAC 15338
Kansas miscellanies. 2d ed. Topeka, Kansas publishing house, 1889.
Prentis, Noble Lovely, 1839–1900.

LAC 16966
Katharine Walton; or, The rebel of Dorchester. New and rev. ed. New York, W. J. Widdleton [1854]
Simms, William Gilmore, 1806–1870.

LAC 40074
The Kearney agitation in California. New York, D. Appleton, 1880.
George, Henry, 1839–1897.

LAC 12924
Kent's commentary on international law, revised with notes and cases brought down to the present time. Ed. by J. T. Abdy. Cambridge, Deighton, Bell, and co.; [etc., etc.] 1866.
Kent, James, 1763–1847.

LAC 12384
Kentucky, a pioneer commonwealth. Boston, Houghton, Mifflin and company, 1885.
Shaler, Nathaniel Southgate, 1841–1906.

LAC 11815
A Kentucky cardinal; a story. Illustrated. New York, Macmillan co., 1900.
Allen, James Lane, 1849–1925.

LAC 13497
The Kentucky resolutions of 1798, an historical study. 2d ed. New York and London, G. P. Putnam's sons, 1894.
Warfield, Ethelbert Dudley, 1861–1936.

LAC 11059
The Kentucky revival; or, A short history of the late extraordinary outpouring of the spirit of God in the western states of America, agreeably to Scripture promises and prophecies concerning the latter day: with a brief account of the entrance and progress of what the world

call Shakerism among the subjects of the late revival in Ohio and Kentucky. Presented to the true Zion-traveler as a memorial of the wilderness journey. New York, Reprinted by E. O. Jenkins, 1846.
McNemar, Richard, 1770–1839.

LAC 40086

The key of libberty, shewing the causes why a free government has always failed, and a remidy against it; written in the year 1798, by William Manning, with notes and a foreword by Samuel Eliot Morison. Billerica, Mass., The Manning association, 1922.
Manning, William, 1747–1814.

LAC 13810

The key to culture; customs, manners and niceties of society. Chicago, The Geographical publishing co. [c1921]
Gilbert, Paul Thomas, 1876–

LAC 40056

A key to the orders in council [respecting trade with French ports] London, Printed for J. Murray, 1812.
Croker, John Wilson, 1780–1857.

LAC 10760

A key to Uncle Tom's cabin; presenting the original facts and documents upon which the story is founded. Together with corroborative statements verifying the truth of the work. Boston, J. P. Jewett & co.; Cleveland, O., Jewett, Proctor & Worthington, 1854, [c1853]
Stowe, Harriet Elizabeth, 1811–1896.

LAC 14019

The keyes of the kingdom of heaven, and power thereof, according to the word of God ... tending to reconcile some present differences about discipline. Boston, Reprinted by Tappan and Dennet, 1843.
Cotton, John, 1584–1652.

LAC 16519

The kidnapped and the ransomed. Being the personal recollections of Peter Still and his wife "Vina," after forty years of slavery. By Mrs. Kate E. R. Pickard. With an introduction, by Rev. Samuel J. May; and an appendix, by William H. Furness, D. D. Syracuse, W. T. Hamilton; New York [etc.] Miller, Orton and Mulligan, 1856.
Pickard, Kate E   R.

LAC 13005

The kindergarten. A manual for the introduction of Froebel's system of primary education into public schools; and for the use of mothers and private teachers. New York, E. Steiger, 1871.
Douai, Adolf, 1819–1888.

LAC 14319

Kindergarten chats on architecture, education and democracy, by Louis H. Sullivan; edited and introduced by Claude F. Bragdon. 1st ed. [Lawrence? Kan.] Scarab fraternity press, 1934.
Sullivan, Louis Henry, 1856–1924.

LAC 40014

Kindergarten education. [Albany, N. Y., J. B. Lyon company, 1900]
Blow, Susan Elizabeth, 1843–1916.

LAC 11770

King Cotton; a historical and statistical review 1790 to 1908. New York, J. L. Watkins & sons [c1908]
Watkins, James Lawrence, 1850–

LAC 11020

The kingdom of Christ on earth; twelve lectures delivered before the students of the theological seminary, Andover. Andover, Warren F. Draper, 1874.
Harris, Samuel, 1814–1899.

LAC 11096

King's Handbook of notable Episcopal churches in the United States, by the Rev. George Wolfe Shinn. One hundred illustrations. Boston, Mass., Moses King corporation, 1889.
Shinn, George Wolfe, 1839–1910.

LAC 14690

King's mountain and its heroes: history of the battle of King's mountain, October 7th, 1780, and the events which led to it. Cincinnati, P. G. Thomson, 1881.
Draper, Lyman Copeland, 1815–1891.

LAC 40149

Kingston and the loyalists of the "Spring fleet" of A. D. 1783. With reminiscenses [!] of early days in Connecticut: a narrative. By Walter Bates. To which is appended a diary written by Sarah Frost on her voyage to St. John, N. B., with the loyalists of 1783. Ed. with notes by W. O. Raymond. Saint John, N. B., Barnes and company, 1889.
Bates, Walter, 1760–1842.

LAC 21946–50

LAC 21134

Kino's historical memoir of Pimeria Alta; a contemporary account of the beginnings of California, Sonora, and Arizona, by Father Eusebio Francisco Kino, S. J., pioneer missionary explorer, cartographer, and ranchman, 1683–1711; pub. for the first time from the original manuscript in the archives of Mexico; tr. into English, ed. and annotated, by Herbert Eugene Bolton. Cleveland, The Arthur H. Clark company, 1919.
Kino, Eusebio Francisco, 1644–1711.

LAC 31304–18

The Knickerbocker; or, New-York monthly magazine. v. 1–22; July 1833–Dec. 1843. New York.

LAC 12010

The Knickerbocker gallery: a testimonial to the editor of the Knickerbocker magazine [i.e. Lewis Gaylord Clark] from its contributors. With forty-eight portraits on steel ... engraved expressly for this work. New-York, S. Hueston, 1855.

LAC 12118

Knickerbocker writers.
Bryant, and his friends: some reminiscences of the Knickerbocker writers... New York, Fords, Howard & Hulbert, 1886, [c1885]
Wilson, James Grant, 1832–1914.

LAC 13380

The Knights of St. Crispin, 1867–1874; a study in the industrial causes of trade unionism. Madison, Wis., 1910.
Lescohier, Don Divance, 1883–

LAC 12484

The Know nothing? Boston, J. P. Jewett & company; [etc., etc.] New York, Sheldon, Lamport, & Blakeman, 1855.

LAC 16444

The Know-Nothing party. A sketch. Washington, The New century press, 1905.
Desmond, Humphrey Joseph, 1858–1932.

LAC 16271

Kokoro: hints and echoes of Japanese inner life. Boston and New York, Houghton, Mifflin and company [c1896]
Hearn, Lafcadio, 1850–1904.

LAC 16584

Kotto ... being Japanese curios, with sundry cobwebs, collected by Lafcadio Hearn. With illustrations by Genjiro Yeto. New York, The Macmillan company; London, Macmillan & co., ltd., 1903, [c1902]
Hearn, Lafcadio, 1850–1904.

LAC 12353

Ku Klux klan, its origin, growth and disbandment, by J. C. Lester and D. L. Wilson; with appendices containing the prescripts of the Ku Klux klan, specimen orders and warnings; with introduction and notes by Walter L. Fleming. New York and Washington, The Neale publishing company, 1905.
Lester, John C.

LAC 16540

Kwaidan: stories and studies of strange things. With an introduction by Oscar Lewis; illustrated by Yasumasa Fujita. New York, Dover [1968]
Hearn, Lafcadio, 1850–1904.

LAC 15417

Labor and administration. New York, The Macmillan company, 1913.
Commons, John Rogers, 1862–1945.

LAC 21946–50

Labor and capital.
Report of the Committee of the Senate upon the relations between labor and capital, and testimony taken by the committee. In five volumes... Washington, Govt. print. off., 1885.
U.S. *Congress. Senate. Committee on Education and Labor.*

LAC 13392

Labor and capital; a discussion of the relations of employer and employed; ed., with an introduction by John P. Peters, D. D. New York and London, G. P. Putnam's sons, 1902.
Peters, John Punnett, 1852–1921, *ed.*

LAC 10705

Labor and capital allies, not enemies. New York, Harper & brothers, 1879.
Atkinson, Edward, 1827–1905.

LAC 14100

Labor and neighbor; an appeal to first principles. Chicago, L. F. Post, 1908.
Crosby, Ernest Howard, 1856–1907.

LAC 15796

Labor and the railroads. Boston and New York, Houghton Mifflin company, 1909.
Fagan, James Octavius, 1859–

LAC 13796

Labor and wages... Philadelphia, American academy of political and social science, 1909.
American Academy of Political and Social Science, *Philadelphia.*

LAC 40086

Labor and wages, at home and abroad: in a series of newspaper articles. Lowell, D. Bixby & co., 1849.
Aiken, John.

LAC 15456

The labor argument in the American protective tariff discussion... Madison, Wis., 1908.
Mangold, George Benjamin, 1876–

LAC 14276

A labor catechism of political economy. A study for the people. Comprising the principal arguments for and against the prominent declarations of the industrial party, requiring that the state assume control of industries. New York [Trow printing co.] 1878.
Ward, Cyrenus Osborne.

LAC 40021

Labor differences and their settlement. A plea for arbitration and conciliation. New York, The Society for political education, 1886.
Weeks, Joseph Dame, 1840–1896.

LAC 15545

The labor history of the Cripple Creek district; a study in industrial evolution. Madison, Wis., 1908.
Rastall, Benjamin McKie.

LAC 14164

Labor in Europe and America; a special report on the rates of wages, the cost of subsistence, and the condition of the working classes in Great Britain, Germany, France, Belgium and other countries of Europe, also in the United States and British America, by Edward Young, chief of the United States Bureau of Statistics. Washington, Govt. Print. Off., 1875.
Young, Edward, 1814–1909.

LAC 13369

Labor in Europe and America, by Samuel Gompers, president of the American federation of labor; personal observations from an American viewpoint of life and conditions of working men in Great Britain, France, Holland, Germany, Italy, etc. New York and London, Harper & brothers, 1910.
Gompers, Samuel, 1850–1924.

LAC 16535

Labor in politics. Chicago, The Socialist party [c1915]
Hunter, Robert, 1874–1942.

LAC 40086

Labor: its history and its prospects. An address delivered before the Young men's mercantile library association of Cincinnati on Tuesday, February 1, 1848. Cincinnati, Herald of truth print, 1848.
Owen, Robert Dale, 1801–1877.

LAC 40086

Labor, its relations in Europe and the United States compared. Boston, Eastburn's press, 1844.
Appleton, Nathan, 1779–1861.

LAC 13378

Labor: its rights and wrongs. Statements and comments by the leading men of our nation on the labor question of to-day. With platforms of the various labor organizations... Washington, D. C., The Labor publishing company, 1886.

LAC 14042

Labor laws and their enforcement, with special reference to Massachusetts, by Charles E. Persons, Mabel Parton, Mabelle Moses and three "fellows"; ed. by Susan M. Kingsbury, PH. D. On the fellowship foundation of the Massachusetts state federation of women's clubs, 1905–1909. New York [etc.] Longmans, Green, and co., 1911.
Kingsbury, Susan Myra, 1870–1949, *ed.*

LAC 13665–66

Labor laws of the United States, with decisions of courts relating thereto. Prepared under the direction of Carroll D. Wright, commissioner of labor. Washington, Govt. print. off., 1904.
U. S. *Bureau of Labor.*

LAC 13428–29

Labor laws of the United States with decisions of courts relating thereto... May, 1925. Washington, Govt. print. off., 1925.
U. S. *Bureau of Labor Statistics.*

LAC 11270

The labor movement in America. New York, T. Y. Crowell & co. [c1886]
Ely, Richard Theodore, 1854–1943.

LAC 13874

The labor movement. The problem of to-day. Comprising a history of capital and labor, and its present status. Associate authors: Dr. Edmund J. James, Terence V. Powderly, Hon. John J. O'Neill [and others] New York, The M. W. Hazen co., 1888.
McNeill, George Edwin, 1837–1906, *ed.*

LAC 40112

The labor party: a speech delivered before the Labor reform league of Worcester, Mass., explaining the ideas and objects of the labor movement–what workingmen want–whom it concerns–and how to get it. 11th thousand. New York, Journeymen printers' co-operative association, 1868.
Heywood, Ezra Hervey, 1829–1893.

LAC 14333

The labor question. Boston, New York [etc.] The Pilgrim press [c1911]
Gladden, Washington, 1836–1918.

LAC 40086

Labor the only true source of wealth; or, The rottenness of the paper money banking system exposed, its sandy foundations shaken, its crumbling pillars overthrown. An oration delivered at the Queen-street theatre, in the city of Charleston, S. C., July, 4th, 1837. [n.p., n.d.]
Fisk, Theophilus.

LAC 40013

Labor through the century, 1833–1933. An illustrated account as prepared by the Bureau of labor statistics of the Department of labor for the Century of progress exposition, Chicago, 1933, 1934. Washington, U.S. Govt. print. off., 1934.
U.S. *Bureau of Labor Statistics.*

LAC 40136

Labor troubles in Idaho. Washington [Govt. print off.] 1899.
U.S. *Congress. Senate. Committee on Military Affairs.*

LAC 40006

Labor-union socialism and socialist labor-unionism. Chicago, C. H. Kerr, 1912.
Walling, William English, 1877–1936.

LAC 13398

The labor-value fallacy. Published by the Patriots' league, Chicago. 3d ed. Chicago, Jeffery printing co., 1887.
Scudder, Moses Lewis, 1848–1917.

LAC 14103

The laborer: a remedy for his wrongs; or, A disquisition on the usages of society. Cincinnati, W. Dealtry, compositor, 1869.
Dealtry, William.

LAC 14169

The laborer and the capitalist. New York, Equitable publishing co. [c1896]
Willey, Freeman Otis.

LAC 15519

Laboring and dependent classes in colonial America, 1607–1783; studies of the economic, educational, and social significance of slaves, servants, apprentices, and poor folk. Chicago, Ill., The University of Chicago press [c1931]
Jernegan, Marcus Wilson, 1872–1949.

LAC 11980

The lady of the Aroostook. Boston, Houghton, Osgood and company, 1879.
Howells, William Dean, 1837–1920.

LAC 12967

The lady, or the tiger? and other stories. New York, C. Scribner's sons, 1909, [c1884]
Stockton, Frank Richard, 1834–1902.

LAC 13143

A lady's life in the Rocky Mountains, by Isabella L. Bird. With illustrations. 7th ed. London, J. Murray, 1910.
Bishop, Isabella Lucy, 1831–1904.

LAC 20685
Lafayette in America in 1824 and 1825; or, Journal of a voyage to the United States: by A. Levasseur. Tr. by J. D. Godman, M. D. Philadelphia, Carey and Lea, 1829.
Levasseur, Auguste.

LAC 12002
Lafcadio Hearn, by Nina H. Kennard, containing some letters from Lafcadio Hearn to his half-sister, Mrs. Atkinson. New York, D. Appleton and company, 1912.
Kennard, Nina H.

LAC 15461
La Follette's autobiography; a personal narrative of political experiences. Madison, Wis., The Robert M. La Follette co. [1919, c1913]
La Follette, Robert Marion, 1855–1925.

LAC 40039
Lake commerce. Letter to the Hon. Robert M'Clelland, chairman of the Committee on commerce in the U.S. House of representatives, in relation to the value and importance of the commerce of the great western lakes. 4th ed.–with additional notes. Buffalo, Press of Jewett, Thomas & co., 1846.
Barton, James L   *d.* 1869.

LAC 10256
Lake shore & Michigan southern railway system, and representative employees; a history of the development of the Lake shore & Michigan southern railway, from its inception, together with introductory and supplementary chapters, tracing the progress of steam railroad transportation from the earliest stages, in America and abroad... Buffalo, N. Y., Chicago, Ill., Biographical publishing company, 1900.
Cary, Ferdinand Ellsworth, 1848–

LAC 10763
Land and its rent. Boston, Little, Brown, and company, 1891, [c1883]
Walker, Francis Amasa, 1840–1897.

LAC 15949
Land and labor in the United States. New York, C. Scribner's sons, 1883.
Moody, William Godwin.

LAC 12217
The land of contrasts.
America, the land of contrasts; a Briton's view of his American kin. [3d ed.] London and New York, J. Lane, 1902.
Muirhead, James Fullarton, 1853–1934.

LAC 11819
The land of little rain. Boston and New York, Houghton, Mifflin and company, 1904, [c1903]
Austin, Mary, 1868–1934.

LAC 13260
The land of Nome; a narrative sketch of the rush to our Bering sea gold-fields, the country, its mines, and its people, and the history of a great conspiracy 1900–1901. New York, The Grafton press [c1902]
McKee, Lanier.

LAC 13812
The land of the almighty dollar, by H. Panmure Gordon; the illustrations by Irving Montagu. London and New York, F. Warne & co. [pref. 1892]
Gordon, H   Panmure.

LAC 13720
The land of the dollar. New York, Dodd, Mead and company, 1897.
Steevens, George Warrington, 1869–1900.

LAC 16434
The land of the lamas; notes of a journey through China, Mongolia and Tibet... New York, The Century co., 1891.
Rockhill, William Woodville, 1854–1914.

LAC 40152
The land politics of the United States. [Cambridge, Riverside press, 1904]
Welling, James Clarke, 1825–1894.

LAC 16641
The land question from various points of view. A study in search of the highest truth and best policy, and not a propaganda reprint. Philadelphia, C. F. Taylor [1898]
Taylor, Charles Fremont, 1856–   *ed.*

LAC 11981
The landlord at Lion's head; a novel, by W. D. Howells, illustrated by W. T. Smedley. New York and London, Harper & brothers, 1908.
Howells, William Dean, 1837–1920.

LAC 12220
Lands of the slave and the free: or, Cuba, the United States, and Canada. By Captain the Hon. Henry A. Murray. London, G. Routledge, 1857.
Murray, Henry Anthony, 1810–1865.

LAC 14558
A landscape book, by American artists and American authors; sixteen engravings on steel, from paintings by Cole, Church, Cropsey, Durand, Gignoux, Kensett, Miller, Richards, Smillie, Talbot, Weir. New York, G. P. Putnam & son; [etc., etc.] 1868.

LAC 12937
La Plata, the Argentine confederation, and Paraguay. Being a narrative of the exploration of the tributaries of the river La Plata and adjacent countries during the years 1853, '54, '55, and '56, under the orders of the United States government. By Thomas J. Page, U. S. N., commander of the expedition. New York, Harper & brothers, 1859.
Page, Thomas Jefferson, 1808–1899.

LAC 10565
The larger aspects of socialism. New York, The Macmillan company, 1913.
Walling, William English, 1877–1936.

LAC 23435–39
The Larkin papers; personal, business, and official correspondence of Thomas Oliver Larkin, merchant and United States consul in California. Edited by George P. Hammond. Berkeley, Published for the Bancroft Library by the University of California Press, 1951–68.
Larkin, Thomas Oliver, 1802–1858.

LAC 16325
The last American frontier. New York, The Macmillan company, 1915, [c1910]
Paxson, Frederic Logan, 1877-1948.

LAC 14066
Last days of Knickerbocker life in New York. Illustrated ed. New York and London, G. P. Putnam's sons, 1897.
Dayton, Abram Child, 1818-1877.

LAC 12046
Last evening with Allston, and other papers. Boston, D. Lothrop and company [1886]
Peabody, Elizabeth Palmer, 1804-1894.

LAC 15144
Last rambles amongst the Indians of the Rocky Mountains and the Andes. London, Sampson Low, son, and Marston, 1868.
Catlin, George, 1796-1872.

LAC 16896
Last words. London, Digby, Long & co., 1902.
Crane, Stephen, 1871-1900.

LAC 12466
The latest studies on Indian reservations. Philadelphia, Indian rights association, 1887.
Harrison, Jonathan Baxter, 1835-1907.

LAC 10457
The launching of a university, and other papers; a sheaf of remembrances. New York, Dodd, Mead & company, 1906.
Gilman, Daniel Coit, 1831-1908.

LAC 13835
The law and policy of annexation, with special reference to the Philippines, together with observations on the status of Cuba. New York [etc.] Longmans, Green, & co., 1901.
Randolph, Carman Fitz, 1856-1920.

LAC 23091-92
The law and practice of marine insurance, deduced from a critical examination of the adjudged cases, the nature and analogies of the subject, and the general usage of commercial nations. New-York, J. S. Voorhies, 1845-46.
Duer, John, 1782-1858.

LAC 16198
The law concerning farms, farmers and farm laborers, together with the game laws of all the states. Boston, C. C. Soule, 1886.
Austin, Henry, 1858-1918.

LAC 12733
Law: its origin, growth and function; being a course of lectures prepared for delivery before the Law school of Harvard university. New York and London, G. P. Putnam's sons, 1907.
Carter, James Coolidge, 1827-1905.

LAC 40027
The law of adultery and ignominious punishments. Worcester, Mass., American antiquarian society, 1896.
Davis, Andrew McFarland, 1833-1920.

LAC 10485
The law of civilization and decay; an essay on history. London, S. Sonnerschein & co., lim.; New York, Macmillan & co., 1895.
Adams, Brooks, 1848-1927.

LAC 20977-78
The law of freedom and bondage in the United States. Boston, Little, Brown & company, New York, D. Van Nostrand, 1858-62.
Hurd, John Codman, 1816-1892.

LAC 10946
The law of growth and other sermons. 9th series. New York, E. P. Dutton and company, 1903, [c1902]
Brooks, Phillips, bp., 1835-1893.

LAC 14009
The law of heredity. A study of the cause of variation, and the origin of living organisms. Baltimore, J. Murphy & co., 1883.
Brooks, William Keith, 1848-1908.

LAC 10530
The law of love and love as a law; or, Moral science, theoretical and practical. New York, C. Scribner, 1869.
Hopkins, Mark, 1802-1887.

LAC 15773
The law of patents for inventions; including the remedies and legal proceedings in relation to patent rights. Boston, American stationers' company; New York, Gould, Banks and company, 1837.
Phillips, Willard, 1784-1873.

LAC 16296
The law of psychic phenomena; a working hypothesis for the systematic study of hypnotism, spiritualism, mental therapeutics, etc... 12th ed. Chicago, A. C. McClurg & co., 1897, [c1893]
Hudson, Thomson Jay, 1834-1903.

LAC 13797
The law of strikes, lockouts and labor organizations. Washington, D. C., W. H. Lowdermilk & co., 1894.
Cogley, Thomas Sydenham, b. 1840.

LAC 14995
The law of the territories. Philadelphia, Printed by C. Sherman & son, 1859.

LAC 40033
The Law school of Harvard college. New York, Hurd and Houghton, 1871.
Parker, Joel, 1795-1875.

LAC 10478
Lawless wealth; the origin of some great American fortunes. New York, B. W. Dodge & company, 1908.
Russell, Charles Edward, 1860-

LAC 11670
Lawn tennis at home and abroad; ed. by A. Wallis Myers, with contributions by H. S. Mahony, H. S. Scrivener, G. W. Hillyard, Mrs. Sterry, and other authorities on the game. London, G. Newnes limited, 1903.
Myers, Arthur Wallis, 1878–   *ed.*

LAC 13613
Lawn tennis, its past, present, and future, by J. Parmly Paret; to which is added a chapter on lacrosse by William Harvey Maddren. New York, The Macmillan company; London, Macmillan & co., ltd., 1904.
Paret, Jahial Parmly, 1870–

LAC 15276
The laws and jurisprudence of England and America: being a series of lectures delivered before Yale university. Boston, Little, Brown, and company, 1894.
Dillon, John Forrest, 1831–1914.

LAC 16677
Laws and ordinances of New Netherland, 1638–1674. Compiled and translated from the original Dutch records in the office of the secretary of state, Albany, N. Y., by E. B. O'Callaghan. Albany, Weed, Parsons and company, printers, 1868.
New York *(Colony) Laws, statutes, etc.*

LAC 40034
Laws and regulations of the American philosophical society, held at Philadelphia, for promoting useful knowledge, as finally amended and adopted, December 16, 1859. Together with the charter of the society and a list of its members. Philadelphia, J. C. Clark & son, printers, 1860.
American Philosophical Society, *Philadelphia.*

LAC 40071
The laws of Connecticut. An exact reprint of the original edition of 1673, with a prefatory note by George Brinley. Hartford, Printed for private distribution, 1865.
Connecticut *(Colony) Laws, statutes, etc.*

LAC 14446
The laws of life with special reference to the physical education of girls. New-York, G. P. Putnam, 1852.
Blackwell, Elizabeth, 1821–1910.

LAC 20245–46
The laws of the British colonies in the West Indies, and other parts of America, concerning real and personal property, and manumission of slaves; with a view of the constitution of each colony. London, W. H. Bond, 1827.
Howard, John Henry,

LAC 14427
Laws of the colonial and state governments, relating to Indians and Indian affairs, from 1633 to 1831, inclusive; with an appendix containing the proceedings of the Congress of the Confederation. And the laws of Congress, from 1800 to 1830, on the same subject. Washington city, Thompson and Homans, 1832.

LAC 11654
Laws of the United States concerning money, banking, and loans, 1778–1909; comp. by A. T. Huntington and Robert J. Mawhinney. Washington, Gov't. print. off., 1910 [i.e. 1911]
U. S. *Laws, statutes, etc.*

LAC 14934
The laws of wages, profits & rent, investigated. New York, A. M. Kelley, bookseller, 1964.
Tucker, George, 1775–1861.

LAC 15074
Laws, treaties, and other documents, having operation and respect to the public lands. Collected and arranged pursuant to an act of Congress, passed April 27, 1810. Washington city, Printed by Joseph Gales, jun. [1810?]
U.S. *Laws, Statutes, etc.*

LAC 40052
Laws, treaty, and regulations relating to the exclusion of Chinese. December, 1903. Washington, Gov't. print. off., 1903.
U.S. *Laws, statutes, etc.*

LAC 13130
The lawyer, the statesman and the soldier. New York, D. Appleton and company, 1887.
Boutwell, George Sewall, 1818–1905.

LAC 13628
The lay preacher; or, Short sermons, for idle readers... Printed at Walpole, Newhampshire, by David Carlisle, jun. and sold at his bookstore, 1796.
Dennie, Joseph, 1768–1812.

LAC 10296
Lead and zinc in the United States; comprising an economic history of the mining and smelting of the metals and the conditions which have affected the development of the industries. New York [etc.] Hill publishing company, 1908.
Ingalls, Walter Renton, 1865–

LAC 13418
Lead poisoning in the smelting and refining of lead. February 17, 1914. Washington, Govt. print. off., 1914.
Hamilton, Alice, 1869–

LAC 15531
Leadership of the new America, racial and religious. New York, George H. Doran company [c1916]
McClure, Archibald, 1890–1931.

LAC 10465
Leading pursuits and leading men. A treatise on the principal trades and manufactures of the United States... Philadelphia, E. Young [c1854]
Freedley, Edwin Troxell, 1827–1904.

LAC 40127
Leah and Rachel, or, The two fruitfull sisters Virginia and Mary-land: their present condition, impartially stated and related. With a removall of such imputations as are scandalously cast on those countries, whereby many deceived souls, chose rather to beg, steal, rot in prison, and come to shame full deaths, then to better their being by going thither, wherein is plenty of all things necessary for humane subsistance. London, Printed by T. Mabb, 1656.
Hammond, John, *fl.* 1655.

LAC 40129
The leather glove industry in the United States. New York, 1913.
Redmond, Daniel Walter, 1876–

LAC 10723
The leaven in a great city. New York, Dodd, Mead & company, 1902.
Betts, Lillian Williams.

LAC 10967
Leavening the nation; the story of American home missions. New York, The Baker & Taylor co. [c1903]
Clark, Joseph Bourne, 1836–1932.

LAC 12632
Leaves from the diary of an army surgeon; or, Incidents of field, camp, and hospital life. New York, J. Bradburn, 1863.
Ellis, Thomas T.

LAC 10616
Leaves of grass. Boston, Thayer and Eldridge, Year 85 of the States, (1860–61)
Whitman, Walt, 1819–1892.

LAC 10696
Leaves of grass; including Sands at seventy, 1st annex, Goodbye my fancy, 2nd annex. A backward glance o'er travel'd roads... Philadelphia, D. McKay, 1891–2.
Whitman, Walt, 1819–1892.

LAC 16838
Leaves of life; a story of twenty years of socialist agitation. Girard, Kan., Printed by Appeal to reason, 1912.
Wayland, Julius Augustus, 1854–1912.

LAC 40091
A lecture on rail roads, delivered January 12, 1829, before the Massachusetts charitable mechanic association. Boston, Printed by Crocker & Brewster, 1829.
Jackson, William, 1783–1855.

LAC 40095
A lecture on the education of females. Delivered before the American institute of instruction, August, 1831. Boston, Hilliard, Gray, Little and Wilkins, 1831.
Emerson, George Barrell, 1797–1881.

LAC 15381
Lectures and annual reports on education. Cambridge [Mass.] The editor, 1867.
Mann, Horace, 1796–1859.

LAC 10938
Lectures and orations. by Henry Ward Beecher; ed. by Newell Dwight Hillis. New York, Chicago [etc.] Fleming H. Revell company [c1913]
Beecher, Henry Ward, 1813–1887.

LAC 14355
Lectures and speeches. London, S. Low, son, and Marston, 1869.
Burritt, Elihu, 1810–1879.

LAC 12009
Lectures on American literature, with remarks on some passages of American history. [New York] Elam Bliss, 1829.
Knapp, Samuel Lorenzo, 1783–1838.

LAC 14547
Lectures on art, and poems, by Washington Allston. Ed. by Richard Henry Dana, jr. New York, Baker and Scribner, 1850.
Allston, Washington, 1779–1843.

LAC 11800
Lectures on colonization and colonies. New York, Augustus M. Kelley, 1967.
Merivale, Herman, 1806–1874.

LAC 16172
Lectures on constitutional law, for the use of the law class at the University of Virginia. Richmond, Printed by Shepherd and Colin, 1843.
Tucker, Henry St. George, 1780–1848.

LAC 13024
Lectures on education. Boston, W. B. Fowle and N. Capen, 1845.
Mann, Horace, 1796–1859.

LAC 40014
Lectures on failures in teaching, delivered before the American institute of instruction, at Bangor, Maine, August, 1848. Boston, W. D. Ticknor & co., 1848.
Kingsbury, John.

LAC 15621
Lectures on female education, comprising the first and second series of a course delivered to Mrs. Garnett's pupils, at Elm-Wood, Essex county, Virginia. By James M. Garnett. To which is annexed, The gossip's manual. 3d ed., with corrections and additions by the author. Richmond, T. W. White, 1825.
Garnett, James Mercer, 1770–1843.

LAC 12726
Lectures on legal history and miscellaneous legal essays; with a memoir. Cambridge, Harvard university press, 1913.
Ames, James Barr, 1846–1910.

LAC 16765
Lectures on modern idealism. New Haven, Yale university press; [etc., etc.] 1919.
Royce, Josiah, 1855–1916.

LAC 14281
Lectures on moral philosophy, by John Witherspoon, ed. under the auspices of the American philosophical association by Varnum Lansing Collins. Princeton, N. J., Princeton university press, 1912.
Witherspoon, John, 1723–1794.

LAC 13089
Lectures on moral science. Delivered before the Lowell institute, Boston. Boston, Gould and Lincoln; New York, Sheldon and company; [etc., etc.] 1862.
Hopkins, Mark, 1802–1887.

LAC 12658
Lectures on physiology, zoology, and the natural history of man, delivered at the Royal college of surgeons. With seven engravings. Salem, Foote and Brown, 1828.
Lawrence, *Sir* William, *bart.*, 1783–1867.

LAC 10999
Lectures on revivals of religion. A new ed., rev. and enl. Oberlin, O., E. J. Goodrich [1868]
Finney, Charles Grandison, 1792–1875.

LAC 11098
Lectures on revivals of religion; by William B. Sprague, with an introductory essay, by Leonard Woods; also, an appendix, consisting of letters from the Rev. Doctors Alexander, Wayland [and others] 2d ed., with additional letters. New York, D. Appleton & co., 1833.
Sprague, William Buell, 1795–1876.

LAC 20395
Lectures on rhetoric and oratory, delivered to the classes of senior and junior sophisters in Harvard university. Cambridge: [Mass.] Printed by Hilliard and Metcalf, 1810.
Adams, John Quincy, *pres. U.S.*, 1767–1848.

LAC 13013
Lectures on school-keeping. Boston, Richardson, Lord and Holbrook, 1829.
Hall, Samuel Read, 1795–1877.

LAC 16786
Lectures on slavery, and its remedy. Boston, New-England anti-slavery society, 1834.
Phelps, Amos Augustus, 1805–1847.

LAC 15724
Lectures on subjects connected with literature and life. 2d ed. Boston, Ticknor, Reed, and Fields, 1850.
Whipple, Edwin Percy, 1819–1886.

LAC 20361–62
Lectures on systematic theology... Oberlin, O., J. M. Fitch, 1846–47.
Finney, Charles Grandison, 1792–1875.

LAC 15585
Lectures on the calling of a Christian woman, and her training to fulfil it. Delivered during the season of Lent, A. D. 1883. New York, D. Appleton and company, 1883.
Dix, Morgan, 1827–1908.

LAC 12751
Lectures on the Constitution of the United States. New York and Albany, Banks and brothers, 1891.
Miller, Samuel Freeman, 1816–1890.

LAC 10506
Lectures on the elements of political economy. 2d ed., with additions. Columbia, S. C., M'Morris and Wilson; London, R. Hunter, 1831.
Cooper, Thomas, 1759–1839.

LAC 40013
Lectures on the elevation of the labouring portion of the community. Boston, W. D. Ticknor, 1840.
Channing, William Ellery, 1780–1842.

LAC 16011
Lectures on the elevation of the laboring portion of the community. Boston, Crosby and Nichols, 1863.
Channing, William Ellery, 1780–1842.

LAC 12026
Lectures on the English language. New-York, C. Scribner; [etc., etc.] 1860.
Marsh, George Perkins, 1801–1882.

LAC 11036
Lectures on the evidences of Christianity, before the Lowell institute, January, 1844. Boston, T. R. Marvin, 1849, [c1846]
Hopkins, Mark, 1802–1887.

LAC 15691
Lectures on the fourteenth article of amendment to the Constitution of the United States, delivered before the Dwight alumni association, New York, April–May, 1898. Boston, Little, Brown and company, 1898.
Guthrie, William Dameron, 1859–1935.

LAC 10115
Lectures on the history of agriculture and rural economics. Columbus, Sheppard & company, printers, 1899.
Hunt, Thomas Forsyth, 1862–1927.

LAC 40002
Lectures on the history of protection in the United States. Delivered before the International free-trade alliance. New York, Pub. for the International free trade alliance by G. P. Putnam's sons, 1877.
Sumner, William Graham, 1840–1910.

LAC 20467
Lectures on the moral government of God. New York, Clark, Austin & Smith, 1859.
Taylor, Nathaniel William, 1786–1858.

LAC 12889
Lectures on the philosophy and practice of slavery, as exhibited in the institution of domestic slavery in the United States; with the duties of masters and slaves. By William A. Smith. Ed. by Thomas O. Summers. Nashville, Tenn., Stevenson and Evans, 1856.
Smith, William Andrew, 1802–1870.

LAC 15376
Lectures on the rational system of society, derived solely from nature and experience, as propounded by Robert Owen, versus socialism, derived from misrepresentation, as explained by the Lord Bishop of Exeter and others; and versus the present system of society... Delivered in London, at the Egyptian hall, Piccadilly, in February, March, and April, 1841. London, The Home colonization society, 1841.
Owen, Robert, 1771–1858.

LAC 13106
Lectures on the restrictive system; delivered to the senior political class of William and Mary college. New York, A. M. Kelley, 1969.
Dew, Thomas Roderick, 1802–1846.

LAC 15130
Lectures on the works and genius of Washington Allston. Boston, Phillips, Sampson and company, 1852.
Ware, William, 1797–1852.

LAC 14225
Lectures on theology. By Rev. Bennet Tyler. With a memoir, by Rev. Nahum Gale, D. D. Boston, J. E. Tilton & company, 1859.
Tyler, Bennet, 1783–1858.

LAC 12992
Lectures read to the seniors in Harvard college. Boston, Ticknor and Fields, 1856.
Channing, Edward Tyrrel, 1790–1856.

LAC 15661
Lectures to female teachers on school-keeping. Boston, Richardson, Lord & Holbrook, 1832.
Hall, Samuel Read, 1795–1877.

LAC 12145
Lectures to young men, on various important subjects.
New York, Derby & Jackson, 1859.
Beecher, Henry Ward, 1813–1887.

LAC 14270
Lectures upon the philosophy of history. Andover, W. F. Draper, 1856.
Shedd, William Greenough Thayer, 1820–1894.

LAC 16872
Legal and historical status of the Dred Scott decision: a history of the case and an examination of the opinion delivered by the Supreme court of the United States, March 6, 1857. Washington, D. C., Cobden publishing company, 1909.
Ewing, Elbert William Robinson, 1867–

LAC 10770
The legal and political status of women in the United States. Cedar Rapids, Ia. [The Torch press] 1912.
Wilson, Jennie Lansley, 1847–

LAC 14247
Legal development in colonial Massachusetts, 1630–1686. New York, Columbia university; [etc., etc.] 1910.
Hilkey, Charles Joseph, 1880–

LAC 14447
Legal education in colonial New York. New York, New York university, Law quarterly review, 1939.
Hamlin, Paul Mahlon, 1896–

LAC 40086
Legal provision respecting the education and employment of children in factories, &c.; with examples of improvement in manufacturing districts. Education and labor; or, The influence of education on the quality and value of labor; and its connection with insanity and crime. Hartford, Printed by Case, Tiffany & Burnham, 1842.
Barnard, Henry, 1811–1900.

LAC 40025
A legal view of the seizure of Messrs Mason and Slidell.
New York, 1861.

LAC 13215
Legends of the West. Philadelphia, H. Hall, 1832.
Hall, James, 1793–1868.

LAC 12742
The legislation of Congress for the government of the organized territories of the United States. 1789–1895.
Newark, N. J., W. A. Baker, printer, 1896.
Farrand, Max, 1869–

LAC 10015
Legislative and documentary history of the Bank of the United States: including the original Bank of North America. Comp. by M. St. Clair Clarke & D. A. Hall.
Washington, Printed by Gales and Seaton, 1832.
Clarke, Matthew St. Clair.

LAC 11572
Legislative and documentary history of the banks of the United States, from the time of establishing the Bank of North America, 1781, to October 1834: with notes and comments. New-York, Sold by G. & C. Carvill & co. [etc.] 1834.
Moulton, R   K.

LAC 16758
Legislative history of the general staff of the army of the United States (its organization, duties, pay, and allowances), from 1775 to 1901. Compiled and annotated under the direction of Major-General Henry C. Corbin, adjutant-general of the army, by Raphael P. Thian, chief clerk, Adjutant-general's office. Washington, Govt. print. off., 1901.
U.S. *Adjutant-general's Office.*

LAC 22383-84
Legislative journals of the Council of colonial Virginia... ed. by H. R. McIlwaine. Richmond, Va. [The Colonial press, Everett Waddey co.] 1918–19.
Virginia *(Colony) Council.*

LAC 12458
Legislative methods.
   The history of legislative methods in the period before 1825. New Haven, Yale university press; [etc., etc.] 1917.
Harlow, Ralph Volney, 1884–1956.

LAC 40006
Legislative program of the Socialist party; record of the work of the Socialist representatives in the state legislatures of the United States, 1899–1913, with account of efforts of the party in direct legislation. Chicago, The Socialist party, National office, 1914.
Mills, Ethelwyn.

LAC 11336
The legislature of the province of Virginia; its internal development. New York, The Columbia university press, the Macmillan company, agents; [etc., etc.] 1907.
Miller, Elmer Isaiah, 1862–

LAC 40045
Leif's house in Vineland. By Eben Norton Horsford. Graves of the Northmen. By Cornelia Horsford. Boston, Damrell and Upham, 1893.
Horsford, Eben Norton, 1818–1893.

LAC 16312
Lena Rivers. New York, A. L. Burt [1899]
Holmes, Mary Jane, 1825–1907.

LAC 14668
L'Enfant and Washington, 1791–1792; published and unpublished documents now brought together for the first time, by Elizabeth S. Kite. Introduction by J. J. Jusserand; foreword by Charles Moore. Baltimore, The Johns Hopkins press, 1929.
Kite, Elizabeth Sarah, 1864–1954, *comp.*

LAC 13251
Leonard's narrative; adventure of Zenas Leonard, fur trader and trapper, 1831–1836; reprinted from the rare original of 1839; ed. by W. F. Wagner. Cleveland, The Burrows brothers company, 1904.
Leonard, Zenas, 1809–1857.

LAC 22666
Leonidas, Polk, bishop and general. New York, Longmans, Green, and co., 1894, [c1893]
Polk, William Mecklenburg, 1844–1918.

LAC 16453
The lepers of Molokai. New ed. enl. Notre Dame, Ind., Ave Maria press [n.d.]
Stoddard, Charles Warren, 1843–1909.

LAC 20322–23
The lesson of popular government. New York, The Macmillan company; London, Macmillan & co., ltd., 1899.
Bradford, Gamaliel, 1831–1911.

LAC 10043
Lessons of the financial crisis. Philadelphia, American academy of political and social science, 1908.
American Academy of Political and Social Science, *Philadelphia.*

LAC 10196
A letter, addressed to Cadwallader D. Colden, esquire. In answer to the strictures, contained in his "Life of Robert Fulton", upon the report of the select committee, to whom was referred a memorial relative to steam navigation, presented to the Legislature of New-York, at the session of 1814. With an appendix, containing the several laws concerning steam boats: the petitions presented for their modification; and the reports of select committees thereupon. Albany: Printed and published by E. and E. Hosford, 1817.
Duer, William Alexander, 1780–1858.

LAC 40042
The letter book of Peleg Sanford of Newport, merchant (later governour of Rhode Island) 1666–1668. Transcribed from the original manuscript in the Massachusetts archives by Howard W. Preston, with an introduction and notes by Howard M. Chapin, and additional notes by G. Andrews Moriarty, jr. Providence, Printed for the Rhode Island historical society, 1928.
Sanford, Peleg, 1639–1701.

LAC 40084
A letter from an American, now resident in London, to a member of Parliament, on the subject of the restraining proclamation; and containing strictures on Lord Sheffield's pamphlet on the commerce of the American states. Said to be written by William Bingham, esquire; late agent for the Congress of the United States, at Martinico. To which are added, Mentor's reply to Phocion's letter, with some observations on trade, addressed to the citizens of New-York. Philadelphia: Printed and sold by Robert Bell, in Third-street, 1784.
Bingham, William, 1752–1804.

LAC 40077
A letter from Gen. Harper, of Maryland, to Elias B. Caldwell, esq., secretary of the American society for colonizing the free people of colour, in the United States, with their own consent. Baltimore: Printed for E. J. Cole, by R. J. Matchett, corner of Gay and Water streets, 1818.
Harper, Robert Goodloe, 1765–1825.

LAC 40030
Letter from His Excellency Governor Bullock, of Georgia, in reply to the Honorable John Scott, United States senator, chairman of the Joint select committee to inquire into the condition of the late insurrectionary states. Atlanta, Ga., 1871.
Georgia. *Governor, 1868–1871 (Rufus B. Bullock)*

LAC 40035
Letter from the Hon. Joseph Holt, upon the policy of the general government, the pending revolution, its objects, its probable results if successful, and the duty of Kentucky in the crisis. 2d ed. Washington, H. Polkinhorn, printer, 1861.
Holt, Joseph, 1807–1894.

LAC 40026
A letter from the Hon. Martin Van Buren ... relative to the Bank of the United States; with an explanatory introduction. London, J. Miller, 1836.
Van Buren, Martin, *pres. U.S.*, 1782–1862.

LAC 40070
A letter from the Hon. Timothy Pickering, a senator of the United States from the state of Massachusetts, exhibiting to his constituents a view of the imminent danger of an unnecessary and ruinous war. Addressed to His Excellency James Sullivan, governor of the said state. Boston, Printed by Greenough and Stebbins, 1808.
Pickering, Timothy, 1745–1829.

LAC 40107
Letter from the Secretary of the Interior communicating the report of Edward F. Beale, Superintendent of Indian affairs in California, respecting the condition of Indian affairs in that state. [Washington, 1853]
U.S. *Congress. Senate. Committee on Indian Affairs.*

LAC 16083
Letter from the Secretary of War, in response to Senate Resolution of Feb. 23, 1903, transmitting a report showing the trials or courts-martial had in the Philippine Islands in consequence of the instructions communicated to Major-General Chaffee on April 15, 1902, together with the action of the President or the Secretary of War thereon. Washington, Govt. print. off., 1903.
U.S. *War Dept.*

LAC 40093

A letter from William Penn, proprietary and governour of Pennsylvania in America, to the committee of the Free society of traders of that province, residing in London. Containing a general description of the said province... Of the natives or aborigines... Of the first planters, the Dutch, &c. ... To which is added, an account of the city of Philadelphia newly laid out. Its scituation [!] between two navigable rivers, Delaware and Skulkill with a portraiture or plat-form thereof... London, Printed and sold by A. Sowle, 1683. [Tottenham, Reprinted by J. Coleman, 1881]
Penn, William, 1644–1718.

LAC 40063

Letter of Hon. R. J. Walker, on the purchase of Alaska, St. Thomas and St. John... [Washington, D. C., Chronicle print, 1868]
Walker, Robert James, 1801–1869.

LAC 40063

Letter of Hon. Robt. J. Walker on the annexation of Nova Scotia and British America... [n.p., 1869]
Walker, Robert James, 1801–1869.

LAC 40100

Letter of Mr. Johnston, of Louisiana, to the secretary of the Treasury, in reply to his circular of the 1st July, 1830, relative to the culture of the sugar cane. Washington, Printed by Gales & Seaton, 1831.
Johnston, Josiah Stoddard, 1784–1833.

LAC 40063

Letter of Mr. Walker, of Mississippi, relative to the annexation of Texas: in reply to the call of the people of Carroll County, Ky., to communicate his views on that subject. Saint Louis, Missourian office, 1844.
Walker, Robert James, 1801–1869.

LAC 40076

Letter of Peter Cooper, on slave emancipation. New York, W. C. Bryant & co., printers, 1863.
Cooper, Peter, 1791–1883.

LAC 40077

A letter on the political obligations of abolitionists. New York, Arno press, 1969.
Birney, James Gillespie, 1792–1857.

LAC 40149

A letter to a friend on the conduct of the adherents to Mr. Burr. New York, 1803.
Cheetham, James, 1772–1810.

LAC 40092

A letter to General Hamilton, occasioned by his letter to President Adams. By a Federalist. [New York, 1800]
Webster, Noah, 1758–1843.

LAC 11602

A letter to the Honorable Brockholst Livingston, esq., one of the justices of the Supreme court of the United States, on the lake canal policy of the state of New York. With a supplement, and additional documents. Albany, Printed by Packard & Van Benthuysen, 1822.
Troup, Robert, 1757–1832.

LAC 40152

Letter to the members of the Gennesee [!] consociation, N. Y. 4th ed. Boston, Beals & Homer, printers, 1829.
Emerson, Joseph, 1777–1833.

LAC 40038

A letter to the Right Honourable Lord Viscount H–e, on his naval conduct in the American war. London, Printed for J. Wilkie, 1779.
Galloway, Joseph, 1731–1803.

LAC 40053

Letter to the secretary of the Treasury, on the history and causes of steamboat explosions, and the means of prevention. Washington, Govt. print. off., 1838.
Redfield, William C   1789–1857.

LAC 14111

Letters, addressed to the people of Pennsylvania respecting the internal improvement, of the Commonwealth by means of roads and canals. New York, B. Franklin [1967]
Duane, William John, 1780–1865.

LAC 12196

Letters addressed to young married women. Philadelphia: From the press of John Turner, November, 1796.
Griffith, Elizabeth, 1720?–1793.

LAC 10477

Letters and diary of John Rowe, Boston merchant, 1759–1762, 1764–1779; ed. by Anne Rowe Cunningham, with extracts from a paper written for the Massachusetts historical society, by Edward Lillie Pierce. Boston, W. B. Clarke company, 1903.
Rowe, John, 1715–1787.

LAC 12048

Letters and documents in the Enoch Pratt free library, edited by Arthur H. Quinn and Richard H. Hart. New York, Scholars' facsimiles & reprints, 1941.
Poe, Edgar Allan, 1809–1849.

LAC 16140

Letters and documents relating to the early history of the lower Cape Fear, with introduction and notes by Kemp P. Battle. Chapel Hill [N. C.] The University, 1903.
Battle, Kemp Plummer, 1831–   ed.

LAC 20420-21

Letters and journals of Samuel Gridley Howe, ed. by his daughter, Laura E. Richards, with notes by F. B. Sanborn. Boston, D. Estes & company [c1909]
Howe, Samuel Gridley, 1801–1876.

LAC 11030

Letters and journals of Thomas Wentworth Higginson, 1846–1906, ed. by Mary Thacher Higginson. Boston and New York, Houghton Mifflin company, 1921.
Higginson, Thomas Wentworth, 1823–1911.

LAC 11536

Letters and journals relating to the war of the American revolution, and the capture of the German troops at Saratoga. By Mrs. General Riedesel. Tr. from the original German, by William L. Stone. Albany, J. Munsell, 1867.
Riedesel, Friederike Charlotte Luise, *freifrau* von, 1746–1808.

LAC 20111
Letters and literary memorials of Samuel J. Tilden; ed. by John Bigelow, LL. D. New York and London, Harper & brothers, 1908.
Tilden, Samuel Jones, 1814–1886.

LAC 20858–62
The letters and papers of Cadwallader Colden... 1711–[1775] New York, Printed for the New York historical society, 1918–37.
Colden, Cadwallader, 1688–1776.

LAC 22550–51
Letters and papers of Charles, lord Barham, admiral of the Red squadron, 1758–1813; edited by Sir John Knox Laughton. [London] Printed for the Navy records society, 1907–11.
Barham, Charles Middleton, *baron*, 1726–1813.

LAC 14322
Letters and papers of Governor John Henry of Maryland, member of Continental Congress 1777–1788, member of United States Senate 1789–1797, governor of Maryland, 1797–1798. With some account of his life, genealogy and descendants, as shown by extracts from records and papers in the Maryland historical society, and original letters and memoranda in the hands of the compiler, one of his great-grandsons, J. Winfield Henry. Baltimore, G. W. King printing co., 1904.
Henry, John, 1750–1798.

LAC 13673
Letters and papers relating chiefly to the provincial history of Pennsylvania, with some notices of the writers. Privately printed. Philadelphia, Crissy & Markley, printers, 1855.
Balch, Thomas, 1821–1877.

LAC 13131
Letters and papers relating to the Alaska frontier. Philadelphia, Press of Allen, Lane & Scott, 1904.
Balch, Edwin Swift, 1856–1927, *ed.*

LAC 20010
Letters and recollections of John Murray Forbes; ed. by his daughter Sarah Forbes Hughes. Boston and New York, Houghton, Mifflin and company, 1899.
Forbes, John Murray, 1813–1898.

LAC 20434–35
The letters and times of the Tylers. Reprinted. New York, Da Capo Press, 1970.
Tyler, Lyon Gardiner, 1853–1935.

LAC 40121
Letters exposing the mismanagement of public affairs by Abraham Lincoln, and the political combinations to secure his re-election. Washington, D. C., Printed at the Constitutional union office, 1864.
Kendall, Amos, 1789–1869.

LAC 13518
Letters from a father to his sons in college. Philadelphia, Grigg and Elliot, 1843.
Miller, Samuel, 1769–1850.

LAC 16342
Letters from a surgeon of the civil war; comp. by Martha Derby Perry; illustrated from photographs. Boston, Little, Brown, and company, 1906.
Perry, John Gardner, 1840–1926.

LAC 13401
Letters from a workingman, by an American mechanic. New York, Chicago [etc.] F. H. Revell company [c1908]
Stelzle, Charles, 1869–1941.

LAC 16885
Letters from Alabama on various subjects: to which is added, an appendix, containing remarks on sundry members of the 20th & 21st Congress, and other high characters, &c. &c. at the seat of government. In one volume. Washington, 1830.
Royall, Anne, 1769–1854.

LAC 16074
Letters from Alabama, (U.S.) chiefly relating to natural history. London, Morgan and Chase, 1859.
Gosse, Philip Henry, 1810–1888.

LAC 20260
Letters from America. London, J. Murray, 1844.
Godley, John Robert.

LAC 16239
Letters from America, historical and descriptive; comprising occurrences from 1769, to 1777, inclusive. London, Printed for the author, 1792.
Eddis, William, 1738–1825.

LAC 14909
Letters from America, 1776–1779; being letters of Brunswick, Hessian, and Waldeck officers with the British armies during the revolution. Boston and New York, Houghton Mifflin company, 1924.
Pettengill, Ray Waldron, 1885–   *tr.*

LAC 11882
Letters from an American farmer; describing certain provincial situations, manners, and customs ... and conveying some idea of the late and present interior circumstances of the British colonies in North America. Written for the information of a friend in England, by J. Hector St. John. London, Printed for T. Davies [etc.] 1782.
Crevecoeur, Michel Guillaume St. Jean de, *called* Saint John de Crevecoeur, 1735–1813.

LAC 15957
Letters from an early settler of Texas. By W. B. Dewees. Comp. by Cara Cardelle [*pseud.*] Louisville, Ky., Morton & Griswold, 1852.
Dewees, William B.

LAC 16747
Letters from Honolulu, written for the Sacramento union by Mark Twain [*pseud.*] Introduction by John W. Vandercook. Honolulu, T. Nickerson, 1939.
Clemens, Samuel Langhorne, 1835–1910.

LAC 11820
Letters from London: written during the years 1802 & 1803. Boston, Printed for W. Pelham, 1804.
Austin, William, 1778–1841.

LAC 14065
Letters from New-York. 2d ed. New-York, C. S. Francis and company; Boston, J. H. Francis, 1844.
Child, Lydia Maria, 1802–1880.

LAC 14156
Letters from Port Royal written at the time of the civil war, ed. by Elizabeth Ware Pearson. Boston, W. B. Clarke company, 1906.
Pearson, Elizabeth Ware, *ed.*

LAC 40005
Letters from Ralph Waldo Emerson to a friend, 1838–1853; ed. by Charles Eliot Norton. Boston and New York, Houghton, Mifflin and company, 1899.
Emerson, Ralph Waldo, 1803–1882.

LAC 13214
Letters from the East and from the West. Washington city, F. Taylor and W. M. Morrison; Baltimore, F. Lucas, jr.; [etc., etc.] 1840.
Hall, Frederick, 1780–1843.

LAC 12961
Letters from the English kings and queens Charles II, James II, William and Mary, Anne, George II, &c. to the governors of the colony of Connecticut, together with the answers thereto, from 1635 to 1749; and other original, ancient, literary and curious documents, comp. from files and records in the office of the secretary of the state of Connecticut. Hartford, J. B. Eldredge, printer, 1836.
Hinman, Royal Ralph, 1785–1868, *comp.*

LAC 40084
Letters from the Hon. Abbott Lawrence to the Hon. William C. Rives, of Virginia. Boston, Eastburn's press, 1846.
Lawrence, Abbott, 1792–1855.

LAC 40055
Letters from the Illinois, 1820. 1821. Containing an account of the English settlement at Albion and its vicinity, and a refutation of various misrepresentations, those more particularly of Mr. Cobbett. By Richard Flower. With a letter from M. Birkbeck; and a preface and notes by Benjamin Flower. London, Printed for J. Ridgway, 1822.
Flower, Richard, 1761?–1829.

LAC 13232
Letters from the Pacific slope; or First impressions. New York, D. Appleton & company, 1870.
Rice, Harvey, 1800–1891.

LAC 40044
Letters from the Rev. Samuel Davies, &c., shewing the state of religion in Virginia, particularly among the Negroes. Likewise an extract of a letter from a gentleman in London to his friend in the country, containing some observations on the same. 2d ed. London, R. Pardon, 1757.
Davies, Samuel, 1723–1761.

LAC 14564
Letters from the slave states. London, J. W. Parker and son, 1857.
Stirling, James, 1805–1883.

LAC 13247
Letters from the South and West; by Arthur Singleton, esq. [*pseud.*] Boston, Pub. by Richardson and Lord, J. H. A. Frost, printer, 1824.
Knight, Henry Cogswell, 1788–1835.

LAC 40078
Letters from the South, on the social, intellectual, and moral condition of the colored people. Boston, T. Todd, printer, 1880.
Emery, E   B.

LAC 40030
Letters from the South, relating to the condition of freedmen, addressed to Major General O. O. Howard, commissioner Bureau R., F., and A. L., by J. W. Alvord, gen. sup't education, Bureau R., F., & A. L. Washington, D. C., Howard university press, 1870.
Alvord, John Watson, 1807–1880.

LAC 20748
Letters from the South, written during an excursion in the summer of 1816. By the author of John Bull and Brother Jonathan. New-York: Published by James Eastburn & co., at the Literary rooms, Broadway, corner of Pine-street. Abraham Paul, printer, 1817.
Paulding, James Kirke, 1778–1860.

LAC 13216
Letters from the West; containing sketches of scenery, manners, and customs; and anecdotes connected with the first settlements of the western sections of the United States. By the Hon. Judge Hall. London, H. Colburn, 1828.
Hall, James, 1793–1868.

LAC 11510
Letters of a Westchester farmer (1774–1775) by the Reverend Samuel Seabury (1729–1796) edited with an introductory essay by Clarence H. Vance. White Plains, N. Y., Pub. for Westchester county by the Westchester county historical society, 1930.
Seabury, Samuel, *bp.*, 1729–1796.

LAC 20904
Letters of Asa Gray, ed. by Jane Loring Gray. Boston and New York, Houghton, Mifflin and company, 1893.
Gray, Asa, 1810–1888.

LAC 16385
Letters of Brunswick and Hessian officers during the American revolution. Tr. by William Stone. (Assisted by August Hund) Albany, N. Y., J. Munsell's sons, 1891.
Stone, William Leete, 1835–1908, *tr.*

LAC 22109-10
Letters of Charles Eliot Norton, with biographical comment by his daughter Sara Norton and M. A. De Wolfe Howe. Boston and New York, Houghton Mifflin company, 1913.
Norton, Charles Eliot, 1827–1908.

LAC 12709

Letters of Chauncey Wright: with some account of his life, by James Bradley Thayer. Privately printed. Cambridge, Press of J. Wilson and son, 1878.
Wright, Chauncey, 1830–1875.

LAC 14486

Letters of Colonel Thomas Westbrook and others relative to Indian affairs in Maine 1722–1726. Boston, Mass., G. E. Littlefield, 1901.
Trask, William Blake, 1812–1906, *ed.*

LAC 23213

Letters of Cortes.
Fernando Cortes: his five letters of relation to the Emperor Charles V, translated and edited, with a biographical introduction and notes compiled from original sources, by Francis Augustus MacNutt. Cleveland, Arthur H. Clark Co., 1908.
Cortes, Hernando, 1485–1547.

LAC 22385

The letters of Emily Dickinson. Edited by Mabel Loomis Todd. Boston, Roberts brothers, 1894.
Dickinson, Emily, 1830–1886.

LAC 16336

Letters of Fredrika Bremer.
America of the fifties: letters of Fredrika Bremer, selected and edited by Adolph B. Benson. New York, The American-Scandinavian foundation; [etc., etc.] 1924.
Bremer, Fredrika, 1801–1865.

LAC 40150

Letters of Gen. Scott and Secretary Marcy relating to the Mexican war. [Washington, Congressional globe office, 1848]
Scott, Winfield, 1786–1866.

LAC 23530

Letters of Hawthorne to William D. Ticknor, 1851–1864... Newark, N. J., The Carteret book club, 1910.
Hawthorne, Nathaniel, 1804–1864.

LAC 23807–8

The letters of Henry James, selected and ed. by Percy Lubbock. New York, C. Scribner's sons, 1920.
James, Henry, 1843–1916.

LAC 15112

Letters of Horatio Greenough to his brother, Henry Greenough. With biographical sketches and some contemporary correspondence. Ed. by Frances Boott Greenough. Boston, Ticknor and company, 1887.
Greenough, Horatio, 1805–1852.

LAC 40065

Letters of James Monroe. Boston, Massachusetts Historical Society, 1909.
Ford, Worthington Chauncey, 1858–1941, *ed.*

LAC 15270

Letters of James Murray, loyalist; edited by Nina Moore Tiffany, assisted by Susan I. Lesley. Boston, printed: not published, 1901.
Murray, James, 1713–1781.

LAC 21319

Letters of John Adams, addressed to his wife. Ed. by his grandson, Charles Francis Adams. Boston, C. C. Little and J. Brown, 1841.
Adams, John, *pres. U.S.,* 1735–1826.

LAC 40149

Letters of John Adams and John Quincy Adams, 1776–1838. [New York, 1906]
Adams, John, *pres. U.S.,* 1735–1826.

LAC 22212

Letters of John James Audubon, 1826–1840, edited by Howard Corning. Boston, The Club of odd volumes, 1930.
Audubon, John James, 1785–1851.

LAC 14509

Letters of John Taylor, of Caroline County, Virginia. [Richmond, Va., Richmond Press, 1908]
Taylor, John, 1753–1824.

LAC 11896

The letters of Joseph Dennie, 1768–1812, edited and annotated by Laura Green Pedder. Orono, Me., Printed at the University press, 1936.
Dennie, Joseph, 1768–1812.

LAC 12485

The letters of Lafayette and Jefferson, with an introduction and notes by Gilbert Chinard... Baltimore, Md., The Johns Hopkins press; Paris, "Les Belles lettres ", 1929.
Lafayette, Marie Joseph Paul Yves Roch Gilbert du Motier, *marquis* de, 1757–1834.

LAC 13105

Letters of Lydia Maria Child, with a biographical introduction by John G. Whittier and an appendix by Wendell Phillips. Boston, New York, Houghton, Mifflin and company, 1884, [c1882]
Child, Lydia Maria, 1802–1880.

LAC 22321–28

Letters of members of the Continental congress, ed. by Edmund C. Burnett. Washington, D. C., The Carnegie institution of Washington, 1921–36.
Burnett, Edmund Cody, 1864–1949, *ed.*

LAC 40096

Letters of Mr. William E. Chandler relative to the so-called southern policy of President Hayes, together with a letter to Mr. Chandler of Mr. William Lloyd Garrison. Concord, N. H., Monitor and statesman office; Washington, Gibson brothers, 1878.
Chandler, William Eaton, 1835–1917.

LAC 11366

Letters of Mrs. Adams, the wife of John Adams. With an introductory memoir by her grandson, Charles Francis Adams. 4th ed., rev. and enl., with an appendix containing the letters addressed by John Q. Adams to his son on the study of the Bible. Boston, Wilkins, Carter, and company, 1848.
Adams, Abigail, 1744–1818.

LAC 20496
Letters of Mrs. James G. Blaine; edited by Harriet S. Blaine Beale. New York, Duffield and company, 1908.
Blaine, Harriet Bailey, 1828–1903.

LAC 11389
Letters of Nathaniel Macon, John Steele and William Barry Grove, with sketches and notes by Kemp P. Battle, LL. D. Chapel Hill, N. C., The University [1902]
Battle, Kemp Plummer, 1831–1919, *ed.*

LAC 10659
Letters of Phineas Bond, British Consul at Philadelphia, to the Foreign office of Great Britain, 1787–1794. Washington, Govt. print. off., 1898.
Bond, Phineas, 1749–1815.

LAC 23399–402
The letters of Ralph Waldo Emerson, edited by Ralph L. Rusk. New York, Columbia university press, 1939.
Emerson, Ralph Waldo, 1803–1882.

LAC 22300–1
The letters of Richard Henry Lee, collected and ed. by James Curtis Ballagh. New York, The Macmillan company, 1911–14.
Lee, Richard Henry, 1732–1794.

LAC 15942
Letters of Roger Williams. 1632–1682. Now first collected. Ed. by John Russell Bartlett. Providence, Printed for the Narragansett club, 1874.
Williams, Roger, 1604?–1683.

LAC 12000
Letters of Sarah Orne Jewett, ed. by Annie Fields. Boston and New York, Houghton Mifflin company [c1911]
Jewett, Sarah Orne, 1849–1909.

LAC 16587
Letters of Sidney Lanier; selections from his correspondence, 1866–1881... New York, C. Scribner's sons, 1899.
Lanier, Sidney, 1842–1881.

LAC 12455
Letters of Ulysses S. Grant to his father and his youngest sister, 1857–78, ed. by his nephew, Jesse Grant Cramer. New York and London, G. P. Putnam's sons, 1912.
Grant, Ulysses Simpson, *pres. U.S.*, 1822–1885.

LAC 20657
The letters of Washington Irving to Henry Brevoort; ed., with an introduction, by George S. Hellman. New York, G. P. Putnam's sons, 1915.
Irving, Washington, 1783–1859.

LAC 40093
Letters of William Fitzhugh [1679–99, in two parts. Richmond, Virginia Historical Society, 1899]
Fitzhugh, William.

LAC 22897
The letters of William James, ed. by his son, Henry James. Boston, The Atlantic monthly press [c1920]
James, William, 1842–1910.

LAC 16831
Letters of Zachary Taylor, from the battle-fields of the Mexican war; reprinted from the originals in the collection of Mr. Williams K. Bixby, of St. Louis, Mo.; with introduction, biographical notes, an appendix, and illustrations from private plates. Rochester, N. Y. [The Genesee press] 1908.
Taylor, Zachary, *pres. U.S.*, 1784–1850.

LAC 12880
Letters on American slavery, addressed to Mr. Thomas Rankin, merchant at Middlebrook, Augusta Co., Va. Boston, Garrison & Knapp, 1833.
Rankin, John, 1793–1886.

LAC 13519
Letters on clerical manners and habits; addressed to a student in the theological seminary, at Princeton, N. J. New York, G. & C. Carvill, 1827.
Miller, Samuel, 1769–1850.

LAC 15833
Letters on college government, and the evils inseparable from the American college system in its present form... New York, D. Appleton & co., 1855.
Barnard, Frederick Augustus Porter, 1809–1889.

LAC 40057
Letters on Irish emigration... Boston, Phillips, Sampson & company, 1852.
Hale, Edward Everett, 1822–1909.

LAC 16206
Letters on practical subjects, from a clergyman of New-England, to his daughter. Hartford, Huntington & Hopkins, 1822.
Sprague, William Buell, 1795–1876.

LAC 12870
Letters on slavery; addressed to the Cumberland congregation, Virginia. By J. D. Paxton, their former pastor. Lexington, Ky., A. T. Skillman, 1833.
Paxton, John D., 1784–1868.

LAC 40007
Letters on the condition of Kentucky in 1825; reprinted from the Richmond enquirer; ed. by Earl Gregg Swem. New York city, Printed for C. F. Heartman, 1916.

LAC 40036
Letters on the condition of the African race in the United States. By a southern lady. Philadelphia, T. K. and P. G. Collins, printers, 1852.
Schoolcraft, Mary.

LAC 40019
Letters on the culture and manufacture of cotton: addressed to Freeman Hunt, esq., editor of Hunt's Merchants' magazine, and published in the numbers of that journal for February and March, 1850, in reply to the communications of A. A. Lawrence, esq., originally published in the Merchants' magazine for Dec. 1849 and January, 1850. New York, Printed by G. W. Wood, 1850.
James, Charles Tillinghast, 1804–1862.

LAC 16294
Letters on the difficulties of religion. By Catharine [!] E. Beecher. Hartford, Belknap & Hamersley, 1836.
Beecher, Catherine Esther, 1800–1878.

LAC 11195
Letters on the equality of the sexes and the condition of woman. Addressed to Mary S. Parker... Boston, I. Knapp, 1838.
Grimke, Sarah Moore, 1792–1873.

LAC 40060
Letters on the internal improvements and commerce of the West. Boston, H. P. Lewis, 1839.
Dearborn, Henry Alexander Scammell, 1783–1851.

LAC 40016
Letters on the internal improvements and commerce of the West. Boston, Dutton and Wentworth, 1839.
Henshaw, David, 1791–1852.

LAC 11141
Letters on the late war between the United States and Great Britain: together with other miscellaneous writings, on the same subject. New-York: Published by J. Belden and co., Van Winkle & Wiley, printers, 1815.
Cobbett, William, 1763–1835.

LAC 40058
Letters on the proposed annexation of Santo Domingo, in answer to certain charges in the newspapers. Boston, Wright & Potter, printers, 1871.
Howe, Samuel Gridley, 1801–1876.

LAC 40102
Letters on the Richmond party. By a Virginian. Originally published in the Washington republican. Washington city, 1823.

LAC 11931
Letters on various interesting and important subjects, by Philip Freneau, with an introduction and a biographical note by Harry Hayden Clark. New York, Scholars' facsimiles & reprints, 1943.
Freneau, Philip Morin, 1752–1832.

LAC 10163
Letters, speeches and addresses of August Belmont... [New York] Priv. print., 1890.
Belmont, August, 1816–1890.

LAC 12451
Letters to a nobleman, on the conduct of the war in the middle colonies. 3d ed. London, Printed for J. Wilkie, 1779.
Galloway, Joseph, 1731–1803.

LAC 10836
Letters to a student in the University of Cambridge, Massachusetts. By John Clarke, minister of a church in Boston. Boston: Printed and sold by Samuel Hall, no. 53, Cornhill. 1796.
Clarke, John, 1755–1798.

LAC 40066
Letters to Alexander Hamilton, king of the Feds. New York, Printed for the Hamilton Club, 1866.
Callender, James Thomson, 1758–1803, *supposed author.*

LAC 12516
Letters to and from Caesar Rodney, 1756–1784; member of the Stamp act congress and the first and second Continental congresses; speaker of the Delaware colonial assembly; president of the Delaware state; major general of the Delaware militia; signer of the Declaration of independence. Edited by George Herbert Ryden. Philadelphia, Pub. for the Historical society of Delaware by the University of Pennsylvania press, 1933.
Rodney, Caesar, 1728–1784.

LAC 40026
Letters to Dr. Adam Seybert, representative in Congress for the city of Philadelphia, on the subject of the renewal of the charter of the Bank of the United States. 2d ed. enl. ... Philadelphia, The author, 1811.
Carey, Mathew, 1760–1839.

LAC 11061
Letters to Presbyterians, on the present crisis in the Presbyterian church in the United States. Philadelphia, A. Finley, 1833.
Miller, Samuel, 1769–1850.

LAC 40084
Letters to the Honorable William M. Meredith. Boston, Phillips, Sampson & co., 1858.
Bradford, Samuel Dexter.

LAC 10621
Letters to the Hon. William Prescott, LL. D., on the free schools of New England, with remarks upon the principle of instruction. Boston, Cummings, Hilliard & co., 1824.
Carter, James Gordon, 1795–1849.

LAC 11728
Letters to the ministry, from Governor Bernard, General Gage and Commodore Hood. And also, memorials to the lords of the treasury, from the commissioners of the customs. With sundry letters and papers annexed to the said memorials. Boston: New-England. Printed by Edes and Gill, printers to the Honourable House of representatives, 1769; and, London, Re-printed for J. Wilkie [1769?]
Massachusetts *(Colony) Governor, 1760–1770 (Francis Bernard)*

LAC 40048
Letters to the people of New Jersey, on the frauds, extortions, and oppressions of the railroad monopoly. By a citizen of Burlington. Philadelphia, Carey and Hart, 1848.
Carey, Henry Charles, 1793–1879.

LAC 16850
Letters to the press, 1758–1775, collected and edited by Verner W. Crane. Chapel Hill, Published for the Institute of Early American History and Culture at Williamsburg, Va., by the University of North Carolina Press [1950]
Franklin, Benjamin, 1706–1790.

LAC 11691
Letters to the Right honourable the Earl of Hillsborough from General Bernard, General Gage, and the honourable His Majesty's Council for the Province of Massachusetts-Bay. With an appendix containing divers proceedings referred to in the said letters. Boston, printed by Edes and Gill, 1769.
Bernard, *Sir* Francis, *bart.*, 1712?–1779.

LAC 20792-94
Letters to Washington, and accompanying papers; published by the Society of the colonial dames of America. Boston and New York, Houghton, Mifflin and company, 1898–1902.
Hamilton, Stanislaus Murray, 1855–1909, *ed.*

LAC 14566
Letters written during the civil war, 1861–1865. [Boston, Mass.] Priv. print., 1898.
Morse, Charles Fessenden, 1839–

LAC 13355
Lewis & Dryden's marine history of the Pacific Northwest; an illustrated review of the growth and development of the maritime industry, from the advent of the earliest navigators to the present time, with sketches and portraits of a number of well known marine men. Portland, Or., The Lewis & Dryden printing company, 1895.
Wright, E   W   *ed.*

LAC 12497
Lewis Cass. Boston and New York, Houghton, Mifflin company [c1891]
McLaughlin, Andrew Cunningham, 1861–

LAC 14416
Libby life: experiences of a prisoner of war in Richmond, Va., 1863–64, by Lieut. Colonel F. F. Cavada, U. S. V. Philadelphia, King & Baird, 1864.
Cavada, Frederic Fernandez, 1832–1871.

LAC 10613
The liberal education of women: the demand and the method. Current thoughts in America and England. Ed. by James Orton. New York and Chicago, A. S. Barnes & company, 1873.
Orton, James, 1830–1877.

LAC 14677
Liberalism and American education in the eighteenth century, by Allen Oscar Hansen. With an introduction by Edward H. Reisner. New York, The Macmillan company, 1926.
Hansen, Allen Oscar.

LAC 15109
Liberia; or, Mr. Peyton's experiments. Upper Saddle River, N. J., Gregg Press [1968]
Hale, Sarah Josepha, 1788–1879.

LAC 40105
La liberte aux Etats-Unis. Paris, Capelle, 1849.
Chevalier, Michel, 1806–1879.

LAC 14772
The Liberty and Free soil parties in the Northwest. Toppan prize essay of 1896. New York [etc.] Longmans, Green, and co., 1897.
Smith, Theodore Clarke, 1870–

LAC 40109
The liberty of the press in the American colonies before the revolutionary war. With particular reference to conditions in the royal colony of New York. New York, T. Whittaker, 1905.
Schuyler, Livingston Rowe, 1868–

LAC 16149
Liberty, union and democracy, the national ideals of America. New York, C. Scribner's sons, 1906.
Wendell, Barrett, 1855–1921.

LAC 21051-58
A library of American literature from the earliest settlement to the present time, comp. and ed. by Edmund Clarence Stedman and Ellen Mackay Hutchinson. New York, C. L. Webster & company, 1888–90.
Stedman, Edmund Clarence, 1833–1908, *ed.*

LAC 20143-51
Library of southern literature; compiled under the direct supervision of southern men of letters. Edwin Anderson Alderman, Joel Chandler Harris, editors in chief; Charles William Kent, literary editor. New Orleans, Atlanta [etc.] The Martin & Hoyt company [c1909–13]

LAC 13867
Life among the Indians; or, Personal reminiscences and historical incidents illustrative of Indian life and character. By Rev. James B. Finley. Ed. by Rev. D. W. Clark, D. D. Cincinnati, Cranston & Curts [1857?]
Finley, James Bradley, 1781–1856.

LAC 14307
Life and achievements of Jay Gould, the wizard of Wall street, being a complete and graphic account of the greatest financier of modern times... Philadelphia, National pub. co. [c1892]
Northrop, Henry Davenport, 1836–1909.

LAC 15030
The life and adventures of Black Hawk: with sketches of Keokuk, The Sac and Fox Indians, and the late Black Hawk war. Cincinnati, G. Conclin, 1838.
Drake, Benjamin, 1794–1841.

LAC 13136
The life and adventures of James P. Beckwourth, mountaineer, scout, and pioneer, and chief of the Crow nation of Indians... Written from his own dictation, by T. D. Bonner. New York, Harper and brothers, 1856.
Beckwourth, James P   1798?–1867.

LAC 16926
Life and adventures of James Williams, a fugitive slave, with a full description of the Underground railroad. 5th ed. Philadelphia, A. H. Sickler & co., 1893.
Williams, James, *b.* 1825.

LAC 11898
The life and adventures of Martin Chuzzlewit. By Charles Dickens. With illustrations by Phiz [*pseud.*] London, Chapman and Hall, 1844.
Dickens, Charles, 1812–1870.

LAC 40143

Life and adventures of Sam Bass, the notorious Union Pacific and Texas train robber... Dallas, Dallas Commercial Steam print, 1878.

LAC 12241

The life and adventures of Seth Wyman, embodying the principal events of a life spent in robbery, theft, gambling, passing counterfeit money, &c., &c. Manchester, N. H., J. H. Cate, printer, 1843.
Wyman, Seth, 1784-1843.

LAC 14617

Life and campaigns of Lieut.-Gen. Thomas J. Jackson, (Stonewall Jackson.) New-York, Blelock & co.; Richmond, Va., and Philadelphia, Pa., National publishing company, 1866.
Dabney, Robert Lewis, 1820-1898.

LAC 15702

The life and campaigns of Major-General J. E. B. Stuart, commander of the cavalry of the Army of northern Virginia. Boston [etc.] Houghton, Mifflin and company; Richmond, Va., J. W. Randolph and English, 1885.
McClellan, Henry Brainerd, 1840-1904.

LAC 14365

The life and character of the late reverend Mr. Jonathan Edwards, president of the college at New-Jersey. Together with a number of his sermons on various important subjects. Boston: Printed and sold by S. Kneeland, opposite to the Probate-office in Queen-street, 1765.
Edwards, Jonathan, 1703-1758.

LAC 13695

Life and correspondence of George Read, a signer of the Declaration of independence; with notices of some of his contemporaries. By his grandson, William Thompson Read. Philadelphia, J. B. Lippincott & co., 1870.
Read, William Thompson.

LAC 20423

Life and correspondence of Henry Ingersoll Bowditch, by his son, Vincent Y. Bowditch. Boston and New York, Houghton, Mifflin and company, 1902.
Bowditch, Vincent Yardley, 1852-1929.

LAC 14621

Life and correspondence of Henry Knox, major-general in the American revolutionary army. Boston, S. G. Drake, 1873.
Drake, Francis Samuel, 1828-1885.

LAC 23312-13

Life and correspondence of James Iredell, one of the associate justices of the Supreme court of the United States. New York, Appleton, 1857-58.
McRee, Griffith John, 1819-1873.

LAC 11544

The life and correspondence of James McHenry, secretary of war under Washington and Adams. Cleveland, The Burrows brothers company, 1907.
Steiner, Bernard Christian, 1867-1926.

LAC 22254

Life and correspondence of John A. Quitman, major-general, U.S.A., and governor of the state of Mississippi. New York, Harper & brothers, 1860.
Claiborne, John Francis Hamtramck, 1809-1884.

LAC 14401

Life and correspondence of John Paul Jones, including his narrative of the campaign of the Liman. From original letters and manuscripts in the possession of Miss Janette Taylor... New York [D. Fanshaw, printer] 1830.
Jones, John Paul, 1747-1792.

LAC 22559-63

The life and correspondence of Rufus King; comprising his letters, private and official, his public documents, and his speeches. Ed. by his grandson Charles R. King. New York, G. P. Putnam's sons, 1894-1900.
King, Rufus, 1755-1827.

LAC 21177-78

Life and correspondence of the Rev. William Smith, D. D., first provost of the College and academy of Philadelphia. First president of Washington college, Maryland... With copious extracts from his writings. By his great-grandson, Horace Wemyss Smith. Philadelphia, Ferguson bros. & co., 1880.
Smith, Horace Wemyss, 1825-1891.

LAC 10936

Life and correspondence of the Right Reverend Samuel Seabury, D. D., first bishop of Connecticut, and of the Episcopal church in the United States of America. 2d ed. Boston, Houghton, Mifflin and company, 1881.
Beardsley, Eben Edwards, 1808-1891.

LAC 23234-35

Life and correspondence of Theodore Parker, minister of Twenty-eighth Congregational society, Boston. New York, D. Appleton & company, 1864.
Weiss, John, 1818-1879.

LAC 14898

Life and death in rebel prisons: giving a complete history of the inhuman and barbarous treatment of our brave soldiers by rebel authorities, inflicting terrible suffering and frightful mortality, principally at Andersonville, Ga., and Florence, S. C., describing plans of escape, arrival of prisoners, with numerous and varied incidents and anecdotes of prison life. By Robert H. Kellogg. Prepared from his daily journal. To which is added as full sketches of other prisons as can be given without repetition of the above, by parties who have been confined therein. Hartford, Conn., L. Stebbins, 1865.
Kellogg, Robert H.

LAC 14171

The life and diary of John Floyd, governor of Virginia, an apostle of secession and the father of the Oregon country. [Richmond, Richmond press, inc., printers, c1918]
Ambler, Charles Henry, 1876-1957.

LAC 16297

Life and labors of Dwight L. Moody... By Rev. Henry Davenport Northrop. Including a chapter entitled "Mr. Moody's ministry to men", by Bishop Williard F. Mallalieu. Springfield, Mass., Hampden pub. co. [c1899]
Northrop, Henry Davenport, 1836-1909.

LAC 13133

Life and labour in the far, far West: being notes of a tour in the western states, British Columbia, Manitoba, and the North-west territory. London, New York [etc.] Cassell & company, 1884.
Barneby, William Henry, 1843–

LAC 15161

The life and letters of Admiral Dewey from Montpelier to Manila, containing reproductions in fac-simile of hitherto unpublished letters of George Dewey during the Admiral's naval career and extracts from his log-book, by Adelbert M. Dewey, assisted by members of the immediate family. Embellished with over two hundred and fifty illustrations. Authorized ed. New York, The Woolfall company, 1899.
Dewey, Adelbert Milton, 1857–

LAC 15165

Life and letters of Alexander Hays, brevet colonel United States army, brigadier general and brevet major general United States volunteers. Ed. and arranged with notes and contemporary history by George Thornton Fleming from data compiled by Gilbert Adams Hays. Pittsburgh, Pa., 1919.
Fleming, George Thornton, 1855–1928.

LAC 13070

The life and letters of Capt. John Brown who was executed at Charlestown, Virginia, Dec. 2, 1859, for an armed attack upon American slavery; with notices of some of his confederates. Ed. by Richard D. Webb. London, Smith, Elder and co., 1861.
Webb, Richard Davis.

LAC 15219

Life and letters of Catharine M. Sedgwick. Ed. by Mary E. Dewey. New York, Harper & brothers, 1872, [c1871]
Sedgwick, Catharine Maria, 1789–1867.

LAC 11881

The life and letters of Christopher Pearse Cranch, by his daughter Leonora Cranch Scott. Boston and New York, Houghton Mifflin company, 1917.
Cranch, Christopher Pearse, 1813–1892.

LAC 22114

Life and letters of Edwin Lawrence Godkin; ed. by Rollo Ogden. New York, The Macmillan company; London, Macmillan & co., ltd., 1907.
Godkin, Edwin Lawrence, 1831–1902.

LAC 12119

The life and letters of Fitz-Greene Halleck. New York, D. Appleton and company, 1869.
Wilson, James Grant, 1832–1914.

LAC 14632

Life and letters of General Thomas J. Jackson (Stonewall Jackson) by his wife, Mary Anna Jackson, with an introduction by Henry M. Field. New York, Harper & brothers, 1892, [c1891]
Jackson, Mary Anna, 1831–1915.

LAC 20125

The life and letters of George Bancroft. New York, C. Scribner's sons, 1908.
Howe, Mark Antony De Wolfe, 1864–1960.

LAC 12491

Life and letters of George Cabot. [2d ed.] Boston, Little, Brown, and company, 1878.
Lodge, Henry Cabot, 1850–1924.

LAC 20227-28

The life and letters of George Gordon Meade, major-general United States army, by George Meade. Ed. by George Gordon Meade. New York, C. Scribner's sons, 1913.
Meade, George Gordon, 1815–1872.

LAC 10965

Life and letters of Horace Bushnell... New York, Charles Scribner's sons, 1903.
Cheney, Mary A   ed.

LAC 23799-800

The life and letters of James Abram Garfield. New Haven, Yale university press; [etc., etc.] 1925.
Smith, Theodore Clarke, 1870–

LAC 12372

The life and letters of James Henley Thornwell ... ex-president of the South Carolina college, late professor of theology in the Theological seminary at Columbia, South Carolina. Richmond, Whittet & Shepperson, 1875.
Palmer, Benjamin Morgan, 1818–1902.

LAC 12951

Life and letters of Joel Barlow, LL. D., poet, statesman, philosopher, with extracts from his works and hitherto unpublished poems. New York & London, G. P. Putnam's sons, 1886.
Todd, Charles Burr, 1849–

LAC 12885

The life and letters of John Brown, liberator of Kansas, and martyr of Virginia. Ed. by F. B. Sanborn. [2d ed.] Boston, Roberts brothers, 1891.
Sanborn, Franklin Benjamin, 1831–1917.

LAC 20120-21

The life and letters of John Fiske. Boston and New York, Houghton Mifflin company, 1917.
Clark, John Spencer, 1835–1920.

LAC 20944

Life and letters of John Greenleaf Whittier. Boston and New York, Houghton, Mifflin and company, 1899, [c1894]
Pickard, Samuel Thomas, 1828–1915.

LAC 20020

The life and letters of John Hay. Boston and New York, Houghton Mifflin company, 1915.
Thayer, William Roscoe, 1859–1923.

LAC 21862-63

Life and letters of John Winthrop, governor of the Massachusetts-Bay company at their emigration to New-England, 1630. 2d ed., with additional letters. Boston, Little, Brown, and co., 1869.
Winthrop, Robert Charles, 1809–1894.

LAC 21182–83
Life and letters of Joseph Story, associate justice of the Supreme court of the United States, and Dane professor of law at Harvard university. Ed. by his son, William W. Story. Boston, C. C. Little and J. Brown, 1851.
Story, William Wetmore, 1819–1895, *ed.*

LAC 12610
Life and letters of Josiah Dwight Whitney. With illustrations. Boston and New York, Houghton Mifflin company, 1909.
Brewster, Edwin Tenney, 1866–

LAC 20637
Life and letters of Oliver Wendell Holmes. Boston and New York, Houghton, Mifflin and company, 1896.
Morse, John Torrey, 1840–1937.

LAC 21348–49
Life and letters of Peter and Susan Lesley, ed. by their daughter, Mary Lesley Ames. New York and London, G. P. Putnam's sons, 1909.
Ames, Mary, *ed.*

LAC 15795
The life and letters of Robert Lewis Dabney. Richmond, Va., The Presbyterian committee of publication [c1903]
Johnson, Thomas Cary, 1859–

LAC 11422
The life and letters of Roscoe Conkling, orator, statesman, advocate. New York, C. L. Webster & company, 1889.
Conkling, Alfred Ronald, 1850–1917.

LAC 14245
Life and letters of Samuel Holden Parsons, major-general in the continental army and chief judge of the Northwestern territory, 1737–1789. Binghamton, N. Y., Otseningo publishing co., 1905.
Hall, Charles Samuel, 1827–

LAC 11162
The life and letters of Samuel Wells Williams, LL. D., missionary, diplomatist, sinologue. By his son Frederick Wells Williams. New York and London, G. P. Putnam's sons, 1889.
Williams, Frederick Wells, 1857–1928.

LAC 15057
Life and letters of Thomas Kilby Smith, brevet major-general, United States volunteers, 1820–1887; by his son, Walter George Smith. New York and London, G. P. Putnam's sons, 1898.
Smith, Walter George, 1854–1924.

LAC 15111
The life and letters of Washington Allston. With reproductions from Allston's pictures. New York, C. Scribner's sons, 1892.
Flagg, Jared Bradley, 1820–1899.

LAC 20631–32
The life and letters of Washington Irving, by his nephew Pierre M. Irving. New York, G. P. Putnam, 1862–1864.
Irving, Pierre Munroe, 1803–1876.

LAC 20918
Life and letters of William Barton Rogers, ed. by his wife, with the assistance of William T. Sedgwick. Boston and New York, Houghton, Mifflin and company, 1896.
Rogers, William Barton, 1804–1882.

LAC 20688
Life and liberty in America; or, Sketches of a tour in the United States and Canada, in 1857–8. London, Smith, Elder and co., 1859.
Mackay, Charles, 1814–1889.

LAC 16363
The life and memoirs of Comte Regis de Trobriand, major-general in the army of the United States, by his daughter, Marie Caroline Post (Mrs. Charles Alfred Post); with two portraits in photogravure. New York, E. P. Dutton & company, 1910.
Post, Marie Caroline, 1845–1926.

LAC 14798
Life and public services of Martin R. Delany, subassistant commissioner, Bureau relief of refugees, freedmen, and of abandoned lands, and late major 104th U.S. colored troops. Boston, Lee and Shepard, 1883.
Rollin, Frank A.

LAC 12757
The life and public services of Salmon Portland Chase, United States senator and governor of Ohio; secretary of the Treasury, and chief-justice of the United States. By J. W. Schuckers. To which is added, the eulogy on Mr. Chase, delivered by William M. Evarts, before the alumni of Dartmouth college, June 24, 1874. New York, D. Appleton and company, 1874.
Schuckers, Jacob W.

LAC 20852–53
The life and public services of Samuel Adams, being a narrative of his acts and opinions, and of his agency in producing and forwarding the American revolution. With extracts from his correspondence, state papers, and political essays. Boston, Little, Brown, and company, 1865.
Wells, William Vincent, 1826–1876.

LAC 10034
The life & public services of Simon Sterne. London, Macmillan and co., limited; New York, The Macmillan company, 1903.
Foord, John, 1842–1922.

LAC 12469
Life and public services of Thomas A. Hendricks with selected speeches and writings, by John W. Holcombe and Hubert M. Skinner. Indianapolis, Carlon and Hollenbeck, 1886.
Holcombe, John Walker, 1853–1940.

LAC 20218
Life and public services of William Pitt Fessenden, United States senator from Maine 1854–1864; secretary of the Treasury 1864–1865; United States senator from Maine 1865–1869, by his son Francis Fessenden. Boston and New York, Houghton, Mifflin and company, 1907.
Fessenden, Francis, 1839–1906.

LAC 14983
The life and reminiscences of Robert G. Ingersoll.
New York, The National weekly publishing co.; [etc.,
etc., 1904]
Smith, Edward Garstin.

LAC 12068
Life and sayings of Mrs. Partington, and others of the
family. New York, J. C. Derby, 1854.
Shillaber, Benjamin Penhallow, 1814–1890, ed.

LAC 16533
Life and sermons of Dwight L. Moody. Containing
the story of his birth and early life–a history of his wonderful power and success as an evangelist; also, twenty-
four of his best sermons–full particulars of his death and
funeral services, comments of the press, and eulogies by
prominent men. Edited by J. S. Ogilvie. With introduction by George R. Scott. New York, J. S. Ogilvie publishing company [c1900]
Moody, Dwight Lyman, 1837–1899.

LAC 11429
Life and speeches of Thomas Corwin: orator, lawyer
and statesman; ed. by Josiah Morrow. Cincinnati, W. H.
Anderson & co., 1896.
Corwin, Thomas, 1794–1865.

LAC 14507
The life and speeches of Thos. E. Watson. 2d ed.
Thomson, Ga., Jeffersonian Pub., 1911.
Watson, Thomas Edward, 1856–1922.

LAC 11289
Life and times in Hopkinton, N. H. ... Concord,
N. H., Republican press association, 1890.
Lord, Charles Chase, 1841–1911.

LAC 15668
The life and times of A. B. Durand. New York, C.
Scribner's sons, 1894.
Durand, John, 1822–1908.

LAC 11517
The life and times of Aaron Burr, lieutenant-colonel in
the army of the revolution, United States senator, vice-
president of the United States, etc. 10th ed. New York,
Mason brothers; [etc., etc.] 1858.
Parton, James, 1822–1891.

LAC 22582–83
Life and times of Benjamin Franklin. New York, Ma-
son brothers; Boston, Mason & Hamlin; [etc., etc.] 1864.
Parton, James, 1822–1891.

LAC 10168
The life and times of C. G. Memminger. Richmond,
Va., Everett Waddey co., 1893.
Capers, Henry Dickson, 1835–1910.

LAC 14308
The life and times of Charles Follen McKim. Boston
and New York, Houghton Mifflin company, 1929.
Moore, Charles, 1855–1942.

LAC 20281–82
Life and times of David Humphreys, soldier–statesman–poet, "belov'd of Washington." New York and London, G. P. Putnam's sons, 1917.
Humphreys, Francis Landon, 1858–

LAC 10981
The life and times of David Zeisberger, the western
pioneer and apostle of the Indians. Philadelphia, J. B.
Lippincott & co., 1870.
De Schweinitz, Edmund Alexander, 1825–1887.

LAC 10829
Life and times of Frederick Douglass, written by himself. His early life as a slave, his escape from bondage,
and his complete history to the present time, including
his connection with the anti-slavery movement... With an
introduction, by Mr. George L. Ruffin. Hartford, Conn.,
Park publishing co., 1884.
Douglass, Frederick, 1817–1895.

LAC 12457
The life and times of Hannibal Hamlin; by his grand-
son, Charles Eugene Hamlin. Cambridge, Printed at the
Riverside press, 1899.
Hamlin, Charles Eugene.

LAC 12498
The life and times of John Kelly, tribune of the people.
New York, The American news company, 1885.
McLaughlin, James Fairfax, 1839–1903.

LAC 11447
The life and times of Nelson Dingley, jr. Kalamazoo,
Mich., Ihling bros. & Everard, 1902.
Dingley, Edward Nelson, 1862–1930.

LAC 23028–29
The life and times of Philip Schuyler. New York, Shel-
don & company [1872]–73.
Lossing, Benson John, 1813–1891.

LAC 10759
Life and times of Red-Jacket, or Sa-go-ye-wat-ha; be-
ing the sequel to the history of the Six nations. New
York and London, Wiley and Putnam, 1841.
Stone, William Leete, 1792–1844.

LAC 20813
The life and times of Samuel Bowles. New York, The
Century co., 1885.
Merriam, George Spring, 1843–1914.

LAC 22660–62
The life and times of Silas Wright. Albany, The Argus
company, 1874.
Gillet, Ransom Hooker, 1800–1876.

LAC 21871–72
The life and times of Sir William Johnson, bart. Al-
bany, J. Munsell, 1865.
Stone, William Leete, 1835–1908.

LAC 20034
The life and times of Stephen Girard, mariner and
merchant. Philadelphia and London, J. B. Lippincott
company, 1918.
McMaster, John Bach, 1852–1932.

LAC 15929
The life and times of Thomas Jefferson. New York, D. Appleton and company, 1903.
Watson, Thomas Edward, 1856–1922.

LAC 10261
The life and times of William Lowndes Yancey. A history of political parties in the United States, from 1834 to 1864; especially as to the origin of the Confederate States. Birmingham [Ala.] Roberts & son, 1892.
Du Bose, John Witherspoon, 1836–1918.

LAC 20727–28
The life and voyages of Christopher Columbus; to which are added those of his companions. Author's rev. ed. ... New York, G. P. Putnam, 1869–1870.
Irving, Washington, 1783–1859.

LAC 12263
The life and work of John Williamson Nevin... Philadelphia, Reformed church publication house, 1889.
Appel, Theodore, 1823–1907.

LAC 21419–20
The life and work of Susan B. Anthony; including public addresses, her own letters and many from her contemporaries during fifty years, by Ida Husted Harper. A story of the evolution of the status of woman... Indianapolis and Kansas City, The Bowen-Merrill company, 1898–1908.
Harper, Ida, 1851–1931.

LAC 12299
The life and work of Thomas Dudley, the second governor of Massachusetts. Boston and New York, Houghton, Mifflin and company, 1899.
Jones, Augustine, 1835–

LAC 21069–71
Life and works of Horace Mann. Boston, Lee and Shepard; New York, C. T. Dillingham, 1891.
Mann, Horace, 1796–1859.

LAC 15107
The life and works of Winslow Homer. Boston and New York, Houghton Mifflin company, 1911.
Downes, William Howe, 1854–

LAC 12446
Life and writings of Alexander James Dallas. By his son George Mifflin Dallas. Philadelphia, J. B. Lippincott & co., 1871.
Dallas, Alexander James, 1759–1817.

LAC 11175
Life and writings of Amelia Bloomer. Boston, Arena publishing co., 1895.
Bloomer, Dexter C   1820–1900.

LAC 15147
The life and writings of De Witt Clinton, by William W. Campbell. New York, Baker and Scribner, 1849.
Clinton, De Witt, 1769–1828.

LAC 12058
Life and writings of Henry David Thoreau. London, W. Scott [1897]
Salt, Henry Stephens, 1851–1939.

LAC 20109–10
The life and writings of Jared Sparks, comprising selections from his journals and correspondence. Boston and New York, Houghton, Mifflin and company, 1893.
Adams, Herbert Baxter, 1850–1901.

LAC 12074
The life and writings of Major Jack Downing [pseud.] of Downingville, away down East in the state of Maine. Written by himself. Boston, Lilly, Wait, Colman, & Holden, 1833.
Smith, Seba, 1792–1868.

LAC 12614
The life and writings of Rafinesque. Prepared for the Filson club and read at its meeting, Monday, April 2, 1894. [Author's ed.] Louisville, Ky., J. P. Morton and company, 1895.
Call, Richard Ellsworth, 1856–

LAC 16936
Life, art, and letters of George Inness, by George Inness, jr., illustrated with portraits and many reproductions of paintings, with an introduction by Elliott Daingerfield. New York, The Century co., 1917.
Inness, George, 1854–

LAC 40075
The life, crime, and capture of John Wilkes Booth, with a full sketch of the conspiracy of which he was the leader, and the pursuit, trial and execution of his accomplices. New York, Dick & Fitzgerald [c1865]
Townsend, George Alfred, 1841–1914.

LAC 40144
The life, experience and gospel labors of the Rt. Rev. Richard Allen, to which is annexed the rise and progress of the African Methodist Episcopal Church in the United States of America. Containing a narrative of the yellow fever in the year of Our Lord 1793. With an address to the people of color in the United States. [Philadelphia, Lee and Yeocum, c1887]
Allen, Richard, bp., 1760–1831.

LAC 13581
The life, history, and travels, of Kah-ge-ga-gah-bowh (George Copway), a young Indian chief of the Ojebwa nation, a convert to the Christian faith, and a missionary to his people for twelve years; with a sketch of the present state of the Ojebwa nation, in regard to Christianity and their future prospects. Also an appeal; with all the names of the chiefs now living, who have been Christianized, and the missionaries now laboring among them. Written by himself. 2d ed. Philadelphia, J. Harmstead, 1847.
Copway, George, Chippewa chief, 1818?–1863.

LAC 11371
Life in a New England town: 1787, 1788. Diary of John Quincy Adams, while a student in the office of Theophilus Parsons at Newburyport. Boston, Little, Brown and company, 1903.
Adams, John Quincy, pres. U.S., 1767–1848.

LAC 15181
Life in Dixie during the war. 1861–1862–1863–1864–1865. 3d ed. (enl.) Atlanta, Ga., C. P. Byrd, 1897.
Gay, Mary Ann Harris, *b.* 1827.

LAC 40086
Life in the iron-mills. [Boston, Ticknor and Fields, 1861]
Davis, Rebecca, 1831–1910.

LAC 11320
Life in the New world; or, Sketches of American society. By Seatsfield [!] Tr. from the German by Gustavus C. Hebbe, L. L. D., and James Mackay, M. A. New York, J. Winchester [c1844]
Sealsfield, Charles, 1793–1864.

LAC 13074
Life in Utah; or, The mysteries and crimes of Mormonism. Being an expose of the secret rites and ceremonies of the Latter-day saints, with a full and authentic history of polygamy and the Mormon sect from its origin to the present time. Philadelphia, Pa., Chicago, Ill. [etc.] National publishing company [c1870]
Beadle, John Hanson, 1840–1897.

LAC 22280–81
Life, journals and correspondence of Rev. Manasseh Cutler, L.L. D. By his grandchildren, William Parker Cutler and Julia Perkins Cutler. Cincinnati, R. Clarke & co., 1888.
Cutler, William Parker, 1812–1889.

LAC 20128–29
Life, letters, and journals of George Ticknor. London, Sampson, Low, Marston, Searle, & Rivington, 1876.
Ticknor, George, 1791–1871.

LAC 20477–78
Life, letters and travels of Father Pierre Jean de Smet, S. J., 1801–1873; missionary labors and adventures among the wild tribes of the North American Indians ... edited from the original unpublished manuscript journals and letter books and from his printed works, with historical, geographical, ethnological and other notes; also a life of Father de Smet by Hiram Martin Chittenden and Alfred Talbot Richardson. New York, F. P. Harper, 1905 [c1904]
Smet, Pierre Jean de, 1801–1873.

LAC 22208
Life, letters, and works of Louis Agassiz. New York and London, Macmillan and co., 1895.
Marcou, Jules, 1824–1898.

LAC 15117
Life masks.
Browere's life masks of great Americans. [New York] Printed at the De Vinne press for Doubleday and McClure company, 1899.
Hart, Charles Henry, 1847–1918.

LAC 15180
Life of A. P. Dostie; or, The conflict of New Orleans. New York, W. P. Tomlinson, 1868.
Reed, Emily Hazen.

LAC 12487
The life of Abraham Lincoln; from his birth to his inauguration as president. Boston, J. R. Osgood and company, 1872.
Lamon, Ward Hill, 1828–1893.

LAC 16404
The life of Adoniram Judson, by his son, Edward Judson. New York, A. D. F. Randolph & company [c1883]
Judson, Edward, 1844–1914.

LAC 11368
The life of Albert Gallatin. Philadelphia and London, J. B. Lippincott & co., 1879.
Adams, Henry, 1838–1918.

LAC 13391
Life of Albert R. Parsons, with brief history of the labor movement in America... Chicago, L. E. Parsons, 1889.
Parsons, Lucy Eldine.

LAC 10240
Life of Alexander H. Stephens, by Richard Malcolm Johnston and William Hand Browne. Philadelphia, J. B. Lippincott, 1878.
Johnston, Richard Malcolm, 1822–1898.

LAC 40066
The life of Alexander Hamilton. By John Williams (Anthony Pasquin) New York, Printed for the Hamilton club, 1865.
Williams, John, 1761–1818.

LAC 14479
Life of Andrew Hull Foote, rear-admiral United States navy. With a portrait and illustrations. New York, Harper & brothers, 1874.
Hoppin, James Mason, 1820–1906.

LAC 20275–77
Life of Andrew Jackson... New York, Mason brothers, 1860.
Parton, James, 1822–1891.

LAC 11420
Life of Andrew Jackson, president of the United States of America. Abridged and comp. by William Cobbett, M. P. for Oldham. London [Printed by Mills, Jowett, and Mills] 1834.
Cobbett, William, 1763–1835.

LAC 14658
The life of Andrew Jackson, to which is added an authentic narrative of the memorable achievements of the American army at New Orleans, in the winter of 1814, '15. New York, Derby & Jackson, 1857.
Walker, Alexander, 1819–1893.

LAC 21427
Life of Arthur Lee, LL. D., joint commissioner of the United States to the court of France, and sole commissioner to the courts of Spain and Prussia, during the revolutionary war. With his political and literary correspondence and his papers on diplomatic and political subjects, and the affairs of the United States during the same period. Boston, Wells and Lilly, 1829.
Lee, Richard Henry, 1794–1865.

LAC 20901
Life of Benjamin Silliman, M.D., LL. D., late professor of chemistry, mineralogy, and geology in Yale college. Chiefly from his manuscript reminiscences, diaries, and correspondence. New York, C. Scribner and company, 1866.
Fisher, George Park, 1827–1909.

LAC 15339
The life of Charles A. Dana. New York and London, Harper & brothers, 1907.
Wilson, James Harrison, 1837–1925.

LAC 21391
The life of Charles Carroll of Carrollton, 1737–1832, with his correspondence and public papers. New York & London, G. P. Putnam's sons, 1898.
Rowland, Kate Mason, d. 1916.

LAC 12626
Life of Charles Henry Davis, rear admiral, 1807–1877; by his son, Captain Charles H. Davis, U. S. N. Boston and New York, Houghton, Mifflin and company, 1899.
Davis, Charles Henry, 1845–1921.

LAC 11033
The life of Charles Hodge, D.D., LL.D., professor in the Theological seminary, Princeton, N. J., by his son, A. A. Hodge. New York, C. Scribner's sons [1880]
Hodge, Archibald Alexander, 1823–1886.

LAC 12504
The life of Charles Jared Ingersoll. By his grandson, William M. Meigs. Philadelphia, J. B. Lippincott company, 1900, [c1897]
Meigs, William Montgomery, 1852–1929.

LAC 13099
The life of Charles Loring Brace, chiefly told in his own letters; ed. by his daughter. With portraits. New York, C. Scribner's sons, 1894.
Brace, Charles Loring, 1826–1890.

LAC 16479
Life of Charles T. Walker... With an introd. by Robert Stuart MacArthur. New York, Negro Universities Press [1969]
Floyd, Silas Xavier, 1869–

LAC 11553
A life of Clement L. Vallandigham, by his brother, Rev. James L. Vallandigham. Baltimore, Turnbull brothers, 1872.
Vallandigham, James Laird, 1812–1904.

LAC 23030
The life of Commodore Oliver Hazard Perry. New-York, Harper & brothers, 1841, [c1840]
Mackenzie, Alexander Slidell, 1803–1848.

LAC 20786–87
Life of Daniel Webster. By George Ticknor Curtis, one of his literary executors. 4th ed. New York, D. Appleton and company, 1872.
Curtis, George Ticknor, 1812–1894.

LAC 15386
The life of David Glasgow Farragut, first admiral of the United States navy, embodying his journal and letters. By his son, Loyall Farragut. New York, D. Appleton and company, 1879.
Farragut, Loyall, 1844–

LAC 11530
Life of Dewitt Clinton. New York, Harper, 1840.
Renwick, James, 1790–1863.

LAC 13655
Life of Dorothea Lynde Dix. Boston and New York, Houghton, Mifflin and company, 1890.
Tiffany, Francis, 1827–1908.

LAC 22644
The life of Edgar Allan Poe, personal and literary, with his chief correspondence with men of letters. Boston and New York, Houghton Mifflin company, 1909.
Woodberry, George Edward, 1855–1930.

LAC 12475
Life of Edward Livingston. By Charles Havens Hunt. With an introduction by George Bancroft. New York, D. Appleton and company, 1864.
Hunt, Charles Havens.

LAC 15330
The life of Edwin Forrest. With reminiscences and personal recollections. By James Rees (Colley Cibber). With portrait and autograph. Philadelphia, T. B. Peterson & brothers [c1874]
Rees, James, 1802–1885.

LAC 20183
The life of Elbridge Gerry. With contemporary letters. To the close of the American revolution. Boston, Wells and Lilly, 1828–29.
Austin, James Trecothick, 1784–1870.

LAC 20871–76
Life of Eleuthere Irenee du Pont from contemporary correspondence ... translated from the French and with an introduction by B. G. du Pont. Newark, Del., University of Delaware press, 1923–27.
Du Pont, Bessie Gardner, ed. and tr.

LAC 13020
The life of Ezra Stiles, D. D., LL. D., a fellow of the American philosophical society; of the American academy of arts and sciences; of the Connecticut society of arts and sciences; a corresponding member of the Massachusetts historical society; professor of ecclesiastical history; and president of Yale college. Boston, Printed by Thomas & Andrews, 1798.
Holmes, Abiel, 1763–1837.

LAC 15783
The life of Father Hecker. By Rev. Walter Elliott. 2d ed. New York, The Columbus press, 1894, [c1891]
Elliott, Walter, 1842–1928.

LAC 15943
The life of Father Isaac Jogues, missionary priest of the Society of Jesus, slain by the Mohawk Iroquois, in the present state of New York, Oct. 18, 1646. By the Rev. Felix Martin, S. J. With Father Jogues' account of

the captivity and death of his companion, Rene Goupil, slain Sept. 29, 1642. Translated from the French by John Gilmary Shea. With a map of the Mohawk country, by Gen. John S. Clark. 3d ed. New York, Cincinnati [etc.] Benziger brothers [c1885]
Martin, Felix, 1804–1886.

LAC 12291
The life of Ferdinand Magellan and the first circumnavigation of the globe. 1480–1521. New York, Dodd, Mead & company [1890]
Guillemard, Francis Henry Hill, 1852–

LAC 15698
Life of Frederick William von Steuben, major general in the revolutionary army. By Friedrich Kapp. With an introduction by George Bancroft. New York, Mason brothers, 1859.
Kapp, Friedrich, 1824–1884.

LAC 14660
The life of General Francis Marion, a celebrated partisan officer, in the revolutionary war, against the British and Tories in South Carolina and Georgia, by Brig. Gen. P. Horry, of Marion's brigade, and M. L. Weems. Philadelphia, J. Allen; sold by J. B. Lippincott, Grambo & co., 1855.
Weems, Mason Locke, 1759–1825.

LAC 20831–32
The life of George Mason, 1725–1792, by Kate Mason Rowland, including his speeches, public papers, and correspondence; with an introduction by General Fitzhugh Lee. New York, London, G. P. Putnam's sons, 1892.
Rowland, Kate Mason, d. 1916.

LAC 21354–55
The life of George Washington, commander in chief of the American forces, during the war which established the independence of his country, and first president of the United States. Comp. under the inspection of the Honourable Bushrod Washington, from original papers... 2d ed., rev. and cor. by the author. Philadelphia, J. Crissy, 1832–1850 [v. 1, 1850]
Marshall, John, 1755–1835, *comp.*

LAC 20848–50
The life of Gouverneur Morris, with selections from his correspondence and miscellaneous papers; detailing events in the American revolution, the French revolution, and in the political history of the United States. Boston, Gray and Bowen, 1832.
Sparks, Jared, 1789–1866.

LAC 13938
Life of Harriet Beecher Stowe, comp. from her letters and journals, by her son Charles Edward Stowe. Boston and New York. Houghton Mifflin and company, 1889.
Stowe, Harriet Elizabeth, 1811–1896.

LAC 12419
The life of Henry A. Wise of Virginia, 1806–1876. By his grandson, the late Barton H. Wise. New York, The Macmillan company; London, Macmillan & co., ltd., 1899.
Wise, Barton Haxall, 1865–1899.

LAC 10280
The life of Henry Bradley Plant, founder and president of the Plant system of railroads and steamships and also of the Southern express company. New York and London, G. P. Putnam's sons, 1898.
Smyth, George Hutchinson, 1837–

LAC 20834
Life of Henry Clay. Boston and New York, Houghton, Mifflin and company, 1888, [c1887]
Schurz, Carl, 1829–1906.

LAC 16667
Life of Henry Dunster, first president of Harvard college. Boston, J. R. Osgood and company, 1872.
Chaplin, Jeremiah, 1813–1886.

LAC 15184
The life of Henry Laurens, with a sketch of the life of Lieutenant-Colonel John Laurens. New York and London, G. P. Putnam's sons, 1915.
Wallace, David Duncan, 1874–

LAC 16170
The life of Hon. Nathaniel Chipman, LL.D. formerly member of the United States Senate, and chief justice of the state of Vermont. With selections from his miscellaneous papers. By his brother, Daniel Chipman. Boston, C. C. Little and J. Brown, 1846.
Chipman, Daniel, 1765–1850.

LAC 11391
The life of Horace Binney, with selections from his letters. Philadelphia and London, J. B. Lippincott company, 1903.
Binney, Charles Chauncey, 1855–1913.

LAC 11518
The life of Horace Greeley, editor of the New York tribune. New York, Mason brothers, 1855.
Parton, James, 1822–1891.

LAC 10060
The life of James Dwight Dana, scientific explorer, mineralogist, geologist, zoologist, professor in Yale university. New York and London, Harper & brothers, 1899.
Gilman, Daniel Coit, 1831–1908.

LAC 22751
The life of James McNeill Whistler, by E. R. and J. Pennell. Philadelphia, J. B. Lippincott company; London, W. Heinemann, 1908.
Pennell, Elizabeth, 1855–1936.

LAC 12476
The life of James Madison. New York, Doubleday, Page & co., 1902.
Hunt, Gaillard, 1862–1924.

LAC 13818
The life of James W. Grimes, governor of Iowa, 1854–1858; a senator of the United States, 1859–1869. New York, D. Appleton and company, 1876.
Salter, William, 1821–1910.

LAC 14207
Life of Jay Gould, how he made his millions... By Murat Halstead and J. Frank Beale, jr.; to which are added Sketches of the great money kings of the present day more or less associated with him. By W. Fletcher Johnson, esq. [Philadelphia] Edgewood publishing co., 1892.
Halstead, Murat, 1829–1908.

LAC 12411
Life of Jefferson Davis, with a secret history of the Southern Confederacy, gathered "behind the scenes in Richmond." Containing curious and extraordinary information of the principal southern characters in the late war, in connection with President Davis, and in relation to the various intrigues of his administration. Philadelphia, Chicago [etc.] National publishing company [c1869]
Pollard, Edward Alfred, 1831–1872.

LAC 21353
The life of John A. Andrew, governor of Massachusetts, 1861–1865. Boston and New York, Houghton, Mifflin and company, 1904.
Pearson, Henry Greenleaf.

LAC 20595
The life of John Adams. Begun by John Quincy Adams. Completed by Charles Francis Adams. Rev. and cor. Philadelphia, J. B. Lippincott & co., 1871.
Adams, Charles Francis, 1807–1886.

LAC 15469
Life of John Albert Johnson, three times governor of Minnesota, by Frank A. Day and Theodore M. Knappen. Chicago, Forbes & company, 1910.
Day, Frank A.

LAC 16552
The life of John Ancrum Winslow, rear-admiral, United States navy, who commanded the U.S. steamer "Kearsarge" in her action with the Confederate cruiser "Alabama". [2d ed.] New York and London, G. P. Putnam's sons, 1905, [c1901]
Ellicott, John Morris, 1859–

LAC 11089
Life of John Boyle O'Reilly, by James Jeffrey Roche. Together with his complete poems and speeches, ed. by Mrs. John Boyle O'Reilly. Introduction by His Eminence, James cardinal Gibbons. New York, Cassell publishing company [c1891]
Roche, James Jeffrey, 1847–1908.

LAC 14157
Life of John C. Calhoun. Being a view of the principal events of his career and an account of his contributions to economic and political science. Charleston, S. C., Walker, Evans & Cogswell co., 1903.
Pinckney, Gustavus M.

LAC 23031
The life of John Collins Warren, M. D., comp. chiefly from his autobiography and journals. Boston, Ticknor and Fields, 1860.
Warren, Edward, 1804–1878, *comp.*

LAC 14962
Life of John Eliot, the apostle to the Indians. Boston, Hilliard, Gray & co., 1836.
Francis, Convers, 1795–1863.

LAC 20894
The life of John Ericsson. New York, C. Scribner's sons, 1890.
Church, William Conant, 1836–1917.

LAC 12705
Life of John Fitch, the inventor of the steam-boat. Philadelphia, J. B. Lippincott & co., 1878.
Westcott, Thompson, 1820–1888.

LAC 20208
The life of John J. Crittenden, with selections from his correspondence and speeches. Ed. by his daughter, Mrs. Chapman Coleman. Philadelphia, J. B. Lippincott & co., 1873, [c1871]
Coleman, Ann Mary Butler, 1813–1891.

LAC 11629
Life of John Jacob Astor. To which is appended a copy of his last will. New York, The American news company, 1865.
Parton, James, 1822–1891.

LAC 12593
The life of John James Audubon, the naturalist. Ed. by his widow. With an introduction by Jas. Grant Wilson. New York, G. P. Putnam & son, 1869.
Audubon, John James, 1785–1851.

LAC 20254–55
The life of John Jay: with selections from his correspondence and miscellaneous papers. By his son, William Jay. New York, J. & J. Harper, 1833.
Jay, William, 1789–1858.

LAC 13317
The life of John Ledyard, the American traveller; comprising selections from his journals and correspondence. Cambridge [Mass.] Hilliard and Brown; New York, G. & C. Carvill; [etc., etc.] 1828.
Sparks, Jared, 1789–1866.

LAC 23003–6
The life of John Marshall. Boston and New York, Houghton Mifflin company [c1916–19]
Beveridge, Albert Jeremiah, 1862–1927.

LAC 21014
Life of John Mitchel. London, K. Paul, Trench & co., 1888.
Dillon, William, 1850–

LAC 12099
The life of John Pendleton Kennedy. New York, G. P. Putnam & sons, 1871.
Tuckerman, Henry Theodore, 1813–1871.

LAC 12892
The life of John Thompson, a fugitive slave; containing his history of 25 years in bondage, and his providential escape. Written by himself. New York, Negro Universities Press [1968]
Thompson, John, *b.* 1812.

LAC 13459

The life of Jonathan Baldwin Turner, by his daughter Mary Turner Carriel. [Jacksonville? Ill.] 1911.
Carriel, Mary, 1845–

LAC 22612–13

Life of Joseph Brant-Thayendanegea: including the border wars of the American revolution, and sketches of the Indian campaigns of Generals Harmar, St. Clair, and Wayne. And other matters connected with the Indian relations of the United States and Great Britain, from the peace of 1783 to the Indian peace of 1795. New York, A. V. Blake, 1838.
Stone, William Leete, 1792–1844.

LAC 12620

The life of Joseph Priestley, LL. D., F. R. S., &c. &c., with critical observations on his works. Birmingham, Printed by Wilks, Grafton, & co., 1804.
Corry, John, *fl.* 1825.

LAC 10750

The life of Joshua R. Giddings. Chicago, A. C. McClurg and co., 1892.
Julian, George Washington, 1817–1899.

LAC 40137

The life of Josiah Henson, formerly a slave, now an inhabitant of Canada, as narrated by himself. Boston, A. D. Phelps, 1849.
Henson, Josiah, 1789–1883.

LAC 11525

Life of Josiah Quincy of Massachusetts. By his son Edmund Quincy. Boston, Ticknor and Fields, 1868, [c1867]
Quincy, Edmund, 1808–1877.

LAC 12555

The life of Lyman Trumbull. Boston and New York, Houghton Mifflin company, 1913.
White, Horace, 1834–1916.

LAC 11431

The life of Martin Van Buren, heir-apparent to the "government," and the appointed successor of General Andrew Jackson. Containing every authentic particular by which his extraordinary character has been formed. With a concise history of the events that have occasioned his unparalleled elevation; together with a review of his policy as a statesman. 16th ed. Philadelphia, R. Wright, 1837, [c1835]
Crockett, David, 1786–1836.

LAC 13970

A life of Matthew Fontaine Maury... Comp. by his daughter, Diana Fontaine Maury Corbin. London, S. Low, Marston, Searle, & Rivington, limited, 1888.
Corbin, Diana Fontaine.

LAC 23460–61

The life of Nathanael Greene, major-general in the army of the revolution... New York, Hurd and Houghton, 1871.
Greene, George Washington, 1811–1883.

LAC 11875

Life of Nathaniel Hawthorne. London, W. Scott; [etc., etc. c1890]
Conway, Moncure Daniel, 1832–1907.

LAC 14145

The life of Nathaniel Macon. Raleigh, N. C., Edwards & Broughton, printers, 1903.
Dodd, William Edward, 1869–1940.

LAC 12911

The life of Olaudah Equiano, or Gustavus Vassa, the African. Written by himself. Two volumes in one. Boston, I. Knapp, 1837.
Equiano, Olaudah.

LAC 20222–23

Life of Oliver P. Morton, including his important speeches. Indianapolis-Kansas City, The Bowen-Merrill company, 1899.
Foulke, William Dudley, 1848–1935.

LAC 11857

The life of P. T. Barnum, written by himself. New-York, Redfield, 1855.
Barnum, Phineas Taylor, 1810–1891.

LAC 11439

Life of Patrick A. Collins, with some of his most notable public addresses; written, compiled, and edited by M. P. Curran. Norwood, Mass., The Norwood press, 1906.
Curran, Michael Philip, 1848–

LAC 22290

The life of Paul Jones. New York, Harper & brothers, 1845.
Mackenzie, Alexander Slidell, 1803–1848.

LAC 15378

Life of Pauline Cushman. The celebrated Union spy and scout. Comprising her early history; her entry into the secret service of the Army of the Cumberland, and exciting adventures with the rebel chieftains and others while within the enemy's lines: together with her capture and sentence to death by General Bragg and final rescue by the Union army under General Rosecrans. The whole carefully prepared from her notes and memoranda. Philadelphia, J. E. Potter, 1865.
Sarmiento, Ferdinand L.

LAC 14464

The life of Philip Schaff, in part autobiographical. New York, C. Scribner's sons, 1897.
Schaff, David Schley, 1852–

LAC 11423

The life of Preston B. Plumb, 1837–1891, United States senator from Kansas for the fourteen years from 1877 to 1891, "a pioneer of the progressive movement in America" ... Chicago, Browne & Howell company, 1913.
Connelley, William Elsey, 1855–1930.

LAC 10339

The life of railway men, together with a brief sketch and history of the great railway organizations, their aims and purposes, also a true and scientific solution of the great labor problem as seen from the inside... Chicago, Press of the H. O. Shepard co. [c1905]
Feick, Fred L   1878–

LAC 20126–27
The life of reason; or, The phases of human progress.
New York, C. Scribner's sons, 1905–26.
Santayana, George, 1863–1952.

LAC 15021
The life of Rev. Charles Nerinckx: with a chapter on the early Catholic missions of Kentucky; copious notes on the progress of Catholicity in the United States of America, from 1800 to 1825; an account of the establishment of the Society of Jesus in Missouri; and an historical sketch of the Sisterhood of Loretto in Kentucky, Missouri, New Mexico, etc. By Rev. Camillus P. Maes. Cincinnati, R. Clarke & co., 1880.
Maes, Camillus Paul, *bp.*, 1846–1915.

LAC 16941
The life of Rev. John Jasper, pastor of Sixth Mt. Zion Baptist church, Richmond, Va.; from his birth to the present time, with his theory on the rotation of the sun. Richmond, Va., R. T. Hill & co., 1884.
Randolph, Edwin Archer, 1854–

LAC 14540
The life of Rev. John Murray... Written by himself. The records contain anecdotes of the writers' infancy, and are extended to some years after the commencement of his public labors in America. To which is added a brief continuation to the closing scene... 7th ed., stereotyped and improved, with notes and appendix, by Rev. L. S. Everett. Utica, N. Y., O. Hutchinson, 1840.
Murray, John, 1741–1815.

LAC 11017
The life of Rev. Michael Schlatter; with a full account of his travels and labors among the Germans in Pennsylvania, New Jersey, Maryland and Virginia; including his services as chaplain in the French and Indian war, and in the war of the revolution. 1716 to 1790. By Rev. H. Harbaugh. Philadelphia, Lindsay & Blakiston, 1857.
Harbaugh, Henry, 1817–1867.

LAC 10064
The life of Robert Fulton and a history of steam navigation. New York and London, G. P. Putnam's sons, 1886.
Knox, Thomas Wallace, 1835–1896

LAC 12618
The life of Robert Fulton, by his friend Cadwallader D. Colden. Read before the Literary and philosophical society of New York. Comprising some account of the invention, progress, and establishment of steam boats. With an appendix. New-York; Published by Kirk & Mercein, no. 22 Wall-street, 1817.
Colden, Cadwallader David, 1769–1834.

LAC 20417
The life of Robert Owen. Written by himself. With selections from his writings and correspondence. v. 1–1A. London, E. Wilson, 1857–58.
Owen, Robert, 1771–1858.

LAC 12375
The life of Robert Toombs. New York, The Macmillan company, 1913.
Phillips, Ulrich Bonnell, 1877–1934.

LAC 11402
The life of Rufus Choate. 2d ed. Boston, Little, Brown, and company, 1870.
Brown, Samuel Gilman, 1813–1885.

LAC 20854–55
The life of Rutherford Birchard Hayes, nineteenth president of the United States. With portraits and other illustrations... Boston and New York, Houghton, Mifflin company, 1914.
Williams, Charles Richard, 1853–1927.

LAC 11488
The life of Sam Houston. (The only authentic memoir of him ever published)... New-York, J. C. Derby; Boston, Phillips, Sampson & co.; [etc., etc.] 1855.
Lester, Charles Edwards, 1815–1890.

LAC 20318
The life of Samuel J. Tilden. New York, Harper & brothers, 1895.
Bigelow, John, 1817–1911.

LAC 12559
Life of Sir Henry Vane the Younger, statesman & mystic (1613–1662) London, The Saint Catherine press, 1913.
Willcock, John, 1853–1931.

LAC 15031
Life of Tecumseh, and his brother the prophet; with a historical sketch of the Shawanoe Indians. Cincinnati, Anderson, Gates & Wright, 1858.
Drake, Benjamin, 1794–1841.

LAC 12752
Life of the Hon. Jeremiah Smith, LL. D., member of Congress during Washington's administration, judge of the United States Circuit court, chief justice of New Hampshire, etc. Boston, C. C. Little and J. Brown, 1845.
Morison, John Hopkins, 1808–1896.

LAC 11021
Life of the Most Reverend John Hughes, D. D., first archbishop of New York. With extracts from his private correspondence. New York, D. Appleton and company, 1866.
Hassard, John Rose Greene, 1836–1888.

LAC 15791
The life of the Most Rev. M. J. Spalding, D. D., archbishop of Baltimore. New York and San Francisco, Christian press association publishing co. [187–?]
Spalding, John Lancaster, *abp.*, 1840–1916.

LAC 11210
The life of Thomas Eddy; comprising an extensive correspondence with many of the most distinguished philosophers and philanthropists of this and other countries. New York, Conner & Cooke, 1834.
Knapp, Samuel Lorenzo, 1783–1838.

LAC 11037
The life of Thomas Hutchinson, royal governor of the province of Massachusetts Bay. Boston and New York, Houghton, Mifflin and company, 1896.
Hosmer, James Kendall, 1834–1927.

LAC 20278–80
The life of Thomas Jefferson. New York, Derby & Jackson, 1858.
Randall, Henry Stephens, 1811–1876.

LAC 14947
The life of Thomas Paine; mover of the "Declaration of independence;" secretary of foreign affairs under the first American Congress; member of the National convention of France; author of "Common sense," "The crisis," "Rights of man," "Age of reason," &c., &c.: the man, whose motto was, "The world is my country; to do good my religion." Embracing practical considerations on human rights; demonstrating that man tends irrepressibly to actual freedom; and showing a liberty-aim connection in the action of the world's three great author-heroes,–Rousseau, Paine, and Comte. New York, D. M. Bennett, 1877.
Blanchard, Calvin, *author of "The religion of science."*

LAC 20261–62
Life of Thurlow Weed including his autobiography and a memoir... [Boston, New York, Houghton, Mifflin and company; etc., etc., 1883–84]
Weed, Thurlow, 1797–1882.

LAC 22651–53
The life of Timothy Pickering. By his son, Octavius Pickering. Boston, Little, Brown, and company, 1867–73.
Pickering, Octavius, 1791–1868.

LAC 13855
A life of travels and researches in North America and south Europe; or, Outlines of the life, travels and researches of C. S. Rafinesque... Containing his travels in North America and the south of Europe; the Atlantic Ocean, Mediterranean, Sicily, Azores, &c., from 1802 to 1835–with sketches of his scientific and historical researches &c. ... Philadelphia, Printed for the author by F. Turner, 1836.
Rafinesque, Constantine Samuel, 1783–1840.

LAC 12561
The life of Ulysses S. Grant, general of the armies of the United States. By Charles A. Dana and J. H. Wilson. Springfield, Mass., Gurdon Bill & company; Cincinnati, H. C. Johnson; [etc., etc.] 1868.
Wilson, James Harrison, 1837–1925.

LAC 11831
A life of Walt Whitman. With thirty-three illustrations. London, Methuen & co. [1905]
Binns, Henry Bryan, 1873–

LAC 23222
Life of Walter Quintin Gresham, 1832–1895. Chicago, Rand, McNally & company, 1919.
Gresham, Matilda, 1839–

LAC 20486–87
The life of Whitelaw Reid. New York, C. Scribner's sons, 1921.
Cortissoz, Royal.

LAC 10964
The life of William Ellery Channing, D. D. The Centenary memorial ed. Boston, American Unitarian association, 1904, [c1880]
Channing, William Henry, 1810–1884.

LAC 40113
Life of William Grimes, the runaway slave. Written by himself. New-York, 1825.
Grimes, William, *b.* 1784.

LAC 10554
Life of William Hickling Prescott. Boston, Ticknor & Fields, 1864.
Ticknor, George, 1791–1871.

LAC 15256
The life of William Penn: with selections from his correspondence and autobiography. 2d ed., rev. ... Philadelphia, Lippincott, Grambo, 1852.
Janney, Samuel Macpherson, 1801–1880.

LAC 12941
The life of William Pinkney, by his nephew, the Rev. William Pinkney. New York, D. Appleton and company, 1853.
Pinkney, William, *bp.*, 1810–1883.

LAC 12513
Life of William Plumer, by his son, William Plumer, junior. Ed., with a sketch of the author's life, by A. P. Peabody. Boston, Phillips, Sampson and company; [etc., etc.] 1857.
Plumer, William, 1789–1854.

LAC 14179
The life of young Sir Henry Vane, governor of Massachusetts Bay, and leader of the Long parliament; with a consideration of the English commonwealth as a forecast of America. London, Sampson Low, Marston, Searle & Rivington, ltd., 1888.
Hosmer, James Kendall, 1834–1927.

LAC 13123
Life on a ranch; ranch notes in Kansas, Colorado, the Indian Territory, and northern Texas. New York, D. Appleton and company, 1884.
Aldridge, Reginald.

LAC 12558
Life on the circuit with Lincoln. With sketches of Generals Grant, Sherman and McClellan, Judge Davis, Leonard Swett, and other contemporaries. Boston, Estes and Lauriat [1892]
Whitney, Henry Clay, 1831–1905.

LAC 15767
Life on the stage; my personal experiences and recollections. New York, McClure, Phillips & co., 1902, [c1901]
Morris, Clara, 1848–1925.

LAC 15435
Life on the westen [!] rivers. Pittsburgh, Pa., McNary & Simpson [1901]
Habermehl, John.

LAC 21320
The life, public services, addresses and letters of Elias Boudinot, LL.D., president of the Continental congress; ed. by J. J. Boudinot. Boston and New York, Houghton, Mifflin and company, 1896.
Boudinot, Elias, 1740–1821.

LAC 11660
A life span and reminiscences of railway mail service.
Philadelphia, Pa., Deemer & Jaisohn [c1910]
White, James E   1846–1916.

LAC 13403
The life, speeches, labors and essays of William H. Sylvis, late president of the Iron-moulders' international union; and also of the National labor union. By his brother James C. Sylvis. Philadelphia, Claxton, Remsen & Haffelfinger, 1872.
Sylvis, William H   1828–1869.

LAC 13202
Life, speeches, state papers and public services of Gov. Oliver P. Morton. Written and compiled by William M. French. Indianapolis, S. L. Marrow [18–]
French, William M.

LAC 10399
The life story of J. Pierpont Morgan; a biography. New York, Sturgis & Walton company, 1911.
Hovey, Carl, 1875–

LAC 13275
The life, studies, and works of Benjamin West, esq., president of the Royal academy of London, composed from materials furnished by himself. London, Printed for T. Cadell and W. Davies; [etc., etc.] 1820.
Galt, John.

LAC 10591
Life, times, and correspondence of James Manning, and the early history of Brown university. Boston, Gould and Lincoln; New York, Sheldon and company; [etc., etc.] 1864.
Guild, Reuben Aldridge, 1822–1899.

LAC 13119
The life, travels and opinions of Benjamin Lundy, including his journeys to Texas and Mexico, with a sketch of contemporary events, and a notice of the revolution in Hayti. Compiled under the direction and on behalf of his children. Philadelphia, W. D. Parrish, 1847.
Lundy, Benjamin, 1789–1839.

LAC 15838
The life, trial, and execution of Captain John Brown, known as Old Brown of Ossawatomie. Compiled from official and authentic sources. New York, Da Capo Press [1969]
Brown, John, 1800–1859, *defendant*.

LAC 12666
Light waves and their uses. Chicago, The University of Chicago press, 1903.
Michelson, Albert Abraham, 1852–1931.

LAC 16221
Lights and shades in San Francisco. With appropriate illustrations... San Francisco, Printed by A. L. Bancroft & company, 1876.
Lloyd, Benjamin E.

LAC 22886–87
Lights and shadows of American life. London, H. Colburn and R. Bentley, 1832.
Mitford, Mary Russell, 1787–1855, *ed.*

LAC 40052
Lights and shadows of Chinatown. [San Francisco, Press of H. S. Crocker company] c1896.
Bode, William Walter.

LAC 16748
The limitations of human responsibility. Boston, Gould, Kendall & Lincoln, 1838.
Wayland, Francis, 1796–1865.

LAC 40146
The limitations of reform. Baccalaureate address, June 17, 1894. Madison, Tracy, Gibbs & co., 1894.
Adams, Charles Kendall, 1835–1902.

LAC 12581–82
Limitations of the taxing power, including limitations upon public indebtedness; a treatise upon the constitutional law governing taxation and the incurrence of public debt in the United States, in the several states, and in the territories. San Francisco, Bancroft-Whitney company, 1906.
Gray, James McIlvaine, 1872–

LAC 40050
The limits of education.
An address on the limits of education, read before the Massachusetts institute of technology, November 16, 1865. By Jacob Bigelow, M. D. Boston, E. P. Dutton & company, 1865.
Bigelow, Jacob, 1787–1879.

LAC 10532
The limits of evolution, and other essays illustrating the metaphysical theory of personal idealism. 2d ed. rev. & enl. New York, The Macmillan company; London, Macmillan & co., ltd., 1905.
Howison, George Holmes, 1834–1917.

LAC 12551
Lincoln and Seward. Remarks upon the memorial address of Chas. Francis Adams, on the late William H. Seward, with incidents and comments illustrative of the measures and policy of the administration of Abraham Lincoln. And views as to the relative positions of the late President and secretary of state. New York, Sheldon & company, 1874.
Welles, Gideon, 1802–1878.

LAC 40064
Lincoln and Stanton; a study of the war administration of 1861 and 1862, with special consideration of some recent statements of Gen. Geo. B. McClellan. New York & London, G. P. Putnam's sons, 1885.
Kelley, William Darrah, 1814–1890.

LAC 40150
Lincoln in caricature. Illustrated with thirty-two plates. [New York, The G. A. Powers printing company] 1903.
Wilson, Rufus Rockwell, 1865–1949.

LAC 13423
Lincoln, labor and slavery; a chapter from the social history of America. New York, Socialist literature co., 1913.
Schluter, Hermann.

LAC 20651
The Linwoods; or, "Sixty years since" in America. By the author of "Hope Leslie", "Redwood", &c. New-York, Harper & brothers, 1835.
Sedgwick, Catherine Maria, 1789–1867.

LAC 40083
The liquor problem. Madison, Wis., 1908.
Edwards, Richard Henry, 1877–1954, *ed.*

LAC 16916
The liquor problem; a summary of investigations conducted by the Committee of fifty, 1893–1903; prepared for the committee by John S. Billings, Charles W. Eliot, Henry W. Farnam, Jacob L. Greene, and Francis G. Peabody. Boston and New York, Houghton, Mifflin and company, 1905.
Peabody, Francis Greenwood, 1847–1936, *ed.*

LAC 10739
The liquor problem in all ages. By Daniel Dorchester, D. D. New York, Phillips & Hunt; Cincinnati, Walden & Stowe, 1884.
Dorchester, Daniel, 1827–1907.

LAC 11249
The liquor problem in its legislative aspects, by Frederick H. Wines and John Koren; an investigation made under the direction of Charles W. Eliot, Seth Low and James C. Carter, sub-committee of fifty to investigate the liquor problem. Boston and New York, Houghton, Mifflin and company, 1897.
Wines, Frederick Howard, 1838–1912.

LAC 10558–59
A list of maps of America in the Library of Congress, preceded by a list of works relating to cartography. By P. Lee Phillips, F. R. G. S., chief of the Division of maps and charts. Washington, Govt. print. off., 1901.
U.S. *Library of Congress. Map Division.*

LAC 40011
List of publications of the United States Bureau of education, 1867–1910. Washington, Govt. print. off., 1910.
U.S. *Office of Education.*

LAC 10490
Literary and historical miscellanies. New York, Harper & brothers, 1855.
Bancroft, George, 1800–1891.

LAC 11834
Literary and social silhouettes. New York, Harper and brothers, 1894.
Boyesen, Hjalmar Hjorth, 1848–1895.

LAC 12104
Literary criticisms and other papers. By the late Horace Binney Wallace. Philadelphia, Parry & McMillan, 1856.
Wallace, Horace Binney, 1817–1852.

LAC 12130
Literary culture in early New England, 1620–1730, by Thomas Goddard Wright. Edited by his wife. New Haven, Yale university press; [etc., etc.] 1920.
Wright, Thomas Goddard, 1885–1918.

LAC 21059–60
The literary diary of Ezra Stiles ... ed. under the authority of the corporation of Yale university by Franklin Bowditch Dexter. New York, C. Scribner's sons, 1901.
Stiles, Ezra, 1727–1795.

LAC 30817–46
The Literary digest. v. 1–30; Mar. 1890–Jun. 1905. New York, Funk & Wagnalls, 1890–1905.

LAC 11982
Literary friends and acquaintance; a personal retrospect of American authorship. New York and London, Harper & brothers, 1901, [c1900]
Howells, William Dean, 1837–1920.

LAC 12110
A literary history of America. New York, C. Scribner's sons, 1900.
Wendell, Barrett, 1855–1921.

LAC 12040
The literary history of Philadelphia. Philadelphia, George W. Jacobs & co. [1906]
Oberholtzer, Ellis Paxson, 1868–1936.

LAC 20660–61
The literary history of the American revolution, 1763–1783. New York & London, G. P. Putnam's sons, 1897.
Tyler, Moses Coit, 1835–1900.

LAC 15230
Literary influences in colonial newspapers, 1704–1750. New York, Columbia university press, 1912.
Cook, Elizabeth Christine, 1876–

LAC 30597–605
The Literary world. v. 1–13; Feb. 6, 1847–Dec. 31, 1853. New York, Osgood & co. [etc.] 1847–53.

LAC 15724
Literature and life.
Lectures on subjects connected with literature and life. 2d ed. Boston, Ticknor, Reed, and Fields, 1850.
Whipple, Edwin Percy, 1819–1886.

LAC 11983
Literature and life; studies by W. D. Howells... New York and London, Harper & brothers, 1902.
Howells, William Dean, 1837–1920.

LAC 20506
The literature of American history; a bibliographical guide in which the scope, character, and comparative worth of books in selected lists are set forth in brief notes by critics of authority. Contributors: Charles M. Andrews [and others] Edited for the American Library Association. Boston, Published for the American Library Association by Houghton, Mifflin, 1902.
Larned, Josephus Nelson, 1836–1913, *ed.*

LAC 11911
A little book of western verse. Chicago, 1889.
Field, Eugene, 1850–1895.

LAC 16302

Little citizens; the humours of school life, by Myra Kelly; illustrated by W. D. Stevens. New York, McClure, Phillips & co., 1905, [c1904]
Kelly, Myra, 1876–1910.

LAC 12107

A little journey in the world. A novel. New York, Harper & brothers, 1895, [c1889]
Warner, Charles Dudley, 1829–1900.

LAC 16330

Little journeys to the homes of great business men. East Aurora, N. Y., The Roycrofters, 1909.
Hubbard, Elbert, 1856–1915.

LAC 11845

Little Lord Fauntleroy, by Frances Hodgson Burnett. New York, C. Scribner's sons, 1886.
Burnett, Frances 1849–1924.

LAC 11811

Little men: life at Plumfield with Jo's boys. Boston, Roberts brothers, 1871.
Alcott, Louisa May, 1832–1888.

LAC 16768

The Little Regiment, and other episodes of the American civil war. New York, D. Appleton, 1896.
Crane, Stephen, 1871–1900.

LAC 11917

The little shepherd of Kingdom Come, by John Fox, jr.; illustrated by F. C. Yohn. New York, C. Scribner's sons, 1904, [c1903]
Fox, John, 1862–1919.

LAC 15568

A little tour in America. By the Very Rev. S. Reynolds Hole, dean of Rochester. London, New York, E. Arnold, 1895.
Hole, Samuel Reynolds, 1819–1904.

LAC 20825

Little visits with great Americans; or, Success, ideals, and how to attain them; ed. by Orison Swett Marden. New York, The Success company, 1905.
Marden, Orison Swett, 1848–1924, *ed.*

LAC 16772

Live questions: including Our penal machinery and its victims. Chicago, Donohue & Henneberry, 1890.
Altgeld, John Peter, 1847–1902.

LAC 12496

The lives and opinions of Benj'n Franklin Butler, United States district attorney for the southern district of New-York, and Jesse Hoyt, counsellor at law, formerly collector of customs for the port of New York; with anecdotes or biographical sketches of Stephen Allen; George P. Barker [etc.]... By William L. Mackeinzie [!] Boston, Cook & co., 1845.
Mackenzie, William Lyon, 1795–1861.

LAC 23017–18

The lives and times of the chief justices of the Supreme court of the United States. Philadelphia, J. B. Lippincott & co.; [etc., etc.] 1869.
Flanders, Henry, 1826–1911.

LAC 12696

Lives and works of civil and military engineers of America. New York, D. Van Nostrand, 1871.
Stuart, Charles Beebe, 1814–1881.

LAC 21180–81

Lives of American merchants. New York, Derby & Jackson; Cincinnati, H. W. Derby & co., 1858.
Hunt, Freeman, 1804–1858, *ed.*

LAC 16028

Lives of eminent American physicians and surgeons of the nineteenth century. Philadelphia, Lindsay & Blakiston, 1861.
Gross, Samuel David, 1805–1884, *ed.*

LAC 16100

Lives of Robert Young Hayne and Hugh Swinton Legare. Charleston, S. C., Walker, Evans & Cogswell, 1878.
Hayne, Paul Hamilton, 1830–1886.

LAC 14613

Lives of the Catholic heroes and heroines of America. New York, Baltimore [etc.] J. Sheehy, 1880.
Murray, John O'Kane, 1847–1885.

LAC 15777

Lives of the governors of New Plymouth, and Massachusetts bay; from the landing of the Pilgrims at Plymouth in 1620, to the union of the two colonies in 1692. Boston, C. D. Strong, 1851.
Moore, Jacob Bailey, 1797–1853.

LAC 13577

Lives of the governors of Pennsylvania, with the incidental history of the state, from 1609 to 1872. Philadelphia, J. K. Simon, 1872.
Armor, William Crawford.

LAC 13396

A living wage, its ethical and economic aspects. New York, The Macmillan company; London, Macmillan & co., ltd., 1906.
Ryan, John Augustine, 1869–1945.

LAC 11888

The living writers of the South. New York, Carleton; [etc., etc.] 1869.
Davidson, James Wood, 1829–1905.

LAC 13253

Lloyd's steamboat directory, and disasters on the western waters; containing the history of the first application of steam, as a motive power; the lives of John Fitch and Robert Fulton... History of the early steamboat navigation on western waters... Full accounts of all the steamboat disasters... A complete list of steamboats and all other vessels now afloat on the western rivers and lakes ... maps of the Ohio and Mississippi rivers... List of plantations on the Mississippi river... One hundred ... engravings, and forty-six maps...Cincinnati, O., J. T. Lloyd & co., 1856.
Lloyd, James T.

LAC 15645

Loans, National, of the U.S.
The national loans of the United States, from July 4, 1776, to June 30, 1880. By Rafael A. Bayley. 2d ed. As prepared for the tenth census of the United States. Washington, Govt. print. off., 1882.
U.S. *Treasury Dept.*

LAC 10468

Location of reserve districts in the United States...
Wash., Govt. print. off., 1914.
U. S. *63d Cong., 2d Sess., 1913–1914. Senate.*

LAC 11409

Loco-foco, or Equal Rights Party.
The history of the Loco-foco, or Equal Rights Party, its movements, conventions and proceedings, with short characteristic sketches of its prominent men. New York, Burt Franklin [1967]
Byrdsall, Fitzwilliam.

LAC 40088

Log cabins and cottages; how to build and furnish them. [5th ed.] New York, Forest and stream publishing co., 1904.
Wicks, William S.

LAC 13121

The log of a cowboy; a narrative of the old trail days, by Andy Adams, illustrated by E. Boyd Smith. Boston and New York, Houghton, Mifflin and company, 1903.
Adams, Andy, 1859–1935.

LAC 20667–68

Logan, a family history. London, Printed for A. K. Newman, 1823.
Neal, John, 1793–1876.

LAC 15841

Logic of history. Five hundred political texts: being concentrated extracts of abolitionism; also, results of slavery agitation and emancipation; together with sundry chapters on despotism, usurpations and frauds. 2d ed. Madison, Wis., 1864.
Carpenter, Stephen D   1821–1906.

LAC 15990

The logic of reason, universal and eternal. Boston, Lee and Shepard; New York, Lee, Shepard and Dillingham, 1875.
Hickok, Laurens Perseus, 1798–1888.

LAC 40142

The logic primer, reprinted from the unique original of 1672; with introduction by Wilberforce Eames. Cleveland, The Burrows brothers company, 1904.
Eliot, John, 1604–1690.

LAC 40007

The London Mathews; containing an account of this celebrated comedian's trip to America, being an annual lecture of peculiarities, characters & manners, founded on his own observations and adventures. To which are prefixed, several original comic songs... Philadelphia, Morgan & Yeager, 1824.
Mathews, Charles, 1796–1835.

LAC 10789

Lone Star ballads.
Allan's Lone Star ballads. A collection of southern patriotic songs, made during Confederate times ... Comp. and rev. by Francis D. Allan. Galveston, Tex., J. D. Sawyer, 1874.
Allan, Francis D   *comp.*

LAC 11829

Looking backward, 2000–1887. 58th Thousand. Boston & New York, Houghton, Mifflin and company, 1889, [c1888]
Bellamy, Edward, 1850–1898.

LAC 40044

A looking glass for the times; or, The former spirit of New England revived in this generation. Providence, S. S. Rider, 1883.
Folger, Peter, 1617?–1690.

LAC 13471

Loom and spindle: or, Life among the early mill girls. With a sketch of "The Lowell offering" and some of its contributors. By Harriet H. Robinson. Introduction by the Honorable Carroll D. Wright. New York, Boston, T. Y. Crowell & company [1898]
Robinson, Harriet Jane, 1825–1911.

LAC 13374

Loose leaves from a busy life. New York, The Macmillan company, 1934.
Hillquit, Morris, 1869–1933.

LAC 13296

Looters of the public domain, by S. A. D. Puter, king of the Oregon land fraud ring, in collaboration with Horace Stevens ... embracing a complete exposure of the fraudulent system of acquiring titles to the public lands of the United States... Portland, Ore., The Portland printing house, 1908.
Puter, Stephen A.   Douglas, 1857–

LAC 15182

The lords Baltimore and the Maryland palatinate; six lectures on Maryland colonial history delivered before the Johns Hopkins university in the year 1902. Baltimore, J. Murphy company, 1902.
Hall, Clayton Colman, 1847–1916.

LAC 10062

The Lords commissioners of trade and plantations, commonly known as the Board of trade, 1748–1782. New Haven, Yale university press; [etc., etc.] 1925.
Basye, Arthur Herbert, 1884–

LAC 15713

Lords of industry. New York and London, G. P. Putnam's sons, 1910.
Lloyd, Henry Demarest, 1847–1903.

LAC 15866

The Lords of trade and plantations 1675–1696. Allentown, Pa., H. R. Haas & co., 1919.
Bieber, Ralph Paul, 1894–

LAC 11290
Los Angeles and vicinity... Los Angeles, The Los Angeles chamber of commerce [c1904]
Los Angeles. Chamber of Commerce.

LAC 12412
The lost cause; a new southern history of the war of the Confederates. Comprising a full and authentic account of the rise and progress of the late southern Confederacy-the campaigns, battles, incidents, and adventures of the most gigantic struggle of the world's history. Drawn from official sources, and approved by the most distinguished Confederate leaders. With numerous splendid steel portraits. New York, E. B. Treat & co.; Baltimore, Md.,L. T. Palmer & co., 1866.
Pollard, Edward Alfred, 1831-1872.

LAC 12377
The lost cause regained. New York, G. W. Carleton & co.; [etc.] 1868.
Pollard, Edward Alfred, 1831-1872.

LAC 11134
Lost chapters recovered from the early history of American Methodism. By J. B. Wakeley, D. D., with a memoir of the author by Rev. William E. Ketcham. New York, W. B. Ketcham [c1889]
Wakeley, Joseph Beaumont, 1809-1875.

LAC 11292
The lost city! drama of the fire fiend! or Chicago, as it was and as it is! and its glorious future! a vivid and truthful picture of all of interest connected with the destruction of Chicago and the terrible fires of the great North-west... By Frank Luzerne. Ed. by John G. Wells. Profusely illustrated with maps and engravings from photographs taken on the spot. New York, Wells & company; [etc., etc.] 1872.
Luzerne, Frank.

LAC 16376
The lost dispatch. Galesburg, Ill., Galesburg printing and publishing company, 1889.

LAC 16416
Lost examples of colonial architecture; bvildings that have disappeared or been so altered as to be denatvred; pvblic bvildings, semi-pvblic, chvrches, cottages, covntry hovses, town hovses, interiors, details, by John Mead Howells; with an introdvction by Fiske Kimball. New York, W. Helbvrn, inc., 1931.
Howells, John Mead, 1868-

LAC 20882
Louis Agassiz, his life and correspondence, ed. by Elizabeth Cary Agassiz. Boston, New York, Houghton, Mifflin and company, 1885.
Agassiz, Elizabeth Cabot, 1822-1907.

LAC 11812
Louisa May Alcott, her life, letters, and journals; ed. by Ednah D. Cheney. Boston, Roberts brothers, 1890, [c1889]
Alcott, Louisa May, 1832-1888.

LAC 15159
Louisbourg journals, 1745, edited by Louis Effingham de Forest. Compiled for and published by the Society of colonial wars in the state of New York, through its Committee on historical documents. New York, 1932.
De Forest, Louis Effingham, 1891-   ed.

LAC 40019
Louisiana and Mississippi's prosperity to be sought in "cotton mills". They should seek the cotton fields. How cotton manufacturing can be made to pay in small country towns and enrich the cotton-grower. Hargrove's letters. New Orleans, The New Orleans picayune, 1899.
Hargrove, H   H.

LAC 11668-69
Louisiana [and South Carolina] in 1878. Report of the United States Senate Committee to inquire into alleged frauds and violence in the elections of 1878, with the testimony and documentary evidence... Washington, Govt. print. off., 1879.
U.S. Congress. Senate. Committee on Alleged Frauds and Violence in Elections of 1878.

LAC 12956
The Louisiana purchase, and our title west of the Rocky mountains, with a review of annexation by the United States. By Binger Hermann, commissioner of the General land office. Washington, Govt. print. off., 1898.
U.S. General Land Office.

LAC 11766
Louisiana rice book; issued by Passenger department of the Southern Pacific Sunset route. [Houston?, Tex., 1901]
Southern Pacific Company.

LAC 23244
The Louisiana-Texas frontier... [Austin, Tex., 1906-13]
Cox, Isaac Joslin, 1873-

LAC 13808
Love and parentage, applied to the improvement of off-spring, including important directions and suggestions to lovers and the married concerning the strongest ties and the most momentous relations of life. 13th ed. New York, Fowlers and Wells, 1850, [c1844]
Fowler, Orson Squire, 1809-1887.

LAC 11223
Love-letters of Margaret Fuller, 1845-1846, with an introduction by Julia Ward Howe; to which are added the reminiscences of Ralph Waldo Emerson, Horace Greeley and Charles T. Congdon. London, T. Fisher Unwin, 1903.
Ossoli, Sarah Margaret, marchesa d', 1810-1850.

LAC 14074
Lowell, as it was, and as it is. By Rev. Henry A. Miles. 2d ed. Lowell, N. L. Dayton [etc.] 1846.
Miles, Henry Adolphus, 1809-1895.

LAC 14187
Lowell hydraulic experiments. Being a selection from experiments on hydraulic motors, on the flow of water over weirs, in open canals of uniform rectangular section, and through submerged orifices and diverging tubes. Made at Lowell, Massachusetts. 4th ed. Rev. and enl., with additional tables, and illustrated with twenty-three copperplate engravings. New York, D. Van Nostrand, 1883.
Francis, James Bicheno, 1815-1892.

LAC 10426
Lowell lectures, on the application of metaphysical and ethical science to the evidences of religion; delivered before the Lowell institute in Boston, in the winters of 1848-1849. Boston, C. C. Little and J. Brown, 1849.
Bowen, Francis, 1811-1890.

LAC 12629
The Lowell lectures on the ascent of man. New York, J. Pott & co., 1894.
Drummond, Henry, 1851-1897.

LAC 40104
The lower depths of the great American metropolis, a discourse ... delivered in the Thirty-fourth street Reformed Dutch Church, New York City, sabbath evening, April 29, 1866. [New York, J. W. Schermerhorn, 1866]
Stryker, Peter, 1826-1900.

LAC 10239
The lower South in American history. New York, The Macmillan company; London, Macmillan & co., ltd., 1902.
Brown, William Garrott, 1868-1913.

LAC 16789
The loyal verses of Joseph Stansbury and Doctor Jonathan Odell; relating to the American revolution. Now first edited by Winthrop Sargent. Albany, J. Munsell, 1860.
Stansbury, Joseph, 1750-1809.

LAC 11460
Loyalism in New York during the American revolution... New York, 1901.
Flick, Alexander Clarence, 1869-1942.

LAC 12065
The loyalist poetry of the revolution... Philadelphia [Collins, printer] 1857.
Sargent, Winthrop, 1825-1870, ed.

LAC 15710
The loyalists in the American revolution. New York, The Macmillan company, 1902.
Van Tyne, Claude Halstead, 1869-1930.

LAC 13142
Loyalty on the frontier, or Sketches of Union men of the South-west; with incidents and adventures in rebellion on the border. St. Louis, R. P. Studley and co., printers, 1863.
Bishop, Albert Webb.

LAC 16808
Loyalty, Philosophy of.
The philosophy of loyalty. New York, The Macmillan company, 1908.
Royce, Josiah, 1855-1916.

LAC 14153
Lucius Q. C. Lamar: his life, times, and speeches. 1825-1893. Nashville, Tenn., Publishing house of the Methodist Episcopal church, South, 1896.
Mayes, Edward, 1846-1917. ·

LAC 11807
Lucy Larcom: life, letters, and diary. Boston and New York, Houghton, Mifflin and company, 1894.
Addison, Daniel Dulany, 1863-1936.

LAC 40118
A lume spento, 1908-1958, a cura di Vanni Scheiwiller. Milano, All'insegna del pesce d'oro [c1958]
Pound, Ezra Loomis, 1885-

LAC 23696
The Luna papers: documents relating to the expedition of Don Tristan de Luna y Arellano for the conquest of La Florida in 1559-1561 ... translated and edited with an historical introduction by Herbert Ingram Priestley. De Land, The Florida state historical society, 1928.
Priestley, Herbert Ingram, 1875-   ed. and tr.

LAC 16257
Lunsford Lane; or, Another helper from North Carolina. By the Rev. William G. Hawkins. Boston, Crosby & Nichols, 1863.
Hawkins, William George, 1823-1909.

LAC 16720
The lust of empire, speech of Hon. George F. Hoar of Massachusetts in the United States Senate, April 17, 1900. New York, The Tucker publishing co. [1900]
Hoar, George Frisbie, 1826-1904.

LAC 21852-56
Luther Burbank, his methods and discoveries and their practical application; prepared from his original field notes covering more than 100,000 experiments made during forty years devoted to plant improvement, with the assistance of the Luther Burbank Society and its entire membership, under the editorial direction of John Whitson and Robert John and Henry Smith Williams... Illustrated with direct color photograph prints produced by a new process devised and perfected for use in these volumes. New York and London, Luther Burbank press, 1914-15.
Burbank, Luther, 1849-1926.

LAC 40097
Luther Burbank; man, methods and achievements; an appreciation. San Francisco, Southern Pacific company [1902?]
Wickson, Edward James, 1848-1923.

LAC 11131
The Lutherans in America. A story of struggle, progress, influence and marvelous growth. By Edmund Jacob Wolf, D.D. With an introduction by Henry Eyster Jacobs. New York, J. A. Hill & company; [Rostock, Ger., E. Volckmann & co.,] 1889, [c1889]
Wolf, Edmund Jacob, 1840-1905.

LAC 12816
Lynch-law; an investigation into the history of lynching in the United States. New York [etc.] Longmans, Green, and co., 1905.
Cutler, James Elbert, 1876-1959.

LAC 14922
McClellan's own story: the war for the Union, the soldiers who fought it, the civilians who directed it and his relations to it and to them. New York, C. L. Webster & company, 1887, [c1886]
McClellan, George Brinton, 1826-1885.

LAC 30777-816

McClure's magazine. v. 1-28; June 1893-Apr. 1907. New York, S. S. McClure.

LAC 12436

The "machine" abolished and the people restored to power, by the organization of all the people on the lines of party organization, by Charles C. P. Clark, M. D. New York & London, G. P. Putnam's sons, 1900. Clark, Charles Cotesworth Pinckney, 1822-1899.

LAC 15651

Machine politics and money in elections in New York city. New York, Harper & brothers, c1887. Ivins, William Mills, 1851-

LAC 40066

Macon papers. Edited by William E. Dodd. Richmond, Va., Richmond press, 1909. Macon, Nathaniel, 1757-1837.

LAC 16699

Macready's reminiscences and selections from his diaries and letters. Ed. by Sir Frederick Pollock. London, Macmillan and co., 1876. Macready, William Charles, 1793-1875.

LAC 16791

McTeague, a story of San Francisco by Frank Norris. Introduction by Charles G. Norris. Illustrations by Otis Oldfield. An exact printing of the text from the first edition. San Francisco, Colt press [1941, c1899] Norris, Frank, 1870-1902.

LAC 12007

The Mc Veys (an episode) Boston and New York, Houghton, Mifflin and company, 1888. Kirkland, Joseph, 1830-1894.

LAC 11855

Madame Delphine. New York, C. Scribner's sons, 1881. Cable, George Washington, 1844-1925.

LAC 11771

Madras versus America: a handbook to cotton cultivation, exhibiting contents of public records in a condensed form, in accordance with the resolution of the government of India. New York, Virtue and Yorston, 1866. Wheeler, James Talboys, 1824-1897.

LAC 11813

Magazine writing and the new literature. New York and London, Harper & brothers, 1908. Alden, Henry Mills, 1836-1919.

LAC 16136

Maggie, a child of the streets... London, W. Heinemann, 1896. Crane, Stephen, 1871-1900.

LAC 13901

The magic city; a massive portfolio of original photographic views of the great World's fair... With graphic descriptions. [Philadelphia, Historical publishing company] 1894. Buel, James William, 1849-1920.

LAC 22361-62

Magnalia Christi americana; or, The ecclesiastical history of New-England, from its first planting in the year 1620, unto the year of Our Lord, 1698. In seven books. By the reverend and learned Cotton Mather. 1st American ed., from the London edition of 1702. Hartford: Published by Silas Andrus. Roberts & Burr, Printers, 1820. Mather, Cotton, 1663-1728.

LAC 11944

Main-travelled roads; being six stories of the Mississippi valley, by Hamlin Garland, with an introduction by W. D. Howells and decorations by H. T. Carpenter. Cambridge and Chicago, Stone and Kimball, 1893. Garland, Hamlin, 1860-1940.

LAC 10725

The Maine liquor law: its origin, history, and results, including a life of Hon. Neal Dow. New York, Pub. for the Maine law statistical society, by Fowler and Wells, 1856. Clubb, Henry Stephen, 1827-1921.

LAC 21095-105

Maintenance of a lobby to influence legislation. Hearings before a subcommittee of the Committee on the Judiciary, United States Senate, Sixty-third Congress, First session, pursuant to S. res. 92, a resolution instructing the Committee on the Judiciary to investigate the charge that a lobby is maintained to influence legislation pending in the Senate... Vol. 1-[4] Washington, Govt. print. off., 1913. U.S. *Congress. Senate. Committee on the Judiciary.*

LAC 14901

Major Andre's journal: operations of the British army under Lieutenant Generals Sir William Howe and Sir Henry Clinton, June, 1777 to November, 1778, recorded by Major John Andre, adjutant general; to which is added The ethics of Major Andre's mission, by C. De W. Willcox, COL. U.S.A. Tarrytown, N. Y., W. Abbatt, 1930. Andre, John, 1751-1780.

LAC 40085

Major General Edward Braddock's orderly books, from February 26 to June 17, 1755. From the originals, in the Congressional library. Cumberland, Md., W. H. Lowdermilk, 1878. Braddock, Edward, 1695?-1755.

LAC 12984

Major Jones's courtship: detailed, with other scenes, incidents, and adventures, in a series of letters, by himself. 8th ed., with additional letters; and twelve illustrations by Darley. Philadelphia, Carey & Hart, 1847. Thompson, William Tappan, 1812-1882.

LAC 16727

The major operations of the navies in the war of American independence. With portraits, maps, and battle plans. New York, Greenwood press [1969, c1913] Mahan, Alfred Thayer, 1840-1914.

LAC 14748

Majority rule and the judiciary: an examination of current proposals for constitutional change affecting the relation of courts to legislation, by William L. Ransom. With an introduction by Theodore Roosevelt. New York, C. Scribner's sons, 1912. Ransom, William Lynn, 1883-

LAC 16233
Making both ends meet; the income and outlay of New York working girls, by Sue Ainslie Clark and Edith Wyatt. New York, The Macmillan company, 1911.
Clark, Sue Ainslie.

LAC 11633
The making of a newspaper; experiences of certain representative American journalists related by themselves and edited by Melville Philips. New York; London, G. P. Putnam's sons, 1893.
Philips, Melville, *ed.*

LAC 23227–32
The making of America. Editorial ed. Robert Marion La Follette, editor-in-chief; William M. Handy, Charles Higgins, managing editors. Chicago, The Making of America co. [c1906]
La Follette, Robert Marion, 1855–1925, *ed.*

LAC 14805
The making of an American. New ed. with numerous illustrations and an introduction by Theodore Roosevelt. New York [etc.] The Macmillan company, 1916, [c1901]
Riis, Jacob August, 1849–1914.

LAC 11125
The making of Methodism: studies in the genesis of institutions. Nashville, Tenn., Publishing house of the Methodist Episcopal church, South. Barbee & Smith, agents, 1898.
Tigert, John James, 1856–1906.

LAC 10412
The making of our middle schools; an account of the development of secondary education in the United States. New York, London [etc.] Longmans, Green, and co., 1903.
Brown, Elmer Ellsworth, 1861–1934.

LAC 11703
The making of Pennsylvania; an analysis of the elements of the population and the formative influences that created one of the greatest of the American states. [8th ed.] Philadelphia, J. B. Lippincott company, 1908, [c1896]
Fisher, Sydney George, 1856–1927.

LAC 15557
Malaeska: the Indian wife of the white hunter. New York, I. P. Beadle [c1860]
Stephens, Ann Sophia, 1813–1886.

LAC 40128
Male continence. 2d ed. Oneida, N. Y., Office of the American socialist, 1877.
Noyes, John Humphrey, 1811–1886.

LAC 13604
The mammon of unrighteousness, by Hjalmar Hjorth Boyeson [!] New York, United States book company [c1891]
Boyesen, Hjalmar Hjorth, 1848–1895.

LAC 13743
Man and labor: a series of short and simple studies. Chicago and New York, Belford, Clarke & co., 1886.
Elder, Cyrus, 1833–1912.

LAC 12710
Man and the glacial period, by G. Frederick Wright. With an appendix on Tertiary man by Prof. Henry W. Haynes. New York, D. Appleton and company, 1892.
Wright, George Frederick, 1838–1921.

LAC 15932
A man in earnest: life of A. H. Conant. Boston, H. B. Fuller; Chicago, J. R. Walsh, 1868.
Collyer, Robert, 1823–1912.

LAC 11187
The man-made world; or, Our androcentric culture. New York, Charlton Co., 1911.
Gilman, Charlotte Stetson, 1860–1935.

LAC 15714
Man, the social creator. New York, Doubleday, Page & company, 1906.
Lloyd, Henry Demarest, 1847–1903.

LAC 13379
Man to man; the story of industrial democracy. New York, B. C. Forbes company [c1919]
Leitch, John, 1868–

LAC 12025
The man with the hoe, and other poems. New York, Doubleday & McClure company, 1899.
Markham, Edwin, 1852–1940.

LAC 16413
Manassas; a novel of the war. New York, The Macmillan company; London, Macmillan & co., ltd., 1904.
Sinclair, Upton Beall, 1878–1968.

LAC 40010
Manila, or Monroe doctrine? New York, Robert Lewis Weed company [c1898]
Chetwood, John, 1859–

LAC 16349
"Manners makyth man." By the author of "How to be happy though married." New York, C. Scribner's sons, 1888.
Hardy, Edward John, 1849–1920.

LAC 11314
Manners; or, Happy homes and good society all the year round. Boston, J. E. Tilton and company, 1868.
Hale, Sarah Josepha, 1788–1879.

LAC 11446
Manoeuvres of horse artillery. Written at Paris in the year 1800, at the request of General Wm. R. Davie, then envoy from the United States to France. Translated, with notes and descriptive plates, by Jonathan Williams. Published by direction of the [U.S. Military Philosophical] Society. New York, Sold by Campbell & Mitchell, 1808.
Kosciuszko, Tadeusz Andrzej Bonawentura, 1746–1817.

LAC 10841
A man's woman. New York, Doubleday, Page & co., 1902, [c1900]
Norris, Frank, 1870–1902.

LAC 14866
Manual for emigrants to America. London, F. Westley and A. H. Davis, 1832.
Colton, Calvin, 1789–1857.

LAC 14198
Manual issued by the Home insurance company of New York, containing general rules and instructions with forms of policies and endorsements, for the use of the agents connected with its Southern department. New York, Pub. under the direction of the Company, 1877.
Home Insurance Company, *New York.*

LAC 40013
The manual laboring class. Baltimore, American economic association, 1888.
Walker, Francis Amasa, 1840–1897.

LAC 13912
A manual of American literature: a text-book for schools and colleges. Philadelphia, Eldredge & brother [c1872]
Hart, John Seely, 1810–1877.

LAC 12631
Manual of botany, for North America: containing generic and specific descriptions of the indigenous plants and common cultivated exotics, growing north of the gulf of Mexico. By Prof. Amos Eaton. 5th ed., rev., cor., and much extended. Albany, Printed by Websters and Skinners, 1829.
Eaton, Amos, 1776–1842.

LAC 15955
Manual of cattle-feeding. A treatise on the laws of animal nutrition and the chemistry of feeding stuffs in their application to the feeding of animals. With illustrations and an appendix of useful tables. Second edition. New York, John Wiley & sons, 1882, [c1880]
Armsby, Henry Prentiss, 1853–1921.

LAC 13097
A manual of historical literature, comprising brief descriptions of the most important histories in English, French and German, together with practical suggestions as to methods and courses of historical study... New York, Harper & brothers, 1882.
Adams, Charles Kendall, 1835–1902.

LAC 40115
Manual of internal rules and regulations for men-of-war. 2d ed., enlarged. New York, D. Van Nostrand, 1862.
Levy, Uriah Phillips, 1795?–1862.

LAC 16073
Manual of jurisprudence and co-operation of the Patrons of husbandry. Pub. by Geo. William Jones. Des Moines, Mills & company, printers, 1875.
Smedley, A   B.

LAC 12624
Manual of mineralogy, including observations on mines, rocks, reduction of ores, and the applications of the science to the arts... 6th ed. New Haven, Durrie & Peck; Philadelphia, H. C. Peck, 1854, [c1848]
Dana, James Dwight, 1813–1895.

LAC 11001
Manual of natural theology. New York, C. Scribner's sons, 1893.
Fisher, George Park, 1827–1909.

LAC 12442
Manual of parliamentary practice. Rules of proceeding and debate in deliberative assemblies. 4th ed. Boston,W. J. Reynolds, 1845.
Cushing, Luther Stearns, 1803–1856.

LAC 10560
The manual of peace, embracing I, Evils and remedies of war, II, Suggestions on the law of nations, III, Considerations of a congress of nations. New-York, Leavitt, Lord, & co., 1836.
Upham, Thomas Cogswell, 1799–1872.

LAC 16554
A manual of pensions, bounty, and pay: containing the laws, forms and regulations relating to pensions, bounty land, bounty money, pay, claims for horses and other property destroyed, etc., etc.; with the opinions of the attorneys-general, and the official regulations and decisions pertaining to these subjects. Cincinnati, R. Clarke & co., 1862.
Raff, George Wertz, 1825–1888.

LAC 13950
A manual of political economy. By Thomas Cooper, M.D. Washington, D. Green, 1833.
Cooper, Thomas, 1759–1839.

LAC 10451
A manual of political economy, with particular reference to the institutions, resources, and condition of the United States. Boston, Hilliard, Gray, Little, and Wilkins, 1828.
Phillips, Willard, 1784–1873.

LAC 22599–600
Manual of political ethics, designed chiefly for the use of colleges and students at law... Boston, C. C. Little and J. Brown, 1838–39.
Lieber, Francis, 1800–1872.

LAC 15910
Manual of psychometry: the dawn of a new civilization. Published by the author. Boston, Holman brothers, press of the Roxbury advocate, 1885.
Buchanan, Joseph Rodes, 1814–1899.

LAC 11568
Manual of public libraries, institutions, and societies, in the United States, and British provinces of North America. By William J. Rhees, chief clerk of the Smithsonian institution. Philadelphia, J. B. Lippincott & co., 1859.
Rhees, William Jones, 1830–1907.

LAC 15804
Manual of the Constitution of the United States of America. Boston, Little, Brown, and company, 1867.
Farrar, Timothy, 1788–1874.

LAC 12639

A manual of the principles and practice of road-making: comprising the location, construction, and improvement of roads, (common, macadam, paved, plank, etc.) and rail-roads. 6th ed., with additions. New York, A. S. Barnes & company, 1853.
Gillespie, William Mitchell, 1816–1868.

LAC 40072

Manual of the state of New-York.
A brief topographical & statistical manual of the state of New-York: exhibiting the situation and boundaries of the several counties ... and designating the principal places and the seat of the courts... Albany, Pub. by J. Frary, State-street, 1811.
Goodenow, Sterling.

LAC 16072

Manual on the cultivation of the sugar cane, and the fabrication and refinement of sugar. Prepared under the direction of the Hon. secretary of the Treasury, in compliance with a resolution of the House of representatives of Jan. 25, 1830. Washington, Printed by F. P. Blair, 1833.
Silliman, Benjamin, 1779–1864.

LAC 14682

The manual training school, comprising a full statement of its aims, methods, and results, with figured drawings of shop exercises in woods and metals. Boston, D. C. Heath & co., 1887.
Woodward, Calvin Milton, 1837–1914.

LAC 15303

Manuductio ad ministerium; directions for a candidate of the ministry, by Cotton Mather. Reproduced from the original edition, Boston, 1726, with a bibliographical note by Thomas J. Holmes and Kenneth B. Murdock. New York, Pub. for the Facsimile text society by Columbia university press, 1938.
Mather, Cotton, 1663–1728.

LAC 11627

The manufacture of iron, in all its various branches... Also, a description of forge hammers, rolling mills, blast machines, hot blast, etc. etc. To which is added, an essay on the manufacture of steel. With one hundred and fifty wood engravings. 2d ed. Philadelphia, H. C. Baird, 1851.
Overman, Frederick, 1803?–1852.

LAC 10332

The manufacture of paper: being a description of the various processes for the fabrication, coloring, and finishing of every kind of paper. Philadelphia, H. C. Baird & co.; London, S. Low, Marston, Searle & Rivington, 1886.
Davis, Charles Thomas.

LAC 40018

Manufacturing in Philadelphia, 1683–1912, with photographs of some of the leading industrial establishments. [Philadelphia] Philadelphia commercial museum, 1912.
Macfarlane, John James, 1846–

LAC 11922

March hares. New York, D. Appleton and company, 1896.
Frederic, Harold, 1856–1898.

LAC 12408

Marching through Georgia. Pen-pictures of every-day life in General Sherman's army, from the beginning of the Atlanta campaign until the close of the war. Illustrated by F. L. Stoddard. Chicago, Donohue & co. [c1884]
Hedley, Fenwick, Y.

LAC 14623

Marching with Gomez; a war correspondent's field notebook, kept during four months with the Cuban army, by Grover Flint; illustrated by the author. With an historical introduction by John Fiske. Boston, New York [etc.] Lamson, Wolffe and company, 1898.
Flint, Grover, 1867–1909.

LAC 11433

Marcus Alonzo Hanna; his life and work. New York, The Macmillan company, 1912.
Croly, Herbert David, 1869–1930.

LAC 23469

Mardi: and a voyage thither. New York, Harper & brothers, 1849.
Melville, Herman, 1819–1891.

LAC 20633

Margaret: A tale of the real and the ideal, blight and bloom; including sketches of a place not before described, called Mons Christi. Rev. ed. ... By the author of "Philo". Boston, Phillips, Sampson, 1851.
Judd, Sylvester, 1813–1853.

LAC 10746

Margaret Fuller Ossoli. Boston, New York, Houghton, Mifflin and company, 1898, [c1884]
Higginson, Thomas Wentworth, 1823–1911.

LAC 12246

Margaret Winthrop, by Alice Morse Earle. New York, C. Scribner's sons, 1895.
Earle, Alice, 1851–1911.

LAC 15561

The margin of profits; how it is now divided, what part of the present hours of labor can now be spared. An address delivered before the Central labor lyceum of Boston ... May 1, 1887. New York & London, G. P. Putnam's sons, 1887.
Atkinson, Edward, 1827–1905.

LAC 11890

Margret Howth; a story of to-day. Boston, Ticknor and Fields, 1862.
Davis, Rebecca, 1831–1910.

LAC 23318

Marie; ou, L'esclavage aux Etats-Unis, tableau de moeurs americaines. Paris, C. Gosselin, 1835.
Beaumont de La Bonniniere, Gustave Auguste de, 1802–1866.

LAC 14890

Marins et soldats francais en Amerique pendant la guerre de l'independance des Etats-Unis (1778–1783) Paris, Perrin et cie, 1903.
Noailles, Amblard Marie Raymond Amedee, *vicomte* de, 1856–1926.

LAC 12316
Maritime enterprise, 1485–1558. Oxford, Clarendon press, 1913.
Williamson, James Alexander, 1886–

LAC 40073
Mark Hanna: his book. 1st ed., with an introduction by Joe Mitchell Chapple. Boston, The Chapple publishing co., ltd., 1904.
Hanna, Marcus Alonzo, 1837–1904.

LAC 14788
Mark Hanna's "moral cranks" and–others. A study of today... By "Mul" [pseud.] Brooklyn, N. Y., G. F. Spinney company, 1900.
Muldoon, William H

LAC 16578
Mark, the match boy; or, Richard Hunter's ward. By Horatio Alger, jr. Boston, Loring [c1869]
Alger, Horatio, 1832–1899.

LAC 21156
Mark Twain's letters, arranged with comment, by Albert Bigelow Paine. New York and London, Harper & brothers [c1917]
Clemens, Samuel Langhorne, 1835–1910.

LAC 15005
"Marked severities" in Philippine warfare.
Secretary Root's record. "Marked severities" in Philippine warfare. An analysis of the law and facts bearing on the action and utterances of President Roosevelt and Secretary Root... Boston, G. H. Ellis co., printers, 1902.
Storey, Moorfield, 1845–1929.

LAC 13475
The market book, containing a historical account of the public markets in the cities of New York, Boston, Philadelphia and Brooklyn, with a brief description of every article of human food sold therein, the introduction of cattle in America, and notices of many remarkable specimens. In two volumes. Vol. I. New York, B. Franklin [1969]
De Voe, Thomas Farrington, 1811–1892.

LAC 14543
Marketing perishable farm products. New York, Columbia university; [etc., etc.] 1916.
Adams, Arthur Barto, 1887–

LAC 40027
Marriage and divorce. New York, McClure, Phillips & co., 1905.
Adler, Felix, 1851–1933.

LAC 22895–96
Marriage and divorce 1867–1906... Washington, Govt. print. off., 1908–09 [v. 2, 1908]
U.S. *Bureau of the Census.*

LAC 16064
Marriage and divorce in the United States: as they are and as they ought to be. Philadelphia, J. B. Lippincott company, 1889.
Convers, Duncan.

LAC 12161
Marriage in the United States. Translated from the French by B. Joy Jeffries. Boston, De Vries, Ibarra & co.; New York, Leypoldt and Holt, 1867.
Carlier, Auguste, 1803–1890.

LAC 15572
Marriage: its history, character, and results... By T. L. Nichols, M. D., and Mrs. Mary S. Gove Nichols. Cincinnati, V. Nicholson & co. [1854]
Nichols, Thomas Low, 1815–1901.

LAC 16065
Marriage, with preludes on current events. Boston, Houghton, Osgood and company, 1879.
Cook, Joseph, 1838–1901.

LAC 23528
"Marse Henry", an autobiography. New York, George H. Doran company [c1919]
Watterson, Henry, 1840–1921.

LAC 11924
Marsena, and other stories of the wartime. New York, C. Scribner's sons, 1894.
Frederic, Harold, 1856–1898.

LAC 40059
Martin Van Buren: lawyer, statesman and man. New York, D. Appleton and company, 1862.
Butler, William Allen, 1825–1902.

LAC 40099
The martyr age of the United States. New York, Arno Press & the New York Times, 1969.
Martineau, Harriet, 1802–1876.

LAC 13331
Marvels of the new West. A vivid portrayal of the stupendous marvels in the vast wonderland west of the Missouri river... Six books in one volume; graphically and truthfully described by William M. Thayer. Illustrated with over three hundred and fifty fine engravings and maps. Norwich, Conn., The Henry Bill publishing company, 1887.
Thayer, William Makepeace, 1820–1898.

LAC 40006
Marx on Mallock; or Facts vs. fiction. An address delivered in Maennerchor hall, New York, Tuesday, January 21, 1908 under the auspices of section New York, Socialist labor party... New York, New York labor news company [1908?]
De Leon, Daniel, 1852–1914.

LAC 14036
Mary and I. Forty years with the Sioux. By Stephen R. Riggs. With an introduction by Rev. S. C. Bartlett. Chicago, W. G. Holmes [c1880]
Riggs, Stephen Return, 1812–1883.

LAC 40147
The Maryland and Virginia boundary controversy (1668–1894) [New York] A. J. Leon, printer [1904]
Whealton, Louis Napoleon, 1872–

LAC 12363
Maryland as a proprietary province. New York, The Macmillan company; London, Macmillan & co., ltd., 1901.
Mereness, Newton Dennison.

LAC 15969
Maryland records: colonial, revolutionary, county, and church, from original sources. Vol. 1. Baltimore, Williams & Wilkins, 1915.
Brumbaugh, Gaius Marcus, 1862–

LAC 12383
Maryland; the land of sanctuary. A history of religious toleration in Maryland from the first settlement until the American revolution. Baltimore, J. H. Furst company, 1907.
Russell, William Thomas, *bp.*, 1863–1927.

LAC 13689
Masonry and anti-masonry. A history of masonry, as it has existed in Pennsylvania since 1792. In which the true principles of the institution are fully developed, and all misrepresentations corrected. Containing the protests, speeches, reports, etc., presented before the Inquisitorial committee, at Harrisburg, Pa. Philadelphia, Lippincott, Grambo & co., 1854.
Creigh, Alfred.

LAC 11684
Mass and class; a survey of social divisions. New York, The Macmillan company; London, Macmillan & co., ltd., 1904.
Ghent, William James, 1866–1942.

LAC 40062
Massachusettensis. Boston, Hews & Goss, 1819.
Leonard, Daniel, 1740–1829.

LAC 11738
The Massachusetts civil list for the colonial and provincial periods, 1630–1774. Being a list of the names and dates of appointment of all the civil officers constituted by authority of the charters, or the local government. Albany, J. Munsell, 1870.
Whitmore, William Henry, 1836–1900.

LAC 11686
Massachusetts; its historians and its history. An object lesson. Boston and New York, Houghton, Mifflin and company, 1893.
Adams, Charles Francis, 1835–1915.

LAC 13940
Massacres of the mountains; a history of the Indian wars of the far West, by J. P. Dunn, jr. New York, Harper & brothers, 1886.
Dunn, Jacob Piatt, 1855–1924.

LAC 40116
Masters of men; a retrospect in presidential politics. With eight contemporary portraits. Columbus, O., McClelland & co., 1915.
Ryan, Daniel Joseph, 1855–

LAC 16813
The Master's slave, Elijah John Fisher; a biography, by his son, Miles Mark Fisher, with an introduction by the Rev. Lacey Kirk Williams, D. D., and an appreciation by the Hon. Martin B. Madden. Philadelphia, Boston [etc.] The Judson press [1922]
Fisher, Miles Mark, 1899–

LAC 14185
Matrimony, as taught by phrenology and physiology. In three parts. Part I.–Love: its nature, laws, and all-controlling power over human destiny. Part II.–Selection: or, Mutual adaptation. Part III.–Courtship and married life: their fatal errors, and how to render all marriages happy. By Prof. O. S. Fowler. Boston, O. S. Fowler [c1859]
Fowler, Orson Squire, 1809–1887.

LAC 12499
Matthew Lyon, the Hampden of Congress, a biography... New York, Wynkoop Hallenbeck Crawford company, 1900.
McLaughlin, James Fairfax, 1839–1903.

LAC 15412
The May-flower and her log, July 15, 1620–May 6, 1621, chiefly from original sources. Boston and New York, Houghton, Mifflin and company, 1901.
Ames, Azel, 1845–1908.

LAC 11254
The meaning of social science. Chicago, Ill., The University of Chicago press [c1910]
Small, Albion Woodbury, 1854–

LAC 10832
The means and ends of universal education. New York, A. S. Barnes & Burr, 1860, [c1856]
Mayhew, Ira, 1814–1894.

LAC 12646–47
Mechanics' and engineers' pocket-book of tables, rules, and formulas pertaining to mechanics, mathematics, and physics... 64th ed. 129th thousand. New York, Harper & brothers, 1899.
Haswell, Charles Haynes, 1809–1907.

LAC 11616
A mechanic's diary, by ex-Gov. Henry C. Brokmeyer. Washington, D. C., E. C. Brokmeyer, c1910.
Brokmeyer, Henry Conrad, 1826–1906.

LAC 15183
The Mecklenburg declaration of independence; a study of evidence showing that the alleged early declaration of independence by Mecklenburg county, North Carolina, on May 20th, 1775, is spurious. New York and London, G. P. Putnam's sons, 1907.
Hoyt, William Henry.

LAC 40024
Mediation and arbitration of railway labor disputes in the United States... By Chas. P. Neill, commissioner of labor. Washington, Govt. print. off., 1912.
Neill, Charles Patrick, 1865–1942.

LAC 22396–405
The medical and surgical history of the war of the rebellion. (1861–65). Prepared, in accordance with the acts of Congress, under the direction of Surgeon general Joseph K. Barnes, United States army. Washington, Govt. print. off., 1875–83.
U.S. *Surgeon-General's Office.*

LAC 40061
A medical discourse; or, An historical inquiry into the ancient and present state of medicine; the substance of which was delivered at opening the Medical school, in the city of New-York. Printed by desire. New-York: Printed by Hugh Gaine, in Hanover-Square, M,DCC,LXIX.
Middleton, Peter, *d.* 1781.

LAC 23262–63
Medical inquiries and observations. The 4th ed. Philadelphia: Printed for Johnson & Warner, Market street. Griggs & Dickinsons, printers, 1815.
Rush, Benjamin, 1745–1813.

LAC 14575
Medical inspection of schools, by Luther Halsey Gulick, M. D., and Leonard P. Ayres, PH. D. New York, Survey associates, inc., 1913.
Gulick, Luther Halsey, 1865–1918.

LAC 12701
The medical men of the revolution, with a brief history of the medical department of the continental army. Containing the names of nearly twelve hundred physicians. An address before the alumni association of Jefferson medical college, March 11, 1876. Philadelphia, Collins printer, 1876.
Toner, Joseph Meredith, 1825–1896.

LAC 14727
Medical recollections of the Army of the Potomac. By Jonathan Letterman, M.D., late surgeon United States army, and medical director of the Army of the Potomac. New York, D. Appleton and company, 1866.
Letterman, Jonathan, 1824–1872.

LAC 16454
Medical schools in America.
A discourse upon the institution of medical schools in America; delivered at a public anniversary commencement, held in the College of Philadelphia, May 30 and 31, 1765. With a preface containing, amongst other things, the author's apology for attempting to introduce the regular mode of practising physic in Philadelphia. Philadelphia, W. Bradford, 1765.
Morgan, John, 1735–1789.

LAC 12012
Meister Karl's sketch-book. Philadelphia, Parry & McMillan, 1855.
Leland, Charles Godfrey, 1824–1903.

LAC 16958
Mellichampe; a legend of the Santee. New and rev. ed. Chicago, Donohue, Henneberry, 1890.
Simms, William Gilmore, 1806–1870.

LAC 10643
Melomaniacs. New York, C. Scribner's sons, 1902.
Huneker, James Gibbons, 1857–1921.

LAC 15614
The melting-pot, drama in four acts. New York, The Macmillan company, 1910, [c1909]
Zangwill, Israel, 1864–1926.

LAC 14287
Memoir and correspondence of Jeremiah Mason. Priv. print. Cambridge, Printed at the Riverside press, 1873.
Mason, Jeremiah, 1768–1848.

LAC 40084
Memoir concerning the commercial relations of the United States with Great Britain. [London, A. J. Valpy, 1814]
Talleyrand-Perigord, Charles Maurice de, *prince de Benevent,* 1754–1838.

LAC 11266
Memoir of a mechanic. Being a sketch of the life of Timothy Claxton, written by himself. Together with miscellaneous papers. Boston, New York, G. W. Light, 1839.
Claxton, Timothy, *b.* 1790.

LAC 10169
Memoir of Abbott Lawrence. With an appendix. Boston, Printed for private distribution [Cambridge, J. Wilson and son] 1883.
Hill, Hamilton Andrews, 1827–1895.

LAC 40080
A memoir of Abijah Hutchinson, a soldier of the Revolution. Rochester [N. Y.] W. Alling, Printer, 1843.
Hutchinson, K   M.

LAC 22347
A memoir of Benjamin Robbins Curtis, LL. D., with some of his professional and miscellaneous writings. Ed. by his son, Benjamin R. Curtis. Boston, Little, Brown, and company, 1879.
Curtis, Benjamin Robbins, 1855–1891, *ed.*

LAC 40080
Memoir of Col. Benjamin Tallmadge, prepared by himself, at the request of his children. New York, T. Holman, book and job printer, 1858.
Tallmadge, Benjamin, 1754–1835.

LAC 11130
Memoir of Commodore David Porter, of the United States navy. By Admiral David D. Porter. With portrait and heliotypes. Albany, N. Y., J. Munsell, 1875.
Porter, David Dixon, 1813–1891.

LAC 14209
Memoir of David Hale, late editor of the Journal of commerce. With selections from his miscellaneous writings. By Joseph P. Thompson. 2d ed. Hartford, Conn., E. Hunt, 1850.
Hale, David, 1791–1849.

LAC 40020
Memoir of Eli Whitney, esq. New Haven, Durrie & Peck, 1846.
Olmsted, Denison, 1791–1859.

LAC 40100
A memoir of February, 1817, upon the subject of the cotton wool cultivation, the cotton trade, and the cotton manufactories of the United States of America. [Philadelphia, 1817]
Coxe, Tench, 1755–1824.

LAC 40085
Memoir of Henry Bouquet, 1719–1765... Prepared on the occasion of the presentation by the society to the city of Philadelphia of a portrait of Colonel Bouquet ... March, 1900. [Philadelphia, G. H. Buchanan and company, 1900?]
Shippen, Edward, 1826–1911.

LAC 15041
A memoir of Hugh Lawson White, judge of the Supreme court of Tennessee, member of the Senate of the United States, etc., etc. With selections from his speeches and correspondence. Philadelphia, J. B. Lippincott & co., 1856.
Scott, Nancy N   *ed.*

LAC 12277
A memoir of Jacques Cartier, sieur de Limoilou, his voyages to the St. Lawrence, a bibliography and a facsimile of the manuscript of 1534, with annotations, etc. New York, Dodd, Mead & company, 1906.
Baxter, James Phinney, 1831–

LAC 11520
A memoir of James De Veaux, of Charleston, S. C., member of the National academy of design, New-York. By Robert W. Gibbes. Columbia, S. C., I. C. Morgan's letter press print, 1846.
De Veaux, James, 1812–1844.

LAC 15175
Memoir of John A. Dahlgren, rear-admiral United States navy, by his widow. Madeleine Vinton Dahlgren. Boston, J. R. Osgood & company, 1882.
Dahlgren, Madeleine, 1825–1898.

LAC 20380–81
Memoir of Madame Jenny Lind-Goldschmidt: her early art-life and dramatic career, 1820–1851. From original documents, letters, ms. diaries, &c., collected by Mr. Otto Goldschmidt. [By] Henry Scott Holland and W. S. Rockstro. With portraits, illustrations, and an appendix of music. London, J. Murray, 1891.
Holland, Henry Scott, 1847–1918.

LAC 20600
A memoir of Ralph Waldo Emerson. Boston and New York, Houghton, Mifflin and company, 1887.
Cabot, James Elliot, 1821–1903.

LAC 11118
Memoir of Rev. Luther Rice, one of the first American missionaries to the East. 2d ed. Nashville, Tenn., Broadman Press [1937]
Taylor, James Barnett, 1804–1871.

LAC 15677
Memoir of Roger Brooke Taney, LL. D., chief justice of the Supreme court of the United States. Baltimore, J. Murphy & co., 1872.
Tyler, Samuel, 1809–1877.

LAC 10313
Memoir of Samuel Slater, the father of American manufactures; connected with a history of the rise and progress of the cotton manufacture in England and America, with remarks on the moral influence of manufactories in the United States. 2d ed. Philadelphia, 1836.
White, George Savage, 1784–1850.

LAC 12633
Memoir of Sir Benjamin Thompson, count Rumford, with notices of his daughter. By George E. Ellis. Pub. in connection with an edition of Rumford's complete works, by the American academy of arts and sciences, Boston. Boston, Estes and Lauriat [1871]
Ellis, George Edward, 1814–1894.

LAC 14318
Memoir of Solomon Willard, architect and superintendent of the Bunker Hill monument. [Boston] Prepared and printed by direction of the Monument association, 1865.
Wheildon, William Willder, 1805–1892.

LAC 40018
Memoir of the Honorable Abbott Lawrence, prepared for the National portrait gallery. Extracted from the work by permission of the publishers. [n. p.] Printed for private distribution, 1856.
Prescott, William Hickling, 1796–1859.

LAC 14410
A memoir of the last year of the war for independence, in the Confederate States of America, containing an account of the operations of his commands in the years 1864 and 1865. By Lieutenant-General Jubal A. Early. [2d ed.] Lynchburg, C. W. Button, 1867.
Early, Jubal Anderson, 1816–1894.

LAC 14024
Memoir of the life and character of Samuel Hopkins, D. D. 2d ed. Boston, Doctrinal Tract and Book Society, 1854.
Park, Edwards Amasa, 1808–1900.

LAC 21075
A memoir of the life and labors of Francis Wayland ... late president of Brown university, including selections from his personal reminiscences and correspondence by his sons, Francis Wayland and H. L. Wayland. New York, Sheldon and company, 1867.
Wayland, Francis, 1826–1904.

LAC 13139
Memoir of the life and public services of John Charles Fremont... New York, Derby & Jackson; Cincinnati, H. W. Derby & co., 1856.
Bigelow, John, 1817–1911.

LAC 11038
A memoir of the life and times of the Rev. Isaac Backus, A. M. Boston, Gould and Lincoln; New York, Sheldon, Blakeman & co.; [etc., etc.] 1859, [c1858]
Hovey, Alvah, 1820–1903.

LAC 13079
Memoir of the life and writings of Rev. Jonathan Mayhew, D. D., pastor of the West church and society in Boston, from June, 1747, to July, 1766. Boston, C. C. Little & co., 1838.
Bradford, Alden, 1765–1843.

LAC 12483
A memoir of the life of Daniel Webster. 2d ed. Rev. and brought down to the present time. New York, J. S. Redfield, 1835.
Knapp, Samuel Lorenzo, 1783–1838.

LAC 20253
Memoir of the life of Henry Ware, jr., by his brother, John Ware. New ed. Boston, American Unitarian Association, 1890, [c1846]
Ware, John, 1795–1864.

LAC 15577
Memoir of the life of Josiah Quincy, jun., of Massachusetts: by his son, Josiah Quincy. Boston, Cummings, Hilliard, & company, 1825.
Quincy, Josiah, 1772–1864.

LAC 22859
Memoir of the life of Richard Henry Lee, and his correspondence with the most distinguished men in America and Europe, illustrative of their characters, and of the events of the American revolution. By his grandson Richard H. Lee, of Leesburg, Virginia. Philadelphia, H. C. Carey and I. Lea, 1825.
Lee, Richard Henry, 1794–1865.

LAC 11214
Memoir of the Rev. Elijah P. Lovejoy; who was murdered in defence of the liberty of the press, at Alton, Illinois, Nov. 7, 1837. By Joseph C. and Owen Lovejoy. With an introduction by John Quincy Adams. New York, J. S. Taylor, 1838.
Lovejoy, Joseph Cammet, 1805–1871.

LAC 14745
Memoir of Theophilus Parsons, chief justice of the Supreme judicial court of Massachusetts; with notices of some of his contemporaries. By his son Theophilus Parsons. Boston, Ticknor and Fields, 1859.
Parsons, Theophilus, 1797–1882.

LAC 15259
A memoir of Thomas Chittenden, the first governor of Vermont; with a history of the constitution during his administration. Middlebury [Vt.] Printed for the author, 1849.
Chipman, Daniel, 1765–1850.

LAC 10291
Memoir of Thomas Handasyd Perkins; containing extracts from his diaries and letters. With an appendix. Boston, Little, Brown and company, 1856, [c1855]
Cary, Thomas Greaves, 1791–1859.

LAC 20347–48
Memoir of William Ellery Channing, with extracts from his correspondence and manuscripts... London [etc.] G. Routledge [1870]
Channing, William Ellery, 1780–1842.

LAC 11006
Memoir of William Henry Channing. Boston and New York, Houghton, Mifflin and company, 1886.
Frothingham, Octavius Brooks, 1822–1895.

LAC 40020
A memoir of William Maclure, esq., late president of the Academy of natural sciences of Philadelphia. Read July 1, 1841, and pub. by direction of the academy. 2d ed. Philadelphia, Merrihew and Thompson, printers, 1844.
Morton, Samuel George, 1799–1851.

LAC 40133
Memoir on slavery, read before the Society for the advancement of learning, of South Carolina, at its annual meeting at Columbia, 1837. By Chancellor Harper. Charleston, J. S. Burges, 1838.
Harper, William, 1790–1847.

LAC 40016
Memoir on the internal improvements contemplated by the legislature of North-Carolina; and on the resources and finances of that state. Raleigh, Printed by J. Gales, 1819.
Murphey, Archibald De Bow, 1777–1832.

LAC 12546
Memoir on the recent surveys, observations, and internal improvements in the United States, with brief notices of the new counties, towns, villages, canals, and railroads, never before delineated. By H. S. Tanner. Intended to accompany his new map of the United States. 2d ed. Philadelphia, The author, 1830.
Tanner, Henry Schenck, 1786–1856.

LAC 15401
Memoir; or, A cursory glance at my different travels & my sojourn in the Creek Nation, by Louis LeClerc de Milford. Translated by Geraldine de Courcy. Edited by John Francis McDermott. Chicago, R. R. Donnelley, 1956.
Milfort, Louis, 1750 (*ca.*)–1817.

LAC 11157
Memoire historique et politique sur la Louisiane, par M. de Vergennes, ministre de Louis XVI, accompagne d'un precis de la vie de ce ministre, et suivi d' autres memoires sur l'Indostan, Saint-Domingue, la Corse et la Guyane... Paris, Lepetit jeune, an x.–1802.
Vergennes, Charles Gravier, *comte* de, 1717–1787.

LAC 40085
Memoire historique sur la negociation de la France & de l'Angleterre, depuis le 26 mars 1761, jusqu'au 20 septembre de la meme annee; avec les pieces justificatives...
A Londres, D. Wilson, T. Becket & P. A. de Hondt, 1761.
Choiseul-Stainville, Etienne Francois, *duc* de, 1719–1785.

LAC 13941
Memoire sur le systeme grammatical des langues de quelques nations indiennes de l'Amerique du Nord...
Paris, A. Pihan de La Forest [etc.] 1838.
Du Ponceau, Peter Stephen, 1760–1844.

LAC 21140
Memoires historiques sur la Louisiane, contenant ce qui y est arrive de plus memorable depuis l'annee 1687 jusqu'a present; avec l'etablissement de la colonie fran-

coise dans cette province de l'Amerique Septentrionale sous la direction de la Compagnie des Indes; le climat, la natur & les productions de ce pays; l'origine et la religion des sauvages qui l'habitent; leurs moeurs & leurs coutumes, &c. Composes sur les memoires de M. Dumont, par M. L. L. M. Paris, C. J. B. Bauche, 1753.
Dumont de Montigny, *lieutenant.*

LAC 14629
Memoirs and adventures of Captain Matthew Phelps; formerly of Harwington in Connecticut, now resident in Newhaven in Vermont. Particularly in two voyages, from Connecticut to the river Mississippi, from December 1773 to October 1780... Compiled from the original journal and minutes kept by Mr. Phelps, during his voyages and revised and corrected according to his present recollection. By Anthony Haswell. From the press of Anthony Haswell, of Bennington, in Vermont. 1802.
Phelps, Matthew, *d.* 1817.

LAC 15150
Memoirs and letters of Dolly Madison, wife of James Madison, president of the United States, ed. by her grand-niece [Lucia B. Cutts] Boston and New York, Houghton, Mifflin and company, 1886.
Madison, Dolly Todd, 1768–1849.

LAC 40045
The memoirs, life and character of the great Mr. Law and his brother at Paris. Down to this present year 1721, with an accurate and particular account of the establishment of the Mississippi company in France... Written by a Scots gentleman. London, Printed for S. Briscoe, 1721.
Gray,

LAC 14825
Memoirs of a Huguenot family: tr. and comp. from the original autobiography of the Rev. James Fontaine, and other family manuscripts; comprising an original journal of travels in Virginia, New-York, etc., in 1715 and 1716. By Ann Maury. With an appendix, containing a translation of the Edict of Nantes, the Edict of revocation, and other interesting historical documents. New York, G. P. Putnam & co., 1872.
Fontaine, Jacques, *b.* 1658.

LAC 15700
Memoirs of a Maryland volunteer. War with Mexico, in the years 1846-7-8. Philadelphia, J. B. Lippincott & co., 1873.
Kenly, John Reese, 1822–1891.

LAC 11352
Memoirs of a New England village choir. With occasional reflections. By a member. Boston, S. G. Goodrich, 1829.
Gilman, Samuel, 1791–1858.

LAC 20192
Memoirs of Aaron Burr. With miscellaneous selections from his correspondence. By Matthew L. Davis. New York, Harper & brothers, 1836–37.
Burr, Aaron, 1756–1836.

LAC 23868–69
Memoirs of American Jews, 1775–1865. Philadelphia, Jewish Publication Society of America, 1955–56, [c1955]
Marcus, Jacob Rader, 1896–   *ed.*

LAC 11964
The memoirs of an American citizen. New York, The Macmillan company; London, Macmillan & co., ltd., 1905.
Herrick, Robert, 1868–1938.

LAC 20679
Memoirs of an American lady, with sketches of manners and scenes in America as they existed previous to the revolution, by Mrs. Anne Grant ... with unpublished letters and a memoir of Mrs. Grant by James Grant Wilson. New York, Dodd, Mead and company, 1901.
Grant, Anne, 1755–1838.

LAC 11502
Memoirs of Andrew Jackson, major-general in the army of the United States; and commander in chief of the Division of the South. Hartford, J. Russell, Jr., 1818.
Waldo, Samuel Putnam, 1780–1826.

LAC 14707
Memoirs of Andrew Sherburne, a pensioner of the navy of the revolution. Written by himself. 2d ed., enl. and improved. Providence, H. H. Brown, 1831.
Sherburne, Andrew, 1765–1831.

LAC 12850
Memoirs of Archy Moore.
The slave: or, Memoirs of Archy Moore, [*pseud.*] 2d ed. Boston, Whipple and Damrell, 1840.
Hildreth, Richard, 1807–1865.

LAC 22882
Memoirs of Baron Hyde de Neuville; outlaw, exile, ambassador; tr. and abridged by Francis Jackson, with 24 illustrations. London [etc.] Sands & co. [pref. 1913]
Hyde de Neuville, Jean Guillaume, *baron*, 1776–1857.

LAC 40038
Memoirs of Brigadier-General John Lacey, of Pennsylvania. Philadelphia, The Historical Society of Pennsylvania, 1901–02.
Lacey, John, 1755–1814.

LAC 15857
The memoirs of Colonel John S. Mosby. ed. by Charles Wells Russell. Boston, Little, Brown, and company, 1917.
Mosby, John Singleton, 1833–1916.

LAC 11893
Memoirs of David Blaustein, educator and communal worker, arranged by Miriam Blaustein. New York, Printed for the author by McBride, Nast & company, 1913.
Blaustein, Miriam.

LAC 20917
Memoirs of Dr. Joseph Priestley, to the year 1795, written by himself: with a continuation, to the time of his decease, by his son, Joseph Priestley: and observations on his writings, by Thomas Cooper and the Rev. William Christie. Northumberland [Pa.] Printed by J. Binns, 1806.
Priestley, Joseph, 1733–1804.

LAC 10955
Memoirs of Elder Thomas Campbell, together with a brief memoir of Mrs. Jane Campbell. Cincinnati, O., H. S. Bosworth, 1861.
Campbell, Alexander, 1788–1866.

LAC 12838
Memoirs of Elleanor Eldridge. Providence, B. J. Albro, printer, 1838.
McDougall, Frances Harriet, 1805–1878.

LAC 11682
Memoirs of Frederick A. P. Barnard ... tenth president of Columbia college in the city of New York. New York and London, Macmillan and co., 1896.
Fulton, John.

LAC 40065
Memoirs of General Andrew Jackson, together with the letter of Mr. Secretary Adams, in vindication of the execution of Arbuthnot and Ambrister, and the other public acts of Gen. Jackson, in Florida. New-York, Published at the Office of the National Union, 1824.

LAC 22477
Memoirs of General William T. Sherman. By himself. New York, D. Appleton and company, 1875.
Sherman, William Tecumseh, 1820–1891.

LAC 20801–02
Memoirs of Gustave Koerner, 1809–1896, lifesketches written at the suggestion of his children: ed. by Thomas J. McCormack. Cedar Rapids, Ia., The Torch press, 1909.
Koerner, Gustave Philipp, 1809–1896.

LAC 20038
Memoirs of Henry Villard, journalist and financier, 1835–1900... Boston and New York, Houghton, Mifflin and company, 1904.
Villard, Henry, 1835–1900.

LAC 11707
Memoirs of his own time. With reminiscences of the men and events of the revolution. By Alexander Graydon. Ed. by John Stockton Littell. Philadelphia, Lindsay & Blakiston, 1846.
Graydon, Alexander, 1752–1818.

LAC 10165
Memoirs of James Gordon Bennett and his times. By a journalist. New York, Stringer & Townsend, 1855.
Pray, Isaac Clark, 1813–1869.

LAC 20210
Memoirs of John Adams Dix; comp. by his son, Morgan Dix. New York, Harper & Brothers, 1883.
Dix, Morgan, 1827–1908.

LAC 16046
Memoirs of John Bannister Gibson, late chief justice of Pennsylvania. With Hon. Jeremiah S. Black's eulogy, notes from Hon. William A. Porter's Essay upon his life and character, etc., etc. Pittsburg, J. Eichbaum & co., 1890.
Roberts, Thomas Pachall, 1843–

LAC 20300–10
Memoirs of John Quincy Adams, comprising portions of his diary from 1795 to 1848. Ed. by Charles Francis Adams. Philadelphia, J. B. Lippincott & co., 1874–77.
Adams, John Quincy, *pres. U. S.*, 1767–1848.

LAC 22558
Memoirs of Lieut.-General Scott, LL. D. Written by himself. New York, Sheldon & company, 1864.
Scott, Winfield, 1786–1866.

LAC 14910
Memoirs of Major-General Heath. Containing anecdotes, details of skirmishes, battles, and other military events, during the American war. Written by himself. Boston, Printed by I. Thomas and E. T. Andrews, 1798.
Heath, William, 1737–1814.

LAC 22885
Memoirs of "Malakoff" [*pseud.*] being extracts from the correspondence and papers of the late William Edward Johnston, ed. by his son R. M. Johnston. London, Hutchinson & co. [pref. 1906]
Johnston, Robert Matteson, 1867–1920, *ed.*

LAC 20424
Memoirs of Margaret Fuller Ossoli. By R. W. Emerson, W. H. Channing and J.F. Clarke. Boston, Roberts brothers, 1874.
Ossoli, Sarah Margaret, *marchesa* d', 1810–1850.

LAC 16524
Memoirs of my life, by John Charles Fremont. Including in the narrative five journeys of western exploration, during the years 1842, 1843-4, 1845-6-7, 1848-9, 1853-4. Together with a sketch of the life of Senator Benton, in connection with western expansion. By Jessie Benton Fremont. A retrospect of fifty years covering the most eventful periods of modern American history... With maps and colored plates. vol. 1. Chicago and New York, Belford, Clarke & company, 1887.
Fremont, John Charles, 1813–1890.

LAC 23026
Memoirs of Rear-Admiral Paul Jones. Now first compiled from his original journals and correspondence; including an account of his services under Prince Potemkin, prepared for publication by himself. Edinburgh, Oliver & Boyd; [etc., etc.] 1830.
Jones, John Paul, 1747–1792.

LAC 11000
Memoirs of Rev. Charles G. Finney. Written by himself. New York, A. S. Barnes & company, 1876.
Finney, Charles Grandison, 1792–1875.

LAC 40012
Memoirs of Roger Clap. 1630. Boston, D. Clapp, jr., 1844.
Clap, Roger, 1609–1691.

LAC 14994
The memoirs of Rufus Putnam and certain official papers and correspondence, published by the National society of the Colonial dames of America in the state of Ohio; comp. and annotated by Miss Rowena Buell. Boston and New York, Houghton, Mifflin and company, 1903.
Putnam, Rufus, 1738–1824.

LAC 14706

Memoirs of service afloat, during the war between the states. By Admiral Raphael Semmes. Baltimore, Kelly, Piet & co.; [etc., etc.] 1869.
Semmes, Raphael, 1809–1877.

LAC 23306

Memoirs of Stephen Burroughs. To which are added, notes, and an appendix. Albany: Published by B. D. Packard, no. 51 State-street. R. Packard, printer, 1811.
Burroughs, Stephen, 1765–1840.

LAC 21321–22

Memoirs of the administrations of Washington and John Adams, edited from the papers of Oliver Wolcott, secretary of the Treasury. New York, Printed for the subscribers [W. Van Norden, printer] 1846.
Gibbs, George, 1815–1873.

LAC 23531–41

Memoirs of the American academy of arts and sciences. v. 1–4; new ser., v. 1–12. Boston [etc.] 1785–1902.
American Academy of Arts and Sciences, *Boston*.

LAC 23814–15

Memoirs of the American revolution, so far as it related to the states of North and South Carolina, and Georgia... New-York, Printed by D. Longworth, 1802.
Moultrie, William, 1730–1805.

LAC 15464

Memoirs of the campaign of the North western army of the United States, A. D. 1812. In a series of letters addressed to the citizens of the United States. With an appendix, containing a brief sketch of the revolutionary services of the author. Boston, True & Greene, 1824.
Hull, William, 1753–1825.

LAC 23395

Memoirs of the Confederate war for independence. New York, P. Smith, 1938.
Borcke, Heros von, 1835–1895.

LAC 14661

Memoirs of the generals, commodores, and other commanders, who distinguished themselves in the American army and navy during the wars of the revolution and 1812, and who were presented with medals by Congress, for their gallant services. Philadelphia, Carey and Hart, 1848.
Wyatt, Thomas.

LAC 21286–93

Memoirs of the Historical society of Pennsylvania. [v. 1–14.] Philadelphia, M'Carty and Davis [etc.] 1826–95.
Pennsylvania. Historical Society.

LAC 16689

Memoirs of the late Reverend Theophilus Lindsey, M. A., including a brief analysis of his works; together with anecdotes and letters of eminent persons, his friends and correspondents: also a general view of the progress of the Unitarian doctrine in England and America. London, Printed for J. Johnson and co., 1812.
Belsham, Thomas, 1750–1829.

LAC 15379

Memoirs of the life and gospel labors of Stephen Grellet. Philadelphia, For sale at friends' book store [n.d.]
Grellet, Stephen, 1773–1855.

LAC 10896

Memoirs of the life and services of Daniel Drake, M.D., physician, professor, and author; with notices of the early settlement of Cincinnati. And some of its pioneer citizens. Cincinnati, Applegate & co., 1855.
Mansfield, Edward Deering, 1801–1880.

LAC 16698

Memoirs of the life and services of the Rt. Rev. Alonzo Potter, D. D., LL. D., bishop of the Protestant Episcopal church in the diocese of Pennsylvania. 2d ed. Philadelphia, J. B. Lippincott & co., 1871.
Howe, Mark Antony DeWolfe, *bp.*, 1808–1895.

LAC 12599

Memoirs of the life of David Rittenhouse, LLD. F. R. S., late president of the American philosophical society, &c. interspersed with various notices of many distinguished men: with an appendix, containing sundry philosophical and other papers, most of which have not hitherto been published. Philadelphia, E. Parker, 1813.
Barton, William, 1754–1817.

LAC 20224

Memoirs of the life of William Wirt, attorney general of the United States. Philadelphia, Lea and Blanchard, 1849.
Kennedy, John Pendleton, 1795–1870.

LAC 21029

Memoirs of the Mexican revolution; including a narrative of the expedition of General Xavier Mina. To which are annexed some observations on the practicability of opening a commerce between the Pacific and Atlantic oceans, through the Mexican isthmus, in the province of Oaxaca, and at the Lake of Nicaragua; and the vast importance of such commerce to the civilized world. London, Printed for Lackington, Hughes, Harding, Mavor, & Lepard, 1821.
Robinson, William Davis.

LAC 12652

Memoirs of the most eminent American mechanics: also, lives of distinguished European mechanics; together with a collection of anecdotes, descriptions, &c. &c., relating to the mechanic arts. Illustrated by fifty engravings. New York, A. V. Blake, 1844.
Howe, Henry, 1816–1893.

LAC 10129

Memoirs of the Philadelphia society for promoting agriculture, containing communications on various subjects in husbandry & rural affairs, to which is added a statistical account of the Schuylkill permanent bridge. Vol. 1. Philadelphia, J. Aitken, 1808.
Philadelphia Society for Promoting Agriculture.

LAC 13928

Memoirs of the private and public life of William Penn; who settled the state of Pennsylvania, and founded the city of Philadelphia. Dover, N. H., S. C. Stevens, 1827.
Clarkson, Thomas, 1760–1846.

LAC 16081
Memoirs of the Protestant Episcopal church in the United States of America, from its organization up to the present day: containing, I. A narrative of the organization and of the early measures of the church; II. Additional statements and remarks; III. An appendix of original papers. Philadelphia, S. Potter, 1820.
White, William, *bp.*, 1748–1836.

LAC 11610
Memoirs of the Rev. David Brainerd; missionary to the Indians on the borders of New-York, New-Jersey, and Pennsylvania: chiefly taken from his own diary. By Rev. Jonathan Edwards. Including his journal, now for the first time incorporated with the rest of his diary, in a regular chronological series. By Sereno Edwards Dwight. New-Haven, S. Converse, 1822.
Brainerd, David, 1718–1747.

LAC 11106
Memoirs of the Rev. Samuel J. Mills, late missionary to the south western section of the United States, and agent of the American colonization society, deputed to explore the coast of Africa. London, Printed for Francis Westley, 1820.
Spring, Gardiner, 1785–1873.

LAC 15780
Memoirs of the Right Reverend Simon Wm. Gabriel Brute, D. D., first bishop of Vincennes, with sketches describing his recollections of scenes connected with the French revolution, and extracts from his journal. By the Rt. Rev. James Roosevelt Bayley. New York, D. & J. Sadlier & co., 1861.
Brute de Remur, Simon Guillaume Gabriel, *bp.*, 1779–1839.

LAC 16738
Memoirs of the "Society of Virginia for promoting agriculture:" containing communications on various subjects in husbandry and rural affairs. Richmond: Printed by Shepherd & Pollard, 1818.
Society of Virginia for Promoting Agriculture.

LAC 21145
Memoirs of the war in the southern department of the United States. Philadelphia: Published by Bradford and Inskeep; and Inskeep and Bradford, New York. Fry and Kammerer, printers, 1812.
Lee, Henry, 1756–1818.

LAC 10808
Memoirs of Theodore Thomas, by Rose Fay Thomas. New York, Moffat, Yard and company, 1911.
Thomas, Rose, 1852–1929.

LAC 12470
Memoirs of W. W. Holden. Durham, N. C., The Seeman printery, 1911.
Holden, William Woods, 1818–1892.

LAC 11404
The memoirs of William Jennings Bryan, by himself and his wife, Mary Baird Bryan. Philadelphia, Chicago [etc.] The John C. Winston company [c1925]
Bryan, William Jennings, 1860–1925.

LAC 10943
Memoirs of William Miller, generally known as a lecturer on the prophecies, and the second coming of Christ. Boston, J. V. Himes, 1853.
Bliss, Sylvester, *d.* 1863.

LAC 21868
Memoirs, official and personal; with sketches of travels among northern and southern Indians; embracing a war excursion, and descriptions of scenes along the western borders. New York, Paine and Burgess, 1846.
McKenney, Thomas Lorraine, 1785–1859.

LAC 11527
Memoirs, speeches and writings of Robert Rantoul, jr. Ed. by Luther Hamilton. Boston, John P. Jewett and company; Cleveland, O., Jewett, Proctor, and Worthington; [etc., etc.] 1854.
Rantoul, Robert, 1805–1852.

LAC 15179
Memoirs, with special reference to secession and the civil war, by John H. Reagan. Ed. by Walter Flavius McCaleb. With introduction by George P. Garrison. New York and Washington, The Neale publishing company, 1906.
Reagan, John Henninger, 1818–1905.

LAC 12557
Memoranda of a residence at the court of London, comprising incidents official and personal from 1819–1825. Including negotiations on the Oregon question, and other unsettled questions between the United States and Great Britain. By Richard Rush, envoy extraordinary and minister plenipotentiary from the United States, from 1817 to 1825. Philadelphia, Lea & Blanchard, 1845.
Rush, Richard, 1780–1859.

LAC 14767
Memoranda relating to the ancestry and family of Hon. Levi Parsons Morton, vice-president of the United States (1889–1893). Cambridge, Printed at the Riverside press, 1894.
Leach, Josiah Granville, 1842–1922.

LAC 20439
Memoria sobre las negociaciones entre Espana y los Estados-Unidos de America, que dieron motivo al tratado de 1819. Con una noticia sobre la estadistica de aquel pais. Acompana un Apendice, que contiene documentos importantes para mayor ilustracion del asunto. Por. d. Luis de Onis, ministro pleni-potenciario. Madrid, Impr. de d. M. de Burgos, 1820.
Onis, Luis de, 1769–1830.

LAC 15983
A memorial addressed to the sovereigns of America. London, Printed for J. Debrett, 1783.
Pownall, Thomas, 1722–1805.

LAC 40107
Memorial and affidavits showing outrages perpetrated by the Apache Indians, in the territory of Arizona, for the years 1869 and 1870. Pub. by authority of the legislature of the territory of Arizona. San Francisco, Francis & Valentine, printers, 1871.
Arizona *(Ter.) Legislative Assembly.*

LAC 12962

A memorial, containing a summary view of facts, with their authorities, in answer to the Observations sent by the English ministry to the courts of Europe. Translated from the French. Philadelphia: Printed, by James Chattin, 1757.
Moreau, Jacob Nicolas, 1717–1804.

LAC 23161–64

The memorial history of Boston, including Suffolk County, Massachusetts. 1630–1880. Ed. by Justin Winsor. Issued... [by] Clarence F. Jewett. Boston, J. R. Osgood and company, 1880–81.
Winsor, Justin, 1831–1897, *ed.*

LAC 20376–77

Memorial history of Louisville from its first settlement to the year 1896; Chicago and New York, American biographical publishing co. [pref. 1896]
Johnston, Josiah Stoddard, 1833– *ed.*

LAC 14061

Memorial history of Syracuse, N. Y., from its settlement to the present time. Syracuse, N. Y., H. P. Smith & co., 1891.
Bruce, Dwight Hall, 1834–1908, *ed.*

LAC 22255–58

Memorial history of the city of New-York and the Hudson river valley from its first settlement to the year 1892. New York, New-York historical company, 1892.
Wilson, James Grant, 1832–1914, *ed.*

LAC 12201

Memorial in regard to a national university. Washington, Govt. print. off., 1892.
Hoyt, John Wesley, 1831–1912.

LAC 16421

A memorial of Horatio Greenough, consisting of a memoir, selections from his writings, and tributes to his genius. New York, G. P. Putnam & co., 1853.
Tuckerman, Henry Theodore, 1813–1871.

LAC 40023

Memorial of the Chicago & northwestern and Chicago, Milwaukee & St. Paul railway companies to the Senate and Assembly of the state of Wisconsin. Chicago, Metropolitan prt'g co., 1875.
Chicago and North Western Railway Company.

LAC 40084

Memorial of the committee appointed by the "Free trade convention," held at Philadelphia, in September and October, 1831, to prepare and present a memorial to Congress, remonstrating against the existing tariff of duties, with an appendix. New York, W. A. Mercein, printer, 1832.
Free Trade Convention, *Philadelphia*, 1831.

LAC 40018

Memorial of the iron manufacturers of New England, asking for a modification of the tariff of 1846. Prepared by John L. Hayes. Philadelphia, C. Sherman, printer, 1850.
Hayes, John Lord, 1812–1887.

LAC 21882–83

A memorial of the town of Hampstead, New Hampshire. Historic and genealogic sketches. Proceedings of the centennial celebration, July 4th, 1849. Proceedings of the 150th anniversary of the town's incorporation, July 4th, 1899... Boston, Mass., G. B. Reed, 1899–1903.
Noyes, Harriette Eliza, 1848– *comp.*

LAC 40082

A memorial representing the present state of religion on the continent of North America. London, Printed by William Downing, for the author, 1700. [Baltimore, Maryland Historical society, 1901]
Bray, Thomas, 1658–1730.

LAC 40028

Memorial to the legislature of Massachusetts, 1843. [Boston, Directors of the Old South work, 1904]
Dix, Dorothea Lynde, 1802–1887.

LAC 12385

Memorials of a southern planter. By Susan Dabney Smedes. Baltimore, Cushings & Bailey, 1888, [c1887]
Smedes, Susan, 1840–1913.

LAC 12625

Memorials of John Bartram and Humphry Marshall; with notices of their botanical contemporaries. Philadelphia, Lindsay & Blakiston, 1849.
Darlington, William, 1782–1863.

LAC 13585

Memorials of Thomas Davidson, the wandering scholar; collected and ed. by William Knight. Boston and London, Ginn and company, 1907.
Knight, William Angus, 1836–1916.

LAC 12651

Memorials of William Cranch Bond, director of the Harvard college observatory, 1840–1859, and of his son, George Phillips Bond, director ... 1859–1865. San Francisco, C. A. Murdock & co.; New York city, Lemcke & Buechner, 1897.
Holden, Edward Singleton, 1846–1914.

LAC 40138

Memorials presented to the Congress of the United States of America, by the different societies instituted for promoting the abolition of slavery, &c. &c. in the states of Rhode-Island, Connecticut, New-York, Pennsylvania, Maryland, and Virginia. Published by order of "The Pennsylvania society for promoting the aboliton of slavery, and the relief of free negroes unlawfully held in bondage, and for improving the condition of the African race." Philadelphia: Printed by Francis Bailey, no. 116, High-street, 1792.
Pennsylvania Society for Promoting the Abolition of Slavery.

LAC 20266

Memories of a hundred years. New York, The Macmillan company; London, Macmillan & co., ltd., 1902.
Hale, Edward Everett, 1822–1909.

LAC 14750

Memories of a musical life. New York, The Century co., 1901.
Mason, William, 1829–1908.

LAC 10032
Memories of an active life; men, and ships, and sealing wax. With 150 illustrations. New York & London, G. P. Putnam's sons, 1923.
Flint, Charles Ranlett, 1850–1934.

LAC 16429
Memories of Hawaii and Hawaiian correspondence; by Julius A. Palmer, jr. Boston, Lee and Shepard, 1894.
Palmer, Julius Auboineau, 1840–1899.

LAC 10758
Memories of the crusade; a thrilling account of the great uprising of the women of Ohio in 1873, against the liquor crime. By Mother Stewart, the leader. 2d ed. Columbus, O., W. G. Hubbard & co., 1889, [c1888]
Stewart, Eliza, 1816–1908.

LAC 11434
Memories of the White House: the home life of our presidents from Lincoln to Roosevelt; being personal recollections of Colonel W. H. Crook... comp. and ed. by Henry Rood. Boston, Little, Brown, and company, 1911.
Crook, William Henry, 1839–1915.

LAC 14407
Memories of two wars; Cuban and Philippine experiences, by Frederick Funston, illustrated by F. C. Yohn. New York, C. Scribner's sons, 1911.
Funston, Frederick, 1865–1917.

LAC 11479
Men and events of forty years. Autobiographical reminiscences of an active career from 1850 to 1891, by the late Josiah Busnell [!] Grinnell. With introduction by Prof. Henry W. Parker, D. D. Boston, D. Lothrop company [c1891]
Grinnell, Josiah Bushnell, 1821–1891.

LAC 13565
Men and manners in America. By the author of Cyril Thornton, etc. Edinburgh, W. Blackwood; [etc., etc., pref. 1833]
Hamilton, Thomas, 1789–1842.

LAC 11319
Men and manners in America one hundred years ago, ed. by H. E. Scudder. New York, Scribner, Armstrong, and company, 1876.
Scudder, Horace Elisha, 1838–1902.

LAC 16599
Men and memories of San Francisco, in the "spring of '50". By T. A. Barry and B. A. Patten. San Francisco, A. L. Bancroft & company, 1873.
Barry, Theodore Augustus, 1825–1881.

LAC 22304
Men and memories; personal reminiscences, by John Russell Young; ed. by his wife, May D. Russell Young. New York, F. T. Neely [c1901]
Young, John Russell, 1841–1899.

LAC 10472
Men and mysteries of Wall street. Boston, Fields, Osgood & co., 1870.
Medbery, James Knowles, 1838–1873.

LAC 14704
Men and things I saw in civil war days. New York, Eaton & Mains; Cincinnati, Curts & Jennings, 1899.
Rusling, James Fowler, 1834–1918.

LAC 11508
Men and times of the revolution; or, Memoirs of Elkanah Watson, including journals of travels in Europe and America, from 1777 to 1842, with his correspondence with public men and reminiscences and incidents of the revolution, ed. by his son, Winslow C. Watson. New-York, Dana and company, 1856.
Watson, Elkanah, 1758–1842.

LAC 20678
Men, women & manners in colonial times. By Sydney Geo. Fisher. Illustrated with photogravures and with decorations by Edward Stratton Holloway. Philadelphia & London, J. B. Lippincott company, 1898.
Fisher, Sydney George, 1856–1927.

LAC 15410
The Mennonites of America. Published by the author. [Scottdale, Pa., Mennonite publishing house] 1909.
Smith, Charles Henry, 1875–

LAC 13042
Mental and moral culture, and popular education, by S. S. Randall. Including a special report on common school libraries, prepared in pursuance of the instructions of the superintendent of common schools; by Henry S. Randall. New York, C. S. Francis & co.; Boston, J. H. Francis, 1844.
Randall, Samuel Sidwell, 1809–1881.

LAC 12594
Mental development in the child and the race, methods and processes. With seventeen figures and ten tables. New York and London, Macmillan and co., 1895.
Baldwin, James Mark, 1861–1934.

LAC 14784
Mental philosophy: including the intellect, sensibilities, and will. Boston, Gould and Lincoln; New York, Sheldon, Blakeman & co.; [etc., etc.] 1857.
Haven, Joseph, 1816–1874.

LAC 11655
Mercantile morals; or, Thoughts for young men entering mercantile life. New-York, C. Scribner, 1852.
Van Doren, William Howard, 1810–1882.

LAC 30640–67
The Merchants' magazine and commercial review. v. 1–22, July 1839–June 1850; v. 44–63, Jan. 1861–Dec. 1870. New York, F. Hunt [etc.]

LAC 16440
Merion in the Welsh tract. With sketches of the townships of Haverford and Radnor. Historical and genealogical collections concerning the Welsh barony in the province of Pennsylvania, settled by the Cymric Quakers in 1682. Printed for the subscribers. Norristown [Pa., Herald press] 1896.
Glenn, Thomas Allen, 1864–

LAC 20638
Merry Mount; a romance of the Massachusetts colony... [1st ed.] Boston and Cambridge, J. Munroe and company, 1849.
Motley, John Lothrop, 1814–1877.

LAC 40056
Message from the President of the U. States, transmitting copies of certain documents obtained from a secret agent of the British government, employed in fomenting disaffection to the constituted authorities, and in bringing about resistance to the laws; and eventually, in concert with a British force, to destroy the union of the United States... Washington city: Printed by R. C. Weightman, 1812.
Henry, John, *British spy.*

LAC 15392
Message from the President of the United States, transmitting the report of the Naval court of inquiry upon the destruction of the United States battle ship Maine in Havana harbor, February 15, 1898, together with the testimony taken before the court. Washington, Govt. print. off., 1898.
U.S. *Naval Court of Inquiry upon Destruction of Battleship Maine.*

LAC 12528
Message of the President of the United States, communicating, in compliance with a resolution of the Senate of the 12th instant, information in relation to the states of the Union lately in rebellion, accompanied by a report of Carl Schurz on the states of South Carolina, Georgia, Alabama, Mississippi, and Louisiana; also a report of Lieutenant General Grant, on the same subject. [Washington, Govt. print. off., 1865]
U.S. *President, 1865–1869 (Johnson)*

LAC 40110
A message to Garcia, being a preachment by Elbert Hubbard. East Aurora, N. Y., The Roycrofters [c1899]
Hubbard, Elbert, 1856–1915.

LAC 23698–99
Messages and letters of William Henry Harrison. Ed. by Logan Esarey. Indianapolis, Indiana historical commission, 1922.
Indiana *(Ter.) Governor, 1801–1812 (Harrison)*

LAC 20814–23
Messages and papers of the presidents, 1789–1897.
A compilation of the messages and papers of the presidents, 1789–1897. Published, by authority of Congress, by James D. Richardson. Washington, Govt. print. off., 1896–99.
U.S. *President.*

LAC 10223
The metallic wealth of the United States, described and compared with that of other countries. Philadelphia, Lippincott, Grambo & co.; [etc., etc.] 1854.
Whitney, Josiah Dwight, 1819–1896.

LAC 14283
Metaphysical essays. Boston, Freedom publishing company, 1895.
Post, Charles Cyrel, 1846–

LAC 15043
The method of instructing children rationally, in the arts of writing and reading. Philadelphia, Printed for the author, 1813.
Neef, Joseph, 1770–1854.

LAC 15404
Methodism and literature; a series of articles from several writers on the literary enterprise and achievements of the Methodist Episcopal church. Ed. by F. A. Archibald, D. D. With a catalogue of select books for the home, the church, and the Sunday-school. Cincinnati, Walden and Stowe; New York, Phillips & Hunt, 1883.
Archibald, Francis A   *ed.*

LAC 10934
Methodism and slavery: with other matters in controversy between the North and the South; being a review of the manifesto of the majority, in reply to the protest of the minority, of the late General conference of the Methodist E. church, in the case of Bishop Andrew. Frankfort, Ky., Hodges, Todd & Pruett, printers, 1845.
Bascom, Henry Bidleman, *bp.*, 1796–1850.

LAC 16459
Methodism and the Negro, edited by I. L. Thomas, D. D. New York, Eaton & Mains; Cincinnati, Jennings & Graham [c1910].
Thomas, Isaac Lemuel, 1860–   *ed.*

LAC 16080
Methodism and the temperance reformation. By Rev. Henry Wheeler. Cincinnati, Walden and Stowe; New York, Phillips & Hunt, 1882.
Wheeler, Henry, 1835–1925.

LAC 10985
Methodism in America: with a personal narrative of the author, during a tour through a part of the United States and Canada. 3d ed. London, Printed for the author; sold by J. Mason, 1849.
Dixon, James, 1788–1871.

LAC 14329
Methods of industrial peace. Boston and New York, Houghton, Mifflin and company; London, Macmillan and company, ltd., 1904.
Gilman, Nicholas Paine, 1849–1912.

LAC 12590
Methods of study in natural history. Boston, Ticknor and Field, 1863.
Agassiz, Louis, 1807–1873.

LAC 13045
Methods of teaching; a hand-book of principles, directions, and working models for common-school teachers. New York, Harper & brothers, 1880.
Swett, John, 1830–1913.

LAC 10834
Methods of teaching history. By Dr. G. [!] Diesterweg, Professors Herbert B. Adams, C. K. Adams, John W. Burgess, E. Emerton, W. F. Allen, and Mr. Thomas Wentworth Higginson. Boston, Ginn, Heath, & co., 1883.

LAC 16778
The Mexican immigrant, his life-story; autobiographic documents collected by Manuel Gamio. Chicago, Ill., The University of Chicago press [c1931]
Gamio, Manuel, 1883–1960, *comp.*

LAC 14923
The Mexican war diary of George B. McClellan, edited by William Starr Myers. Princeton, Princeton university press; [etc., etc.] 1917.
McClellan, George Brinton, 1826–1885.

LAC 12949
Mexico and the United States; a story of revolution, intervention and war. Illustrated with photographs and maps. Chicago, The Bible house [c1914]
Starr, Frederick, 1858–1933.

LAC 12935
Mexico as it was and as it is. With numerous illustrations on wood, engraved by Butler from drawings by the author. New-York, J. Winchester; [etc., etc.] 1844.
Mayer, Brantz, 1809–1879.

LAC 13706
Mexico under Maximilian. Philadelphia, Pa.; Boston, Mass.; [etc.] National publishing company [c1867]
Flint, Henry Martyn, 1829–1868.

LAC 10644
Mezzotints in modern music; Brahms, Tschaikowsky, Chopin, Richard Strauss, Liszt, and Wagner. 3d ed. New York, Scribner, 1901.
Huneker, James Gibbons, 1857–1921.

LAC 15541
Michael Heilprin and his sons: a biography. New York, Dodd, Mead and company, 1912.
Pollak, Gustav, 1849–1919.

LAC 11425
Michigan: a history of governments. 4th ed., Boston, New York, Houghton, Mifflin and co., 1889, [c1885]
Cooley, Thomas McIntyre, 1824–1898.

LAC 21152–53
Michigan as a province, territory and state, the twenty-sixth member of the federal Union, by Henry M. Utley, Byron M. Cutcheon: advisory editor, Clarence M. Burton... [New York] The Publishing society of Michigan, 1906.
Utley, Henry Munson, 1836–1917.

LAC 10675
The Michigan fur trade. Lansing, Michigan historical commission, 1919.
Johnson, Ida Amanda.

LAC 23505–6
The Middle Kingdom; a survey of ... the Chinese empire and its inhabitants, with a new map of the empire, and illustrations, principally engraved by T. W. Orr, by S. Wells Williams. 3d ed. ... New York, G. P. Putnam, 1848.
Williams, Samuel Wells, 1812–1884.

LAC 13766
The middle period, 1817–1858. New York, C. Scribner's sons, 1898, [c1897]
Burgess, John William, 1844–1931.

LAC 14574
The middle West Side; a historical sketch. New York, Survey associates, inc., 1914.
Cartwright, Otho Grandford.

LAC 16760
The middle years. London [etc.] W. Collins sons & co., ltd. [c1917]
James, Henry, 1843–1916.

LAC 14534
Might and right; by a Rhode Islander. Providence, A. H. Stillwell, 1844.
McDougall, Frances Harriet Greene, 1805–1878.

LAC 40083
The mighty destroyer displayed, in some account of the dreadful havock made by the mistaken use as well as abuse of distilled spirituous liquors. By a lover of mankind. Philadelphia: Printed by Joseph Crukshank, between Second and Third streets, in Market-street, 1774.
Benezet, Anthony, 1713–1784.

LAC 40105
Migrations from Connecticut prior to 1800. [New Haven] Published for the Tercentenary commission by the Yale university press, 1934.
Rosenberry, Lois Mathews, 1873–

LAC 13381
The militant proletariat. Chicago, C. H. Kerr & company, co-operative [c1911]
Lewis, Austin.

LAC 15462
The military and civil history of Connecticut during the war of 1861–65. Comprising a detailed account of the various regiments and batteries, through march, encampment, bivouac, and battle; also instances of distinguished personal gallantry, and biographical sketches of many heroic soldiers: together with a record of the patriotic action of citizens at home, and of the liberal support furnished by the state in its executive and legislative departments. By W. A. Croffut and John M. Morris. 3d ed., rev. New York, L. Bill, 1869.
Croffut, William Augustus, 1835–1915.

LAC 14697
Military education in the United States, by Captain Ira L. Reeves. Burlington, Free press printing co., 1914.
Reeves, Ira Louis, 1872–

LAC 23122–24
Military history of Ulysses S. Grant, from April, 1861, to April, 1865. New York, D. Appleton and company, 1868–81.
Badeau, Adam, 1831–1895.

LAC 14649
A military journal during the American revolutionary war, from 1775 to 1783; describing interesting events and transactions of this period; with numerous historical facts and anecdotes, from the original manuscript. To which is added an appendix, containing biographical sketches of several general officers. Boston, Richardson and Lord, 1823.
Thacher, James, 1754–1844.

LAC 14255
The military laws of the United States, relating to the army, Marine corps, volunteers, militia, and to bounty lands and pensions, from the foundation of the government to the year 1858. Baltimore, J. Murphy & co., 1858.
Callan, John F *comp.*

LAC 15168
Military miscellanies. New York, Brentano's, 1889.
Fry, James Barnet, 1827–1894.

LAC 22466–67
The military operations of General Beauregard in the war between the states, 1861 to 1865; including a brief personal sketch and a narrative of his services in the war with Mexico, 1846–8. New York, Harper & brothers [c1883]
Roman, Alfred, 1824–

LAC 14655
The military policy of the United States. By Brevet Maj. Gen. Emory Upton, United States army. 3d impression. Washington, Govt. print. off., 1911.
Upton, Emory, 1839–1881.

LAC 40053
The military profession in the United States, and the means of promoting its usefulness and honour; an address, delivered before the Dialectic society of the corps of cadets of the Military academy, Westpoint, at the close of the annual examination, June 19th, 1839. New-York, S. Colman, 1839.
Butler, Benjamin Franklin, 1795–1858.

LAC 15391
Military road from Fort Benton to Fort Walla-Walla... The report of Lieutenant Mullan, in charge of the construction of the military road from Fort Benton to Fort Walla-Walla. [Washington, Govt. print. off., 1861]
U.S. *Army. Corps of Topographical Engineers.*

LAC 14423
The military services and public life of Major-General John Sullivan, of the American revolutionary army. Port Washington, N. Y., Kennikat Press [1968]
Amory, Thomas Coffin, 1812–1889.

LAC 22395
The military telegraph during the Civil war in the United States, with an exposition of ancient and modern means of communication, and of the federal and Confederate cipher systems; also a running account of the war between the states. Chicago, Jansen, McClurg & co., 1882.
Plum, William Rattle, 1845–1927.

LAC 15463
The military unpreparedness of the United States; a history of American land forces from colonial times until June 1, 1915, by Frederic Louis Huidekoper. With an introduction by Major General Leonard Wood. New York, The Macmillan company, 1915.
Huidekoper, Frederic Louis, 1874–

LAC 11744
The milk supply of two hundred cities and towns. By Henry E. Alvord and R. A. Pearson. Washington, Govt. print. off., 1903.
Alvord, Henry Elijah, 1844–1904.

LAC 11758
The milk trade of New York and vicinity, giving an account of the sale of pure and adulterated milk... By John Mullaly. With an introduction by R. T. Trall, M. D. New York, Fowlers and Wells, 1853.
Mullaly, John.

LAC 21937–38
Millard Fillmore papers... Ed. by Frank H. Severance. Buffalo, N. Y., The Buffalo historical society, 1907.
Fillmore, Millard, *pres. U.S.*, 1800–1874.

LAC 13864
The millennium; or, The thousand years of prosperity, promised to the Church of God... [*Anon.*] Elizabethtown, S. Kollock, 1794.
Bellamy, Joseph, 1719–1790.

LAC 15029
Miller's guide.
The young mill-wright and miller's guide; illus. by twenty-eight descriptive plates. 9th ed., with additions and corrections, by Thomas P. Jones, and a description of an improved merchant flour-mill, with engravings, by C. and O. Evans, engineers. Philadelphia, Carey, Lea & Blanchard, 1836.
Evans, Oliver, 1755–1819.

LAC 16098
Millionaires of a day: an inside history of the great southern California "boom". New York, Fords, Howard & Hulbert, 1890.
Van Dyke, Theodore Strong, *b.* 1842.

LAC 10889
Milwaukee. Milwaukee, Wis., Schnellpressendruck des "Herold," 1871.
Koss, Rudolph A.

LAC 16214
Milwaukee municipal campaign book 1912, Social-democratic party ... pub. by order of the County central committee of the Social-democratic party, Milwaukee County, Wis. [Milwaukee, The Co-operative printery, 1912]
Socialist Party *(U.S.) Wisconsin.*

LAC 13014
Mind and hand; manual training, the chief factor in education. Being the 3d ed. of "Manual training, the solution of social and industrial problems." New York, American book co. [c1900]
Ham, Charles Henry, 1831–1902.

LAC 15991
Mind in evolution. London, Macmillan and co., limited; New York, The Macmillan company, 1901.
Hobhouse, Leonard Trelawney, 1864–

LAC 16255
The mind of the Negro as reflected in letters written during the crisis, 1800–1860. New York, Negro Universities Press [1969]
Woodson, Carter Godwin, 1875–1950, *ed.*

LAC 16304
Mineral springs and health resorts of California, with a complete chemical analysis of every important mineral water in the world. Illustrated. A prize essay. Annual prize of the Medical society of the state of California, awarded April 20, 1889. San Francisco, The Bancroft company, 1890.
Anderson, Winslow.

LAC 13409
Miners' strike in Westmoreland County, Pa.
Report on the miners' strike in bituminous coal field in Westmoreland County, Pa., in 1910–11. Prepared under the direction of Chas. P. Neill, commissioner of labor. June 22, 1912.–Referred to the Committee on labor and ordered to be printed. Washington [Govt. print. off.] 1912.
U. S. *Bureau of Labor.*

LAC 15641
Mines, mills, and furnaces of the Pacific states and territories: an account of the condition, resources, and methods of the mining and metallurgical industry in those regions, chiefly relating to the precious metals. A sequel to "American mines and mining." New-York, J. B. Ford and company, 1871.
Raymond, Rossiter Worthington, 1840–1918.

LAC 16094
The mines of Colorado. Springfield, Mass., S. Bowles & company, 1867.
Hollister, Ovando James, 1834–1892.

LAC 11959
Mingo, and other sketches in black and white. Boston, James R. Osgood and company, 1884.
Harris, Joel Chandler, 1848–1908.

LAC 10303
The mining advance into the inland empire; a comparative study of the beginnings of the mining industry in Idaho and Montana, eastern Washington and Oregon, and the southern interior of British Columbia; and of institutions and laws based upon that industry. Madison, Wis., 1914.
Trimble, William Joseph, 1871–

LAC 14948
Mining-camps; a study in American frontier government. New York, C. Scribner's sons, 1885.
Shinn, Charles Howard, 1852–1924.

LAC 11396
Mining in the Pacific states of North America. San Francisco, H. H. Bancroft and company, 1861.
Hittell, John Shertzer, 1825–1901.

LAC 13715
Ministerial court of the United States in Japan.
Outline lectures on the history, organization, jurisdiction, and practice of the ministerial and consular courts of the United States of America in Japan, by G. H. Scidmore, LL. B. Tokio, Igirisu horitsu gakko, 1887.
Scidmore, George Hawthorne, 1854–1922.

LAC 11984
The minister's charge; or, The apprenticeship of Lemuel Barker. Boston and New York, Houghton Mifflin and company [c1886]
Howells, William Dean, 1837–1920.

LAC 13881
The ministry of art. Boston and New York, Houghton Mifflin company, 1914.
Cram, Ralph Adams, 1863–

LAC 13128
Minnesota and Dacotah: in letters descriptive of a tour through the North-west, in the autumn of 1856. With information relative to public lands, and a table of statistics. Washington, R. Farnham, 1857.
Andrews, Christopher Columbus, 1829–1922.

LAC 16116
Minnesota and its resources; to which are appended Campfire sketches, or, Notes of a trip from St. Paul to Pembina and Selkirk settlement on the Red river of the North. Chicago, Keen & Lee; Philadelphia, C. DeSilver, 1856.
Bond, John Wesley, 1825–1903.

LAC 40072
Minnesota: its advantages to settlers, 1868. Being a brief synopsis of its history and progress, climate, soil, agricultural and manufacturing facilities, commercial capacities, and social status; its lakes, rivers and railroads; homestead and exemption laws; embracing a concise treatise on its climatology, in a hygienic and sanitary point of view... St. Paul, 1868.
Hewitt, Girart.

LAC 11084
Minutes and letters of the Coetus of the German reformed congregations in Pennsylvania, 1747–1792. Together with three preliminary reports of Rev. John Philip Boehm, 1734–1744. Published by authority of the eastern synod of the Reformed church in the United States. Philadelphia, Reformed church publishing board, 1903.
Reformed Church in the United States.

LAC 13908
The minutes from 1685–1705. With an introductory essay by George J. Miller. Perth Amboy, 1949.
Board of General Proprietors of the Eastern Division of New Jersey.

LAC 20449–53
Minutes of the Common council of the city of New York, 1675–1776. In eight volumes. Pub. under the authority of the city of New York. New York, Dodd, Mead and company, 1905.
New York *(City) Common Council.*

LAC 15578
Minutes of the Convention of the commonwealth of Pennsylvania, which commenced at Philadelphia, on Tuesday the twenty-fourth day of November, in the year of Our Lord one thousand seven hundred and eighty-nine, for the purpose of reviewing, and if they see occasion, altering and amending, the constitution of this state. Philadelphia: Printed by Zachariah Poulson, jun. in Fourth-street, between Market-street and Arch-street, 1789.
Pennsylvania. *Constitutional Convention,* 1789–1790.

LAC 16839
Minutes of the Council and General court of colonial Virginia, 1622–1632, 1670–1676, with notes and excerpts from original Council and General court records, into 1683, now lost. Ed. by H. R. McIlwaine. Richmond, Va. [The Colonial press, Everett Waddey co.] 1924.
Virginia *(Colony) Council.*

LAC 15951
Minutes of the Philadelphia society for the promotion of agriculture, from its institution in February, 1785, to March, 1810. Philadelphia, J. C. Clark & son, printers, 1854.
Philadelphia Society for Promoting Agriculture.

LAC 40138
Miscegenation. [n.p., n.d.]
Croly, David Goodman, 1829–1889.

LAC 13094
Miscellanea: comprising reviews, lectures, and essays, on historical, theological, and miscellaneous subjects. Louisville, Ky., Webb, Gill & Levering, 1855.
Spalding, Martin John, *abp.*, 1810–1872.

LAC 10527
Miscellaneous essays and discourses. Boston, T. R. Marvin, 1847.
Hopkins, Mark, 1802–1887.

LAC 22607–8
The miscellaneous essays and occasional writings of Francis Hopkinson, esq. Philadelphia: Printed by T. Dobson, at the stone-house, no. 41, Second street, 1792.
Hopkinson, Francis, 1737–1791.

LAC 16777
Miscellaneous publications of the Socialist labor party. [n. p.] 1898–1951.
Socialist Labor Party.

LAC 16723
Miscellaneous trifles in prose. Philadelphia: Printed for the author, by Lang and Ustick, M.DCC.XCVI.
Carey, Mathew, 1760–1839.

LAC 15233
The miscellaneous works of Colonel Humphreys. New York, Printed by Hodge, Allen, and Campbell; and sold at their respective book-stores, 1790.
Humphreys, David, 1752–1818.

LAC 11932
The miscellaneous works of Mr. Philip Freneau containing his essays, and additional poems. Philadelphia: Printed by Francis Bailey, at Yorick's head, in Market street. M DCC LXXXVIII.
Freneau, Philip Morin, 1752–1832.

LAC 10991
Miscellaneous writings, 1883–1896, by Mary Baker Eddy. Boston, A. V. Stewart, 1917.
Eddy, Mary, 1821–1910.

LAC 14511
The miscellaneous writings of Joseph Story, ed. by his son, William W. Story. Boston, C. C. Little and J. Brown, 1852.
Story, Joseph, 1779–1845.

LAC 12479
Miscellaneous writings on slavery. Boston, J. P. Jewett & company; Cleveland, O., Jewett, Proctor, and Worthington; [etc., etc.] 1853.
Jay, William, 1789–1858.

LAC 10247
Miscellanies of Georgia, historical, biographical, descriptive, etc. In three parts. Atlanta, Ga., J. F. Meegan [1874]
Chappell, Absalom Harris, 1801–1878.

LAC 10180
Miss Beecher's domestic receipt book: designed as a supplement to her Treatise on domestic economy. New York, Harper & brothers, 1852.
Beecher, Catherine Esther, 1800–1878.

LAC 11830
Miss Ludington's sister; a romance of immortality. Boston, J. R. Osgood and company, 1885, [c1884]
Bellamy, Edward, 1850–1898.

LAC 11894
Miss Ravenel's conversion from secession to loyalty. New York, Harper & brothers, 1867.
De Forest, John William, 1826–1906.

LAC 14127
Missionary explorers among the American Indians. New York, C. Scribner's sons, 1913.
Humphreys, Mary Gay, *d.* 1915, *ed.*

LAC 10992
The missionary gazetteer; comprising a geographical and statistical account of the various stations of the American and foreign Protestant missionary societies of all denominations, with their progress in evangelization and civilization. Boston, W. Hyde & co., 1832.
Edwards, Bela Bates, 1802–1852.

LAC 11032
Missionary history of the Pacific Northwest, containing the wonderful story of Jason Lee, with sketches of many of his co-laborers, all illustrating life on the plains and in the mountains in pioneer days. Portland, H. K. Hines; San Francisco, J. D. Hammond [1899]
Hines, Harvey K   1828–1902.

LAC 10024
The Mississippi and Ohio rivers: containing plans for the protection of the delta from inundation; and investigations of the practicability and cost of improving the navigation of the Ohio and other rivers by means of reservoirs, with an appendix, on the bars at the mouths of the Mississippi. Philadelphia, Lippincott, Grambo, and co., 1853.
Ellet, Charles, 1810–1862.

LAC 14370
Mississippi, as a province, territory and state, with biographical notices of eminent citizens. vol. 1. Jackson, Miss., Power & Barksdale, 1880.
Claiborne, John Francis Hamtramck, 1809–1884.

LAC 15053
The Mississippi basin... The struggle in America between England and France, 1697–1763, with full cartographical illustrations from contemporary sources. Boston and New York, Houghton, Mifflin and company, 1898, [c1895]
Winsor, Justin, 1831–1897.

LAC 12409
Mississippi-fahrten. Reisebilder aus dem amerikanischen Suden (1879-1880). Von Ernst von Hesse-Wartegg. Mit zahlreichen abbildungen. Leipzig, C. Reissner, 1881.
Hesse-Wartegg, Ernst von, 1854-1918.

LAC 10252
Mississippi scenes; or, Sketches of southern and western life and adventure, humorous, satirical, and descriptive, including the legend of Black Creek. 2d ed. Philadelphia, A. Hart, 1851.
Cobb, Joseph Beckham, 1819-1858.

LAC 14058
Missouri's contribution to American architecture; a history of the architectural achievements in this state from the time of the earliest settlements down to the present year. Compiled and edited by John Albury Bryan. [St. Louis, Saint Louis architectural club] 1928.
Bryan, John Albury, 1890–   *ed.*

LAC 40094
Mistakes of educated men. An address. [2d ed.] Philadelphia, J. C. Garrigues, 1862.
Hart, John Seely, 1810-1877.

LAC 14634
Mr. Ambrose's letters on the rebellion. New York, Hurd & Houghton; Baltimore, J. S. Waters, 1865.
Kennedy, John Pendleton, 1795-1870.

LAC 11902
Mr. Dooley in peace and in war. Boston, Small, Maynard & company, 1898.
Dunne, Finley Peter, 1867-1936.

LAC 15188
Mr. Fish and the Alabama claims; a chapter in diplomatic history. Boston and New York, Houghton, Mifflin and company, 1892.
Davis, John Chandler Bancroft, 1822-1907.

LAC 40007
Mr. Greeley's letters from Texas and the lower Mississippi: to which are added his address to the farmers of Texas, and his speech on his return to New York, June 12, 1871. New York, Tribune office, 1871.
Greeley, Horace, 1811-1872.

LAC 12061
Mr. Incoul's misadventure; a novel. New York, W. E. Benjamin & Bell, 1887, [c1888]
Saltus, Edgar Evertson, 1855-1921.

LAC 40070
Mr. Madison's war. A dispassionate inquiry into the reasons alleged by Mr. Madison for declaring an offensive and ruinous war against Great-Britain. Together with some suggestions as to a peaceable and constitutional mode of averting that dreadful calamity. By a New-England farmer. Boston: Printed by Russell & Cutler, 1812.
Lowell, John, 1769-1840.

LAC 16879
Mitchell's compendium of the internal improvements of the United States; comprising general notices of all the most important canals and rail-roads ... with a brief notice of internal improvement in Canada and Nova Scotia. Philadelphia, Mitchell & Hinman, 1835.
Mitchell, Samuel Augustus, 1792-1868.

LAC 14714
Mobile of the five flags; the story of the river basin and coast about Mobile from the earliest times to the present. Mobile, The Gill printing company, 1913.
Hamilton, Peter Joseph, 1859-1927.

LAC 40084
The mode of protecting domestic industry, consistently with the desires both of the South and the North, by operating on the currency. New York, McElrath & Bangs, 1833.
Roosevelt, Clinton, 1804-1898.

LAC 22262
The model architect. A series of original designs for cottages, villas, suburban residences, etc., accompanied by explanations, specifications, estimates, and elaborate details. Prepared expressly for the use of projectors and artisans throughout the United States. A new edition, with new drawings and large additions. Philadelphia, J. B. Lippincott, 1868.
Sloan, Samuel, 1815-1884.

LAC 40081
A model factory in a model city. A social study. [New York, Press of Brown, Green & Adams] 1887.
Winton, John G.

LAC 15892
The model of the government of the province of East New Jersey in America. From the original edition published at Edinburgh, 1685. Newark, N. J., 1874.
Scot, George, *d.* 1685.

LAC 14584
A model tenement house law. New York, Charities publication committee, 1910.
Veiller, Lawrence Turnure.

LAC 13786
The model town; or, The right and progressive organization of industry for the production of material and moral wealth. By Beta [*pseud.*] Cambridge, Printed for the author, 1869.
Bassett, Edward Barnard.

LAC 40023
Moderate houses for moderate means. An argument for cheap trains as essential to independent homes for the working classes; and an address before the Quincy homestead association, and the requirements for admission. Boston, Wright & Potter, 1871.
Quincy, Josiah, 1802-1882.

LAC 11386
Modern agitators; or, Pen portraits of living American reformers. By David W. [!] Bartlett, New York, Auburn [N. Y.] Miller, Orton & Mulligan, 1856, [c1854]
Bartlett, David Vandewater Golden, 1828-1912.

LAC 10849
Modern American school buildings. Being a treatise upon and designs for, the construction of school buildings. With 89 full-page illustrations. 1st ed. 1st thousand. New York, J. Wiley & sons; London, Chapman & Hall, Limited, 1899.
Briggs, Warren Richard.

LAC 40115
Modern armor for national defence, presenting practical information about material, methods of manufacture, cost, development, tests and application, effects of fire, resistance of plates, and a comparison of the results that have been obtained at the most important competitive trials, together with statistics. New York & London, G. P. Putnam's sons, 1886.
Jaques, William Henry, 1848–

LAC 14671
The modern builders' guide. Illustrated by eighty-seven copper plate engravings. New York, W. D. Smith, 1841.
Lafever, Minard.

LAC 16307
Modern chivalry, by Hugh Henry Brackenridge; edited, with introduction, chronology, and bibliography, by Claude M. Newlin. New York, Cincinnati [etc.] American book company [c1937]
Brackenridge, Hugh Henry, 1748–1816.

LAC 15137
Modern church brotherhoods; a survey of the practical activities of the churchmen's clubs and brotherhoods. New York, Chicago [etc.] Fleming H. Revell company [c1911]
Patterson, William B.

LAC 13472
Modern cities and their religious problems, by Samuel Lane Loomis. With an introduction by Rev. Josiah Strong, D.D. New York, The Baker & Taylor company [c1887]
Loomis, Samuel Lane, 1856–

LAC 13927
Modern cities; progress of the awakening for their betterment here and in Europe, by Horatio M. Pollock and William S. Morgan. New York and London, Funk & Wagnalls company, 1913.
Pollock, Horatio Milo, 1868–

LAC 15035
The modern city and its problems. New York, Chicago [etc.] C. Scribner's sons [c1915]
Howe, Frederic Clemson, 1867–

LAC 13522
Modern civic art; or, The city made beautiful. New York and London, G. P. Putnam's sons, 1903.
Robinson, Charles Mulford, 1869–1917.

LAC 40098
The modern distributive process. Studies of competition and its limits ... by John B. Clark, and Franklin H. Giddings. Boston, Ginn & company, 1888.
Clark, John Bates, 1847–1938.

LAC 40020
Modern farming; the passing of the horse. Minneapolis, Gas traction company [1908]
Gas Traction Company.

LAC 16532
The modern horse doctor: containing practical observations on the causes, nature, and treatment of disease and lameness in horses... 15th thousand. New York, Orange Judd & co. [n. d.]
Dadd, George H   b. 1813.

LAC 40108
Modern industrialism and the negroes of the United States. Washington, D. C., The Academy, 1908.
Grimke, Archibald Henry, 1849–1930.

LAC 16945
Modern industry in relation to the family, health, education, morality. New York [etc.] Longmans, Green, and co., 1914.
Kelley, Florence, 1859–1932.

LAC 10497
Modern inquiries: classical, professional, and miscellaneous. [2d ed.] Boston, Little, Brown, and company, 1867.
Bigelow, Jacob, 1787–1879.

LAC 16313
A modern instance, a novel. Boston, J. R. Osgood and company, 1882.
Howells, William Dean, 1837–1920.

LAC 11198
Modern methods of charity; an account of the systems of relief, public and private, in the principal countries having modern methods, by Charles Richmond Henderson, assisted by others. New York, The Macmillan company; London, Macmillan & co., ltd., 1904.
Henderson, Charles Richmond, 1848–1915.

LAC 13529
Modern methods of sewage disposal, for towns, public institutions, and isolated houses; by Geo. E. Waring, jr. New York, D. Van Nostrand company, 1894.
Waring, George Edwin, 1833–1898.

LAC 12635
The modern philosopher; or Terrible tractoration! In four cantos, most respectfully addressed to the Royal college of physicians, London. By Christopher Caustick [pseud.] 2d American ed., rev., cor., and much enl. by the author. Philadelphia: From the Lorenzo press of E. Bronson, 1806.
Fessenden, Thomas Green, 1771–1837.

LAC 11199
Modern prison systems. Their organization and regulation in various countries of Europe and America. International prison commission reports. Samuel J. Barrows, commissioner for the United States. Washington, Govt. print. off., 1903.
Henderson, Charles Richmond, 1848–1915.

LAC 10561
Modern socialism. New York, Commonwealth co. [c1897]
Vail, Charles Henry, 1866–

LAC 22640
Modern spiritualism; a history and a criticism. London, Methuen & co., 1902.
Podmore, Frank, 1856–1910.

LAC 15798
Modern tendencies in sculpture; the Scammon lectures for 1917. Chicago, Ill., Pub. for the Art institute of Chicago by the University of Chicago press [c1921]
Taft, Lorado, 1860–1936.

LAC 11234
The modern woman's rights movement; a historical survey, by Dr. Kaethe Schirmacher; tr. from the 2d German ed. by Carl Conrad Eckhardt. New York, The Macmillan company, 1912.
Schirmacher, Kathe, 1865–1930.

LAC 40085
A Modest and Impartial narrative Of several Grievances and Great Oppressions That the Peaceable and most Considerable Inhabitants of Their Majesties Province of New-York in America Lye Under, By the Extravagant and Arbitrary Proceedings of Jacob Leysler and his Accomplices. Printed at New-York, and Reprinted at London, 1690. [Boston, 1927]

LAC 22421–22
Moeurs des sauvages ameriquains, comparees aux moeurs des premiers temps. Par le P. Lafitau. Ouvrage enrichi de figures en taille-douce... Paris, Saugrain l'aine [etc.] 1724.
Lafitau, Joseph Francois, 1681–1746.

LAC 15867
Mohonk addresses, by Edward Everett Hale and David J. Brewer, with introduction by Edwin D. Mead. Boston, Published for the International school of peace, Ginn and company, 1910.
Hale, Edward Everett, 1822–1909.

LAC 15069
The Molly Maguires. New York, International publishers [c1932]
Bimba, Anthony.

LAC 13741
The Molly Maguires and the detectives. New and enl. ed. New York, G. W. Dillingham co. [c1905]
Pinkerton, Allan, 1819–1884.

LAC 16402
The Molly Maguires. The origin, growth, and character of the organization. Philadelphia, J. B. Lippincott & co., 1877.
Dewees, Francis Percival.

LAC 10308
Money. New York, H. Holt and company, 1878, [c1877]
Walker, Francis Amasa, 1840–1897.

LAC 10315
Money and banking illustrated by American history. Boston and London, Ginn & company, 1896, [c1895]
White, Horace, 1834–1916.

LAC 10067
Money and legal tender in the United States. New York, G. P. Putnam's sons, 1877.
Linderman, Henry Richard, 1825–1879.

LAC 15916
Money found: recovered from its hiding-places, and put into circulation through confidence in government banks. Rev. ed. with a glossary of financial terms, and general information relating to finance. Chicago, C. H. Kerr & company, 1894.
Hill, Thomas Edie, 1832–1915.

LAC 10309
Money in its relations to trade and industry. London, Macmillan and co., 1880.
Walker, Francis Amasa, 1840–1897.

LAC 10224
Money inflation in the United States; a study in social pathology. New York and London, G. P. Putnam's sons, 1905.
Wildman, Murray Shipley, 1868–1930.

LAC 40001
Money, its history, evils and remedy. Albany, Printed by B. Taylor, 1858.
Dealtry, William.

LAC 10009
Monopolies and the people. New York and London, G. P. Putnam's sons, 1890, [c1889]
Baker, Charles Whiting, 1865–1941.

LAC 10017
Monopolies and the people. Davenport, Iowa, Day, Egbert & Fidlar, 1873.
Cloud, D   C.

LAC 10025
Monopolies and trusts. New York, The Macmillan company; London, Macmillan & co., ltd., 1912, [c1900]
Ely, Richard Theodore, 1854–1943.

LAC 13836
The Monroe doctrine. 2d ed. New York, G. E. Stechert & co. [France printed] 1905.
Reddaway, William Fiddian, 1872–1949.

LAC 11137
The Monroe doctrine, an obsolete shibboleth. New Haven, Yale university press; [etc., etc.] 1913.
Bingham, Hiram, 1875–1956.

LAC 40085
The monster of monsters: a true and faithful narrative of a most remarkable phoenomenon lately seen in this metropolis; to the great surprize and terror of His Majesty's good subjects: humbly dedicated to all the virtuosi of New-England. [Boston] Printed [by Zechariah Fowle] in July 1754.
Thumb, Thomas, *pseud.*

LAC 10487

Mont Saint Michel and Chartres. Washington, 1912.
Adams, Henry, 1838–1918.

LAC 13031

The Montessori method; scientific pedagogy as applied to child education in "The children's houses" with additions and revisions by the author, by Maria Montessori; tr. from the Italian by Anne E. George; with an introduction by Professor Henry W. Holmes, with thirty-two illustrations from photographs. 2d ed. New York, Frederick A. Stokes company, 1912.
Montessori, Maria, 1870–1952.

LAC 40123

The Montessori system examined. Boston, New York [etc.] Houghton Mifflin company [c1914]
Kilpatrick, William Heard, 1871–

LAC 30237–42

The Monthly anthology and Boston review. v. 1–10, no. 5; Nov. 1803–May 1811. Boston, T. B. Wait [etc.]

LAC 11455

Monument to the memory of General Andrew Jackson: containing twenty-five eulogies and sermons delivered on occasion of his death. To which is added an appendix, containing General Jackson's proclamation, his farewell address, and a certified copy of his last will. The whole preceded by a short sketch of his life. Troy, J. Hanna, 1846.
Dusenbery, Benjamin M   *comp.*

LAC 16954

Moorhead bill.
The origin of the national banking system. Washington, Govt. Print. Off., 1910.
Davis, Andrew McFarland, 1833–1920.

LAC 11042

The moral and religious challenge of our times; the guiding principle in human development, reverence for personality. New York, The Macmillan company, 1911.
King, Henry Churchill, 1858–1934.

LAC 13903

Moral aspects of city life. A series of lectures by Rev. E. H. Chapin. New York, H. Lyon; Boston, A. Tompkins; [etc., etc.] 1856.
Chapin, Edwin Hubbell, 1814–1880.

LAC 14792

The moral damage of war. Boston, For the International union, Ginn & company, 1906.
Walsh, Walter, 1857–1931.

LAC 10521

Moral philosophy: including theoretical and practical ethics. Boston, Gould and Lincoln; New York, Sheldon and company; [etc., etc.] 1859.
Haven, Joseph, 1816–1874.

LAC 40080

A moral review of the revolutionary war, or some of the evils of that event considered. A discourse delivered at the Unitarian church, Augusta, Sabbath evening, March 13th, 1842. With an introductory address, and notes. Hallowell [Me.] Glazier, Masters & Smith, printers, 1842.
Judd, Sylvester, 1818–1853.

LAC 16082

Moralism and Christianity; or, Man's experience and destiny. In three lectures. New-York, J. S. Redfield, 1850.
James, Henry, 1811–1882.

LAC 16263

Morals in modern business, addresses delivered in the Page lecture series, 1908, before the senior class of the Sheffield scientific school, Yale university. New Haven, Conn., Yale university press; [etc., etc.] 1909.
Yale University. *Sheffield Scientific School.*

LAC 10158

Moran of the Lady Letty; a story of adventure off the California coast. New York, Doubleday & McClure co., 1898.
Norris, Frank, 1870–1902.

LAC 11004

The Moravians in Georgia, 1735–1740. Raleigh. N. C., Printed for the author by Edwards & Broughton [c1905]
Fries, Adelaide Lisetta, 1871–1949.

LAC 11806

More fables, by George Ade. Illustrated by Clyde J. Newman. Chicago & New York, H. S. Stone and company, 1900.
Ade, George, 1866–1944.

LAC 16703

Moreau de St. Mery's American journey (1793–1798) translated and edited by Kenneth Roberts and Anna M. Roberts. Preface by Kenneth Roberts. Introduction by Stewart L. Mims. Frontispiece painting by James Bingham. Garden City, N. Y., Doubleday & company, inc., 1947.
Moreau de Saint-Mery, Mederic Louis Elie, 1750–1819.

LAC 11041

Mormonism and the Mormons: a historical view of the rise and progress of the sect self-styled Latter-day saints. New-York, G. Lane & C. P. Tippett for the Methodist Episcopal church, 1844, [c1842]
Kidder, Daniel Parish, 1815–1891.

LAC 13076

Mormonism exposed.
The history of the saints; or, An expose of Joe Smith and Mormonism. Boston, Leland & Whiting; New York, Bradbury, Soden, & co.; [etc., etc.] 1842.
Bennett, John C.

LAC 16295

Mormonism unvailed [!]: or, A faithful account of that singular imposition and delusion, from its rise to the present time. With sketches of the characters of its propagators... Painesville [O.] Printed and pub. by the author, 1834.
Howe, Eber D   *b.* 1798.

LAC 14181

The Mormons, or, Latter-day saints, in the valley of the Great Salt Lake: a history of their rise and progress, peculiar doctrines, present condition, and prospects, derived from personal observation: during a residence among them. Philadelphia, J. B. Lippincott & co., 1856.
Gunnison, John Williams, 1812–1853.

LAC 40058
The morning of my life in China; comprising an outline of the history of foreign intercourse from the last year of the regime of Honorable East India Company, 1833, to the imprisonment of the foreign community in 1839. Canton, 1872.
Nye, Gideon, 1812–1888.

LAC 23433–34
Morris's memorial history of Staten Island, New York... New York [etc.] Memorial publishing co. [etc., c1898–1900]
Morris, Ira K.

LAC 40097
Morse's patent. Full exposure of Dr. Chas. T. Jackson's pretensions to the invention of the American electro-magnetic telegraph. Washington, Printed by J. T. Towers, 1852.
Kendall, Amos, 1789–1869.

LAC 40078
Mortality among Negroes in cities. Proceedings of the Conference for investigations of city problems held at Atlanta university, May 26–27, 1896. Ed. by Thomas N. Chase. Atlanta, Ga., Atlanta university press, 1903.
Conference for the Study of the Negro Problems. *1st, Atlanta University*, 1896.

LAC 13776
Mosby's men, by John H. Alexander, of Mosby's rangers (Co. A) illustrated by portraits. New York and Washington, The Neale publishing company, 1907.
Alexander, John Henry, 1846–

LAC 15989
Mosby's rangers: a record of the operations of the Forty-third battalion Virginia cavalry, from its organization to the surrender, from the diary of a private, supplemented and verified with official reports of federal officers and also of Mosby; with personal reminiscences, sketches of skirmishes, battles and bivouacs, dashing raids and daring adventures, scenes and incidents in the history of Mosby's command ... Muster rolls, occupation and present whereabouts of surviving members. New York, R. B. Kenyon, 1896.
Williamson, James Joseph, 1834–1915.

LAC 12100
Moses Coit Tyler, 1835–1900; selections from his letters and diaries, made and ed. by Jessica Tyler Austen. Garden City, New York, Doubleday, Page & company, 1911.
Tyler, Moses Coit, 1835–1900.

LAC 13558
The mother at home; or, The principles of maternal duty familiarly illustrated. 4th ed., stereotyped. Boston, Crocker and Brewster, 1834.
Abbott, John Stevens Cabot, 1805–1877.

LAC 14573
Mothers who must earn. New York, Survey associates, inc., 1914.
Anthony, Katharine Susan, 1877–

LAC 14331
Motion study, a method for increasing the efficiency of the workman, by Frank B. Gilbreth, with an introduction by Robert Thurston Kent. New York, D. Van Nostrand company, 1911.
Gilbreth, Frank Bunker, 1868–1924.

LAC 14032
The mound builders; being an account of a remarkable people that once inhabited the valleys of the Ohio and Mississippi, together with an investigation into the archaeology of Butler county, O. Illustrated with over one hundred figures. Cincinnati, R. Clarke & co., 1887, [c1879]
MacLean, John Patterson, 1848–1939.

LAC 16193
The Mountain Meadows massacre. Who were guilty of the crime? An address by Elder Charles W. Penrose, October 26, 1884. Also a supplement containing important additional testimony subsequently received. Salt Lake City, The Desert News, 1906.
Penrose, Charles William, 1832–1925.

LAC 15357
Mountain playmates. Boston and New York, Houghton, Mifflin and company, 1900.
Albee, Helen, 1864–

LAC 16443
Mountaineering in the Sierra Nevada. Boston, New York, C. Scribner's sons, 1926, [c1902]
King, Clarence, 1842–1901.

LAC 13671
Mountains and molehills; or, Recollections of a burnt journal. With illustrations by the author. New York, Harper & brothers, 1855.
Marryat, Francis Samuel, 1826–1855.

LAC 13272
The mountains of California. London, T. Fisher Unwin, 1894.
Muir, John, 1838–1914.

LAC 16396
Mourt's relation or journal of the plantation at Plymouth, with an introduction and notes by Henry Martyn Dexter. Boston, J. K. Wiggin, 1865.
Mourt's Relation.

LAC 40016
The movement for better roads. An address before the Board of Trade, at Hartford, Mass. [*i.e. Conn.*] February 11, 1890. [Boston? 1890]
Pope, Albert Augustus, 1843–1909.

LAC 15799
Moving pictures, how they are made and worked. Philadelphia, J. B. Lippincott company; [etc., etc.] 1912.
Talbot, Frederick Arthur Ambrose, 1880–

LAC 11315
Mrs. Hale's new cook book. A practical system for private families in town and country; with directions for carving, and arranging the table for parties, etc. Also, preparations of food for invalids and for children. Philadelphia, T. B. Peterson [c1857]
Hale, Sarah Josepha, 1788–1879.

LAC 12068

Mrs. Partington.
Life and sayings of Mrs. Partington, and others of the family. New York, J. C. Derby, 1854.
Shillaber, Benjamin Penhallow, 1814–1890, *ed.*

LAC 12053

Mrs. Wiggs of the cabbage patch, by Alice Caldwell Hegan. New York, The Century co., 1902. [c1901]
Rice, Alice Caldwell, 1870–1942.

LAC 10374

Municipal administration. New York, London, Macmillan & co., ltd., 1901.
Fairlie, John Archibald, 1872–1947.

LAC 40009

Municipal consolidation... Historical sketch of the greater New York. [New York, Press of Stettiner, Lambert & co.] 1895.
Henschel, Albert Edward, 1862–

LAC 10838

Municipal engineering and sanitation. New York, The Macmillan company; London, Macmillan & co., ltd., 1906, [c1901]
Baker, Moses Nelson, 1864–

LAC 21207–08

Municipal franchises: a description of the terms and conditions upon which private corporations enjoy special privileges in the streets of American cities. Chicago, University of Chicago press [c1910–11]
Wilcox, Delos Franklin, 1873–1928.

LAC 14459

A municipal history of the town and city of Boston, during two centuries. From September 17, 1630, to September 17, 1830. Boston, C. C. Little and J. Brown, 1852.
Quincy, Josiah, 1772–1864.

LAC 14992

Municipal monopolies; a collection of papers by American economists and specialists. New York, Boston, T. Y. Crowell & company [1899]
Bemis, Edward Webster, 1860–1930, *ed.*

LAC 10801

Municipal ownership of gas in the United States. [Baltimore] American economic association, 1891.
Bemis, Edward Webster, 1860–1930.

LAC 11217

A municipal program; report of a committee of the National municipal league, adopted by the league, November 17, 1899, together with explanatory and other papers. New York, London, Pub. for the National municipal league, the Macmillan company, 1900.
National Municipal League.

LAC 11243

Municipal reform movements in the United States, by William Howe Tolman, with an introductory chapter by the Rev. Charles H. Parkhurst. New-York, Chicago [etc.] Fleming H. Revell company, 1895.
Tolman, William Howe, 1861–

LAC 40043

Municipal socialism; the conservative victory in Cleveland. Washington, D. C., Press of G. E. Howard, 1905.
Newcomb, Harry Turner, 1867–1944.

LAC 10887

Municipal utilities, Regulation of.
The regulation of municipal utilities. New York and London, D. Appleton and company, 1912.
King, Clyde Lyndon, 1879–1937, *ed.*

LAC 15104

Mural painting in America; the Scammon lectures, delivered before the Art institute of Chicago, March, 1912, and since greatly enlarged, by Edwin Howland Blashfield; with numerous reproductions of representative works. New York, C. Scribner's sons, 1913.
Blashfield, Edwin Howland, 1848–1936.

LAC 12094

Murvale Eastman, Christian socialist. New York, Fords, Howard, & Hulbert [c1890]
Tourgee, Albion Winegar, 1838–1905.

LAC 40123

Museum history and museums of history. Washington, Govt. print. off., 1901.
Goode, George Brown, 1851–1896.

LAC 15883

Music and culture. Comprising a number of lectures and essays. Philadelphia, T. Presser [c1890]
Merz, Karl, 1836–1890.

LAC 10797

Music and musicians in Chicago; the city's leading artists, organizations and art buildings, progress and development... Gathered and comp. by Florence Ffrench, representative of the Musical courier for Chicago and the central western states... Chicago, F. Ffrench [c1899]
Ffrench, Florence, *comp.*

LAC 40047

"Music and snobs;" or, A few funny facts regarding the disabilities of music in America. New York, R. A. Saalfield [c1888]
Hopkins, Jerome, 1836–1898.

LAC 16811

Music and some highly musical people: containing brief chapters on I. A description of music. II. The music of nature. III. A glance at the history of music. IV. The power, beauty, and uses of music. Following which are given sketches of the lives of remarkable musicians of the colored race. With portraits; and an appendix containing copies of music composed by colored men. Boston, Lee and Shepard, 1878; New York, Johnson reprint corporation [1968]
Trotter, James M.

LAC 10809

Musical memories; my recollections of celebrities of the half century, 1850–1900. Chicago, A. C. McClurg & co., 1908.
Upton, George Putnam, 1834–1919.

LAC 14106
Mutual aid a factor of evolution. New York, McClure, Phillips & co., 1902.
Kropotkin, Petr Alekseevich, *kniaz*, 1842–1921.

LAC 16119
My attainment of the Pole; being the record of the expedition that first reached the boreal center, 1907–1909, with the final summary of the polar controversy, by Dr. Frederick A. Cook. New York, The Polar publishing co., 1911.
Cook, Frederick Albert, 1865–

LAC 12493
My autobiography. New York, Frederick A. Stokes company [c1914]
McClure, Samuel Sidney, 1857–1949.

LAC 14349
My campaigns in America: a journal kept by Count William de Deux-Ponts, 1780–81. Translated from the French manuscript, with an introduction and notes, by Samuel Abbott Green. Boston, J. K. Wiggin & W. P. Lunt, 1868.
Deux-Ponts, Guillaume, *comte* de.

LAC 16204
My dark companions and their strange stories. New York, C. Scribner's sons, 1893.
Stanley, *Sir* Henry Morton, 1841–1904.

LAC 11918
"My dear girl" ; the correspondence of Benjamin Franklin with Polly Stevenson, Georgiana and Catherine Shipley. By James Madison Stifler. New York, George H. Doran company [c1927]
Franklin, Benjamin, 1706–1790.

LAC 14432
My diary North and South. Boston, T. O. H. P. Burnham; New York, O. S. Felt, 1863.
Russell, *Sir* William Howard, 1820–1907.

LAC 14738
My farm of Edgewood: a country book. By the author of "Reveries of a bachelor". New York, C. Scribner, 1863.
Mitchell, Donald Grant, 1822–1908.

LAC 16620
My first summer in the Sierra, by John Muir, with illustrations from drawings made by the author in 1869 and from photographs by Herbert W. Gleason. Boston and New York, Houghton Mifflin company, 1911.
Muir, John, 1838–1914.

LAC 11592
My forty years in New York, by Reverend C. H. Parkhurst. New York, The Macmillan company, 1923.
Parkhurst, Charles Henry, 1842–1933.

LAC 16706
My friend the Indian. Boston and New York, Houghton Mifflin company, 1926.
McLaughlin, James, 1842–1923.

LAC 13116
My generation; an autobiographical interpretation, by William Jewett Tucker, president emeritus of Dartmouth college. Boston and New York, Houghton Mifflin company, 1919.
Tucker, William Jewett, 1839–1926.

LAC 15009
My imprisonment and the first year of abolition rule at Washington. London, R. Bentley, 1863.
Greenhow, Rose, 1814–1864.

LAC 15231
My lady Pokahontas. A true relation of Virginia. Writ by Anas Todkill, puritan and pilgrim [*pseud.*] With notes by John Esten Cooke. Boston, New York, Houghton, Mifflin and company, 1885.
Cooke, John Esten, 1830–1886.

LAC 15888
My Lady Vaudeville and her White rats, by George Fuller Golden, founder and first big chief of the White rats of America. New York, Pub. under the auspices of the Board of directors of the White rats of America, 1909.
Golden, George Fuller.

LAC 16022
My life and experiences among our hostile Indians; a record of personal observations, adventures, and campaigns among the Indians of the great West, with some account of their life, habits, traits, religion, ceremonies, dress, savage instincts, and customs in peace and war, by Major-General O. O. Howard. Beautifully illustrated with full page engravings, chiefly from photographs supplied by the Bureau of ethnology, Washington, and a series of colored plates showing Indian objects of interest and curiosity in facsimile... Hartford, Conn., A. D. Worthington & company [c1907]
Howard, Oliver Otis, 1830–1909.

LAC 15865
My life and my lectures. New York and Washington, The Neale publishing company, 1908.
Fontaine, Lamar, 1829–

LAC 16473
My life and work, by Henry Ford, in collaboration with Samuel Crowther. Garden City, N. Y., Doubleday, Page & company [c1922]
Ford, Henry, 1863–

LAC 15613
My life in China and America, by Yung Wing, A.B., LL.D. (Yale) commissioner of the Chinese Educational Commission, associate Chinese minister in Washington, expectant Tao-Tai of Kiang Su. New York, H. Holt and company, 1909.
Yung Wing, 1828–1912.

LAC 10302
My life in many states and in foreign lands, dictated in my seventy-fourth year. London, William Heinemann, 1902.
Train, George Francis, 1829–1904.

LAC 11985
My literary passions. New York, Harper & brothers, 1895.
Howells, William Dean, 1837–1920.

LAC 16516
My memories of eighty years. New York, C. Scribner's sons, 1923, [c1922]
Depew, Chauncey Mitchell, 1834–1928.

LAC 11310
My native land. The United States: its wonders, its beauties, and its people; with descriptive notes, character sketches, folk lore, traditions, legends and history... St. Louis, Blair Pub. Co., 1895.
Cox, James, 1851–1901.

LAC 10344
My own story. San Francisco, The Call publishing co., 1919.
Older, Fremont, 1856–1935.

LAC 40094
My pedagogic creed, by Professor John Dewey, and The demands of sociology upon pedagogy, by Professor Albion W. Small. Chicago, A. Flanagan company [1910?]
Dewey, John, 1859–1952.

LAC 16526
My sixty years on the plains trapping, trading, and Indian fighting, by W. T. Hamilton ("Bill Hamilton") ed. by E. T. Sieber; with eight full-page illustrations by Charles M. Russell. Columbus, O., Reprinted by Long's college book co., 1951.
Hamilton, William Thomas, 1822–1908.

LAC 15840
My southern home; or, The South and its people. Upper Saddle River, N. J., Gregg Press [1968]
Brown, William Wells, 1815–1884.

LAC 15817
My story, by Tom L. Johnson; ed. by Elizabeth J. Hauser. New York, B. W. Huebsch, 1911.
Johnson, Tom Loftin, 1854–1911.

LAC 14639
My story of the war: a woman's narrative of four years personal experience as nurse in the Union army, and in relief work at home, in hospitals, camps, and at the front during the war of the rebellion. With anecdotes, pathetic incidents, and thrilling reminiscences portraying the lights and shadows of hospital life and the sanitary service of the war. Hartford, A. D. Worthington and company, 1889.
Livermore, Mary Ashton, 1820–1905.

LAC 15635
My thirty years in baseball, by John J. McGraw, with an introduction by George M. Cohan. New York, Boni and Liveright [1923]
McGraw, John Joseph, 1873–1934.

LAC 16254
My village home.
'Black mammy,' a song of the sunny South, in three cantos; and "My village home." Cheyenne, Wyo. [Sun steam print.] 1885.
Visscher, William Lightfoot, 1842–1924.

LAC 40005
My year in a log cabin. New York, Harper & brothers, 1893.
Howells, William Dean, 1837–1920.

LAC 11272
Mysteries and miseries of America's great cities, embracing New York, Washington city, San Francisco, Salt Lake City, and New Orleans. St. Louis and Philadelphia, Historical publishing co., 1883.
Buel, James William, 1849–1920.

LAC 13569
The mysteries of New York, a tale of real life. By Ned Buntling [*pseud.*] London, Milner [n.d.]
Judson, Edward Zane Carroll, 1822?–1886.

LAC 11076
The mystical presence. A vindication of the Reformed or Calvinistic doctrine of the Holy Eucharist. Philadelphia, J. B. Lippincott & co., 1846.
Nevin, John Williamson, 1803–1886.

LAC 12231
The myth of Hiawatha, and other oral legends, mythologic and allegoric, of the North American Indians. Philadelphia, J. B. Lippincott & co.; [etc., etc.] 1856.
Schoolcraft, Henry Rowe, 1793–1864.

LAC 15636
Mythology of the Blackfoot Indians. By Clark Wissler and D. C. Duvall. New York, The Trustees, 1908.
Wissler, Clark, 1870–1947.

LAC 21430
Myths and legends of our own land. Philadelphia & London, J. P. Lippincott company [c1896]
Skinner, Charles Montgomery, 1852–1907.

LAC 16431
Na Motu; or, Reef-rovings in the South Seas... New York, Pudney & Russell, 1854.
Perkins, Edward T.

LAC 12552
Names of persons who took the oath of allegiance to the state of Pennsylvania between the years 1777 and 1789, with a history of the "test laws" of Pennsylvania. Baltimore, Genealogical Pub. Co., 1965.
Westcott, Thompson, 1820–1888.

LAC 11453
Narrative and correspondence concerning the removal of the deposites, and occurrences connected therewith. Philadelphia, 1838.
Duane, William John, 1780–1865.

LAC 13528
Narrative history. A history of Dover, Massachusetts, as a precinct, parish, district, and town. Dover, Mass., The town, 1897.
Smith, Frank, 1854–

LAC 13309
Narrative journal of travels through the northwestern regions of the United States; extending from Detroit through the great chain of American lakes, to the

sources of the Mississippi river. Performed as a member of the expedition under Governor Cass. In the year 1820. With a map and eight copper plate engravings. Albany, E. & E. Hosford, 1821.
Schoolcraft, Henry Rowe, 1793–1864.

LAC 15011
The narrative of a blockade-runner. New York, Sheldon & co., 1877.
Wilkinson, John, 1821–1891.

LAC 22866
The narrative of a Japanese; what he has seen and the people he has met in the course of the last forty years. Edited by James Murdoch. San Francisco, American-Japanese publishing association [n.d.]
Heco, Joseph, 1837–1897.

LAC 13334
Narrative of a journey across the Rocky mountains, to the Columbia river, and a visit to the Sandwich islands, Chili, &c.; with a scientific appendix. Philadelphia, H. Perkins; Boston, Perkins & Marvin, 1839.
Townsend, John Kirk, 1809–1851.

LAC 40087
Narrative of a journey down the Ohio and Mississippi in 1789–90. By Maj. Samuel S. Forman; with a memoir and illustrative notes by Lyman C. Draper. Cincinnati, R. Clarke & co., 1888.
Forman, Samuel S   1765–1862.

LAC 13200
Narrative of a journey to the shores of the polar sea, in the years 1819, 20, 21, and 22. By John Franklin, captain R. N. With an appendix on various subjects relating to science and natural history. London, J. Murray, 1823.
Franklin, *Sir* John, 1786–1847.

LAC 40044
A narrative of a new and unusual American imprisonment of two Presbyterian ministers: and prosecution of Mr. Francis Makemie one of them, for preaching one sermon at the city of New-York. By a learner of law, and lover of liberty. [Boston] Printed for the publisher, 1707.
Makemie, Francis, 1658–1708, *supposed author.*

LAC 40072
Narrative of a tour from the state of Indiana to the Oregon territory in the years 1841-2, by Joseph Williams, with an introduction by James C. Bell, jr. New York, The Cadmus book shop, 1921.
Williams, Joseph.

LAC 23403–4
Narrative of a tour in North America; comprising Mexico, the mines of Real del Monte, the United States, and the British colonies: with an excursion to the island of Cuba. In a series of letters, written in the years 1831-2. London, J. Duncan, 1834.
Tudor, Henry.

LAC 14882
A narrative of a tour of observation, made during the summer of 1817, by James Monroe, president of the United States, through the north-eastern and north-western departments of the Union: with a view to the examination of their several military defences. With an appendix. Philadelphia: Published by S. A. Mitchell & H. Ames, Clark & Raser, Printers, 1818.

LAC 23602
Narrative of a tour through Armenia, Kurdistan, Persia and Mesopotamia, with an introduction, and occasional observations upon the condition of Mohammedanism and Christianity in those countries. By the Rev. Horatio Southgate. New-York, D. Appleton & co., 1840.
Southgate, Horatio, 1812–1894.

LAC 21107
Narrative of a voyage to the Pacific and Beering's strait, to co-operate with the polar expeditions: performed in His Majesty's ship Blossom, under the command of Captain F. W. Beechey in the years 1825, 26, 27, 28... London, H. Colburn and R. Bentley, 1831.
Beechey, Frederick William, 1796–1856.

LAC 15904
Narrative of a voyage to the Spanish Main, in the ship "Two friends;" the occupation of Amelia island by M'Gregor, &c.-sketches of the province of East Florida; and anecdotes illustrative of the habits and manners of the Seminole Indians: with an appendix, containing a detail of the Seminole war, and the execution of Arbuthnot and Ambrister... London, Printed for J. Miller, 1819.

LAC 15693
A narrative of Col. Ethan Allen's captivity, from the time of his being taken by the British, near Montreal, on the 25th day of September, in the year 1775, to the time of his exchange, on the 6th day of May, 1778. Containing his voyages and travels, with the most remarkable occurrences respecting himself, and many other continental prisoners ... particularly the destruction of the prisoners at New-York, by General Sir William Howe, in the years 1776 and 1777; interspersed with some political observations. Written by himself, and now published for the information of the curious in all nations... To which are now added a considerable number of explanatory and occasional notes, together with an index... Walpole, N. H., Published by Thomas & Thomas. From the press of Charter & Hale, 1807.
Allen, Ethan, 1737–1789.

LAC 40113
Narrative of Henry Box Brown, who escaped from slavery enclosed in a box 3 feet long and 2 wide. Written from a statement of facts made by himself. With remarks upon the remedy for slavery, by Charles Stearns. Boston, Brown & Stearns [1849]
Brown, Henry Box, *b.* 1816.

LAC 40138
The narrative of James Roberts, soldier in the revolutionary war and at the battle of New Orleans. Chicago: printed for the author, 1858. Hattiesburg, Miss., The Book farm, 1945.
Roberts, James, *b.* 1753.

LAC 14481
The narrative of Lieut. Gen. Sir William Howe, in a committee of the House of commons, on the 29th of April, 1779, relative to his conduct, during his late command of the King's troops in North America: to which are added, some observations upon a pamphlet, entitled, Letters to a nobleman. 3d ed. London, Printed by H. Baldwin, 1781.
Howe, William Howe, *5th viscount,* 1729–1814.

LAC 14400

Narrative of military operations, directed, during the late war between the states, by Joseph E. Johnston, general, C. S. A. New York, D. Appleton and co., 1874.
Johnston, Joseph Eggleston, 1807–1891.

LAC 40038

Narrative of Mr. John Dodge during his captivity at Detroit, reproduced in facsimile from the 2d ed. of 1780, with an introductory note by Clarence Monroe Burton. Cedar Rapids, Ia., The Torch press, 1909.
Dodge, John, 1751–1800.

LAC 40130

The narrative of Mr. John Soren, a native of the United States of America, piratically captured on the high seas, in requital for an act of humanity, in saving a British transport ... from sinking. With an appendix, containing the documents referred to in the narrative, a letter from the American Minister, and testimonials of the truth of the statement from Major Mansergh, the commanding officer of the troops, and Captain Davis. London, printed at the Oriental Press by Wilson & co., 1800.
Soren, John, *b.* 1757.

LAC 14653

Narrative of privations and sufferings of United States officers and soldiers while prisoners of war in the hands of the Rebel authorities. Being the report of a commission of inquiry, appointed by the United States sanitary commission. With an appendix, containing the testimony. Philadelphia, Printed for the U.S. sanitary commission by King and Baird, 1864.
United States Sanitary Commission.

LAC 11173

Narrative of riots at Alton: in connection with the death of Rev. Elijah P. Lovejoy. By Rev. Edward Beecher. Alton [Ill.] G. Holton, 1838.
Beecher, Edward, 1803–1895.

LAC 40113

A narrative of the adventures and escape of Moses Roper, from American slavery; with a preface by the Rev. T. Price. Philadelphia, Merrihew & Gunn, printers, 1838. [Philadelphia, Rhistoric Publications, n.d.]
Roper, Moses.

LAC 14477

A narrative of the captivity and adventures of John Tanner (U.S. interpreter at the Saut de Ste. Marie) during thirty years residence among the Indians in the interior of North America. Prepared for the press by Edwin James. Minneapolis, Ross & Haines, 1956.
Tanner, John, 1780?–1847.

LAC 40089

Narrative of the captivity of William Biggs among the Kickapoo Indians in Illinois in 1788, written by himself. [New York, C. F. Heartman] 1922.
Biggs, William, 1755–1827.

LAC 15301

A narrative of the captivity, sufferings, and removes, of Mrs. Mary Rowlandson, who was taken prisoner by the Indians; with several others... Written by her own hand. Boston: re-printed and sold by Thomas and John Fleet, at the Bible and Heart, Cornhill, 1791. [Boston] The Mass. Sabbath school society, 1856.
Rowlandson, Mary.

LAC 12999

A narrative of the embarrassments and decline of Hamilton college. [Clinton? 1833?]
Davis, Henry, 1771–1852.

LAC 21026–28

Narrative of the expedition of an American squadron to the China seas and Japan, performed in the years 1852, 1853 and 1854, under the command of Commodore M. C. Perry, United States navy, by order of the government of the United States... Pub. by order of the Congress of the United States. Washington, A. O. P. Nicholson, printer, 1856.
Perry, Matthew Calbraith, 1794–1858.

LAC 15227

A narrative of the great revival which prevailed in the southern armies during the late civil war between the states of the federal union. Philadelphia, Claxton, Remsen & Haffelfinger, 1877.
Bennett, William Wallace, 1821–1887.

LAC 40030

A narrative of the leading incidents of the organization of the first popular movement in Virginia in 1865 to reestablish peaceful relations between the northern and southern states, and of the subsequent efforts of the "Committee of nine," in 1869, to secure the restoration of Virginia to the Union. Richmond, Va., W. E. Jones, printer, 1888.
Stuart, Alexander Hugh Holmes, 1807–1891.

LAC 13657

Narrative of the life and adventures of Henry Bibb, an American slave, written by himself. With an introduction by Lucius C. Matlack. New York, The author, 1849.
Bibb, Henry, *b.* 1815.

LAC 11885

A narrative of the life of David Crockett (1834) Philadelphia, J. E. Potter, 1865.
Crockett, David, 1786–1836.

LAC 16660

Narrative of the life of Frederick Douglass, an American slave. Written by himself. Boston, Pub. at the Antislavery office, 1845.
Douglass, Frederick, 1817?–1895.

LAC 40113

A narrative of the life of Rev. Noah Davis, a colored man. Written by himself, at the age of fifty-four. Baltimore, J. F. Weishampel [c1859]
Davis, Noah, 1804–

LAC 40142

A narrative of the Lord's wonderful dealings with John Marrant, a black (A preacher of the gospel in Nova-Scotia) born in New-York, in North-America. Taken down from his own relation, arranged and corrected by the Rev. Mr. Aldridge. 3d ed. Yarmouth, J. Barnes, 1824.
Marrant, John, *b.* 1755.

LAC 14705

A narrative of the manner in which the campaign against the Indians, in the year one thousand seven hundred and ninety-one, was conducted, under the command of Major General St. Clair, together with his observations on the statements of the secretary of war and the

quarter master general, relative thereto, and the reports of the committees appointed to inquire into the causes of the failure thereof: taken from the files of the House of representatives in Congress. Philadelphia, Jane Aitken, 1812.
St. Clair, Arthur, 1734–1818.

LAC 40012
A narrative of the miseries of New England, by reason of an arbitrary government erected there under Sir Edmond Andros. Boston, Old South meeting house, 1884.
Mather, Increase, 1639–1723.

LAC 11025
A narrative of the mission of the United Brethren among the Delaware and Mohegan Indians, from its commencement, in the year 1740, to the close of the year 1808. Comprising all the remarkable incidents which took place at their missionary stations during that period. Interspersed with anecdotes, historical facts, speeches of Indians, and other interesting matter. Philadelphia: Published by McCarty & Davis, 1820.
Heckewelder, John Gottlieb Ernestus, 1743–1823.

LAC 40128
A narrative of the proceedings of the black people, during the late awful calamity in Philadelphia, in the year 1793: and a refutation of some censures, thrown upon them in some late publications. By A. J. and R. A. Philadelphia: Printed for the authors, by William W. Woodward, at Franklin's head, no. 41, Chesnut-street, 1794.
Jones, Absalom.

LAC 40092
A narrative of the suppression by Col. Burr, of the History of the administration of John Adams, late President of the United States, written by John Wood. To which is added a biography of Thomas Jefferson, President of the United States; and of General Hamilton: with strictures on the conduct of John Adams, and on the character of General C. C. Pinckney. Extracted verbatim from the suppressed history. By a citizen of New-York. New-York, Printed by Denniston and Cheetham, 1802.
Cheetham, James, 1772–1810.

LAC 13241
Narrative of the Texan Santa Fe expedition, comprising a tour through Texas, and capture of the Texans. [London] Sherwood, Gilbert, and Piper [etc.]; Bristol, Office of the Great Western advertiser and chronicle [1845?]
Kendall, George Wilkins, 1809–1867.

LAC 40080
A narrative of the transactions, imprisonment, and sufferings, of John Connolly, an American loyalist, and lieutenant-colonel in His Majesty's service. In which are shewn, the unjustifiable proceedings of Congress, in his treatment and detention. London, Printed in the year 1783. [New York, Reprinted for C. L. Woodward, 1889]
Connolly, John, 1750?–1813.

LAC 21869–70
Narrative of the travels and adventures of Monsieur Violet, in California, Sonora, & Western Texas. Written by Capt. Marryat. London, Longman, Brown, Green, & Longmans, 1843.
Marryat, Frederick, 1792–1848.

LAC 15306
A narrative of the troubles with the Indians in New-England, from the first planting thereof in the year 1607, to this present year 1677. But chiefly of the late troubles in the two last years, 1675 and 1676. To which is added a discourse about the warre with the Pequods in the year 1637. By W. Hubbard, minister of Ipswich. Pnblished [!] by authority. Boston; Printed by John Foster, in the year 1677.
Hubbard, William, 1621–1704.

LAC 20926–29
Narrative of the United States exploring expedition during the years 1838, 1839, 1840, 1841, 1842. With illustrations and maps. In five volumes. Philadelphia, Lea and Blanchard, 1845.
Wilkes, Charles, 1798–1877.

LAC 20485
A narrative of the visit to the American churches, by the deputation from the Congregational union of England and Wales. By Andrew Reed and James Matheson. New York, Harper & brothers, 1835.
Reed, Andrew, 1787–1862.

LAC 12794
Narrative of William W. Brown, a fugitive slave. Written by himself. Boston, The Anti-slavery office, 1847.
Brown, William Wells, 1815–1884.

LAC 16465
Narratives of colored Americans... Printed by order of the Trustees of the residuary estate of Lindley Murray. New York, W. Wood & co., 1877.
Mott, Abigail, 1766–1851, *comp.*

LAC 15809
Narratives of early Virginia, 1606–1625. With a map and two facsimiles. New York, C. Scribner's sons, 1907.
Tyler, Lyon Gardiner, 1853–1935, *ed.*

LAC 16826
Narratives of New Netherland, 1609–1664. With three maps and a facsimile. New York, C. Scribner's sons, 1909.
Jameson, John Franklin, 1859–1937, *ed.*

LAC 15933
Narratives of remarkable conversions and revival incidents: including a review of revivals, from the day of Pentecost to the great awakening in the last century–conversions of eminent persons–instances of remarkable conversions and answers to prayer–an account of the rise and progress of the great awakening of 1857-'8. New York, Derby & Jackson, 1858.
Conant, William C.

LAC 20773
Narratives of the career of Hernando de Soto in the conquest of Florida, as told by a knight of Elvas, and in a relation by Luys Hernandez de Biedma, factor of the expedition; translated by Buckingham Smith, together with an account of de Soto's expedition based on the diary of Rodrigo Ranjel, his private secretary, translated from Oviedo's Historia general y natural de las Indias; edited with an introduction by Edward Gaylord Bourne. New York, Allerton book co., 1922.
Bourne, Edward Gaylord, 1860–1908, *ed.*

LAC 12812
Narratives of the sufferings of Lewis and Milton Clarke, sons of a soldier of the revolution, during a captivity of more than twenty years among the slaveholders of Kentucky, one of the so called Christian states of North America. Dictated by themselves. Boston, B. Marsh, 1846.
Clark, Lewis Garrard, 1812–1897.

LAC 13306
Narratives of voyages towards the North-west, in search of a passage to Cathay and India. 1496 to 1631. With selections from the early records of the honourable the East India company and from mss. in the British museum. London, Printed for the Hakluyt society, 1849.
Rundall, Thomas, *ed.*

LAC 40140
The Nasby papers. Letters and sermons containing the views on the topics of the day, of Petroleum V. Nasby [*pseud.*]... Indianapolis, C. O. Perrine & co., 1864.
Locke, David Ross, 1833–1888.

LAC 12683
Nathan Read: his invention of the multi-tubular boiler and portable high-pressure engine, and discovery of the true mode of applying steam-power to navigation and railways. A contribution to the early history of the steamboat and locomotive engine. By his friend and nephew, David Read. New York, Hurd and Houghton, 1870.
Read, David, 1799–1881.

LAC 15298
Nathaniel Hawthorne. Boston and New York, Houghton, Mifflin and company, 1902.
Woodberry, George Edward, 1855–1930.

LAC 21255
Nathaniel Hawthorne and his wife. Boston and New York, Houghton, Mifflin company [c1884]
Hawthorne, Julian, 1846–1934.

LAC 11825
Nathaniel Parker Willis. Boston and New York, Houghton, Mifflin and company [c1885]
Beers, Henry Augustin, 1847–

LAC 31039–87
The Nation, a weekly journal devoted to politics, literature, science, drama, music, art, finance. v. 1–80; July 1866–June 1905. New York.

LAC 40046
A nation saved by its prosperity only by the gospel. A discourse in behalf of the American home missionary society, preached in the cities of New York and Brooklyn, May, 1853, by Rev. Laurens P. Hickok, D. D. New York, American home missionary society, 1853.
Hickok, Laurens Perseus, 1798–1888.

LAC 12506
The nation: the foundations of civil order and political life in the United States. New York, Hurd & Houghton, 1870.
Mulford, Elisha, 1833–1885.

LAC 12916
The national and private "Alabama claims" and their "final and amicable settlement". By Charles C. Beaman, jr. Washington city, D. C., Printed by W. H. Moore [1871]
Beaman, Charles Cotesworth.

LAC 40115
The National Armories, a review of the system of superintendency, civil and military, particularly with reference to economy, and general management at the Springfield Armory. 2d ed. Springfield, Mass., G. W. Wilson's Steam Power Presses, 1852.

LAC 10826
A national bank, or no bank; an appeal to the common sense of the people of the United States, especially of the laboring classes. New York, W. E. Dean, 1842.
Hurd, John R.

LAC 16954
National banking system.
The origin of the national banking system. Washington, Govt. Print. Off., 1910.
Davis, Andrew McFarland, 1833–1920.

LAC 10417
National banking system.
History of crises under the national banking system. Washington, Govt. print. off., 1910 [*i.e.* 1911]
Sprague, Oliver Mitchell Wentworth, 1873–1953.

LAC 12066
National characteristics.
The cabin book: or, National characteristics. By Charles Sealsfield. Tr. from the German by Sarah Powell. With numerous engravings. London, Ingram, Cooke, & co., 1852.
Sealsfield, Charles, 1793–1864.

LAC 14321
National conference on industrial conciliation under the auspices of the National civic federation, held at rooms of Board of trade and transportation, New York, December 16 and 17, 1901. New York, The Knickerbocker press, 1902.
National Conference on Industrial Conciliation, *New York*, 1901.

LAC 12507
National conference on practical reform of primary elections held at the rooms of the New York Board of trade and transportation ... New York city. Thursday and Friday, January 20 and 21, 1898. Chicago, W. C. Hollister-& bro., printers [1898]
National Conference on Practical Reform of Primary Elections, *New York*, 1898.

LAC 10066
National consolidation of the railways of the United States. New-York, Dodd, Mead & company, 1893.
Lewis, George Henry, 1842–

LAC 10409
National education in Europe; being an account of the organization, administration, instruction and statistics of public schools of different grades in the principal states. 2d ed. New York, C. B. Norton, 1854.
Barnard, Henry, 1811–1900.

LAC 13009

National education in the United States of America, by Du Pont de Nemours; translated from the second French edition of 1812 and with an introduction, by B. G. du Pont. Newark, Del., University of Delaware press, 1923.
Du Pont de Nemours, Pierre Samuel, 1739–1817.

LAC 40094

National institution ... for the education of children, necessity of a.
Proposal to demonstrate the necessity of a national institution in the United States of America for the education of children of both sexes. To which is joined, a project of organization, &c. Philadelphia, Printed for G. Decombaz, bookseller, 1797.
Lafitte du Courteil, Amable Louis Rose de.

LAC 11244

The national land system, 1785–1820. New York, E. B. Treat & company, 1910.
Treat, Payson Jackson, 1879–

LAC 15623

National legislation concerning education; its influence and effect in the public land states east of the Mississippi River admitted prior to 1820... New York, 1899.
Germann, George Balthasar.

LAC 10544

National life and character, a forecast. London and New York, Macmillan and co., 1893.
Pearson, Charles Henry, 1830–1894.

LAC 15645

The national loans of the United States, from July 4, 1776, to June 30, 1880. By Rafael A. Bayley. 2d ed. As prepared for the tenth census of the United States. Washington, Govt. print. off., 1882.
U.S. *Treasury Dept.*

LAC 10795

The national music of America and its sources. Boston, L. C. Page and company (incorporated) 1900.
Elson, Louis Charles, 1848–1920.

LAC 10994

National perils and opportunities; the discussions of the General Christian Conference held in Washington, D. C., December 7th, 8th, and 9th, 1887, under the auspices and direction of the Evangelical Alliance for the United States. New York, Baker & Taylor Co., 1887.
Evangelical Alliance for the United States of America. *General Christian Conference. 1st, Washington, D. C.,* 1887.

LAC 40091

National plan of an Atlantic and Pacific rail road, and remarks of Albert Pike, made thereon, at Memphis, November, 1849. Little Rock, Ark., Gazette and democrat, print. [1849]
Memphis. *Board of Mayor and Aldermen.*

LAC 14958

National sermons. Sermons, speeches and letters on slavery and its war: from the passage of the Fugitive slave bill to the election of President Grant. Boston, Lee and Shepard, 1869.
Haven, Gilbert, *bp.,* 1821–1880.

LAC 12637

National vitality, its wastes and conservation. Extract from report of the National conservation commission, Senate document no. 676, vol. III, Sixtieth Congress, second session. Washington, Govt. print. off., 1910.
Fisher, Irving, 1867–

LAC 15859

The nation's peril. Twelve years' experience in the South. Then and now. The Ku Klux klan, a complete exposition of the order: its purpose, plans, operations, social and political significance; the nation's salvation... New York, Pub. by the friends of the compiler, 1872.

LAC 40083

The nation's responsibility for peace. Address delivered at the New England convention of the National reform association held at Boston in February, 1895. Boston, The American peace society, 1898.
Trueblood, Benjamin Franklin, 1847–1916.

LAC 11740

The natural and civil history of Vermont. By Samuel Williams, LL. D. member of the Meteorological society in Germany, of the Philosophical society in Philadelphia, and of the Academy of arts and sciences in Massachusetts. Published according to act of Congress. Printed at Walpole, Newhampshire, by Isaiah Thomas and David Carlisle, jun. Sold at their bookstore, in Walpole, and by said Thomas, at his bookstore, in Worcester. MDCCXCIV.
Williams, Samuel, 1743–1817.

LAC 10632

The natural and political history of the state of Vermont. Montpelier, Vermont historical society, 1870.
Allen, Ira, 1751–1814.

LAC 10868

Natural and statistical view, or picture of Cincinnati and the Miami county, illustrated by maps. With an appendix, containing observations on the late earthquakes, the aurora borealis, and south-west wind. Cincinnati, Printed by Looker and Wallace, 1815.
Drake, Daniel, 1785–1852.

LAC 23885

The natural history of Carolina, Florida, and the Bahama islands: containing the figures of birds, beasts, fishes, serpents, insects, and plants; particularly, those not hitherto described, or incorrectly figured by former authors, with their descriptions in English and French. To which is prefixed, a new and correct map of the countries; with observations on their natural state, inhabitants, and productions. By the late Mark Catesby. Revised by Mr. Edwards. To the whole is now added a Linnaean index of the animals and plants... Histoire naturelle de la Caroline, de la Floride, et des isles de Bahama: contenant les desseins des oiseaux, des quadrupedes, des poissons, des serpens, des insectes, & des plantes, qui se trouvent dans ces pays-la; et en particulier, de ceux qui n'ont point ete decrits jusqu'a present par les auteurs, ou peu exactement dessines. Avec leurs descriptions en francois & en anglois. On trouve au commencement une carte de ces pays, avec des remarques ser leur etat naturel, leurs habitans, & leurs productions. Par feu Monsieur Marc Catesby... Reveue par monsieur Edwards... On y a ajoute une table selon le systeme de Linnaeus... London, Printed for B. White, 1771.
Catesby, Mark, 1679?–1749.

LAC 16194

The natural history of North-Carolina. With an account of the trade, manners, and customs of the Christian and Indian inhabitants. Illustrated with copper-plates, whereon are curiously engraved the map of the country, several strange beasts', birds, fishes, snakes, insects, trees, and plants, &c. By John Brickell, M. D. Dublin: Printed by James Carson. For the author, 1737. [Raleigh, Reprinted by authority of the Trustees of the public libraries, 1911]
Brickell, John, 1710?–1745.

LAC 16921

The natural history of secession; or, Despotism and democracy at necessary, eternal, exterminating war. New York, J. Bradburn; Cincinnati, Rickey & Carroll; [etc., etc.] 1864.
Goodwin, Thomas Shepard.

LAC 10571

Natural law in the business world. Boston, Lee and Shepard; New York, C. T. Dillingham, 1887.
Wood, Henry, 1834–1909.

LAC 11069

Natural law in the spiritual world. New York, J. Pott & co. [1884]
Drummond, Henry, 1851–1897.

LAC 40005

Natural religion.
Uncollected lectures by Ralph Waldo Emerson; reports of lectures on American life and Natural religion, reprinted from the Commonwealth. Edited by Clarence Gohdes. New York, W. E. Rudge, 1932.
Emerson, Ralph Waldo, 1803–1882.

LAC 12643

Natural science and religion; two lectures delivered to the Theological school of Yale college. New York, C. Scribner's sons, 1880.
Gray, Asa, 1810–1888.

LAC 15793

The natural wealth of California; comprising early history; geography, topography, and scenery; climate; agriculture and commercial products; geology, zoology, and botany; mineralogy, mines, and mining processes; manufactures; steamship lines, railroads, and commerce; immigration, population and society; educational institutions and literature; together with a detailed description of each county... San Francisco, New York, H. H. Bancroft & company, 1868.
Cronise, Titus Fey.

LAC 13886

The nature and function of art, more especially of architecture. New York, A. C. Armstrong & son; [etc., etc.] 1881.
Eidlitz, Leopold, 1823–1908.

LAC 14860

Nature and man in America. New York, C. Scribner's sons, 1893, [c1891]
Shaler, Nathaniel Southgate, 1841–1906.

LAC 11757

Nature and reason harmonized in the practice of husbandry. By the late John Lorain. With an alphabetical index. Philadelphia, H. C. Carey & I. Lea, 1825.
Lorain, John.

LAC 10954

Nature and the supernatural, as together constituting the one system of God. 3rd ed. New York, C. Scribner; London, Sampson, Low, son & co., 1858.
Bushnell, Horace, 1802–1876.

LAC 40001

The nature and uses of money and mixed currency, with a history of the Wickaboag bank. Boston, Crosby, Nichols & company, 1857.
Walker, Amasa, 1799–1875.

LAC 14804

The nature-study idea; being an interpretation of the new school-movement to put the child in sympathy with nature. New York, Doubleday, Page & company, 1903.
Bailey, Liberty Hyde, 1858–1954.

LAC 14034

Navaho legends. Collected and tr. by Washington Matthews. With introduction, notes, illustrations, texts, interlinear translations, and melodies. Boston and New York, Pub. for the American folk-lore society, by Houghton, Mifflin and company; [etc., etc.] 1897.
Matthews, Washington, 1843–1905.

LAC 14917

Naval administration and warfare, some general principles, with other essays, by Captain A. T. Mahan. Boston, Little, Brown, and company, 1908.
Mahan, Alfred Thayer, 1840–

LAC 23605–12

Naval documents of the American Revolution. Editor: William Bell Clark. Washington [For sale by the Supt. of Doc., U.S. Govt. Print. Off.] 1964–69.
U.S. *Naval History Division.*

LAC 22784–89

Naval documents related to the United States wars with the Barbary powers... Published under direction of the Honorable Claude A. Swanson, secretary of the navy. Prepared by the Office of naval records and library, Navy department, under the supervision of Captain Dudley W. Knox, U.S. Navy (ret.) Washington, U.S. Govt. print off., 1939–44.
U.S. *Office of Naval Records and Library.*

LAC 23552

Naval history of the United States, from the commencement of the revolutionary war to the present time. 2d ed. Philadelphia, M. Carey, 1814.
Clark, Thomas, 1787–1860.

LAC 14657

Naval scenes and reminiscences of the civil war in the United States, on the southern and western waters during the years 1861, 1862 and 1863. With the history of that period. Compared and corrected from authentic sources. By Rear-Admiral H. Walke. New York, F. R. Reed & co., 1877.
Walke, Henry, 1808–1896.

LAC 16379
Naval strategy compared and contrasted with the principles and practice of military operations on land; lectures delivered at U.S. Naval war college, Newport, R. I., between the years 1887 and 1911, by Captain A. T. Mahan. Boston, Little, Brown, and company, 1911.
Mahan, Alfred Thayer, 1840–1914.

LAC 11288
The navigator: containing directions for navigating the Monongahela, Allegheny, Ohio, and Mississippi rivers; with an ample account of these much admired waters, from the head of the former to the mouth of the latter, and a concise description of their towns, villages, harbours, settlements, &c. With accurate maps of the Ohio and Mississippi. To which is added, an appendix, containing an account of Louisiana, and of the Missouri and Columbia rivers, as discovered by the voyage under Captains Lewis and Clarke. 7th ed.–improved and enl. Pittsburgh, Printed and pub. by Cramer, Spear & Eichbaum, and sold at their bookstore, Franklin's head, Market, between Front and Second streets, 1811.
Cramer, Zadok, 1773–1813.

LAC 16822
The navy of the American revolution; its administration, its policy and its achievements... Chicago [The Burrows brothers company] 1906.
Paullin, Charles Oscar, 1868 *or* 9–1944.

LAC 16553
The navy of the United States, from the commencement, 1775 to 1853; with a brief history of each vessel's service and fate... Comp. by Lieut. George F. Emmons, under the authority of the Navy dept. To which is added a list of private armed vessels, fitted out under the American flag ... also a list of the revenue and coast survey vessels, and principal ocean steamers, belonging to citizens of the United States in 1850. Washington, Printed by Gideon & co., 1853.
Emmons, George Foster, 1811–1884.

LAC 16181
The Negro a menace to American civilization. Boston, R. G. Badger, 1907.
Shufeldt, Robert Wilson, 1850–1934.

LAC 15846
The Negro American artisan; report of a social study made by Atlanta university under the patronage of the trustees of the John F. Slater fund; with the proceedings of the 17th annual conference for the study of the Negro problems, held at Atlanta university, on Monday, May 27th, 1912; ed. by W. E. Burghardt Du Bois and Augustus Granville Dill. Atlanta, Ga., The Atlanta university press, 1912.
Du Bois, William Edward Burghardt, 1868–1963, *ed.*

LAC 12820
The Negro American family; report of a social study made principally by the college classes of 1909 and 1910 of Atlanta University, under the patronage of the trustees of the John F. Slater fund; together with the proceedings of the 13th annual Conference for the study of the Negro problems, held at Atlanta University on Tuesday, May the 26th, 1908; New York, Negro Universities Press [1969]
Du Bois, William Edward Burghardt, 1868–1963, *ed.*

LAC 40078
The negro and the intelligence and property franchise. Address of Wm. A. MacCorkle, late governor of West Virginia, before the Southern conference on race problems, Montgomery, Alabama, May 9, 1900. Cincinnati, The R. Clarke company, printers, 1900.
MacCorkle, William Alexander, 1857–1930.

LAC 12864
The Negro and the nation; a history of American slavery and enfranchisement. New York, H. Holt and company, 1906.
Merriam, George Spring, 1843–1914.

LAC 15852
The negro and the white man. Philadelphia, A. M. E. publishing house, 1897.
Gaines, Wesley John, *bp.*, 1840–

LAC 16398
The Negro at home: an inquiry after his capacity for self-government and the government of whites for controlling, leading, directing, or co-operating in; the civilization of the age; its material, intellectual, moral, religious, social and political interests; the objects of society and government, the business and duties of our race; the offenses of legislation. New York, The author, 1868.
Spring, Lindley.

LAC 12842
The Negro at work in New York city; a study in economic progress. New York, Columbia university, Longmans, Green & co., agents; [etc., etc.] 1912.
Haynes, George Edmund, 1880–1960.

LAC 15847
The Negro church; report of a social study made under the direction of Atlanta university; together with the Proceedings of the eighth Conference for the study of the Negro problems, held at Atlanta university, May 26th, 1903. Atlanta, Ga., The Atlanta university press, 1903.
Du Bois, William Edward Burghardt, 1868–1963, *ed.*

LAC 16923
The Negro common school; report of a social study made under the direction of Atlanta university; together with the proceedings of the sixth Conference for the study of the Negro problems, held at Atlanta university, on May 28th, 1901. Atlanta, Ga., University press, 1901.
Du Bois, William Edward Burghardt, 1868–1963, *ed.*

LAC 12847
A negro explorer at the North pole, by Matthew A. Henson; with a foreword by Robert E. Peary and an introduction by Booker T. Washington; with illustrations from photographs. New York, Frederick A. Stokes company [c1912]
Henson, Matthew Alexander, 1866–1955.

LAC 12893
The Negro in Africa and America. New York, for the American economic association by the Macmillan company; [etc., etc.] 1902.
Tillinghast, Joseph Alexander.

LAC 40108
The negro in America; an address delivered before the Philosophical institution of Edinburgh, 16th October, 1907. [Philadelphia, Press of E. A. Wright bank note co., 1907?]
Carnegie, Andrew, 1835-1919.

LAC 12867
The negro in America, and the ideal American republic. Philadelphia, American Baptist publication society [c1898]
Morgan, Thomas Jefferson, 1839-1902.

LAC 16476
The Negro in American history; men and women eminent in the evolution of the American of African descent. Washington, The American Negro academy, 1914.
Cromwell, John Wesley, 1846-

LAC 15360
The Negro in business. Boston, Chicago, Hertel, Jenkins & co. [c1907]
Washington, Booker Taliaferro, 1859?-1915.

LAC 40078
The Negro in business: report of a social study made under the direction of Atlanta university; together with the proceedings of the fourth Conference for the study of the Negro problems, held at Atlanta university, May 30-31, 1899. Atlanta, Ga. [Atlanta university] 1899.
Du Bois, William Edward Burghardt, 1868-1963, ed.

LAC 16256
The negro in Pennsylvania; a study in economic history... By Richard R. Wright, jr. [Philadelphia, A. M. E. book concern, printers, 1912]
Wright, Richard Robert, 1878-

LAC 12795
The negro in the American rebellion, his heroism and his fidelity. Boston, Lee & Shepard, 1867.
Brown, William Wells, 1815-1884.

LAC 40078
The Negro in the black belt: some social sketches, by W. E. B. Du Bois. Washington, Govt. print. off., 1899.
U.S. *Bureau of Labor.*

LAC 15936
The Negro in the Christian pulpit; or, The two characters and two destinies, as delineated in twenty-one practical sermons, by J. W. Hood. With an appendix, containing specimen sermons by other bishops of the same church. Introd. by A. G. Haygood. Raleigh, Edwards, Broughton, 1884.
Hood, James Walker.

LAC 13062
The Negro in the cities of the North. New York, Charity Organization Society, 1905.
The Survey *(East Stroudsburg, Pa.)*

LAC 16196
The Negro in the South, his economic progress in relation to his moral and religious development; being the William Levi Bull lectures for the year 1907, by Booker T. Washington and W. E. Burghardt Du Bois. Philadelphia, G. W. Jacobs & company [1907]
Washington, Booker Taliaferro, 1859?-1915.

LAC 40111
The negro labor question. By a New-York merchant. New-York, J. A. Gray, printer, 1858.

LAC 40068
The negro law of South Carolina, collected and digested by John Belton O'Neall, one of the judges of the courts of law and errors of the said state, under a resolution of the State agricultural society of South Carolina: read before them, at their September semi-annual meeting, 1848, at Spartanburg Court House-by them directed to be submitted to the governor, with a request that he would lay it before the legislature, at its approaching session, November, 1848, and by him ordered to be published for the information of the members. Columbia, Printed by J. G. Bowman, 1848.
O'Neall, John Belton, 1793-1863, *comp.*

LAC 40078
Negro lynching in the South. Treating of the negro. His past and present condition, of the cause of lynching, and of the means to remedy the evil... Washington, D. C., T. W. Cadick, 1899.
Presley, Samuel C

LAC 14085
Negro myths from the Georgia coast told in the vernacular. Boston and New York, Houghton, Mifflin and company, 1888.
Jones, Charles Colcock, 1831-1893.

LAC 12905
Negro orators and their orations. Washington, D. C., The Associated publishers, inc., [c1925]
Woodson, Carter Godwin, 1875-1950 *ed.*

LAC 16834
The Negro problem; a series of articles by representative American Negroes of today; contributions by Booker T. Washington, W. E. Burghardt Du Bois, Paul Laurence Dunbar, Charles W. Chesnutt, and others. New York, J. Pott & company, 1903.

LAC 12873
The Negro problem; Abraham Lincoln's solution. New York and London, G. P. Putnam's sons, 1909.
Pickett, William Passmore, 1855-

LAC 12881
The negro problem solved; or, Africa as she was, as she is, and as she shall be. Her curse and her cure. By Rev. Hollis Read. New York, A. A. Constantine, 1864.
Read, Hollis, 1802-1887.

LAC 12798
The Negro question. New York, C. Scribner's sons, 1903, [c1890]
Cable, George Washington, 1844-1925.

LAC 20976
The Negro races, a sociological study, v. 1-2. New York, The Macmillan company; London, Macmillan & co., ltd., 1907-14.
Dowd, Jerome, 1864-

LAC 40152
Negro slavery unjustifiable. A discourse by the late Rev. Alexander McLeod ... 1802. 10th ed. New York, A. McLeod, 1860.
McLeod, Alexander, 1774–1833.

LAC 13661
The Negro; the southerner's problem. New York, C. Scribner's sons, 1904.
Page, Thomas Nelson, 1853–1922.

LAC 16486
Negroes and their treatment in Virginia from 1865 to 1867. Pulaski, Va., Printed by B. D. Smith & brothers [c1910]
McConnell, John Preston, 1866–

LAC 12843
The negroes in negroland; the negroes in America; and negroes generally. Also, the several races of white men, considered as the involuntary and predestined supplanters of the black races. New York, G. W. Carleton; [etc., etc.] 1868.
Helper, Hinton Rowan, 1829–1909, *comp.*

LAC 16253
Negroes in the United States. Washington, Govt. print. off., 1904.
U.S. *Bureau of the Census.*

LAC 40108
The Negroes of Cinclare central factory and Calumet plantation, Louisiana. By J. Bradford Laws. Washington, Govt. print. off., 1902.
U.S. *Bureau of Labor.*

LAC 40108
The Negroes of Columbia, Missouri; a concrete study of the race problem ... by William Wilson Elwang, M. A.; with a preface by Charles A. Ellwood. [Columbia, Mo.] Dept. of sociology, University of Missouri, 1904.
Elwang, William Wilson.

LAC 40108
The Negroes of Farmville, Virginia: a social study. By W. E. B. Du Bois. Washington, Govt. print. off., 1898.
U.S. *Bureau of Labor.*

LAC 40138
The negroes of St. Louis. Boston, 1903.
Brandt, Lilian, 1873–

LAC 40078
The Negroes of Xenia, Ohio: a social study, by Richard R. Wright. Washington, Govt. print. off., 1903.
U.S. *Bureau of Labor.*

LAC 12801
Negro-mania: being an examination of the falsely assumed equality of the various races of men; demonstrated by the investigations of Champollion, Wilkinson, Rosellini, Van-Amringe, Gliddon, Young, Morton, Knox, Lawrence, Gen. J. H. Hammond, Murray, Smith, W. Gilmore, Simms, English, Conrad, Elder, Prichard, Blumenbach, Cuvier, Brown, Le Vaillant, Carlyle, Cardinal Wiseman, Burckhardt, and Jefferson. Together with a concluding chapter, presenting a comparative statement of the condition of the Negroes in the West Indies before and since emancipation. Philadelphia, Campbell & Power, 1851.
Campbell, John, 1810–1874.

LAC 12779
The negro's progress in fifty years. Philadelphia, American academy of political and social science, 1913.
American Academy of Political and Social Science, *Philadelphia.*

LAC 10728
Neighbourhood guilds; an instrument of social reform. 2d ed. London, S. Sonnenschein & co., 1892.
Coit, Stanton, 1857–

LAC 16918
Neither bond nor free. (A plea.)... New York, J. S. Ogilvie publishing company [c1902]
Pryor, George Langhorne, 1857.

LAC 10813
The nether side of New York; or, The vice, crime and poverty of the great metropolis. New York, Sheldon & company, 1872.
Crapsey, Edward.

LAC 12930
Neutral relations of England and the United States. New York, D. Appleton and company, 1863.
Loring, Charles Greely, 1794–1867.

LAC 16192
Nevada and her resources. A brief sketch of the advantages and possibilities of the state, and the opportunities and inducements offered to capitalists and homeseekers. Comp. under the direction of the State bureau of immigration. Carson City, J. E. Eckley, 1894.
Nevada. *State Bureau of Immigration.*

LAC 16134
Nevada: the land of silver. San Francisco, Bacon & company, printers, 1876.
Powell, John J.

LAC 10259
New America. Complete in one volume. Philadelphia, J. B. Lippincott & co., 1867.
Dixon, William Hepworth, 1821–1879.

LAC 10004
New American farm book. Originally by R. L. Allen. Rev. and enl. by Lewis F. Allen. New York, Orange Judd company, 1870, [c1869]
Allen, Richard Lamb, 1803–1869.

LAC 23027
The new American navy, by John D. Long, secretary of the navy, 1897–1902; illustrated with drawings by Henry Reuterdahl and with photographs. New York, The Outlook company, 1903.
Long, John Davis, 1838–1915.

LAC 12608
The new American practical navigator: being an epitome of navigation; containing all the tables necessary to be used with the Nautical almanac in determining the latitude, and the longitude by lunar observations, and keeping a complete reckoning at sea ... the whole exemplified in a journal, kept from Boston to Madeira ... with an appendix, containing methods of calculating eclipses of the sun and moon, and occultations of the fixed stars... By Nathaniel Bowditch and, since his decease, continued by his son, J. Ingersoll Bowditch. 28th stereotype edition. New York, E. & G. W. Blunt, 1859.
Bowditch, Nathaniel, 1773–1838.

LAC 14453
New Amsterdam and its people; studies, social and topographical, of the town under Dutch and early English rule. New York, C. Scribner's sons, 1902.
Innes, John H.

LAC 10360
New Amsterdam, New Orange, New York: a chronologically arranged account of engraved views of the city from the first picture published in MDCLI until the year MDCCC. New York, Dodd, Mead and company, 1897.
Andrews, William Loring, 1837-1920.

LAC 40012
A new and accurate account of the provinces of South Carolina and Georgia: with many curious and useful observations on the trade, navigation and plantations of Great Britain, compared with her most powerful maritime neighbors in ancient and modern times. London, 1733.
Oglethorpe, James Edward, 1696-1785.

LAC 12657
The new astronomy. Boston and New York, Houghton, Mifflin and company, 1891, [c1887]
Langley, Samuel Pierpont, 1834-1906.

LAC 10542
The new basis of civilization. The Kennedy lectures for 1905, in the School of philanthropy conducted by the Charity organization society of the city of New York. New York, The Macmillan company; London, Macmillan & co., ltd., 1913, [c1907]
Patten, Simon Nelson, 1852-1922.

LAC 15508
New Britain. A narrative of a journey, by Mr. Ellis, to a country so called by its inhabitants, discovered in the vast plain of the Missouri, in North America, and inhabited by a people of British origin... London, W. Simpkin and R. Marshall, 1820.
Ellis, G   A.

LAC 11635
A new chapter in the early life of Washington, in connection with the narrative history of the Potomac company. New York, D. Appleton & co., 1856.
Pickell, John, 1802?-1865.

LAC 13843
The new chemistry. New York, D. Appleton and company, 1876.
Cooke, Josiah Parsons, 1827-1894.

LAC 20443-44
A new collection of laws, charters and local ordinances of the governments of Great Britain, France and Spain, relating to the concessions of land in their respective colonies; together with the laws of Mexico and Texas on the same subject. To which is prefixed Judge Johnson's translation of Azo and Manuel's Institutes of the civil law of Spain. Philadelphia, T. & J. W. Johnson, 1839.
White, Joseph M   1781-1839, *comp.*

LAC 16657
New Colorado and the Santa Fe trail. London, C. K. Paul & co., 1881.
Hayes, Augustus Allen, 1837-1892.

LAC 16906
The new competition; an examination of the conditions underlying the radical change that is taking place in the commercial and industrial world–the change from a competitive to a cooperative basis. 4th ed., completely rev., with full texts of Clayton and Federal trade commission laws, and comments thereon. Chicago, A. C. McClurg & co., 1920, [c1915]
Eddy, Arthur Jerome, 1859-1920.

LAC 12553
The new democracy; an essay on certain political and economic tendencies in the United States. New York, The Macmillan company, 1912.
Weyl, Walter Edward, 1873-1919.

LAC 40029
The new departure in the common schools of Quincy and other papers on educational topics. By Charles F. Adams, jr. Boston, Estes and Lauriat, 1879.
Adams, Charles Francis, 1835-1915.

LAC 20899-900
A new dictionary of medical science and literature, containing a concise account of the various subjects and terms; with the synonymes in different languages; and formulae for various officinal and empirical preparations, &c. &c. Boston, C. Bowen, 1833.
Dunglison, Robley, 1798-1869.

LAC 13059
A new discovery of a vast country in America, extending above four thousand miles, between New France and New Mexico. With a description of the Great lakes, cataracts, rivers, plants, and animals: also, the manners, customs, and languages, of the several native Indians; and the advantage of commerce with those different nations. With a continuation: giving an account of the attempts of the Sieur de la Salle upon the mines of St. Barbe, &c. The taking of Quebec by the English; with the advantages of a shorter cut to China and Japan. Both parts illustrated with maps and figures, and dedicated to his Majesty K. William. By L. Hennepin, now resident in Holland. To which are added, several new discoveries in North-America, not publish'd in the French edition. London: Printed for M. Bentley, J. Tonson, H. Bonwick, T. Goodwin, and S. Manship, 1698.
Hennepin, Louis, *17th cent.*

LAC 14781
The new economy; a peaceable solution of the social problem. Chicago and New York, H. S. Stone & company, 1898.
Gronlund, Laurence, 1846-1899.

LAC 14110
A New England boyhood and other bits of autobiography. Boston, Little, Brown and company, 1915.
Hale, Edward Everett, 1822-1909.

LAC 15247
The New-England farmer: or, Georgical dictionary: containing a compendious account of the ways and methods in which the most important art of husbandry, in all its various branches, is, or may be, practised to the greatest advantage in this country. By Samuel Deane, A. M. Fellow of the American academy of arts and sciences. Printed at Worcester, Mass. By Isaiah Thomas...1790.
Deane, Samuel, 1733-1814.

LAC 12205

A New England girlhood ... with an introductory sketch and portrait. Boston, New York, Houghton Mifflin company, 1889.
Larcom, Lucy, 1824–1893.

LAC 15920

New England judged by the spirit of the Lord. In two parts. Part first, containing a brief relation of the sufferings of the people called Quakers in New England, from the time of their first arrival there in the year 1656 to the year 1660... In answer to the declaration of their persecutors apologizing for the same, 1659. Second part, being a further relation of the cruel and bloody sufferings of the people called Quakers in New England, continued from anno 1660 to anno 1665. Beginning with the sufferings of William Leddra, whom they put to death. Formerly published by George Bishop, and now somewhat abbreviated. With an appendix containing the writings of several of the sufferers ... and a postscript of the judgments of God that have befallen divers of their persecutors. Also, an answer to Cotton Mather's abuses of the said people, in his late history of New England, printed anno 1702. The whole being at this time published in the said peoples' vindication, as a reply to all his slanderous calumnies. London, T. Sowle, 1703 [Philadelphia, T. W. Stuckey, 1875]
Bishop, George, d. 1668.

LAC 11928

A New England nun, and other stories, by Mary E. Wilkins. New York, Harper & brothers, 1891.
Freeman, Mary Eleanor, 1852–1930.

LAC 11002

The New-England primer; a reprint of the earliest known edition, with many facsimiles and reproductions, and an historical introduction. Ed. by Paul Leicester Ford. New York, Dodd, Mead and company, 1899.

LAC 12067

A New-England tale; or, Sketches of New-England character and manners. New York, E. Bliss & E. White, 1822.
Sedgwick, Catharine Maria, 1789–1867.

LAC 10466

New England, what it is and what it is to be. Boston, Boston chamber of commerce, 1911.
French, George, 1853–1935, ed.

LAC 40044

New-Englands Jonas cast up at London: or, A relation of the proceedings of the court at Boston in New-England against divers honest and godly persons, for petitioning for government in the common-wealth, according to the lawes of England, and for admittance of themselves and children to the sacraments in their churches; and in case that should not be granted, for leave to have ministers and church-government according to the best reformation of England and Scotland. Together with a confutation of some reports of a fained miracle upon the foresaid petition, being thrown overboard at sea; as also a breif answer to some passages in a late book (entituled Hypocrisie unmasked) set out by Mr. Winslowe, concerning the independent churches holding communion with the reformed churches. By Major John Childe. London, Printed for T. R. and E. M., 1647.
Child, John.

LAC 12033

New-England's memorial; or, A brief relation of the most memorable and remarkable passages of the providence of God manifested to the planters of New-England in America: with special reference to the first colony thereof, called New-Plimouth. As also a nomination of divers of the most eminent instruments deceased, both of church & common wealth... Published for the use and benefit of present and future generations. Boston, Reprinted for Daniel Henchman, 1721.
Morton, Nathaniel, 1613–1685.

LAC 14726

New Englands rarities discovered: in birds, beasts, fishes, serpents, and plants of that country. Together with the physical and chyrurgical remedies wherewith the natives constantly use to cure their distempers, wounds, and sores. Also a perfect description of an Indian squa, in all her bravery; with a poem not improperly conferr'd upon her. Lastly a chronological table of the most remarkable passages in that country amongst the English... London, Printed for G. Widdowes, 1672.
Josselyn, John, fl. 1630–1675.

LAC 12267

The new epoch for faith. Boston and New York, Houghton, Mifflin and company, 1901.
Gordon, George Angier, 1853–1929.

LAC 11113

The new era; or, The coming kingdom, by Rev. Josiah Strong. New York, The Baker & Taylor co. [c1893]
Strong, Josiah, 1847–1916.

LAC 40148

New governments west of the Alleghanies before 1780. (Introductory to a study of the organization and admission of new states) Madison, Wis., The University, 1897.
Alden, George Henry, 1866–

LAC 13287

A new guide for emigrants to the West, containing sketches of Michigan, Ohio, Indiana, Illinois, Missouri, Arkansas with the territory of Wisconsin, and the adjacent parts. New ed. Boston, Gould, Kendall and Lincoln, 1843, [c1836]
Peck, John Mason, 1789–1858.

LAC 10779

New Hampshire; an epitome of popular government. Boston and New York, Houghton, Mifflin and company, 1904.
Sanborn, Franklin Benjamin, 1831–1917.

LAC 14753

New Hampshire as a royal province. New York, Columbia university, Longmans, Green, agents, 1908.
Fry, William Henry, 1875–

LAC 13949

New Hampshire as it is... Comp. ... by Edwin A. Charlton. Claremont, N. H., Tracy and Sanford, 1855.
Charlton, Edwin Azro, 1828–1896.

LAC 11213

The New Harmony movement, by George B. Lockwood, with the collaboration of Charles A. Prosser in the preparation of the educational chapters. New York, D. Appleton and company, 1905.
Lockwood, George Browning, 1872–

LAC 13245

A new home—who'll follow? or, Glimpses of western life. By Mrs. Mary Clavers [*pseud.*] 4th ed. Rev. by the author, and illustrated by engravings from designs by F. O. C. Darley. New York, C. S. Francis, 1850.
Kirkland, Caroline Matilda, 1801–1864.

LAC 10213

New ideals in business, an account of their practice and their effects upon men and profits. New York, The Macmillan company, 1917, [c1916]
Tarbell, Ida Minerva, 1857–1944.

LAC 10454

New ideals in rural schools. Boston, New York [etc.] Houghton Mifflin company [c1913]
Betts, George Herbert, 1868–1934.

LAC 13995

New ideas on population: with remarks on the theories of Malthus and Godwin. Boston, O. Everett, 1823.
Everett, Alexander Hill, 1790–1847.

LAC 15548

The new immigration; a study of the industrial and social life of southeastern Europeans in America. New York, The Macmillan company, 1912.
Roberts, Peter, 1859–

LAC 11639

The new industrial day, a book for men who employ men. New York, The Century co., 1912.
Redfield, William Cox, 1858–1932.

LAC 10077

A new industry, or, Raising the Angora goat, and mohair, for profit. Embracing the historical, commercial, and practical features of the industry... [Fort Worth, Tex., Keystone printing company, 1900]
Black, William Leslie, 1843–1931.

LAC 14441

New Jersey as a royal province, 1738–1776. New York, Columbia university, Longmans, Green & co., agents; [etc., etc.] 1911.
Fisher, Edgar Jacob, 1885–

LAC 16753

The new Laokoon; an essay on the confusion of the arts. Boston and New York, Houghton Mifflin company, 1910.
Babbitt, Irving, 1865–1933.

LAC 16780

New letters of Abigail Adams, 1788–1801; ed. with an introd. by Stewart Mitchell. Boston, Houghton Mifflin Co., 1947.
Adams, Abigail, 1744–1818.

LAC 21121–22

New light on the early history of the greater Northwest. The manuscript journals of Alexander Henry and of David Thompson, 1799–1814. Exploration and adventure among the Indians on the Red, Saskatchewan, Missouri and Columbia rivers. Ed., with copious critical commentary, by Elliott Coues. New York, F. P. Harper, 1897.
Henry, Alexander, *d.* 1814.

LAC 16244

The new man. Twenty-nine years a slave. Twenty-nine years a free man. Recollections of H. C. Bruce. York, Pa., P. Anstadt & sons, 1895.
Bruce, Henry Clay, 1836–1902.

LAC 40145

New Mexico. Otherwise, the voiage of Anthony of Espeio, who in the yeare 1583. with his company, discouered a lande of 15. prouinces, replenished with townes and villages, with houses of 4. or 5. stories height, it lieth northward, and some suppose that the same way men may by places inhabited go to the lande tearmed De Labrador. Translated out of the Spanish copie printed first at Madreed, 1586. and afterward at Paris, in the same yeare. Imprinted at London for Thomas Cadman. [1587] [Lancaster, Pa., Lancaster press, inc., 1928]
Espejo, Antonio de.

LAC 40046

New missionary field; a report to the Female missionary society for the poor of the city of New-York, and its vicinity at their quarterly prayer meeting, March, 1817. New-York, Printed by J. Seymour, 1817.
Stafford, Ward, 1790?–1851.

LAC 10751

A new monetary system: the only means of securing the respective rights of labor and property, and of protecting the public from financial revulsions. By Edward Kellogg. Rev. from his work on "Labor and other capital," with numerous additions from his manuscripts. 8th ed. To which is prefixed a biographical sketch of the author. Ed. by his daughter, Mary Kellogg Putnam. New York, The American Sentry, 1883, [c 1861]
Kellogg, Edward, 1790–1853.

LAC 40006

The new movement in humanity from liberty to unity; an oration delivered before the [Phi Beta Kappa] fraternity of Harvard university, June 30, 1892. Boston and New York, Houghton, Mifflin and company, 1892.
Tucker, William Jewett, 1839–1926.

LAC 12517

The new nationalism., By Theodore Roosevelt. With an introduction by Ernest Hamlin Abbott. New York, The Outlook company, 1910.
Roosevelt, Theodore, *pres. U.S.*, 1858–1919.

LAC 16484

The new Negro: an interpretation, edited by Alain Locke; book decoration and portraits by Winold Reiss. New York, A. and C. Boni, 1925.
Locke, Alain Le Roy, 1886–1954, *ed.*

LAC 16733

A new Negro for a new century; an accurate and up-to-date record of the upward struggles of the Negro race. The Spanish-American War, causes of it; vivid descriptions of fierce battles; superb heroism and daring deeds of the Negro soldier... Education, industrial schools, colleges, universities and their relationship to the race problem, by Prof. Booker T. Washington. Reconstruction and industrial advancement by N. B. Wood... The colored woman and her part in race regeneration ... by Fannie Barrier Williams. Miami, Fla., Mnemosyne Pub. Inc. [1969]
Washington, Booker Taliaferro, 1859?–1915.

LAC 11207
The new peace movement. Boston, The World peace foundation, 1912.
Hull, William Isaac, 1868–1939.

LAC 12273
A new philosophy of life. New York, Dodge Publishing company [c1911]
Randall, John Herman, 1871–1946.

LAC 16891
The new politics, and other papers. Boston and New York, Houghton Mifflin company, 1914.
Brown, William Garrott, 1868–1913.

LAC 40046
The new psychic studies in their relation to Christian thought. By Franklin Johnson, D. D. New York [etc.] Funk & Wagnalls, 1887.
Johnson, Franklin, 1836–1916.

LAC 21120
The new purchase: or, Seven and a half years in the far West. By Robert Carleton, esq. [*pseud.*] New-York, D. Appleton & co.; Philadelphia, G. S. Appleton, 1843.
Hall, Baynard Rush, 1798–1863.

LAC 11202
The new redemption. A call to the church to reconstruct society according to the gospel of Christ. New York, Boston, T. Y. Crowell & company [c1893]
Herron, George Davis, 1862–1925.

LAC 15818
The new right; a plea for fair play through a more just social order, by Hon. Samuel M. Jones. Introductory and a chapter on co-operation by N. O. Nelson. New York, Eastern book concern, 1899.
Jones, Samuel Milton, 1846–1904.

LAC 10275
The new South. By Henry W. Grady, with a character sketch of Henry W. Grady by Oliver Dyer. New York, Robert Bonner's sons, 1890.
Grady, Henry Woodfin, 1815–1889.

LAC 12337
The new South. A description of the southern states, noting each state separately, and giving their distinctive features and most salient characteristics. Baltimore, The Manufacturers' record co., 1887.
Hillyard, M   B.

LAC 40030
The new South: gratitude, amendment, hope. A Thanksgiving sermon for November 25, 1880. Oxford, Ga., 1880.
Haygood, Atticus Green, *bp.*, 1839–1896.

LAC 16347
The new South investigated. Detroit, Mich., Ferguson printing company, 1888.
Straker, David Augustus, *d.* 1908.

LAC 40034
A new statement of the aim of the ethical culture societies. New York, New York society for ethical culture [1904]
Adler, Felix, 1851–

LAC 11705
A new survey of the West-Indies, 1648, The English-American. Edited with an introduction by A. P. Newton. New York, R. M. McBride, 1929.
Gage, Thomas, 1603?–1656.

LAC 14656
A new system of infantry tactics, double and single rank. Adapted to American topography and improved fire-arms. New York, D. Appleton and company, 1873.
Upton, Emory, 1839–1881.

LAC 15875
A new system of paper currency. Boston, Printed by Stacy & Richardson, 1861.
Spooner, Lysander, 1808–1887.

LAC 15775
A new system of phrenology. New York, C. Blanchard, 1857.
Hittell, John Shertzer, 1825–1901.

LAC 10974
New themes for the Protestant clergy: creeds without charity, theology without humanity, and Protestantism without Christianity: with notes on the literature of charity, population, pauperism, political economy, and Protestantism. 2d ed. rev. Philadelphia, Lippincott, Grambo & co., 1853, [c1851]
Colwell, Stephen 1800–1871.

LAC 22279
New tracks in North America. A journal of travel and adventure whilst engaged in the survey for a southern railroad to the Pacific Ocean during 1867–8. London, Chapman and Hall, 1869.
Bell, William Abraham.

LAC 12154
New travels in the United States of America. Performed in 1788... Translated from the French... London, J. S. Jordan, 1792.
Brissot de Warville, Jacques Pierre, 1754–1793.

LAC 13755
A new universal dictionary of the marine; being, a copious explanation of the technical terms and phrases usually employed in the construction, equipment, machinery, movements, and military, as well as naval operations of ships: with such parts of astronomy, and navigation, as will be found useful to practical navigators. Illustrated with a variety of modern designs of shipping, &c., together with separate views of the masts, yards, sails and rigging. To which is annexed, a vocabulary of French sea-phrases and terms of art, collected from the best authorities. Originally compiled by William Falconer. Now modernized and much enlarged by William Burney. London, T. Cadell, 1815.
Falconer, William, 1732–1769.

LAC 40012
New views of early Virginia history, 1606–1619. Liberty, Va., The Bedford index print, 1886.
Brown, Alexander, 1843–1906.

LAC 13825
New views of the Constitution of the United States. Washington City, Printed for the author, by Way and Gideon, 1823.
Taylor, John, 1753–1824.

LAC 15385
New views of the origin of the tribes and nations of America. Philadelphia, Printed, for the author, by John Bioren, 1797.
Barton, Benjamin Smith, 1766–1815.

LAC 15970
The new Virginia justice, comprising the office and authority of a justice of the peace, in the commonwealth of Virginia. Together with a variety of useful precedents adapted to the laws now in force. To which is added, an appendix containing all the most approved forms of conveyancing, commonly used in this country... Also, the duties of a justice of the peace, arising under the laws of the United States. Richmond–Printed By Aug: Davis, 1799.
Hening, William Waller, 1768–1828.

LAC 20729
New voyages to North-America, by the Baron de Lahontan; reprinted from the English edition of 1703, with facsimiles of original title-pages, maps, and illustrations, and the addition of introduction, notes, and index, by Reuben Gold Thwaites. Chicago, A. C. McClurg & co., 1905.
Lahontan, Louis Armand de Lom d'Arce, *baron* de, 1666–1715?

LAC 15046
New wars for old, being a statement of radical pacifism in terms of force versus non-resistance, with special reference to the facts and problems of the great war. New York, Dodd, Mead and company, 1916.
Holmes, John Haynes, 1879–

LAC 13047
The new West as related to the Christian college and the home missionary. 3d ed., illustrated. Cambridge [Mass.] Printed at the Riverside press, 1878.
Tenney, Edward Payson, 1835–1916.

LAC 14435
The new West; or, California in 1867–1868. New York [etc.] G. P. Putnam & son, 1869.
Brace, Charles Loring, 1826–1890.

LAC 10666
New York: a historical sketch of the rise and progress of the metropolitan city of America. By a New Yorker. New-York, Carlton & Phillips, 1853.
Curry, Daniel, 1809–1887.

LAC 11299
New York and its institutions, 1609–1872. A library of information, pertaining to the great metropolis, past and present... New York, E. B. Treat, 1872.
Richmond, John Francis.

LAC 12308
New York as an eighteenth century municipality prior to 1731. New York, Columbia university; [etc., etc.] 1917.
Peterson, Arthur Everett, 1871–1943.

LAC 15448
New York by gas-light, with here and there a streak of sunshine. New York, M. J. Ivers [1850?]
Foster, George G   *d.* 1850.

LAC 13871
New York city during the American revolution. Being a collection of original papers (now first published) from the manuscripts in the possession of the Mercantile library association, of New York city. [New York] Priv. print. for the Association, 1861.
New York. Mercantile Library Association.

LAC 40009
The New York city "Ring": its origin, maturity and fall, discussed in a reply to the New York times. New York, Press of John Polhemus, 1873.
Tilden, Samuel Jones, 1814–1886.

LAC 10902
New York considered and improved, 1695, by John Miller, published from the original ms. in the British museum; with introduction and notes by Victor Hugo Paltsits. Cleveland, The Burrows brothers company, 1903.
Miller, John, 1666–1724.

LAC 15643
The New-York conspiracy, or a history of the Negro plot, with the Journal of the proceedings against the conspirators at New York in the years 1741–2... New York, Negro Universities Pr., 1969.
Horsmanden, Daniel, 1694–1778.

LAC 40100
New-York convention. Report on the production and manufacture of cotton. Boston, J. T. & E. Buckingham, 1832.
Friends of Domestic Industry.

LAC 15344
New York in bondage. By Hon. John D. Townsend. New York, 1901.
Townsend, John Drake, 1835–1896.

LAC 40079
The New York national bank presidents' conspiracy against industry and property; a history of the panic of 1893, its organization and methods. Chicago, The American Bimetallic Union [1894]
Schuckers, Jacob W.

LAC 10714
New-York: past, present, and future; comprising a history of the city of New-York, a description of its present condition, and an estimate of its future increase. 3d ed. New-York, Prall, Lewis & co.; Philadelphia, G. S. Appleton; [etc., etc.] 1850.
Belden, Ezekiel Porter, 1823–1911.

LAC 14956
The New York pulpit in the revival of 1858. A memorial volume of sermons. New York, Sheldon, 1860.

LAC 14685
New-York state conventions for "rescuing the canals from the ruin with which they are threatened".
Proceedings of the New-York state conventions for "rescuing the canals from the ruin with which they are threatened" : by exposing and resisting "the railroad conspiracy" for "discrediting the canals, and diminishing their revenues with a view of bringing them under the hammer" ... and adopting measures for counteracting "the ruinous competition with railroads, permitted by the state..." Arranged by Henry O'Rielly and Hugh Allen for the Clinton league... New York, The Clinton league, 1859.
O'Rielly, Henry, 1806–1886, ed.

LAC 10151
The New York stock exchange. New York, Greenwood Press, 1968.
Eames, Francis L   1844–

LAC 15876
The New York Stock Exchange; its history, its contribution to national prosperity, and its relation to American finance at the outset of the twentieth century. New York, Greenwood Press [1969, c1905]
Stedman, Edmund Clarence, 1833–1908.

LAC 10397
New York stock exchange manual, containing its principles, rules, and its different modes of speculation: also, a review of the stocks dealt in on 'change... New York, J. F. Trow, 1865.
Hamon, Henry.

LAC 20187-88
New York university; its history, influence, equipment and characteristics, with biographical sketches and portraits of founders, benefactors, officers and alumni; editor-in-chief: General Joshua L. Chamberlain; special editors ... historical: Henry M. MacCracken, Professor Ernest G. Sihler; biographical: Willis Fletcher Johnson. Introduction by Hon. William T. Harris. Boston, R. Herndon company, 1901–03
Chamberlain, Joshua Lawrence, 1828–1914, ed.

LAC 16600
New York's Chinatown; an historical presentation of its people and places. New York, Bohemia publishing company [1898]
Beck, Louis Joseph, 1867–

LAC 40009
New York's hundred lodging-houses; the evil conditions under which a great floating population is housed. New York, 1905.
Kennaday, Paul.

LAC 14855
New York's inferno explored. Scenes full of pathos powerfully portrayed–Siberian desolation caused by vice and drink–Tenements packed with misery and crime... New York, The Salvation army headquarters, 1891.
Booth, Ballington, 1859–

LAC 12934
The new-born Cuba. New York and London, Harper & brothers, 1899.
Matthews, Franklin, 1858–1917.

LAC 14454
The Newburgh survey; reports of limited investigations of social conditions in Newburgh, N. Y., by the Department of surveys and exhibits, Russell Sage foundation, Zenas L. Potter, director, field work. [Newburgh, N. Y., The News co., 1913]
Russell Sage Foundation, *New York. Dept. of Surveys and Exhibits.*

LAC 16544
Newer ideals of peace. New York, The Macmillan company; London, Macmillan & co., ltd., 1907.
Addams, Jane, 1860–1935.

LAC 10363
Newport: our social capital, by Mrs. John King Van Rensselaer...with frontispiece in color by Henry Hutt, many illustrations in photogravure and double-tone and from drawings by Edward Stratton Holloway. Philadelphia and London, J. B. Lippincott company, 1905.
Van Rensselaer, May, 1848–1925.

LAC 40127
Newes from Virginia.
A good speed to Virginia (1609) [by] Robert Gray. Newes from Virginia (1610) [by] R. Rich. [New York, 1937]
Gray, Robert, *fl.* 1609.

LAC 11114
The next great awakening. New York, The Baker & Taylor company, 1902.
Strong, Josiah, 1847–1916.

LAC 16561
Nez Perce Joseph, an account of his ancestors, his lands, his confederates, his enemies, his murders, his war, his pursuit and capture. Boston, Lee and Shepard, 1881.
Howard, Oliver Otis, 1830–1909.

LAC 16063
Niagara.
Echoes from Niagara: historical, political, personal. By Mrs. Richard Crowley. Buffalo, C. W. Moulton, 1890.
Crowley, Julia M.

LAC 40016
"The Niagara ship canal" : and "Reciprocity" : papers written for the "Buffalo commercial advertiser," by J. D. Hayes, esq.; together with the speech of Hon. Israel T. Hatch, in the convention at Detroit, July 14, 1865... Buffalo, Matthews & Warren, 1865.
Hayes, John D.

LAC 40060
The Nicaragua canal, the gateway between the oceans. Published by authority of the Chamber of commerce of San Francisco, the Board of trade of San Francisco, the Chamber of commerce of Portland, Oregon, the Chamber of commerce of San Diego. San Francisco, Cal., Press of Commercial pub co., 1895.
Merry, William Lawrence, 1842–1911.

LAC 11832
Nick of the woods; or, The Jibbenainosay; a tale of Kentucky, by Robert Montgomery Bird; edited, with introduction, chronology, and bibliography, by Cecil B. Williams. New York, Cincinnati [etc.] American book company [c1939]
Bird, Robert Montgomery, 1806–1854.

LAC 11868
A night in Acadie. Chicago, Way & Williams, 1897.
Chopin, Kate, 1851–1904.

LAC 11960
Nights with Uncle Remus; myths and legends of the old plantation. Boston, J. R. Osgood, 1883.
Harris, Joel Chandler, 1848–1908.

LAC 31263–73
Niles' national register, containing political, historical, geographical, scientifical, statistical, economical, and biographical documents, essays and facts: together with notices of the arts and manufactures, and a record of the events of the times. v. 53–75; Sept. 2, 1837–June 27, 1849. Philadelphia.

LAC 31236–62
Niles' weekly register, containing political, historical, geographical, scientifical, statistical, economical, and biographical documents, essays and facts; together with notices of the arts and manufactures, and a record of the events of the times. v. 7–52; Sept. 10, 1814–Aug. 26, 1837. Baltimore.

LAC 31014
Niles' weekly register. General index to the first twelve volumes, or first series ... from September, 1811, to September, 1817. Baltimore, Franklin Pr., 1818.

LAC 15903
The nineteen local governments in Chicago, a multiplicity of overlapping taxing bodies with many elective officials; Chicago's greatest needs are the unification of its local governments and a short ballot, report prepared by the Chicago bureau of public efficiency. [Chicago, 1913]
Chicago Bureau of Public Efficiency.

LAC 15163
Nineteen months a prisoner of war. Narrative of Lieutenant G. E. Sabre, Second Rhode Island cavalry, of his experience in the war prisons and stockades of Morton, Mobile, Atlanta, Libby, Belle island, Andersonville, Macon, Charleston, and Columbia, and his escape ... list of officers confined at Columbia, during the winter of 1864 and 1865. New York, The American news company, 1865.
Sabre, Gilbert E.

LAC 23470
Nippur; or, Explorations and adventures on the Euphrates; the narrative of the University of Pennsylvania expedition to Babylonia in the years 1888–1890. New York and London, G. P. Putnam's sons, 1897.
Peters, John Punnett, 1852–1921.

LAC 23182–83
Nitrocellulose industry; a compendium of the history, chemistry, manufacture, commercial application and analysis of nitrates, acetates and xanthates of cellulose as applied to the peaceful arts, with a chapter on gun cotton, smokeless powder and explosive cellulose nitrates. 324 illustrations. New York, D. Van Nostrand company, 1911.
Worden, Edward Chauncey, 1875–

LAC 40059
No just cause for a dissolution of the Union in any thing which has hitherto happened; but the Union the only security for southern rights. An oration, delivered before the citizens of Tuscaloosa, Ala., July 4, 1851. Furnished for publication by request of the mayor and aldermen of the city. Tuscaloosa, Printed by J. W. & J. F. Warren, 1851.
Barnard, Frederick Augustus Porter, 1809–1889.

LAC 14675
No sex in education; or, An equal chance for both boys and girls. Being a review of Dr. E. H. Clarke's "Sex in education". Philadelphia, J. M. Stoddart & co. [c1874]
Duffey, Eliza Bisbee, d. 1898.

LAC 12844
Nojoque; a question for a continent. New York, G. W. Carleton & co.; [etc., etc.] 1867.
Helper, Hinton Rowan, 1829–1909.

LAC 16131
Nome and Seward Peninsula; history, description, biographies and stories. [Seattle, Wash., E. S. Harrison, c1905]
Harrison, Edward Sanford.

LAC 16126
Nome nuggets. Some of the experiences of a party of gold seekers in northwestern Alaska in 1900. By L. H. French. In charge of the expedition of the Cape Nome hydraulic mining company. New York, Montross, Clarke & Emmons, 1901.
French, Leigh Hill, 1863–

LAC 16068
Der nordamerikanische landwirth. Ein handbuch fur ansiedler in den Vereinigten Staaten. Mit 246 original-holzschnitten. Frankfurt am Main, G. F. Heyer, 1848.
Fleischmann, Carl Ludwig.

LAC 15042
The normal; or, Methods of teaching the common branches, orthoepy, orthography, grammar, geography, arithmetic and elocution... New York, A. S. Barnes & Burr, 1860, [c1859]
Holbrook, Alfred, 1816–1909.

LAC 20625
Norman Leslie. A tale of the present times... New-York, Harper & brothers, 1835.
Fay, Theodore Sedgwick, 1807–1898.

LAC 16441
The Norse discovery of America; a compilation in extenso of all the sagas, manuscripts, and inscriptive memorials relating to the finding and settlement of the New World in the eleventh century, with presentations of freshly discovered proofs, in the form of church records supplied by the Vatican of Rome, never before published. Translations and deductions by Arthur Middleton Reeves, North Ludlow Beamish, [and] Rasmus B. Anderson. Rasmus B. Anderson, ed. in chief, J. W. Buel, managing ed. London, Norroena Society, 1907, [c1905]

LAC 13335
North America. New York, Harper & Brothers, 1862.
Trollope, Anthony, 1815–1882.

LAC 14740
North America, its agriculture and climate; containing observations on the agriculture and climate of Canada, the United States, and the island of Cuba. Edinburgh, A. and C. Black, 1857.
Russell, Robert, *d.* 1871.

LAC 22410–20
The North American Indian; being a series of volumes picturing and describing the Indians of the United States, and Alaska, written, illustrated, and published by Edward S. Curtis; edited by Frederick Webb Hodge, foreword by Theodore Roosevelt; field research conducted under the patronage of J. Pierpont Morgan... New York, Johnson reprint corp. [1970, c1907–30]
Curtis, Edward S   1868–

LAC 30273–400
The North American review. v. 1–173; May 1815–Dec. 1901. New York [etc.]

LAC 30985
The North American review index... v. I.–CXXV., 1815–1877. By William Cushing. Cambridge, J. Wilson, 1878.

LAC 20913–14
The North American sylva; or, A description of the forest trees of the United States, Canada and Nova Scotia. Considered particularly with respect to their use in the arts and their introduction into commerce. To which is added a description of the most useful of the European forest trees... Tr. from the French of F. Andrew Michaux, with notes by J. Jay Smith. Philadelphia, Rice, Rutter & co., 1865.
Michaux, Francois Andre, 1770–1855.

LAC 13507
The North and the South: being a statistical view of the condition of the free and slave states. By Henry Chase and C. H. Sanborn. Comp. from official documents. [2d ed.] Boston, J. P. Jewett and company; Cleveland, O.,H. P. B. Jewett, 1857.
Chase, Henry.

LAC 14929
North Atlantic coast fisheries arbitration. The case of the United States before the Permanent court of arbitration at the Hague under the provisions of the Special agreement between the United States of America and Great Britain concluded January 27, 1909. Washington, D.C., Govt. print. off., 1909.
United States.

LAC 13266
North Carolina, a study in English colonial government. New York, The Macmillan company; London, Macmillan & co., ltd., 1904.
Raper, Charles Lee, 1870–

LAC 15234
North of Boston. London, D. Nutt [1914]
Frost, Robert, 1874–1963.

LAC 16324
The North pole, its discovery in 1909 under the auspices of the Peary Arctic club, by Robert E. Peary; with an introduction by Theodore Roosevelt and a foreword by Gilbert H. Grosvenor, with eight full-page illustrations reproducing photographic enlargements colored by hand; one hundred illustrations in black-and-white, from photographs; and with a map in colors by Gilbert H. Grosvenor. New York, Frederick A. Stokes company, 1910.
Peary, Robert Edwin, 1856–1920.

LAC 16037
The Northmen, Columbus and Cabot, 985–1503: The voyages of the Northmen, ed. by Julius E. Olson. The voyages of Columbus and of John Cabot, ed. by Edward Gaylord Bourne. With maps and a facsimile reproduction. New York, C. Scribner's sons [c1906]

LAC 15142
A north-side view of slavery. The refugee: or, The narratives of fugitive slaves in Canada. Related by themselves, with an account of the history and condition of the colored population of Upper Canada. Boston, J. P. Jewett and company; New York, Sheldon, Lamport and Blakeman; [etc., etc.] 1856.
Drew, Benjamin.

LAC 13325
The northwest coast; or, Three years' residence in Washington territory. New York, Harper & brothers, 1857.
Swan, James Gilchrist.

LAC 15752
Norwegian immigrant contributions to America's making. New York [The International press] 1921.
Sundby-Hansen, Harry, *ed.*

LAC 22861–62
Norwegian migration to America... Northfield, Minn., The Norwegian-American historical association, 1931–40.
Blegen, Theodore Christian, 1891–

LAC 15542
Norwegian settlement in the United States. Northfield, Minn. [Norwegian-American historical association] 1938.
Qualey, Carlton Chester, 1904–

LAC 20330–32
Norwich university, 1819–1911; her history, her graduates, her roll of honor, pub. by Major-General Grenville M. Dodge; comp. and ed. by William Arba Ellis. Montpelier, Vt., The Capital city press, 1911.
Ellis, William Arba, 1869–   *comp. and ed.*

LAC 11824
Norwood; or, Village life in New England. New York, C. Scribner & company, 1868.
Beecher, Henry Ward, 1813–1887.

LAC 16219
Nos hommes et notre histoire; notices biographiques accompagnees de reflexions et de souvenirs personnels, hommage a la population creole, en souvenir des grands hommes qu'elle a produits et des bonnes choses qu'elle a accomplies. Montreal, Arbour & Dupont, 1911.
Desdunes, Rodolphe L.

LAC 15923
Notas e impresiones de los Estados Unidos. Santiago de Chile, Impr. Cervantes, 1904.
Gutierrez, Alberto.

LAC 40110
Notes nouvelles sur Edgar Poe. [Paris, Michel Levy freres, 1857]
Baudelaire, Charles Pierre, 1821–1867.

LAC 20190–91
Notes of a busy life. With portraits and other illustrations. Cincinnati, Stewart & Kidd company, 1916.
Foraker, Joseph Benson, 1846–

LAC 15528
Notes of a journey through Canada, the United States of America, and the West Indies... Edinburgh [etc.] Fraser and co., 1838.
Logan, James, *advocate, of Edinburgh.*

LAC 10641
Notes of a pianist. During his professional tours in the United States, Canada, the Antilles, and South America. Preceded by a short biographical sketch with contemporaneous criticisms. Edited by his sister, Clara Gottschalk. Translated from the French by Robert E. Peterson. Philadelphia, London, J. B. Lippincott & co., 1881.
Gottschalk, Louis Moreau, 1829–1869.

LAC 16762
Notes of a son and brother. New York, C. Scribner's sons, 1914.
James, Henry, 1843–1916.

LAC 16722
Notes of a war correspondent. New York, C. Scribner's sons, 1911, [c1910]
Davis, Richard Harding, 1864–1916.

LAC 15384
Notes of talks on teaching, given by Francis W. Parker, at the Martha's Vineyard summer institute, July 17 to August 19, 1882. Reported by Lelia E. Patridge. New York, E. L. Kellogg & co., 1883.
Parker, Francis Wayland, 1837–1902.

LAC 16382
Notes of the Mexican war 1846–47–48. Comprising incidents, adventures and everyday proceedings and letters while with the United States army in the Mexican war; also extracts from ancient histories of Mexico, giving an accurate account of the first and original settlers of Mexico, etc.; also the names and numbers of the different rulers of Mexico; also influence of the church. Rev. 1885... Philadelphia, 1885.
Oswandel, J   Jacob.

LAC 12146
Notes on a journey in America, from the coast of Virginia to the territory of Illinois. The 4th ed. London, Printed by Severn and co., for J. Ridgway, 1818.
Birkbeck, Morris, 1764–1825.

LAC 11679
Notes on American schools and training colleges...
London and New York, Macmillan and co., 1890.
Fitch, *Sir* Joshua Girling, 1824–1903.

LAC 13615
Notes on duels and duelling, alphabetically arranged, with a preliminary historical essay. Boston, Crosby, Nichols, and company, 1855.
Sabine, Lorenzo, 1803–1877.

LAC 15326
Notes on Italy. Written during a tour in the years 1829 and 1830. Philadelphia, Carey & Lea, 1831.
Peale, Rembrandt, 1778–1860.

LAC 16761
Notes on novelists, with some other notes. [London] J. M. Dent & sons, ltd., 1914.
James, Henry, 1843–1916.

LAC 14277
Notes on political economy, as applicable to the United States. By a southern planter. New York, Leavitt, Trow & co., 1844.
Ware, Nathaniel A 1780–1854.

LAC 12233
Notes on public subjects, made during a tour in the United States and in Canada. London, J. Murray, 1852.
Tremenheere, Hugh Seymour, 1804–1893.

LAC 10155
Notes on railroad accidents. New York, G. P. Putnam's sons, 1879.
Adams, Charles Francis, 1835–1915.

LAC 40140
Notes on the burning of theatres and public halls. Reflections on some of the causes of the great mortality occasionally attending them, with suggestions as to improved security to life. The antiquity of the drama and the introduction of theatres into America with a chronological list of theatres and other public edifices burned. [Washington] R. O. Polkinhorn, printer, 1876.
Toner, Joseph Meredith, 1825–1896.

LAC 13161
Notes on the early settlement of the North-western territory. Cincinnati, Derby, Bradley & co., 1847.
Burnet, Jacob, 1770–1853.

LAC 13002
Notes on the first planting of New Hampshire and on the Piscataqua patents. Priv. print. Portsmouth, Printed by L. W. Brewster, 1878.
Jenness, John Scribner, 1827–1879.

LAC 12866
Notes on the history of slavery in Massachusetts.
New-York, D. Appleton & co., 1866.
Moore, George Henry, 1823–1892.

LAC 13310
Notes on the Iroquois: or, Contributions to the statistics, aboriginal history, antiquities and general ethnology of western New York. New York, Bartlett & Welford, 1846.
Schoolcraft, Henry Rowe, 1793–1864.

LAC 40151
Notes on the law of territorial expansion, with especial reference to the Philippines. Submitted to the Committee on the judiciary of the Senate of the United States, March 16, 1900... [New York, De Vinne press, 1900]
Randolph, Carman Fitz, 1856–1920.

LAC 13153
Notes on the Northwest, or valley of the upper Mississippi. New York and London, Wiley and Putnam, 1846.
Bradford, William John Alden, 1791–1858.

LAC 40063
Notes on the survey of the boundary line between Mexico and the United States. Cincinnati, Morgan & Overend, printers [1851]
Emory, William Hemsley, 1811–1887.

LAC 20895
Notes on the United States of North America, during a phrenological visit in 1838-9-40. Philadelphia, Carey & Hart, 1841.
Combe, George, 1788–1858.

LAC 14725
Notes on the use of anthracite in the manufacture of iron. With some remarks on its evaporating power. Boston, C. C. Little and J. Brown, 1841.
Johnson, Walter Rogers, 1794–1852.

LAC 40144
Notes on witchcraft. Worcester, Mass., American antiquarian society, 1907.
Kittredge, George Lyman, 1860–1941.

LAC 40041
Notices concerning Cincinnati. Cincinnati, Press of Jennings and Graham, 1908.
Drake, Daniel, 1785–1852.

LAC 16857
Notices of Florida and the campaigns. By M. M. Cohen, (an officer of the left wing.) Charleston, S. C., Burges & Honour; New-York, B. B. Hussey, 1836.
Cohen, Myer M.

LAC 11566
Notices of public libraries in the United States of America. Printed by order of Congress, as an appendix to the Fourth annual report of the Board of regents of the Smithsonian institution. Washington, 1851.
Jewett, Charles Coffin, 1816–1868.

LAC 22555
Notices of the war of 1812. New-York, G. Dearborn, 1836-40.
Armstrong, John, 1758–1843.

LAC 20675
Notions of the Americans: picked up by a travelling bachelor. London, H. Colburn, 1828.
Cooper, James Fenimore, 1789–1851.

LAC 13672
Nova Francia, a description of Acadia, 1606; tr. by P. Erondelle, 1609. With an introduction by H. P. Biggar... New York and London, Harper & brothers [1928]
Lescarbot, Marc.

LAC 23995–010
The novels and tales of Henry James. New York ed. [New York, C. Scribner's sons, 1907–17]
James, Henry, 1843–1916.

LAC 22879–81
The novels of Charles Brockden Brown... With a memoir of the author. Boston, S. G. Goodrich, 1827.
Brown, Charles Brockden, 1771–1810.

LAC 13110
Noyesism unveiled: a history of the sect self-styled Perfectionists; with a summary view of their leading doctrines. By Rev. Hubbard Eastman. Brattleboro, The author, 1849.
Eastman, Hubbard, d. 1891.

LAC 40035
Nullification and compromise; a retrospective view. New York, Francis & Loutrel, printers, 1863.
Williams, John Mason, 1780–1868.

LAC 14640
Numbers and losses in the Civil war in America, 1861–65. [2d ed.] Boston and New York, Houghton, Mifflin and company, 1901.
Livermore, Thomas Leonard, 1844–1918.

LAC 15007
Nurse and spy in the Union army: comprising the adventures and experiences of a woman in hospitals, camps, and battle-fields. By S. Emma E. Edmonds. Hartford, W. S. Williams & co.; Philadelphia [etc.] Jones bros. & co., 1865.
Edmundson, Sarah Emma, 1841–1898.

LAC 15434
Obed Hussey, who, of all inventors, made bread cheap; being a true record of his life and struggles to introduce his greatest invention, the reaper, and its success, as gathered from pamphlets published heretofore by some of his friends and associates, and reprinted in this volume, together with some additional facts and testimonials from other sources. [Rochester, N. Y., The Rochester herald publishing company] 1912.
Greeno, Follett Lamberton, 1889–   ed.

LAC 40033
Oberlin. Its origin, progress and results. An address, prepared for the alumni of Oberlin college, assembled August 22, 1860. By Pres. J. H. Fairchild. Oberlin, R. Butler, printer, 1871.
Fairchild, James Harris, 1817–1902.

LAC 10786
Oberlin: the colony and the college. 1833–1883. Oberlin, O., E. J. Goodrich, 1883.
Fairchild, James Harris, 1817–1902.

LAC 40011
The obligation of the state to provide for the education of its citizens; the extent of the obligation; and the grounds on which it rests. Education and the state: an address delivered before the Regents of the University of the state of New York at their first annual commencement, held in the state capitol at Albany, July 10, 1879. New York, The S. W. Green typesetting machines, 1879.
Barnard, Frederick Augustus Porter, 1809–1889.

LAC 16024

Observations in husbandry. London, Printed by J. Hughs [etc.] 1757.
Lisle, Edward, 1666?–1722.

LAC 40119

Observations leading to a fair examination of the system of government, proposed by the late convention; and to several essential and necessary alterations in it. In a number of letters from the Federal farmer to the Republican. [New-York] Printed in the year M.DCC.LXXXVII.
Lee, Richard Henry, 1732–1794.

LAC 40080

Observations on Mr. Stedman's History of the American war. By Lieutenant-General Sir Henry Clinton, K. B. London, Printed for J. Debrett, 1794.
Clinton, *Sir* Henry, 1738?–1795.

LAC 10757

Observations on penal jurisprudence, and the reformation of criminals. With an appendix; containing the latest reports of the state-prisons or penitentiaries of Philadelphia, New-York, and Massachusetts; and other documents. London, Printed for T. Cadell and W. Davies [etc.] 1819.
Roscoe, William, 1753–1831.

LAC 12192

Observations on professions, literature, manners, and emigration, in the United States and Canada, made during a residence there in 1832. By the Rev. Isaac Fidler. New York, J. & J. Harper, 1833.
Fidler, Isaac,

LAC 40065

Observations on public principles and characters; with reference to recent events [in the U.S.] November, 1820. [n.p., 1820]

LAC 15694

Observations on some parts of the Answer of Earl Cornwallis to Sir Henry Clinton's Narrative. To which is added an appendix: containing extracts of letters and other papers, to which reference is necessary. London, Printed for J. Debrett, 1783.
Clinton, *Sir* Henry, 1738?–1795.

LAC 40089

Observations on the aboriginal monuments of the Mississippi Valley; the character of the ancient earthworks, and the structure, contents, and purposes of the mounds; with notices of the minor remains of ancient art... [New York, Bartlett & Welford, 1848]
Squier, Ephraim George, 1821–1888.

LAC 40040

Observations on the act of Parliament commonly called the Boston port-bill; with thoughts on civil society and standing armies. By Josiah Quincy, jun'r. Boston: N. E. Printed for and sold by Edes and Gill, in Queen-Street, 1774.
Quincy, Josiah, 1744–1775.

LAC 40135

Observations on the agriculture of the United States of America. London, W. Bulmer and co., 1801.
Strickland, William, *of Yorkshire.*

LAC 40056

Observations on the American treaty. First published in "The Sun," under the signature of Decius. London, J. Budd, 1808.
Courtenay, Thomas Peregrine, 1782–1841.

LAC 13792

Observations on the charter and conduct of the Society for the propagation of the gospel in foreign parts; designed to shew their non-conformity to each other. With remarks on the mistakes of East Apthorp, M. A., missionary at Cambridge, in quoting, and representing the sense of said charter, &c. As also various incidental reflections relative to the Church of England, and the state of religion in North-America, particularly in New-England. By Jonathan Mayhew, D. D., pastor of the West-church in Boston. Boston, New-England: Printed by Richard and Samuel Draper, in Newbury-street, Edes and Gill, in Queen-street, and Thomas and John Fleet at the Heart and crown in Cornhill, M,DCC,LXIII.
Mayhew, Jonathan, 1720–1766.

LAC 40106

Observations on the commerce of the American states with Europe and the West Indies; including the several articles of import and export. Philadelphia, R. Bell, 1783.
Sheffield, John Baker Holroyd, *1st earl of,* 1735–1821.

LAC 40089

Observations on the Creek and Cherokee Indians. By William Bartram. 1789. With prefatory and supplementary notes. By E. G. Squier. [New-York, G. P. Putnam, 1853]
Bartram, William, 1739–1823.

LAC 10682

Observations on the dispute between the United States and France, addressed by Robert Goodloe Harper, esq., one of the representatives in Congress for the state of South Carolina to his constituents, in May, 1797... 2d ed. Philadelphia, printed; London, Reprinted by direction of the editor, at the Philanthropic press, 1798.
Harper, Robert Goodloe, 1765–1825.

LAC 16892

Observations on the distinguishing views and practices of the Society of Friends. 2d American, from the 7th London ed. New York, S. S. & W. Wood, 1856.
Gurney, Joseph John, 1788–1847.

LAC 40056

Observations on the fifth article of the treaty with America; and on the necessity of appointing a judicial enquiry into the merits and losses of the American loyalists. Printed by order of their agents. [London] 1783.
Galloway, Joseph, 1731–1803.

LAC 13729

Observations on the financial position and credit of such of the states of the North American Union as have contracted public debts... London, Longman, Orme, Brown, Green, and Longmans, 1839.
Trotter, Alexander.

LAC 12659

Observations on the geology of the United States of America; with some remarks on the effect produced on the nature and fertility of soils, by the decomposition of the different classes of rocks; and an application to the fertility of every state in the Union, in reference to the accompanying geological map... Philadelphia, Printed for the author by A. Small, 1817.
Maclure, William, 1763–1840.

LAC 40089

Observations on the Indian language, by Experience Mayhew. Now published from the original ms. by John S. H. Fogg, Boston [Press of D. Clapp & son] 1884.
Mayhew, Experience, 1673–1758.

LAC 14492

Observations on the inhabitants, climate, soil, rivers, productions, animals, and other matters worthy of notice. Made by Mr. John Bartram, in his travels from Pensilvania to Onondago, Oswego and the Lake Ontario, in Canada. To which is annex'd, a curious account of the cataracts at Niagara. By Mr. Peter Kalm. London, Printed for J. Whiston and B. White, 1751.
Bartram, John, 1699–1777.

LAC 40068

Observations on the inslaving, importing and purchasing of negroes; with some advice thereon, extracted from the epistle of the yearly-meeting of the people called Quakers held at London in the year 1748... 2d ed. Germantown: Printed by Christopher Sower, 1760.
Benezet, Anthony, 1713–1784.

LAC 40085

Observations on the late and present conduct of the French, with regard to their encroachments upon the British colonies in North America. Together with remarks on the importance of these colonies to Great-Britain. Boston: printed and sold by S. Kneeland in Queen-street, 1755. Tarrytown, N. Y., Reprinted, W. Abbatt, 1917.
Clarke, William, M. D., fl. 1755.

LAC 15827

Observations on the means of preserving the health of soldiers and sailors; and on the duties of the Medical department of the army and navy: with remarks on hospitals and their internal arrangement. Philadelphia: Printed for Thomas Dobson, at the Stone house, no. 41, South second street. Fry and Kammerer, printers, 1808.
Cutbush, Edward.

LAC 40119

Observations on the new Constitution, and on the federal and state conventions. By a Columbian patriot. Boston printed, New-York re-printed, 1788.
Warren, Mercy, 1728–1814.

LAC 40071

Observations on the pernicious practice of the law. As published occasionally in the Independent chronicle, in the year 1786, and republished at the request of a number of respectable citizens. With an address never before published. Corrected and amended. By Honestus [pseud.] With remarks on the rights of jury as judges of law and evidence. Boston, Printed by True & Weston, 1819.
Austin, Benjamin, 1752–1820.

LAC 40104

Observations on the river Potomack, the country adjacent, and the city of Washington. New-York: Printed by Samuel Loudon and Son, No. 5, Water-street, 1793 [reprinted 1905]
Lear, Tobias, 1762–1816.

LAC 40133

Observations on the slavery of the Africans and their descendants, and on the use of the produce of their labour. Recommended to the serious perusal, and impartial consideration of the citizens of the United States of America, and others concerned. New-York, S. Wood, 1814.
Hicks, Elias, 1748–1830.

LAC 40147

Observations upon certain passages in Mr. Jefferson's Notes on Virginia, which appear to have a tendency to subvert religion, and establish a false philosophy. New-York, 1804.
Moore, Clement Clarke, 1779–1863.

LAC 40149

Observations upon the government of the United States of America. Boston, Printed and sold by S. Hall, 1791.
Sullivan, James, 1744–1808.

LAC 15893

Observations upon the Peloponnesus and Greek islands, made in 1829. Boston, Crocker and Brewster; New-York, J. Leavitt, 1830.
Anderson, Rufus, 1796–1880.

LAC 12153

Occasional productions, political, diplomatic, and miscellaneous. Including, among others, a glance at the court and government of Louis Philippe and the French revolution of 1848, while the author resided as envoy extraordinary and minister plenipotentiary from the United States at Paris. By the late Richard Rush. Edited by his executors. Philadelphia, J. B. Lippincott & co., 1860.
Rush, Richard, 1780–1859.

LAC 13404

The occupational diseases; their causation, symptoms, treatment and prevention. New York and London, D. Appleton and company, 1914.
Thompson, William Gilman, 1856–1927.

LAC 13208

Ocean to ocean on horseback; being the story of a tour in the saddle from the Atlantic to the Pacific; with especial reference to the early history and development of cities and towns along the route; and regions traversed beyond the Mississippi... By Captain Willard Glazier. Philadelphia, P. W. Ziegler company [c1895]
Glazier, Willard, 1841–1905.

LAC 40046

Octavius Brooks Frothingham and the new faith. New York, G. P. Putnam's sons, 1876.
Stedman, Edmund Clarence, 1833–1908.

LAC 40054

The octoroon. Original complete edition. London, J. Dicks [n.d.]
Boucicault, Dion, 1820?–1890.

LAC 15273

Oddities of colonial legislation in America, as applied to the public lands, primitive education, religion, morals, Indians, etc., etc., with authentic records of the origin and growth of pioneer settlements, embracing also a condensed history of the states and territories, with a summary of the territorial expansion, civil progress and development of the nation. Indianapolis, R. Douglass, 1879.
Dillon, John Brown, 1808?–1879.

LAC 12134

Of the newe landes and of ye people founde
The first three English books on America. (?1511)–1555 A. D. Being chiefly translations, compilations, &c.,

by Richard Eden, from the writings, maps, &c., of Pietro Martire, of Anghiera (1455–1526) ... Sebastian Munster, the cosmographer (1489–1552) ... Sebastian Cabot, of Bristol (1474–1557) ... with extracts, &c., from the works of other Spanish, Italian, and German writers of the time. Ed. by Edward Arber. Birmingham [Printed by Turnbull & Spears, Edinburgh] 1885.
Arber, Edward, 1836–1912, *ed.*

LAC 40069
Of the rate of interest; and of its influence on the relations of capital and labor. Speech of H. C. Carey in the Constitutional convention of Pennsylvania, May 15, 1873. Philadelphia, Collins, printer, 1873.
Carey, Henry Charles, 1793–1879.

LAC 16317
Offenbach in America. Notes of a travelling musician. By Jacques Offenbach. With a biographical preface by Albert Wolff. Translated from advance sheets of the original Paris edition. New York, G. W. Carleton & co.; Paris, C. Levy, 1877.
Offenbach, Jacques, 1819–1880.

LAC 12567
The Office and Duty of Sheriffs.
Conductor Generalis: or, the Office, Duty and Authority of Justices of the Peace, High-Sheriffs, Under-Sheriffs, Coroners, Constables, Goalers [!] Jury-Men, and Overseers of the Poor. As also, the Office of Clerks of Assize and of the Peace, &c. To which are added, Several Choice Maxims in Law, &c. Compiled chiefly from Burn's Justice, and the several other Books on those Subjects. By James Parker, Esquire, late Justice of the Peace in Middlesex County, in New Jersey. Adapted to these United States. The whole Alphabetically digested under the several Titles; with a Table directing to the ready finding out the proper Matter under those Titles. New-York: Printed by John Patterson, for Robert Hodge, 1788.

LAC 40043
The office of mayor in the United States; a study in administrative law... [New York?] 1895.
Bayles, George James, 1869–1914.

LAC 23335–36
Official correspondence of the Texan revolution, 1835–1836. New York, London, D. Appleton-Century company, incorporated [c1936]
Binkley, William Campbell, 1889–   *ed.*

LAC 11294
Official documents, addresses, etc., of George Opdyke, mayor of the city of New York during the years 1862 and 1863. New York, Hurd and Houghton, 1866.
New York (*City*) *Mayor, 1862–1864 (George Opdyke)*

LAC 15324
Official illustrated catalogue, fine arts exhibit, United States of America, Paris exposition of 1900. Boston, Noyes, Platt & company [c1900]
U.S. *Commission to the Paris Exposition, 1900. Dept. of Fine Arts.*

LAC 40059
Official journal of the conference convention, held at Washington city, February, 1861. By Crafts J. Wright, secretary. Washington, M'Gill & Witherow, printers, 1861.
Washington, D. C. Peace Conference, 1861.

LAC 14345
Official journal of the Constitutional convention of the state of Alabama, held in the city of Montgomery, commencing on Tuesday, November 5th, A. D. 1867. Montgomery, Ala., Barrett & Brown, printers, 1868.
Alabama. *Constitutional Convention, 1867.*

LAC 14720
Official journal of the proceedings of the Constitutional convention of the state of Louisiana, held in New Orleans, Tuesday, February 8, 1898. And calendar. By authority. New Orleans, Printed by H. J. Hearsey, 1898.
Louisiana. *Constitutional Convention, 1898.*

LAC 14719
Official journal of the proceedings of the Convention, for framing a constitution for the state of Louisiana. By authority. New Orleans, J. B. Roudanez & co., printers to the Convention, 1867–1868.
Louisiana. *Constitutional Convention, 1867–1868.*

LAC 20776–78
Official letter books of W. C. C. Claiborne, 1801–1816; ed. by Dunbar Rowland. Jackson, Miss., State department of archives and history, 1917.
Claiborne, William Charles Cole, 1775–1817.

LAC 14250
Official letters of the military and naval officers of the United States, during the war with Great Britain in the years 1812, 13, 14, & 15. With some additional letters and documents elucidating the history of that period. Collected and arranged by John Brannan. Washington city, Printed by Way & Gideon, for the editor, 1823.
Brannan, John, *comp.*

LAC 21684–706
Official opinions of the attorneys general of the United States, advising the President and heads of departments in relation to their official duties... v. 1–25 [Aug. 21, 1791–Dec. 1906] Washington, U.S. Govt. print. off. [etc.] 1852–1906.
U.S. *Dept. of Justice.*

LAC 12764–65
Official proceedings of the Constitutional convention of the state of Alabama, held in the city of Montgomery, commencing May 21st, 1901. With an index prepared by the secretary. Montgomery, The Brown printing company, 1901.
Alabama. *Constitutional Convention, 1901.*

LAC 11443
Official proceedings of the Democratic national convention held in Chicago, Ill., July 7th, 8th, 9th, 10th and 11th, 1896. Containing, also, the preliminary proceedings of the Democratic national committee, etc. with an appendix... Reported for the Convention by Edward B. Dickinson, official stenographer. Logansport, Ind., Wilson, Humphreys & co., 1896.
Democratic Party. *National Convention, Chicago, 1896.*

LAC 40023
Official proceedings of the Mississippi Valley railroad convention, held at the Varieties' theatre, in St. Louis, Monday and Tuesday, 15th & 16th Nov., 1852, together with the memorial to Congress, and address to the people of the Mississippi Valley, ordered by said convention. Also, the official proceedings of the North Missouri railroad convention, held at the court house, in St. Charles, Wednesday, the 10th November, 1852, with their memorial to Congress, asking for a grant of land. St. Louis, Printed by M. Niedner [1852]
Mississippi Valley Railroad Convention, *St. Louis,* 1852.

LAC 12448
Official proceedings of the National Democratic convention, held in Chicago, Ill., July 8th, 9th, 10th, and 11th, 1884. Containing also, the preliminary proceedings of the National Democratic committee and the Committee of arrangements, with an appendix... Reported for the Convention by Edward B. Dickinson, official stenographer. New York, D. Taylor's Democratic printing house [1884]
Democratic Party. *National Convention, Chicago,* 1884.

LAC 12450
Official proceedings of the National Democratic convention, held in Chicago, Ill., June 21st, 22nd and 23rd, 1892. Containing, also, the preliminary proceedings of the National Democratic committee and the Committee of arrangements, with an appendix... Reported for the Convention by Edward B. Dickinson, official stenographer. Chicago, Cameron, Amberg & co., 1892.
Democratic Party. *National Convention, Chicago,* 1892.

LAC 22140–74
Official records of the Union and Confederate armies.
The war of the rebellion: a compilation of the official records of the Union and Confederate armies. Pub. under the direction of the ... secretary of war. Washington, Govt. print. off., 1880–1901.
U.S. *War Dept.*

LAC 23758–96
Official records of the Union and Confederate Navies in the War of the Rebellion. ser. 1, v. 1–27; ser. 2, v. 1–3. Washington, Govt. Print. Off., 1894–1927.
U.S. *Naval War Records Office.*

LAC 40037
Official report of Gen. John O'Neill, president of the Fenian brotherhood; on the attempt to invade Canada, May 25th, 1870. The preparations therefor, and the cause of its failure, with a sketch of his connection with the organization, and the motives which led him to join it: also a report of the battle of Ridgeway, Canada West, fought June 2d, 1866... New York, J. J. Foster, 1870.
O'Neill, John, 1834–1878.

LAC 21345–47
Official report of the debates and proceedings in the State convention, assembled May 4th, 1853, to revise and amend the constitution of the commonwealth of Massachusetts. Boston, White & Potter, printers, 1853.
Massachusetts, *Constitutional Convention,* 1853.

LAC 12773
Official report of the debates and proceedings in the Constitutional convention of the state of Nevada, assembled at Carson City, July 4, 1864, to form a constitution and state government. Andrew J. Marsh, official reporter. San Francisco, F. Eastman, printer, 1866.
Nevada. *Constitutional Convention,* 1864.

LAC 40099
Official report of the Niger Valley exploring party. By M. R. Delany, chief commissioner to Africa. New York, T. Hamilton; [etc., etc.] 1861.
Niger Valley Exploring Party.

LAC 22490–97
Official report of the proceedings and debates in the Convention assembled at Frankfort, on the eighth day of September, 1890, to adopt, amend, or change the constitution of the state of Kentucky... Frankfort, Ky., E. P. Johnson, printer to the Convention, 1890 [1891]
Kentucky. *Constitutional Convention,* 1890–1891.

LAC 21190–92
Official report of the proceedings and debates of the convention assembled at Salt Lake City on the fourth day of March 1895, to adopt a constitution for the state of Utah. Salt Lake City, Star printing company, 1898.
Utah. *Constitutional Convention,* 1895.

LAC 13744–45
Official report of the proceedings and debates of the first Constitutional convention of North Dakota, assembled in the city of Bismarck, July 4th to Aug. 17th, 1889. R. M. Tuttle, official stenographer. Bismarck, N. D., Tribune, state printers, 1889.
North Dakota. *Constitutional Convention.* 1889.

LAC 22674–79
Official report of the proceedings and debates of the Third constitutional convention of Ohio, assembled in the city of Columbus, on Tuesday, May 13, 1873. J. G. Adel, official reporter. Cleveland, W. S. Robison & co., printers to the Convention, 1873–74.
Ohio. *Constitutional Convention,* 1873–1874.

LAC 11444
Official report of the proceedings of the Democratic national convention held in St. Louis, Mo., July 6, 7, 8, and 9, 1904, resulting in the nomination of Hon. Alton B. Parker (of New York) for president and Hon. Henry G. Davis (of West Virginia) for vice-president. Reported by Milton W. Blumenberg. [New York, Press of the publishers' printing company, 1904?]
Democratic Party. *National Convention, St. Louis,* 1904.

LAC 12857
An official report of the trials of sundry Negroes, charged with an attempt to raise an insurrection in the state of South Carolina: preceded by an introduction and narrative; and in an appendix, a report of the trials of four white persons on indictments for attempting to excite the slaves to insurrection. Prepared and published at the request of the court. By Lionel H. Kennedy & Thomas Parker. Charleston, Printed by James R. Schenck, 1822.
Kennedy, Lionel H.

LAC 13769–70
Official reports of the debates and proceedings of the Ohio state convention, called to alter, revise or amend the constitution of the state, held at Columbus, commencing May 6, 1850, and at Cincinnati, commencing December 2, 1850. Reported by J. V. Smith, official reporter to the Convention. Columbus, Printed by Scott & Bascom, 1851.
Ohio. *Constitutional Convention,* 1850–1851.

LAC 10021
Official retrospective exhibition of the development of harvesting machinery for the Paris exposition of 1900. Made by Deering harvester company, Chicago, U. S. A. Paris [Chicago, R. R. Donnelley & sons co., printers, 1900?]
Deering Harvester Company.

LAC 20076–77
Ohio falls cities.
History of the Ohio falls cities and their counties, with illustrations and bibliographical sketches... Cleveland, O., L. A. Williams & co., 1882.

LAC 22461–63
Ohio in the war: her statesmen, her generals, and soldiers. Cincinnati, New York, Moore, Wilstach & Baldwin, 1868.
Reid, Whitelaw, 1837–1912.

LAC 14012
Oil-finding; an introduction to the geological study of petroleum, by E. H. Cunningham Craig. With an introduction by Sir Boverton Redwood, bart. London, E. Arnold; New York, Longmans, Green and co. [1912]
Cunningham-Craig, Edward Hubert, 1874–

LAC 16262
The oil regions of Pennsylvania. Showing where petroleum is found; how it is obtained, and at what cost... New York, Harper & brothers, 1865.
Wright, William, 1824–1866.

LAC 40051
The Ojibway conquest, a tale of the Northwest. By Kah-ge-ga-gah-bowh, or G. Copway, chief of the Ojibway nation. New York, G. P. Putnam, 1850.
Clark, Julius Taylor, 1814–1908.

LAC 40003
The old and new ideal of scholars; a baccalaureate address delivered June 18, 1905. Ann Arbor, Mich., The University, 1905.
Angell, James Burrill, 1829–1916.

LAC 14759
The old and new Republican parties: their origin, similitude and progress from the administration of Washington to that of Chester A. Arthur. With a biographical sketch of James A. Garfield. Boston, A. C. Getchell, 1881.
Allen, Stephen Merrill, 1819–1894.

LAC 10962
Old and new Unitarian belief. Boston, G. H. Ellis, 1894.
Chadwick, John White, 1840–1904.

LAC 12122
The Old bachelor... [2d ed.] Printed at the Enquirer press, Richmond, Virginia: for Thomas Ritchie & Fielding Lucas. 1814.

LAC 11589
The old brewery, and the new mission house at the Five Points. By the ladies of the mission... New York, Stringer & Townsend, 1854.

LAC 15040
Old Catholic Maryland and its early Jesuit missionaries. Swedesboro, N. J. [1889]
Treacy, William P.

LAC 20763–64
Old churches, ministers and families of Virginia. By Bishop Meade. Philadelphia, J. B. Lippincott & co., 1857.
Meade, William, *bp.*, 1789–1862.

LAC 20315
The old colonial system, 1660–1754. New York, The Macmillan company, 1912.
Beer, George Louis, 1872–1920.

LAC 11856
Old Creole days. New York, C. Scribner's sons, 1879.
Cable, George Washington, 1844–1925.

LAC 15629
Old days in Chapel Hill, being the life and letters of Cornelia Phillips Spencer. With illustration by the author. Chapel Hill, The University of North Carolina press; [etc., etc.] 1926.
Chamberlain, Hope Summerell.

LAC 13512
Old Deadwood days. New York, J. H. Sears & company, inc. [c1928]
Bennett, Estelline.

LAC 14970
Old diary leaves, the true story of the Theosophical society. New York and London, G. P. Putnam's sons; [etc., etc.] 1895.
Olcott, Henry Steel, 1832–1907.

LAC 16490
The Old Dominion; her making and her manners. New York, C. Scribner's sons, 1914, [c1908]
Page, Thomas Nelson, 1853–1922.

LAC 12202
Old Drury of Philadelphia; a history of the Philadelphia stage, 1800–1835 [edited] by Reese D. James. Philadelphia, University of Pennsylvania Press, 1932.
Wood, William Burke, 1779–1861.

LAC 12157
Old England and New England, in a series of views taken on the spot. Two volumes of the London ed. complete in one. London, R. Bentley; Philadelphia, Reprinted by A. Hart, late Carey and Hart, 1853.
Bunn, Alfred, 1796?–1860.

LAC 22890
Old family letters: copied from the originals for Alexander Biddle... Series A[–B.] Philadelphia, Press of J. B. Lippincott company, 1892.

LAC 11426
An old-fashioned senator: Orville H. Platt, of Connecticut; the story of a life unselfishly devoted to the public service. New York and London, G. P. Putnam's sons, 1910.
Coolidge, Louis Arthur, 1861–1925.

LAC 12001
Old friends and new. Boston, Houghton, Osgood and company, 1879.
Jewett, Sarah Orne, 1849–1909.

LAC 15853
Old homes of new Americans; the country and the people of the Austro-Hungarian monarchy and their contribution to the New world. With illustrations from photographs. Boston and New York, Houghton Mifflin company, 1913.
Clark, Francis Edward, 1851–1927.

LAC 15034
The old Indian chronicle: being a collection of exceeding rare tracts, written and published in the time of King Philip's war, by persons residing in the country. To which are now added an introduction and notes, by Samuel G. Drake. Boston, S. A. Drake, 1867.
Drake, Samuel Gardner, 1798–1875, *ed.*

LAC 16528
Old Jules. Boston, Little, Brown, and company, 1935.
Sandoz, Mari, 1907–1966.

LAC 14448
Old Kent: the eastern shore of Maryland; notes illustrative of the most ancient records of Kent County, Maryland, and of the parishes of St. Paul's, Shrewsbury and I. U., and genealogical histories of old and distinguished families of Maryland, and their connections by marriage, &c., with an introduction. Baltimore, Regional Pub. co., 1967.
Hanson, George Adolphus.

LAC 20035–36
The old merchants of New York city. By Walter Barrett, clerk [*pseud.*] [First–fifth series] New York, Carleton, 1863–89.
Scoville, Joseph Alfred, 1811–1864.

LAC 14527
The old national road; a chapter of American expansion. Columbus, F. J. Heer, 1901.
Hulbert, Archer Butler, 1873–

LAC 14053
Old New England churches and their children, by Dolores Bacon [*pseud.*] Thirty-three illustrations in photogravure and half-tone, from photographs. New York, Doubleday, Page & company, 1906.
Bacon, Mary Schell, 1870–

LAC 13224
The Old Northwest; the beginnings of our colonial system. Rev. ed. Boston, New York [etc.] Silver, Burdett and company [c1899]
Hinsdale, Burke Aaron, 1837–1900.

LAC 11247
The old order changeth; a view of American democracy. New York, The Macmillan company, 1910.
White, William Allen, 1868–

LAC 10209
The old pike. A history of the National road, with incidents, accidents, and anecdotes thereon. Illustrated. Uniontown, Pa., The author, 1894.
Searight, Thomas Brownfield.

LAC 13236
The old Santa Fe trail; the story of a great highway, by Colonel Henry Inman. New York, The Macmillan company; London, Macmillan & co., ltd., 1897.
Inman, Henry, 1837–1899.

LAC 15973
The old silver of American churches. Letchworth, England. Priv. print. for the National society of colonial dames of America, at the Arden press, 1913.
Jones, Edward Alfred, 1872–1943.

LAC 40096
The old South. Addresses delivered before the Confederate survivors' association in Augusta, Georgia, on the occasion of its ninth annual reunion, on Memorial day, April 26, 1887, by his excellency, Governor John B. Gordon, and by Col: Charles C. Jones, jr. Printed by order of the association. Augusta, Ga., Chronicle publishing company, 1887.
Gordon, John Brown, 1832–1904.

LAC 14151
The old South and the new. A series of letters by Hon. William D. Kelley. New York and London, G. P. Putnam's sons, 1888.
Kelley, William Darrah, 1814–1890.

LAC 12371
The old South: essays social and political. New York, C. Scribner's sons, 1896, [c1892]
Page, Thomas Nelson, 1853–1922.

LAC 20267–68
Old time notes of Pennsylvania; a connected and chronological record of the commercial, industrial and educational advancement of Pennsylvania, and the inner history of all political movements since the adoption of the constitution of 1838. Illustrated with portraits of over one hundred distinguished men of Pennsylvania, including all the governors, senators, judges of the courts of today, leading statesmen, railroad presidents, business men and others of note. Autograph ed. Philadelphia, The J. C. Winston company, 1905.
McClure, Alexander Kelly, 1828–1909.

LAC 10600
Old-time schools and school-books. With many illustrations collected by the author. New York, The Macmillan company; London, Macmillan & co., ltd., 1904.
Johnson, Clifton, 1865–1940.

LAC 16468
Old times on the upper Mississippi; the recollections of a steamboat pilot from 1854 to 1863. Cleveland, O., The A. H. Clark company, 1909, [c1908]
Merrick, George Byron, 1841–1931.

LAC 15550
The Old world in the New; the significance of past and present immigration to the American people. Illustrated with many photographs. New York, The Century co., 1914.
Ross, Edward Alsworth, 1866–1951.

LAC 23314–15
The Olden time; a monthly publication devoted to the preservation of documents and other authentic infor-

mation in relation to the early explorations and the settlement and improvement of the country around the head of the Ohio... Ed. by Neville B. Craig, esq. Pittsburgh, Dumars & co. [etc.] 1846–48; Cincinnati, Reprinted by R. Clarke & co., 1876.

LAC 15842
Olden-time music; a compilation from newspapers and books, by Henry M. Brooks. With an introduction by Professor Edward S. Morse. Boston, Ticknor and company, 1888.
Brooks, Henry Mason, 1822–1898.

LAC 16261
The oldest and the newest empire: China and the United States. Hartford, Conn., S. S. Scranton and company, 1870.
Speer, William, 1822–1904.

LAC 12987
The oldest school in America. An oration by Phillips Brooks, D. D., and a poem by Robert Grant, at the celebration of the two hundred and fiftieth anniversary of the foundation of the Boston Latin school, April 23, 1885. Boston and New York, Houghton, Mifflin and company, 1885.
Boston Latin School Association.

LAC 15500
Ole Bull, a memoir; with Ole Bull's Violin notes and A. B. Crosby's Anatomy of the violinist. Boston, Houghton Mifflin, 1886, [c1882]
Bull, Sara Chapman, 1850–1911.

LAC 40105
Ole Rynning's True account of America, translated and edited by Theodore C. Blegen. [St. Paul, Minnesota Historical society, 1917]
Rynning, Ole, 1809–1838.

LAC 40129
Oleomargarine butter: the new article of commerce. Chemically analyzed by the most skillful and distinguished scientists, demonstrating its purity... New York, Commercial manufacturing company, 1880.
Commercial Manufacturing Company.

LAC 15426
The olive branch, or Faults on both sides, Federal and Democratic. A serious appeal on the necessity of mutual forgiveness and harmony, to save our common country from ruin. 3d ed., greatly enl. and improved. Boston: Reprinted by Rowe and Hooper, Feb. 1815.
Carey, Mathew, 1760–1839.

LAC 13606
Oliver Wendell Holmes, poet, litterateur, scientist. Boston, S. E. Cassino and company, 1883.
Kennedy, William Sloane, 1850–1929.

LAC 11424
Omitted chapters of history disclosed in the life and papers of Edmund Randolph, governor of Virginia; first attorney-general United States, secretary of state. 2d ed. New York & London, G. P. Putnam's sons, 1889, [c1888]
Conway, Moncure Daniel, 1832–1907.

LAC 14461
On becoming an American; some meditations of a newly naturalized immigrant. Boston, Marshall Jones company, 1919.
Bridges, Horace James, 1880–

LAC 11211
On civil liberty and self-government. Enl. ed. in one volume. Philadelphia, J. B. Lippincott, 1859.
Lieber, Francis, 1800–1872.

LAC 40061
On criminal abortion; a lecture introductory to the course on obstetrics, and diseases of women and children. University of Pennsylvania, session 1854-5. By Hugh L. Hodge, M. D. Philadelphia, T. K. and P. G. Collins, printers, 1854.
Hodge, Hugh Lenox, 1796–1873.

LAC 14987
On representative government and personal representation. Based in part upon Thomas Hare's treatise, entitled "The election of representatives, parliamentary and municipal". Philadelphia, J. B. Lippincott & co., 1871.
Sterne, Simon, 1839–1901.

LAC 12349
On Sherman's track; or, The South after the war. London, Seeley, Jackson, and Halliday, 1867.
Kennaway, *Sir* John Henry, *bart.*, 1837–1919.

LAC 40097
On small differences of sensation... By C. S. Peirce and J. Jastrow. [Washington, Govt. print. off., 1885]
Peirce, Charles Santiago Sanders, 1839–1914.

LAC 11777
On sugar cultivation in Louisiana, Cuba, &c., and the British possessions. By an European and colonial sugar manufacturer. London, P. Ollivier, 1848.
Leon, John A

LAC 15917
On the arrangement, care, and operation of woodworking factories and machinery: forming a complete operator's handbook. New York, E. & F. N. Spon, 1885.
Richards, John, 1834–

LAC 13186
On the discovery of the Mississippi, and on the southwestern, Oregon, and north-western boundary of the United States. With a translation from the original ms. of memoirs, etc. relating to the discovery of the Mississippi, by Robert Cavelier de La Salle and the Chevalier Henry de Tonty. London, S. Clarke, 1844.
Falconer, Thomas, 1805–1882.

LAC 40028
On the duty of females to promote the cause of peace, by Philanthropos [*pseud.*] Boston, American peace society, 1836.
Ladd, William, 1778–1841.

LAC 40104
On the enforcement of law in cities; a reply to a letter from representatives of the Federation of churches. 2d ed. Toledo [O.] Rosengarten & co., 1910.
Whitlock, Brand, 1869–1934.

LAC 40116

On the evils of a weak government. A sermon, preached on the general election at Hartford, in Connecticut, May 8, 1800. By John Smalley, A. M., pastor of a church in Berlin. Hartford: Printed by Hudson and Goodwin, 1800.
Smalley, John, 1734–1820.

LAC 14352

On the great highway; the wanderings and adventures of a special correspondent. Boston, Lothrop publishing company [c1901]
Creelman, James, 1859–1915.

LAC 40003

On the growth of American colleges and their present tendency to the study of science. Boston, American institute of instruction, 1871.
Gilman, Daniel Coit, 1831–1908.

LAC 40128

On the influence of trades, professions, and occupations in the United States, in the production of disease. Albany, E. W. and C. Skinner, 1837.
McCready, Benjamin William, 1813–1892.

LAC 13991

On the mental illumination and moral improvement of mankind; or, An inquiry into the means by which a general diffusion of knowledge and moral principle may be promoted. Illustrated with engravings. Philadelphia, Key & Biddle, 1836.
Dick, Thomas, 1774–1857.

LAC 40142

On the origin of the native races of America. A dissertation by Hugo Grotius. To which is added a Treatise on foreign languages and unknown islands. By Peter Albinus. Tr. from the original Latin, and enriched with biographical notes and illustrations, by Edmund Goldsmid, F. R. H. S. Edinburgh, Priv. print. [London, etc., Unwin bros., printers] 1884.
Grotius, Hugo, 1583–1645.

LAC 13964

On the penitentiary system in the United States, and its application in France; with an appendix on penal colonies, and also, statistical notes. By G. de Beaumont and A. de Tocqueville. Tr. from the French, with an introduction, notes and additions. By Francis Lieber. Philadelphia, Carey, Lea & Blanchard, 1833.
Beaumont de La Bonniniere, Gustave Auguste de, 1802–1866.

LAC 40075

On the present state of political parties in America. Edinburgh and London, W. Blackwood and sons, 1866.
Oliphant, Laurence, 1829–1888.

LAC 40020

On the principles of classification in the animal kingdom; on the structure of the halcyonoid polypi; on the morphology of the *Medusae*. Charleston, S. C., Press of Walker and James, 1850.
Agassiz, Louis, 1807–1873.

LAC 40100

On the production and consumption of cotton. A paper read before the American geographical and statistical society, on the 16th of March, 1865... New York, Printed by the Society, 1865.
Conkling, Frederick Augustus, 1816–1891.

LAC 40130

On the recognition of the Southern confederation. 3d ed. London, R. Bentley, 1862.
Spence, James, *b.* 1816.

LAC 12304

On the Spanish Main; or, Some English forays on the Isthmus of Darien. With a description of the buccaneers and a short account of old-time ships and sailors. With twenty-two illustrations and a map. London, Methuen & co. [1906]
Masefield, John, 1878–1967.

LAC 14544

On the storied Ohio; an historical pilgrimage of a thousand miles in a skiff, from Redstone to Cairo. Being a new and rev. ed. of "Afloat on the Ohio," with new preface, and full-page illustrations from photographs. Chicago, A. C. McClurg & co., 1903.
Thwaites, Reuben Gold, 1853–1913.

LAC 14539

On the threshold. Boston, Houghton, Mifflin and company, 1883.
Munger, Theodore Thornton, 1830–1910.

LAC 20082

On the trail of a Spanish pioneer; the diary and itinerary of Francisco Garces (missionary priest) in his travels through Sonora, Arizona, and California, 1775–1776; translated from an official contemporaneous copy of the original Spanish manuscript, and ed., with copious critical notes, by Elliott Coues. New York, F. P. Harper, 1900.
Garces, Francisco Tomas Hermenegildo, 1738–1781.

LAC 15609

On the trail of the immigrant. New York, Chicago [etc.] F. H. Revell company [c1906]
Steiner, Edward Alfred, 1866–1956.

LAC 13779

One American's opinion of the European war; an answer to Germany's appeals. New ed. with an appendix. New York, E. P. Dutton & company [c1914]
Whitridge, Frederick Wallingford, 1852–1916.

LAC 12584

The one fair woman. London, Chapman and Hall; New York, G. W. Carleton & co., 1876.
Miller, Joaquin, 1841–1913.

LAC 40144

100 selected editorials from the secular press of America on the Zionist movement. New York city, Publicity department (A. H. Fromenson, director) the Zionist organization of America, 1918.
Zionist Organization of America, *New York.*

LAC 14328

One hundred years of medicine and surgery in Missouri; historical and biographical review of the careers of the physicians and surgeons of the state of Missouri, and sketches of some of its notable medical institutions. [St. Louis] St. Louis star, 1900.
Goldstein, Max Aaron, 1870–   *ed.*

LAC 13967

One hundred years of temperance. A memorial volume of the Centennial temperance conference held in Philadelphia, Pa., September, 1885. New York, National temperance society and publication house, 1886.
Centennial Temperance Conference, *Philadelphia*, 1885.

LAC 13717

One hundred years of the African Methodist Episcopal Zion Church; or, The centennial of African Methodism, by Bishop J. W. Hood. New York, A. M. E. Zion Book Concern, 1895.
Hood, James Walker, 1831–1918.

LAC 12084

One of a thousand, a series of biographical sketches of one thousand representative men resident in the commonwealth of Massachusetts, A.D. 1888–'89; comp. under the editorial supervision of John C. Rand. Boston, First national publishing company, 1890.
Rand, John Clark, 1842–   *ed.*

LAC 15516

One of them, chapters from a passionate autobiography. Boston and New York, Houghton Mifflin company [c1918]
Hasanovitz, Elizabeth.

LAC 14455

One thousand homeless men; a study of original records, by Alice Willard Solenberger. New York, Charities publication committee, 1911.
Solenberger, Alice, *d.* 1910.

LAC 40004

One woman's work for farm women; the story of Mary A. Mayo's part in rural social movements. Boston, Whitcomb & Barrows, 1908.
Buell, Jennie.

LAC 10993

The Oneida community: a record of an attempt to carry out the principles of Christian unselfishness and scientific race-improvement. London, G. Redway, 1900.
Estlake, Allan.

LAC 13813

Onward to fame and fortune; or, Climbing life's ladder. Containing seventy-five superb portraits and numerous other illustrations. New York, The Christian herald, 1897.
Thayer, William Makepeace, 1820–1898.

LAC 16274

The open boat, and other tales of adventure. New York, Doubleday & McClure co., 1898.
Crane, Stephen, 1871–1900.

LAC 13280

The opening of the Mississippi; a struggle for supremacy in the American interior. New York, The Macmillan company; London, Macmillan & co., ltd., 1904.
Ogg, Frederic Austin, 1878–1951.

LAC 16843

The operations of the French fleet under the Count de Grasse in 1781–2, as described in two contemporaneous journals. New York, 1864.

LAC 40129

Operatives' reply to ... Jere. Clemens, being a sketch of factory life and factory enterprise, and a brief history of manufacturing by machinery. Lowell, S. J. Varney, 1850.
Farley, Harriet, 1817–1907.

LAC 40084

Opinions respecting the commercial intercourse between the United States of America, and the dominions of Great-Britain, including observations upon the necessity and importance of an American navigation act. By a citizen of Massachusetts. Boston, S. Hall, 1797.
Bowdoin, James, 1752–1811.

LAC 14518

Opportunities for industry and the safe investment of capital; or, A thousand chances to make money. London, S. Low, son, & co., 1859.
Freedley, Edwin Troxell, 1827–1904.

LAC 40021

An oration delivered before the trades union of Boston and vicinity, on Fort Hill, Boston, on the fifty-eighth anniversary of American independence. Boston, C. Douglas, 1834.
Robinson, Frederick.

LAC 16041

Oration delivered in Wallingford, on the 11th of March 1801, before the Republicans of the state of Connecticut, at their general thanksgiving, for the election of Thomas Jefferson to the presidency and of Aaron Burr to the vice presidency of the United States of America. New Haven: Printed by William W. Morse, 1801.
Bishop, Abraham, 1763–1844.

LAC 40066

Oration, in honor of the election of President Jefferson, and the peaceable acquisition of Louisiana, delivered at the National festival, in Hartford, on the 11th of May, 1804. [New Haven] Printed for the general committee of Republicans. From Sidney's press, 1804.
Bishop, Abraham, 1763–1844.

LAC 40132

An oration on the abolition of the slave trade; delivered in the African church, in the city of New-York, January 1, 1808... By Peter Williams, jun., a descendant of Africa. New York: Printed by Samuel Wood, no. 362 Pearl-street, 1808.
Williams, Peter, 1780?–1840.

LAC 40034

An oration on the influence of moral causes on national character, delivered before the Phi Beta Kappa society on their anniversary, 28 August, 1817. By William Crafts, jun. Cambridge [Mass.] University press, Hilliard and Metcalf, 1817.
Crafts, William, 1787–1826.

LAC 40133
An oration upon the moral and political evil of slavery. Delivered at a public meeting of the Maryland society, for promoting the abolition of slavery, and the relief of free negroes, and others unlawfully held in bondage. Baltimore, July 4th, 1791. Baltimore, Printed by Philip Edwards, 1793.
Buchanan, George, 1763-1808.

LAC 21306-9
Orations, addresses and speeches of Chauncey M. Depew; ed. by John Denison Champlin. New York, Priv. print., 1910.
Depew, Chauncey Mitchell, 1834-1928.

LAC 22334-37
Orations and speeches on various occasions... Boston, Little, Brown and co., 1868-70.
Everett, Edward, 1794-1865.

LAC 15160
Orderly book of the three battalions of loyalists, commanded by Brigadier-General Oliver De Lancey, 1776-1778; to which is appended a list of New York loyalists in the city of New York during the war of the revolution – comp. by William Kelby. New York, Printed for the New York historical society, 1917.
De Lancey's Brigade (loyalist) 1776-1778.

LAC 16725
Ordnance manual for the use of the officers of the United States Army [compiled by the Ordnance Board] Washington, J. and G. S. Gideon, printers, 1841.
U.S. *Ordnance Dept.*

LAC 13160
Oregon and Eldorado; or, Romance of the rivers [Columbia and Amazon] Boston, J. E. Tilton and company, 1866.
Bulfinch, Thomas, 1796-1867.

LAC 15101
Oregon and its institutions; comprising a full history of the Willamette university, the first established on the Pacific coast. By Rev. Gustavus Hines. New York, Carlton & Porter [1868]
Hines, Gustavus, 1809-1873.

LAC 16184
The Oregon Territory, and the British North American fur trade. With an account of the habits and customs of the principal native tribes on the northern continent. Philadelphia, G. B. Zieber & co., 1845.
Dunn, John.

LAC 15682
The Oregon territory, its history and discovery, including an account of the convention of the Escurial; also, the treaties and negotiations between the United States and Great Britain, held at various times for the settlement of a boundary line. And an examination of the whole question in respect to facts and the law of nations. New York, D. Appleton & co.; Philadelphia, G. S. Appleton; [etc., etc.] 1846.
Twiss, *Sir* Travers, 1809-1897.

LAC 13135
Oregon; the struggle for possession. 2d ed. Boston, New York, Houghton, Mifflin and company, 1884, [c1883]
Barrows, William, 1815-1891.

LAC 20343-44
Orestes A. Brownson's ... life... Detroit, Mich., H. F. Brownson, 1898-1900.
Brownson, Henry Francis, 1835-1913.

LAC 14736
Organic chemistry in its applications to agriculture and physiology. By Justus Liebig. Ed. from the manuscript of the author by Lyon Playfair. 1st American ed., with an introduction, notes, and appendix, by John W. Webster. Cambridge, J. Owen; Boston, J. Munroe and company; [etc., etc.] 1841.
Liebig, Justus, *freiherr* von, 1803-1873.

LAC 10915
Organic scientific philosophy.
Scientific theism. London, Macmillan and co., 1885.
Abbot, Francis Ellingwood, 1836-1903.

LAC 10504
Organismic theories of the state; nineteenth century interpretations of the state as organism or as person. New York, Columbia university, Longmans, Green & co., agents; [etc., etc.] 1910.
Coker, Francis William, 1878-

LAC 20601
The organization and administration of the Union army, 1861-1865. Cleveland, The Arthur H. Clark company, 1928.
Shannon, Fred Albert, 1893-

LAC 14206
The organization and history of the Chicago, Milwaukee & St. Paul railway company, by John W. Cary, general counsel. [Milwaukee, Wis., Press of Cramer, Aikens & Cramer, 1892?]
Cary, John W   1817-1895.

LAC 40107
Organization of a new Indian territory, east of the Missouri River. Arguments and reasons submitted to the Honorable the members of the Senate and House of representatives of the 31st Congress of the United States: by the Indian chief Kah-ge-ga-gah-bouh, or Geo. Copway. New York, S. W. Benedict, 1850.
Copway, George, *Chippewa chief*, 1818-1863?

LAC 40008
Organization of the agricultural experiment stations in the United States. February, 1889. Washington, Govt. print. off., 1889.
U.S. *Office of Experiment Stations.*

LAC 13388
Organized labor, its problems, purposes and ideals and the present and future of American wage earners. Philadelphia, Pa., American book and Bible house [c1903]
Mitchell, John, 1870-1919.

LAC 40021

Organized labor. Its struggles, its enemies and fool friends. By Samuel Gompers, president, American federation of labor. Washington, D. C., American federation of labor [1904?]
Gompers, Samuel, 1850–1924.

LAC 13734

Organized self-help. A history and defence of the American labor movement. New York, P. Eckler [c1901]
Casson, Herbert Newton, 1869–

LAC 16567

Oriental America. Official and authentic records of the dealings of the United States with the natives of Luzon and their former rulers... Chicago [etc.] Oriental American pub. co., 1899.
Williams, Ora.

LAC 40029

Origin and development of the New York common school system. An address delivered before the New York state teachers' association, at Saratoga Springs, N. Y., Tuesday evening, July 8, 1890. Albany, J. B. Lyon, state printer, 1890.
Draper, Andrew Sloan, 1848–1913.

LAC 14998

The origin and growth of the American Constitution; an historical treatise in which the documentary evidence as to the making of the entirely new plan of federal government embodied in the existing Constitution of the United States is, for the first time, set forth as a complete and consistent whole. Boston and New York, Houghton Mifflin company, 1911.
Taylor, Hannis, 1851–1922.

LAC 14776

Origin and history of the Federal council of the churches of Christ in America. Hartford, Conn., The S. S. Scranton company [c1916]
Sanford, Elias Benjamin, 1843–1932.

LAC 40016

Origin and history of the measures that led to the construction of the Erie canal... Written at the request of the Buffalo historical society, by George Geddes. 1866. Syracuse, Summers & company, 1866.
Geddes, George, 1809–1883.

LAC 40017

The origin and nature of the representative and federative institutions of the United States of America; an anniversary discourse, delivered before the New-York historical society, on the 19th of April, 1832. New-York, G. & C. & H. Carvill, 1832.
Lawrence, William Beach, 1800–1881.

LAC 40121

Origin and objects of the slaveholders' conspiracy against Democratic principles, as well as against the national union–illustrated in the speeches of Andrew Jackson Hamilton, in the statements of Lorenzo Sherwood, ex-member of the Texas Legislature, and in the publications of the Democratic league, &c. The slave aristocracy against democracy. Statements addressed to loyal men of all parties, concerning the antagonistic principles involved in the rebellion–By Henry O'Rielly. New York, Baker & Godwin, printers, 1862.
O'Rielly, Henry, 1806–1886, *ed.*

LAC 14768

The origin and progress of the American party in politics; embracing a complete history of the Philadelphia riots in ... 1844 ... and a refutation of the arguments founded on the charges of religious proscription and secret combinations. Philadelphia, Elliott & Gihon, 1855.
Lee, John Hancock.

LAC 11773

Origin and progress of the order of the Patrons of Husbandry in the United States; a history from 1866 to 1873. Philadelphia, Pa., J. A. Wagenseller, 1875.
Kelley, Oliver Hudson, 1826–1913.

LAC 14711

Origin and traditional history of the Wyandotts, and sketches of other Indian tribes of North America. True traditional stories of Tecumseh and his league, in the years 1811 and 1812. Toronto, Hunter, Rose & co., 1870.
Clarke, Peter Dooyentate.

LAC 40120

Origin, history and principles of the Farmers' educational and co-operative union of America. [Greenfield, Tenn.] National union farmer print [1908?]
Brooks, Thomas Joseph, 1870–

LAC 40062

The origin of the American contest with Great-Britain, or The present political state of the Massachusetts-Bay, in general, and the town of Boston in particular. Exhibiting the rise and progress of the disordered state of that country, in a series of weekly essays, published at Boston, under the signature of Massachusettensis, a native of New-England. New-York, Printed by J. Rivington, 1775.
Leonard, Daniel, 1740–1829.

LAC 40053

Origin of the American navy.
Extracts relating to the origin of the American navy. Boston, The New England historic genealogical society, 1890.
Waite, Henry Edward, *comp.*

LAC 40060

Origin of the Erie canal. Embracing a synopsis of the essays of the Hon. Jesse Hawley, published in 1807. Read before the society, February 21, 1866. [Buffalo, Bigelow Brothers, 1880]
Hawley, Merwin S.

LAC 16019

The origin of the Land grant act of 1862 (the so-called Morrill act) and some account of its author, Jonathan B. Turner. Urbana-Champaign, University press [c1910]
James, Edmund Janes, 1855–1925.

LAC 14921

The origin of the late war: traced from the beginning of the Constitution to the revolt of the southern states. New York, D. Appleton and company, 1866.
Lunt, George, 1803–1885.

LAC 13052

The origin of the moving school in Massachusetts. New York city, Teachers college, Columbia university, 1908.
Updegraff, Harlan, 1874–

LAC 16954
The origin of the national banking system. Washington, Govt. Print. Off., 1910.
Davis, Andrew McFarland, 1833–1920.

LAC 16085
The origin of the national scientific and educational institutions of the United States. New York & London, G. P. Putnam's sons [1890]
Goode, George Brown, 1851–1896.

LAC 15088
The origin of the North American Indians; with a faithful description of their manners and customs ... their religions, languages, dress, and ornaments; including various specimens of Indian eloquence, as well as historical and biographical sketches of almost all the distinguished nations and celebrated warriors, statesmen and orators, among the Indians of North America. New ed., improved and enlarged. Sheldon, Blakeman & co., 1858.
McIntosh, John.

LAC 15063
The origin, progress, and conclusion of the Florida war; to which is appended a record of officers, non-commissioned officers, musicians, and privates of the U.S. army, navy, and marine corps, who were killed in battle or died of disease. As also the names of officers who were distinguished by brevets, and the names of others recommended. Together with the orders for collecting the remains of the dead in Florida, and the ceremony of interment at St. Augustine, East Florida, on the fourteenth day of August, 1842. New York, D. Appleton & company; Philadelphia,G. S. Appleton, 1848.
Sprague, John Titcomb, 1810–1878.

LAC 14224
Origin, rise, and progress of Mormonism. Biography of its founders and history of its church. Personal remembrances and historical collections hitherto unwritten. New York, D. Appleton and company, 1867.
Tucker, Pomeroy, 1802–1870.

LAC 40085
The original account of Capt. John Lovewell's "great fight" with the Indians, at Pequawket, May 8, 1725; by Rev. Thomas Symmes. A new ed. with notes, by Nathaniel Bouton. Concord, N. H., P. B. Cogswell, 1861.
Symmes, Thomas, 1678–1725.

LAC 10932
An original church of Christ: or, A Scriptural vindication of the orders and powers of the ministry of the Methodist Episcopal church. New-York, Published by T. Mason and G. Lane, for the Methodist Episcopal church, 1837.
Bangs, Nathan, 1778–1862.

LAC 22365–68
Original journals of the Lewis and Clark expedition, 1804–1806; printed from the original manuscripts in the library of the American philosophical society and by direction of its committee on historical documents, together with manuscript material of Lewis and Clark from other sources, including note-books, letters, maps, etc., and the journals of Charles Floyd and Joseph Whitehouse, now for the first time published in full and exactly as written; ed., with introduction, notes, and index, by Reuben Gold Thwaites. New York, Dodd, Mead & company, 1904–59.
Lewis, Meriwether, 1774–1809.

LAC 40053
The original steam-boat supported; or, A reply to Mr. James Rumsey's pamphlet. Shewing the true priority of John Fitch, and the false datings, &c. of James Rumsey. Philadelphia, Printed by Z. Poulson, junr., 1788. [Albany, Weed Parsons, 1850]
Fitch, John, 1743–1798.

LAC 12667
Ormsby Macknight Mitchel, astronomer and general; a biographical narrative, by his son F. A. Mitchel. Boston and New York, Houghton, Mifflin and company, 1887.
Mitchel, Frederick Augustus, 1889–1918.

LAC 20885–89
Ornithological biography, or An account of the habits of the birds of the United States of America; accompanied by descriptions of the objects represented in the work entitled The birds of America, and interspersed with delineations of American scenery and manners. Edinburgh, A. Black; [etc., etc.] 1831–1849 [i.e. 1839]
Audubon, John James, 1785–1851.

LAC 10968
Orthodoxy: its truths and errors. 5th ed. Boston, American Unitarian association, 1868, [c1866]
Clarke, James Freeman, 1810–1888.

LAC 16270
The O'Ruddy, a romance by Stephen Crane, and Robert Barr. With frontispiece by C. D. Williams. New York, F. A. Stokes company [c1903]
Crane, Stephen, 1871–1900.

LAC 14928
The other man's country; an appeal to conscience. Philadelphia, J. B. Lippincott company, 1900.
Welsh, Herbert, 1851–1941.

LAC 14167
The other side. A social study based on fact. Cleveland, O., Ingham, Clarke & co.; Washington, D. C., Gray & Clarkson, 1886.
Foran, Martin Ambrose, 1844–1921.

LAC 40057
The other side of the Chinese question; to the people of the United States and the honorable the Senate and House of representatives; testimony of California's leading citizens; read and judge. San Francisco, February, 1886. [San Francisco, Woodward & co., printers, 1886]
Bee, Fred A.

LAC 40040
The other side of the question: or, A defence of the liberties of North-America. In answer to a late Friendly address to all reasonable Americans, on the subject of our political confusions. By a citizen. New-York, Printed by James Rivington, 1774. Tarrytown, N. Y., Reprinted, W. Abbatt, 1916.
Livingston, Philip, 1716–1778.

LAC 16112
The other side of war; with the Army of the Potomac. Letters from the headquarters of the United States sanitary commission during the peninsular campaign in Virginia in 1862. Boston, Ticknor and company, 1889, [c1888]
Wormeley, Katharine Prescott, 1830–1908.

LAC 14424
The other side: or, Notes for the history of the war between Mexico and the United States. Written in Mexico. Translated from the Spanish, and ed., with notes, by Albert C. Ramsey. New York and London, J. Wiley, 1850.
Alcaraz, Ramon.

LAC 12510
Otis' letters in defence of the Hartford convention, and the people of Massachusetts. Boston, S. Gardner, 1824.
Otis, Harrison Gray, 1765–1848.

LAC 16852
Otzinachson; or, A history of the West Branch valley of the Susquehanna: embracing a full account of its settlement-trials and privations endured by the first pioneers-full accounts of the Indian wars, predatory incursions, abductions, massacres, &c., together with an account of the fair play system; and the trying scenes of the big runaway; interspersed with biographical sketches of some of the leading settlers, families, etc., together with pertinent anecdotes, statistics, and much valuable matter entirely new. Philadelphia, H. B. Ashmead, 1857.
Meginness, John Franklin, 1827–1899.

LAC 40051
Ouabi: or The virtues of nature. An Indian tale. In four cantos. By Philenia, a lady of Boston. Printed at Boston, by I. Thomas and E. T. Andrews, at Faust's statue, no. 45, Newbury street, MDCCXC.
Morton, Sarah Wentworth, 1759–1846.

LAC 12796
Ought American slavery to be perpetuated? A debate between Rev. W. G. Brownlow and Rev. A. Pryne. Held at Philadelphia, September, 1858. Philadelphia, Pub. for the authors by J. B. Lippincott & co. [1858]
Brownlow, William Gannaway, 1805–1877.

LAC 40047
Our American artists. With portraits, studios, and engravings of paintings. Boston, D. Lothrop and company [c1879]
Benjamin, Samuel Greene Wheeler, 1837–1914.

LAC 16045
Our army on the Rio Grande. Being a short account of the important events transpiring from the time of the removal of the "Army of occupation" from Corpus Christi, to the surrender of Matamoros; with descriptions of the battles of Palo Alto and Resaca de la Palma, the bombardment of fort Brown, and the ceremonies of the surrender of Matamoros: with descriptions of the city, etc. etc. Illustrated by twenty-six engravings. Philadelphia, Carey and Hart, 1846.
Thorpe, Thomas Bangs, 1815–1878.

LAC 10434
Our benevolent feudalism. New York, The Macmillan company; London, Macmillan & co., ltd., 1902.
Ghent, William James, 1866–1942.

LAC 40057
Our brethren of the tenements and the ghetto. New York, J. S. Ogilvie publishing company [c1899]
McKenna, Mary J.

LAC 16482
Our brother in black: his freedom and his future. New York, Phillips & Hunt; Cincinnati, Walden & Stowe, 1881.
Haygood, Atticus Greene, *Bp.*, 1839–1896.

LAC 13571
Our brothers and cousins: a summer tour in Canada and the States. London, Seeley, Jackson, and Halliday, 1859.
MacGregor, John, 1825–1892.

LAC 40150
Our burden and our strength, or, A comprehensive and popular examination of the debt and resources of our country, present and prospective. New York, Loyal publication society, 1864.
Wells, David Ames, 1828–1898.

LAC 12275
Our Christian heritage. By James, cardinal Gibbons. Baltimore, J. Murphy and company; London, R. Washbourne, 1889.
Gibbons, James, *cardinal*, 1834–1921.

LAC 10811
Our church music... New-York, Dana and company, 1856.
Willis, Richard Storrs, 1819–1900.

LAC 15206
Our colonial curriculum, 1607–1776. Washington, D. C., Capital publishing co., 1907.
Meriwether, Colyer, *d.* 1920.

LAC 13882
Our colonial homes. Boston, Lee and Shepard, 1894.
Drake, Samuel Adams, 1833–1905.

LAC 13003
Our common school system. By Gail Hamilton [*pseud.*] Boston. Estes & Lauriat [c1880]
Dodge, Mary Abigail, 1833–1896.

LAC 15527
Our country: its danger and duty. By Rev. Andrew A. Lipscomb. New-York, American and foreign Christian union, 1857.
Lipscomb, Andrew Adgate, 1816–1890.

LAC 12539
Our country: its possible future and its present crisis. By Rev. Josiah Strong. With an introduction by Prof. Austin Phelps. Rev. ed., based on the census of 1890. New York, Pub. by Baker and Taylor for the American home missionary society [c1891]
Strong, Josiah, 1847–1916.

LAC 13982–83
Our country's wealth and influence. Shown by tracing in historical form from year to year and decade to decade, from 1620 to 1880, the rapid increase of population, and progress in the development of our ... resources... By eminent literary and scientific writers. Education, by Henry Barnard, L.L.D. Illustrated with four hundred engravings. Ed. by L. P. Brockett. Hartford, Conn., L. Stebbins, 1882.
Brockett, Linus Pierpont, 1820–1893, *ed.*

LAC 14782

Our destiny; the influence of socialism on morals and religion; an essay in ethics. 2d ed. London, S. Sonnenschein & co., 1891.
Gronlund, Laurence, 1846–1899.

LAC 10646

Our familiar songs and those who made them; three hundred standard songs of the English-speaking race, arranged with piano accompaniment, and preceded by sketches of the writers and histories of the songs, by Helen Kendrick Johnson. New York, H. Holt and company, 1881.
Johnson, Helen, 1844–1917.

LAC 16035

Our farming; or, How we have made a run-down farm bring both profit and pleasure... Philadelphia, The Farmer company, 1893.
Terry, Theodore Brainard, 1843–1916.

LAC 11593

Our fight with Tammany. By Rev. Charles H. Parkhurst, D. D. New York, C. Scribner's sons, 1895.
Parkhurst, Charles Henry, 1842–1933.

LAC 15287

Our first war in Mexico. New York, C. Scribner's sons, 1916.
Bishop, Farnham, 1886–1930.

LAC 15089

Our Indian wards. Cincinnati, R. Clarke & co., 1880.
Manypenny, George Washington, 1808–1893.

LAC 10219

Our inland seas, their shipping & commerce for three centuries. With illustrations from photographs and maps and drawings. Chicago, A. C. McClurg & co., 1910.
Mills, James Cooke.

LAC 15209

Our island empire; a hand-book of Cuba, Porto Rico, Hawaii, and the Philippine Islands. Philadelphia, J. B. Lippincott company, 1899.
Morris, Charles, 1833–1922.

LAC 16751

Our Italy. [Hartford, Conn., The American publishing co., 1904]
Warner, Charles Dudley, 1829–1900.

LAC 16430

Our journey to the Hebrides. By Joseph Pennell and Elizabeth Robins Pennell. New York, Harper & brothers, 1889.
Pennell, Joseph, 1857–1926.

LAC 14861

Our labor difficulties: the cause, and the way out; including the paper on the displacement of labor by improvements in machinery, by a committee appointed by the American social science association, composed of Lorin Blodget, Rev. Edward E. Hale, W. Godwin Moody [and others] ... read before the association at their annual meeting in Cincinnati, May 24, 1878. Boston, A. Williams & co., 1878.
Moody, William Godwin.

LAC 11659

Our merchant marine; how it rose, increased, became great, declined and decayed, with an inquiry into the conditions essential to its resuscitation and future prosperity. New York, G. P. Putnam's sons, 1882.
Wells, David Ames, 1828–1898.

LAC 10830

Our money wars; the example and warning of American finance. Boston, Arena publishing company, 1894.
Leavitt, Samuel.

LAC 13273

Our national parks. Boston and New York, Houghton, Mifflin [c1901]
Muir, John, 1838–1914.

LAC 14422

Our navy and the Barbary corsairs. Boston and New York, Houghton Mifflin company [c1905]
Allen, Gardner Weld, 1856–

LAC 15061

Our navy in the war with Spain. New York, C. Scribner's sons, 1898.
Spears, John Randolph, 1850–1936.

LAC 16451

Our navy in time of war (1861–1898) New York, D. Appleton and company, 1899.
Matthews, Franklin, 1858–1917.

LAC 16130

Our new Alaska; or, The Seward purchase vindicated. By Charles Hallock. Illustrated from sketches by T. J. Richardson. New York, Forest and stream publishing co., 1886.
Hallock, Charles, 1834–1917.

LAC 11159

Our new possessions... A graphic account, descriptive and historical, of the tropic islands of the sea which have fallen under our sway... Book I. The Philippine islands. Book II. Puerto Rico. Book III. Cuba. Book IV. The Hawaiian islands... [N. P. 1898]
White, Trumbull, 1868–1941.

LAC 13708

Our new possessions. Natural riches, industrial resources ... of Cuba, Porto Rico, Hawaii, the Ladrones and the Philippine islands, with episodes of their early history... Chicago, The Dominion co., 1898.
Halstead, Murat, 1829–1908.

LAC 13782

Our new prosperity. New York, Doubleday & McClure company, 1900.
Baker, Ray Stannard, 1870–1946.

LAC 16118

Our new West. Records of travel between the Mississippi river and the Pacific ocean. Over the plains–over the mountains–through the great interior basin–over the Sierra Nevadas–to and up and down the Pacific coast. With details of the wonderful natural scenery, agriculture, mines, business, social life, progress, and prospects ... including a full description of the Pacific railroad; and of the life of the Mormons, Indians, and Chinese. With map, portraits, and twelve full page illustrations. Hartford, Conn., Hartford publishing co.; New-York, J. D. Dennison; [etc., etc.] 1869.
Bowles, Samuel, 1826–1878.

LAC 11167
Our penal machinery and its victims. New and rev. ed. Chicago, A. C. McClurg, 1886.
Altgeld, John Peter, 1847–1902.

LAC 16772
Our penal machinery and its victims.
Live questions: including Our penal machinery and its victims. Chicago, Donohue & Henneberry, 1890.
Altgeld, John Peter, 1847–1902.

LAC 15498
Our racial and national minorities; their history, contributions, and present problems, edited by Francis J. Brown and Joseph Slabey Roucek. New York, Prentice-Hall, inc., 1937.
Brown, Francis James, 1894–   *ed.*

LAC 40002
Our revenue system and the civil service. Shall they be reformed? New York, Pub. for the New York free trade club, by G. P. Putnam's sons, 1878.
Earle, Abraham L.

LAC 40010
Our right to acquire and hold foreign territory; an address delivered before the New York state bar association at its annual meeting at Albany, January 18th, 1899. New York & London, G. P. Putnam's sons, 1899.
Gardiner, Charles Alexander, 1855–

LAC 10022
Our sheep and the tariff. Philadelphia, University of Pa. press co., 1890.
Lewis, Willliam Draper, 1867.

LAC 15493
Our Slavic fellow citizens. New York, Charities publication committee, 1910.
Balch, Emily Greene, 1867–1961.

LAC 22294–95
Our struggle for the fourteenth colony: Canada, and the American revolution. 315 illustrations and 23 maps... New York & London, G. P. Putnam's sons, 1907.
Smith, Justin Harvey, 1857–1930.

LAC 40009
Our suburbs. A resume of the origin, progress and present status of Chicago and environs... Presented by the Blue island land and building company, George R. Clarke, agent. Chicago [1873]
The Blue Island Land and Building Company.

LAC 15336
Our theatres to-day and yesterday. Beginning of the drama on Manhattan island and the troublous days of early managers and players, with anecdotal account of the growth of the amusement industry. Stories and personal sketches of men and women connected with famous houses in a bygone era, as well as the present. From 1732 to 1913. New York, The H. K. Fly company [c1913]
Dimmick, Ruth Crosby.

LAC 40010
Our treaty with Spain; triumphant diplomacy; annotated by Charles Henry Butler. Washington, D. C., Washington law book company, 1898.
Butler, Charles Henry, 1859–   *ed.*

LAC 10748
Our vanishing wild life; its extermination and preservation. With maps and illustrations. New York, C. Scribner's sons, 1913.
Hornaday, William Temple, 1854–1937.

LAC 13261
Our western border, its life, combats, adventures, forays, massacres, captivities, scouts, red chiefs, pioneer women, one hundred years ago... Carefully written and compiled by Charles McKnight. Philadelphia, Cincinnati [etc.] J. C. McCurdy & co., 1875.
McKnight, Charles, 1826–1881.

LAC 16741
Out of Mulberry street; stories of tenement life in New York city. New York, The Century co., 1898.
Riis, Jacob August, 1849–1914.

LAC 16273
"Out of the east." Reveries and studies in new Japan. Boston and New York, Houghton, Mifflin and company [c1895]
Hearn, Lafcadio, 1850–1904.

LAC 16218
Out of work; a study of employment agencies: their treatment of the unemployed, and their influence upon homes and business. Published for the Inter-municipal committee on household research. New York and London, G. P. Putnam's sons, 1904.
Kellor, Frances Alice, 1873–1952.

LAC 14944
Outdoor relief in Missouri; a study of its administration by county officials, by George A. Warfield, prepared under the direction of Thomas J. Riley. New York, Survey associates, inc., 1915.
Warfield, George Alfred, 1871–

LAC 13715
Outline lectures on the history, organization, jurisdiction, and practice of the ministerial and consular courts of the United States of America in Japan, by G. H. Scidmore, LL. B. Tokio, Igirisu horitsu gakko, 1887.
Scidmore, George Hawthorne, 1854–1922.

LAC 40122
An outline of a course of architectural instruction. Boston, Press of J. Wilson, 1866.
Ware, William Robert, 1832–1915.

LAC 10969
An outline of Christian theology. 4th ed. New York, C. Scribner's sons, 1899, [c1898]
Clarke, William Newton, 1841–1912.

LAC 40069
Outline of lectures upon political economy, prepared for the use of students at the Johns Hopkins university ... and the University of Michigan... Baltimore [Amherst, Mass., Press of C. A. Bangs & co.] 1881.
Adams, Henry Carter, 1851–1921.

LAC 14027
An outline of the documentary history of the Zuni tribe. Boston, Houghton, Mifflin, 1892.
Bandelier, Adolph Francis Alphonse, 1840–1914.

LAC 12533
An outline of the public life and services of Thomas F. Bayard, senator of the United States from the state of Delaware, 1869–1880. With extracts from his speeches and the debates of Congress. New York, D. Appleton and company, 1880.
Spencer, Edward.

LAC 10531
An outline study of man; or, The body and mind in one system. With illustrative diagrams, and a method for blackboard teaching. New York, Scribner [c1878]
Hopkins, Mark, 1802–1887.

LAC 16809
Outlines of a critical theory of ethics. Ann Arbor, Michigan Register publishing company, 1891.
Dewey, John, 1859–1952.

LAC 40084
Outlines of American political economy, in a series of letters addressed by Frederick List to Charles J. Ingersoll. To which is added the celebrated letters of Mr. Jefferson to Benjamin Austin, and of Mr. Madison to the editors of the Lynchburg Virginian. Philadelphia, Printed by S. Parker, 1827.
List, Friedrich, 1789–1846.

LAC 12703
Outlines of imperfect and disordered mental action. New-York, Harper & brothers, 1840.
Upham, Thomas Cogswell, 1799–1872.

LAC 16264
Outlines of Louis F. Post's lectures on the single tax, absolute free trade, the labor question, progress and poverty, the land question, the elements of political economy, socialism, hard times; with illustrative notes and charts. New York, The Sterling library, c1894.
Post, Louis Freeland, 1849–

LAC 40083
Outlines of penology. [Philadelphia? 1874]
Chandler, Joseph Ripley, 1792–1880.

LAC 10548
Outlines of psychology; an elementary treatise, with some practical applications. New York, London, The Macmillan company, 1903.
Royce, Josiah, 1855–1916.

LAC 11039
Outlines of social theology. New York and London, Macmillan and co., 1895.
Hyde, William De Witt, 1858–1917.

LAC 10612
Outlines of the first course of Yale agricultural lectures. By Henry S. Olcott. With an introduction by John A. Porter. New York, C. M. Saxton, Barker & co., 1860.
Olcott, Henry Steel, 1832–1907, ed.

LAC 40022
Outlines of the mineralogy and geology of Boston and its vicinity, with a geological map. By J. F. Dana and S. L. Dana. Boston, American academy of arts and sciences, 1818.
Dana, James Freeman, 1793–1827.

LAC 31394–439
The Outlook. v. 48–81; Jan. 1, 1893–Dec. 1905. New York, The Outlook company.

LAC 11256
The outlook for industrial peace... Philadelphia, American academy of political and social science, 1912.
American Academy of Political and Social Science, *Philadelphia.*

LAC 10444
The outlook for the average man. New York, The Macmillan company, 1907.
Shaw, Albert, 1857–1947.

LAC 12151
Outre-mer: impressions of America. London, T. Fisher, 1895.
Bourget, Paul Charles Joseph, 1852–1935.

LAC 12224
Over the Alleghanies and across the prairies. Personal recollections of the far West, one and twenty years ago. 2d ed. London, Simpkin, Marshall and co., 1870.
Peyton, John Lewis, 1824–1896.

LAC 13354
Over the range to the Golden Gate; a complete tourist's guide to Colorado, New Mexico, Utah, Nevada, California, Oregon, Puget Sound, and the great Northwest. Chicago, R. R. Donnelley & sons co., 1902, [c1894]
Wood, Stanley.

LAC 14499
The overcoming life and other sermons. New York, Chicago [etc.] Fleming H. Revell company [1896]
Moody, Dwight Lyman, 1837–1899.

LAC 13269
Overland in a covered wagon; an autobiography, by Joaquin Miller, edited by Sidney G. Firman, illustrations by Esther M. Mattson. New York, London, D. Appleton and company, 1930.
Miller, Joaquin, 1841?–1913.

LAC 13210
An overland journey, from New York to San Francisco, in the summer of 1859. New York, C. M. Saxton, Barker & co.; San Francisco, H. H. Bancroft & co., 1860.
Greeley, Horace, 1811–1872.

LAC 31198–207
The Overland monthly, devoted to the development of the country. v. 1–15; July 1868–Dec. 1875. San Francisco, J. H. Carmany & Company [etc.]

LAC 40091
The overland route to the Pacific. A report on the condition, capacity and resources of the Union Pacific and Central Pacific railways. October, 1869. Boston, Lee & Shepard, 1869.
Derby, Elias Hasket, 1803–1880.

LAC 13301

The overland stage to California. Personal reminiscences and authentic history of the great overland stage line and pony express from the Missouri river to the Pacific ocean. By Frank A. Root and William Elsey Connelley. Published by the authors. Topeka, Kan., 1901. Columbus, O., Reprinted by Long's College Book Co., 1950.
Root, Frank Albert, 1837–

LAC 10776

The Pacific railroad–open. How to go: what to see. Guide for travel to and through western America. Boston, Fields, Osgood & co., 1869.
Bowles, Samuel, 1826–1878.

LAC 13352

The Pacific tourist. Williams' illustrated trans-continental guide of travel, from the Atlantic to the Pacific Ocean. Containing full descriptions of railroad routes... A complete traveler's guide of the Union and Central Pacific railroads... by Henry T. Williams, editor. With special contributions by Prof. F. V. Hayden, Maj. J. W. Powell, Clarence King, Capt. Dutton, A. C. Peale, Joaquin Miller, J. B. Davis, F. E. Shearer. New York, H. T. Williams, 1876.
Williams, Henry T   ed.

LAC 10159

The packers, the private car lines, and the people. Philadelphia, H. Altemus company [1906]
Armour, Jonathan Ogden, 1863–1927.

LAC 12675

The painter, gilder, and varnisher's companion: containing rules and regulations in every thing relating to the arts of painting, gilding, varnishing, and glass-staining ... 8th ed. Philadelphia, H. C. Baird, 1861, [c1860]

LAC 15131

Painters, sculptors, architects, engravers and their works. A handbook. By Clara Erskine Clement. With monograms. 2d ed. New York, Hurd and Houghton, 1874.
Waters, Clara Clement, 1834–1916.

LAC 20915

Paley's natural theology, with illustrative notes, by Henry Lord Brougham and Sir Charles Bell. With numerous wood-cuts. London, C. Knight; New York, W. Jackson, 1836.
Paley, William, 1743–1805.

LAC 15690

The palladium of conscience; or, The foundation of religious liberty displayed, asserted, and established, agreeable to its true and genuine principles, above the reach of all petty tyrants, who attempt to lord it over the human mind, containing Furneaux's Letters to Blackstone. Priestley's Remarks on Blackstone. Blackstone's Reply to Priestley. And Blackstone's Case of the Middlesex-election; with some other curious tracts ... being a necessary companion for every lover of religious liberty. And An interesting appendix to Blackstone's Commentaries on the laws of England. America: Printed for the subscribers, by Robert Bell, at the late Union library, in Third-street, Philadelphia, 1773.

LAC 13283

Palmer's journal of travels over the Rocky mountains, 1845–1846. New York, AMS press, 1966.
Palmer, Joel, 1810–1881.

LAC 15688

Pamphlets on the Constitution of the United States, published during its discussion by the people, 1787–1788. Ed. with notes and a bibliography, by Paul Leicester Ford. Brooklyn, N. Y., 1888.
Ford, Paul Leicester, 1865–1902, ed.

LAC 14839

Panama canal tolls. Symposium of views protesting against a surrender of American rights and upholding the side of the United States in the toll controversy. A discussion of the Hay-Pauncefote treaty, of the right of foreign nations to interfere in our domestic affairs, and of the influences back of the effort to repeal the sections of the Panama canal act beneficial to American commerce. Extracts from Congressional record and public documents comp. by Hon. Joseph R. Knowland. 1912–1913. Washington [Govt. print. off.] 1913.
Knowland, Joseph Russell, 1873–   comp.

LAC 14989

Panama; the canal, the country and the people, by Arthur Bullard (Albert Edwards) Rev. ed. with additional chapters... New York, The Macmillan company, 1914.
Bullard, Arthur, 1879–1929.

LAC 11156

Pan-Americanism: a forecast of the inevitable clash between the United States and Europe's victor. New York, The Century co., 1915.
Usher, Roland Greene, 1880–

LAC 12649

The panorama of professions and trades; or Every man's book. Philadelphia, U. Hunt, 1836.
Hazen, Edward.

LAC 10937

The papal conspiracy exposed, and Protestantism defended, in the light of reason, history, and scripture. New York, M. W. Dodd, 1855.
Beecher, Edward, 1803–1895.

LAC 40119

Papers of Dr. James McHenry on the Federal convention of 1787, edited by J. Franklin Jameson. [New York, 1906]
McHenry, James, 1753–1816.

LAC 10654

Papers of James A. Bayard, 1796–1815. Ed. by Elizabeth Donnan. Washington, 1915.
Bayard, James Asheton, 1767–1815.

LAC 22277–78

The papers of Randolph Abbott Shotwell, edited by J. G. de Roulhac Hamilton, with the collaboration of Rebecca Cameron. Raleigh, The North Carolina historical commission, 1929–36.
Shotwell, Randolph Abbott, 1844—1885.

LAC 22423-42
The papers of Sir William Johnson. Prepared for publication by the Division of archives and history... Albany, The University of the state of New York, 1921-62.
Johnson, *Sir* William, *bart.*, 1715-1774.

LAC 23575-77
Papers of the American historical association. v. 1-5 [1885-91] New York & London, G. P. Putnam's sons, 1886-91.
American Historical Association.

LAC 20758-60
The papers of Thomas Ruffin; collected and ed. by J. G. de Roulhac Hamilton. Raleigh, Edwards & Broughton printing co., state printers, 1918-20.
Ruffin, Thomas, 1787-1870.

LAC 14849
Papers relating to America. Presented to the House of commons, 1809. London, Printed by A. Strahan, 1810.
Gt. Brit. *Foreign Office.*

LAC 11335
Papers relating to public events in Massachusetts preceding the American revolution. Philadelphia, Printed for the Seventy-six society, 1856.

LAC 12926
Papers relating to the condemnation of the British barque "Springbok" and her cargo, by the District prize court of New York, U.S.; with the opinions of the press thereon... London, Printed for the owners, 1864.

LAC 40116
Papers relating to the election of senators by direct vote of the people... Washington, Gov't print. off., 1908.
U.S. *Congress. Senate.*

LAC 21707-79
Papers relating to the foreign relations of the United States. New York, Kraus reprint corporation, 1881-1966.
U.S. *Dept. of State.*

LAC 14380
Papers relating to the improvement of the city of Washington, District of Columbia. Compiled by Glenn Brown, Secretary of the American institute of architects; with an introduction by Charles Moore, Clerk of Senate committee on the District of Columbia. Washington, Govt. print. off., 1901.
U.S. *Congress. Senate. Committee on the District of Columbia.*

LAC 23208-12
Papers relating to the treaty of Washington... Washington, Govt. print. off., 1872-74.
U.S. *Dept. of State.*

LAC 40021
Papers relative to labor troubles at Goldfield, Nev. Message from the President ... transmitting report of Special commission on labor troubles at Goldfield, Nev., and papers relating thereto... [Washington, Gov't print. off., 1908]
U.S. *Special Commission on Labor Troubles at Goldfield, Nev.*

LAC 14469
Paquita, the Indian heroine. A true story ... presenting graphic pictures of Indian home life in peace and war, as beheld by the author during his residence of four years among the red men. Hartford, Conn., American publishing company [1881]
Miller, Joaquin, 1841-1913.

LAC 10569
Paradise found; the cradle of the human race at the North pole; a study of the prehistoric world. With original illustrations. 5th ed. Boston, New York, Houghton, Mifflin and company, 1885.
Warren, William Fairfield, 1833-1929.

LAC 40081
The paradise within the reach of all men, without labor, by powers of nature and machinery. An address to all intelligent men. In two parts. 2d English ed. London, printed by James H. Young; and published by J. Cleave, 1842.
Etzler, John Adolphus.

LAC 15304
Parentator. Memoirs of remarkables in the life and the death of the ever-memorable Dr. Increase Mather. Who expired, August 23, 1723... Boston: Printed by B. Green, for Nathaniel Belknap, at the corner of Scarlets-Wharff, 1724.
Mather, Cotton, 1663-1728.

LAC 10429
The parent's friend; or, Letters on the government and education of children and youth. By the Rev. Daniel Smith. New-York, T. Mason and G. Lane, 1838.
Smith, Daniel, 1806-1852.

LAC 11799
Paris in '67; or, The great exposition, its side-shows and excursions. New York, G. W. Carleton & co. [etc., etc.] 1867.
Morford, Henry, 1823-1881.

LAC 15721
Paris universal exposition MDCCCLXXVIII. The catalogue of the United States collective exhibition of education, comp. by John D. Philbrick and published by direction of the commissioner-general. London, Printed at the Chiswick press, 1878.
Philbrick, John Dudley, 1818-1886, *comp.*

LAC 40029
Parish education in colonial Virginia. New York city, Teachers college, Columbia university, 1923.
Wells, Guy Fred, 1880-

LAC 16807
Partial portraits. London, Macmillan and co. [etc.] 1888.
James, Henry, 1843-1916.

LAC 16883
A particular history of the five years French and Indian war in New England and parts adjacent, from its declaration by the King of France, March 15, 1744, to the treaty with the eastern Indians, Oct. 16, 1749, sometimes called Governor Shirley's war. With a memoir of Major-general Shirley, accompanied by his portrait and other engravings. Albany, J. Munsell, 1870.
Drake, Samuel Gardner, 1798-1875.

LAC 40092
Particulars of the late duel, fought at Hoboken, July 11, between Aaron Burr and Alexander Hamilton, esqrs., in which the latter unfortunately fell. Containing all the papers relating to that event, together with the will of Gen. Hamilton, and letters of Bishop Moore, and the Rev. J. M. Mason. New-York: Printed by A. Forman, 91, Beekman-street, 1804.

LAC 16959
The partisan: a romance of the revolution. New and rev. ed. Chicago, Donohue, Henneberry, 1890.
Simms, William Gilmore, 1806–1870.

LAC 20658
The partisan leader; a tale of the future. By Edward William Sidney [pseud.] Printed for the publishers, by J. Caxton, 1856 [i.e. Washington, Printed by D. Green, 1836] Caxton, 1856.
Tucker, Nathaniel Beverley, 1784–1851.

LAC 14906
The Partisan rangers of the Confederate States army; ed. by William J. Davis. Louisville, Ky., G. G. Fetter company, 1904.
Johnson, Adam Rankin, 1834–

LAC 11548
Party leaders of the time; character studies of public men at Washington, Senate portraits, House etchings, snapshots at executive officers and diplomats, and flashlights in the country at large. New York, G. W. Dillingham company [1906]
Thompson, Charles Willis, 1871–1946.

LAC 14717
Party leaders; sketches of Thomas Jefferson, Alex'r Hamilton, Andrew Jackson, Henry Clay, John Randolph, of Roanoke, including notices of many other distinguished American statesmen. New York, D. Appleton and company; [etc., etc.] 1855.
Baldwin, Joseph Glover, 1815–1864.

LAC 23257–58
The Passaic Valley, New Jersey, in three centuries. New York, The New Jersey genealogical company, 1901.
Whitehead, John, 1819–

LAC 10599
The passing of Spain and the ascendency of America. Springfield, Mass., The King-Richardson publishing co., 1898.
Crabtree, Jerome Bruce.

LAC 12296
The passing of the idle rich. London, Hodder & Stoughton, 1911.
Martin, Frederick Townsend, 1849–1914.

LAC 11970
Passion-flowers. Boston, Ticknor, Reed, and Fields, 1854.
Howe, Julia, 1819–1910.

LAC 14816
The passport question; reprint from the American Jewish year book 5672. New York, The American Jewish committee, 1911.
American Jewish Year Book.

LAC 13096
The past and present condition of public hygiene and state medicine in the United States. [Boston, Wright & Potter printing company, 1900]
Abbott, Samuel Warren, 1837–1904.

LAC 23426–27
Past and present of Jasper County, Iowa. Gen. James B. Weaver, editor-in-chief. Indianapolis, Ind., B. F. Bowen & company, 1912.
Weaver, James Baird, 1833–1912.

LAC 40098
Past and present of life insurance. [New York, D. A. Gorton, 1877]

LAC 10499
The past, the present, and the future. Philadelphia, Carey & Hart, 1848.
Carey, Henry Charles, 1793–1879.

LAC 13515
Path breaking; an autobiographical history of the equal suffrage movement in Pacific coast states. [Portland, Ore., James, Kerns & Abbott co., 1914]
Duniway, Abigail, 1834–1915.

LAC 11522
The path I trod; the autobiography of Terence V. Powderly, edited by Harry J. Carman, Henry David and Paul N. Guthrie. New York, Columbia university press, 1940.
Powderly, Terence Vincent, 1849–1924.

LAC 40026
The path to riches. An inquiry into the origin and use of money; and into the principles of stocks and banks. To which are subjoined some thoughts respecting a bank for the Commonwealth. By a citizen of Massachusetts. Boston, I. Thomas and E. T. Andrews, 1792.
Sullivan, James, 1744–1808.

LAC 12396
Patrician and plebeian in Virginia; or, The origin and development of the social classes of the Old Dominion. Pub. by the author. Charlottesville, Va., The Michie company, printers, 1910.
Wertenbaker, Thomas Jefferson, 1879–1966.

LAC 12392
Patrick Henry. Boston and New York, Houghton, Mifflin and company, 1888, [c1887]
Tyler, Moses Coit, 1835–1900.

LAC 23454–56
Patrick Henry; life, correspondence and speeches. New York, Charles Scribner's sons, 1891.
Henry, William Wirt, 1831–1900.

LAC 13520
The patriot preachers of the American revolution. With biographical sketches. 1766-1783. [New York] Printed for the subscribers, 1860.
Moore, Frank, 1828-1904, *ed.*

LAC 11412
Patriotic addresses in America and England, from 1850 to 1885, on slavery, the civil war, and the development of civil liberty in the United States, by Henry Ward Beecher. Ed., with a review of Mr. Beecher's personality and influence in public affairs, by John R. Howard. New York, Fords, Howard & Hulbert, 1891, [c1887]
Beecher, Henry Ward, 1813-1887.

LAC 10439
Patriotism, and other papers. With a biographical sketch by Hon. Richard Frothingham. Boston, Tompkins, 1864.
King, Thomas Starr, 1824-1864.

LAC 22275-76
The patriotism of Illinois. A record of the civil and military history of the state in the war for the Union, with a history of the campaigns in which Illinois soldiers have been conspicuous, sketches of distinguished officers, the roll of the illustrious dead, movements of the sanitary and Christian commissions. Chicago, Clarke & co., 1865-66.
Eddy, Thomas Mears, 1823-1874.

LAC 15947
The Patrons of husbandry on the Pacific coast. Being a complete history of the origin, condition and progress of agriculture in different parts of the world; of the origin and growth of the order of Patrons, with a general and special grange directory, and full list of charter members of the subordinate granges of California. Also, of the foes of the farmers, or monopolies of land, water, transportation and education; of a protective tariff, currency and banking. San Francisco, A. L. Bancroft and company, 1875.
Carr, Ezra Slocum, 1819-1894.

LAC 40120
The Patrons' parliamentary guide... Washington, Gibson brothers, printers, 1874.
Patrons of Husbandry. *National Grange.*

LAC 15948
The Patron's pocket companion. In four parts. Cincinnati, R. W. Carroll & co., 1875.
Cramer, J   A.

LAC 15359
Paul Revere and his engraving. New York, C. Scribner's sons, 1901.
Andrews, William Loring, 1837-1920.

LAC 13945
Pawnee hero stories and folk-tales, with notes on the origin, customs and character of the Pawnee people, by George Bird Grinnell. To which is added a chapter on the Pawnee language by John B. Dunbar. New York, C. Scribner's sons, 1912, [c1890]
Grinnell, George Bird, 1849-1938.

LAC 10687
The peace conference at The Hague, and its bearings on international law and policy. New York, The Macmillan company; London, Macmillan & co., ltd., 1900.
Holls, Frederick William, 1857-1903.

LAC 40121
The "Peace Convention" at Washington and the Virginia Convention at Richmond. New York, Dodge & Grattan, Printers, 1861.

LAC 14353
The peace negotiations of 1782 and 1783. An address delivered before the New York historical society on its seventy-ninth anniversary, Tuesday, November 27, 1883. New York, Printed for the Society, 1884.
Jay, John, 1817-1894.

LAC 10083
The peace negotiations of 1782-1783. With a critical essay on the sources of information, and editorial notes. Boston & New York, Houghton, Mifflin [c1888]
Jay, John, 1817-1894.

LAC 16704
The peace problem, the task of the twentieth century, by Frederick Lynch, with an introduction by Andrew Carnegie. New York, Chicago [etc.] Fleming H. Revell company [c1911]
Lynch, Frederick Henry, 1867-

LAC 40025
Peace without dishonour-war without hope. Being a calm and dispassionate enquiry into the question of the Chesapeake, and the necessity and expediency of war. By a Yankee farmer. Boston: Printed by Greenough and Stebbins, 1807.
Lowell, John, 1769-1840.

LAC 40082
The pearl of great price: being a choice selection from the revelations, translations, and narrations of Joseph Smith, first prophet, seer, and revelator to the Church of Jesus Christ of Latter-day saints. Liverpool, F. D. Richards, 1851.
Smith, Joseph, 1805-1844.

LAC 14097
The Pearl of the Antilles. London, Chapman and Hall, 1873.
Gallenga, Antonio Carlo Napoleone, 1810-1895.

LAC 12720
Peck's bad boy, no. 2. The grocery man and Peck's bad boy. Being a continuation of Peck's bad boy and his pa. Chicago and New York, Belford, Clarke & co., 1883.
Peck, George Wilbur, 1840-1916.

LAC 14069
Peculiarities of American cities. By Captain Willard Glazier. Philadelphia, Hubbard brothers, 1886, [c1883]
Glazier, Willard, 1841-1905.

LAC 16774
Pedestrian tour in Europe. Views a-foot: or, Europe seen with knapsack and staff, by J. Bayard Taylor. With a preface by N. P. Willis, with additions, and a portrait from a sketch by T. B. Read. New York, G. P. Putnam, 1848.
Taylor, Bayard, 1825-1878.

LAC 16059

Pedro Menendez de Aviles, adelantado, governor and captain-general of Florida, memorial by Gonzalo Solis de Meras; first published in La Florida, su conquista y colonizacion por Pedro Menendez de Aviles, by Eugenio Ruidiaz y Caravia; translated from the Spanish with notes, by Jeannette Thurber Connor. Deland, Fla., The Florida state historical society, 1923.
Solis de Meras, Gonzalo.

LAC 40129

A peep into Catharine street, or The mysteries of shopping. By a late retailer. New York, J. Slater, 1846.

LAC 15335

Un peintre des enfants et des meres, Mary Cassatt. 2. ed. Paris, P. Ollendorff, c1913.
Segard, Achille, 1872-1936.

LAC 11929

Pembroke, by Mary E. Wilkins. New York and London, Harper & brothers, 1900, [c1899]
Freeman, Mary Eleanor, 1852-1930.

LAC 16403

Pen and pencil sketches of the great riots. An illustrated history of the railroad and other great American riots. Including all riots in the early history of the country. New York, E. B. Treat, 1882, [c1877]
Headley, Joel Tyler, 1813-1897.

LAC 16388

Pen and powder, by Franc B. Wilkie (Poliuto) Boston, Ticknor and company, 1888.
Wilkie, Franc Bangs, 1832-1892.

LAC 11798

Pen illustrations of New Orleans, 1881-82. Trade, commerce and manufactures... New Orleans, Pub. by the author, 1882.
Land, John E.

LAC 16514

Pencillings by the way: written during some years of residence and travel in France, Italy, Greece, Asia Minor, Turkey, and England. 1st complete ed. New York, Morris & Willis, 1844.
Willis, Nathaniel Parker, 1806-1867.

LAC 16548

The Peninsular campaign and its antecedents, as developed by the report of Maj.-Gen. Geo. B. McClellan, and other published documents. New York, D. Van Nostrand, 1864.
Barnard, John Gross, 1815-1882.

LAC 16290

The Peninsular campaign in Virginia; or, Incidents and scenes on the battle-fields and in Richmond. By Rev. J. J. Marks, D. D. Philadelphia, J. B. Lippincott & co., 1864.
Marks, James Junius, 1809-1899.

LAC 15670

The Pennsylvania academy of the fine arts and other collections of Philadelphia, including the Pennsylvania museum, the Wilstach collection, and the collections of Independence hall and the Historical society of Pennsylvania. Boston, L. C. Page & company, 1911.
Henderson, Helen Weston, 1874-

LAC 22635-37

Pennsylvania, colonial and federal; a history, 1608-1903. Philadelphia, Pennsylvania historical publishing association, 1903.
Jenkins, Howard Malcolm, 1842-1902, ed.

LAC 11704

Pennsylvania, colony and commonwealth. Philadelphia, H. T. Coates and company, 1897.
Fisher, Sydney George, 1856-1927.

LAC 14246

Pennsylvania Constitutional convention 1872 and 1873: its members and officers and the result of their labors. Philadelphia, Inquirer book and job print, 1873.
Harlan, Abram Douglas, 1833-

LAC 15416

"Pennsylvania Dutch," and other essays. By Phebe Earle Gibbons. 3d ed., rev. and enl. Philadelphia, J. B. Lippincott & co., 1882.
Gibbons, Phebe H.   b. 1821.

LAC 15549

The Pennsylvania Germans; a sketch of their history and life, of the Mennonites, and of side lights from the Rosenberger family. Chicago, Ill., The University of Chicago press [c1923]
Rosenberger, Jesse Leonard, 1860-

LAC 11730

Pennsylvania in American history. Philadelphia, W. J. Campbell, 1910.
Pennypacker, Samuel Whitaker, 1843-1916.

LAC 20513-14

Pennsylvania, province and state; a history from 1609 to 1790. Philadelphia and New York, J. Wanamaker, 1899.
Bolles, Albert Sidney, 1846-1939.

LAC 10183

The Pennsylvania railroad: its origin, construction, condition, and connections. Embracing historical, descriptive, and statistical notices of cities, towns, villages, stations, industries, and objects of interest on its various lines in Pennsylvania and New Jersey. By William B. Sipes. Illustrated with drawings by Thomas Moran, James Hamilton, F. B. Schell, F. O. C. Darley, J. D. Woodward, G. Perkins, W. H. Gibson, and others, engraved by James W. Lauderbach. Philadelphia [Pennsylvania railroad co.] the Passenger dept., 1875.
Sipes, William B   d. 1905.

LAC 40016

The Pennsylvania tunnel franchise. Some of the reasons why it should be granted; Stated by the Merchants' association of New York at the hearing before the railroad committee of the Board of Aldermen, November 26, 1902. [New York, 1902]
Merchants' Association of New York.

LAC 11571

The people and the railways; a popular discussion of the railway problem in the United States, by way of answer to "The railways and the republic," by James F. Hudson, and with an examination of the Interstate commerce law. New York and Chicago, Belford, Clarke & company, 1888.
Morgan, James Appleton, 1845-1928.

LAC 15600

The people at play; excursions in the humor and philosophy of popular amusements, with illustrations drawn by the author from prints and photographs. Boston and New York, Houghton Mifflin company, 1909.
Hartt, Rollin Lynde, 1869–1946.

LAC 13805

The people of the abyss. With many illustrations from photographs. New York, The Macmillan company; London, Macmillan & co., ltd., 1904, [c1903]
London, Jack, 1876–1916.

LAC 12365

The People's Party campaign book. Author's ed. [n.p., n.d.]
Watson, Thomas Edward, 1856–1922.

LAC 40112

People's party shot and shell. Chicago, C. H. Kerr and company, 1892.
Bland, Thomas Augustus, 1830–

LAC 40116

The people's power; or, How to wield the ballot. San Francisco, W. M. Hinton & co., printers, 1883.
Stetson, Simeon.

LAC 40012

The people's right to election or alteration of goverment [!] in Connecticott, argued in a letter; by Gershom Bulkeley, esq; one of Their Majesties justices of the peace in the county of Hartford. Together with a letter to the said Bulkeley, from a friend of his in the Bay. To which is added, the writing delivered to James Russell of Charlestown esq; warning him and others concerned not to meet to hold a court at Cambridge, within the county of Middlesex. By Thomas Greaves. And also his answer to Mr. Broadstreete and the gentlemen mett at the Town-house in Boston concerning the same. Published for the information & satisfaction of Their Majesties loyall (but abused) subjects in New England. Philadelphia, Printed by assignes of William Bradford, 1689.
Bulkeley, Gershom, 1636–1713.

LAC 13851

Perfumery: its manufacture and use... From the French of Celnart [pseud.] and other late authorities. With additions and improvements by Campbell Morfit. 2d ed. rev. Philadelphia, H. C. Baird, 1853.
Morfit, Campbell, 1820–1897.

LAC 40024

The perils of the nation. Bribery, dishonesty, usurpations and despotism of the railway corporations, and their relation to the politics of the day, the remedy to be used. Read–discuss–diffuse. Address by John Livingston, before the Workingmen and farmers' union, at Owego, Tioga County, New York, September 22, 1877. [New York, Evening post print, 1877?]
Livingston, John.

LAC 15821

Perpetual war, the policy of Mr. Madison. Being a candid examination of his late message to Congress, so far as respects the following topicks ... viz., the pretended negotiations for peace ... the important and interesting subject of a conscript militia ... and the establishment of an immense standing army of guards and spies, under the name of a local volunteer force... By a New England farmer. Boston, Printed by C. Stebbins, 1812.
Lowell, John, 1769–1840.

LAC 16292

Perry's saints; or, The fighting parson's regiment in the war of the rebellion. Boston, D. Lothrop company [1886]
Nichols, James Moses, 1835–1886.

LAC 14348

Personal and military history of Philip Kearny, major-general United States volunteers... New York, Rice and Gage; Newark, N. J., Bliss & co., 1869.
De Peyster, John Watts, 1821–1907.

LAC 40071

Personal liberty laws, (Statutes of Massachusetts,) and Slavery in the territories, (Case of Dred Scott.) Boston, Wright & Potter, printers, 1861.
Parker, Joel, 1795–1875.

LAC 12818

Personal memoir of Daniel Drayton, for four years and four months a prisoner (for charity's sake) in Washington jail. Including a narrative of the voyage and capture of the schooner Pearl... Boston, B. Marsh; New York, American and foreign anti-slavery society, 1855.
Drayton, Daniel, b. 1802.

LAC 20115

Personal memoirs and recollections of editorial life. Boston, Ticknor, Reed, and Fields, 1852.
Buckingham, Joseph Tinker, 1779–1861.

LAC 22475–76

Personal memoirs of P. H. Sheridan, general, United States army. New York, C. L. Webster & company, 1888.
Sheridan, Philip Henry, 1831–1888.

LAC 20790–91

Personal memoirs of U. S. Grant... New York, C. L. Webster & co., 1885–86.
Grant, Ulysses Simpson, pres. U.S., 1822–1885.

LAC 13764

Personal memories, social, political and literary, with sketches of many noted people, 1803–1843. Cincinnati, R. Clarke & co., 1879.
Mansfield, Edward Deering, 1801–1880.

LAC 12283

Personal narrative of the first voyage of Columbus to America. From a manuscript recently discovered in Spain. Tr. from the Spanish. Boston, T. B. Wait and son [1827]
Colombo, Cristoforo.

LAC 13196

Personal narrative of travels in Virginia, Maryland, Pennsylvania, Ohio, Indiana, Kentucky; and of a residence in the Illinois Territory: 1817–1818, by Elias Pym Fordham; with facsimiles of the author's sketches and plans; ed. by Frederic Austin Ogg. Cleveland, The Arthur H. Clark company, 1906.
Fordham, Elias Pym.

LAC 15704

Personal recollections and observations of General Nelson A. Miles, embracing a brief view of the Civil war; or, From New England to the Golden gate, and the

story of his Indian campaigns, with comments on the exploration, development and progress of our great western empire; copiously illustrated with graphic pictures by Frederic Remington and other eminent artists. Chicago, New York, The Werner company, 1896.
Miles, Nelson Appleton, 1839–1925.

LAC 11477
Personal recollections of Abraham Lincoln and the civil war, by James R. Gilmore. (Edmund Kirke). Boston, L. C. Page and company, 1898.
Gilmore, James Roberts, 1822–1903.

LAC 15706
Personal recollections of distinguished generals. New York, Harper & brothers, 1866.
Shanks, William Franklin Gore, 1837–1905.

LAC 14769
Personal recollections of John M. Palmer; the story of an earnest life. Cincinnati, The R. Clarke company, 1901.
Palmer, John McAuley, 1817–1900.

LAC 16203
Personal recollections of Nathaniel Hawthorne. New York, Harper & brothers, 1893.
Bridge, Horatio, 1806–1893.

LAC 23504
Personal recollections of notable people at home and abroad. With other papers. London, R. Bentley and son, 1895.
Tuckerman, Charles Keating, 1821–1896.

LAC 16881
Personal recollections of the drama, or Theatrical reminiscences, embracing sketches of prominent actors and actresses, their chief characteristics, original anecdotes of them, and incidents connected therewith. Albany, C. Van Benthuysen & sons, 1873.
Stone, Henry Dickinson.

LAC 15340
Personal recollections of the stage, embracing notices of actors, authors, and auditors, during a period of forty years. Philadelphia, H. C. Baird, 1855.
Wood, William Burke, 1779–1861.

LAC 10678
Personal reminiscences. 2d ed., rev., to which is added rambling recollections connected with China. Boston, Little, Brown, and company, 1882.
Forbes, Robert Bennet, 1804–1889.

LAC 12347
Personal reminiscences, anecdotes, and letters of Gen. Robert E. Lee. By Rev. J. William Jones. (Published by authority of the Lee family, and of the faculty of Washington and Lee university.) New-York, D. Appleton and company, 1874.
Jones, John William, 1836–1909.

LAC 12432
Personal reminiscences, including Lincoln and others, 1840–1890. New York, Richmond, Croscup, 1893.
Chittenden, Lucius Eugene, 1824–1900.

LAC 13190
Personal reminiscences of early days in California. New York, Da Capo Press, 1968.
Field, Stephen Johnson, 1816–1899.

LAC 21301
Personal reminiscences of the life and times of Gardiner Spring... New York, C. Scribner & co., 1866.
Spring, Gardiner, 1785–1873.

LAC 16291
Personal reminiscences of the war of 1861–5; in camp–en bivouac–on the march–on picket–on the skirmish line–on the battlefield–and in prison. Lynchburg, Va., J. P. Bell company, inc., 1911.
Morgan, William Henry, 1836–

LAC 14452
The personality of American cities, by Edward Hungerford, with frontispiece by E. Horter. New York, McBride Nast & company, 1913.
Hungerford, Edward, 1875–

LAC 12254
Personally conducted. Illustrated by Joseph Pennell, Alfred Parsons, and others. London, S. Low, Marston, Searle, and Rivington, 1889.
Stockton, Frank Richard, 1834–1902.

LAC 16386
Peru; incidents of travel and exploration in the land of the Incas. New York, H. Holt and co. [c1877]
Squier, Ephraim George, 1821–1888.

LAC 13587
Pestalozzi: his life, work, and influence. Cincinnati, New York, Wilson, Hinkle & co. [c1903]
Krusi, Hermann, 1817–1903.

LAC 40008
Peter Henderson, gardener–author–merchant. A memoir. New York, Press of McIlroy & Emmet, 1890.
Henderson, Alfred.

LAC 40067
Petition favoring suspension of hostilities in the Philippine Islands. [Washington, Govt. print. off., 1902]
U.S. *Congress. Senate. Committee on the Philippines.*

LAC 10152
Petroleum: a history of the oil region of Venango County, Pennsylvania. Its resources, mode of development, and value: embracing a discussion of ancient oil operations... Philadelphia, J. P. Skelly & co., 1866.
Eaton, Samuel John Mills, 1820–1889.

LAC 11640
Petroleum in California; a concise and reliable history of the oil industry of the state ... comp. by Lionel V. Redpath. Los Angeles, Cal., L. V. Redpath, 1900.
Redpath, Lionel V.

LAC 40022
Petroleum, its production; distribution and its purchasing power, from the report of the Philadelphia board of trade, for 1865. [Philadelphia, 1865?]
Philadelphia. Board of Trade.

LAC 10639
Phases of modern music... New York and London, Harper & brothers, 1904.
Gilman, Lawrence, 1878–1939.

LAC 13127
Philadelphia and her merchants as constituted fifty – seventy years ago; illustrated by diagrams of the river front, and portraits of some of the prominent occupants, together with sketches of character, and incidents and anecdotes of the day. Philadelphia, The author, 1860.
Ritter, Abraham.

LAC 11277
Philadelphia and its manufactures; a handbook of the great manufactories and representative mercantile houses of Philadelphia, in 1867. Philadelphia, E. Young & co. [1867]
Freedley, Edwin Troxell, 1824–1904.

LAC 40091
Philadelphia and Reading railroad company; its financial history. By George M'Henry, with the suppressed report of the committee of directors... 3d ed., rev. and corrected. Philadelphia, January, 1881.
McHenry, George, of *Philadelphia*.

LAC 12075
The Philadelphia magazines and their contributors, 1741–1850. Philadelphia, R. M. Lindsay, 1892.
Smyth, Albert Henry, 1863–1907.

LAC 15848
The Philadelphia Negro; a social study by W. E. Burghardt Du Bois. Together with a special report on domestic service by Isabel Eaton. Philadelphia, Published for the University, 1899.
Du Bois, William Edward Burghardt, 1868–1963.

LAC 13937
The philanthropic work of Josephine Shaw Lowell; containing a biographical sketch of her life, together with a selection of her public papers and private letters, collected and arranged for publication. New York, The Macmillan company, 1911.
Stewart, William Rhinelander, 1852–1929.

LAC 13645
Philanthropy and social progress; seven essays ... delivered before the school of applied ethics at Plymouth, Mass., during the session of 1892. With introduction by Professor Henry C. Adams. New York, Boston, T. Y. Crowell & company [c1893]

LAC 16695
Philanthropy in the history of American higher education. Washington, Govt. print. off., 1922.
Sears, Jesse Brundage, 1876–

LAC 16419
Philip Hooker; a contribution to the study of the renaissance in America. New York, C. Scribner's sons, 1929.
Root, Edward Wales.

LAC 22667
Philip Vickers Fithian, journal and letters, 1767–1774, student at Princeton college, 1770–72, tutor at Nomini Hall in Virginia, 1773–74; edited for the Princeton historical association by John Rogers Williams. Princeton, N. J., The University library, 1900–34.
Fithian, Philip Vickers, 1747–1776.

LAC 11150
Philippine affairs; a retrospect and outlook; an address, by Jacob Gould Schurman. 2d ed. New York, C. Scribner's sons, 1902.
Schurman, Jacob Gould, 1854–

LAC 40031
The Philippine Islands and America's interests in the Far East. An address delivered by John Barrett before the Shanghai general chamber of commerce, January 12th, 1899, together with extracts from addresses delivered before the Oriental society of Tokio and the Odd volumes society of Hongkong. [Hongkong, Printed by Kelly & Walsh, 1899]
Barrett, John, 1866–

LAC 12964
The Philippine islands and their people; a record of personal observation and experience, with a short summary of the more important facts in the history of the archipelago. New York, The Macmillan company; London, Macmillan & co., ltd., 1899, [c1898]
Worcester, Dean Conant, 1866–1924.

LAC 40010
Philippine policy, History of the.
An epitome of historical events and of official and other correspondence connected with the acquisition and other dealings of the United States with the Philippine Islands. Prepared by Erving Winslow. May 29, 1902.– Ordered to be printed as a document. Washington, Govt. print. off., 1902.
Winslow, Erving, 1839–1922.

LAC 40124
The Philippine situation. Testimony and statements of witnesses, American and foreign, concerning conduct of our army, reconcentration, effect of our administration on the people, Filipino self-government and effect of American withdrawal, foreign testimony on Filipino character and the situation... Washington, Govt. print. off., 1902.
U.S. *Congress. Senate. Committee on the Philippines.*

LAC 13600
The Philippines and round about, by Major G. J. Younghusband, with illustrations and map. New York, The Macmillan company; [etc., etc.] 1899.
Younghusband, *Sir* George John, 1859–1944.

LAC 13774
The Philippines and the purpose. Being the facts concerning the Philippines and the acts of the administration in relation thereto, as officially transmitted by the President to Congress–proving the purpose of imperialism. [Washington, D. C., The Jeffersonian Democrat pub. co., 1900]
Thomas, Aretas W.

LAC 14674

The Philippines: The first civil governor, by Theodore Roosevelt; Civil government in the Philippines, by William H. Taft... New York, The Outlook company, 1902.

LAC 16556

The Philippines: the war and the people; a record of personal observations and experiences. New York, McClure, Phillips & co., 1901.
Robinson, Albert Gardner, 1855–1932.

LAC 15314

Philosophical and miscellaneous papers. Lately written by B. Franklin. London: Printed for C. Dilly, M.DCC.LXXXVII.
Franklin, Benjamin, 1706–1790.

LAC 16870

A philosophical and political history of the British settlements and trade in North America. From the French of Abbe Raynal. With an introductory preface, not in the first edition. To which is annexed, An impartial history of the present war in America: from its commencement, to the present time. Edinburgh, Printed by C. Denovan, 1779.
Raynal, Guillaume Thomas Francois, 1713–1796.

LAC 16810

Philosophical discussions, by Chauncey Wright; with a biographical sketch of the author, by Charles Eliot Norton. New York, H. Holt and company, 1877.
Wright, Chauncey, 1830–1875.

LAC 13998

Philosophy as absolute science, founded in the universal laws of being, and including ontology, theology, and psychology made one, as spirit, soul, and body. By E. L. & A. L. Frothingham. Vol. 1. Boston, Walker, Wise and company, 1864.
Frothingham, Ephraim Langdon.

LAC 14512

The philosophy of education; being the foundations of education in the related natural and mental sciences. New York, The Macmillan company; London, Macmillan & co., ltd., 1904.
Horne, Herman Harrell, 1874–1946.

LAC 10539

The philosophy of Friedrich Nietzsche. Boston, Luce and company, 1908.
Mencken, Henry Louis, 1880–1956.

LAC 14713

The philosophy of human nature. Gainesville, Fla., Scholars' Facsimiles & Reprints, 1969.
Buchanan, Joseph, 1785–1829.

LAC 16808

The philosophy of loyalty. New York, The Macmillan company, 1908.
Royce, Josiah, 1855–1916.

LAC 16902

The philosophy of Negro suffrage. Washington, D. C., 1897.
Riley, Jerome R.

LAC 11364

The philosophy of price, and its relation to domestic currency. Chicago, The Chicago sentinel publishing co. [c1887]
Dunning, Nelson A.

LAC 40086

The philosophy of the labor movement. Boston, G. H. Ellis, printer, 1874.
Hinckley, Frederic Allen.

LAC 40074

The philosophy of the labor movement. A paper read before the International labor congress, Chicago, Ill., September, 1893. [New York, The American federation of labor, 1893?]
McNeill, George Edwin, 1837–1906.

LAC 11821

The philosophy of the plays of Shakspere unfolded. By Delia Bacon. With a preface by Nathaniel Hawthorne. London, Groombridge and sons, 1857.
Bacon, Delia Salter, 1811–1859.

LAC 10503

The philosophy of wealth. Economic principles newly formulated. Boston, Ginn & company, 1886.
Clark, John Bates, 1847–1938.

LAC 23146–50

The photographic history of the civil war... Francis Trevelyan Miller, editor-in-chief; Robert S. Lanier, managing editor. Thousands of scenes photographed 1861–65, with text by many special authorities. New York, The Review of reviews co., 1911–12 [v. 1–2, 1912]
Miller, Francis Trevelyan, 1877–   *ed.*

LAC 14186

Phrenology proved, illustrated, and applied, accompanied by a chart ... together with a view of the moral and theological bearing of the science. By O. S. & L. N. Fowler, assisted by Samuel Kirkham. 4th ed. Philadelphia, Fowler and Brevoort, 1839.
Fowler, Orson Squire, 1809–1887.

LAC 12663

The physical geography of the sea. New York, Harper & brothers, 1855.
Maury, Matthew Fontaine, 1806–1873.

LAC 15774

Physical observations, and medical tracts and researches, on the topography and diseases of Louisiana. New-York: Printed by T. and J. Swords, 1817.
Heustis, Jabez Wiggins, 1784–1841.

LAC 12690

The physical papers of Henry Augustus Rowland ... Johns Hopkins university, 1876–1901; collected for publication by a committee of the faculty of the university. Baltimore, The Johns Hopkins press, 1902.
Rowland, Henry Augustus, 1848–1901.

LAC 12592
The physicians and surgeons of the United States.
Philadelphia, C. Robson, 1878.
Atkinson, William Biddle, 1832–1909, *ed.*

LAC 10873
The physiology of New York boarding-houses. With illus. on wood, designed and drawn by the "Triangle," A. R. Waud, and the author, and engraved by John Andrew. New York, Mason Brothers, 1857.
Gunn, Thomas Butler.

LAC 20078
Pianos and their makers. Covina, Cal., Covina publishing company, 1911–13.
Dolge, Alfred, 1848–

LAC 22568–69
The pictorial field-book of the revolution; or, Illustrations, by pen and pencil, of the history, biography, scenery, relics, and traditions of the war for independence. By Benson J. Lossing. With eleven hundred engravings on wood, by Lossing and Barritt, chiefly from original sketches by the author. New York, Harper & brothers, 1859–60.
Lossing, Benson John, 1813–1891.

LAC 14918–19
The pictorial field-book of the war of 1812; or, Illustrations, by pen and pencil, of the history, biography, scenery, relics, and traditions of the last war for American independence. By Benson J. Lossing. With several hundred engravings on wood, by Lossing and Barritt, chiefly from original sketches by the author. New York, Harper & brothers, 1869, [c1868]
Lossing, Benson John, 1813–1891.

LAC 13709
Pictorial history of America's new possessions, the isthmian canals, and the problem of expansion ... with chapters on the policy of American expansion, contributed by President William McKinley, Ex-Pres. Grover Cleveland ... [and others] Chicago, The Dominion company [c1898]
Halstead, Murat, 1829–1908.

LAC 22570–71
Pictorial history of the civil war in the United States of America. By Benson J. Lossing. Illustrated by engravings on wood, by Lossing and Barritt, from sketches by the author and others. Philadelphia, D. McKay, 1874–1900.
Lossing, Benson John, 1813–1891.

LAC 13435
The pictorial sketch-book of Pennsylvania. Or, its scenery, internal improvements, resources, and agriculture, popularly described. [2d ed.] Philadelphia, W. Bromwell, 1853.
Bowen, Eli, *b.* 1824.

LAC 10900
The picture of Philadelphia, giving an account of its origin, increase and improvements in arts, sciences, manufactures, commerce and revenue. With a compendious view of its societies, literary, benevolent, patriotic, & religious. Its police–the public buildings–the prison and penetentiary [!] system–institutions, monied and civil–museum. Philadelphia: Published by B. & T. Kite, no. 20. N. Third-street. For sale by them and Joseph Delaplaine. 1811.
Mease, James, 1771–1846.

LAC 12784
Picture of slavery in the United States of America...
Boston, I. Knapp, 1838, [c1834]
Bourne, George, 1780–1845.

LAC 12250
Pictures of Rhode Island in the past, 1642–1833, by travellers and observers. Providence, R. I., Preston & Rounds co., 1900.
Kimball, Gertrude Selwyn, 1863–1910, *ed.*

LAC 12860
Pictures of slavery in church and state; including personal reminiscences, biographical sketches, anecdotes, etc. etc. with an appendix, containing the views of John Wesley and Richard Watson on slavery. By Rev. John Dixon Long. 3d ed. Auburn, W. J. Moses, 1859.
Long, John Dixon, 1817–1894.

LAC 15860
Pictures of southern life, social, political, and military. Written for the London times. New York, J. G. Gregory, 1861.
Russell, *Sir* William Howard, 1820–1907.

LAC 23144–45
Picturesque America; or, The land we live in. A delineation by pen and pencil of the mountains, rivers, lakes, forests, water-falls, shores, canons, valleys, cities, and other picturesque features of our country. With illustrations on steel and wood, by eminent American artists. New York, D. Appleton and company [c1872–74]
Bryant, William Cullen, 1794–1878, *ed.*

LAC 40088
The picturesque beauties of the Hudson River and its vicinity; illustrated in a series of views, from original drawings, taken expressly for this work, and engraved on steel, by distinguished artists. With historical and descriptive illustrations. [pt. I–II] New-York, J. Disturnell, 1835–36.
Knapp, Samuel Lorenzo, 1783–1838.

LAC 23304–5
A pilgrimage in Europe and America, leading to the discovery of the sources of the Mississippi and Bloody river; with a description of the whole course of the former, and of the Ohio. By J. C. Beltrami. London, Hunt and Clarke, 1828.
Beltrami, Giacomo Constantino, 1779–1855.

LAC 14864
Pilgrims of '48; one man's part in the Austrian revolution of 1848, and a family migration to America, by Josephine Goldmark; with a preface by Josef Redlich. New Haven, Yale university press; London, H. Milford, Oxford university press, 1930.
Goldmark, Josephine Clara, 1877–

LAC 10792
Pine tree ballads: rhymed stories of unplaned human natur' up in Maine. Boston, Small, Maynard & company, 1902.
Day, Holman Francis, 1865–1935.

LAC 16012
The Pinkerton labor spy. New York, Wilshire book co. [c1907]
Friedman, Morris, 1883–

LAC 15136
Pinkerton's national detective agency and its connection with labor troubles at Homestead, Penn., July 6th, 1892, with extracts from proofs before the judiciary committees of the U.S. Senate and House of representatives. [New York, 1892]
Pinkerton's National Detective Agency.

LAC 13223
Pioneer history: being an account of the first examinations of the Ohio valley, and the early settlement of the Northwest territory. Chiefly from original manuscripts... Cincinnati, For the Historical society of Cincinnati, by H. W. Derby & co., 1848.
Hildreth, Samuel Prescott, 1783–1863.

LAC 10854
Pioneer life in and around Cedar Rapids, Iowa, from 1839 to 1849. Cedar Rapids, Ia., Times printing and binding house, 1895.
Carroll, George Ryerson, 1831–1895.

LAC 10997
Pioneer life in the West.
Autobiography of Rev. James B. Finley; or, Pioneer life in the West. Edited by W. P. Strickland, D. D. Cincinnati, Printed at the Methodist book concern, for the author, 1854, [c1853]
Finley, James Bradley, 1781–1856.

LAC 16346
Pioneer papers, comprising a collection of the recollections of early events of Bloomington, Iowa, now Muscatine, and its surroundings, being a short history of the business men, the schools, the churches, and the early politics of the pioneers. Muscatine, 1899.
Walton, Josiah Proctor, 1826–1899.

LAC 40148
The pioneer press of Kentucky, from the printing of the first paper west of the Alleghanies, Aug. 11, 1787, to the establishment of the daily press in 1830. [Louisville, Ky.] J. P. Morton & company, 1888.
Perrin, William Henry, *d.* 1892?

LAC 13265
Pioneer reminiscences of Puget sound; the tragedy of Leschi; an account of the coming of the first Americans and the establishment of their institutions; their encounters with the native race; the first treaties with the Indians and the war that followed; seven years of the life of Isaac I. Stevens in Washington territory; cruise of the author on Puget sound fifty years ago; Nisqually house and the Hudson bay company... Seattle, Wash., Lowman & Hanford stationery and printing co., 1905.
Meeker, Ezra, 1830–1928.

LAC 13184
Pioneer women of the West. New York, C. Scribner, 1852.
Ellet, Elizabeth Fries, 1818–1877.

LAC 16882
Pioneering the West, 1846 to 1878; Major Howard Egan's diary, also thrilling experiences of pre-frontier life among Indians, their traits, civil and savage, and part of autobiography, inter-related to his father's by Howard R. Egan, ed., comp., and connected in nearly chronological order, by Wm. M. Egan. Richmond, Utah, Howard R. Egan estate, 1917.
Egan, Howard, 1815–1878.

LAC 12327
The pioneers of Massachusetts, a descriptive list, drawn from records of the colonies, towns, and churches, and other contemporaneous documents. Baltimore, Genealogical Pub. co., 1965.
Pope, Charles Henry, 1841–1918.

LAC 14836
Pioneers of modern physical training. 2d ed., rev. and enl. New York [etc.] Association press, 1915.
Leonard, Fred Eugene, 1866–1922.

LAC 14592
Pioneers of religious liberty in America; being the Great and Thursday lectures delivered in Boston in nineteen hundred and three. Boston, American Unitarian association, 1903.

LAC 14118
Pioneers of science in America; sketches of their lives and scientific work. Reprinted with additions from the Popular science monthly. Ed. and rev. by William Jay Youmans. New York, D. Appleton and company, 1896.
Youmans, William Jay, 1838–1901.

LAC 15294
The pioneers of the West; or, Life in the woods. New-York, Carlton & Porter; Boston, J. P. Magee [c1856]
Strickland, William Peter, 1809–1884.

LAC 15193
Pioneers of the Western Reserve. Boston, Lee and Shepard; New York, C. T. Dillingham, 1883.
Rice, Harvey, 1800–1891.

LAC 14943
The pioneers of Utica: being sketches of its inhabitants and its institutions, with the civil history of the place, from the earliest settlement to the year 1825,—the era of the opening of the Erie canal. Utica, N. Y., Curtiss & Childs, 1877.
Bagg, Moses Mears, *d.* 1900.

LAC 40132
Piracy and the slave trade, a charge to the grand jury, first delivered in the Circuit court of the United States, for the judicial district of Maine, at its first session in Portland, May 8, 1820. [Boston, Little and Brown, 1852]
Story, Joseph, 1779–1845.

LAC 13203
The pirates of the Mississippi. Tr. from the German. London and New York, G. Routledge & co., 1856.
Gerstacker, Friedrich Wilhelm Christian, 1816–1872.

LAC 11304
Pittsburgh and Allegheny in the centennial year. Pittsburgh, A. A. Anderson & son, book and job printers, 1876.
Thurston, George Henry, 1822–

LAC 11303
Pittsburgh as it is; or, Facts and figures, exhibiting the past and present of Pittsburgh; its advantages, resources, manufactures, and commerce. Pittsburgh, W. S. Haven, printer, 1857.
Thurston, George Henry, *b.* 1822.

LAC 22524-27

The Pittsburgh survey; findings in six volumes, edited by Paul Underwood Kellogg. New York, Charities publication committee, 1909-14.

LAC 15093

A plain and faithful narrative of the original design, rise, progress and present state of the Indian charity-school at Lebanon, in Connecticut. Boston, R. and S. Draper, 1763.
Wheelock, Eleazar, 1711-1779.

LAC 10984

Plain and familiar discourses for the instruction of the unlearned.
Plantation sermons; or, Plain and familiar discourses for the instruction of the unlearned. By the Rev. A. F. Dickson. Philadelphia, Presbyterian board of publication [c1856]
Dickson, Andrew Flinn, 1825-1879.

LAC 10075

Plain and pleasant talk about fruits, flowers and farming. New York, Derby & Jackson, 1859.
Beecher, Henry Ward, 1813-1887.

LAC 13390

A plain man's talk on the labor question. New York, Harper & brothers, 1886.
Newcomb, Simon, 1835-1909.

LAC 16795

Plaine path-way to plantations; that is, A discourse in generall, concerning the plantation of our English people in other countries. Wherein is declared, that the attempts or actions, in themselues are very good and laudable, necessary also for our country of England. Doubts thereabout are answered: and some meanes are shewed, by which the same may, in better sort then hitherto, be prosecuted and effected. Written for the perswading and stirring vp of the people of this land, chiefly the poorer and common sort to affect and effect these attempts better then yet they doe. With certaine motiues for a present plantation in New-foundland aboue the rest. Made in the manner of a conference, and diuided into three parts, for the more plainnesse, ease, and delight to the reader. By Richard Ebvrne of Hengstridge in the countie of Somerset. [London] Printed by G. P. for Iohn Marriot, 1624.
Eburne, Richard.

LAC 40036

Plain reasons for the great Republican movement. What we want; why we want it; and what will come if we fail. Remarks made at a public meeting in Geneva, N. Y., July 19, 1856. 2d ed. New York, Dix, Edwards & co., 1856.
Henry, Caleb Sprague, 1804-1884.

LAC 12200

Plain talks on familiar subjects. A series of popular lectures. New York, C. Scribner & co., 1866.
Holland, Josiah Gilbert, 1819-1881.

LAC 40125

Plain truth; addressed to the inhabitants of America, containing remarks on a late pamphlet, entitled Common sense... Written by Candidus [pseud.] Philadelphia: Printed, and sold, by R. Bell, in Third-street, 1776.
Chalmers, James, 1727?-1806.

LAC 40001

Plan of an improved system of the money-concerns of the Union. Philadelphia: Printed for the author. William Fry, printer, Walnut, near Fifth street, 1816.
Bollmann, Erick, 1769-1821.

LAC 40036

A plan of brotherly copartnership of the North and South, for the peaceful extinction of slavery. New York, Dayton and Burdick, 1856.
Burritt, Elihu, 1810-1879.

LAC 40041

The plan of the city of Columbus; report made to the Honorable Charles A. Bond, mayor, to the Honorable Board of public service, and to the Honorable City council, by Austin W. Lord, Albert Kelsey, Charles N. Lowrie, Charles Mulford Robinson, H. A. MacNeil, plan commission, February, 1908. [Columbus, 1908]
Columbus, O. Plan Commission.

LAC 10853

A plan of the city of Hartford. Preliminary report by Carrere & Hastings, advisory architects, to the Commission on the city plan of the city of Hartford, Connecticut, in relation to the rectification of the present plan and the development and extension of the city... Hartford, Case, Lockwood & Brainard company, 1912.
Carrere & Hastings, architects.

LAC 16953

Plans and sections of the obelisk on Bunker's Hill. With the details of experiments made in quarrying the granite. Boston [Printed by S. N. Dickinson] 1843.
Willard, Solomon, 1783-1861.

LAC 21119

Plantation and frontier, 1649-1863. New York, B. Franklin [1969]
Phillips, Ulrich Bonnell, 1877-1934, ed.

LAC 12797

The plantation negro as a freeman; observations on his character, condition, and prospects in Virginia. New York [etc.] G. P. Putnam's sons, 1889.
Bruce, Philip Alexander, 1856-1933.

LAC 10984

Plantation sermons; or, Plain and familiar discourses for the instruction of the unlearned. By the Rev. A. F. Dickson. Philadelphia, Presbyterian board of publication [c1856]
Dickson, Andrew Flinn, 1825-1879.

LAC 12791

The planter: or, Thirteen years in the South. By a northern man. Philadelphia, H. Hooker, 1853.
Brown, David, 1786-1875.

LAC 40093

The planters plea. Boston, Massachusetts historical society, 1930.
White, John, 1575-1648.

LAC 11191

Platform echoes: or, Living truths for head and heart... With a history of Mr. Gough's life and work, by Rev. Lyman Abbott, D. D. Superbly illustrated with two hundred and twenty-five engravings... Hartford, Conn., A. D. Worthington & co., 1890.
Gough, John Bartholomew, 1817-1886.

LAC 15596
A platform of church discipline.
A vindication of the government of New England churches. Boston, John Boyles, 1772.
Wise, John, 1652–1725.

LAC 15328
Players of a century. A record of the Albany stage. Including notices of prominent actors who have appeared in America. Albany, J. McDonough, 1880.
Phelps, Henry Pitt, 1844–

LAC 16335
Plays and players. New York, Hurd and Houghton, 1875.
Hutton, Laurence, 1843–1904.

LAC 13601–2
Plays and poems. 2d ed. Boston, Ticknor and Fields, 1857.
Boker, George Henry, 1823–1890.

LAC 13300
Plays, prose and poetry. Philadelphia, E. H. Butler & co., 1848.
Barnes, Charlotte Mary Sanford, 1819?–1863.

LAC 40077
A plea for Africa. A sermon preached October 26, 1817, in the First Presbyterian church in the city of New-York, before the Synod of New-York and New-Jersey, at the request of the board of directors of the African school established by the synod. Pub. by request of the board. New-York, Gould, printer, 1817.
Griffin, Edward Dorr, 1770–1837.

LAC 10149
A plea for colleges. 2d ed. Cincinnati, Truman and Smith, 1836.
Beecher, Lyman, 1775–1863.

LAC 40109
A plea for religious liberty and the rights of conscience. An argument delivered in the Supreme court of the United States, April 28, 1886, in three cases of Lorenzo Snow, plaintiff in error, *v.* The United States, on writs of error to the Supreme court of Utah territory. Washington, D. C., Printed for the author, by Gibson bros., 1886.
Curtis, George Ticknor, 1812–1894.

LAC 40081
A plea for social and popular repose; being an address delivered before the Philomathean and Eucleian societies of the University of the city of New-York, July 1, 1845. New-York, Tribune job printing establishment, 1845.
Barnard, Daniel Dewey, 1797–1861.

LAC 40003
A plea for the smaller college. An address delivered on Founder's day at Alma College, June 16, 1897. Detroit, J. Bornman, 1898.
Cooper, David Mack, 1827–1908.

LAC 40050
A plea for the training of the hand, by D. C. Gilman. Manual training and the public school, by H. H. Belfield. Ed. by Nicholas Murray Butler. New York, Industrial education association, 1888.
Butler, Nicholas Murray, 1862–1947, *ed.*

LAC 10453
A plea for the West. 2d ed. Cincinnati, Truman & Smith; New York, Leavitt, Lord & co., 1835.
Beecher, Lyman, 1775–1863.

LAC 12724
The plum tree, by David Graham Phillips. Illustrated by E. M. Ashe. Indianapolis, The Bobbs-Merrill company [1905]
Phillips, David Graham, 1867–1911.

LAC 11538
Plunkitt of Tammany Hall; a series of very plain talks on very practical politics, delivered by Ex-senator George Washington Plunkitt, the Tammany philosopher, from his rostrum–the New York County courthouse bootblack stand–and recorded by William I. Riordon. New York, McClure, Phillips & co., 1905.
Riordon, William L.

LAC 12039
Plutocracy; or, American white slavery; a politico-social novel. New York, The American News company, 1888.
Norwood, Thomas Manson, 1830–1913.

LAC 40118
A poem, on the rising glory of America; being an exercise delivered at the public commencement at Nassau-hall, September 25, 1771... Philadelphia: Printed by Joseph Crukshank, for R. Aitken, bookseller, opposite London-coffee-house, in Front-street, M.DCC.LXXII.
Freneau, Philip Morin, 1752–1832.

LAC 16183
Poems by Emily Dickinson. Ed. by Mabel Loomis Todd and T. W. Higginson. Boston, Roberts brothers, 1890.
Dickinson, Emily, 1830–1886.

LAC 16334
Poems by Emily Dickinson, edited by two of her friends, T. W. Higginson and Mabel Loomis Todd. Second series. Boston, Roberts brothers, 1892.
Dickinson, Emily, 1830–1886.

LAC 12674
Poems, by Emily Dickinson, ed. by Mabel Loomis Todd. 3d series. Boston, Roberts brothers, 1896.
Dickinson, Emily, 1830–1886.

LAC 13452
Poems. Freeport, N. Y., Books for libraries press, 1970.
Harper, Frances Ellen Watkins, 1825–1911.

LAC 13557
Poems. Boston and New York, Houghton, Mifflin and company [c1899]
Hay, John, 1838–1905.

LAC 12076
Poems. Collected by Ina Coolbrith. New York, J. Lane, 1917.
Stoddard, Charles Warren, 1843–1909.

LAC 12097
Poems. Boston, Ticknor and Fields, 1864.
Tuckerman, Frederick Goddard, 1821–1873.

LAC 21845–49
The poems and prose sketches of James Whitcomb Riley... [Homestead ed.] New York, C. Scribner's sons, 1904–1914, [c1897–1914]
Riley, James Whitcomb, 1849–1916.

LAC 20608
Poems and prose writings. New York, Baker and Scribner, 1850, [c1849]
Dana, Richard Henry, 1787–1879.

LAC 11909
The poems and prose writings of Sumner Lincoln Fairfield. In two volumes. Vol. I. Philadelphia, Printed for the proprietor, 1841.
Fairfield, Sumner Lincoln, 1803–1844.

LAC 20382
Poems; descriptive, dramatic, legendary and contemplative. New York, Redfield, 1853.
Simms, William Gilmore, 1806–1870.

LAC 40123
Poems for our children: designed for families, Sabbath schools, and infant schools. Written to inculcate moral truths and virtuous sentiments. Boston, Marsh, Capen & Lyon, 1830.
Hale, Sarah Josepha, 1788–1879.

LAC 11858
The poems of Alice and Phoebe Cary. New York, Hurst & company [n.d.]
Cary, Alice, 1820–1871.

LAC 11966
The poems of Charles Fenno Hoffman. Collected and edited by his nephew, Edward Fenno Hoffman. Philadelphia, Porter & Coates, 1873.
Hoffman, Charles Fenno, 1806–1884.

LAC 20636
The poems of Emma Lazarus... Boston and New York, Houghton, Mifflin and company, 1889.
Lazarus, Emma, 1849–1887.

LAC 11844
The poems of H. C. Bunner... New ed. New York, C. Scribner's sons, 1899.
Bunner, Henry Cuyler, 1855–1896.

LAC 14990
Poems of Henry Timrod; with memoir and portrait. Boston and New York, Houghton, Mifflin and company, 1899.
Timrod, Henry, 1828–1867.

LAC 12116
Poems of passion, by Ella Wheeler. Chicago, W. B. Conkey company [c1883]
Wilcox, Ella, 1855–1919.

LAC 20626–27
The poems of Philip Freneau, poet of the American revolution; edited for the Princeton historical association by Fred Lewis Pattee... Princeton, N. J., The University library, 1902–07.
Freneau, Philip Morin, 1752–1832.

LAC 11804
Poems of religion and society, by John Quincy Adams, sixth president of the United States ... with notices of his life and character, by John Davis and T. H. Benton. [4th thousand] Auburn and Buffalo, Miller, Orton & Mulligan, 1854, [c1848]
Adams, John Quincy, pres. U. S., 1767–1848.

LAC 12673
The poems of Roger Wolcott, esq: 1725. Boston, The Club of odd volumes, 1898.
Wolcott, Roger, 1679–1767.

LAC 11859
Poems of sixty-five years, by Ellery Channing; selected and ed. by F. B. Sanborn. Philadelphia and Concord, J. H. Bentley, 1902.
Channing, William Ellery, 1818–1901.

LAC 15558
The poems of Trumbull Stickney. Boston and New York, Houghton, Mifflin & co., 1905.
Stickney, Trumbull, 1874–1904.

LAC 40015
The poems of Washington Irving, brought together from various sources by William R. Langfeld. New York, The New York public library, 1931.
Irving, Washington, 1783–1859.

LAC 40118
Poems on miscellaneous subjects, by Frances Ellen Watkins. 10th thousand. Philadelphia, Merrihew & Thompson, printers, 1857. [Philadelphia, Rhistoric Publications, n.d.]
Harper, Frances Ellen, 1825–1911.

LAC 40118
Poems on several occasions; by a gentleman of Virginia; edited by Earl Gregg Swem. New York, Reprinted for C. F. Heartman, 1920.

LAC 14458
Poems on several occasions, by Mather Byles; reproduced from the edition of 1744, with an introduction by C. Lennart Carlson. New York, Pub. for the Facsimile text society by Columbia university press, 1940.
Byles, Mather, 1707–1788.

LAC 15317
Poems on several occasions, with some other compositions. By Nathaniel Evans, A. M., late missionary (appointed by the Society for propagating the gospel) for Gloucester county, in New-Jersey; and chaplain to the Lord Viscount Kilmorey, of the kingdom of Ireland. Philadelphia: Printed by John Dunlap, in Market-street, M.DCC.LXXII.
Evans, Nathaniel, 1742–1767.

LAC 12968
Poems on various subjects, religious and moral. By Phillis Wheatley, negro servant to Mr. John Wheatley, of Boston, in New-England. London: Printed for A. Bell, bookseller, Aldgate; and sold by Messrs. Cox and Berry, King-street, Boston, 1773.
Wheatley, Phillis, *afterwards* Phillis Peters, 1753?–1784.

LAC 12086
The poetical works of Bayard Taylor. Household ed. Boston and New York, Houghton Mifflin, 1899, [c1894]
Taylor, Bayard, 1825–1878.

LAC 15556
The poetical works of Edmund Clarence Stedman. Household ed. Boston and New York, Houghton, Mifflin and company [c1891]
Stedman, Edmund Clarence, 1833–1908.

LAC 12087
The poetical works of Edward Taylor, edited with an introduction and notes by Thomas H. Johnson. New York, Rockland editions [c1939]
Taylor, Edward, 1642–1729.

LAC 11956
The poetical works of Fitz-Greene Halleck. Now first collected. Illustrated with steel engravings, from drawings by American artists. New York, D. Appleton & company; Philadelphia, G. S. Appleton, 1847.
Halleck, Fitz-Greene, 1790–1867.

LAC 16866
The poetical works of James Madison Bell... Lansing, Mich., Press of Wynkoop, Hallenbeck, Crawford co. [1904?]
Bell, James Madison, 1826–1902.

LAC 20655
The poetical works of John Trumbull, LL. D. Containing M'Fingal, a modern epic poem, revised and corrected, with copious explanatory notes; The progress of dulness: and a collection of poems on various subjects, written before and during the revolutionary war... Hartford: Printed for Samuel G. Goodrich, by Lincoln & Stone, MDCCCXX.
Trumbull, John, 1750–1831.

LAC 11842
The poetical works of William Cullen Bryant. Ed. by Parke Godwin. New York, D. Appleton and company, 1883.
Bryant, William Cullen, 1794–1878.

LAC 11952
The poets and poetry of America. With an historical introduction. 2d ed., rev. ... Philadelphia, Carey and Hart, 1842.
Griswold, Rufus Wilmot, 1815–1857.

LAC 11872
The poets and poetry of the West: with biographical and critical notices. New York, Follett, Foster & co., 1860.
Coggeshall, William Turner, 1824–1867.

LAC 16205
Poets of America. Boston and New York, Houghton Mifflin company [c1885]
Stedman, Edmund Clarence, 1833–1908.

LAC 16859
The poets of transcendentalism, an anthology. With introductory essay and biographical notes. Boston and New York, Houghton, Mifflin and company, 1903.
Cooke, George Willis, 1848–1923, *ed.*

LAC 12845
The police control of the slave in South Carolina... Emory, Va., 1914.
Henry, Howell Meadoes, 1879–

LAC 14949
The police power of the state and decisions thereon as illustrating the development and value of case law. Chicago, Callaghan & company, 1900.
Russell, Alfred, 1830–1906.

LAC 12743
The police power, public policy and constitutional rights. Chicago, Callaghan & company, 1904.
Freund, Ernst, 1864–1932.

LAC 15495
The Polish Jew, his social and economic value. New York, The Macmillan company, 1906.
Baskerville, Beatrice C.

LAC 23197–99
The Polish peasant in Europe and America; monograph of an immigrant group, by William I. Thomas and Florian Znaniecki. Boston, R. G. Badger [c1918–20]
Thomas, William Isaac, 1863–1947.

LAC 40054
Politian, an unfinished tragedy, by Edgar A. Poe, edited from the original sources, including the autograph ms. in the Pierpont Morgan library, with notes and a commentary, by Thomas Ollive Mabbott. Menasha, Wis., George Banta publishing company, 1923.
Poe, Edgar Allan, 1809–1849.

LAC 40090
The political activity of Wisconsin Germans, 1854–1860. [Madison, Democratic Printing Co., state printer, 1902]
Bruncken, Ernest, 1865–1933.

LAC 20956–57
A political and civil history of the United States of America, from the year 1763 to the close of the administration of President Washington, in March, 1797: including a summary view of the political and civil state of the North American colonies, prior to that period. New Haven, H. Howe and Durrie & Peck, 1828.
Pitkin, Timothy, 1766–1847.

LAC 14754
Political and constitutional law of the United States of America. St. Louis, G. I. Jones and company, 1876.
Bateman, William O.

LAC 13730
A political and constitutional study of the Cumberland road... Chicago, 1902.
Young, Jeremiah Simeon, 1866–

LAC 13749
The political and economic doctrines of John Marshall, who for thirty-four years was chief justice of the United States. And also his letters, speeches, and hitherto unpublished and uncollected writings, by John Edward Oster. New York, The Neale publishing company, 1914.
Marshall, John, 1755–1835.

LAC 11286
The political and financial opinions of Peter Cooper. Ed. by Prof. J. C. Zachos. New York, Trow's printing and bookbinding company, 1877.
Cooper, Peter, 1791–1883.

LAC 14237
Political and official papers. New York, G. P. Putnam & sons, 1872.
Kennedy, John Pendleton, 1795–1870.

LAC 16742
Political and philosophical speculations on the distinguishing characteristics of the present century ... with occasional reflections on the probable effects of American independency... London, printed for Fielding and Walker, 1778.
Linguet, Simon Nicolas Henri, 1736–1794.

LAC 12541
The political class book; intended to instruct the higher classes in schools, in the origin, nature, and use of political power... By William Sullivan. With an appendix upon studies for practical men; with notices of books suited to their use. By George B. Emerson. Boston, Richardson, Lord & Holbrook, 1830.
Sullivan, William, 1774–1839.

LAC 10108
Political, commercial, and moral reflections on the late cession of Louisiana to the United States. Lexington, Ky., printed by D. Bradford, 1803.
Magruder, Allan Bowie, 1775–1822.

LAC 12426
The political conspiracies preceding the rebellion; or, The true stories of Sumter and Pickens. New York, G. P. Putnam's sons, 1882.
Anderson, Thomas McArthur, 1836–1917.

LAC 40056
The political correspondence of the late Hon. George N. Sanders, Confederate commissioner to Europe during the civil war... To be sold at unrestricted public sale by order of the owner at the American art galleries, May 13th, 1914. [New York, 1914]
Sanders, George N.

LAC 11459
A political crime; the history of the great fraud. New York, W. S. Gottsberger, 1885.
Gibson, Albert M.

LAC 15486
The political detection; or, The treachery and tyranny of administration, both at home and abroad; displayed in a series of letters, signed Junius Americanus. London, J. and W. Oliver, 1770.
Lee, Arthur, 1740–1792.

LAC 11394
Political discussions, legislative, diplomatic, and popular 1856–1886. Norwich, Conn., The Henry Bill publishing company, 1887.
Blaine, James Gillespie, 1830–1893.

LAC 14935
Political economy for the people. New York, A. M. Kelley, 1970.
Tucker, George, 1775–1861.

LAC 40111
Political economy: founded in justice and humanity. In a letter to a friend. By W. T., Washington. City of Washington, Printed by S. H. Smith, 1804.
Thornton, William, 1761–1828.

LAC 14604
Political economy: its objects, uses, and principles, considered with reference to the condition of the American people. With a summary for the use of students. New York, Harper & Brothers, 1862.
Potter, Alonzo, 1800–1865.

LAC 40069
Political economy, or Interest, usury and taxation, showing the dangers of the hour. New York, J. Wiley & sons, 1877.
Disturnell, John, 1801–1877.

LAC 22213–15
Political essay on the kingdom of New Spain... With physical sections and maps. Tr. from the original French by John Black. London, Longman, Hurst, Rees, Orme, and Brown, 1811–1814.
Humboldt, Alexander, *freiherr* von, 1769–1859.

LAC 11673
Political essays. New York, Dix, Edwards & co., 1856.
Godwin, Parke, 1816–1904.

LAC 40040
The political family: or A discourse pointing out the reciprocal advantages, which flow from an uninterrupted union between Great Britain and her American colonies. Numb. 1. Philadelphia: Printed, By James Humphreys, junior, 1775.
Hunt, Isaac, 1742?–1809.

LAC 10358
Political history of Chicago. 1st ed. (covering the period from 1837 to 1887) Local politics from the city's birth; Chicago's mayors, aldermen and other officials; county and federal officers; the fire and police departments; the Haymarket horror; miscellaneous. Chicago, Donohue & Henneberry, printers and binders, 1886.
Ahern, M   L.

LAC 13156
Political history of Oregon. Provisional government. Treaties, conventions, and diplomatic correspondence on the boundary question; historical introduction of the explorations on the Pacific coast; history of the provisional government from year to year, with election returns and official reports; history of the Cayuse war, with original documents. Vol. I. Portland, W. B. Allen, 1892.
Brown, Joseph Henry, 1837–1898.

LAC 20311–14
A political history of the state of New York. New York, H. Holt, 1906–1923.
Alexander, De Alva Stanwood, 1846–

LAC 11543
A political history of the state of New York, 1865–1869. New York, Columbia university; [etc., etc.] 1913.
Stebbins, Homer Adolph, 1884–

LAC 12502
The political history of the United States of America, during the great rebellion, from November 6, 1860, to July 4, 1864; including a classified summary of the legislation of the second session of the Thirty-sixth Congress, the three sessions of the Thirty-seventh Congress, the first session of the Thirty-eighth Congress, with the votes thereon, and the important executive, judicial, and politico-military facts of that eventful period; together with the organization, legislation, and general proceedings of the rebel administration. Washington, D. C., Philp & Solomons; [etc., etc.] 1864.
McPherson, Edward, 1830–1895.

LAC 12501
The political history of the United States of America during the period of reconstruction, (from April 15, 1865 to July 15, 1870,) including a classified summary of the legislation of the Thirty-ninth, Fortieth, and Forty-first congresses. With the votes thereon: together with the action, congressional and state, on the fourteenth and fifteenth amendments to the Constitution of the United States, and the other important executive, legislative, politico-military, and judicial facts of that period. By Hon. Edward McPherson... New York, Negro universities [reprinted 1969]
McPherson, Edward, 1830–1895.

LAC 13763
Political parties in the United States, 1846–1861. New York, The Macmillan company; London, Macmillan & co., ltd., 1900.
Macy, Jesse, 1842–1919.

LAC 12486
The political philosophy of Robert M. La Follette as revealed in his speeches and writings. Comp. by Ellen Torelle, assisted by Albert O. Barton and Fred L. Holmes. Madison, Wis., The Robert M. La Follette co. [c1920]
La Follette, Robert Marion, 1855–1925.

LAC 12482
Political recollections, 1840 to 1872. Chicago, Jansen, McClurg & company, 1884.
Julian, George Washington, 1817–1899.

LAC 11465
Political reform by the representation of minorities. New York, The author, 1894.
Forney, Matthias Nace, 1835–1908.

LAC 11445
Political reminiscences including a sketch of the origin and history of the "Statesman party" of Boston. Boston, Printed for the author, by Homer & Palmer, 1835.
Derby, John Barton, 1793–1867.

LAC 20186
Political science and comparative constitutional law... Boston and London, Ginn & company, 1891, [c1890]
Burgess, John William, 1844–1931.

LAC 11504
The political science of John Adams; a study in the theory of mixed government and the bicameral system. New York and London, G. P. Putnam's sons, 1915.
Walsh, Correa Moylan, 1862–

LAC 20067–68
Political science; or, The state theoretically and practically considered. New York, Scribner, Armstrong & company, 1878.
Woolsey, Theodore Dwight, 1801–1889.

LAC 10655
The political shame of Mexico. New York, McBride, Nast & company, 1914.
Bell, Edward I.

LAC 11419
The political text-book, or encyclopedia. Containing everything necessary for the reference of the politicians and statesmen of the United States. 2d ed. Philadelphia, J. B. Smith & co., Washington, C. Wendell, 1858, [c1857]
Cluskey, Michael W   ed.

LAC 15687
Political thuggery; or, Bribery a national issue. Missouri's battle with the boodlers, including the great fight led by Hon. Joseph W. Folk, and the uprising of the people of the state... St. Louis, Puritan publishing co., 1904.
Tyrrell, Frank G.

LAC 20081
The political writings of John Dickinson, esquire, late president of the state of Delaware, and of the commonwealth of Pennsylvania... Wilmington [Del.] Printed and sold by Bonsal and Niles. Also, sold at their book-store, no. 173, Market-street, Baltimore, 1801.
Dickinson, John, 1732–1808.

LAC 15445
Politics and mysteries of life insurance. Boston, Lee and Shepard, 1873.
Wright, Elizur, 1804–1885.

LAC 11327
Politics and pen pictures at home and abroad. New York [etc.] G. P. Putnam's sons, 1892.
Hilliard, Henry Washington, 1808–1892.

LAC 10798

Politics and politicians of Chicago, Cook county, and Illinois. Memorial volume, 1787–1887. A complete record of municipal, county, state and national politics from the earliest period to the present time. Comp. by Fremont O. Bennett, and an account of the Haymarket massacre of May 4, 1886, and the anarchist trials... Chicago, The Blakely printing company, 1886.
Bennett, Fremont O.

LAC 40066

The politicks and views of a certain party, displayed. [n. p.] Printed in the year 1792.
Smith, William Loughton, 1758–1812.

LAC 14175

Politics for American Christians: a word upon our example as a nation, our labour, our trade, elections, education, and congressional legislation. Philadelphia, Lippincott, Grambo & co., 1852.
Colwell, Stephen, 1800–1871.

LAC 11549

Politics in a democracy; an essay. New York, Longmans, Green, and co., 1893.
Thompson, Daniel Greenleaf, 1850–1897.

LAC 11144

Polonica in English; annotated catalogue of the Archives and museum of the Polish Roman Catholic union. With 4 illustrations. By Alphonse S. Wolanin. Chicago, Polish Roman Catholic union of America, Archives and museum, 1945.
Polish Roman Catholic Union of America. *Archives and Museum.*

LAC 12062

The pomps of Satan... New York, Brentano's [1923?]
Saltus, Edgar Evertson, 1855–1921.

LAC 14038

Ponteach: or, The savages of America. A tragedy. London, Printed for the author, and sold by J. Millan, opposite the Admiralty, Whitehall, M.DCC.LXVI.
Rogers, Robert, 1731–1795.

LAC 15331

Pony tracks, written and illustrated by Frederic Remington. New York, Harper & brothers, 1895.
Remington, Frederic, 1861–1909.

LAC 30981

Poole's index to periodical literature; third supplement from Jan. 1, 1892 to Dec. 31, 1896, by William I. Fletcher, and Franklin O. Poole. With the cooperation of the American library association. Boston and New York, Houghton, Mifflin and co., 1897.

LAC 30982

Poole's index to periodical literature; fourth supplement from January 1, 1897, to January 1, 1902, by William I. Fletcher and Mary Poole. With the cooperation of the American library association. Boston and New York, Houghton, Mifflin and company, 1903.

LAC 30983

Poole's index to periodical literature; fifth supplement from January 1, 1902 to January 1, 1907, by William I. Fletcher and Mary Poole. With the cooperation of many librarians. Boston and New York, Houghton, Mifflin and company, 1908.

LAC 40144

The poore dovbting Christian drawne unto Christ. In one sermon. Wherein the maine letts and hindrances which keepe men from comming to Christ are discovered and removed... London, Printed in the year 1629.

LAC 40054

The poor of New York. A drama in five acts. By the—club. To which are added a description of the costume–cast of the characters ... stage business. As performed at Wallack's theatre, December, 1857. New York, S. French [c1857]
Boucicault, Dion, 1820?–1890.

LAC 14269

The poor rich man, and the rich poor man, by the author of "Hope Leslie," "The Linwoods," &c. New York, Harper & brothers [c1864]
Sedgwick, Catharine Maria, 1789–1867.

LAC 31121–67

The Popular science monthly. v. 1–47; May 1872–Oct. 1895. New York, D. Appleton and company.

LAC 30986

The Popular science monthly index... for the twenty volumes from 1872 to 1882, and of the three volumes of the supplement; embracing the titles of the articles in the several departments of the magazine. New York, D. Appleton, 1883.

LAC 30986

Popular science monthly index... from 1872 to 1892.
The Popular science monthly index... for the twenty volumes from 1872 to 1882, and of the three volumes of the supplement; embracing the titles of the articles in the several departments of the magazine. New York, D. Appleton, 1883.

LAC 13482

A popular treatise on the currency question written from a southern point of view. New York, G. P. Putnam's sons, 1879.
Hughes, Robert William, 1821–1901.

LAC 16890

A popular view of the doctrines of Charles Fourier. 2d ed. New York, J. S. Redfield, 1844.
Godwin, Parke, 1816–1904.

LAC 16823

Population of the city of New York, 1890–1930... compiled and edited by Walter Laidlaw, executive secretary... Publication committee: Robert E. Chaddock, Neva R. Deardorff [and] Haven Emerson. New York city, Cities census committee, inc. [c1932]
Cities Census Committee, Inc., *New York.*

LAC 40112

The Populist movement. New York, Pub. for the American economic association by the Macmillan company; London, S. Sonnenschein & co., 1896.
McVey, Frank Le Rond, 1869–

LAC 20196–207

Porcupine's works; containing various writings and selections, exhibiting a faithful picture of the United States of America; of their government, laws, politics, and resources; of the characters of their presidents, governors, legislators, magistrates, and military men; and of the customs, manners, morals, religion, virtues and vices of the people: comprising also a complete series of historical documents and remarks, from the end of the war, in 1783, to the election of the President, in March, 1801. In twelve volumes. (A volume to be added annually.)...
London, Printed for Cobbett and Morgan, 1801.
Cobbett, William, 1763–1835.

LAC 31440–84

The Port folio. By Oliver Oldschool, esq. v. 1–5, 1801–05; new ser., v. 1–6, 1806–08; new [3d] ser., v. 1–8, 1809–12; 3d [i.e. 4th] ser., v. 1–6, 1813–15; 4th [i.e. 5th] ser., v. 1–20, 1816–25. Philadelphia, Printed by H. Maxwell; [etc., etc.] 1801–26.

LAC 12829

Port Royal mission.
Slavery in South Carolina and the ex-slaves; or, The Port Royal mission. New York, W. M. French, 1862.
French, Austa Malinda, 1810–1880.

LAC 11930

The portion of labor, by Mary E. Wilkins. New York and London, Harper & brothers, 1901.
Freeman, Mary Eleanor, 1852–1930.

LAC 16227

Portrait gallery of the Chamber of commerce of the state of New-York. Catalogue and biographical sketches. Comp. by George Wilson, secretary. New-York, Press of the Chamber of commerce, 1890.
New York. Chamber of Commerce of the State of New York.

LAC 40051

Portraits of North American Indians, with sketches of scenery, etc., painted by J. M. Stanley. Deposited with the Smithsonian institution. Washington, Smithsonian institution, 1852.
Stanley, John Mix, 1814–1872.

LAC 12309

Portraits of places. London, Macmillan and co., 1883.
James, Henry, 1843–1916.

LAC 16855

A portraiture of domestic slavery, in the United States: proposing national measures for the education and gradual emancipation of the slaves, without impairing the legal privileges of the possessor; and a project of a colonial asylum for free people of color; including memoirs of facts on the interior traffic in slaves, and on kidnapping. 2d ed. Ballston Spa, Published by the author, 1818.
Torrey, Jesse, fl. 1787–1834.

LAC 10975

The position of Christianity in the United States, in its relations with our political institutions, and specially with reference to religious instruction in the public schools. Philadelphia, Lippincott, Grambo & co., 1854.
Colwell, Stephen, 1800–1871.

LAC 40034

The positive community: glimpse of the regenerated future of the human race... Modern Times (Thompson,) L. I., 1864.
Edger, Henry, 1820–1888.

LAC 16674

The pottery and porcelain of the United States; an historical review of American ceramic art from the earliest times to the present day. 2d ed., rev. and enl., with 277 illustrations. New York, London, G. P. Putnam's sons, 1901.
Barber, Edwin Atlee, 1851–1916.

LAC 40083

Poverty. Madison, Wis., 1909.
Edwards, Richard Henry, 1877–1954, ed.

LAC 11208

Poverty. New York, The Macmillan company; London, Macmillan & co., ltd., 1912, [c1904]
Hunter, Robert, 1874–1942.

LAC 40083

Poverty. [Boston, Wright & Potter, state printers, 1873]
Steward, Ira, 1831–1883.

LAC 14986

Poverty: its illegal causes and legal cure. Part first. Boston, B. Marsh, 1846.
Spooner, Lysander, 1808–1887.

LAC 10101

Power and the plow, by L. W. Ellis and Edward A. Rumely. Garden City, N. Y., Doubleday, Page & company, 1911.
Ellis, Lynn Webster, 1882–

LAC 16763

The power of Christian benevolence illustrated in the life and labors of Mary Lyon. Comp. by Edward Hitchcock with the assistance of others. 6th ed. Northampton, Hopkins, Bridgman, and company; Philadelphia, Thomas, Cowperthwait, & co., 1852.
Hitchcock, Edward, 1793–1864.

LAC 12739

Power of federal judiciary over legislation: its origin; the power to set aside laws; boundaries of the power; judicial independence; existing evils and remedies. New York and London, G. P. Putnam's sons, 1912.
Dougherty, John Hampden, 1849–1918.

LAC 22878

The power of sympathy. Reproduced from the first edition. With a bibliographical note by Milton Ellis. New York, Published for the Facsimile text society, 1937.
Brown, William Hill, 1766–1793.

LAC 14783

The power of tolerance, and other speeches. New York and London, Harper & brothers, 1911.
Harvey, George Brinton McClellan, 1864–1928.

LAC 10927

Practical Christian socialism: a conversational exposition of the true system of human society; in three parts, viz: I. Fundamental principles. II. Constitutional polity. III. Superiority to other systems. Hopedale [Mass.] The author; New York, Fowlers and Wells, 1854.
Ballou, Adin, 1803–1890.

LAC 16849

Practical Christian sociology; a series of lectures at Princeton theological seminary and Marietta college on moral reforms and social problems, with 20th-century statistics. Rev. 4th ed. New York and London, Funk & Wagnalls company, 1907.
Crafts, Wilbur Fisk, 1850–1922.

LAC 40117

A practical description of Herron's patent trellis railway structure ... also, the patent wrought iron railway chairs, new and improved mode of joining the ends of railway bars, scarfing timbers, and improved fastenings: illustrated by four large plates of working plans ... with a compendious account of the process of kyanizing, in use on the English railways, for preserving the timber from decay: and the recent discoveries of M. Boucherie by means of the pyrolignite of iron... Philadelphia, E. G. Dorsey, printer, 1841.
Herron, James.

LAC 11667

A practical detail of the cotton manufacture of the United States of America; and the state of the cotton manufacture of that country contrasted and compared with that of Great Britain; with comparative estimates of the cost of manufacturing in both countries... Glasgow, J. Niven; New York, D. Appleton & co.; [etc., etc.] 1840; New York, Johnson reprint [1968]
Montgomery, James.

LAC 10355

Practical economics; a collection of essays respecting certain of the recent economic experiences of the United States. New York & London, G. P. Putnam's sons, 1885.
Wells, David Ames, 1828–1898.

LAC 22443

Practical education: by Maria Edgeworth and by Richard Lovell Edgeworth. 1st American ed. New York, Printed by G. F. Hopkins, for self, and Brown & Stansbury, 1801.
Edgeworth, Maria, 1767–1849.

LAC 16099

Practical essays on American government. New York, Longmans, Green and co., 1905, [c1893]
Hart, Albert Bushnell, 1854–1943.

LAC 12627

Practical essays on medical education, and the medical profession, in the United States. Cincinnati, O., Roff & Young, 1832.
Drake, Daniel, 1785–1852.

LAC 10322

Practical money making: or, How to succeed in any occupation, trade, or profession. A home and a competence for every attentive man and woman. Based on the experiences of the best financiers and most successful business and professional men of the present century. Boston, Palestine publishing company, 1885.
Crabtre, Addison Darre.

LAC 40022

The practical of spiritualism. Biographical sketch of Abraham James. Historic description of his oil-well discoveries in Pleasantville, Pa., through spirit direction. Chicago, Horton & Leonard, printers, 1868.
Peebles, James Martin, 1822–1922.

LAC 40048

Practical remarks on the present state of life insurance in the United States... To which are added the valuable tables of associated actuaries... 14th ed. Rev. and cor. to July 1, 1851. Philadelphia, The author [J. Harding, printer] 1851.
Tuckett, Harvey Garnett Phipps, d. 1854.

LAC 11120

Practical sermons. New York, Clark, Austin & Smith, 1858.
Taylor, Nathaniel William, 1786–1858.

LAC 23604

The practical tourist; or, Sketches of the state of the useful arts, and of society, scenery, &c. &c. in Great-Britain, France and Holland. Providence, A. S. Beckwith; Boston, Richardson, Lord and Holbrook [etc.] 1832.
Allen, Zachariah, 1795–1882.

LAC 14858

A practical treatise on business: or How to get, save, spend, give, lend, and bequeath money: with an inquiry into the chances of success and causes of failure in business. Also, prize essays, statistics, miscellanies, and numerous private letters from successful and distinguished business men. 12th thousand. Philadelphia, Lippincott, Grambo & co., 1853.
Freedley, Edwin Troxell, 1827–1904.

LAC 15826

A practical treatise on dyeing, and callicoe printing: exhibiting the processes in the French, German, English, and American practice of fixing colours on woollen, cotton, silk, and linen. By Thomas Cooper, esq. professor of chemistry in Dickenson college, Carlisle, Pennsylvania. Philadelphia: Published by Thomas Dobson, at the Stone house, no. 41, South Second street. William Fry, printer, 1815.
Cooper, Thomas, 1759–1839.

LAC 13921

A practical treatise on labor. New York, G. W. Carleton & co.; Wilkes Barre, Morton & co., 1871.
Wright, Hendrick Bradley, 1808–1881.

LAC 11601

A practical treatise on rail-roads and carriages, showing the principles of estimating their strength, proportions, expense, and annual produce, and the conditions which render them effective, economical, and durable; with the theory, effect, and expense of steam carriages, stationary engines, and gas machines... New-York, E. Bliss and E. White, 1825.
Tredgold, Thomas, 1788–1829.

LAC 14115

A practical treatise on rail-roads, and interior communication in general ... with tables of the comparative value of canals and rail-roads, and the power of the present locomotive engines... 1st American, from the 2d English ed., with corrections, notes, and additions; also, an appendix, containing a detailed account of a number of railroads in Europe, and in the United States... Philadelphia, Carey & Lea, 1832.
Wood, Nicholas.

LAC 12900

A practical treatise on the law of slavery. Being a compilation of all the decisions made on that subject, in the several courts of the United States, and state courts. With copious notes and references to the statutes and other authorities, systematically arranged. New York, A. Pollock, jr.; New Orleans, B. Levy, 1837.
Wheeler, Jacob D.

LAC 11283

A practical treatise on the revenue laws of the United States. Boston, Little, Brown and company, 1858.
Andrews, Christopher Columbus, 1829–1922.

LAC 15278

Pragmatism, a new name for some old ways of thinking; popular lectures on philosophy. New York [etc.] Longmans, Green, and co., 1907.
James, William, 1842–1910.

LAC 12467

Prairie experiences in handling cattle and sheep, with illustrations from sketches by the author. London, Chapman and Hall, limited, 1884.
Shepherd, William, 1824–

LAC 16711

The Prairie Flower; or, Adventures in the far West. Cincinnati and St. Louis, Stratton & Barnard, 1849.
Bennett, Emerson, 1822–1905.

LAC 13263

The prairie traveler. A hand-book for overland expeditons. With maps, illustrations, and itineraries of the principal routes between the Mississippi and the Pacific. Published by authority of the War department. New York, Harper & brothers, 1859.
Marcy, Randolph Barnes, 1812–1887.

LAC 11756

The prairies of the western states: their advantages and their drawbacks. Toronto, Printed at the 'Leader' & 'Patriot' steam-press, 1860.
Lindsey, Charles, 1820–1908.

LAC 14117

Preadamites; or, A demonstration of the existence of men before Adam; together with a study of their condition, antiquity, racial affinities, and progressive dispersion over the earth... Chicago, S. C. Griggs and company; [etc., etc.] 1880.
Winchell, Alexander, 1824–1891.

LAC 40025

Precedents of American neutrality, in reply to the speech of Sir Roundell Palmer, attorney-general of England, in the British House of commons, May 13, 1864.
Boston, Little, Brown and company, 1864.
Bemis, George, 1816–1878.

LAC 15453

Precepts of Mother Ann Lee and the elders.
Testimonies of the life, character, revelations and doctrines of Mother Ann Lee, and the elders with her, through whom the word of eternal life was opened in this day of Christ's second appearing, collected from living witnesses, in union with the church... 2d ed. Albany, N. Y., Weed, Parsons & co., printers, 1888.
Shakers.

LAC 12280

The precursors of Jacques Cartier, 1497–1534, a collection of documents relating to the early history of the Dominion of Canada, ed. by H. P. Biggar. Pub. by authority of the minister of agriculture under the direction of the archivist, Ottawa, Government printing bureau, 1911.
Biggar, Henry Percival, 1872–   ed.

LAC 16462

A preface to politics. New York and London, M. Kennerley, 1914, [c1913]
Lippmann, Walter, 1889–

LAC 14403

The preliminaries of the American revolution as seen in the English press, 1763–1775. New York, Columbia university press, 1926.
Hinkhouse, Fred Junkin, 1895–

LAC 40037

A preliminary report on the treaty of reciprocity with Great Britain, to regulate the trade between the United States and the provinces of British North America. Prepared by E. H. Derby, at the request of the secretary of the Treasury of the United States. Washington, Treasury dept., 1866.
Derby, Elias Hasket, 1803–1880.

LAC 40105

A preliminary sketch of the history of Ohio. Cincinnati, Corey & Fairbank, 1833.
Chase, Salmon Portland, 1808–1873.

LAC 13826

A preliminary treatise on evidence at the common law. Boston, Little, Brown, and company, 1898.
Thayer, James Bradley, 1831–1902.

LAC 10543

The premises of political economy; being a re-examination of certain fundamental principles of economic science. Philadelphia, J. B. Lippincott company, 1885.
Patten, Simon Nelson, 1852–1922.

LAC 40120

Premium essay on agricultural education. Submitted to the Executive committee of the Southern central agricultural association. By Edmund Ruffin, of Virginia. 2d ed. Richmond, Va., J. W. Randolph, 1853.
Ruffin, Edmund, 1794–1865.

LAC 14054

Pre-revolutionary Dutch houses and families in northern New Jersey and southern New York, by Rosalie Fellows Bailey, A. B.; with an introduction by Franklin D. Roosevelt; photography by Margaret De M. Brown; prepared under the auspices of the Holland society of New York. New York, W. Morrow & company, 1936.
Bailey, Rosalie Fellows, 1908–

LAC 15792
The Presbyterian movement in the reign of Queen Elizabeth as illustrated by the Minute book of the Dedham classis, 1582–1589; edited for the Royal historical society, from the ms. in the possession of J. F. Gurney, esquire, Keswick hall, Norfolk, by Roland G. Usher. London, Royal historical society, 1905.
Dedham Classis *(Presbyterian)*

LAC 12262
Presbyterianism, its relation to the negro. Illustrated by the Berean Presbyterian church, Philadelphia, with sketch of the church and autobiography of the author, by Matthew Anderson. With introductions by Francis J. Grimke and John B. Reeve. Philadelphia, J. M. White & co. [c1897]
Anderson, Matthew.

LAC 40136
The present aspect of the labor problem. Four lectures given in All Souls church, New York, May, 1886. New York, The Day Star, 1886.
Newton, Richard Heber, 1840–1914.

LAC 40025
The present attempt to dissolve the American union, a British aristocratic plot. By B. New York, Printed for the author, 1862.
Morse, Samuel Finley Breese, 1791–1872.

LAC 13011
Present college questions; six papers read before the National educational association, at the sessions held in Boston, July 6 and 7, 1903, by Charles W. Eliot, Andrew F. West, William R. Harper, Nicholas Murray Butler. New York, D. Appleton and company, 1903.

LAC 14445
The present condition of Mexico. Message from the President of the United States in answer to resolution of the House of the 3d of March last, transmitting report from the Department of state regarding the present condition of Mexico. [With accompanying documents] [Washington, 1862]
U.S. *Dept. of State.*

LAC 40021
The present conflict of labor and capital... A discourse. Chicago, Chicago legal news co., 1886.
Bonney, Charles Carroll, 1831–1903.

LAC 40001
The present crisis, or The currency; a tract of the times for every man who can read: by Bank Crash, esq. [*pseud.*][Rochester] 1857.
Dutton, George.

LAC 12544
Present day problems; a collection of addresses delivered on various occasions. New York, Dodd, Mead & company, 1908.
Taft, William Howard, *pres. U.S.,* 1857–1930.

LAC 13086
Present day theology. Columbus, O., McClelland & company [c1913]
Gladden, Washington, 1836–1918.

LAC 11109
Present day theology; a popular discussion of leading doctrines of the Christian faith, by Lewis French Stearns, with a biographical sketch by George L. Prentiss. New York, C. Scribner's sons, 1893.
Stearns, Lewis French, 1847–1892.

LAC 40062
The present political state of the province
The origin of the American contest with Great-Britain, or The present political state of the Massachusetts-Bay, in general, and the town of Boston in particular. Exhibiting the rise and progress of the disordered state of that country, in a series of weekly essays, published at Boston, under the signature of Massachusettensis, a native of New-England. New-York, Printed by J. Rivington, 1775.
Leonard, Daniel, 1740–1829.

LAC 14197
The present state of Great Britain and North America, with regard to agriculture, population, trade, and manufactures, impartially considered... London, T. Becket [etc.] 1767.
Mitchell, John, *d.* 1768.

LAC 16197
The present state of Virginia. New York, Reprinted for J. Sabin, 1865.
Jones, Hugh, 1669–1760.

LAC 16259
The present state of Virginia and the college, by Henry Hartwell, James Blair, and Edward Chilton; edited, with an introduction, by Hunter Dickinson Farish. Charlottesville [Va.] Dominion books [1964, c1940]
Hartwell, Henry.

LAC 10520
Present status of social science. A review, historical and critical, of the progress of thought in social philosophy. New York, H. L. Hinton, 1873.
Hamilton, Robert S.

LAC 40003
Present status of the honor system in colleges and universities, by Bird T. Baldwin, assisted by Henry L. Messner and Grace W. Greene. Washington, Govt. print. off., 1915.
Baldwin, Bird Thomas, 1875–

LAC 15659
President Garfield's speeches and addresses on education and educators. [Boston, J. R. Osgood, 1882]
Hinsdale, Burke Aaron, 1837–1900.

LAC 14508
The presidential campaign of 1860. New York, The Macmillan company, 1911.
Fite, Emerson David, 1874–1953.

LAC 11393
Presidential nominations and elections; a history of American conventions, national campaigns, inaugurations and campaign caricature, with numerous illustrations. New York, C. Scribner's sons, 1916.
Bishop, Joseph Bucklin, 1847–1928.

LAC 12440
Presidential problems. New York, The Century co.,
1904.
Cleveland, Grover, *pres. U.S.*, 1837–1908.

LAC 13896
The President's cabinet; studies in the origin, formation and structure of an American institution. New Haven, Yale university press; [etc., etc.] 1912.
Learned, Henry Barrett, 1868–1931.

LAC 40010
The President's policy; war and conquest abroad, deg-
radation of labor at home; address by Hon. George S.
Boutwell ... at Masonic hall, Washington, D. C., January 11, 1900. Chicago, American anti-imperialist league,
1900.
Boutwell, George Sewall, 1818–1905.

LAC 13559
The presumption of sex, and other papers. Boston, Lee
and Shepard, 1892.
Adams, Oscar Fay, 1855–1919.

LAC 23319
The pretensions of Thomas Jefferson to the presidency
examined; and the charges against John Adams refuted.
Addressed to the citizens of America in general; and par-
ticularly to the electors of the president. United States
[Philadelphia?] 1796.
Smith, William Loughton, 1758–1812.

LAC 40062
A pretty story written in the year of Our Lord 2774.
By Peter Grievous, esquire, A. B. C. D. E. Williamsburg;
Printed by John Pinkney, for the Benefit of Clementina
Rind's children, 1774.
Hopkinson, Francis, 1737–1791.

LAC 11692
Prices in colonial Pennsylvania, by Anne Bezanson,
Robert D. Gray [and] Miriam Hussey. Philadelphia, Uni-
versity of Pennsylvania press, 1935.
Bezanson, Anne.

LAC 40061
The primary surgery of Gen. Sherman's campaigns.
By E. Andrews and J. M. Woodworth. Chicago, G. H.
Fergus, printer, 1866.
Andrews, Edmund, 1824–1904.

LAC 20916
A primer of forestry. Washington, Govt. print. off.,
1899–1905.
Pinchot, Gifford, 1865–

LAC 40002
A primer of tariff reform. London, New York, etc.,
Cassell, 1885.
Wells, David Ames, 1828–1898.

LAC 14113
Primitive piety revived, or, The aggressive power of
the Christian church. A premium essay. By Rev. Henry
C. Fish. Boston, Congregational board of publication,
1857, [c1855]
Fish, Henry Clay, 1820–1877.

LAC 10978
Primitive traits in religious revivals; a study in mental
and social evolution. New York, The Macmillan company; London, Macmillan & co., ltd., 1905.
Davenport, Frederick Morgan, 1866–1956.

LAC 12602
Prince Henry the Navigator: the hero of Portugal and
of modern discovery, 1394–1460 A. D. With an account
of geographical progress throughout the middle ages as
the preparation for this work. New York [etc.] G. P. Putnam's sons, 1895.
Beazley, *Sir* Charles Raymond, 1868–1955.

LAC 15310
The prince of Parthia, a tragedy, by Thomas Godfrey;
ed., with introduction, historical, biographical, and critical, by Archibald Henderson. Boston, Little, Brown, and
company, 1917.
Godfrey, Thomas, 1736–1763.

LAC 15045
Princeton. New York, Oxford university press, Ameri-
can branch; [etc., etc.] 1914.
Collins, Varnum Lansing, 1870–1936.

LAC 12976
Princeton college during the eighteenth century. New
York, A. D. F. Randolph & company [c1872]
Alexander, Samuel Davies, 1819–1894.

LAC 14465
The principle of Protestantism as related to the pre-
sent state of the church. By Philip Schaf [!] Translated
from the German with an introduction by John W. Nevin.
Chambersburg, Pa., "Publication Office" of the German
Reformed Church, 1845.
Schaff, Philip, 1819–1893.

LAC 12508
Principles and acts of the revolution in America; or,
An attempt to collect and preserve some of the speeches,
orations, & proceedings, with sketches and remarks on
men and things, and other fugitive or neglected pieces,
belonging to the revolutionary period in the United
States... Baltimore, Printed and pub. for the editor, by
W. O. Niles, 1822.
Niles, Hezekiah, 1777–1839.

LAC 40004
The principles and aims of the Patrons of husbandry.
Their origin, rapid growth, and general statistics. A sup-
plement to The footprints of time. Burlington, Ia., R. T.
Root, 1874.
Smedley, A   B.

LAC 15261
Principles and purposes of our form of government as
set forth in public papers of Grover Cleveland. Comp. by
Francis Gottsberger. New York, G. G. Peck, 1892.
Cleveland, Grover, *pres. U.S.*, 1837–1908.

LAC 40010
Principles of colonial government adapted to the present
needs of Cuba and Porto Rico, and of the Philippines.
Boston, L. C. Page and company, 1899.
Fisher, Horace Newton, 1836–1916.

LAC 15566
The principles of courtesy: with hints and observations of manners and habits. New York, Harper & brothers, 1852.
Hervey, George Winfred.

LAC 15560
Principles of domestic science; as applied to the duties and pleasures of home. A text-book for the use of young ladies in schools, seminaries, and colleges. By Catherine E. Beecher and Harriet Beecher Stowe. New York, J. B. Ford and company, 1870.
Beecher, Catherine Esther, 1800–1878.

LAC 12431
Principles of government; a treatise on free institutions. Including the Constitution of the United States. Burlington [Vt.] E. Smith, 1833.
Chipman, Nathaniel, 1752–1843.

LAC 14022
Principles of nature; or, A development of the moral causes of happiness and misery among the human species. America printed; London, Re-printed and published by R. Carlile, 1819.
Palmer, Elihu, 1764–1806.

LAC 16596
Principles of ornamental art. London, New York [etc.] Cassell, Petter & Galpin [1875]
Hulme, Frederick Edward, 1841–1909.

LAC 20116–17
Principles of political economy... Philadelphia, Carey, Lea & Blanchard, 1837–40.
Carey, Henry Charles, 1793–1879.

LAC 10449
Principles of political economy. New York, C. Scribner's sons, 1891, [c1890]
Perry, Arthur Latham, 1830–1905.

LAC 10427
The principles of political economy applied to the condition, the resources, and the institutions of the American people. Boston, Little, Brown, and company, 1865, [c1856]
Bowen, Francis, 1811–1890.

LAC 10492
The principles of psychology. New York, G. P. Putnam's sons, 1877, [c1869]
Bascom, John, 1827–1911.

LAC 20001–2
The principles of psychology. New York, H. Holt and company, 1890.
James, William, 1842–1910.

LAC 15878
The principles of scientific management. New York and London, Harper & brothers, 1919, [c1911]
Taylor, Frederick Winslow, 1856–1915.

LAC 16626
The principles of social progress. A study of civilization. Rochester, N. Y., E. Darrow & company, 1901.
Morman, James Bale, 1862–1930.

LAC 20118–19
Principles of social science. Philadelphia, J. B. Lippincott & co.; London, Trubner & co.; [etc., etc.] 1877, [c1858]
Carey, Henry Charles, 1793–1879.

LAC 10437
The principles of sociology. An analysis of the phenomena of association and of social organization. [3d ed.] New York, The Macmillan company; London, Macmillan & co., ltd., 1921, [c1896]
Giddings, Franklin Henry, 1855–1931.

LAC 15224
The principles of teaching, based on psychology. New York, A. G. Seiler, 1920, [c1906]
Thorndike, Edward Lee, 1874–1949.

LAC 40040
The principles of the Revolution vindicated in a sermon preached before the University of Cambridge, on Wednesday, May 29, 1776. Cambridge, Eng., J. Archdeacon, 1776.
Watson, Richard, *bp. of Llandaff*, 1737–1816.

LAC 10438
Principles of western civilisation. New York, The Macmillan company; London, Macmillan & co., ltd., 1902.
Kidd, Benjamin, 1858–1916.

LAC 12591
Principles of zoology: touching the structure, development, distribution, and natural arrangement of the races of animals, living and extinct, with numerous illustrations. Pt. I. Comparative physiology. For the use of schools and colleges. By Louis Agassiz and A. A. Gould. Rev. ed. Boston, Gould and Lincoln; [etc., etc.] 1858, [c1851]
Agassiz, Louis, 1807–1873.

LAC 40098
Principles that should control the interference of the state of industries.
Relations of the state to industrial action... [Baltimore] American economic association, 1887.
Adams, Henry Carter, 1851–1921.

LAC 11258
The printers; a study in American trade unionism. Cambridge, Mass., American econimic association; [etc., etc.] 1909.
Barnett, George Ernest, 1873–1938.

LAC 11880
Prismatics, by Richard Haywarde [*pseud.*] Illustrated with wood engravings from designs by Elliott, Darley, Kensett, Hicks, and Rossiter. New York, London, D. Appleton & company, 1853.
Cozzens, Frederick Swartwout, 1818–1869.

LAC 15460
Prison discipline in America. London, J. Murray, 1848.
Gray, Francis Calley, 1790–1856.

LAC 11242
Prison life and reflections; or, A narrative of the arrest, trial, conviction, imprisonment, treatment, observations, reflections, and deliverance of Work, Burr, and Thompson, who suffered an unjust and cruel imprisonment in Missouri penitentiary for attempting to aid some slaves to liberty... By George Thompson, one of the prisoners. 3d ed. Hartford, A. Work, 1849.
Thompson, George, *d.* 1893.

LAC 40035
Prison life during the rebellion. Being a brief narrative of the miseries and sufferings of six hundred Confederate prisoners sent from Fort Delaware to Morris' Island to be punished. Written by Fritz Fuzzlebug [*pseud.*] one of their number. Pub. by the author. Singer's Glen, Va., J. Funk's sons, printers, 1869.
Dunkle, John J.

LAC 16681
Prison life in the Old capitol and reminiscences of the civil war, by James J. Williamson; illustrations by B. F. Williamson. West Orange, N. J., 1911.
Williamson, James Joseph, 1834–1915.

LAC 15285
Prison life in the South: at Richmond, Macon, Savannah, Charleston, Columbia, Charlotte, Raleigh, Goldsborough, and Andersonville, during the years 1864 and 1865. New York, Harper & brothers, 1865.
Abbott, Allen O.

LAC 10254
Prison life of Jefferson Davis. Embracing details and incidents in his captivity, particulars concerning his health and habits, together with many conversations on topics of great public interest. New York, Carleton; [etc., etc.] 1866.
Craven, John J.

LAC 10722
Prison memoirs of an anarchist. New York, Mother Earth publishing association, 1912.
Berkman, Alexander, 1870–1936.

LAC 11171
Prison systems of the United States. Reports prepared for the International prison commission. S. J. Barrows, commissioner for the United States. Washington, Govt. print. off., 1900.
International Penal and Prison Commission.

LAC 11176
Prisoners and paupers; a study of the abnormal increase of criminals, and the public burden of pauperism in the United States; the causes and remedies. New York [etc.] G. P. Putnam's sons, 1893.
Boies, Henry Martyn, 1837–1903.

LAC 15064
The prisoners of Perote: containing a journal kept by the author, who was captured by the Mexicans at Mier, December 25, 1842, and released from Perote, May 16, 1844. Austin, Texas, The Steck company, 1935.
Stapp, William Preston.

LAC 16105
Prisoners of war and military prisons; personal narratives of experience in the prisons of Richmond, Danville, Macon, Andersonville, Savannah, Millen, Charleston, and Columbia ... with a list of officers who were prisoners of war from January 1, 1864. By Asa B. Isham, Henry M. Davidson and Henry B. Furness. Cincinnati, Lyman & Cushing, 1890.
Isham, Asa Brainerd, 1844–1912.

LAC 22198–202
Private and official correspondence of Gen. Benjamin F. Butler, during the period of the civil war... Privately issued. [Norwood, Mass., The Plimpton press] 1917.
Butler, Benjamin Franklin, 1818–1893.

LAC 40064
The private and public life of Abraham Lincoln; comprising a full account of his early years, and a succinct record of his career as statesman and president. New York, Beadle and company [1864]
Victor, Orville James, 1827–1910.

LAC 15169
A private chapter of the war. (1861–5) St. Louis, G. I. Jones and company, 1880.
Bailey, George W   *b.* 1841.

LAC 14200
Private freight cars and American railways. New York, Columbia university, Longmans, Green & co., agents [etc., etc.] 1908.
Weld, Louis Dwight Harvell, 1882–

LAC 20193
The private journal of Aaron Burr, during his residence of four years in Europe; with selections from his correspondence. Ed. by Matthew L. Davis. New York, Harper & brothers, 1838.
Burr, Aaron, 1756–1836.

LAC 40085
The private journals kept by Rev. John, [*i.e.* Thomas] Buckingham, of the expedition against Canada, in the years 1710 & 1711. From the original manuscripts. New-York, Wilder & Campbell, 1825.
Buckingham, Thomas, 1671–1731.

LAC 13894
The private life of Daniel Webster. New York, Harper & brothers, 1856, [c1852]
Lanman, Charles, 1819–1895.

LAC 14249
The private soldier under Washington. New York, C. Scribner's sons, 1902.
Bolton, Charles Knowles, 1867–1950.

LAC 16374
Privateering and piracy in the colonial period: illustrative documents, edited under the auspices of the National society of the colonial dames of America, by John Franklin Jameson. New York, The Macmillan company, 1923.
Jameson, John Franklin, 1859–   *ed.*

LAC 15801

Prize essays on a Congress of nations, for the adjustment of international disputes, and for the promotion of universal peace without resort to arms. Together with a sixth essay, comprising the substance of the rejected essays. Boston, Pub. by Whipple & Damrell, for the American peace society, 1840.

LAC 12931

The problem of Asia and its effect upon international policies. Boston, Little, Brown and company, 1900.
Mahan, Alfred Thayer, 1840–1914.

LAC 40057

The problem of Jewish education in America and the Bureau of education of the Jewish community of New York city. Washington, Govt. print. off., 1914.
Friedlaender, Israel, 1876–1920.

LAC 40043

The problem of municipal government in the United States. An address given before the Historical and political science association of Cornell university, March 16, 1887, by the Hon. Seth Low. Ithaca, N. Y., Pub. for the University by Andrews & Church [1887?]
Low, Seth, 1850–1916.

LAC 10987

The problem of religious progress. New York, Phillips & Hunt; Cincinnati, Walden & Stowe, 1881.
Dorchester, Daniel, 1827–1907.

LAC 15640

The problem of success for young men and how to solve it; an educational symposium, by successful men and leaders of thought for the guidance of all young men ambitious to succeed in life. New York, W. R. Hearst, 1903.

LAC 15757

The problem of the immigrant; a brief discussion, with a summary of conditions, laws, and regulations governing the movement of population to and from the British empire, United States, France, Belgium, Switzerland, Germany, Italy, Austria-Hungary, Spain, Portugal, Netherlands, Denmark, Scandinavia and Russia. London, Chapman & Hall, ld., 1905.
Whelpley, James Davenport, 1863–

LAC 14600

Problems in modern education; addresses and essays. Boston, Sherman, French & company, 1913.
Sutton, William Seneca, 1860–

LAC 14210

Problems in railway regulations. New York, The Macmillan company, 1911.
Haines, Henry Stevens, 1836–1923.

LAC 11147

Problems of expansion, as considered in papers and addresses. New York, The Century co., 1900.
Reid, Whitelaw, 1837–1912.

LAC 11672

Problems of modern democracy; political and economic essays. New York, C. Scribner's sons, 1898, [c1896]
Godkin, Edwin Lawrence, 1831–1902.

LAC 12367

Problems of the present South; a discussion of certain of the educational, industrial and political issues in the southern states. New York, The Macmillan company; London, Macmillan & co., ltd., 1904.
Murphy, Edgar Gardner, 1869–1913.

LAC 10026

Problems of to-day; a discussion of protective tariffs, taxation, and monopolies. New ed., rev. and greatly enl. New York, T. Y. Crowell & company [c1888]
Ely, Richard Theodore, 1854–1943.

LAC 20422

Proceedings. Boston, Hiram Tupper [etc.] 1831–1833.
American Lyceum.

LAC 16645

Proceedings. [n. p., n. d.]
National Negro Conference, *New York*, 1909.

LAC 20337–40

Proceedings and debates of the British parliaments respecting North America, edited by Leo Francis Stock. Washington, Carnegie Institution of Washington, 1924–1941.
Gt. Brit. *Parliament.*

LAC 15371–72

Proceedings and debates of the Constitutional convention held in the city of Helena, Montana, July 4th, 1889, August 17th, 1889... Helena, Mont., State publishing company, 1921.
Montana *(Ter.) Constitutional Convention*, 1889.

LAC 22898–900

Proceedings and debates of the Constitutional convention of Idaho, 1889; ed. and annotated by I. W. Hart. Caldwell, Id., Caxton printers, ltd., 1912.
Idaho. *Constitutional Convention*, 1889.

LAC 14718

Proceedings and debates of the convention.
Kansas Constitutional convention. A reprint of the proceedings and debates of the convention which framed the constitution of Kansas at Wyandotte in July, 1859. Also, the constitution annotated to date, historical sketches, etc. By authority of the state Legislature. Topeka, Printed by Kansas state printing plant, Imri Zumwalt, state printer, 1920.
Kansas. *(Ter.) Constitutional Convention*, 1859.

LAC 13701

Proceedings and debates of the Convention of North Carolina, called to amend the constitution of the state, which assembled at Raleigh, June 4, 1835. To which are subjoined the convention act and the amendments to the constitution... Raleigh, Printed by J. Gales and son, 1836.
North Carolina. *Constitutional Convention*, 1835.

LAC 21277–85
Proceedings and debates of the Convention of the commonwealth of Pennsylvania, to propose amendments to the constitution, commenced ... at Harrisburg, on the second day of May, 1837. Reported by John Agg; stenographer to the Conventions; assisted by Messrs. Kingman, Drake, and M'Kinley. Harrisburg, Printed by Packer, Barrett, and Parke, 1837–39.
Pennsylvania. *Constitutional Convention, 1837–1838.*

LAC 14833
Proceedings and list of delegates. California Chinese Exclusion Convention ... held at Metropolitan Temple, San Francisco, November 21 and 22, 1901 ... also California's memorial to the President and the Congress of the United States. San Francisco, Star Press [1901]
Chinese Exclusion Convention, *San Francisco*, 1901.

LAC 12393
Proceedings in the Ku Klux trials, at Columbia, S. C. in the United States Circuit court, November term, 1871. Printed from government copy. Columbia, S. C., Republican printing company, state printers, 1872.
U.S. *Circuit Court (4th Circuit)*

LAC 40150
The proceedings of a convention of delegates, from the states of Massachusetts, Connecticut, and Rhode Island; the counties of Cheshire and Grafton, in the state of New-Hampshire; and the county of Windham, in the state of Vermont; convened at Hartford, in the state of Connecticut, December 15th, 1814. 3d ed., cor. and improved. Boston, Wells and Lilly, 1815.
Hartford Convention, 1814.

LAC 16771
Proceedings of a general court martial for the trial of Major General Arnold. With an introduction, notes, and index. New York, Priv. print., 1865.
Arnold, Benedict, 1741–1801, *defendant.*

LAC 14502
Proceedings of a general court martial, held at Brunswick, in the state of New-Jersey, by order of his Excellency General Washington ... for the trial of Major General Lee. July 4th, 1778. Major General Lord Stirling, president. Philadelphia, J. Dunlap, 1778.
Lee, Charles, 1731–1782, *defendant.*

LAC 21402–8
Proceedings of the Alaskan boundary tribunal, convened at London, under the treaty between the United States of America and Great Britain, concluded at Washington, January 24, 1903, for the settlement of questions ... with respect to the boundary line between the territory of Alaska and the British possessions in North America... Washington, Govt. print. off., 1904.
Alaskan Boundary Tribunal.

LAC 16464
Proceedings of the American Anti-slavery Society at its third decade. New York, Arno Press and New York Times, 1969.
American Anti-slavery Society.

LAC 23518–27
Proceedings of the annual congress of the National Prison Association. 1874–1906. New York [etc.]
American Correctional Association.

LAC 21235–43
Proceedings of the ... annual convention. [1st]–29th, 1889–1917. Washington, Govt. print. off.; [etc., etc.] 1889–[1917]
National Association of Railroad and Utilities Commissioners.

LAC 16802
Proceedings of the Constitutional convention held in Denver, December 20, 1875, to frame a constitution for the state of Colorado, together with the enabling act passed by the Congress of the United States and approved March 3, 1875, the address to the people issued by the Convention, the constitution as adopted and the President's proclamation. Pub. by authority, Timothy O'Connor, secretary of state. Denver, Col., The Smith-Brooks press, state printers, 1907.
Colorado. *Constitutional Convention, 1875–1876.*

LAC 11532
Proceedings of the eighth Republican national convention held at Chicago, Illinois, June 3, 4, 5, and 6, 1884. [Chicago] Printed by order of the Republican national committee [1884]
Republican Party. *National Convention. 8th, Chicago,* 1884.

LAC 40077
Proceedings of the first annual meeting of the New-York state anti-slavery society, convened at Utica, October 19, 1836. Utica, N. Y., Pub. for the Society, 1836.
New York State Anti-slavery Society.

LAC 13622
Proceedings of the first ten years. To which is added a brief view of the principal religious tract societies throughout the world. [Boston?] Printed for the American Tract Society by Flagg and Gould, 1824.
American Tract Society, *Boston.*

LAC 16629
Proceedings of the fourth New-England anti-slavery convention, held in Boston, May 30, 31, and June 1 and 2, 1837. Boston, Printed by I. Knapp, 1837.
New England Anti-slavery Convention. *4th, Boston,* 1837.

LAC 40023
Proceedings of the friends of a rail-road to San Francisco, at their public meeting, held at the U.S. Hotel, in Boston, April 19, 1849. Including an address to the people of the United States; showing ... P. P. F. Degrand's plan... 4th ed. Boston, Dutton and Wentworth, printers, 1849.

LAC 40068
Proceedings of the meeting in Charleston, S. C., May 13–15, 1845, on the religious instruction of the negroes, together with the report of the committee, and the address to the public. Pub. by order of the meeting. Charleston, S. C., Printed by B. Jenkins, 1845.
Charleston, S. C. Meeting on Religious Instruction of Negroes.

LAC 40004
Proceedings of the National agricultural convention, held at Washington, D. C., February 15, 16, 17, 1872. Washington, Govt. print. off., 1872.
National Agricultural Convention, *Washington, D. C.,* 1872.

LAC 23925-29
Proceedings of the ... National conference on city planning. 2d-16th; 1910-24. Boston [etc.] 1910-24.
National Conference on City Planning.

LAC 16755
Proceedings of the national convention to secure the religious amendment of the Constitution of the United States. Held in Pittsburg, February 4, 5, 1874. With an account of the origin and progress of the movement. Philadelphia, Printed by the Christian statesman association, 1874.
National Reform Association *(Founded 1863)*

LAC 40138
Proceedings of the National emigration convention of colored people; held at Cleveland, Ohio, on ... the 24th, 25th and 26th of August, 1854... Pittsburgh, Printed by A. A. Anderson, 1854.
National Emigration Convention of Colored People, *Cleveland*, 1854.

LAC 40023
Proceedings of the National railroad convention, which assembled in the city of St. Louis, on the fifteenth of October, 1849. To which is prefixed the proceedings of the primary meetings of the citizens of St. Louis, held previous to the meeting of said convention. St. Louis, Printed by Chambers & Knapp, 1850.
National Railroad Convention, *St. Louis*, 1849.

LAC 11663
Proceedings of the National ship-canal convention, held at the city of Chicago, June 2 and 3, 1863. Chicago, Tribune company's book and job printing office, 1863.
National Ship-canal Convention, *Chicago*, 1863.

LAC 40099
Proceedings of the New-England anti-slavery convention, held in Boston on the 27th, 28th and 29th of May, 1834. Boston, Garrison & Knapp, 1834.
New England Anti-slavery Convention. *Boston*, 1834.

LAC 40077
Proceedings of the New England anti-slavery convention: held in Boston, May 24, 25, 26, 1836. Boston, Printed by I. Knapp, 1836.
New England Anti-slavery Convention. *3d, Boston*, 1836.

LAC 14685
Proceedings of the New-York state conventions for "rescuing the canals from the ruin with which they are threatened" : by exposing and resisting "the railroad conspiracy" for "discrediting the canals, and diminishing their revenues with a view of bringing them under the hammer" ... and adopting measures for counteracting "the ruinous competition with railroads, permitted by the state..." Arranged by Henry O'Rielly and Hugh Allen for the Clinton league... New York, The Clinton league, 1859.
O'Rielly, Henry, 1806-1886, *ed.*

LAC 11531
Proceedings of the Republican national convention, held at Chicago, Illinois, Wednesday, Thursday, Friday, Saturday, Monday and Tuesday, June 2d, 3d, 4th, 5th, 7th and 8th, 1880. Resulting in the following nominations: for president, James A. Garfield, of Ohio. For vice-president, Chester A. Arthur, of New York. Reported by Eugene Davis, official stenographer to the convention. Chicago, Ill., The Jno. B. Jeffery printing and publishing house, 1881.
Republican Party. *National Convention. 7th, Chicago*, 1880.

LAC 40099
Proceedings of the Rhode-Island anti-slavery convention, held in Providence, on the 2d, 3d, and 4th of February, 1836. Providence, H. H. Brown, printer, 1836.
Rhode Island State Anti-slavery Convention, *Providence*, 1836.

LAC 11533
Proceedings of the tenth Republican national convention, held in the city of Minneapolis, Minn., June 7, 8, 9 and 10, 1892... Reported by Theodore C. Rose and James F. Burke. [Minneapolis, Minn., Harrison & Smith, printers, 1892]
Republican Party. *National Convention. 10th, Minneapolis*, 1892.

LAC 13437
The proceedings of the United States anti-masonic convention, held at Philadelphia, September 11, 1830. Embracing the journal of proceedings, the reports, the debates, and the address to the people. Philadelphia, I. P. Trimble; New York, Skinner and Dewey; [etc., etc.] 1830.
United States Anti-Masonic Convention, *Philadelphia*, 1830.

LAC 13702
The proceedings relative to calling the conventions of 1776 and 1790. The minutes of the convention that formed the present constitution of Pennsylvania, together with the charter to William Penn, the constitutions of 1776 and 1790, and a view of the proceedings of the convention of 1776, and the Council of censors. Harrisburg, Printed by J. S. Wiestling, 1825.
Pennsylvania. *Constitutional Convention*, 1776.

LAC 11751
Productive farming.
The farmer's mine, or source of wealth, being a compilation, with the addition of new and important information on the subject of manure, together with the most approved methods for the manufacture of vegetable manure, by which the farmer can obtain in the shortest possible time, as much manure of the richest quality as he pleases. To which is added, Productive farming, by Joseph A. Smith. By Henry Heermance. Rev. and cor. by A. B. Allen. New York, H. Heermance, 1843.
Heermance, Henry.

LAC 13966
Professional criminals of America. New York, Cassell & company, limited [c1886]
Byrnes, Thomas, 1842-1910.

LAC 15226
The professional training of secondary teachers in the United States. New York, The Macmillan co.; [etc., etc.] 1903.
Luckey, George Washington Andrew, 1855-1933.

LAC 40128
Prof. Agassiz on the origin of species. [New Haven, 1860]
Agassiz, Louis, 1807-1873.

LAC 14332
Profit sharing between employer and employee; a study in the evolution of the wages system. Boston and New York, Houghton, Mifflin and company, 1889.
Gilman, Nicholas Paine, 1849-1912.

LAC 15945
Profitable advice for rich and poor. In a dialogue, or discourse between James Freeman, a Carolina planter, and Simon Question, a west-country farmer. Containing a description, or true relation of South Carolina, an English plantation or colony, in America: with propositions for the advantageous settlement of people, in general, but especially the laborious poor, in that fruitful, pleasant, and profitable country, for its inhabitants... London, Printed by J. Howe, 1712.
Norris, John, *of Charleston, S. C., fl.* 1712.

LAC 40018
Profits on manufactures at Lowell. A letter from the treasurer of a corporation to John S. Pendleton, esq., Virginia. Boston, C. C. Little & J. Brown, 1845.
Cary, Thomas Greaves, 1791–1859.

LAC 40017
"Progress and poverty." A review of the doctrines of Henry George. Cambridge [Mass.] J. Wilson and son, 1882.
Dixwell, George Basil.

LAC 20390–92
The progress of America, from the discovery by Columbus to the year 1846. London, Whittaker and co., 1847.
MacGregor, John, 1797–1857.

LAC 14011
The progress of invention in the nineteenth century. New York, Munn & co., 1900.
Byrn, Edward Wright, 1849–1921.

LAC 12899
The progress of slavery in the United States. Washington, D. C., The author, 1857.
Weston, George Melville, 1816–1887.

LAC 14936
Progress of the United States in population and wealth in fifty years, as exhibited by the decennial census. New-York, Press of Hunt's merchants' magazine; Boston, Little & Brown, 1843.
Tucker, George, 1775–1861.

LAC 40013
Progress toward shorter hours, 1900–1910. Albany, State department of labor, 1912.
New York *(State) Bureau of Labor Statistics.*

LAC 10732
Progressive democracy. New York, The Macmillan company, 1914.
Croly, Herbert David, 1869–1930.

LAC 13971
Progressive men, women, and movements of the past twenty-five years, by B. O. Flower, founder of "the Arena" and "the Twentieth century magazine". Boston, Mass., The New Arena [c1914]
Flower, Benjamin Orange, 1858–1918.

LAC 13107
The progressive movement; a non-partisan, comprehensive discussion of current tendencies in American politics. New York, The Macmillan company, 1915.
De Witt, Benjamin Parke.

LAC 12272
Progressive orthodoxy: a contribution to the Christian interpretation of Christian doctrines, by the editors of "The Andover review"... Boston and New York, Houghton, Mifflin and company, 1892, [c1885]

LAC 13960
Progressive Pennsylvania; a record of the remarkable industrial development of the Keystone state, with some account of its early and its later transportation systems, its early settlers, and its prominent men. Philadelphia, J. B. Lippincott company, 1908.
Swank, James Moore, 1832–1914.

LAC 10764
Progressivism–and after. New York, The Macmillan company, 1914.
Walling, William English, 1877–1936.

LAC 10222
A project for a railroad to the Pacific. New York, Printed by G. W. Wood, 1849.
Whitney, Asa, 1797–1872.

LAC 20593
Promenade en Amerique; Etats-Unis–Cuba–Mexique. Nouv. ed. entierement revue. Paris, Michel Levy freres, 1867.
Ampere, Jean Jacques Antoine, 1800–1864.

LAC 40152
The promise of American architecture. Addresses at the annual dinner of the American institute of architects, 1905; compiled with an introduction by Charles Moore. Washington, American institute of architects, 1905.
Moore, Charles, 1855–   *comp.*

LAC 10733
The promise of American life. New York, The Macmillan company, 1914.
Croly, Herbert David, 1869–1930.

LAC 40005
The prompter; a commentary on common sayings and subjects which are full of common sense, the best sense in the world. [n.p.] 1801.
Webster, Noah, 1758–1843.

LAC 16177
Proofs of a conspiracy, against Christianity, and the government of the United States; exhibited in several views of the union of church and state in New-England. Hartford, J. Babcock, printer, 1802.
Bishop, Abraham, 1763–1844.

LAC 12437
Proofs of the corruption of Gen. James Wilkinson, and of his connexion with Aaron Burr, with a full refutation of his slanderous allegations in relation to the character of the principal witness against him. Wm. Hall, jun. & Geo. W. Pierie, printers, no. 51 Market-street, Philadelphia, 1809.
Clark, Daniel, 1766–1813.

LAC 13090

Proofs of the real existence, and dangerous tendency, of illuminism. Containing an abstract of the most interesting parts of what Dr. Robison and the Abbe Barruel have published on this subject; with collateral proofs and general observations. Charlestown: [Mass.] Printed by Samuel Etheridge, for the author, 1802.
Payson, Seth, 1758–1820.

LAC 11071

The prophet of the Great Smoky mountains, by Charles Egbert Craddock *pseud.* Boston and New York, Houghton, Mifflin and company, 1885.
Murfree, Mary Noailles, 1850–1922.

LAC 40043

Proportional representation. The Gove system. Notes on the inequality and injustice of existing methods of electing representatives of the people, with the true remedy. Worcester, Mass., 1892.
Berry, John M.

LAC 40060

Proposal of a design for the promotion of the interests of the United States of America ... by means of inland navigable communications... New York, Printed for the author, by S. Wood, 1808.
Colles, Christopher, 1738–1821.

LAC 40094

Proposal to demonstrate the necessity of a national institution in the United States of America for the education of children of both sexes. To which is joined, a project of organization, &c. Philadelphia, Printed for G. Decombaz, bookseller, 1797.
Lafitte du Courteil, Amable Louis Rose de.

LAC 40107

Proposals for an Indian state, 1778–1878. [Washington, Govt. print. off., 1908]
Abel, Annie Heloise, 1873–

LAC 40050

Proposals relating to the education
Benjamin Franklin's Proposals for the education of youth in Pennsylvania, 1749. Ann Arbor [Mich.] The William L. Clements library, 1927.
Franklin, Benjamin, 1706–1790.

LAC 40056

The proposed Anglo-American alliance; an address delivered before the American social science association at its annual meeting at Saratoga, August 31st, 1898. New York & London, G. P. Putnam's sons, 1898.
Gardiner, Charles Alexander, 1855–

LAC 11634

Propositions concerning protection and free trade. Boston, C. C. Little and J. Brown, 1850.
Phillips, Willard, 1784–1873.

LAC 40119

Propositions for amending the Constitution of the United States, submitted by Mr. Hillhouse to the Senate, on the twelfth day of April, 1808, with his explanatory remarks. [2d ed., rev.] New-Haven [Conn.] Printed by O. Steele & co., 1808.
Hillhouse, James, 1754–1832.

LAC 16787

Prose and poetry of the live stock industry of the United States. With outlines of the origin and ancient history of our live stock animals. With a new introduction by Ramon F. Adams. Prepared by authority of the National live stock association. New York, Antiquarian press, 1959, [c1905]

LAC 16752

Prose sketches and poems, written in the western country. Boston, Light & Horton, 1834.
Pike, Albert, 1809–1891.

LAC 15312

The prose writers of America. With a survey of the history, condition, and prospects of American literature. Illustrated with portraits from original pictures. Philadelphia, Carey and Hart, 1847.
Griswold, Rufus Wilmot, 1815–1857.

LAC 11963

Prose writers of Germany. Illustrated with portraits. 2d ed. Philadelphia, Carey and Hart, 1849.
Hedge, Frederic Henry, 1805–1890.

LAC 15299

Prose writings of Nathaniel Parker Willis, selected by Henry A. Beers. New York, C. Scribner's sons, 1885.
Willis, Nathaniel Parker, 1806–1867.

LAC 22285

Prose writings of William Cullen Bryant. Ed. by Parke Godwin. New York, D. Appleton and company, 1884.
Bryant, William Cullen, 1794–1878.

LAC 12378

The pro-slavery argument; as maintained by the most distinguished writers of the southern states, containing the several essays, on the subject, of Chancellor Harper, Governor Hammond, Dr. Simms, and Professor Dew. Charleston, Walker, Richards & co., 1852.

LAC 40066

A prospect from the Congress-gallery, during the session, begun December 7, 1795. Containing, the President's speech, the addresses of both houses, some of the debates in the Senate, and all the principal debates in the House of representatives... With occasional remarks, by Peter Porcupine [*pseud.*] The 2d ed. Philadelphia, T. Bradford, 1796.
Cobbett, William, 1763–1835.

LAC 40047

The prospects of art in the United States. An address before the Artists' fund society of Philadelphia, at the opening of their exhibition, May, 1840. Philadelphia, Printed for the Artists' fund society, by J. C. Clark, 1840.
Bethune, George Washington, 1805–1862.

LAC 40101

The prospects of the small college. Chicago, The University of Chicago press, 1900.
Harper, William Rainey, 1856–1906.

LAC 40011
Prospectus of a national institution, to be established in the United States. Washington, Printed by S. H. Smith, 1806.
Barlow, Joel, 1754–1812.

LAC 13658
The prosperity of the South dependent upon the elevation of the Negro. Richmond, E. Waddey, 1889.
Blair, Lewis Harvie, 1834–1916.

LAC 12376
The prostrate state: South Carolina under Negro government. New York, D. Appleton and company, 1874, [c1873]
Pike, James Shepherd, 1811–1882.

LAC 10392
Protection and free trade: an inquiry whether protective duties can benefit the interests of a country in the aggregate; including an examination into the nature of value, and the agency of the natural forces in producing it. New York, G. P. Putnam's sons, 1875.
Butts, Isaac, 1816–1874.

LAC 40084
Protection and free trade. The question stated and considered. New-York, Greeley & McElrath [1844]
Greeley, Horace, 1811–1872.

LAC 11651
Protection of home industry. Four lectures delivered in Harvard university, January, 1885. New York, D. Appleton & company, 1886.
Thompson, Robert Ellis, 1844–1924.

LAC 40071
Protection to private property from public attack. An address delivered before the graduating classes at the sixty-seventh anniversary of Yale law school, on June 23, 1891, by Hon. D. J. Brewer. New Haven, Conn., Hoggson & Robinson, printers, 1891.
Brewer, David Josiah, 1837–1910.

LAC 10401
Protection versus free trade. The scientific validity and economic operation of defensive duties in the United States. New York, D. Appleton and company, 1886, [c1885]
Hoyt, Henry Martyn, 1830–1892.

LAC 10973
Protestant Jesuitism. By a Protestant. New-York, Harper & Brothers, 1836.
Colton, Calvin, 1789–1857.

LAC 11083
Protestantism in Michigan: being a special history of the Methodist Episcopal church and incidentally of other denominations. Notices of the origin and growth of the principal towns and cities of the state; biographical sketches of many prominent pastors and laymen connected with the birth and growth of Protestantism in Michigan. Detroit, R. D. S. Tyler & co. [1878]
Pilcher, Elijah Holmes, 1810–1887.

LAC 40044
A Protestant's resolution: shewing his reasons why he will not be a Papist... London, Printed for T. Field, 1761.

LAC 40079
Proudhon and his "bank of the people," being a defence of the great French anarchist, showing the evils of a specie currency, and that interest on capital can and ought to be abolished by a system of free and mutual banking; a series of newspaper articles. New York, B. R. Tucker, 1896.
Dana, Charles Anderson, 1819–1897.

LAC 40015
Provenca; poems selected from Personae, Exultations, and Canzoniere of Ezra Pound. Boston, Small, Maynard and company [c1910]
Pound, Ezra Loomis, 1885–

LAC 11596
Providence in colonial times, by Gertrude Selwyn Kimball, with an introduction by J. Franklin Jameson. Boston & New York, Houghton Mifflin company, 1912.
Kimball, Gertrude Selwyn, 1863–1910.

LAC 23151–53
Province and court records of Maine. Portland, Maine Historical Society, 1928–1958.
Maine *(Colony)*

LAC 40102
The provincial council and committees of safety in North Carolina. Chapel Hill [N. C.] The University press, 1908.
Whitaker, Bessie Lewis.

LAC 16044
The provincial councillors of Pennsylvania who held office between 1733 and 1776, and those earlier councillors who were some time chief magistrats of the province and their descendants. Philadelphia, 1883.
Keith, Charles Penrose, 1854–1939.

LAC 14765
The provincial governor in the English colonies of North America. New York [etc.] Longmans, Green and co., 1898.
Greene, Evarts Boutell, 1870–1947.

LAC 10405
Provisional and permanent constitutions, of the Confederate States. Richmond, Tyler, Wise, Allegre and Smith, printers, 1861.
Confederate States of America. *Constitution.*

LAC 13450
The provisional government of Nebraska Territory and The journals of William Walker, provisional governor of Nebraska Territory. Ed. by William E. Connelley. Lincoln, Neb., State journal company, printers, 1899.
Connelley, William Elsey, 1855–1930, *ed.*

LAC 40029
The Prussian primary school system as seen by a Virginia traveler a century ago, with suggestions as to its application to the state of Virginia. A report submitted

to the Governor of Virginia on January 15, 1839, by the
Rev. Benjamin Mosby Smith of Danville, Virginia, re-
printed from a photostat of House document 26, Virginia.
Foreword by Charles William Dabney. [Staunton, Va.,
The McClure co., printers, 1936]
Smith, Benjamin Mosby, 1811–1893.

LAC 10567
The psychic factors of civilization. Boston, Ginn &
company, 1893.
Ward, Lester Frank, 1841–1913.

LAC 13015
Psychologic foundations of education; an attempt to
show the genesis of the higher faculties of the mind. New
York, D. Appleton and company, 1898.
Harris, William Torrey, 1835–1909.

LAC 13990
Psychology. New York, Harper & brothers, 1887.
Dewey, John, 1859–1952.

LAC 14046
Psychology and industrial efficiency. Boston and New
York, Houghton Mifflin company, 1913.
Munsterberg, Hugo, 1863–1916.

LAC 12261
The psychology of religious experience. Boston and
New York, Houghton Mifflin company [c1910]
Ames, Edward Scribner, 1870–1958.

LAC 14279
The psychology of the Salem witchcraft excitement of
1692, and its practical application to our own time. New
York, G. P. Putnam's sons, 1882.
Beard, George Miller, 1839–1883.

LAC 14265
Psychology, or, Elements of a new system of mental
philosophy, on the basis of consciousness and common
sense. Designed for colleges and academies. New-York,
Harper & brothers, 1842.
Schmucker, Samuel Simon, 1799–1873.

LAC 14789
Psychology; or the science of mind. Rev. Oliver S.
Munsell. New York, D. Appleton and company, 1871.
Munsell, Oliver Spencer, 1825–1905.

LAC 23184–86
The public and general statutes passed by the Congress of the United States of America. From 1789 to
1827 inclusive, whether expired, repealed, or in force;
arranged in chronological order, with marginal references, and a copious index. To which is added the Constitution of the United States, and an appendix.
Published under the inspection of Joseph Story. Boston,
Wells and Lilly, 1827–28.
U.S. *Laws, statutes, etc.*

LAC 22209
Public and private economy. New-York, Harper &
brothers, 1836–39.
Sedgwick, Theodore, 1780–1839.

LAC 11186
The public debt of the United States. Its organization;
its liquidation; administration of the Treasury; the financial system. New York, C. Scribner & co.; [etc., etc.]
1867.
Gibbons, James Sloan, 1810–1892.

LAC 10156
Public debts: an essay in the science of finance. New
York, D. Appleton and company, 1887.
Adams, Henry Carter, 1851–1921.

LAC 15908
Public documents concerning the Ohio canals, which
are to connect lake Erie with the Ohio river, comprising
a complete official history of these great works of internal improvement, from their commencement down to the
close of the session of the legislature of 1831–32. Columbus, I. N. Whiting, 1832.
Kilbourn, John, 1787–1833.

LAC 14202
Public documents, relating to the New-York canals,
which are to connect the western and northern lakes,
with the Atlantic ocean; with an introduction. Printed
under the direction of the New-York corresponding association, for the promotion of internal improvements.
New-York, W. A. Mercein, printer, 1821.
New York Corresponding Association for the Promotion
of Internal Improvements.

LAC 16829–30
The public domain. Its history, with statistics, to June
30 and December 1, 1883. Prepared in pursuance of the
acts of Congress of March 3, 1879, June 16, 1880, and
August 7, 1882. Author's edition. Washington, Govt.
print. off., 1884.
Donaldson, Thomas Corwin, 1843–1898.

LAC 40094
Public education: an address; delivered in the hall of
the House of representatives, in the Capitol at Lansing,
on the evening of January 28th, 1857. Detroit, Printed by
H. Barns, 1857.
Tappan, Henry Philip, 1805–1881.

LAC 14602
Public education in California; its origin and develop-
ment, with personal reminiscences of half a century.
New York, Cincinnati [etc.] American book company
[c1911]
Swett, John, 1830–1913.

LAC 10578
Public education in the city of New York: its history,
condition. And statistics. An official report to the Board
of education. By Thomas Boese, clerk of the board. New
York, Harper & brothers, 1869.
New York *(City) Board of education.*

LAC 13638
Public hygiene in America: being the centennial discourse delivered before the International medical congress, Philadelphia, September, 1876. By Henry I.
Bowditch, M. D. With extracts from correspondence
from the various states. Together with a digest of American sanitary law, by Henry G. Pickering, esq. Boston,
Little, Brown, and company; [etc., etc.] 1877.
Bowditch, Henry Ingersoll, 1808–1892.

LAC 14324
The public land policies, A history of.
A history of the public land policies. New York, The Macmillan company, 1924.
Hibbard, Benjamin Horace, 1870–

LAC 14381-82
Public libraries in the United States of America. Part I. 1876 report. [Urbana] University of Illinois [n.d.]
U.S. *Office of Education.*

LAC 40123
The public library movement in the United States.
Boston, Warren F. Kellogg, 1893.
Harrison, Joseph Leroy, 1862–

LAC 13953
The public library movement in The United States 1853-1893. From 1876, reminiscences of the writer. Boston, The Boston book company, 1913.
Green, Samuel Swett, 1837–1918.

LAC 12361
The public life and diplomatic correspondence of James M. Mason, with some personal history, by his daughter. Roanoke, Va., The Stone printing and manufacturing co., 1903.
Mason, Virginia, 1833–1920, *ed. and comp.*

LAC 11528
The public life of Capt. John Brown, by James Redpath, with an auto-biography of his childhood and youth.
Boston, Thayer and Eldridge, 1860.
Redpath, James, 1833–1891.

LAC 11597
The public life of Joseph Dudley; a study of the colonial policy of the Stuarts in New England, 1660–1715. New York [etc.] Longmans, Green, and co., 1911.
Kimball, Everett, 1873–

LAC 20833
Public men and events from the commencement of Mr. Monroe's administration, in 1817, to the close of Mr. Fillmore's administration, in 1853. Philadelphia, J. B. Lippincott & co., 1875, [c1874]
Sargent, Nathan, 1794–1875.

LAC 10351
Public opinion and popular government. New York [etc.] Longmans, Green, and co., 1913.
Lowell, Abbott Lawrence, 1856–1943.

LAC 16387
Public opinion and the Spanish-American war; a study in war propaganda. Baton Rouge, Louisiana state university press, 1932.
Wilkerson, Marcus Manley.

LAC 40048
The public ownership of monopolies. 6th ed. Philadelphia, Bureau of Nationalist Literature [c1894]
Parsons, Frank, 1854–1908.

LAC 15263
Public papers and addresses of Benjamin Harrison, twenty-third president of the United States. March 4, 1889, to March 4, 1893. Washington, Govt. print. off., 1893.
Harrison, Benjamin, *pres. U.S.*, 1833–1901.

LAC 21875-77
Public papers of Daniel D. Tompkins, governor of New York, 1807-1817. Military-vol. I-III. With an introduction by Hugh Hastings, state historian. Published by the state of New York. New York and Albany, Wynkoop Hallenbeck, Crawford co., state printers [etc.] 1898-1902.
New York *(State) Governor, 1807–1817 (Daniel D. Tompkins)*

LAC 23441-51
Public papers of George Clinton, first governor of New York, 1777-1795, 1801-1804... Pub. by the state of New York. New York and Albany, 1899–1914.
New York *(State) Governor, 1777–1795 (George Clinton)*

LAC 13897
Public parks, being two papers read before the American social science association in 1870 and 1880, entitled, respectively, public parks and the enlargement of towns and A consideration of the justifying value of a public park. Brookline, Mass., 1902.
Olmsted, Frederick Law, 1822–1903.

LAC 14344
Public parks: their effects upon the moral, physical and sanitary condition of the inhabitants of large cities; with special reference to the city of Chicago. Chicago, S. C. Griggs & company, 1869.
Rauch, John Henry, 1828–1894.

LAC 12530
Public record: including speeches, messages, proclamations, official correspondence, and other public utterances of Horatio Seymour; from the campaign of 1856 to the present time. With an appendix. Comp. from the most authentic sources, and printed exclusively for the use of editors and public speakers. Comp. and ed. by Thomas M. Cook and Thomas W. Knox. New York, I. W. England, 1868.
Seymour, Horatio, 1810–1886.

LAC 20579-89
The public records of the colony of Connecticut [1636-1776] ... transcribed and published, (in accordance with a resolution of the General assembly) Hartford, Press of the Case, Lockwood & Brainard company [etc.] 1850-90.
Connecticut *(Colony)*

LAC 10052
The public regulation of railways. New York & London, G. P. Putnam's sons, 1889.
Dabney, Walter Davis, 1853–1899.

LAC 13643
Public relief and private charity, by Josephine Shaw Lowell. New York & London, G. P. Putnam's sons, 1884.
Lowell, Josephine, 1843–1905.

LAC 16092
The public school. History of common school education in New York from 1633 to 1904, by Charles E. Fitch. Prepared under the direction of Charles R. Skinner, superintendent of public instruction. Albany, N. Y., J. B. Lyon company, printers [1904?]
New York *(State) Dept. of Public Instruction.*

LAC 10623
The public-school system of the United States. New York, The Century co., 1893.
Rice, Joseph Mayer, 1857–1934.

LAC 14139
The public schools of colonial Boston, 1635–1775. Cambridge, Harvard university press, 1935.
Seybolt, Robert Francis, 1888–1951.

LAC 22035–107
The public statutes at large of the United States of America... v. 1–38; 1789–1845—1913–1915. Boston, C. C. Little and J. Brown.
U.S. *Laws, statutes, etc.*

LAC 14201
Public utility economics; a series of ten lectures delivered before the West side Young men's Christian association, New York. [New York? 1914]

LAC 15038
Public worship; a study in the psychology of religion. Chicago, The Open court publishing company; London, K. Paul, Trench, Trubner & co., ltd., 1901.
Hylan, John Perham, 1870–

LAC 23886–89
Publications of the Narragansett club. (First series) v. 1–6. Providence [Providence press co., printers] 1866–74.
Narragansett Club, *Providence.*

LAC 24054–66
The publications of the Prince society... Boston, The Prince society, 1865–1903.
Prince Society, *Boston.*

LAC 16173
Puerto Rico; its conditions and possibilities. With illustrations and photographs by the author. New York and London, Harper & bros., 1899.
Dinwiddie, William, 1867–1934.

LAC 11124
The pulpit of the American revolution: or, The political sermons of the period of 1776. With a historical introduction, notes, and illustrations. Boston, Gould and Lincoln; New York, Sheldon and company; [etc., etc.] 1860.
Thornton, John Wingate, 1818–1878, *ed.*

LAC 10586
Pupil self-government, its theory and practice. New York, The Macmillan company; London, Macmillan & company, ltd., 1908, [c1907]
Cronson, Bernard, 1866–1916.

LAC 10343
Pure oil trust *vs.* Standard oil company, being the report of an investigation by the United States Industrial commission. Comp. from private and official sources by the Oil City derrick, 1899–1900. Oil City, Pa., Derrick publishing co., printer, 1901.
Oil City Derrick.

LAC 10568
Pure sociology; a treatise on the origin and spontaneous development of society. New York, The Macmillan company; London, Macmillan & co., ltd., 1903.
Ward, Lester Frank, 1841–1913.

LAC 14810
The Puritan commonwealth. An historical review of the Puritan government in Massachusetts in its civil and ecclesiastical relations from its rise to the abrogation of the first charter. Together with some general reflections on the English colonial policy, and on the character of Puritanism. By the late Peter Oliver. Boston, Little, Brown and company, 1856.
Oliver, Peter, 1822–1855.

LAC 40076
Put up thy sword. A discourse delivered before Theodore Parker's society, at the Music hall, Boston, Sunday, March 11, 1860. Boston, R. F. Wallcut, 1860.
Furness, William Henry, 1802–1896.

LAC 30871–79
Putnam's monthly magazine of American literature, science and art. v. 1–9; Jan. 1853–July 1857. New York, G. P. Putnam & co.; etc., etc.

LAC 20649
The quadroon; or, A lover's adventures in Louisiana. London, G. W. Hyde, 1856.
Reid, Mayne, 1818–1883.

LAC 20961–62
The quadrupeds of North America, by John James Audubon, and the Rev. John Bachman. New York, V. G. Audubon [1849–1854]
Audubon, John James, 1785–1851.

LAC 16371
Quaint and historic forts of North America. With seventy-one illustrations. Philadelphia & London, J. B. Lippincott company, 1915.
Hammond, John Martin, 1886–1939.

LAC 12016
The Quaker City; or, The monks of Monk-Hall. A romance of Philadelphia life, mystery, and crime. [16th ed.] Philadelphia, T. B. Peterson [c1876]
Lippard, George, 1822–1854.

LAC 16179
A Quaker experiment in government. Philadelphia, A. J. Ferris, 1898.
Sharpless, Isaac, 1848–

LAC 16061
The Quaker invasion of Massachusetts. 3d ed. Boston, Houghton, Mifflin and company, 1884, [c1883]
Hallowell, Richard Price, 1835–1904.

LAC 11095
Quakerism and politics; essays by Isaac Sharpless. Philadelphia, Ferris & Leach, 1905.
Sharpless, Isaac, 1848–1920.

LAC 11986
The quality of mercy; a novel. New York and London, Harper & brothers [c1891]
Howells, William Dean, 1837–1920.

LAC 15003
Quantrill and the border wars. Cedar Rapids, Ia., The Torch press, 1910.
Connelley, William Elsey, 1855–1930.

LAC 15849
The quest of the silver fleece; a novel. Illustrated by H. S. DeLay. College Park, Md., McGrath Pub. Co. [1969, c1911]
Du Bois, William Edward Burghardt, 1868–1963.

LAC 14683
La question Chinoise aux Etats-Unis et dans les possessions des puissances europeennes. Paris, A. Rousseau, 1898.
Cailleux, Edouard.

LAC 13727
The question of ships; the navy and the merchant marine. New York, C. Scribner's sons, 1884.
Kelley, James Douglas Jerrold, 1847–1922.

LAC 12993
The question of the hour: the Bible and the school fund. Boston, Lee and Shepard, 1870.
Clark, Rufus Wheelwright, 1813–1886.

LAC 40010
The question of the Philippines; an address delivered before the Graduate club of Leland Stanford junior university, on February 14, 1899. Palo Alto, Cal., Printed for the Graduate club by the courtesy of J. J. Valentine, 1899.
Jordan, David Starr, 1851–1931.

LAC 10431
Questions of the day: economic and social. Philadelphia, H. C. Baird, 1871.
Elder, William, 1806–1885.

LAC 11133
Questions of the soul. 5th ed. New York, D. Appleton & co., 1864, [c1855]
Hecker, Isaac Thomas, 1819–1888.

LAC 40015
A quiet road. Portland, Me., T. B. Mosher, 1916.
Reese, Lizette Woodworth, 1856–

LAC 13526
The "Quincy methods" illustrated. Pen photographs from the Quincy schools. New York, E. L. Kellogg [c1885]
Patridge, Lelia E.

LAC 12728
The quit-rent system in the American colonies, by Beverley W. Bond, jr., with an introduction by Charles M. Andrews. New Haven, Yale university press; [etc., etc.] 1919.
Bond, Beverley Waugh, 1881–

LAC 12865
Race adjustment; essays on the negro in America. New York and Washington, The Neale publishing company, 1910, [c1909]
Miller, Kelly, 1863–

LAC 15979
Race distinctions in American law. New York and London, D. Appleton and company, 1910.
Stephenson, Gilbert Thomas, 1884–

LAC 16895
Race orthodoxy in the South, and other aspects of the negro question. New York, The Neale publishing company, 1914.
Bailey, Thomas Pearce, 1867–1949.

LAC 16216
Race problems of the South; report of the proceedings of the first annual conference held under the auspices of the Southern Society for the Promotion of the Study of Race Conditions and Problems in the South, at Montgomery, Alabama, May 8, 9, 10, A. D. 1900. New York, Negro Universities Press [1969]
Southern Society for the Promotion of the Study of Race Conditions and Problems in the South.

LAC 16493
Race questions, provincialism, and other American problems. New York, The Macmillan company, 1908.
Royce, Josiah, 1855–1916.

LAC 12852
Race traits and tendencies of the American Negro. New York, Pub. for the American economic association by the Macmillan company; [etc., etc.] 1896.
Hoffman, Frederick Ludwig, 1865–1946.

LAC 12611
Races and peoples: lectures on the science of ethnography. Philadelphia, D. McKay, 1901.
Brinton, Daniel Garrison, 1837–1899.

LAC 12609
The races of the Old world: a manual of ethnology. New York, C. Scribner, 1863.
Brace, Charles Loring, 1826–1890.

LAC 16605
Racial integrity and other features of the Negro problem. Nashville, Tenn., Dallas, Tex., Printed for the author, Publishing house of the M. E. church, South, 1907.
Shannon, Alexander Harvey, 1869–

LAC 13986
The radical: and advocate of equality; presenting a series of expostulatory animadversions on the present state of practical politics and morals; with a view to an access of improvement. Addressed to the people of the United States. By the author of "A disquisition on faith" and "A dialogue on commonwealths". Albany, Printed by Stone and Munsell, 1834.
Brown, Paul.

LAC 14148
Radical empiricism.
Essays in radical empiricism. New York [etc.] Longmans, Green, and co., 1912.
James, William, 1842–1910.

LAC 13073

Radical problems. Boston, Roberts brothers, 1872.
Bartol, Cyrus Augustus, 1813–1900.

LAC 11305

Ragged Dick; or, Street life in New York with the bootblacks. Boston, Loring [1868]
Alger, Horatio, 1832–1899.

LAC 15428

The raid on prosperity. New York, D. Appleton and company, 1908, [c1907]
Day, James Roscoe, 1845–1923.

LAC 22826–28

Railroad charters.
The railroad laws and charters of the United States, now for the first time collated, arranged in chronological order, and published with a synopsis and explanatory remarks. By W. P. Gregg and Benjamin Pond. New York, J. R. Halstead, 1851.
Gregg, Washington Parker, 1802–1892, *ed.*

LAC 16327

Railroad finance, by Frederick A. Cleveland and Fred Wilbur Powell. New York and London, D. Appleton and company, 1912.
Cleveland, Frederick Albert, 1865–1946.

LAC 22826–28

The railroad laws and charters of the United States, now for the first time collated, arranged in chronological order, and published with a synopsis and explanatory remarks. By W. P. Gregg and Benjamin Pond. New York, J. R. Halstead, 1851.
Gregg, Washington Parker, 1802–1892, *ed.*

LAC 10715

Rail road manual, or, A brief exposition of principles and deductions applicable in tracing the route of a rail road. In two parts. Baltimore, W. Wooddy, printer, 1829.
Long, Stephen Harriman, 1784–1864.

LAC 40048

The railroad monopoly.
Letters to the people of New Jersey, on the frauds, extortions, and oppressions of the railroad monopoly. By a citizen of Burlington. Philadelphia, Carey and Hart, 1848.
Carey, Henry Charles, 1793–1879.

LAC 12169

Railroad promotion and capitalization in the United States, by Frederick A. Cleveland, PH. D. and Fred Wilbur Powell, A. M. New York [etc.] Longmans, Green, and co., 1909.
Cleveland, Frederick Albert, 1865–1946.

LAC 10172

The railroad question; a historical and practical treatise on railroads, and remedies for their abuses. 3rd ed. Chicago, The Schulte publishing company, 1893.
Larrabee, William, 1832–1912.

LAC 40024

Railroad rings, and their relation to the railroad question in this country. New York, D. H. Gildersleeve & co., printers, 1876.
Hassler, Charles William.

LAC 40117

The railroad, the conqueror. Columbia, S. C., The State company, 1913.
Jervey, Theodore Dehon, 1859–

LAC 10266

Railroad transportation; its history and its laws. 10th impression. New York and London, G. P. Putnam's sons, 1899.
Hadley, Arthur Twining, 1856–1930.

LAC 40117

Railroads and their management. Concord [N. H.] Steam printing works of McFarland & Jenks, 1856.
Whiton, James M.

LAC 10204

Railroads; finance & organization, with 29 maps and diagrams. New York [etc.] Longmans, Green, and co., 1915.
Ripley, William Zebina, 1867–

LAC 40143

The Railroads of Chicago; a comprehensive history, containing a map of the lines within a radius of five hundred miles. Pub. by the Western news company, Chicago, Ill. Chicago, Horton & Leonard, printers [1872]

LAC 12140

The railroads of the United States. A potent factor in the politics of that country and of Great Britain. Boston, A. Williams and company, 1880.
Atkinson, Edward, 1827–1905.

LAC 10033

The railroads of the United States; their history and statistics: comprising the progress and present condition of the various lines with their earnings and expenses... To which are added a synopsis of the railroad laws of the United States, and an article on the comparative merits of iron and steel rails. Philadelphia, John E. Potter and company, 1868.
Flint, Henry Martyn, 1829–1868.

LAC 10157

Railroads: their origin and problems. New York, G. P. Putnam's sons, 1878.
Adams, Charles Francis, 1835–1915.

LAC 13395

Railway conductors; a study in organized labor. New York, Columbia university; Longmans, Green & co., agents; [etc., etc.] 1914.
Robbins, Edwin Clyde, 1883–

LAC 10294

Railway control by commissions. New York & London, G. P. Putnam's sons, 1900.
Hendrick, Frank.

LAC 10065

Railway co-operation. An investigation of railway traffic associations and a discussion of the degree and form of co-operation that should be granted competing railways in the United States. By Charles S. Langstroth and Wilson Stilz, with an introduction by Martin A. Knapp. Philadelphia, The University, 1899.
Langstroth, Charles Souder.

LAC 40098
Railway discriminations ! as given to the Standard Oil Trust. [Marietta, Ohio, 1888]
Rice, George.

LAC 10171
Railway economy: a treatise on the new art of transport, its management, prospects and relations... New York, Harper & brothers, 1855.
Lardner, Dionysius, 1793–1859.

LAC 40024
Railway mail service: an historical sketch; being a lecture delivered at the University of Chicago and at the University of Minnesota. Chicago, R. R. Donnelley & sons co., 1902.
Tunell, George Gerard.

LAC 10210
The railway problem... St. Paul, Minn., D. D. Merrill company, 1891.
Stickney, Alpheus Beede, 1840–1916.

LAC 15870
Railway problems; ed., with an introduction, by William Z. Ripley. Boston, New York [etc.] Ginn & company [c1907]
Ripley, William Zebina, 1867–   ed.

LAC 11609
Railway property. A treatise on the construction and management of railways... New York, Phinney, Blakeman & Mason, 1861.
Jervis, John Bloomfield, 1795–1885.

LAC 10048
Railway secrecy and trusts. New York & London, G. P. Putnam's sons, 1890.
Bonham, John Milton.

LAC 40117
The railway, the farmer and the public. New York, The Society for political education, 1885.
Atkinson, Edward, 1827–1905.

LAC 10198
The railways and the republic. New York, Harper & brothers, 1886.
Hudson, James Fairchild, 1846–1915.

LAC 23225–26
Railways in the United States in 1902. A twenty-two year review of railway operations; a forty-year review of changes in freight tariffs; a fifteen-year review of federal railway regulation; a twelve-year review of state railway regulation; and a twelve-year review of state railway taxation. Pt. II, IV–V. Washington, Govt. print. off., 1903.
U.S. *Interstate Commerce Commission.*

LAC 16236
Railways in the United States; their history, their relation to the state, and an analysis of the legislation in regard to their control, with supplementary notes continuing the record to 1911. New York and London, G. P. Putnam's sons, 1912.
Sterne, Simon, 1839–1901.

LAC 20393
The railways, the trusts, and the people ... by Prof. Frank Parsons. With the assistance of Ralph Albertson. Ed. by C. F. Taylor. Philadelphia, C. F. Taylor [1905]
Parsons, Frank, 1854–

LAC 40047
Ralph Albert Blakelock. New York, Priv. print., 1914.
Daingerfield, Elliott, 1859–

LAC 12126
Ralph Waldo Emerson. New York [etc.] The Macmillan company, 1907.
Woodberry, George Edward, 1855–1930.

LAC 11876
Ralph Waldo Emerson: his life, writings, and philosophy. Boston, J. R. Osgood and company, 1881.
Cooke, George Willis, 1848–1923.

LAC 11581
Ralph Waldo Emerson, philosopher and seer; an estimate of his character and genius, in prose and verse. [2d ed.] Boston, Cupples & Hurd [c1888]
Alcott, Amos Bronson, 1799–1888.

LAC 21137
The rambler in North America: MDCCCXXXII–MDCCCXXXIII. London, R. B. Seeley and W. Burnside [etc.] 1835.
Latrobe, Charles Joseph, 1801–1875.

LAC 20515
Rambles about Portsmouth. Sketches of persons, localities, and incidents of two centuries: principally from tradition and unpublished documents. Portsmouth, N. H., C. W. Brewster & son, 1859–69.
Brewster, Charles Warren, 1802–1868.

LAC 16337
Rambles by land and water, or Notes of travel in Cuba and Mexico; including a canoe voyage up the river Panuco, and researches among the ruins of Tamaulipas... New-York, Paine & Burgess; New Orleans, B. M. Norman, 1845.
Norman, Benjamin Moore, 1809–1860.

LAC 16191
Rambles in north-western America, from the Pacific ocean to the Rocky mountains. Being a description of the physical geography, climate, soil, productions, industrial and commercial resources, scenery, population, educational institutions, arboreal botany, and game animals of Oregon, Washington territory, Idaho, Montana, Utah, and Wyoming. London, Chapman and Hall, 1879.
Murphy, John Mortimer.

LAC 16568
Rambles overland. A trip across the continent. Boston, Universalist publishing house, 1884.
Gunnison, Almon, 1844–1917.

LAC 15124
Ramblings in California; containing a description of the country, life at the mines, state of society, &c. Interspersed with characteristic anecdotes, and sketches from life, being the five years' experience of a gold digger. Toronto, J. Bain [1857?]
Shaw, Pringle.

LAC 11998
Ramona; a story. By Helen Jackson (H. H.) Boston, Roberts brothers, 1884.
Jackson, Helen Maria Hunt, 1831–1885.

LAC 20769
Ramsay's History of South Carolina, from its first settlement in 1670 to the year 1808. Newberry, S. C., W. J. Duffie, 1858.
Ramsay, David, 1749–1815.

LAC 15858
Random recollections. [New York] Priv. print. [The De Vinne press] 1905.
Munford, Beverly Bland, 1856–1910.

LAC 12534
Random recollections. 3rd ed. New York, Harper & brothers, 1887.
Stanton, Henry Brewster, 1805–1887.

LAC 13551
Random recollections of Albany, from 1800 to 1808. 3d ed., with notes by the publisher. Albany, N. Y., J. Munsell, 1866.
Worth, Gorham A. *d.* 1856–

LAC 12473
Random recollections of an old political reporter, by William C. Hudson, with introduction by St. Clair McKelway, LL. D. New York, Cupples & Leon company, 1911.
Hudson, William Cadwalader, 1843–1915.

LAC 16534
Random reminiscences of men and events. New York, Doubleday, Page & company, 1909.
Rockefeller, John Davison, 1839–1937.

LAC 20761
Random shots and southern breezes, containing critical remarks on the southern states and southern institutions, with semi-serious observations on men and manners. New-York, Harper & brothers, 1842.
Tasistro, Louis Fitsgerald.

LAC 14941
Rapid transit in New York city and in other great cities. Prepared for the Chamber of commerce of the state of New York by its special committee on recognition of services of members of the Chamber on the Rapid transit commission. [New York, Blumenberg press] 1905.
New York. Chamber of Commerce of the State of New York.

LAC 14787
Rational cosmology; or, The eternal principles and the necessary laws of the universe. New York [etc.] D. Appleton & company, 1858.
Hickok, Laurens Perseus, 1798–1888.

LAC 10523
Rational psychology: or, The subjective idea and the objective law of all intelligence. Schenectady, G. Y. Van Debogert, 1854, [c1848]
Hickok, Laurens Perseus, 1798–1888.

LAC 13626
The real Billy Sunday, the life and work of Rev. William Ashley Sunday, D. D., the baseball evangelist, by Elijah P. Brown, D. D. (Ram's Horn Brown) New York, Chicago [etc.] Fleming H. Revell company [c1914]
Brown, Elijah P *b.* 1842.

LAC 13599
The real Hawaii; its history and present condition, including the true story of the revolution. (A revised and enlarged ed. of "The Boston at Hawaii") by Lucien Young, U. S. N. New York, Doubleday & McClure company, 1899.
Young, Lucien, 1852–1912.

LAC 40076
The real issue–union or disunion. Letter of Hon. S. S. Marshall, on the parties and politics of the day, to the freemen of the Ninth congressional district of Illinois. Washington, Printed at the Union office, 1856.
Marshall, Samuel Scott, 1824–1890.

LAC 14450
The real New York, by Rupert Hughes; drawings by H. Mayer. New York, London, The Smart set publishing company, 1904.
Hughes, Rupert, 1872–1956.

LAC 14536
The real world. New York, The Macmillan company; London, Macmillan & co., ltd., 1901.
Herrick, Robert, 1868–1938.

LAC 11026
Reason in religion. Boston, Walker, Fuller and company, 1865.
Hedge, Frederic Henry, 1805–1890.

LAC 16692
Reason the only oracle of man; with an introduction by John Pell. New York, Scholars Facsimiles & Reprints, 1940.
Allen, Ethan, 1737–1789.

LAC 40074
Reasons for pardoning Fielden, Neebe and Schwab, by John P. Altgeld, governor of Illinois. [Chicago, 1893]
Altgeld, John Peter, 1847–1902.

LAC 15413
Rebel, priest and prophet; a biography of Dr. Edward McGlynn. New York, The Devin-Adair company, 1937.
Bell, Stephen, 1864–

LAC 20746
A Rebel war clerk's dairy at the Confederate States capital. Philadelphia, J. B. Lippincott & co., 1866.
Jones, John Beauchamp, 1810–1866.

LAC 12429
The rebellion: its consequences, and the congressional committee, denominated the reconstruction committee, with their action. By Investigator. New Orleans, Commercial print, 1866.
Barker, Jacob, 1779–1871.

LAC 22449-60

The Rebellion record: a diary of American events, with documents, narratives, illustrative incidents, poetry, etc. Ed. by Frank Moore. With an introductory address on the causes of the struggle, and the great issues before the country, by Edward Everett... New York, G. P. Putnam, 1862-63; D. Van Nostrand, 1864-69.

LAC 14413

A Rebel's recollections. New York, Hurd and Houghton; Cambridge, The Riverside press, 1875.
Eggleston, George Cary, 1839-1911.

LAC 10311

Recent economic changes, and their effect on the production and distribution of wealth and the well-being of society. New York, D. Appleton and company, 1899, [c1889]
Wells, David Ames, 1828-1898.

LAC 12402

The recent past from a southern standpoint. Reminiscences of a grandfather... New York, T. Whittaker, 1887.
Wilmer, Richard Hooker, *bp.*, 1816-1900.

LAC 14728

The recent progress of astronomy; especially in the United States. 3d ed., mostly rewritten, and much enlarged. New York, Harper & brothers, 1856.
Loomis, Elias, 1811-1889.

LAC 20811-12

Recherches historiques et politiques sur les Etats-Unis de l'Amerique Septentrionale, ou l'on traite des etablissemens des treize colonies, de leurs rapports & de leurs dissentions avec la Grande-Bretagne, de leurs gouvernemens avant & apres la revolution, &c. Par un citoyen de Virginie. Avec quatre lettres d'un bourgeois de New-Heaven [Condorcet] sur l'unite de la legislation. A Colle, et se trouve a Paris, chez Froulle, 1788.
Mazzei, Filippo, 1730-1816.

LAC 12928

Reciprocity, by J. Laurence Laughlin and H. Parker Willis. New York, The Baker & Taylor co. [c1903]
Laughlin, James Laurence, 1850-1933.

LAC 10082

Reclaiming the arid West; the story of the United States reclamation service. New York, Dodd, Mead and company, 1917.
James, George Wharton, 1858-1923.

LAC 11478

Recollection of men and things at Washington, during the third of a century. Philadelphia, Claxton, Remsen & Haffelfinger; Washington, W. H. & O. H. Morrison, 1869.
Gobright, Lawrence Augustus, 1816-1879.

LAC 11188

Recollections. Boston and New York, Houghton Mifflin company [c1909]
Gladden, Washington, 1836-1918.

LAC 16903

Recollections and experiences of an abolitionist; from 1855 to 1865. Toronto, Rowsell and Hutchison, 1875.
Ross, Alexander Milton, 1832-1897.

LAC 11007

Recollections and impressions, 1822-1890. New York, London, G. P. Putnam's sons, 1891.
Frothingham, Octavius Brooks, 1822-1895.

LAC 15108

Recollections and impressions of James A. McNeill Whistler. Philadelphia & London, J. B. Lippincott company, 1903.
Eddy, Arthur Jerome, 1859-1920.

LAC 14504

Recollections and letters of General Robert E. Lee, by his son, Captain Robert E. Lee. New York, Doubleday, Page & company, 1905, [c1904]
Lee, Robert Edward, 1843-1914.

LAC 15468

Recollections and private memoirs of Washington, by his adopted son, George Washington Parke Custis, with a memoir of the author, by his daughter; and illustrative and explanatory notes. By Benson J. Lossing. New York, Derby & Jackson, 1860.
Custis, George Washington Parke, 1781-1857.

LAC 15958

Recollections 1837-1910. Chicago, Farm implement news company, 1910.
Marsh, Charles W   1834-

LAC 12478

Recollections, historical, political, biographical, and social, of Charles J. Ingersoll. By experience, presenting annals, with portraiture of personages of this country, from Genet's arrival in 1792, to the purchase of Louisiana in 1803... In two volumes. Vol. 1. Philadelphia, J. B. Lippincott & co., 1861.
Ingersoll, Charles Jared, 1782-1862.

LAC 11193

Recollections of a busy life: including reminiscences of American politics and politicians, from the opening of the Missouri contest to the downfall of slavery; to which are added miscellanies ... also, a discussion with Robert Dale Owen of the law of divorce. New York, J. B. Ford & co.; Boston, H. A. Brown & co. [etc., etc.] 1868.
Greeley, Horace, 1811-1872.

LAC 12481

Recollections of a Georgia loyalist, by Elizabeth Lichtenstein Johnston, written in 1836; edited by Rev. Arthur Wentworth Eaton. New York and London, M. F. Mansfield & company [c1901]
Johnston, Elizabeth, 1764-1848.

LAC 11399

Recollections of a lifetime. 2d ed. Cincinnati, The Robert Clarke company, 1904, [c1900]
Brinkerhoff, Roeliff, 1828-1911.

LAC 20374-75
Recollections of a lifetime, or Men and things I have seen: in a series of familiar letters to a friend, historical, biographical, anecdotal, and descriptive. New York, C. M. Saxon, 1859.
Goodrich, Samuel Griswold, 1793–1860.

LAC 15292
Recollections of a long life, 1829–1915. Chicago, Priv. print. [by R. R. Donnelley & sons company] 1915.
Stephenson, Isaac, 1829–1918.

LAC 21048
Recollections of a minister to France, 1869–1877. New York, C. Scribner's sons, 1887.
Washburne, Elihu Benjamin, 1816–1887.

LAC 14386
Recollections of a New York chief of police. New York, Caxton book concern, limited, 1887.
Walling, George Washington, 1823–

LAC 14885
Recollections of a private soldier in the Army of the Potomac. London, G. Redway, 1898.
Wilkeson, Frank, 1848–

LAC 12921
Recollections of a varied career. With nine illustrations from photographs. Boston, Little, Brown, and company, 1908.
Draper, Willaim Franklin, 1842–1910.

LAC 14896
Recollections of a Virginian in the Mexican, Indian, and Civil wars; by General Dabney Herndon Maury. New York, C. Scribner's sons, 1894.
Maury, Dabney Herndon, 1822–1900.

LAC 12226
Recollections of a visit to the United States and British provinces of North America, in the years 1847, 1848, and 1849. Edinburgh [etc.] T. Constable and co., 1856.
Playfair, Robert.

LAC 40080
Recollections of an old soldier. The life of Captain David Perry, a soldier of the French and revolutionary wars. Containing many extraordinary occurrences relating to his own private history, and an account of some interesting events in the history of the times in which he lived... Written by himself. Windsor, Vt., Printed at the Republican & yeoman printing office, 1822.
Perry, David, b. 1741.

LAC 12970
Recollections of eminent men, with other papers, by Edwin Percy Whipple, with introduction by Rev. C. A. Bartol, D. D. Boston, Ticknor and company, 1887.
Whipple, Edwin Percy, 1819–1886.

LAC 12543
Recollections of full years, by Mrs. William Howard Taft. New York, Dodd, Mead & company, 1914.
Taft, Helen, 1861–

LAC 13228
Recollections of life in Ohio, from 1813 to 1840, by William Cooper Howells. With an introduction by his son, William Dean Howells. Cincinnati, The Robert Clarke company, 1895.
Howells, William Cooper, 1807–1894.

LAC 14931
Recollections of Mexico. New York & London, Wiley and Putnam, 1846.
Thompson, Waddy, 1798–1868.

LAC 14369
Recollections of Mississippi and Mississippians. Boston and New York, Houghton, Mifflin and company, 1890.
Davis, Reuben, 1813–1890.

LAC 13152
Recollections of persons and places in the West. 2d ed., enl. Philadelphia, J. B. Lippincott & co., 1868.
Brackenridge, Henry Marie, 1786–1871.

LAC 12433
Recollections of President Lincoln and his administration. New York, Harper & brothers [c1891]
Chittenden, Lucius Eugene, 1824–1900.

LAC 10145
Recollections of Samuel Breck, with passages from his notebooks (1771–1862) ed. by H. E. Scudder. Philadelphia, Porter & Contes, 1877.
Breck, Samuel, 1771–1862.

LAC 14900
Recollections of seventy years, by Augustus L. Chetlain, brigadier, and brevet major general U.S. vols., civil war. 1861–65. Galena, The Gazette publishing company, 1899.
Chetlain, Augustus Louis, 1824–1914.

LAC 20411
Recollections of seventy years, by F. B. Sanborn, of Concord... Boston, R. G. Badger, 1909.
Sanborn, Franklin Benjamin, 1831–1917.

LAC 14618
Recollections of the civil war; with the leaders at Washington and in the field in the sixties. New York, D. Appleton and company, 1902, [c1898]
Dana, Charles Anderson, 1819–1897.

LAC 10648
Recollections of the inhabitants, localities, superstitions and Kuklux outrages of the Carolinas. By a "carpetbagger" who was born and lived there. [Cleveland? O.] 1880.
Green, John Paterson, 1845–

LAC 16608
Recollections of the last ten years, passed in occasional residences and journeyings in the valley of the Mississippi, from Pittsburgh and the Missouri to the Gulf of Mexico, and from Florida to the Spanish frontier; in a series of letters to the Rev. James Flint, of Salem, Massachusetts. Boston, Cummings, Hilliard, and company, 1826.
Flint, Timothy, 1780–1840.

LAC 13028
Recollections of the log school house period, and sketches of life and customs in pioneer days. By Jno. S. Minard. Illustrated by R. J. Tucker. Cuba, N. Y., Free press print, 1905.
Minard, John Stearns, 1834–1920.

LAC 11555
Recollections of thirteen presidents. Illustrated. Freeport, N.Y., Books for libraries press [1968]
Wise, John Sergeant, 1846–1913.

LAC 11535
Recollections of war times; reminiscences of men and events in Washington, 1860–1865. New York [etc.] G. P. Putnam's sons, 1895.
Riddle, Albert Gallatin, 1816–1902.

LAC 12078
Recollections, personal and literary, by Richard Henry Stoddard; ed. by Ripley Hitchcock. With an introduction by Edmund Clarence Stedman. New York, A. S. Barnes and company, 1903.
Stoddard, Richard Henry, 1825–1903.

LAC 13344
Reconnaissances in the Cape Nome and Norton Bay regions, Alaska, in 1900, by Alfred H. Brooks, George B. Richardson, Arthur J. Collier and Walter C. Mendenhall. Washington, Govt. print. off., 1901.
U.S. *Geological Survey.*

LAC 10242
Reconstruction and the Constitution, 1866–1876. New York, C. Scribner's sons, 1902.
Burgess, John William, 1844–1931.

LAC 12758
Reconstruction during the Civil war in the United States of America. Boston and New York, Houghton, Mifflin and company, 1895.
Scott, Eben Greenough, 1836–1919.

LAC 10269
Reconstruction in Mississippi. New York, London, The Macmillan company, 1901.
Garner, James Wilford, 1871–1938.

LAC 12382
Reconstruction in South Carolina, 1865–1877. New York, Negro Universities Press [1969]
Reynolds, John Schreiner, 1848–

LAC 12380
Reconstruction in Texas... [n.p.] 1910.
Ramsdell, Charles William, 1877–

LAC 12404
The reconstruction of Georgia. New York, 1901.
Woolley, Edwin Campbell, 1878–1916.

LAC 40030
The reconstruction of states. Letter of Major-General Banks to Senator Lane. New-York, Harper & brothers, 1865.
Banks, Nathaniel Prentice, 1816–1894.

LAC 40064
The reconstruction of the government of the United States of America: a Democratic empire advocated, and an imperial constitution proposed. New-York, J. H. Tingley, 1861.
Wedgwood, William B.

LAC 16470
Reconstruction, political and economic, 1865–1877. New York and London, Harper & brothers [c1907]
Dunning, William Archibald, 1857–1922.

LAC 40096
Reconstruction. Speech of the Hon. Thaddeus Stevens, delivered in the city of Lancaster, September 7th, 1865. Lancaster, Pa., Examiner and herald print, 1865.
Stevens, Thaddeus, 1792–1868.

LAC 13037
Record of a school: exemplifying the general principles of spiritual culture... Boston, J. Munroe and company [etc.] 1835.
Peabody, Elizabeth Palmer, 1804–1894.

LAC 10624
A record of education. The schools and teachers of Dedham, Massachusetts, 1644–1904. [Dedham] Dedham Transcript press, 1905.
Slafter, Carlos, 1825–1909.

LAC 14301
Record of engagements with hostile Indians within the Military division of the Missouri, from 1868 to 1882, Lieutenant General P. H. Sheridan, commanding. Compiled at headquarters, Military Division of the Missouri, from official records. Washington, Govt. print. off., 1882. [Bellevue, Neb., Old Army press, 1969]
U.S. *Army. Military Division of the Missouri.*

LAC 11552
The record of Hon. C. L. Vallandigham on abolition, the union, and the civil war... 5th ed. Columbus, O., J. Walter & co., 1863.
Vallandigham, Clement Laird, 1820–1871.

LAC 15362
Record of the courts of Chester County, Pennsylvania, 1681–1697, pub. by the Colonial society of Pennsylvania. Philadelphia, Pa., Printed by Patterson & White company 1910.
Chester Co., *Pa. Court.*

LAC 23215–20
Record of the proceedings of the General Assembly. 4th–26th regular session; Sept. 1880–Nov. 1902. [n. p.]
Knights of Labor.

LAC 21878–81
The records of New Amsterdam from 1653 to 1674 anno Domini; ed. by Berthold Fernow. New York, Pub. under the authority of the city by the Knickerbocker press, 1897.
New York (City) Burgomasters and Schepens.

LAC 21940
Records of Salem witchcraft, copied from the original documents. Roxbury, Mass., Priv. print. for W. E. Woodward, 1864.

LAC 11339

Records of the colony and plantation of New Haven, from 1638 to 1649. Transcribed and edited in accordance with a resolution of the General assembly of Connecticut. With occasional notes and an appendix. By Charles J. Hoadly. Hartford, Printed by Case, Tiffany and company, 1857.
New Haven (Colony)

LAC 20738–42

Records of the colony of New Plymouth, in New England. Printed by order of the legislature of the commonwealth of Massachusetts. Ed. by Nathaniel B. Shurtleff and David Pulsifer. Boston, Press of W. White, 1855–61.
New Plymouth Colony.

LAC 20169–75

Records of the colony of Rhode Island and Providence Plantations, in New England. Printed by order of the General assembly. Ed. by John Russell Bartlett, secretary of state. Providence, A. C. Greene and brother, state printers [etc.] 1856–65.
Rhode Island (Colony)

LAC 21343–4

Records of the Court of assistants of the colony of the Massachusetts bay, 1630–1692... Boston, Pub. by the county of Suffolk, 1901–28.
Massachusetts (Colony) Court of Assistants.

LAC 23259–61

The records of the Federal convention of 1787, ed. by Max Farrand. New Haven, Yale university press; [etc., etc.] 1911.
U.S. Constitutional Convention, 1787.

LAC 20551–55

Records of the governor and company of the Massachusetts Bay in New England. Printed by order of the legislature. Ed. by Nathaniel B. Shurtleff. Boston, W. White, printer to the commonwealth, 1853–54.
Massachusetts (Colony)

LAC 15441

Records of the National general ticket agents' association. From March, 1855, to March, 1878, inclusive. Chicago, J. M. W. Jones stationary and printing company, 1878.
National General Ticket Agents' Association.

LAC 22749–50

Records of the New York stage, from 1750 to 1860. New York, T. H. Morrell, 1866–67.
Ireland, Joseph Norton, 1817–1898.

LAC 12271

Records of the Presbyterian church in the United States of America embracing the minutes of the Presbytery of Philadelphia, from A. D. 1706 to 1716; minutes of the Synod of Philadelphia, from A. D. 1717 to 1758; minutes of the Synod of New York, from A. D. 1745 to 1758; minutes of the Synod of New York and Philadelphia, from A. D. 1758 to 1788. Philadelphia, Presbyterian board of publication [1841]
Presbyterian Church in the U.S.A. General Assembly.

LAC 10847

Records of the town of Braintree. 1640 to 1793. Ed. by Samuel A. Bates. Randolph, Mass., D. H. Huxford, printer, 1886.
Braintree, Mass.

LAC 13547

The records of the town of Cambridge (formerly Newtowne) Massachusetts. 1630–1703. The records of the town meetings, and of the selectmen, comprising all of the first volume of records, and being volume II. of the printed records of the town. Printed by order of the City council under the direction of the city clerk. Cambridge, 1901.
Cambridge, Mass.

LAC 23154–55

Records of the town of Plymouth; pub. by order of the town. Plymouth, Avery & Doten, book and job printers, 1889–1903.
Plymouth, Massachusetts.

LAC 20878–80

The records of the Virginia company of London ... edited, with an introduction and bibliography, by Susan Myra Kingsbury. Washington, Govt. print. off., 1906–35.
Virginia Company of London.

LAC 16276

The red badge of courage; an episode of the American civil war. New York, D. Appleton and co., 1896.
Crane, Stephen, 1871–1900.

LAC 12598

The Red cross in peace and war. [Washington, D. C.] American historical press, 1910, [c1898]
Barton, Clara Harlowe, 1821–1912.

LAC 10433

The red man and the white man in North America, from its discovery to the present time. Boston, Little, Brown, and company, 1882.
Ellis, George Edward, 1814–1894.

LAC 12042

Red Rock; a chronicle of reconstruction. New York, C. Scribner's sons, 1900, [c1898]
Page, Thomas Nelson, 1853–1922.

LAC 16411

Redburn: his first voyage. Being the sailor-boy confessions and reminiscences of the son-of-gentleman, in the merchant service. New York, Harper & brothers, 1855, [c1849]
Melville, Herman, 1819–1891.

LAC 12117

The redeemed captive returning to Zion: or, A faithful history of remarkable occurrences in the captivity and deliverance of Mr. John Williams, minister of the gospel in Deerfield; who, in the desolation which befel that plantation, by an incursion of French and Indians, was by them carried away, with his family and his neighbourhood, into Canada. Drawn up by himself. Annexed to which, is a sermon, preached by him upon his return. Also, an appendix, by the Rev. Mr. Williams of Springfield. Likewise, an appendix, by the Rev. Mr. Taylor, of Deerfield. With a conclusion to the whole, by the Rev. Mr. Prince, of Boston. New-Haven. Printed by W. W. Morse, 1802.
Williams, John, 1664–1729.

LAC 14268
The redemption of the city, by Charles Hatch Sears. Introduction by Edward Judson, D. D. Philadelphia, Boston [etc.] The Griffith & Rowland press [1911]
Sears, Charles Hatch, 1870–

LAC 14327
Redemptioners and indentured servants in the colony and commonwealth of Pennsylvania. New Haven, Conn., The Tuttle, Morehouse & Taylor co. [1901]
Geiser, Karl Frederick, 1869–

LAC 22681
Redwood; a tale... New-York, E. Bliss and E. White, 1824.
Sedgwick, Catharine Maria, 1789–1867.

LAC 11222
The referendum in America; together with some chapters on the initiative and the recall. New ed., with supplement covering the years from 1900 to 1911. New York, C. Scribner's sons, 1912, [c1911]
Oberholtzer, Ellis Paxson, 1868–1936.

LAC 11189
Reflections and comments, 1865–1895. New York, C. Scribner's sons, 1895.
Godkin, Edwin Lawrence, 1831–1902.

LAC 40113
Reflections, occasioned by the late disturbances in Charleston. By Achates [pseud.] Charleston, Printed and sold by A. E. Miller, 1822.
Pinckney, Thomas, 1750–1828.

LAC 10108
Reflections on the late cession of Louisiana.
Political, commercial, and moral reflections on the late cession of Louisiana to the United States. Lexington, Ky., printed by D. Bradford, 1803.
Magruder, Allan Bowie, 1775–1822.

LAC 40052
Reflections on the subject of emigration from Europe, with a view to settlement in the United States: containing brief sketches of the moral and political character of this country... 3d ed., corr. and enl. Philadelphia, H. C. Carey & I. Lea, 1826.
Carey, Mathew, 1760–1839.

LAC 10663
Reflections upon the present state of England, and the independence of America. 4th ed.: with additions. London, Printed for J. Stockdale, 1783.
Day, Thomas, 1748–1789.

LAC 40001
Reflections upon the present state of the currency in the United States. Boston, Printed by E. Lincoln, 1837.
Adams, Charles Francis, 1807–1886.

LAC 40124
Reform in the consular service. A paper read at the annual meeting of the National civil-service reform league, December 13, 1894. Published for the National civil-service reform league. [Washington, D. C., Press of Good government] 1894.
Straus, Oscar Solomon, 1850–

LAC 40073
Reform or revolution. Address delivered under the auspices of the People's union, at Well's memorial hall, Boston, January 26, 1896. New York, New York labor news co., 1934.
De Leon, Daniel, 1852–1914.

LAC 12983
Reformatory education. Papers on preventive, correctional and reformatory institutions and agencies, in different countries. Hartford, F. C. Brownell, 1857.
Barnard, Henry, 1811–1900.

LAC 10979
The Reformed church in America. Its origin, development and characteristics. 4th ed. Rev. and enl. New York, Board of publication of the Reformed church in America, 1889.
Demarest, David D   1819–1898.

LAC 16250
The refugees from slavery in Canada West. Report to the Freedmen's inquiry commission. Boston, Wright & Potter, printers, 1864.
Howe, Samuel Gridley, 1801–1876.

LAC 40111
A refutation of the calumnies circulated against the southern and western states, respecting the institution and existence of slavery among them. To which is added, a minute and particular account of the actual state and condition of their negro population. Together with historical notices of all the insurrections that have taken place since the settlement of the country... By a South-Carolinian. Charleston, Printed by A. E. Miller, 1822.
Holland, Edwin Clifford, 1794–1824.

LAC 11822
The regicides.
Tales of the Puritans. The regicides.–The fair Pilgrim.–Castine. New-Haven, A. H. Maltby; New-York, G. and C. and H. Carvill, and J. Leavitt; [etc., etc.] 1831.
Bacon, Delia Salter, 1811–1859.

LAC 14624
Regimental losses in the American civil war, 1861–1865. A treatise on the extent and nature of the mortuary losses in the Union regiments, with full and exhaustive statistics compiled from the offical records on file in the state military bureaus and at Washington. Albany, Albany pub. co., 1889.
Fox, William Freeman, 1840–1909.

LAC 11733
The register book of the lands and houses in the "New Towne" and the town of Cambridge, with the records of the proprietors of the common lands, being the records generally called "the proprietors' records" [1634–1829] Printed by order of the City council under the direction of the city clerk. Cambridge [J. Wilson & son] 1896.
Cambridge, *Mass. Proprietors.*

LAC 12730
Regulation of commerce under the federal Constitution. Northport, N. Y., Edward Thompson company, 1907.
Calvert, Thomas Henry, 1868–

LAC 10887
The regulation of municipal utilities. New York and London, D. Appleton and company, 1912.
King, Clyde Lyndon, 1879–1937, *ed.*

LAC 10005
Regulation of railway rates on interstate freight traffic. 2d ed. New York, The Evening post job printing office, 1905.
Fink, Henry, 1831–1912.

LAC 11168
Regulation of the liquor traffic. Philadelphia, American academy of political and social science, 1908.
American Academy of Political and Social Science, *Philadelphia.*

LAC 12225
The reign of gilt. New York, J. Pott & co., 1905.
Phillips, David Graham, 1867–1911.

LAC 10622
Rejoinder to the "Reply" of the Hon. Horace Mann, secretary of the Massachusetts Board of education, to the "Remarks" of the Association of Boston Masters, upon his Seventh annual report. Boston, C. C. Little and J. Brown, 1845.
Association of Masters of the Boston Public Schools.

LAC 21454–56
Relaciones geograficas de Indias. Publicalas el Ministerio de fomento. Peru... Madrid, Tip. de M. G. Hernandez, 1881–97.
Spain. *Ministerio de Fomento.*

LAC 40020
Relation of a voyage from Boston to Newfoundland, for the observation of the transit of Venus, June 6, 1761. By John Winthrop, esq.; Hollisian professor of mathematics and philosophy at Cambridge, N. E. [*Two lines in Latin*] Boston: N. E. Printed and sold by Edes and Gill, in Queen-street, M,DCC,LXI.
Winthrop, John, 1714–1779.

LAC 14343
The relation of religion to civil government in the United States of America; a state without a church, but not without a religion. New York, Putnam, 1895.
Cornelison, Isaac Amada, 1829–1911.

LAC 40117
The relation of the railroads of the United States to the people and the commercial and financial interests of the country. The elements that determine the rates that shall be charged... Chicago, Cameron, Amberg & co. [c1885]
Kirkman, Marshall Monroe, 1842–1921.

LAC 40041
The relation of the social survey to public health authorities [by] Franz Schneider, jr. Department of surveys and exhibits, Russell Sage foundation, New York city. [Toronto?] 1913.
Schneider, Franz, 1887–

LAC 21946–50
Relations between labor and capital.
Report of the Committee of the Senate upon the relations between labor and capital, and testimony taken by the committee. In five volumes... Washington, Govt. print. off., 1885.
U.S. *Congress. Senate. Committee on Education and Labor.*

LAC 40004
The relations between the federal Department of agriculture and the agricultural colleges and experiment stations. An address. Urbana, Ill., 1913.
Davenport, Eugene, 1856–1941.

LAC 40037
Relations between the United States and northwest British America. Washington, Govt. print. off., 1862.
U.S. *Treasury Dept.*

LAC 40086
The relations of Christianity to labor and capital. An essay read before the third Methodist state convention, in Trinity Church, Charlestown, Oct. 27, 1870. Boston, Printed at the office of the "Weekly American Workman" [1870]
Rogers, Edward H.

LAC 16340
The relations of geography & history. Oxford, Clarendon press, 1901.
George, Hereford Brooke, 1838–1910.

LAC 12520
The relations of Pennsylvania with the British government, 1696–1765. [Philadelphia] University of Pennsylvania; New York, D. Appleton and company, agents, 1912.
Root, Winfred Trexler, 1879–1947.

LAC 40098
Relations of the state to industrial action... [Baltimore] American economic association, 1887.
Adams, Henry Carter, 1851–1921.

LAC 10662
The relations of the United States and Spain, diplomacy. New York, C. Scribner's sons, 1909.
Chadwick, French Ensor, 1844–1919.

LAC 23459
The relations of the United States and Spain: the Spanish-American war. New York, C. Scribner's sons, 1911.
Chadwick, French Ensor, 1844–1919.

LAC 40039
The relative position in our system of industry of foreign commerce, domestic production, and internal trade. By Jonathan B. Wise [*pseud.*] Philadelphia, Lindsay and Blakiston, 1850.
Colwell, Stephen, 1800–1872.

LAC 16373
A relic of the revolution, containing a full and particular account of the sufferings and privations of all the American prisoners captured on the high seas, and carried into Plymouth, England, during the revolution of

1776; with the names of the vessels taken–the names and residence of the several crews, and time of their commitment–the names of such as died in prison, and such as made their escape, or entered on board English men-of-war; until the exchange of prisoners, March 15, 1779. Also, an account of the several cruises of the squadron under the command of Commodore John Paul Jones, prizes taken, etc., etc. By Charles Herbert, of Newburyport, Mass., who was taken prisoner in the brigantine Dolton, Dec., 1776, and served in the U.S. frigate Alliance, 1779–80. Boston, Pub. for the proprietor, by C. H. Peirce, 1847.
Herbert, Charles, 1757–1808.

LAC 13093
Religion, agnosticism and education. Chicago, A. C. McClurg & co., 1902.
Spalding, John Lancaster, *abp.*, 1840–1916.

LAC 14834
Religion and education in America: with notices of the state and prospects of American Unitarianism, popery, and African colonization. London, T. Ward and co., 1840.
Lang, John Dunmore, 1799–1878.

LAC 10350
Religion and science. A series of Sunday lectures on the relation of natural and revealed religion, or the truths revealed in nature and Scripture. New York, D. Appleton and company, 1874.
Le Conte, Joseph, 1823–1901.

LAC 13087
Religion and the higher life; talks to students. Chicago, The University of Chicago press, 1904.
Harper, William Rainey, 1856–1906.

LAC 15931
La religion dans la societe aux Etats-Unis. Paris, A. Colin, 1902.
Bargy, Henry, 1872–1927.

LAC 10924
Religion in America; or, An account of the origin, relation to the state, and present condition of the evangelical churches in the United States. With notices of the unevangelical denominations. New York, Harper & brothers, 1856.
Baird, Robert, 1798–1863.

LAC 14337
Religion in New Netherland; a history of the development of the religious conditions in the province of New Netherland 1623–1664... Rochester, N. Y., J. P. Smith printing company, 1910.
Zwierlein, Frederick James, 1881–

LAC 11117
Religion in social action, by Graham Taylor, with an introduction by Jane Addams. New York, Dodd, Mead and company, 1913.
Taylor, Graham, 1851–1938.

LAC 10345
The religion of duty. New York, McClure, Phillips & co., 1905.
Adler, Felix, 1851–

LAC 15938
The religion of evolution. Boston, G. E. Ellis, 1900, [c1876]
Savage, Minot Judson, 1841–1918.

LAC 12650
The religion of geology and its connected sciences. Boston, Phillips, Sampson, and company, 1851.
Hitchcock, Edward, 1793–1864.

LAC 13979
The religion of science; or, The art of actualizing liberty, and of perfecting and satisfactorily prolonging happiness: being a practical answer to the great question,–"If you take away my religion, what will you give me in its stead?" New York, C. Blanchard, 1860.
Blanchard, Calvin.

LAC 10960
The religion worth having. Boston and New York, Houghton Mifflin company, 1912.
Carver, Thomas Nixon, 1865–1961.

LAC 40034
Religio-political physics: or, The science and art of man's deliverance from ignorance-engendered mysticism, and its resulting theo-moral quackery and governmental brigandage. New York, C. Blanchard, 1861.
Blanchard, Calvin.

LAC 11055
The religious aspect of evolution. Enl. and improved ed. New York, Charles Scribner's sons, 1890.
McCosh, James, 1811–1894.

LAC 11091
The religious aspect of philosophy; a critique of the bases of conduct and of faith. Boston and New York, Houghton Mifflin company [c1885]
Royce, Josiah, 1855–1916.

LAC 15750
The religious aspects of Swedish immigration; a study of immigrant churches. Minneapolis, The University of Minnesota press, 1932.
Stephenson, George Malcolm, 1883–

LAC 11023
The religious creeds and statistics of every Christian denomination in the United States and British provinces. With some account of the religious sentiments of the Jews, American Indians, Deists, Mahometans, &c., alphabetically arranged. Boston, J. Hayward, 1836.
Hayward, John, 1781–1862.

LAC 15935
Religious denominations in the United States: their past history, present condition, and doctrines. Accurately set forth in fifty-three carefully-prepared articles, written by eminent clerical and lay authors connected with the respective persuasions ... together with ... statistics, to which is added a historical summary of religious denominations in England and Scotland. Philadelphia, C. Desilver, 1861.
Rupp, Israel Daniel, 1803–1878, *ed.*

LAC 15850
The religious development of the Negro in Virginia ...
by Joseph B. Earnest, jr. Charlottesville, Va., The Michie
company, printers, 1914.
Earnest, Joseph Brummell, 1889–

LAC 14229
Religious experience of John Humphrey Noyes,
founder of the Oneida Community. New York, Macmillan, 1923.
Noyes, George Wallingford, *ed.*

LAC 16217
The religious instruction of the Negroes in the United
States. New York, Negro Universities Press [1969]
Jones, Charles Colcock, 1804–1863.

LAC 11097
The religious revolution of to-day. Boston and New
York, Houghton Mifflin company, 1913.
Shotwell, James Thomson, 1874–

LAC 13841
Reliquiae Baldwinianae: selections from the correspondence of the late William Baldwin ... with occasional notes, and a short biographical memoir. Comp. by
William Darlington. Philadelphia, Kimber and Sharpless,
1843.
Baldwin, William, 1779–1819.

LAC 13025
The remains of the Rev. James Marsh, D.D., late
president and professor of moral and intellectual philosophy, in the University of Vermont; with a memoir of his
life... Boston, Crocker and Brewster, 1843.
Marsh, James, 1794–1842.

LAC 15579
Remarks by Bill Nye (Edgar W. Nye)... With over one
hundred and fifty illustrations, by J. H. Smith. Chicago,
A. E. Davis & company, 1887.
Nye, Edgar Wilson, 1850–1896.

LAC 11492
Remarks concerning the government and the laws of
the United States of America: in four letters, addressed
to Mr. Adams. From the French of the Abbe de Mably.
New York, Burt Franklin [1964]
Mably, Gabriel Bonnot de, 1709–1785.

LAC 15567
Remarks during a journey through North America in
the years 1819, 1820, and 1821, in a series of letters:
with an appendix, containing an account of several of the
Indian tribes and the principal missionary stations, &c.
Also a letter to M. Jean Baptiste Say, on the comparative expense of free and slave labor... Collected, arranged, and published by Samuel Whiting. New-York [J.
Seymour, printer] 1823.
Hodgson, Adam.

LAC 13679
Remarks made during a tour through the United
States of America, in the years 1817, 1818, and 1819. In
a series of letters to friends in England. London, Sherwood, Neely, & Jones, 1821.
Harris, William Tell.

LAC 40103
Remarks of George P. Marsh, of Vermont, on slavery
in the territories of New Mexico, California and Oregon; delivered in the House of representatives, August
3d, 1848. [Burlington, Vt., Free press office print, 1848]
Marsh, George Perkins, 1801–1882.

LAC 40026
Remarks on banks and banking and the skeleton of a
project for a national bank. By a citizen of Boston. Boston, Torrey & Blair, printers, 1840.
Williams, Henry, *of Boston.*

LAC 40033
Remarks on changes lately proposed or adopted, in
Harvard university. [Boston] Cummings, Hilliard & co.,
1825.
Ticknor, George, 1791–1871.

LAC 40058
Remarks on China and the China trade. Boston, S. N.
Dickinson, printer, 1844.
Forbes, Robert Bennet, 1804–1889.

LAC 40094
Remarks on classical and utilitarian studies, read
before the American academy of arts and sciences, Dec.
20, 1866. Boston, Little, Brown, and company, 1867.
Bigelow, Jacob, 1787–1879.

LAC 40079
Remarks on currency and banking; having reference
to the present derangement of the circulating medium in
the United States. Boston, C. C. Little and J. Brown,
1841.
Appleton, Nathan, 1779–1861.

LAC 40050
Remarks on education: illustrating the close connection between virtue and wisdom. To which is annexed, a
system of liberal education. Which, having received the
premium awarded by the American philosophical society, December 15th, 1797, is now published by their
order. Philadelphia: Printed for John Ormrod, 1798.
Smith, Samuel Harrison, 1772–1845.

LAC 40081
Remarks on Europe, relating to education, peace and
labor; and their reference to the United States. New
York, C. S. Francis and company, 1846.
Brooks, Charles, 1795–1872.

LAC 40130
Remarks on Governor Johnstone's speech in Parliament; with a collection of all the letters and authentic
papers, relative to his proposition to engage the interest
of one of the delegates of the state of Pennsylvania, in
the Congress of the United States of America, to promote the views of the British commissioners. Philadelphia, Printed by Francis Bailey, 1779.
Reed, Joseph, 1741–1785.

LAC 40017
Remarks on popular sovereignty, as maintained and
denied respectively by Judge Douglas, and Attorney-General Black. By a southern citizen. Baltimore, Murphy
& co., 1859.
Johnson, Reverdy, 1796–1876.

LAC 40028
Remarks on some of the provisions of the laws of Massachusetts, affecting poverty, vice, and crime; being the general topics of a charge to the Grand jury of the county of Suffolk, in March term, 1822. Cambridge, Printed at the University press, 1822.
Quincy, Josiah, 1772–1864.

LAC 13590
Remarks on the classical education of boys. By a teacher. Boston, Hilliard, Gray & company, 1834.
Cleveland, Henry Russell, 1808–1843.

LAC 40139
Remarks on the musical conventions in Boston, &c.
Northampton, Printed for the author, 1844.
Lucas, George Washington, b. 1800.

LAC 16017
Remarks on the past and its legacies to American society... Louisville, Ky., Morton & Griswold, 1847.
Nourse, James Duncan, 1817–1854.

LAC 40107
Remarks on the practicability of Indian reform, embracing their colonization; with an appendix. 2d. ed.
New-York; Printed by Gray and Bunce, 1829.
McCoy, Isaac, 1784–1846.

LAC 40049
Remarks on the proposed plan of a federal government, addressed to the citizens of the United States of America, and particularly to the people of Maryland, by Aristides [pseud.] Annapolis, Printed by F. Green, printer to the state, 1788. [New York, N.Y., Reprinted W. Abbatt, 1933]
Hanson, Alexander Contee, 1749–1806.

LAC 40028
Remarks on the relation between education and crime, in a letter to the Right Rev. William White... By Francis Lieber. To which are added, some observations by N. H. Julius. Philadelphia, 1835.
Lieber, Francis, 1800–1872.

LAC 11903
Remarks on the Review of Inchiquin's letters, published in the Quarterly review; addressed to the Right Honourable George Canning, esquire. By an inhabitant of New-England. Boston: Published by Samuel T. Armstrong, No. 50, Cornhill, 1815.
Dwight, Timothy, 1752–1817.

LAC 16215
Remarks on the review of the Controversy between Great Britain and her colonies. In which the errors of its authors are exposed, and the claims of the colonies vindicated, upon the evidence of historical facts and authentic records. To which is subjoined, a proposal for terminating the present unhappy dispute with the colonies; recovering their commerce; reconciliating their affection; securing their rights; and establishing their dependence on a just and permanent basis. Humbly submitted to the consideration of the British legislature.
London, Printed in the year 1769. New-London, in New-England, Re-printed and sold by T. Green, 1771.
Bancroft, Edward, 1744–1821.

LAC 40111
Remarks on the slavery of the black people; addressed to the citizens of the United States, particularly to those who are in legislative or executive stations in the general or state governments; and also to such individuals as hold them in bondage. Philadelphia, Printed for the author, by Kimber, Conrad, & co., 1806.
Parrish, John, 1729–1807.

LAC 11516
Remarks on the statistics and political institutions of the United States, with some observations on the ecclesiastical system of America, her sources of revenue, &c. To which are added statistical tables, &c. Philadelphia, Carey & Lea, 1832.
Ouseley, Sir William Gore, 1797–1866.

LAC 40126
Remarks upon the Bank of the United States, being an examination of the Report of the Committee of Ways and Means, made to Congress, April, 1830. By a merchant. Boston, Printed by True and Greene, 1831.
Henshaw, David, 1791–1852.

LAC 40048
Remarks upon the rights and powers of corporations, and of the rights, powers, and duties of the legislature toward them. Embracing a review of the opinion of the Supreme court of the United States, in the case of Dartmouth college, in New Hampshire, given in 1819. By a citizen of Boston. Boston, Beals and Greene, 1837.
Henshaw, David, 1791–1852.

LAC 40065
The remedy by state interposition, or nullification; explained and advocated by Chancellor Harper in his speech at Columbia, (S. C.) on the twentieth September, 1830... Charleston, State rights and free trade association, 1832.
Harper, William, 1790–1847.

LAC 40027
The remedy for duelling. A sermon, delivered before the presbytery of Long-Island, at the opening of their session, at Aquebogue, April 16, 1806. First published by request of the presbytery. Re-published by subscription. To which is annexed, the resolutions and address of the Anti-duelling association of New-York. New-York: Sold at the theological and classical book-store of Williams and Whiting, no. 118, Pearl-street. J. Seymour, printer, 1809.
Beecher, Lyman, 1775–1863.

LAC 11512
Remembered yesterdays. Boston, Little, Brown, and company, 1923.
Johnson, Robert Underwood, 1853–1937.

LAC 40112
A reminiscence of the Free-soil movement in New Hampshire, 1845. Cambridge, J. Wilson and son, 1885.
Hayes, John Lord, 1812–1887.

LAC 14967
Reminiscences. Boston and New York, Houghton Mifflin company [c1915]
Abbott, Lyman, 1835–1922.

LAC 14364

Reminiscences, by Isaac M. Wise; tr. from the German and ed. with an introduction by David Philipson. Cincinnati, L. Wise and company, 1901.
Wise, Isaac Mayer, 1819–1900.

LAC 12461

Reminiscences and anecdotes of Daniel Webster. Boston, Little, Brown, and company, 1877.
Harvey, Peter, 1810–1877.

LAC 12397

Reminiscences and memoirs of North Carolina and eminent North Carolinians. Columbus, O., Columbus printing works, 1884.
Wheeler, John Hill, 1806–1882.

LAC 11205

Reminiscences, 1819–1899, by Julia Ward Howe. Boston and New York, Houghton, Mifflin and company, 1899.
Howe, Julia, 1819–1910.

LAC 16917

Reminiscences, 1827–1897, Governor Robert M. McLane. [n. p.] Priv. print., 1903.
McLane, Robert Milligan, 1815–1898.

LAC 14554

Reminiscences of a dramatic critic, with an essay on the art of Henry Irving. Boston and New York, Houghton, Mifflin and company, 1902.
Clapp, Henry Austin, 1841–1904.

LAC 11421

Reminiscences of a journalist. Boston, J. R. Osgood and company, 1880.
Congdon, Charles Taber, 1821–1891.

LAC 13608

Reminiscences of a Mosby guerilla. New York, Moffat, Yard and company, 1906.
Munson, John William, 1845–

LAC 15118

Reminiscences of a portrait painter. Chicago, A. C. McClurg and company, 1894.
Healy, George Peter Alexander, 1813–1894.

LAC 13137

Reminiscences of a ranger; or, Early times in Southern California. Los Angeles, Yarnell, Caystile & Mathes, printers, 1881.
Bell, Horace, 1830–1918.

LAC 15334

The reminiscences of a very old man, 1808–1897. New York, D. Appleton and company, 1900, [c1899]
Sartain, John, 1808–1897.

LAC 11540

Reminiscences of a war-time statesman and diplomat, 1830–1915, by Frederick W. Seward, assistant secretary of state during the administrations of Lincoln, Johnson, and Hayes. New York and London, G. P. Putnam's sons, 1916.
Seward, Frederick William, 1830–1915.

LAC 11534

Reminiscences of Abraham Lincoln by distinguished men of his time, collected and edited by Allen Thorndike Rice. New York, North American publishing company, 1886.
Rice, Allen Thorndike, 1851–1889, *ed.*

LAC 16234

Reminiscences of an American loyalist, 1738–1789, being the autobiography of the Revd. Jonathan Boucher, Rector of Annapolis in Maryland, and afterwards Vicar of Epsom, Surrey, England. Edited by his grandson, Jonathan Bouchier. Port Washington, N. Y., Kennikat Press, 1967.
Boucher, Jonathan, 1738–1804.

LAC 12672

The reminiscences of an astronomer. Boston and New York, Houghton, Mifflin and company, 1903.
Newcomb, Simon, 1835–1909.

LAC 16513

The reminiscences of an idler. New York, Fords, Howard, & Hulbert, 1880.
Wikoff, Henry, 1813–1884.

LAC 14946

Reminiscences of an interesting decade, the ardent eighties, by Gregory Weinstein. With a foreword by Lillian D. Wald. New York, The International press [c1928]
Weinstein, Gregory, 1864–

LAC 22638–39

The reminiscences of Carl Schurz ... illustrated with portraits and original drawings. New York, The McClure company, 1907–08.
Schurz, Carl, 1829–1906.

LAC 15647

Reminiscences of Charleston. Charleston, J. Walker, printer, 1866.
Cardozo, Jacob Newton.

LAC 11276

Reminiscences of Charleston, lately published in the Charleston Courier, and now rev. and enl. by the author, Charles Fraser. Charleston, J. Russell, 1854.
Fraser, Charles, 1782–1860.

LAC 13718

Reminiscences of Chicago during the forties and fifties, with an introduction by Mabel McIlvaine. Chicago, R. R. Donnelley & sons company, 1913.
McIlvaine, Mabel, *comp.*

LAC 13765

Reminiscences of Congress. New York, Baker and Scribner, 1850.
March, Charles Wainwright, 1815–1864.

LAC 12615

Reminiscences of Dr. Spurzheim and George Combe: and a review of the science of phrenology, from the period of its discovery by Dr. Gall, to the time of the visit of George Combe to the United States, 1838, 1840. New York, Fowler & Wells, [etc.] 1881.
Capen, Nahum, 1804–1886.

LAC 40077
Reminiscences of early anti-slavery days. [Cambridge, Mass., The Riverside press] Priv. print., 1893.
Southwick, Sarah H   1821–

LAC 23692–93
Reminiscences of famous Georgians, embracing episodes and incidents in the lives of the great men of the state, also an appendix devoted to extracts from speeches and addresses... 1st ed. Atlanta, Ga., Franklin-Turner company, 1907–08.
Knight, Lucian Lamar, 1868–1933.

LAC 14620
Reminiscences of forts Sumter and Moultrie in 1860–'61. New York, Harper & brothers, 1876.
Doubleday, Abner, 1819–1893.

LAC 10297
Reminiscences of glass-making. 2d ed., enl. New York, Hurd and Houghton, 1865.
Jarves, Deming, 1790–1869.

LAC 11401
Reminiscences of Gov. R. J. Walker; with the true story of the rescue of Kansas from slavery. Rockford, Ill., The author, 1902.
Brown, George Washington, 1820–1915.

LAC 14444
The reminiscences of James Burrill Angell. New York [etc.] Longmans, Green, and co., 1912.
Angell, James Burrill, 1829–1916.

LAC 12734
Reminiscences of Jeremiah Sullivan Black. By Mary Black Clayton. St. Louis, Christian publishing company, 1887.
Clayton, Mary.

LAC 12815
Reminiscences of Levi Coffin, the reputed president of the Underground railroad; being a brief history of the labors of a lifetime in behalf of the slave, with the stories of numerous fugitives, who gained their freedom through his instrumentality, and many other incidents. Cincinnati, Western tract society [1876]
Coffin, Levi, 1798–1877.

LAC 10740
The reminiscences of Neal Dow. Recollections of eighty years... Portland, Me., The Evening express publishing company, 1898.
Dow, Neal, 1804–1897.

LAC 10878
Reminiscences of New York by an octogenarian (1816 to 1860). New York, Harper & brothers [c1896]
Haswell, Charles Haynes, 1809–1907.

LAC 11524
Reminiscences of peace and war. Rev. and enl. ed. New York, The Macmillan company; [etc., etc.] 1905.
Pryor, Sara Agnes, 1830–1912.

LAC 40105
Reminiscences of pioneer life in the Mississippi valley. Davenport [Ia.] Griggs, Watson & Day, 1872. [Chicago, Lakeside press, 1942]
Spencer, John W   1801–1878.

LAC 10270
Reminiscences of public men in Alabama, for thirty years. With an appendix. Atlanta, Ga., Plantation publishing company's press, 1872.
Garrett, William, 1809–

LAC 12373
Reminiscences of public men, with speeches and addresses, by ex-Gov. Benjamin Franklin Perry. 2d series... Greenville, S. C., Shannon & co., printers, 1889.
Perry, Benjamin Franklin, 1805–1886.

LAC 20321
Reminiscences of sixty years in public affairs. New York, Greenwood Press, 1968 [New York, McClure, Phillips & co., c1902]
Boutwell, George Sewall, 1818–1905.

LAC 10274
Reminiscences of the civil war. New York, C. Scribner's sons, 1903.
Gordon, John Brown, 1832–1904.

LAC 15162
Reminiscences of the "filibuster" war in Nicaragua. New York and London, G. P. Putnam's sons, 1886.
Doubleday, Charles William, 1829–

LAC 14304
Reminiscences of the Indians. By the Rev. Cephas Washburn, A. M., many years superintendent of the Dwight mission among the Cherokees of the Arkansas. With a biography of the author. By Rev. J. W. Moore. And an introduction by J. L. Wilson. Richmond, Presbyterian committee of publication [c1869]
Washburn, Cephas, 1793–1860.

LAC 12004
Reminiscences of Walt Whitman, with extracts from his letters and remarks on his writings. Paisley and London, A. Gardner, 1896.
Kennedy, William Sloane, 1850–1929.

LAC 14626
Reminiscences of Winfield Scott Hancock, by his wife. New York, C. L. Webster & company, 1887.
Hancock, Almira.

LAC 15533
Reminiscences: the story of an emigrant. Saint Paul, D. D. Merrill company, 1891.
Mattson, Hans, 1832–1893.

LAC 15813
Removal of causes from state courts to federal courts, with forms adapted to the several acts of Congress on the subject. 3d ed., rev. and enl. St. Louis, Mo., W. H. Stevenson, 1881.
Dillon, John Forrest, 1831–1914.

LAC 21865
The removal of the Cherokee Indians from Georgia. By Wilson Lumpkin. Including his speeches in the United States Congress on the Indian question, as representative and senator of Georgia; his official correspondence on the removal of the Cherokees during his two terms as governor of Georgia, and later as United States commissioner to the Cherokees, 1827–1841, together with a sketch of his life and conduct while holding many public offices under the government of Georgia and the United States, prior to 1827, and after 1841... Wormsloe [Ga.] Priv. print.; New York, Dodd, Mead & company, 1907.
Lumpkin, Wilson, 1783–1870.

LAC 40036
The rendition of Anthony Burns. Its causes and consequences. A discourse on Christian politics, delivered in Williams hall, Boston, on Whitsunday, June 4, 1854. Boston, Crosby, Nichols, & co. [etc.] 1854.
Clarke, James Freeman, 1810–1888.

LAC 13714
Reply to an "American's examination" of the "right of search": with observations on some of the questions at issue between Great Britain and the United States, and on certain positions assumed by the North American government. By an Englishman. London, J. Rodwell, 1842.
Ouseley, *Sir* William Gore, 1797–1866.

LAC 13552
A reply to Mr. Burke's invective against Mr. Cooper, and Mr. Watt, in the House of commons, on the 30th of April, 1792. London, J. Johnson; [etc., etc.] 1792.
Cooper, Thomas, 1759–1839.

LAC 10611
Reply to the "Remarks" of thirty-one Boston schoolmasters on the Seventh annual report of the secretary of the Massachusetts Board of education. By Horace Mann, secretary of the board. Boston, W. B. Fowle and N. Capen, 1844.
Mann, Horace, 1796–1859.

LAC 22302
Report. 1st–2d; 1844–46. New York, J. W. Bell, 1845?–46.
Prison Association of New York.

LAC 16736–37
Report. Feb. 27, 1877. Washington, Govt. Print. Off., 1877.
U.S. *Congress. Joint Special Committee to Investigate Chinese Immigration.*

LAC 15755
Report. [Washington, Govt. print. off., 1893]
U.S. *Congress. Senate. Committee on Immigration.*

LAC 20459–64
Report and proceedings of the Senate committee appointed to investigate the Police department of the city of New York. Albany, J. B. Lyon, state printer, 1895.
New York *(State) Legislature. Senate. Committee on Police Dept. of the City of New York.*

LAC 40060
Report by the New Jersey commissioners upon the subject of a canal, from the Delaware to the Raritan. Made November, 1824. Trenton, Printed by J. Justice, 1824.
New Jersey. *Commission for the Purpose of Ascertaining the Practicability and Expediency of a Canal, to Unite the Delaware and Raritan Rivers.*

LAC 13586
A report from the chief of the Bureau of statistics, in response to a resolution of the House calling for information in regard to the range and ranch cattle traffic in the western states and territories. Washington, Govt. print. off., 1885.
U.S. *Bureau of Statistics (Treasury Dept.)*

LAC 13596
Report of a committee of the citizens of Boston and vicinity, opposed to a further increase of duties on importations. Boston, Press of N. Hale, 1827.
Lee, Henry, 1782–1867.

LAC 40093
Report of a French Protestant refugee, in Boston, 1687: translated from the French by E. T. Fisher. Brooklyn, N. Y. [Albany, J. Munsell, printer] 1868.

LAC 13282
Report of a geological survey of Wisconsin, Iowa, and Minnesota; and incidentally of a portion of Nebraska territory. Made under instructions from the United States Treasury department. By David Dale Owen, United States geologist. Philadelphia, Lippincott, Grambo & co., 1852.
Owen, David Dale, 1807–1860.

LAC 40007
Report of a missionary tour through that part of the United States which lies west of the Allegany mountains; performed under the direction of the Massachusetts missionary society. By Samuel J. Mills and Daniel Smith. Andover: Flagg and Gould, 1815.
Mills, Samuel John, 1783–1818.

LAC 40050
Report of a sub-committee of the School Committee recommending various improvements in the system of instruction in the grammar and writing schools of this city. Boston, N. Hale, City printer, 1828.
Boston. *School Committee.*

LAC 40087
Report of an exploration and survey of the territory on the Aroostook River, during the spring and autumn of 1838. Augusta, Smith & Robinson, printers to the state, 1839.
Holmes, Ezekiel, 1801–1865.

LAC 11796
Report of Benj. P. Johnson, agent of the state of New-York, appointed to attend the Exhibition of the industry of all nations, held in London, 1851. Albany, C. Van Benthuysen, public printer, 1852.
Johnson, Benjamin Pierce, 1793–1869.

LAC 40104

Report of Capt. Henry C. Long, on the condition and prospects of the city of Cairo. September 2, 1850. Submitted by Col. S. H. Long. New York, Narine & co., printers, 1850.
Long, Henry C.

LAC 13458

Report of Commission on occupational diseases to His Excellency Governor Charles S. Deneen. January, 1911. [Chicago, Warner printing company] 1911.
Illinois. *Commission on Occupational Diseases.*

LAC 40060

Report of experiments on the navigation of the Chesapeake and Delaware canal by steam. From the Journal of the Franklin institute. Philadelphia, Printed by J. Harding, 1834.
Bache, Alexander Dallas, 1806–1867.

LAC 22668–69

Report of explorations for a railway route, near the thirty-fifth parallel of north latitude, from the Mississippi River to the Pacific Ocean. By Lieut. A. W. Whipple, corps of topographical engineers. [Washington, 1856]
U.S. *Army. Corps of Topographical Engineers.*

LAC 16501

Report of explorations for a route for the Pacific railroad ... near the 38th and 39th parallels of north latitude, from the mouth of the Kansas river, Mo., to the Sevier lake, in the Great Basin, by Lieut. E. G. Beckwith. [Washington, 1855]
U.S. *War Dept.*

LAC 40091

Report of explorations for that portion of a railway route, near the 32d parallel of latitude, lying between Dona Ana, on the Rio Grande, and Pimas villages, on the Gila. By Lieut. Jno. G. Parke, U.S.A. [Washington, 1855?]
U.S. *Army. Corps of Topographical Engineers.*

LAC 40071

The report of Hiram Maxwell's case, decided at the City-hall of the city of New-York, on the 3d day of February, 1823; with the speech and doctrine advanced by John A. Graham, L.L.D., on the practice of taking the examinations and confessions in the police office of prisoners charged with crime; together with the letters and opinions of many of the greatest and wisest philosophers, civilians, orators, and statesmen in the United States. New-York, Gould & Banks; [etc., etc.] 1823.
Graham, John Andrew, 1764–1841.

LAC 14438

Report of J. Ross Browne on the mineral resources of the states and territories west of the Rocky Mountains. Washington, Govt. print. off., 1867.
U.S. *Treasury Dept.*

LAC 40121

Report of Lieutenant-General U.S. Grant, of the armies of the United States—1864–'65... New York, D. Appleton and company, 1865.
U.S. *Army.*

LAC 15719

Report of Major-General E. S. Otis on military operations and civil affairs in the Philippine Islands. 1899. Washington, Govt. print. off., 1899.
Philippine Islands. *Military Governor, 1898–1900 (Otis)*

LAC 13876

Report of proceedings of the twenty-seventh–[twenty-eighth] annual session. New York, 1879–80.
International Typographical Union of North America.

LAC 15872

Report of Samuel B. Ruggles, commissioner appointed by the governor of the state of New York, under the concurrent resolution of the Legislature, of April 22, 1862, in respect to the enlargement of the canals for national purposes. Transmitted by the governor to the Legislature, April 8th, 1863. Albany, Comstock & Cassidy, printers, 1863.
New York *(State) Commissioner on Enlargement of Canals for National Purposes.*

LAC 40107

Report of special agent John G. Ames, in regard to the condition of the Mission Indians of California. With recommendations. [Washington, Gov't print. off., 1873]
Ames, John Griffith, 1834–1910.

LAC 40008

Report of the agricultural meeting, held in Boston, January 13, 1840, containing the remarks on that occasion of the Hon. Daniel Webster, and of Professor Silliman, with notes by Henry Colman. Salem, Printed at the Gazette office, 1840.
Massachusetts. *Agricultural Survey.*

LAC 11573

Report of the case of the trustees of Dartmouth college against William H. Woodward. Argued and determined in the Superior court of judicature of the state of New Hampshire, November 1817. And on error in the Supreme court of the United States, February 1819. Portsmouth, N. H., J. W. Foster; [etc., etc., 1819]
Farrar, Timothy.

LAC 15389

Report of the Commission appointed by the President to investigate the conduct of the War department in the war with Spain... Washington, Gov't print. off., 1899.
U.S. *Commission appointed by the President to Investigate the Conduct of the War Dept. in the War with Spain.*

LAC 20056–57

Report of the commissioner of corporations on the tobacco industry... Washington, Govt. print. off., 1909–15.
U.S. *Bureau of Corporations.*

LAC 15672

Report of the Committee of fifteen, by W. T. Harris, LL. D., A. S. Draper, LL. D., and H. S. Tarbell, read at the Cleveland meeting of the Department of superintendence, February 19–21, 1895, with the debate. Boston, The New England publishing company, 1895.
National Education Association of the United States. *Committee of Fifteen on Elementary Education.*

LAC 21946-50

Report of the Committee of the Senate upon the relations between labor and capital, and testimony taken by the committee. In five volumes... Washington, Govt. print. off., 1885.
U.S. *Congress. Senate. Committee on Education and Labor.*

LAC 14203

Report of the Committee on general laws on the investigation relative to trusts. Transmitted to the Legislature, March 6, 1888. [Troy?] Troy press company, printers, 1888.
New York *(State) Legislature. Senate. Committee on General Laws on the Investigation Relative to Trusts.*

LAC 40033

Report of the Committee on organization, presented to the trustees of the Cornell university. October 21st, 1866. Albany, C. Van Benthuysen & sons, printing house, 1867.
Cornell University.

LAC 40104

Report of the committee on tenement houses of the Citizens' Association of Chicago. September, 1884. Chicago, G. K. Hazlitt, 1884.
Citizens' Association of Chicago. *Committee on Tenement Houses.*

LAC 10863

Report of the Council of hygiene and public health of the Citizens' association of New York upon the sanitary condition of the city... 2d ed. New York, D. Appleton and company, 1866, [c1865]
Citizens' Association of New York. *Council of Hygiene and Public Health.*

LAC 40004

Report of the Country life commission. Special message from the President of the United States transmitting the report... Washington, Govt. print. off., 1909.
U.S. *Country Life Commission.*

LAC 12434

A report of the debates and proceedings in the secret sessions of the conference convention, for proposing amendments to the Constitution of the United States, held at Washington, D. C., in February, A. D. 1861. By L. E. Chittenden, one of the delegates. New York, D. Appleton & company, 1864.
Chittenden, Lucius Eugene, 1824-1900.

LAC 13829

Report of the debates in the Convention of California, on the formation of the state constitution, in September and October, 1849. By J. Ross Browne. Washington, Printed by J. T. Towers, 1850.
California. *Constitutional Convention,* 1849.

LAC 11797

Report of the director-general, H. I. Kimball. New York, D. Appleton & company, 1882.
Atlanta. International Cotton Exposition, 1881.

LAC 10882

Report of the economic survey of Pittsburgh. [Pittsburgh, 1912.]
Holdsworth, John Thom, 1873-

LAC 16125

Report of the exploring expedition to the Rocky mountains in the year 1842, and to Oregon and north California in the years 1843-'44. By Brevet Captain J. C. Fremont, of the topographical engineers, under the orders of Col. J. J. Abert, chief of the Topographical bureau. Printed by order of the Senate of the United States. Washington, Gales and Seaton, printers, 1845.
Fremont, John Charles, 1813-1890.

LAC 15189

Report of the geology of the route, near the thirty-second parallel: prepared from the collection and notes of Capt. Pope, by William P. Blake. Washington, D. C., 1856.
U.S. *Army. Corps of Topographical Engineers.*

LAC 22006-27

Reports of the Industrial commission... Washington, Govt. print. off., 1900-02.
U.S. *Industrial commission.*

LAC 13877

Report of the Industrial commission on prison labor. Prepared in conformity with act of Congress approved June 18, 1898... Washington, Govt. print. off., 1900.
U.S. *Industrial Commission.*

LAC 14565

Report of the joint committee on reconstruction, at the first session, Thirty-ninth Congress. Washington, Govt. print. off., 1866.
U.S. *Congress. Joint Committee on Reconstruction.*

LAC 22371-80

[Report of the Joint select committee appointed to inquire into the condition of affairs in the late insurrectionary states, so far as regards the execution of the laws, and the safety of the lives and property of the citizens of the United States and Testimony taken. Washington, Govt. print. off., 1872]
U.S. *Congress. Joint Select Committee on the Condition of Affairs in the Late Insurrectionary States.*

LAC 10716

A report of the labors of John Augustus, for the last ten years, in aid of the unfortunate: containing a description of his method of operations; striking incidents, and observations upon the improvement of some of our city institutions, with a view to the benefit of the prisoner and of society. Published by request... Boston, Wright & Hasty, 1852.
Augustus, John, 1785-1859.

LAC 20106-8

Report of the Merchant marine commission together with the testimony taken at the hearings. In three volumes... Washington, Govt. print. off., 1905.
U. S. *Merchant Marine Commission.*

LAC 13777

Report of the military governor of the Philippine Islands on civil affairs. Washington, Govt. print. off., 1900.
U.S. *War Dept.*

LAC 22632-34

Report of the National conservation commission. February, 1909. Special message from the President of the United States transmitting a report of the National conservation commission, with accompanying papers... Ed. under the direction of the executive committee by Henry Gannett. Washington, Govt. print. off., 1909.
National Conservation Commission, *Washington, D. C.*

LAC 10286

Report of the organization and proceedings of the Union Pacific railroad co. New York, W. G. Bryant & co., printers, 1864.
Union Pacific Railroad Company. (1862–1880)

LAC 21042–45

Report of the Philippine commission to the President. January 31, 1900[–December 20, 1900] Washington, Govt. print. off., 1900–01.
U.S. *Philippine Commission*, 1899–1900.

LAC 21173–76

Report of the proceedings and debates of the Constitutional convention, state of Virginia. Held in the city of Richmond, June 12, 1901, to June 26, 1902... Richmond, Va., The Hermitage press, 1906.
Virginia. *Constitutional Convention*, 1901–1902.

LAC 10697

Report of the Public lands commission, created by the act of March 3, 1879, relating to public lands in the western portion of the United States and to the operation of existing land laws. Washington, Govt. print. off., 1880.
U.S. *Public Lands Commission.*

LAC 15390

Report of the secretary of war, communicating, in compliance with a resolution of the Senate of February 2, 1857, information respecting the purchase of camels for the purposes of military transportation. Washington, A. O. P. Nicholson, printer, 1857.
U.S. *War Dept.*

LAC 40087

Report of the secretary of war on the several Pacific railroad explorations. Washington, A. O. P. Nicholson, 1855.
U.S. *War Dept.*

LAC 40146

Report of the Select committee appointed to examine into the condition of tenant houses in New-York and Brooklyn. [Albany, C. Van Benthuysen, 1857]
New York *(State) Legislature. Assembly. Select Committee to Examine Condition of Tenant Houses in New-York and Brooklyn.*

LAC 11551

Report [of] the Select committee of the Senate appointed to inquire into the late invasion and seizure of the public property at Harper's Ferry... [Washington, 1860]
U.S. *Congress. Senate. Select Committee on the Harper's Ferry Invasion.*

LAC 40090

Report of the select committee of the Senate of the United States on the sickness and mortality on board emigrant ships. [Washington, B. Tucker, Senate printer, 1854]
U.S. *Congress. Senate. Select Committee on Sickness and Mortality on Board Emigrant Ships.*

LAC 15977

Report of the Select committee on the New Orleans riots. Washington, Govt. print. off., 1867.
U.S. *Congress. House. Select Committee on New Orleans Riots.*

LAC 40026

Report of the "Union committee" appointed by the meeting of the signers of the memorial to Congress, held on the 11th day of February, 1834, at the Merchants' exchange, in the city of New-York. New York, Harper & brothers, 1834.
Union Committee, *New York*, 1834.

LAC 40136

Report of West Virginia Mining investigation commission, appointed by Governor Glasscock on the 28th day of August, 1912... [Charleston, W. Va., Tribune printing co., 1912]
West Virginia. *Mining Investigation Commission*, 1912.

LAC 21547–55

Report on condition of woman and child wage-earners in the United States. In 19 volumes... Prepared under the direction of Chas. P. Neill, commissioner of labor. Washington, Govt. print off., 1910–13.
U.S. *Bureau of Labor.*

LAC 21162–65

Report on conditions of employment in the iron and steel industry in the United States. In 4 volumes... Prepared under the direction of Chas. P. Neill, commissioner of labor. Washington, Govt. print. off., 1911–13.
U. S. *Bureau of Labor.*

LAC 10597

Report on education. Washington, Govt. print. off., 1870.
Hoyt, John Wesley, 1831–1912.

LAC 14803

Report on education in Europe, to the trustees of the Girard college for orphans. Philadelphia, Printed by Lydia R. Bailey, 1839.
Bache, Alexander Dallas, 1806–1867.

LAC 40050

Report on elementary public instruction in Europe, made to the Thirty-sixth General assembly of the state of Ohio, December 19, 1837. Re-printed by order of the House of representatives of the legislature of Massachusetts, March 29, 1838. Boston, Dutton and Wentworth, state printers, 1838.
Stowe, Calvin Ellis, 1802–1886.

LAC 10839

Report on introducing pure water into the city of Boston. 2d ed., with additions. Boston, Hilliard, Gray and co., 1835.
Baldwin, Loammi, 1780–1838.

LAC 13798

A report on labor disturbances in the state of Colorado, from 1880 to 1904, inclusive, with correspondence relating thereto. Prepared under the direction of Carroll D. Wright, commissioner of labor... Washington, Govt. print. off., 1905.
U.S. *Bureau of Labor.*

LAC 11329–30

A report on marriage and divorce in the United States, 1867–1886; including an appendix relating to marriage and divorce in certain countries in Europe. By Carroll D. Wright, commissioner of labor. February, 1889: Rev. ed. Washington, Govt. print. off., 1891.
U.S. *Bureau of Labor.*

LAC 13662
Report on strike at Bethlehem steel works, South Bethlehem, Pennsylvania. Prepared under the direction of Chas. P. Neill, commissioner of labor... Washington, Govt. print. off., 1910.
U.S. *Bureau of Labor.*

LAC 13667
Report on strike of textile workers in Lawrence, Mass., in 1912. Prepared under the direction of Chas. P. Neill, commissioner of labor. Washington, Govt. print. off., 1912.
U.S. *Bureau of Labor.*

LAC 40016
Report on survey for ship canal across peninsula of Florida. Washington, C. Wendell, 1856.
Abert, John James, 1788–1863.

LAC 10698
Report on the agriculture and geology of Mississippi. Embracing a sketch of the social and natural history of the state. By B. L. C. Wailes, geologist of Mississippi... [n.p.] L. Barksdale, state printer, 1854.
Mississippi. *State Geologist.*

LAC 40011
Report on the American system of graded free schools, to the Board of trustees and visitors of common schools. Printed by order of the board. Cincinnati, Printed at the office of the Daily times, 1851.
Barney, Hiram H.

LAC 40043
Report on the causes of municipal corruption in San Francisco, as disclosed by the investigations of the Oliver grand jury, and the prosecution of certain persons for bribery and other offenses against the state. William Denman, chairman. Committee appointed by the mayor, October 12, 1908. Pub. by order of Board of supervisors, city and county of San Francisco, January 5, 1910. Reprinted with a preface and index of names and subjects by the California weekly...
San Francisco. *Committee on the Causes of Municipal Corruption.*

LAC 13664
Report on the Chicago strike of June–July, 1894, by the United States Strike commission ... with appendices containing testimony, proceedings, and recommendations. Washington, Govt. print. off., 1895.
U. S. *Strike Commission.*

LAC 13917
Report on the Colorado strike. By George P. West. Washington, D. C. [Chicago, Barnard & Miller print] 1915.
U.S. *Commission on Industrial Relations.*

LAC 16563
Report on the condition and improvement of the public schools of Rhode Island, submitted Nov. 1, 1845. Pub. by order of the General assembly. Providence, B. Cranston & co., 1846.
Barnard, Henry, 1811–1900.

LAC 13997
Report on the cotton production of the state of Louisiana, with a discussion of the general agricultural features of the state. [Washington, 1884]
Hilgard, Eugene Woldemar, 1833–1916.

LAC 40079
A report on the currency. New York, J. F. Trow, 1858.
Committee on Currency, *New York.*

LAC 10865
Report on the desirability of establishing an employment bureau in the city of New York. Printed privately. New York, Charities publication committee, 1909.
Devine, Edward Thomas, 1867–

LAC 13343
Report on the exploration of the Yellowstone river, by Bvt. Brig. Gen. W. F. Raynolds. Communicated by the secretary of war, in compliance with a resolution of Senate, February 13, 1866. Washington, Govt. print. off., 1868.
U.S. *Army. Corps of Engineers.*

LAC 14513
Report on the factory system of the United States. By Carroll D. Wright. [Washington, Govt. print. off., 1883]
U.S. *47th Cong., 2d Sess., 1882–1883. House.*

LAC 16167
Report on the forests of North America (exclusive of Mexico). Washington, Govt. print. off., 1884.
Sargent, Charles Sprague, 1841–1927.

LAC 10057
Report on the geological and agricultural survey of the State of Rhode-Island, made under a resolve of legislature in the year 1839. Providence, B. Cranston, 1840.
Jackson, Charles Thomas, 1805–1880.

LAC 13294
Report on the lands of the arid region of the United States, with a more detailed account of the lands of Utah. With maps. By J. W. Powell. 2d ed. Washington, Govt. print. off., 1879.
U.S. *Geographical and Geological Survey of the Rocky Mountain Region.*

LAC 14978
Report on the manufacture of coke. By Jos. D. Weeks, special agent. [Washington, Govt. print. off., 1884]
Weeks, Joseph Dame, 1840–1896.

LAC 13409
Report on the miners' strike in bituminous coal field in Westmoreland County, Pa., in 1910–11. Prepared under the direction of Chas. P. Neill, commissioner of labor. June 22, 1912.–Referred to the Committee on labor and ordered to be printed. Washington [Govt. print. off.] 1912.
U. S. *Bureau of Labor.*

LAC 40122
Report on the new Treasury buildings and Patent office at Washington: made at the request of the Committee of the House of representatives on public buildings and grounds, by Thomas U. Walter, architect. January 29, 1838. Philadelphia, Printed by L. R. Bailey, 1838.
Walter, Thomas Ustick, 1804–1887.

LAC 16854
Report on the production, technology, and uses of petroleum and its products. Washington, Govt. print. off., 1885.
Peckham, Stephen Farnum, 1839–1918.

LAC 40126
Report on the removal of the deposites, made by Mr. Webster, from the Committee on finance of the Senate, on the 5th of February, 1834. Washington, Printed by Duff Green, 1834.
U.S. *Congress. Senate. Committee on Finance.*

LAC 10396
Report on the ship-building industry of the United States. Washington, Govt. print. off., 1884.
Hall, Henry, 1845–

LAC 40037
Report on the state of trade between the United States and British possessions in North America, prepared for the secretary of the Treasury... Washington, Govt. print. off., 1871.
Larned, Josephus Nelson, 1836–1913.

LAC 23054–55
Report on the United States and Mexican boundary survey, made under the direction of the secretary of the Interior, by William H. Emory, major First Cavalry, and the United States commissioner. Washington, C. Wendell, printer, 1857–59.
U.S. *Dept. of the Interior.*

LAC 13305
A report on Washington territory. New York, Seattle, Lake Shore and eastern railway, 1889.
Ruffner, William Henry, 1824–1908.

LAC 40043
A report relating to the federal civil service in Indiana since March 4, 1885. [Indianapolis? 1886]
Swift, Lucius B   1844–

LAC 40095
Report submitted to the trustees of Cornell university, in behalf of a majority of the committee on Mr. Sage's proposal to endow a college for women. Albany, February 13, 1872. Ithaca, N. Y., University press, 1872.
Cornell University.

LAC 40096
Report. (To accompany bill S. no. 141.) [Washington, Govt. print. off., 1864]
U.S. *Congress. Senate. Select Committee on Slavery and the Treatment of Freedmen.*

LAC 40063
Report: (To accompany Senate bill no. 206.) [Washington] Blair & Rives, printers [1838]
U.S. *Cong. Senate. Select Committee on Bill to Authorize the President to Occupy the Oregon Territory.*

LAC 40100
Report to the Boston Board of Trade on the cotton manufacture of 1862. [Boston, 1863]
Atkinson, Edward, 1827–1905.

LAC 40101
Report to the corporation of Brown university, on changes in the system of collegiate education, read March 28, 1850. Providence, G. H. Whitney, 1850.
Brown University.

LAC 13408
Report to the President on the anthracite coal strike of May–October, 1902, by the Anthracite coal strike commission. Washington, Govt. print. off., 1903; [Philadelphia, Anthracite bureau of information, 1920]
U.S. *Anthracite Coal Strike Commission, 1902–1903.*

LAC 14128
A report to the secretary of war of the United States, on Indian affairs, comprising a narrative of a tour performed in the summer of 1820, under a commission from the President of the United States, for the purpose of ascertaining, for the use of the government, the actual state of the Indian tribes in our country... By the Rev. Jedidiah Morse. New Haven, Printed by S. Converse, 1822.
Morse, Jedidiah, 1761–1826.

LAC 40011
A report to the trustees of the College of New Jersey; relative to a revival of religion among the students of said college, in the winter and spring of the year 1815. With an appendix. Philadelphia, Printed for Benjamin B. Hopkins, 1815.
Green, Ashbel, 1762–1848.

LAC 40120
A report upon a plan for the organization of colleges for agriculture and the mechanic arts, with especial reference to the organization of the Agricultural college of Pennsylvania, in view of the endowment of this institution by the land scrip fund, donated by Congress to the state of Pennsylvania; addressed to the board of trustees of the Agricultural college of Pennsylvania, convened at Harrisburg, January 6, 1864: by Dr. E. Pugh, president of the faculty. Harrisburg, Singerly & Myers, printers, 1864.
Pugh, Evan, 1828–1864.

LAC 40022
Report upon forestry. From the committee appointed to memorialize Congress and the state legislatures, regarding the cultivation of timber and the preservation of forests. Salem, The Salem press, 1878.
Hough, Franklin Benjamin, 1822–1885.

LAC 40060
Report upon the finances and internal improvements of the state of New-York. 1838. New-York, J. S. Taylor [1838]
New York (State) Legislature. Assembly. Committee on Ways and Means.

LAC 40117
Report upon the locomotive engines and the police and management of several of the principal rail roads in the northern and middle states, being a sequel to the Report of the 8th of January, 1838 upon railway structures. Baltimore, Lucas & Deaver, 1838.
Knight, Jonathan, 1787–1858.

LAC 21592–99
Report upon United States Geographical surveys west of the one hundredth meridian, in charge of First. Lieut. Geo. M. Wheeler under the direction of the chief of engineers, U.S. army. Published by authority of ... the secretary of war in accordance with acts of Congress of June 23, 1874, and February 15, 1875. In seven volumes and one supplement, accompanied by one topographic and one geologic atlas... Washington, Gov't print. off., 1875–89.
U.S. *Geographical Surveys West of the 100th Meridian.*

LAC 14506
Reports of cases argued and adjudged in the Superior court of judicature of the province of Massachusetts bay, between 1761 and 1772. By Josiah Quincy, junior. Printed from his original manuscript in the possession of his son, Josiah Quincy, and edited by his greatgrandson, Samuel M. Quincy. With an appendix upon the writs of assistance. Boston, Little, Brown, and company, 1865.
Massachusetts *(Colony) Superior Court of Judicature.*

LAC 21970–005
Reports of the Immigration commission... Washington, Govt. print. off., 1911.
U.S. *Immigration Commission, 1907–1910.*

LAC 15753–54
Reports of the Industrial commission on immigration, including testimony, with review and digest, and special reports. And on education, including testimony, with review and digest... Washington, Govt. print. off., 1901.
U.S. *Industrial Commission.*

LAC 13033
Reports of the Mosely educational commission to the United States of America, October–December, 1903. London, Pub. for the proprietor by the Co-operative printing society, limited, 1904.
Mosley Educational Commission to the United States of America, Oct.–Dec. 1903.

LAC 12755
Reports of the proceedings and debates of the convention of 1821, assembled for the purpose of amending the constitution of the state of New York: containing all the official documents, relating to the subject, and other valuable matter. By Nathaniel H. Carter and William L. Stone, reporters; and Marcus T. C. Gould, stenographer. Albany, E. and E. Hosford, 1821.
New York *(State) Constitutional Convention, 1821.*

LAC 12957
Reports of the Taft Philippine commission. [June–November 1900] Message from the President of the United States, transmitting a report of the secretary of war, containing the reports of the Taft commission, its several acts of legislation, and other important information relating to the condition and immediate wants of the Philippine islands... Washington, Govt. print. off., 1901.
U.S. *Philippine Commission, 1900–1916.*

LAC 20194–95
Reports of the trials of Colonel Aaron Burr, (late vice president of the United States,) for treason, and for a misdemeanor, in preparing the means of a military expedition against Mexico, a territory of the King of Spain, with whom the United States were at peace. In the Circuit court of the United States, held at the city of Richmond, in the district of Virginia, in the summer term of the year 1807. To which is added, an appendix, contain-

ing the arguments and evidence in support and defence of the motion afterwards made by the counsel for the United States, to commit A. Burr, H. Blannerhassett[!] and I. Smith to be sent for trial to the state of Kentucky, for treason or misdemeanor, alleged to be committed there. Taken in short hand by David Robertson. Philadelphia: Published by Hopkins and Earle. Fry and Kammerer, printers, 1808.
Burr, Aaron, 1756–1836, *defendant.*

LAC 14221
Reports of the United German Evangelical Lutheran congregations in North America, specially in Pennsylvania; with preface by Dr. John Ludwig Schulze. Volume I. Reading, Pa., Pilger book-store [c1882]
Hallesche Nachrichten.

LAC 40033
Reports on the course of instruction in Yale college; by a committee of the corporation and the academical faculty. New Haven, Printed by H. Howe, 1828.
Yale University.

LAC 16637
Reports on the law of civil government in territory subject to military occupation by the military forces of the United States. Submitted to Hon. Elihu Root, secretary of war, by Charles E. Magoon, law officer, Bureau of insular affairs, War department. Published by order of the secretary of war. 3d ed. Bureau of insular affairs, War dept. Washington, Govt. print. off., 1903.
U.S. *Bureau of Insular Affairs.*

LAC 13775
The reports on the present state of the United provinces of South America; drawn up by Messrs. Rodney and Graham, commissioners sent to Buenos Ayres by the government of North America, and laid before the Congress of the United States; with their accompanying documents; occasional notes by the editor; and an introductory discourse, intended to present, with the reports and documents, a view of the present state of the country, and of the progress of the independents... London, Baldwin, Cradock and Joy, 1819.
U.S. *President, 1817–1825 (Monroe)*

LAC 12572
Reports, specifications, and estimates of public works in the United States of America: comprising the Philadelphia gas works; reservoir dam across the Swatara; twin locks on the Schuylkill canal; Delaware breakwater; Philadelphia water works; dam and lock on the Sandy and Beaver canal; dam on the James River and Kanawha canal, Virginia; locks of eight feet lift, on the same; aqueducts across Rivanna River and Byrd Creek, on the same; superstructure, etc., of farm bridges, on the same; lock gates and mitre sills. Ed. by William Strickland, Edward H. Gill, Henry R. Campbell. Explantory of the atlas folio of detailed engravings elucidating the engineering works herein described. London, J. Weale, 1841.
Strickland, William, 1787–1854, *ed.*

LAC 12691
A reprint of annual reports and other papers on the geology of the Virginias. By the late William Barton Rogers. New York, D. Appleton and company, 1884.
Rogers, William Barton, 1804–1882.

LAC 40041

Reprint of "Recollections of Cincinnati." Cincinnati, The Abingdon press [1916]
Worth, Gorham A   d. 1856.

LAC 16888

Reprints of Littell's Political transactions in and concerning Kentucky and Letter of George Nicholas to his friend in Virginia, also General Wilkinson's memorial; with an introduction by Temple Bodley. Louisville, Ky., J. P. Morton & company, incorporated, 1926.
Littell, William, 1768-1824.

LAC 11066

The republic of God. An institute of theology. 6th ed. Boston, Houghton, Mifflin and company, 1882, [c1881]
Mulford, Elisha, 1833-1885.

LAC 40099

Republic of Liberia. Facts for thinking men: showing the present condition of slave labor and free labor, in tropical and semi-tropical countries; and the indispensable necessity of African colonization; being letters originally addressed to the citizens of Cleveland, Ohio, through the Herald and the Plain dealer, daily papers of this city.- Feb. 1852. [Cleveland, O., Harris, Fairbanks & co., printers] 1852.
Christy, David, b. 1802.

LAC 16735

Republic or empire? The Philippine question. By William Jennings Bryan, Adlai E. Stevenson, Andrew Carnegie and others. Chicago, The Independence company, 1899.

LAC 11060

Republican Christianity: Or, true liberty, as exhibited in the life, precepts, and early disciples of the Great Redeemer. Cincinnati, David Anderson; Boston, Gould, Kendall and Lincoln, 1849.
Magoon, Elias Lyman, 1810-1886.

LAC 12197

The republican court; or, American society in the days of Washington. A new ed., with the author's last additions and corrections. With twenty-five portraits of distinguished women, engraved from original pictures by Wollaston, Copley, Gainsborough, Stuart, Peale, Trumbull, Pine, Malbone, and other contemporary painters. New York [etc.] D. Appleton and company, 1867, [c1854]
Griswold, Rufus Wilmot, 1815-1857.

LAC 20784-85

The Republican party; a history of its fifty years' existence and a record of its measures and leaders, 1854-1904, by Francis Curtis. With a foreword, by President Roosevelt, and introductions by William P. Frye and J. G. Cannon. New York [etc.] G. P. Putnam's sons, 1904.
Curtis, Francis, 1858-

LAC 11480

The Republican party and its presidential candidates... With ... sketches ... of Fremont and Dayton. New York and Auburn, Miller, Orton & Mulligan, 1856.
Hall, Benjamin Franklin, 1814-1891.

LAC 12492

The Republican party; its history, principles, and policies. Ed. by Hon. John D. Long. New York, The M. W. Hazen co., 1888.
Long, John Davis, 1838-1915, ed.

LAC 11498

Republicanism in America: a history of the colonial and republican governments of the United States of America, from the year 1607 to the year 1869. To which is added constitutions, proclamations, platforms, resolutions, decisions of courts, laws... Also, a brief history of all the existing republics in the world... San Francisco, R. J. Trumbull & co.; [etc., etc.] 1869.
McClellan, Rolander Guy.

LAC 12529

The repudiation of state debts; a study in the financial history of Mississippi, Florida, Alabama, North Carolina, South Carolina, Georgia, Louisiana, Arkansas, Tennessee, Minnesota, Michigan, and Virginia. New York, Boston, Thomas Y. Crowell & co. [1893]
Scott, William Amasa, 1862-

LAC 12920

The rescue of Cuba; an episode in the growth of free government, Boston, New York [etc.] Silver, Burdett and company, 1899.
Draper, Andrew Sloan, 1848-1913.

LAC 12945

A residence at the court of London. London, R. Bentley, 1833.
Rush, Richard, 1780-1859.

LAC 13077

A residence of twenty-one years in the Sandwich Islands; or, The civil, religious, and political history of those islands: comprising a particular view of the missionary operations connected with the introduction and progress of Christianity and civilization among the Hawaiian people. 2d ed. Hartford [Conn.] H. Huntington; New York, S. Converse, 1848, [c1847]
Bingham, Hiram, 1789-1869.

LAC 13987

Resist not evil. Chicago, C. H. Kerr & company, 1903.
Darrow, Clarence Seward, 1857-

LAC 10282

A resource of war-The credit of the government made immediately available. History of the legal tender paper money issued during the great rebellion. Being a loan without interest and a national currency. [2d ed.] Buffalo, Express printing company, 1869 [pref. 1875]
Spaulding, Elbridge Gerry, 1809-1897.

LAC 40104

Resources and advantages of Lynchburg, Virginia, and tributary country. Prepared and pub. by order of the City council of Lynchburg. Lynchburg, Virginian job office print, 1872.
Lynchburg, *Va. City Council.*

LAC 15959

The resources and opportunities of Montana, 1914 ed., by the Department of agriculture and publicity. J. M. Kennedy, commissioner. Helena, Mont., Independent publishing company, state printers, 1914.
Montana. *Dept. of Agriculture and Publicity.*

LAC 10450
Resources and prospects of America, ascertained during a visit to the States in the autumn of 1865. New-York, A. Strahan & co.; Philadelphia, J. B. Lippincott & co., 1866.
Peto, *Sir* Samuel Morton, *bart.*, 1809-1889.

LAC 15197
The resources of California, comprising agriculture, mining, geography, climate, commerce, etc., etc., and the past and future development of the state. San Francisco, A. Roman & company; New York, W. J. Widdleton, 1863.
Hittell, John Shertzer, 1825-1901.

LAC 10942
Re-statements of Christian doctrine, in twenty-five sermons. New York, D. Appleton and company, 1860, [c1859]
Bellows, Henry Whitney, 1814-1882.

LAC 40083
The restoration of the criminal. A sermon ... preached on Prison Sunday, Oct. 21, 1888, at Springfield, Illinois. Springfield, H. W. Rokker, 1888.
Wines, Frederick Howard, 1838-1912.

LAC 40057
Restriction of immigration. (Rev. ed.) Madison, The University, 1909.
Wisconsin. University. *University Extension Division. Dept. of Debating and Public Discussion.*

LAC 12811
The results of emancipation. By Augustin Cochin. Translated by Mary L. Booth. Boston, Walker, Wise, and company, 1863.
Cochin, Augustin, 1823-1872.

LAC 21951-53
Retail prices and wages. Report by Mr. Aldrich, from the Committee on finance, July 19, 1892... Washington, Gov't. print. off., 1892.
U.S. *Congress. Senate. Committee on Finance.*

LAC 40031
The retention of the Philippine Islands. Speech of Hon. Henry Cabot Lodge, of Massachusetts, in the Senate of the United States, March 7, 1900. Washington [Govt. print. off.] 1900.
Lodge, Henry Cabot, 1850-1924.

LAC 14489
Retrospect and prospect; studies in international relations, naval and political. Boston, Little, Brown, and company, 1902.
Mahan, Alfred Thayer, 1840-1914.

LAC 20363
A retrospect of fifty years, by James cardinal Gibbons, archbishop of Baltimore. Baltimore, New York, John Murphy company; [etc., etc., c1916]
Gibbons, James, *cardinal*, 1834-1921.

LAC 11408
A retrospect of forty years, 1825-1865, by William Allen Butler, ed. by his daughter, Harriet Allen Butler. New York, C. Scribner's sons, 1911.
Butler, William Allen, 1825-1902.

LAC 20696
Retrospect of western travel. London, Saunders and Otley; New York, Sold by Harper & brothers, 1838.
Martineau, Harriet, 1802-1876.

LAC 16623
Retrospection and introspection. Boston, The trustees under the will of Mary Baker G. Eddy [c1892]
Eddy, Mary, 1821-1910.

LAC 16910
Retrospections of America, 1797-1811, by John Bernard. Edited from the manuscript by Mrs. Bayle Bernard, with an introduction, notes, and index by Laurence Hutton and Brander Matthews. New York, B. Blom [1969]
Bernard, John, 1756-1828.

LAC 20425-28
Retrospections of an active life. New York, The Baker & Taylor co., 1909-13.
Bigelow, John, 1817-1911.

LAC 16589
Retrospects and prospects; descriptive and historical essays. New York, C. Scribner's sons, 1899.
Lanier, Sidney, 1842-1881.

LAC 11547
The return of the Democratic party to power in 1884. New York, Columbia university; [etc., etc.] 1919.
Thomas, Harrison Cook, 1888-

LAC 11925
The return of the O'Mahony; a novel. By Harold Frederic. With illustrations by Warren B. Davis. New York, G. W. Dillingham, 1899, [c1892]
Frederic, Harold, 1856-1898.

LAC 40082
The reunion of the Old and New-school Presbyterian churches. By Rev. Charles Hodge, D.D. Reprinted from the Princeton repertory for July. With a preface by the author noticing some objections. New York, C. Scribner & co., 1867.
Hodge, Charles, 1797-1878.

LAC 12859
The Rev. J. W. Loguen, as a slave and as a freeman. A narrative of real life. New York, Negro Universities Press [1968]
Loguen, Jermain Wesley, 1814-1872.

LAC 40044
The Reverend Mr. James Davenport's Confession & retractations. Boston, Printed and sold by S. Kneeland and T. Green, in Queenstreet, 1744.
Davenport, James, 1716-1757.

LAC 11731
The Rev. Samuel Peters' LL. D. General history of Connecticut, from its first settlement under George Fenwick to its latest period of amity with Great Britain prior to the revolution; including a description of the country, and many curious and interesting anecdotes. With an appendix, pointing out the causes of the rebellion in America; together with the particular part taken by the people of Connecticut in its promotion. By a gentleman of the province. London: 1781. To which are added, additions to appendix, notes, and extracts from letters, By Samuel Jarvis McCormick. New York, D. Appleton and company, 1877.
Peters, Samuel, 1735-1826.

LAC 14586
Reveries of a bachelor, or, A book of the heart. By Ik.
Marvel [*pseud.*] New ed. New York, Scribner, Armstrong, 1873, [c1863]
Mitchell, Donald Grant, 1822–1908.

LAC 40133
A review and refutation of Helper's "Impending crisis." Middletown, N. Y., 1860.
Beebe, Gilbert J.

LAC 12522
The review of American colonial legislation by the King in council. New York, Columbia university; [etc., etc.] 1915.
Russell, Elmor Beecher, 1885–

LAC 40077
Review of pamphlets on slavery and colonization. First published in the Quarterly Christian spectator; for March, 1833. 2d separate ed. New-Haven, A. H. Maltby; Boston, Pierce and Parker, 1833.
Bacon, Leonard, 1802–1881.

LAC 13926
A review of the administration and civil police of the state of New-York, from the year 1807, to the year 1819... New York, Printed by E. Conrad, 1819.
Pell, Ferris.

LAC 14953
Review of the Constitution of the United States; including changes by interpretation and amendment; for lawyers and those not learned in the law. Cincinnati, The Robert Clarke company, 1899.
Bullitt, William Grigsby.

LAC 40017
Review of the decade 1857–67. Philadelphia, Collins, 1867.
Carey, Henry Charles, 1793–1879.

LAC 11045
A review of the evidences of Christianity; in a series of lectures, delivered in Broadway hall, New-York, August, 1829. To which is prefixed, an extract from Wyttenbach's Opuscula, on the ancient notices of the Jewish nation previous to the time of Alexander the Great. 6th ed. Boston, Office of the Investigator [1835?]
Kneeland, Abner, 1774–1844.

LAC 40061
A review of the improvements, progress and state of medicine in the XVIIIth century. Read on the first day of the XIX century, before the Medical society of South-Carolina, in pursuance of their vote, and published at their request. By David Ramsay, M. D. Charleston: Printed by W. P. Young, Franklin's head, no. 43, Broad-street [1801]
Ramsay, David, 1749–1815.

LAC 16781
A review of the life of William Ladd, "The apostle of peace." By Jacob S. Willets. Abridged mainly from a memoir by John Hemmenway. With an introduction to Sabbath schools by Elihu Burritt. New Vienna, O., Peace association of friends in America, 1875.
Hemmenway, John.

LAC 13773
A review of the negociations between the United States of America and Great Britain, respecting the commerce of the two countries, and more especially concerning the trade of the former with the West Indies. By the Hon. Littleton W. Tazewell. London, J. Murray, 1829.
Tazewell, Littleton Waller, 1774–1860.

LAC 16422
Review of the New York musical season 1885–1886, containing programmes of noteworthy occurrences, with numerous criticisms. New York, Novello, Ewer & co., 1886.
Krehbiel, Henry Edward, 1854–1923.

LAC 40143
A review of the relative commercial progress of the cities of New-York & Philadelphia, tracing the decline of the latter to state development, and showing the necessity of trans-Atlantic steamship communication to re-establish foreign trade. Philadelphia, Jackson, printer, 1859.
Baker, G   W.

LAC 40066
A review of the rise, progress and tendency of the present system of national policy. Addressed to the people of the United States. Boston: Printed at the Repertory office, 1808.

LAC 40026
Review of the veto. Containing an examination of the principles of the President's message, and his objections to the bill ... rechartering the Bank of the United States. Philadelphia, 1832.

LAC 12416
The reviewers reviewed; a supplement to the "War between the states," etc., with an appendix in review of "Reconstruction," so called. New York, D. Appleton and company, 1872.
Stephens, Alexander Hamilton, 1812–1883.

LAC 16455
Revival sketches and manual... By Rev. Heman Humphrey. New York, American tract society [c1859]
Humphrey, Heman, 1779–1861.

LAC 40085
The revolution in New-England justified, and the people there vindicated from the aspersions cast upon them by Mr. John Palmer, in his pretended answer to the Declaration published by the inhabitants of Boston, and the country adjacent, on the day when they secured their late oppressors, who acted by an illegal and arbitrary commission from the late King James. To which is added, A narrative of the proceedings of Sir Edmond Androsse and his accomplices. Who also acted by an illegal and arbitrary commission from the late King James, during his government in New-England. By several gentlemen who were of his Council. Printed in the year 1691. Boston: Reprinted and sold by Isaiah Thomas, 1773. [Gloucester, Mass., Peter Smith, 1963]
Rawson, Edward, 1615–1693.

LAC 15911
The revolution in the mind and practice of the human race; or, The coming change from irrationality to rationality. London, Wilson, 1849.
Owen, Robert, 1771–1858.

LAC 14886
The revolution on the upper Ohio, 1775–1777; compiled from the Draper manuscripts in the library of the Wisconsin historical society and published at the charge of the Wisconsin society of the Sons of the American revolution; ed. by Reuben Gold Thwaites and Louise Phelps Kellogg. Madison, Wisconsin historical society, 1908.
Thwaites, Reuben Gold, 1853–1913, *ed.*

LAC 23476–82
The revolutionary diplomatic correspondence of the United States. Edited under direction of Congress by Francis Wharton, with preliminary index, and notes historical and legal. Pub. in conformity with act of Congress of August 13, 1888. Washington, Govt. print off., 1889.
U.S. *Dept. of State.*

LAC 11034
The revolutionary function of the modern church. New York and London, G. P. Putnam's sons, 1912.
Holmes, John Haynes, 1879–

LAC 15170
The revolutionary journal of Col. Jeduthan Baldwin. 1775–1778; ed., with a memoir and notes, by Thomas Williams Baldwin. Bangor, Printed for the DeBurians [by C. H. Glass & company] 1906.
Baldwin, Jeduthan, 1732–1788.

LAC 12488
The revolutionary movement in Pennsylvania 1760 –1776. Philadelphia, The University, 1901.
Lincoln, Charles Henry, 1869–

LAC 20755–57
The revolutionary records of the state of Georgia... Comp. and pub. under authority of the Legislature by Allen D. Candler. Atlanta, Ga., The Franklin Turner company, 1908.

LAC 14414
Revolutionary services and civil life of General William Hull; prepared from his manuscripts, by his daughter, Mrs. Maria Campbell: together with the history of the campaign of 1812, and surrender of the post of Detroit, by his grandson, James Freeman Clarke. New-York, D. Appleton & co.; Philadelphia, G. S. Appleton, 1848.
Campbell, Maria, 1788–1845.

LAC 11271
Revolutionary syndicalism, an exposition and a criticism. London, P. S. King & son, 1913.
Estey, James Arthur, 1886–

LAC 15387
The revolutionary war and the military policy of the United States. New York, C. Scribner's sons, 1911.
Greene, Francis Vinton, 1850–1921.

LAC 15805
Revolutionary war journals of Henry Dearborn, 1775–1783, edited from the original manuscripts by Lloyd A. Brown and Howard H. Peckham; with a biographical essay by Hermon Dunlap Smith. Chicago, The Caxton club, 1939.
Dearborn, Henry, 1751–1829.

LAC 15899
Rhode Island, a study in separatism. Boston and New York, Houghton, Mifflin and company, 1905.
Richman, Irving Berdine, 1861–

LAC 14969
Rhode Island and the formation of the Union. New York, 1898.
Bates, Frank Greene, 1868–

LAC 14130
Rhode Island architecture, by Henry-Russell Hitchcock, jr. Providence, Rhode Island museum press, 1939.
Hitchcock, Henry Russell, 1903–

LAC 23156–60
Rhode Island historical tracts. [1st series] no. 1–20; 2d series, no. 1–5. Providence, S. S. Rider, 1877–96.

LAC 15280
Rhode Island in the Continental Congress, with the Journal of the convention that adopted the Constitution. 1765–1790. By Hon. William R. Staples. Ed. by Reuben Aldridge Guild. Providence, Providence press company, printers to the state, 1870.
Staples, William Read, 1798–1868.

LAC 20168
Rhode Island; its making and its meaning; a survey of the annals of the commonwealth from its settlement to the death of Roger Williams, 1636–1683, by Irving Berdine Richman; with an introduction by James Bryce. New York and London, G. P. Putnam's sons, 1902.
Richman, Irving Berdine, 1861–

LAC 14341
Rich and poor in the New Testament: a study of the primitive-Christian doctrine of earthly possessions. New York, The Macmillan company; London, A. & C. Black, 1902.
Cone, Orello, 1835–1905.

LAC 15591
The rich men of Massachusetts: containing a statement of the reputed wealth of about two thousand persons, with brief sketches of nearly fifteen hundred characters. 2d ed., greatly enl. and improved. Boston, Printed for Redding & co. [etc.] 1852.
Forbes, Abner.

LAC 11871
Richard Carvel, by Winston Churchill. With illustrations by Carlton T. Chapman and Malcolm Fraser. New York, The Macmillan company, 1899.
Churchill, Winston, 1871–1947.

LAC 10892

Richard Croker. New York, Life publishing company, 1901.
Lewis, Alfred Henry, 1857–1914.

LAC 13605

Richard Edney and the governor's family. A rusurban tale ... of morals, sentiment, and life ... containing, also, hints on being good and doing good. By the author of "Margaret." Boston, Roberts brothers, 1880.
Judd, Sylvester, 1813–1853.

LAC 20877

Richard Henry Dana, a biography. Boston and New York, Houghton, Mifflin and company, 1890.
Adams, Charles Francis, 1835–1915.

LAC 16965

Richard Hurdis; a tale of Alabama. New and rev. ed. Chicago [etc.] Belford, Clarke & Co., 1889.
Simms, William Gilmore, 1806–1870.

LAC 15268

Richard Olney and his public service, by Henry James; with documents including unpublished diplomatic correspondence. Boston and New York, Houghton Mifflin company, 1923.
James, Henry, 1879–1947.

LAC 16625

Richmond during the war: four years of personal observation. By a Richmond lady. New York, G. W. Carleton & co.; [etc., etc.] 1867.
Putnam, Sallie A   b. 1845?

LAC 14891

The Richmond examiner during the war; or, The writings of John M. Daniel. With a memoir of his life, by his brother, Frederick S. Daniel. New York, Printed for the author, 1868.
Daniel, John Moncure, 1825–1865.

LAC 10861

Richmond, her past and present. Richmond, Va., Manufactured by L. H. Jenkins, 1912.
Christian, William Asbury, 1866–1936.

LAC 10069

The riddle of the sphinx. A discussion of the economic questions relating to agriculture, land, transportation, money, taxation, and cost of interchange: a consideration of possible remedies for existing inequalities, and an outline of the position of agriculture in the industrial world; with a comprehensive history of the leading farm organizations, their constitutions and by-laws. Chicago, Mercantile publishing and advertising co., 1892, [c1890]
Ashby, N   B.

LAC 10519

The riddle of the universe at the close of the nineteenth century, by Ernst Haeckel. Tr. by Joseph McCabe. New York and London, Harper & brothers [c1900]
Haeckel, Ernst Heinrich Philipp August, 1834–1919.

LAC 13268

The rifle, axe, and saddle-bags, and other lectures. By William Henry Milburn. With introduction by Rev. J. McClintock. New York, Derby & Jackson; Cincinnati, H. W. Derby & co., 1857.
Milburn, William Henry, 1823–1903.

LAC 16322

Right of the Bible in our public schools. New York, R. Carter, 1859.
Cheever, George Barrell, 1807–1890.

LAC 40113

Right on the scaffold, or, The martyrs of 1822. Washington, D. C., The Academy, 1901.
Grimke, Archibald Henry, 1849–1930.

LAC 12810

The right way the safe way, proved by emancipation in the British West Indies, and elsewhere. New York, 1862.
Child, Lydia Maria, 1802–1880.

LAC 40040

The rights of colonies examined. Pub. by authority. Providence, Printed by W. Goddard, 1765.
Hopkins, Stephen, 1707–1785.

LAC 12906

Rights of colored men to suffrage, citizenship and trial by jury: being a book of facts, arguments and authorities, historical notices and sketches of debates–with notes. Philadelphia, Printed by Merrihew and Gunn, 1838.
Yates, William, 1767–1857.

LAC 40109

The rights of conscience inalienable, and therefore religious opinions not cognizable by law: or, The high-flying church-man, stript of his legal robe, appears a Yaho. New-London, Printed by T. Green & son, M.DCC.XCI.
Leland, John, 1754–1841.

LAC 14271

The rights of man to property! Being a proposition to make it equal among the adults of the present generation: and to provide for its equal transmission to every individual of each succeding generation, on arriving at the age of maturity. Addressed to the citizens of the state of New-York, particularly, and to the people of other states and nations, generally... New-York, Printed for the author by A. Ming, jr., 1829.
Skidmore, Thomas.

LAC 40040

The rights of the British colonies asserted and proved. Boston, Printed and sold by Edes and Gill, 1764.
Otis, James, 1725–1783.

LAC 11767

The rise and decline of the wheat growing industry in Wisconsin. Madison, Wis., 1909.
Thompson, John Giffin, 1873–

LAC 23428–29

The rise and fall of the Confederate government. New York, D. Appleton and co., 1881.
Davis, Jefferson, 1808–1889.

LAC 11462

The rise and growth of American politics; a sketch of constitutional development. New York, The Macmillan company; [etc., etc.] 1898.
Ford, Henry Jones, 1851–1925.

LAC 11625
The rise and progress of the Standard oil company.
New York and London, Harper & brothers, 1903.
Montague, Gilbert Holland, 1880–1961.

LAC 14516
The rise of local school supervision in Massachusetts
(the school committee, 1635–1827) New York, Teachers
college, Columbia university, 1906.
Suzzallo, Henry, 1875–1933.

LAC 12566
The rise of modern democracy in old and New England, by Charles Borgeaud. Tr. by Mrs. Birkbeck Hill,
with a preface by C. H. Firth. London, S. Sonnenschein
& co.; New York, C. Scribner's sons, 1894.
Borgeaud, Charles.

LAC 10970
The rise of religious liberty in America; a history.
New York, The Macmillan company; London, Macmil-
lan & co., ltd., 1902.
Cobb, Sanford Hoadley, 1838–1910.

LAC 11987
The rise of Silas Lapham. Boston, Ticknor and com-
pany, 1885.
Howells, William Dean, 1837–1920.

LAC 16819
The rise of the republic of the United States. 7th ed.
Boston, Little, Brown, and company, 1899.
Frothingham, Richard, 1812–1880.

LAC 11267
The rise of the working-class. New York, The Century
co., 1914.
Crapsey, Algernon Sidney, 1847–

LAC 40061
The rise, progress, and present state of medicine. A
discourse, delivered at Concord, July 6th, 1791. Before
the Middlesex medical association. Boston, Printed by
T. and J. Fleet, 1792.
Waterhouse, Benjamin, 1754–1846.

LAC 40082
The rise, progress and travels of the Church of Jesus
Christ of latter-day saints, being a series of answers to
questions, including the revelation on celestial marriage,
and a brief account of the settlement of Salt Lake Valley, with interesting statistics, by President George A.
Smith. 2d ed. Salt Lake City, Printed at the Deseret news
office, 1872.
Smith, George Albert, 1817–1875.

LAC 40118
The rising glory of America.
A poem, on the rising glory of America; being an exer-
cise delivered at the public commencement at Nassau-
hall, September 25, 1771... Philadelphia: Printed by
Joseph Crukshank, for R. Aitken, bookseller, opposite
London-coffee-house, in Front-street, M.DCC.LXXII.
Freneau, Philip Morin, 1752–1832.

LAC 15839
The rising son; or, The antecedents and advancement
of the colored race. Miami, Fla., Mnemosyne Pub. Inc.,
1969.
Brown, William Wells, 1815–1884.

LAC 13347
The river of the West. Life and adventure in the
Rocky mountains and Oregon; embracing events in the
life-time of a mountain-man and pioneer: with the early
history of the north-western slope, including an account
of the fur traders... Also, a description of the country...
By Mrs. Frances Fuller Victor. Hartford, Conn., and
Toledo, Ohio: 1870. [Columbus, O., Reprinted by Long's
College Book Co., 1950]
Victor, Frances, 1826–1902.

LAC 13537
Riverside buildings, 1890.
Improved dwellings for the working classes, 1877.
1879; Better homes for workingmen, 1885; Riverside
buildings, 1890. [n.p., 1891?]
White, Alfred Tredway, 1846–1921.

LAC 14111
Roads and canals.
Letters, addressed to the people of Pennsylvania respecting the internal improvement, of the Commonwealth
by means of roads and canals. New York, B. Franklin
[1967]
Duane, William John, 1780–1865.

LAC 20750–51
The Roanoke voyages, 1584–1590; documents to illustrate the English voyages to North America under the
patent granted to Walter Raleigh in 1584. London, Hakluyt Society, 1955.
Quinn, David Beers, *ed.*

LAC 23503
Roba di Roma. 4th ed. ... London, Chapman & Hall;
New York, D. Appleton & co., 1864.
Story, William Wetmore, 1819–1895.

LAC 12399
Robert Barnwell Rhett: father of secession. New
York, London, The Century co. [c1931]
White, Laura Amanda.

LAC 12106
Robert Elsmere, by Mrs. Humphry Ward. Chicago,
J. S. Ogilvie [1888]
Ward, Mary Augusta, 1851–1920.

LAC 14971
Robert Owen's opening speech, and his reply to the
Rev. Alex. Campbell, in the recent public discussion in
Cincinnati, to prove that the principles of all religions
are erroneous, and that their practice is injurious to the
human race. Also, Mr. Owen's Memorial to the republic
of Mexico, and a narrative of the proceedings thereon ...
for the purpose of establishing a new political and moral
system of government, founded on the laws of nature, as
explained in the above debate with Mr. Campbell. Cincinnati, Pub. for R. Owen, 1829.
Owen, Robert, 1771–1858.

LAC 40087
Rocky mountain letters, 1869. "Letters written to my wife during a trip to the Rocky Mountains July to September, 1869." Denver, Col., Colorado mountain club, 1930.
Brewer, William Henry, 1828–1910.

LAC 16138
Rocky Mountain life; or, Startling scenes and perilous adventures in the far West, during an expedition of three years. Boston, Wentworth & co., 1857.
Sage, Rufus B., 1817–1893.

LAC 40148
The Rocky Mountain locust, or grasshopper, being the report of proceedings of a conference of the governors of several Western states and territories, together with several other gentlemen, held at Omaha, Nebraska, on the 25th and 26th days of October, 1876, to consider the locust problem; Also, a summary of the best means now known for counteracting the evil. St. Louis, R. P. Studley, 1876.

LAC 23378
The Rocky Mountains: or, Scenes, incidents, and adventures in the far West; digested from the journal of Capt. B. L. E. Bonneville and illustrated from various other sources. Philadelphia, Carey, Lea, & Blanchard, 1837.
Irving, Washington, 1783–1859.

LAC 12129
Rodman the keeper, southern sketches. New York, Harper & brothers, 1886.
Woolson, Constance Fenimore, 1840–1894.

LAC 40107
Roman Catholics and Indian education, an address ... delivered in Music Hall, Boston, Mass., Sunday, April 16, 1893. Revised. [Boston, The American Citizen Co., 1893]
Morgan, Thomas Jefferson, 1839–1902.

LAC 10273
The romance of steel: the story of a thousand millionaires. New York, A. S. Barnes & company, 1907.
Casson, Herbert Newton, 1869–

LAC 16272
The romance of the Milky Way, and other studies & stories. Boston and New York, Houghton, Mifflin and company [1905]
Hearn, Lafcadio, 1850–1904.

LAC 13217
The romance of western history; or, Sketches of history, life, and manners, in the West. Cincinnati, R. Clarke & co., 1885, [c1857]
Hall, James, 1793–1868.

LAC 10947
Romanism in the light of prophecy and history: its final downfall: and the triumph of the church of Christ. New York, American and Foreign Christian union, 1857.
Brownlee, William Craig, 1784–1860.

LAC 13004
Romanism versus the public school system. By Daniel Dorchester, D. D. New York, Phillips & Hunt; [etc., etc.] 1888.
Dorchester, Daniel, 1827–1907.

LAC 16775
Rome: as seen by a New-Yorker in 1843-4... New-York & London, Wiley and Putnam, 1845.
Gillespie, William Mitchell, 1816–1868.

LAC 10335
Room at the top: or, How to reach success, happiness, fame and fortune, with biographical notices of successful, self-made men, who have risen from obscurity to fame ... also, rules for behavior in society. Chicago, H. A. Sumner and company, 1883.
Craig, Adam, *comp.*

LAC 11945
Rose of Dutcher's Coolly. Chicago, Stone & Kimball, 1895.
Garland, Hamlin, 1860–1940.

LAC 16425
Roumania; the border land of the Christian and the Turk, comprising adventures of travel in eastern Europe and western Asia. New York, Rudd & Carleton, 1857.
Noyes, James Oscar, 1829–1872.

LAC 12024
The round table. London, James Nishet & co. [1913?]
Lowell, James Russell, 1819–1891.

LAC 13168
The round trip by way of Panama through California, Oregon, Nevada, Utah, Idaho, and Colorado; with notes on railroads, commerce, agriculture, mining, scenery, and people. New York, G. P. Putnam's sons, 1879.
Codman, John, 1814–1900.

LAC 14530
Route across the Rocky mountains, by Overton Johnson and Wm. H. Winter, of the emigration of 1843. Reprinted, with preface and notes by Carl L. Cannon, from the edition of 1846. Princeton, Princeton university press, 1932.
Johnson, Overton.

LAC 12882
The roving editor: or, Talks with slaves in the southern states. New York, Negro Universities Press [1968]
Redpath, James, 1833–1891.

LAC 13561
Rowing and Track athletics; Rowing, by Samuel Crowther; Track athletics, by Arthur Ruhl. New York, The Macmillan company; London, Macmillan & co., ltd., 1905.
Crowther, Samuel, 1880–1947.

LAC 11906
Roxy. New York, Charles Scribner's sons [c1878]
Eggleston, Edward, 1837–1902.

LAC 13831

The Royal commission on the losses and services of American loyalists, 1783 to 1785, being the notes of Mr. Daniel Parker Coke, M. P., one of the commissioners during that period; ed. by Hugh Edward Egerton. Oxford, Printed for presentation to the members of the Roxburghe club [by H. Hart, at the University press] 1915.
Coke, Daniel Parker, 1745–1825.

LAC 20808

Royal instructions to British colonial governors, 1670–1776, collated and edited by Leonard Woods Labaree. New York, London, D. Appleton-Century company, incorporated [c1935]
Labaree, Leonard Woods, 1897–   *ed.*

LAC 40048

The rule of reason in Texas. The man who was imprisoned, tried and convicted without authority of law by the Senate of the state of Texas in the summer of 1911, relates a story of what went on under cover of the great agitation of that year—some things about which the committee did not question him... Houston, Tex., W. H. Gray, c1912.
Gray, William Henry, 1877–

LAC 16350

Rules of etiquette and home culture; or what to do and how to do it. By Walter R. Houghton [and others]. 11th ed. Chicago, Rand-McNally, 1887, [c1884]

LAC 11013

Ruling ideas of the present age. Boston and New York, Houghton, Mifflin and company, 1895.
Gladden, Washington, 1836–1918.

LAC 40118

The ruling passion.
Hasty-pudding: a poem, in three cantos. Written at Chamrery [!] in Savoy, January, 1793, by Joel Barlow... Together with, The ruling passion. By Robert T. Paine, jr., esq. Exeter, N. H., A. Brown [182-?]
Barlow, Joel, 1754–1812.

LAC 40074

Rulings as to meaning or application of the award. Arbitration between the western railroads represented by a Conference committee of managers and Brotherhood of locomotive engineers and Brotherhood of locomotive firemen and enginemen. Submitted to arbitration, under the provisions of the act of Congress approved July 15, 1913, by agreement dated August 3, 1914. Chicago, Illinois, August 30, 1915. New York, Law reporting company, official reporters [1915]
Board of Arbitration in the Controversy Between the Western Railroads and the Brotherhood of Locomotive Engineers and the Brotherhood of Locomotive Firemen and Enginemen, 1914–1915.

LAC 20697

A run through the United States, during the autumn of 1840. London, H. Colburn, 1841.
Maxwell, Archibald Montgomery.

LAC 12717

Running a thousand miles for freedom; or, The escape of William and Ellen Craft from slavery. London, W. Tweedie, 1860.
Craft, William.

LAC 20865–69

Rural affairs; a practical and copiously illustrated register of rural economy and rural taste, including country dwellings, improving and planting grounds, fruits and flowers... By J. J. Thomas. v. 1–9; 1855–57 to 1879–81. Albany, N. Y., L. Tucker & son, 1858–81.

LAC 14052

Rural architecture. Being a complete description of farm houses, cottages, and out buildings, comprising wood houses, workshops ... &c. ... Also, the best method of conducting water into cattle yards and houses. New York, C. M. Saxton, 1852.
Allen, Lewis Falley, 1800–1890.

LAC 15081

The rural church movement. New York, Cincinnati, The Methodist book concern [c1914]
Earp, Edwin Lee, 1867–

LAC 12573

Rural credits. Joint hearings before the subcommittees of the committees on banking and currency of the Senate and of the House of representatives, charged with the investigation of rural credits, Sixty-third Congress, second session... Washington, Govt. print. off., 1914.
U.S. *Congress. Senate. Committee on Banking and Currency.*

LAC 10111

Rural credits, land and cooperative, by Myron T. Herrick and R. Ingalls. New York and London, D. Appleton and company, 1914.
Herrick, Myron Timothy, 1854–1929.

LAC 11755

Rural economy: containing a treatise on pise building, as recommended by the Board of Agriculture in Great Britain, with improvements by the author; on buildings in general; particularly on the arrangement of those belonging to farms: on the culture of the vine; and on turnpike roads. New-Brunswick, N. J., Printed by W. Elliot for I. Riley, New-York, 1806.
Johnson, Stephen William.

LAC 10097

Rural essays. Ed., with a memoir of the author, by George William Curtis, and a letter to his friends, by Frederika Bremer. New York, The H. W. Hagemann Publishing co., 1894, [c1869]
Downing, Andrew Jackson, 1815–1852.

LAC 14317

Rural homes: or, Sketches of houses suited to American country life, with original plans, designs, &c. Auburn and Rochester, Alden and Beardsley, 1855.
Wheeler, Gervase.

LAC 15213

The rural life problem of the United States; notes of an Irish observer. New York, The Macmillan company, 1911, [c1910]
Plunkett, *Sir* Horace Curzon, 1854–1932.

LAC 16070

The rural Socrates. [London, T. Becket, 1773]
Hirzel, Hans Kaspar, 1725–1803.

LAC 10118

Rural studies, with hints for country places. By the author of "My farm of Edgewood." New York, C. Scribner & co., 1867.
Mitchell, Donald Grant, 1822–1908.

LAC 16127

Russian expansion on the Pacific, 1641–1850; an account of the earliest and later expeditions made by the Russians along the Pacific coast of Asia and North America; including some related expeditions to the Arctic regions. Cleveland, The Arthur H. Clark company, 1914.
Golder, Frank Alfred, 1877–1929.

LAC 15073

The Russian Jew in the United States; studies of social conditions in New York, Philadelphia, and Chicago, with a description of rural settlements; planned and ed. by Charles S. Bernheimer, PH. D. Philadelphia, The J. C. Winston co., 1905.
Bernheimer, Charles Seligman, 1868–   *ed.*

LAC 12186

The Sabbath in Puritan New England. New York, C. Scribner's sons, 1891.
Earle, Alice, 1851–1911.

LAC 40139

Sabbath school songs: or, Hymns and music suitable for Sabbath schools. Prepared for the Massachusetts Sabbath school society, and revised by the Committee on publication. 7th ed. Boston, Massachusetts Sabbath school society, 1836.
Mason, Lowell, 1792–1872.

LAC 12908

The sable cloud: a southern tale, with northern comments. By the author of "A south-side view of slavery." Boston, Ticknor and Fields, 1861.
Adams, Nehemiah, 1806–1878.

LAC 40064

Sack and destruction of the city of Columbia, S. C. To which is added a list of the property destroyed. Columbia, S. C., Power press of Daily phoenix, 1865.
Simms, William Gilmore, 1806–1870.

LAC 15895

Safety fund banking system in New York.
State banking before the civil war, by Davis R. Dewey and The safety fund banking system in New York, 1829–1866, by Robert E. Chaddock. Washington, Govt. print. off., 1910 [*i.e.* 1911]
Dewey, Davis Rich, 1858–1942.

LAC 15480

The safety of appearing at the day of judgment, in the righteousness of Christ: opened and applied. By Solomon Stoddard, pastor to the church of Northampton in New-England. The 2d ed., cor. With some addition by the author. Boston: Re-printed for D. Henchman, at his shop in Corn-hill, MDCCXXIX.
Stoddard, Solomon, 1643–1729.

LAC 40151

The sage of Hickory Hill, a story of Thomas E. Watson. [n. p., n. d.]
Hutchings, James Key.

LAC 12628

The sailing ships of New England. Series three. Salem Mass., Marine research society, 1928.
Dow, George Francis, 1868–

LAC 16367

A sailor's log; recollections of forty years of naval life. New York, D. Appleton and company, 1901.
Evans, Robley Dunglison, 1846–1912.

LAC 12319

Sailors narratives of voyages along the New England coast, 1524–1624; with notes by George Parker Winship. Boston, Houghton, Mifflin & company, 1905.
Winship, George Parker, 1871–1952, *ed.*

LAC 15174

The St. Albans raid; or, Investigation into the charges against Lieut. Bennett H. Young and command, for their acts at St. Albans, Vt., on the 19th October, 1864. Being a complete and authentic report of all the proceedings on the demand of the United States for their extradition, under the Ashburton treaty. Before Judge Coursol, J. S. P., and the Hon. Mr. Justice Smith, J. S. C. With the arguments of counsel and the opinions of the judges revised by themselves. Comp. by L. N. Benjamin, B. C. L. Montreal, Printed by J. Lovell, 1865.
Benjamin, L   N   *comp.*

LAC 22617–18

The St. Clair papers. The life and public services of Arthur St. Clair, soldier of the revolutionary war; president of the Continental congress; and governor of the North-western territory; with his correspondence and other papers, arranged and annotated by William Henry Smith. Cincinnati, R. Clarke & co., 1882.
Smith, William Henry, 1833–1896.

LAC 10885

Saint Tammany and the origin of the Society of Tammany, or Columbian order in the city of New York. New York [Columbia university] 1913.
Kilroe, Edwin Patrick, 1880–

LAC 40010

The St. Thomas treaty. A series of letters to the Boston daily advertiser. New York [Sutton, Browne & co., printers] 1869.
Andrews, Sidney, 1837–1880.

LAC 22182–83

Salem witchcraft; with an account of Salem village and a history of opinions on witchcraft and kindred subjects. New York, F. Ungar, 1969.
Upham, Charles Wentworth, 1802–1875.

LAC 16110

Sally Wister's journal, a true narrative; being a Quaker maiden's account of her experiences with officers of the Continental army, 1777–1778, edited by Albert Cook Myers, with reproductions of portraits, manuscripts, relics and views. Philadelphia, Ferris & Leach [c1902]
Wister, Sarah, 1761–1804.

LAC 10720

The saloon problem and social reform. Boston, Mass., The Everett press, 1905.
Barker, John Marshall, 1849–

LAC 10773
Saloon, Substitutes for the.
Substitutes for the saloon, by Raymond Calkins; an investigation made for the Committee of fifty under the direction of Francis G. Peabody, Elgin R. L. Gould and William M. Sloane, sub-committee on substitutes for the saloon. Boston and New York, Houghton, Mifflin and company [1901]
Calkins, Raymond, 1869–

LAC 14591
The salvation of all men strictly examined; and the endless punishment of those who die impenitent, argued and defended against the objections and reasonings of the late Rev. Doctor Chauncy, of Boston in his book entitled "The salvation of all men," &c. New-Haven, Printed by A. Morse, M,DCC,XC.
Edwards, Jonathan, 1745–1801.

LAC 15751
The Salzburgers and their descendants: being the history of a colony of German (Lutheran) Protestants, who emigrated to Georgia in 1734, and settled at Ebenezer, twenty-five miles above the city of Savannah. By Rev. P. A. Strobel. Baltimore, T. N. Kurtz, 1855.
Strobel, Philip A.

LAC 15012
Sam Houston and the war of independence in Texas. Boston and New York, Houghton, Mifflin and company, 1893.
Williams, Alfred Mason, 1840–1896.

LAC 15201
Samson and Delilah; America effeminately vanquished; loss of national character... [Seattle, E. Clayson, sr., 1899]
Clayson, Edward, *sr.*

LAC 15087
Samson Occom, and the Christian Indians of New England. Boston, Chicago, The Pilgrim press [c1899]
Love, William De Loss, 1851–1918.

LAC 12472
Samuel Adams. Boston and New York, Houghton, Mifflin and company, 1900, [c1885]
Hosmer, James Kendall, 1834–1927.

LAC 13064
Samuel Chapman Armstrong; a biographical study, by Edith Armstrong Talbot. New York, Doubleday, Page & company, 1904.
Talbot, Edith.

LAC 23048–49
Samuel F. B. Morse; his letters and journals, ed. and supplemented by his son Edward Lind Morse; illustrated with reproductions of his paintings and with notes and diagrams bearing on the invention of the telegraph... Boston and New York, Houghton Mifflin company, 1914.
Morse, Samuel Finley Breese, 1791–1872.

LAC 14236
Samuel Sewall and the world he lived in; by Rev. N. H. Chamberlain. Boston, De Wolfe, Fiske & company, 1897.
Chamberlain, Nathan Henry, 1831–1901.

LAC 20071–72
San Francisco, a history of the Pacific coast metropolis. San Francisco, Chicago, The S. J. Clarke publishing company [pref. 1912]
Young, John Philip, 1849–1921.

LAC 40009
The sanitary condition of the laboring population of New York. With suggestions for its improvement. A discourse (with additions) delivered on the 30th December, 1844, at the repository of the American institute. New York, Harper & brothers, 1845.
Griscom, John Hoskins, 1809–1874.

LAC 10073
The sanitation of a country house. With sixteen illustrations. 1st ed. 1st thousand. New York, J. Wiley & sons, 1905.
Bashore, Harvey Brown, 1864–1934.

LAC 15345
Satellite cities; a study of industrial suburbs. New York and London, D. Appleton and company, 1915.
Taylor, Graham Romeyn, 1880–

LAC 13570
Save the girls. 12th ed. 110th thousand. Fort Wayne, Ind., M. Long [c1888]
Long, Mason, 1842–1903.

LAC 15367
Sawdust & spangles; stories and secrets of the circus. Washington, P. A. Ruddell [1961, c1901]
Coup, William Cameron, 1837–1895.

LAC 40110
The sayings of Poor Richard; wit, wisdom, and humor of Benjamin Franklin in the proverbs and maxims of Poor Richard's almanacks for 1733 to 1758, condensed and edited by Thomas Herbert Russell. [n. p.] Americanization department, Veterans of foreign wars of the United States [1926]
Franklin, Benjamin, 1706–1790.

LAC 22338–39
The scalp hunters; or, Romantic adventures in northern Mexico. London, C. J. Skeet, 1851.
Reid, Mayne, 1818–1883.

LAC 15601
A scamper through America; or, Fifteen thousand miles of ocean and continent in sixty days. London, Griffith & Farran; New York, E. P. Dutton & co., 1882.
Hudson, T   S.

LAC 14824
The Scandinavian-American, by Alfred O. Fonkalsrud, PH. D., with the collaboration of Beatrice Stevenson, M. A. Minneapolis, Minn. [K. C. Holter publishing company] 1915.
Fonkalsrud, Alfred O   1874–

LAC 15492
The Scandinavian element in the United States. Urbana, The University of Illinois [c1914]
Babcock, Kendric Charles, 1864–1932.

LAC 13211

Scandinavians as a social force in America... Brooklyn, N. Y., Heiberg printery [1914]
Fonkalsrud, Alfred O   1874–

LAC 40087

The scenery of the Catskill mountains as described by Irving, Cooper, Bryant, W. G. Clark, N. P. Willis, Miss Martineau, Tyrone Power, Park Benjamin, Thomas Cole, Bayard Taylor and other eminent writers. Catskill [N. Y.] J. Joesbury, printer, 1864.

LAC 16550

Scenes and adventures in the army: or, Romance of military life. Philadelphia, Lindsay & Blakiston, 1857.
Cooke, Philip St. George, 1809–1895.

LAC 14529

Scenes and scenery in the Sandwich Islands, and a trip through Central America: being observations from my note-book during the years 1837–1842. Boston, J. Munroe and company, 1843.
Jarves, James Jackson, 1820–1888.

LAC 13125

Scenes in the Hawaiian islands and California. New York, American tract society [c1865]
Anderson, Mary Eleanor, 1840–1916.

LAC 40052

Schemes to "distribute" immigrants. [n.p.] 1911.
Gompers, Samuel, 1850–1924.

LAC 10904

Schenectady, ancient and modern; a complete and connected history of Schenectady from the granting of the first patent in 1661 to 1914, presenting also many historic pictures and portraits of those who have been conspicuous figures in its history. [Geneva, N. Y., Press of W. F. Humphrey] 1914.
Monroe, Joel Henry.

LAC 12980

The scholar's companion; containing exercises in the orthography, derivation, and classification of English words. With an introduction and a copious index, by Rufus W. Bailey. A new ed., thoroughly rev. Philadelphia, E. H. Butler & co., 1870, [c1863]
Butter, Henry, 1794–1885.

LAC 15778

The school and society; being three lectures by John Dewey. Supplemented by a statement of the University elementary school. Chicago, The University of Chicago press; New York, McClure, Phillips & company, 1907, [c1900]
Dewey, John, 1859–1952.

LAC 15535

The school and the immigrant. Cleveland, O., The Survey committee of the Cleveland foundation, 1916.
Miller, Herbert Adolphus, 1875–1951.

LAC 13041

The school and the schoolmaster. A manual for the use of teachers, employers, trustees, inspectors, &c., &c., of common schools. In two parts. Part I. By Alonzo Potter. Part II. By George B. Emerson. Boston, W. B. Fowle & N. Capen, 1843.
Potter, Alonzo, bp., 1800–1865.

LAC 10455

School funds and their apportionment; a consideration of the subject with reference to a more general equalization of both the burdens and the advantages of education. New York, Teachers college, Columbia university, 1905.
Cubberley, Ellwood Patterson, 1868–1941.

LAC 14796

A school history of the negro race in America, from 1619 to 1890, with a short introduction as to the origin of the race; also a short sketch of Liberia. Rev. ed., Chicago, W. B. Conkey company, 1897, [c1891]
Johnson, Edward Augustus, 1860–1944.

LAC 40027

The school of good manners. Composed for the help of parents in teaching their children how to carry it in their places during their minority. Exeter, Eng., Printed by C. Norris & co., 1813.

LAC 13040

School supervision. New York, D. Appleton and company, 1890.
Pickard, Josiah Little, 1824–1914.

LAC 14598

The schools of Cincinnati, and its vicinity. Cincinnati, C. F. Bradley & co.'s power press, 1855.
Foote, John Parsons, 1783–1865.

LAC 11047

The Schwenkfelders in Pennsylvania, a historical sketch... By Howard Wiegner Kriebel. Illustrated by Julius F. Sachse, LITT. D. Lancaster, Pa. [The New era printing company] 1904.
Kriebel, Howard Wiegner.

LAC 15718

Science and art. Systems, institutions and statistics of scientific instruction, applied to national industries in different countries. Vol. I... New York, E. Steiger, 1872.
Barnard, Henry, 1811–1900.

LAC 14273

Science and revolution. Chicago, C. H. Kerr & company, 1905.
Untermann, Ernest.

LAC 14259

The science of logic; or, An analysis of the laws of thought. By Rev. Asa Mahan. New-York, A. S. Barnes & co., 1857.
Mahan, Asa, 1800–1889.

LAC 15716

The science of mechanics, as applied to the present improvements in the useful arts in Europe, and in the United States of America: adapted as a manual for mechanics and manufacturers, and containing tables and calculations of general practical utility. Providence, Hutchens & Cory, 1829.
Allen, Zachariah, 1795–1882.

LAC 15963
Science of moral philosophy. Oberlin, O., J. M. Fitch, 1848.
Mahan, Asa, 1800–1889.

LAC 11177
The science of penology; the defence of society against crime; collated and systematized by Henry M. Boies. New York and London, G. P. Putnam's sons, 1901.
Boies, Henry Martyn, 1837–1903.

LAC 20399–407
The science of railways... The whole profusely embellished and illustrated by engravings, prepared expressly for this work... [Rev. and enl. ed.] New York, The world railway pub. co., 1902.
Kirkman, Marshall Monroe, 1842–1921.

LAC 14778
The science of society. no. 1–[2]... New York, Fowlers and Wells, 1852.
Andrews, Stephen Pearl, 1812–1886.

LAC 13996
The science of thought; a system of logic. Boston, W. V. Spencer, 1869.
Everett, Charles Carroll, 1829–1900.

LAC 10564
The science of wealth: a manual of political economy. Embracing the laws of trade, currency and finance... [Student's ed.] Philadelphia, J. B. Lippincott, 1872.
Walker, Amasa, 1799–1875.

LAC 10493
Science, philosophy and religion. Lectures delivered before the Lowell institute, Boston. New York, G. P. Putnam & sons, 1872, [c1871]
Bascom, John, 1827–1911.

LAC 31485–593
Scientific American. v. 1–14, Aug. 28, 1845–June 25, 1859; new ser., v. 1–93, July 2, 1859–Dec. 30, 1905. New York, Munn & co.

LAC 13760
Scientific correspondence of Joseph Priestley. Ninety-seven letters addressed to Josiah Wedgwood, Sir Joseph Banks, Capt. James Keir, James Watt, Dr. William Withering, Dr. Benjamin Rush, and others. Together with an appendix: I. The likenesses of Priestley in oil, ink, marble, and metal. II. The Lunar society of Birmingham. III. Inventory of Priestley's laboratory in 1791. Ed., with copious biographical, bibliographical, and explanatory notes, by Henry Carrington Bolton. New York, Privately printed [Philadelphia, Collins printing house] 1892.
Priestley, Joseph, 1733–1804.

LAC 16235
Scientific management; a collection of the more significant articles describing the Taylor system of management. Cambridge, Harvard university press; [etc., etc.] 1914.
Thompson, Clarence Bertrand, 1882–   ed.

LAC 40117
Scientific management and railroads; being part of a brief submitted to the Interstate commerce commission. New York, The Engineering magazine, 1911.
Brandeis, Louis Dembitz, 1856–1941.

LAC 20905
Scientific papers of Asa Gray, selected by Charles Sprague Sargent. Boston and New York, Houghton, Mifflin and company, 1889.
Gray, Asa, 1810–1888.

LAC 21859
The scientific papers of J. Willard Gibbs. London, New York and Bombay, Longmans, Green and co., 1906.
Gibbs, Josiah Willard, 1839–1903.

LAC 40097
Scientific propagation.
Essay on scientific propagation. Oneida, N. Y., Oneida community [1875?]
Noyes, John Humphrey, 1811–1886.

LAC 10915
Scientific theism. London, Macmillan and co., 1885.
Abbot, Francis Ellingwood, 1836–1903.

LAC 20906–7
Scientific writings of Joseph Henry... Washington, The Smithsonian institution, 1886.
Henry, Joseph, 1797–1878.

LAC 15748
The Scot in America. New York, The Raeburn book company, 1896.
Ross, Peter, 1847–1902.

LAC 14827
The Scotch-Irish in America. Princeton, N. J., Princeton university press; [etc., etc.] 1915.
Ford, Henry Jones, 1851–1925.

LAC 40052
The Scotch-Irish in America. A paper read as the report of the Council of the American antiquarian society, at the semi-annual meeting, April 24, 1895, with correspondence called out by the paper. Worcester, Mass., Press of C. Hamilton, 1895.
Green, Samuel Swett, 1837–1918.

LAC 23039–43
The Scotch-Irish in America. Proceedings... [1st]–9th; 1889–1896, 1900. Cincinnati, R. Clarke [etc.] 1899–1900.
The Scotch-Irish Society of America.

LAC 22864–65
The Scotch-Irish; or, The Scot in North Britain, north Ireland, and North America. New York and London, G. P. Putnam's sons, 1902.
Hanna, Charles Augustus, 1863–1950.

LAC 15497
Scotch Irish pioneers in Ulster and America, by Charles Knowles Bolton. With maps and illustrations drawn by Ethel Stanwood Bolton. Boston, Bacon and Brown, 1910.
Bolton, Charles Knowles, 1867–

LAC 23248–50

Scotch-Irish settlement in Virginia.
Chronicles of the Scotch-Irish settlement in Virginia; extracted from the original court records of Augusta County, 1745–1800, by Lyman Chalkley; pub. by Mary S. Lockwood. Rosslyn, Va., Printers: The Commonwealth printing co. [c1912–13]
Augusta Co., *Va.*

LAC 16964

The scout; or, The Black riders of Congaree. New and rev. ed. New York, W. J. Widdleton, 1868.
Simms, William Gilmore, 1806–1870.

LAC 14698

The scouting expeditions of McCulloch's Texas rangers; or, The summer and fall campaign of the army of the United States in Mexico–1846; including skirmishes with the Mexicans, and ... the storming of Monterey; also, the daring scouts at Buena Vista; together with anecdotes, incidents, descriptions of country, and sketches of the lives of ... Hays, McCulloch, and Walker. By Samuel C. Reid, jr. Philadelphia, G. B. Zieber and co., 1848, [c1847]
Reid, Samuel Chester, 1818–1897.

LAC 15288

Scouts, spies, and heroes of the great civil war. Including thrilling adventures, daring deeds, heroic exploits, wonderful escapes of spies, scouts, and detectives with songs, ballads, anecdotes, witty sayings, watchwords, battle-cries, and humorous and pathetic incidents of the war. By Captain Joseph Powers Hazelton [*pseud.*] Jersey City, Star publishing company, 1892.
Brockett, Linus Pierpont, 1820–1893.

LAC 40041

Scranton in quick review. The report of a pathfinder survey of living conditions which point the need of a more intensive local survey–made for the Century club of Scranton by the Department of surveys and exhibits, Russell Sage foundation. Scranton, Pa., Pub. by the Century club of Scranton, 1913.
Russell Sage Foundation, *New York. Dept. of Surveys and Exhibits.*

LAC 12514

Scrap book on law and politics, men and times. Lexington, Ky., A. W. Elder, 1855.
Robertson, George, 1790–1874.

LAC 16132

Scraps of California history.
A biographical sketch of the life of William B. Ide: with a minute and interesting account of one of the largest emigrating companies ... from the East to the Pacific coast. And ... account of "the virtual conquest of California, in June, 1846, by the Bear flag party," as given by its leader, the late Hon. William Brown Ide... [Claremont, N. H., S. Ide, 1880]
Ide, Simeon, 1794–1889.

LAC 30715–37

Scribner's monthly, an illustrated magazine for the people. Conducted by J. G. Holland. v. 1–22; Nov. 1870–October 1881. New York, Scribner & co. [etc.] 1870–81.

LAC 12891

Scriptural and statistical views in favor of slavery. 4th ed., with additions. Richmond, J. W. Randolph, 1856.
Stringfellow, Thornton.

LAC 11035

A scriptural, ecclesiastical, and historical view of slavery, from the days of the patriarch Abraham, to the nineteenth century. Addressed to the Right Rev. Alonzo Potter... New York, W. I. Pooley & co. [1864]
Hopkins, John Henry, *bp.*, 1792–1868.

LAC 16245

A Scriptural examination of the institution of slavery in the United States; with its objects and purposes. [Perry?] Ga., Printed for the author, 1856.
Cobb, Howell, 1815–1868.

LAC 14488

A scriptural view of the character, causes, and ends of the present war. By Alexander M'Leod, D. D., pastor of the Reformed Presbyterian church, New-York. New-York: Published by Eastburn, Kirk and co.; Whiting and Watson; and Smith and Forman. Paul & Thomas, printers, 1815.
McLeod, Alexander, 1774–1833.

LAC 23462–63

Sea power in its relations to the war of 1812, by Captain A. T. Mahan. Boston, Little, Brown, and company, 1905.
Mahan, Alfred Thayer, 1840–1914.

LAC 11895

Seacliff; or, The mystery of the Westervelts. Boston, Phillips, Sampson and company, 1859.
De Forest, John William, 1826–1906.

LAC 22572–76

Seal and salmon fisheries and general resources of Alaska... Washington, Govt. print. off., 1898.
U.S. *Treasury Dept. Special Agents Division.*

LAC 10053

The seaman's friend; containing a treatise on practical seamanship, with plates; a dictionary of sea terms; customs and usages of the merchant service; laws relating to the practical duties of master and mariners. Boston, C. C. Little & J. Brown, 1844.
Dana, Richard Henry, 1815–1882.

LAC 13787

A search of truth in the science of the human mind, part first. By the Rev. Frederick Beasley. Philadelphia, S. Potter and co., 1822.
Beasley, Frederick, 1777–1845.

LAC 15807

Seasonable thoughts on the state of religion in New-England, a treatise in five parts ... With a preface giving an account of the antinomians, familists and libertines, who infected these churches, above an hundred years ago: very needful for these days; the like spirit and errors prevailing now as did then. The whole being intended, and calculated, to serve the interest of Christ's kingdom. Boston, Printed by Rogers and Fowle, for Samuel Eliot in Cornhill, 1743.
Chauncy, Charles, 1705–1787.

LAC 13170
The seat of empire. By Charles Carleton Coffin, "Carleton". Boston, J. R. Osgood and company, 1870.
Coffin, Charles Carleton, 1823–1896.

LAC 12019
The sea-wolf, by Jack London, with illustrations by W. J. Aylward. New York, The Macmillan company, London, Macmillan & co., ltd., 1904.
London, Jack, 1876–1916.

LAC 10264
The secession and reconstruction of Tennessee... Chicago, The University of Chicago press, 1898.
Fertig, James Walter.

LAC 10292
The second bank of the United States. Chicago, The University of Chicago press, 1903, [c1902]
Catterall, Ralph Charles Henry, 1866–1914.

LAC 20686
A second visit to the United States of North America... New York, Harper & brothers, London, J. Murray, 1849.
Lyell, *Sir* Charles, *bart.*, 1797–1875.

LAC 14039
The second William Penn; a true account of incidents that happened along the old Santa Fe trail in the sixties. Kansas City, Mo., Press of Frank T. Riley publishing co. [c1913]
Ryus, William Henry, 1839–

LAC 40094
Secondary education. By Thomas H. Briggs. Washington, Govt. print. off., 1919.
U.S. *Office of Education.*

LAC 13034
Secondary education in Pennsylvania.
A history of secondary education in Pennsylvania. Philadelphia, The author, 1933.
Mulhern, James, 1890–

LAC 15453
The secret book of the elders.
Testimonies of the life, character, revelations and doctrines of Mother Ann Lee, and the elders with her, through whom the word of eternal life was opened in this day of Christ's second appearing, collected from living witnesses, in union with the church... 2d ed. Albany, N. Y., Weed, Parsons & co., printers, 1888.
Shakers.

LAC 15576
The secret of a happy home. By Marion Harland [*pseud.*] New York, The Christian herald [c1896]
Terhune, Mary Virginia, 1830–1922.

LAC 21012
The secret service of the Confederate States in Europe; or, How the Confederate cruisers were equipped. New York, G. P. Putnam's sons, 1884.
Bulloch, James Dunwody, 1823–1901.

LAC 15005
Secretary Root's record. "Marked severities" in Philippine warfare. An analysis of the law and facts bearing on the action and utterances of President Roosevelt and Secretary Root... Boston, G. H. Ellis co., printers, 1902.
Storey, Moorfield, 1845–1929.

LAC 13716
The secrets of the great city: a work descriptive of the virtues and the vices, the mysteries, miseries, and crimes of New York city. By Edward Winslow Martin [*pseud.*] Philadelphia, Chicago [etc.] Jones brothers & co. [1868]
McCabe, James Dabney, 1842–1883.

LAC 10230
Sectionalism in Virginia from 1776 to 1861. Chicago, The University of Chicago press, 1910.
Ambler, Charles Henry, 1876–1957.

LAC 14752
The secularization of American education as shown by state legislation, state constitutional provisions and state Supreme court decisions. New York city, Teachers college, Columbia university, 1912.
Brown, Samuel Windsor, 1875–

LAC 40025
The seizure of the "Peterhoff"; being a statement of the facts, the reason, the law and the consequences. With the correspondence. London, E. Wilson, 1863.

LAC 14075
Select cases of the Mayor's court of New York city, 1674–1784, edited by Richard B. Morris. Washington, D. C., The American historical association, 1935.
New York *(City) Mayor's Court.*

LAC 13442
Select charters and other documents illustrative of American history, 1606–1775, ed. with notes by William MacDonald. New York, The Macmillan company; London, Macmillan & co., ltd., 1899.
MacDonald, William, 1863–1938, *ed.*

LAC 20641–44
The Select journal of foreign periodical literature, v. 1–4; Jan. 1833–Oct. 1834. Boston, C. Bowen, 1833–34.

LAC 12619
Select letters of Christopher Columbus, with other original documents, relating to his four voyages to the New world. Tr. and ed. by R. H. Major. London, Printed for the Hakluyt society, 1847.
Colombo, Cristoforo.

LAC 10620
Select works of Robert Goodloe Harper; consisting of speeches on political and forensic subjects; with the answer drawn up by him to the articles of impeachment against Judge Chase, and sundry political tracts. Collated from the original publications and carefully rev. Vol. 1. Baltimore, O. H. Neilson, 1814.
Harper, Robert Goodloe, 1765–1825.

LAC 12977
Selected addresses. New York [etc.] Longmans, Green, and co., 1912.
Angell, James Burrill, 1829–1916.

LAC 15546
Selected articles on immigration. White Plains, N. Y., and New York city, The H. W. Wilson company, 1915.
Reely, Mary Katharine, 1881–   *comp.*

LAC 14603
Selected articles on woman suffrage. Minneapolis, the H. W. Wilson company, 1910.
Phelps, Edith May, 1881–   *comp.*

LAC 11231
Selected articles on world peace including international arbitration and disarmament. White Plains, N. Y., and New York city, The H. W. Wilson company, 1914.
Reely, Mary Katharine, 1881–   *comp.*

LAC 10551
Selected essays of William Graham Sumner, edited by Albert Galloway Keller and Maurice Rea Davie. New Haven, Yale university press; [etc., etc.] 1924.
Sumner, William Graham, 1840–1910.

LAC 12532
Selected speeches and reports on finance and taxation, from 1859 to 1878. New York, D. Appleton and company, 1879.
Sherman, John, 1823–1900.

LAC 15295
Selected speeches of Booker T. Washington, edited by E. Davidson Washington. Garden City, N. Y., Doubleday, Doran & company, inc., 1932.
Washington, Booker Taliaferro, 1859?–1915.

LAC 11839
Selected works of Artemus Ward [*pseud.*]; edited with an introduction by Albert Jay Nock. New York, A. & C. Boni, 1924.
Browne, Charles Farrar, 1834–1867.

LAC 15026
Selected writings of Isaac M. Wise, with a biography by the editors, David Philipson and Louis Grossmann. Published under the auspices of the Alumnal association of the Hebrew union college. Cincinnati, The Robert Clarke company, 1900.
Wise, Isaac Mayer, 1819–1900.

LAC 15784
A selection from the miscellaneous writings of the late Isaac Harby, esq. Arranged and published by Henry L. Pinckney and Abraham Moise, for the benefit of his family. To which is prefixed, a memoir of his life, by Abraham Moise. Charleston [N. C.] Printed by J. S. Burges, 1829.
Harby, Isaac, 1788–1828.

LAC 10653
Selections from the correspondence of Thomas Barclay, formerly British consul-general at New York, ed. by George Lockhart Rives. New York, Harper & brothers, 1894.
Barclay, Thomas, 1753–1830.

LAC 10707
Selections from the economic history of the United States, 1765–1860, with introductory essays by Guy Stevens Callender. Boston, New York [etc.] Ginn and company [c1909]
Callender, Guy Stevens, 1865–1915, *ed.*

LAC 16729
Selections from the letters and speeches of the Hon. James H. Hammond, of South Carolina. New York, J. F. Trow & co., printers, 1866.
Hammond, James Henry, 1807–1864.

LAC 11938
Selections from the poetical literature of the West...
Cincinnati, U. P. James, 1841.
Gallagher, William Davis, 1808–1894, *ed.*

LAC 14143
Selections from the speeches and writings of Hon. Thomas L. Clingman, of North Carolina, with additions and explanatory notes. 2d ed. Raleigh, J. Nichols, 1878.
Clingman, Thomas Lanier, 1812–1897.

LAC 12830
Selections from the writings and speeches of William Lloyd Garrison. With an appendix... Boston, R. F. Wallcut, 1852.
Garrison, William Lloyd, 1805–1879.

LAC 40040
A self-defensive war lawful, proved in a sermon, preached at Lancaster, before Captain Ross's company of militia, in the Presbyterian church, on Sabbath morning, June 4, 1775. By the Rev. John Carmichael, A. M. Now pub. at the request of the author, and corrected by himself from the copy printed at Lancaster... Philadelphia, J. Dean, 1775. [Tarrytown, N. Y., Reprinted, W. Abatt, 1929]
Carmichael, John, 1728–1785.

LAC 40048
The self-made man in American life. New York, Boston, T. Y. Crowell & company [c1897]
Cleveland, Grover, *pres. U.S.*, 1837–1908.

LAC 13925
Semi-centennial history of the city of Rochester, with illustrations and biographical sketches of some of its prominent men and pioneers. Syracuse, N. Y., D. Mason & co., 1884.
Peck, William Farley, 1840–

LAC 16749
Semi-tropical California: its climate, healthfulness, productiveness, and scenery... by Major Ben. C. Truman. San Francisco, A. L. Bancroft & company, 1874.
Truman, Benjamin Cummings, 1835–1916.

LAC 40075
The Senate from 1907 to 1912; the story of the stewardship of those United States senators whose terms expire March third, nineteen thirteen. [Washington, D. C., The National capital press] c1912.
Haines, Lynn, 1876–1929.

LAC 40126
The senator unmasked: being a letter to Mr. Daniel Webster, on his speech in the Senate of the United States asking leave to bring a bill to continue for six years the charter of the Bank of the United States. Philadelphia, The author, 1834.
Brothers, Thomas.

LAC 12064
The sense of beauty; being the outlines of aesthetic theory. New York, C. Scribner's sons, 1907, [c1896]
Santayana, George, 1863-1952.

LAC 15351
Separate and unequal; public school campaigns and racism in the Southern Seaboard States, 1901-1915. Chapel Hill, University of North Carolina Press [1958]
Harlan, Louis R.

LAC 15408
Separation of church and state in Virginia; a study in the development of the revolution. Special report of the Department of archives and history, H. J. Eckenrode, archivist. Richmond, D. Bottom, superintendent of public printing, 1910.
Virginia. State Library, *Richmond. Archives Division.*

LAC 40050
Sequel to the so called correspondence between the Rev. M. H. Smith and Horace Mann, surreptitiously published by Mr. Smith; containing a letter from Mr. Mann, suppressed by Mr. Smith, with the reply therein promised. Boston, W. B. Fowle, 1847.
Mann, Horace, 1796-1859.

LAC 15084
Se-quo-yah, the American Cadmus and modern Moses. A complete biography of the greatest of redmen, around whose wonderful life has been woven the manners, customs and beliefs of the early Cherokees, together with a recital of their wrongs and wonderful progress toward civilization. By Geo. E. Foster. Illustrated by Miss C. S. Robbins. Philadelphia, Office of the Indian rights association; Tahlequah, Cherokee nation, H. B. Stone; [etc., etc.] 1885.
Foster, George Everett, 1849-

LAC 10929
A series of lecture sermons, delivered at the Second Universalist meeting, in Boston. By Hosea Ballou, pastor. 3d ed., stereotyped. Revised by the author. Boston, A. Tompkins, 1854, [c1832]
Ballou, Hosea, 1771-1852.

LAC 12762
A series of lectures on the science of government; intended to prepare the student for the study of the Constitution of the United States. Philadelphia, Carey and Hart, 1845.
Tucker, Nathaniel Beverley, 1784-1851.

LAC 20433
A series of letters from London written during the years 1856, '57, '58, '59, and '60. By George Mifflin Dallas, then minister of the United States at the British court. Ed. by his daughter Julia. Philadelphia, J. B. Lippincott & co., 1869.
Dallas, George Mifflin, 1792-1864.

LAC 40028
Serious considerations on several important subjects; viz. on war and its inconsistency with the gospel: observations on slavery. And remarks on the nature and bad effects of spirituous liquors... Philadelphia, Printed by Joseph Crukshank, in Market-street, between Second and Third-streets, 1778.
Benezet, Anthony, 1713-1784.

LAC 40066
Serious considerations on the election of a president: addressed to the citizens of the United States. New-York: Printed and sold by John Furman, at his blank, stamp, and stationary shop, opposite the City hall, 1800.
Linn, William, 1752-1808.

LAC 16757
A serious inquiry into the nature and effects of the stage: and a letter respecting play actors. By the Rev. John Witherspoon... Also a sermon, on the burning of the theatre at Richmond, &c. By Samuel Miller. Together with an introductory address, by several ministers in New-York, &c. New-York: Published by Whiting & Watson, 96 Broadway. [Printed by D. & G. Bruce] 1812.
Witherspoon, John, 1723-1794.

LAC 40070
A sermon, preached in Boston, August 20, 1812, the day of humiliation and prayer, appointed by the President of the United States, in consequence of the declaration of war against Great Britain. Published at the request of the hearers. Boston: Printed by C. Stebbins, no. 4, Suffolk buildings, 1812.
Channing, William Ellery, 1780-1842.

LAC 40070
Sermon. The question of war with Great Britain, examined upon moral and Christian principles... Boston, Printed by Snelling & Simons, 1808.
McKean, Joseph, 1776-1818.

LAC 40133
Sermons addressed to masters and servants, and published in the year 1743 [!], now republished by the Rev. William Meade. Winchester, Va., John Heiskell, printer [1813?]
Bacon, Thomas, 1700 (*ca.*)-1768.

LAC 13988
Sermons, by the Rev. Samuel Davies. With a funeral sermon by the Rev. Samuel Finley and some account of President Davies by the Rev. Thomas Gibbons and the Rev. David Bostwick. Containing also an introductory memoir of President Davies, by the Rev. William B. Sprague. Vol. 1. Philadelphia, Presbyterian board of publication [1864]
Davies, Samuel, 1723-1761.

LAC 14847
Sermons of the city. New York, E. P. Dutton & company, 1881.
Potter, Henry Codman, *bp.*, 1834-1908.

LAC 10998
Sermons on important subjects. New York, John S. Taylor [1836]
Finney, Charles Grandison, 1792-1875.

LAC 15788

Sermons upon the following subjects, viz. On hearing the word: On receiving it with meekness: On renouncing gross immoralities: On the necessity of obeying the gospel: On being found in Christ: On justification by faith: On the nature, principle and extent of evangelical obedience: On the deceitfulness of the heart and God's knowledge thereof: On the shortness and vanity of human life: and On the true value, use and end of life: together with the conduciveness of religion to prolong, and make it happy. Boston, Richard Draper, 1755.
Mayhew, Jonathan, 1720–1766.

LAC 16640

Service afloat and ashore during the Mexican war. Cincinnati, W. H. Moore & co., 1851.
Semmes, Raphael, 1809–1877.

LAC 14892

Serving the Republic; memoirs of the civil and military life of Nelson A. Miles. New York and London, Harper & brothers, 1911.
Miles, Nelson Appleton, 1839–1925.

LAC 13619

Seth Jones; or, The captives of the frontier. London, Beadle and company [1861]
Ellis, Edward Sylvester, 1840–1916.

LAC 11926

Seth's brother's wife. A study of life in the greater New York. New York, C. Scribner's sons, 1887.
Frederic, Harold, 1856–1898.

LAC 14077

Settlement in the West. Sketches of Rochester; with incidental notices of western New-York... Arranged by Henry O'Reilly [!] Rochester, W. Alling, 1838.
O'Rielly, Henry, 1806–1886.

LAC 15733

The settlement of the German coast of Louisiana and the Creoles of German descent. Philadelphia, Americana germanica press, 1909.
Deiler, John Hanno, 1849–1909.

LAC 14791

The settlement of the Jews in North America. By Charles P. Daly, ed., with notes and appendices, by Max J. Kohler. New York, P. Cowen, 1893.
Daly, Charles Patrick, 1816–1899.

LAC 16033

The settler's guide in the United States and British North American provinces... New York, Davis & Kent, 1862.
Spence, Thomas, *land surveyor.*

LAC 16091

The settler's new home; or, The emigrant's location, being a guide to emigrants in the selection of a settlement, and the preliminary details of the voyage. London, J. Kendrick, 1849.
Smith, Sidney.

LAC 11554

Seven decades of the Union. The humanities and materialism, illustrated by a memoir of John Tyler, with reminiscences of some of his great contemporaries. The transition state of this nation, its dangers and their remedy. Philadelphia, J. B. Lippincott & co., 1876, [c1871]
Wise, Henry Alexander, 1806–1876.

LAC 15010

Seven months a prisoner. New York, Charles Scribner's sons, 1898.
Hadley, John Vestal, 1840–

LAC 13521

Seven years' street preaching in San Francisco, California; embracing incidents, triumphant death scenes, etc., by Rev. William Taylor. Ed. by W. P. Strickland. 7th thousand. New-York, Pub. for the author by Carlton & Porter [c1856]
Taylor, William, *bp.*, 1821–1902.

LAC 20009

1795–1895. One hundred years of American commerce ... a history of American commerce by one hundred Americans, with a chronological table of the important events of American commerce and invention within the past one hundred years. Issued in commemoration of the completion of the first century of American commercial progress as inaugurated by the treaty ... negotiated by Chief Justice Jay and approved by President Washington in 1795. New York, D. O. Haynes & co., 1895.
Depew, Chauncey Mitchell, 1834–1928, *ed.*

LAC 13262

Seventy years on the frontier; Alexander Majors' memoirs of a lifetime on the border. With a preface by "Buffalo Bill" (General W. F. Cody) Edited by Colonel Prentiss Ingraham. Columbus, O., Reprinted by Long's College Book Co., 1950.
Majors, Alexander, 1814–1900.

LAC 12575

Several essays in political arithmetick. 4th ed., cor. To which are prefix'd, memoirs of the author's life. London, Printed for D. Browne [etc.] 1755.
Petty, *Sir* William, 1623–1687.

LAC 10806

Sewage disposal in the United States, by Geo. W. Rafter and M. N. Baker. New York, D. Van Nostrand company; [etc., etc.] 1894.
Rafter, George W   1851–

LAC 30880–88

The Sewanee review, quarterly. v. 1–13. Nov. 1892–Oct. 1905. Sewanee, Tenn., The University press; [etc., etc.] 1892–1905.

LAC 10596

Sex and education. A reply to Dr. E. H. Clarke's "Sex in education". Ed., with an introduction, by Mrs. Julia Ward Howe. Boston, Roberts brothers, 1874.
Howe, Julia, 1819–1910, *ed.*

LAC 12994
Sex in education: or, A fair chance for the girls. Boston, J. R. Osgood and company, 1874, [c1873]
Clarke, Edward Hammond, 1820–1877.

LAC 40061
Sexual health. A companion to "Modern domestic medicine." A plain and practical guide for the people in all matters concerning the organs of reproduction in both sexes and all ages. By Henry G. Hanchett. Issued after careful revision by A. H. Laidlaw. New York, C. T. Hurlburt, 1887.
Hanchett, Henry Granger, 1853–

LAC 11432
Seymour and Blair, their lives and services with an appendix containing a history of reconstruction. New York, Richardson and company, 1868.
Croly, David Goodman, 1829–1889.

LAC 12831
Shadow and light; an autobiography with reminiscences of the last and present century. By Mifflin Wistar Gibbs. With an introduction by Booker T. Washington. Washington, D. C., 1902.
Gibbs, Mifflin Wistar.

LAC 16549
Shadowings. Boston, Little, Brown, and company, 1919, [c1900]
Hearn, Lafcadio, 1850–1904.

LAC 10990
Shaker sermons: scripto-rational. Containing the substance of Shaker theology. Together with replies and criticisms logically and clearly set forth. Shakers, N. Y., The Shaker manifesto, 1879.
Eads, Harvey L   *b.* 1807.

LAC 14233
Shakers. Compendium of the origin, history, principles, rules and regulations, government, and doctrines of the United Society of believers in Christ's second appearing. With biographies of Ann Lee, William Lee, Jas. Whittaker, J. Hocknell, J. Meacham, and Lucy Wright. New York, D. Appleton and company, 1859.
Evans, Frederick William, 1808–1893.

LAC 13861
Shakers of Ohio; fugitive papers concerning the Shakers of Ohio, with unpublished manuscripts. Columbus, O., The F. J. Heer printing co., 1907.
MacLean, John Patterson, 1848–1939.

LAC 40002
Shall we have peace? Peace financial, and peace political? Letters to the president elect of the United States. Philadelphia, Collins, printer, 1869.
Carey, Henry Charles, 1793–1879.

LAC 40066
The sham-patriot unmasked; or, An exposition of the fatally successful arts of demagogues, to exalt themselves, by flattering and swindling the people; in a variety of pertinent facts, drawn from sacred and profane history. By Historicus [*pseud.*] Concord [N. H.] Printed by George Hough, 1805.
Sampson, Ezra, 1749–1823.

LAC 20152
Sharps and flats, by Eugene Field; collated by Slason Thompson. New York, Scribner's sons, 1900.
Field, Eugene, 1850–1895.

LAC 10131
The sheep. A historical and statistical description of sheep and their products. The fattening of sheep. Their diseases, with prescriptions for scientific treatment. The respective breeds of sheep and their fine points. Government inspection, etc., with other valuable information ... also an appendix containing sheep breeders' directory. [New York] The Buffalo review co., 1899.
Rushworth, William Arthur.

LAC 15215
Sheep husbandry in the South: comprising a treatise on the acclimation of sheep in the southern states and an account of the different breeds. Also, a complete manual of breeding, summer and winter management, and of the treatment of diseases... In a series of letters from Henry S. Randall ... to R. F. W. Allston... Philadelphia, J. S. Skinner & son, 1848.
Randall, Henry Stephens, 1811–1876.

LAC 13320
Sheldon Jackson, pathfinder and prospector of the missionary vanguard in the Rocky mountains and Alaska. New York, Chicago [etc.] F. H. Revell company [c1908]
Stewart, Robert Laird, 1840–1916.

LAC 15699
Sheridan's troopers on the borders: a winter campaign on the plains. Philadelphia, Claxton, Remsen & Haffelfinger, 1870.
Keim, De Benneville Randolph.

LAC 16954
Sherman act.
The origin of the national banking system. Washington, Govt. Print. Off., 1910.
Davis, Andrew McFarland, 1833–1920.

LAC 11541
The Sherman letters; correspondence between General and Senator Sherman from 1837 to 1891, ed. by Rachel Sherman Thorndike. With portraits. New York, C. Scribner's sons, 1894.
Sherman, William Tecumseh, 1820–1891.

LAC 12423
Sherman's march through the South. With sketches and incidents of the campaign. By Capt. David P. Conyngham. New York, Sheldon and co., 1865.
Conyngham, David Power, 1840–1883.

LAC 12698
The ship; or, Sketches of the vessels of various countries, with the manner of building and navigating them. With sixteen engravings. Boston, Carter, Hendee & co., 1834.
Taylor, Isaac, 1759–1829.

LAC 16617

Ship subsidies; an economic study of the policy of subsidizing merchant marines. Boston and New York, Houghton Mifflin and company [c1907]
Dunmore, Walter Thomas, 1877–

LAC 13724

The shipmaster's assistant, and commercial digest: containing information useful to merchants, owners, and masters of ships... [2d ed.] New York, E. & G. W. Blunt, 1837.
Blunt, Joseph, 1792–1860.

LAC 10390

Shoe and leather trade of the last hundred years. Boston, Mass., S. Bryant, 1891.
Bryant, Seth, 1800–1897.

LAC 16537

Shop management, by Frederick Winslow Taylor. With an introduction by Henry R. Towne. New York and London, Harper & brothers [c1911]
Taylor, Frederick Winslow, 1856–1915.

LAC 40068

A short account of that part of Africa, inhabited by the Negroes. With respect to the fertility of the country; the good disposition of many of the natives, and the manner by which the slave trade is carried on. Extracted from divers authors, in order to shew the iniquity of that trade, and the falsity of the arguments usually advanced in its vindication. With quotations from the writings of several persons of note, viz. George Wallis, Francis Hutcheson, and James Foster, and a large extract from a pamphlet, lately published in London, on the subject of the slave trade. 2d ed., with large additions and amendments... Philadelphia: Printed by W. Dunlap, in the year M.DCC.LXII.
Benezet, Anthony, 1713–1784.

LAC 40022

A short account of the big trees of California... Washington, Govt. print. off., 1900.
U.S. *Forest Service.*

LAC 40044

A short account of the people called Quakers; their rise, religious principles and settlement in America, mostly collected from different authors, for the information of all serious inquirers, particularly foreigners. Philadelphia: Printed by Joseph Crukshank, in Market-street, between Second and Third streets, 1780.
Benezet, Anthony, 1713–1784.

LAC 14800

A short description of the province of New Sweden. Now called, by the English, Pennsylvania, in America. Compiled from the relations and writings of persons worthy of credit, and adorned with maps and plates. By Thomas Campanius Holm. Translated from the Swedish, for the Historical society of Pennsylvania. With notes. By Peter S. Du Ponceau. [Philadelphia, M'Carty & Davis, 1834]
Holm, Thomas Campanius, *ca.* 1670–1702.

LAC 40018

A short history of American shoemaking. [Salem, Mass., Newcomb & Gauss, printers, c1912]
Gannon, Frederic Augustus, 1881–

LAC 14442

A short history of Barbados, from its first discovery and settlement to the present time. A new ed., cor. and enl. London, J. Dodsley, 1768.
Frere, George.

LAC 10037

A short history of paper money and banking in the United States, including an account of provincial and continental paper money. To which is prefixed, An inquiry into the principles of the system... Philadelphia, Printed by T. W. Ustick, 1833.
Gouge, William M   1796–1863.

LAC 16538

A short history of the American labor movement. New York, Harcourt, Brace and Howe, 1920.
Beard, Mary, 1876–1958.

LAC 10257

A short history of the Confederate States of America. New York, Bedford co., 1890.
Davis, Jefferson, 1808–1889.

LAC 11049

A short history of the Methodists, in the United States of America; beginning in 1766, and continued till 1809. To which is prefixed, a brief account of their rise in England, in the year 1729, &c. Baltimore, Printed by Magill and Clime, 1810.
Lee, Jesse, 1758–1816.

LAC 13227

A short history of the Mississippi valley. Boston and New York, Houghton, Mifflin and company, 1901.
Hosmer, James Kendall, 1834–1927.

LAC 40020

A short history of the printing press and of the improvements in printing machinery from the time of Gutenberg up to the present day. New York, R. Hoe, 1902.
Hoe, Robert, 1839–1909.

LAC 14884

A short history of the war with Spain. New York, F. A. Stokes company [c1898]
Wilcox, Marrion, 1858–1926.

LAC 16642

A short history of women's rights from the days of Augustus to the present time. With special reference to England and the United States. 2d ed. rev., with additions. New York and London, G. P. Putnam's sons, 1914.
Hecker, Eugene Arthur, 1884–

LAC 14174

Short studies in party politics. New York, C. Scribner's sons, 1895.
Brooks, Noah, 1830–1903.

LAC 40053

A short treatise on the application of steam, whereby is clearly shewn, from actual experiments, that steam may be applied to propel boats or vessels of any burthen against rapid currents with great velocity. Great velocity [!] The same principles are also introduced with effect, by a machine of simple and chep [!] construction, for the

purpose of raising water sufficient for the working of grist-mills, saw-mills, &c., and for watering meadows and other purposes of agriculture. Philadelphia, Printed by J. James, 1788.
Rumsey, James, 1743?–1792.

LAC 15964
Short-horn cattle; a series of historical sketches, memoirs and records of the breed and its development in the United States and Canada. 2d ed. Chicago, Sanders publishing co., 1909.
Sanders, Alvin Howard, 1860–

LAC 22340–41
Siberia and the exile system. New York, The Century co., 1891.
Kennan, George, 1845–1924.

LAC 14985
Sidelights on contemporary socialism. New York, B. W. Heubsch, 1911.
Spargo, John, 1876–1966.

LAC 12364
Sidney Lanier. Boston and New York, Houghton Mifflin and company, 1905.
Mims, Edwin, 1872–1959.

LAC 12414
Sieben monate in den rebellen-staaten wahrend des nordamerikanischen krieges 1863, von Scheibert. Hierzu vier gefechts und situationsplane. Stettin, T. von der Nahmer, 1868.
Scheibert, Justus, 1831–1904.

LAC 14068
The sights and secrets of the national capital: a work descriptive of Washington city in all its various phases, by Dr. John B. Ellis. New York, United States publishing company, 1869.
Ellis, John B.

LAC 10036
The significance of the frontier in American history... (From Proceedings of the forty-first annual meeting of the State historical society of Wisconsin) Madison, State historical society of Wisconsin, 1894.
Turner, Frederick Jackson, 1861–1932.

LAC 40047
Sigr. R. Abecco's sentimental songster. Eureka theatre, San Francisco. San Francisco, D. E. Appleton & co., 1864.
Abecco, Raffaell, *comp.*

LAC 16229
The silent war, by John Ames Mitchell. Illustrations by William Balfour Ker. New York, Life publishing company, 1906.
Mitchell, John Ames, 1845–1918.

LAC 11891
Silhouettes of American life, by Rebecca Harding Davis. New York, C. Scribner's sons, 1892.
Davis, Rebecca, 1831–1910.

LAC 40019
Silk culture in Louisiana and in the southern states. New Orleans, Southern knight print, 1882.
Johnson, Emma B.

LAC 10422
The silk goods of America: a brief account of the recent improvements and advances of silk manufacture in the United States. Published under the auspices of the Silk association of America. 2d ed. New York [E. O'Keefe, printer] 1880.
Wyckoff, William Cornelius, 1832–1888.

LAC 16097
Silver and gold: an account of the mining and metallurgical industry of the United States, with reference chiefly to the precious metals. New York, J. B. Ford and company, 1876, [c1873]
Raymond, Rossiter Worthington, 1840–1918.

LAC 16658
The silver country; or, The great Southwest; a review of the mineral and other wealth, the attractions and material development of the former kingdom of New Spain, comprising Mexico and the Mexican concessions to the United States in 1848 and 1853. New York, G. P. Putnam's sons, 1877.
Anderson, Alexander Dwight.

LAC 40079
The silver question, the dollar of the fathers versus the dollar of the sons; also an extract from an article in the North American review, November, 1877, on the unconstitutionality of the repeal of the obligations of the resumption act. New York, G. P. Putnam's sons, 1877.
Wells, David Ames, 1828–1898.

LAC 12547
The silver situation in the United States. New York [etc.] G. P. Putnam's sons, 1896, [c1893]
Taussig, Frank William, 1859–1940.

LAC 15293
The Silverado squatters. Boston, Roberts brothers, 1884.
Stevenson, Robert Louis, 1850–1894.

LAC 13250
Silverland. By the author of "Guy Livingstone," &c. London, Chapman and Hall, 1873.
Lawrence, George Alfred, 1827–1876.

LAC 14924
Simcoe's military journal. A history of the operations of a partisan corps, called the Queen's rangers, commanded by Lieut. Col. J. G. Simcoe, during the war of the American revolution... Now first published, with a memoir of the author and other additions. New York, Bartlett & Welford, 1844.
Simcoe, John Graves, 1752–1806.

LAC 40109
The simple cobler of Aggawam in America. Willing to help amend his native country, lamentably tattered, both in the upper-leather and sole, with all the honest stitches he can take. And as willing never to be paid for his work by old English wonted pay. It is his trade to patch all the year long, gratis. Therefore I pray gentlemen keep your purses. By Theodore de la Guard [*pseud.*] The 5th ed., with some amendments... London, Printed by J. D. & R. I. for S. Bowtell, 1647. Reprinted at Boston, for D. Henchman, 1713.
Ward, Nathaniel, 1578?–1652.

LAC 21000
Sinfulness of American slavery: proved from its evil sources: its injustice: its wrongs: its contrariety to many Scriptural commands, prohibitions, and principles, and to the Christian spirit: and from its evil effects: together with observations on emancipation, and the duties of American citizens in regard to slavery. By Rev. Charles Elliott, D. D. Ed. by Rev. B. F. Tefft. Cincinnati, L. Swormstedt & J. H. Power, 1851, [1850]
Elliott, Charles, 1792–1869.

LAC 40139
Singing of Psalmes, a gospel-ordinance; or, A treatise, wherein are handled these foure particulars. 1. Touching the duty it selfe. 2. Touching the matter to be sung. 3. Touching the singers. 4. Touching the manner of singing. London, Printed by M. S. for Hannah Allen, at the Crowne in Popes-Head-Alley: and John Rothwell at the Sunne and Fountaine in Pauls-Church-Yard, 1647.
Cotton, John, 1584–1652.

LAC 11901
Sister Carrie. New York, Doubleday, Page & co., 1900.
Dreiser, Theodore, 1871–1945.

LAC 40134
Situations: lawyers, clergy, physicians, men and women. London, J. Watson, 1839.
Owen, Robert Dale, 1801–1877.

LAC 11051
The six days of creation; or, The Scriptural cosmology, with the ancient idea of ... time-worlds, in distinction from worlds in space. Schenectady, G. Y. van Debogert; London, John Chapman, 1855.
Lewis, Tayler, 1802–1877.

LAC 14396
Six lectures on architecture, by Ralph Adams Cram, Thomas Hastings, Claude Bragdon. The Scammon lectures for 1915. Chicago, Ill., Pub. for the Art institute of Chicago by the University of Chicago press [c1917]
Cram, Ralph Adams, 1863–

LAC 40001
Six letters on the necessity and practicability of a national currency, and the principles and measures essential to it. New York, A. D. F. Randolph, 1862.
Lord, Eleazar, 1788–1871.

LAC 11414
Six months at the White House with Abraham Lincoln. The story of a picture. New York, Hurd and Houghton, 1866.
Carpenter, Francis Bicknell, 1830–1900.

LAC 14122
Six months in a convent, or, The narrative of Rebecca Theresa Reed, who was under the influence of the Roman Catholics about two years, and an inmate of the Ursuline convent on Mount Benedict, Charlestown, Mass., nearly six months, in the years 1831–2. With some preliminary suggestions by the Committee of publication. Boston, Russell, Odiorne & Metcalf; New-York, Leavitt, Lord and co.; [etc., etc.] 1835.
Reed, Rebecca Theresa, b. ca. 1813.

LAC 11324
Six months in America. Philadelphia, T. T. Ash, 1833.
Vigne, Godfrey Thomas, 1801–1863.

LAC 12179
Six months in the federal states. London and Cambridge, Macmillan and co., 1863.
Dicey, Edward, 1832–1911.

LAC 12686
Six months in the gold mines: from a journal of three years residence in upper and lower California. 1847–8–9. Philadelphia, Lea and Blanchard, 1850.
Buffum, Edward Gould, 1820–1867.

LAC 11169
Six nights with the Washingtonians; and other temperance tales. Philadelphia, T. B. Peterson & brothers [c1871]
Arthur, Timothy Shay, 1809–1885.

LAC 10721
Six sermons on the nature, occasions, signs, evils, and remedy of intemperance. 10th ed. New York, American tract society, 1843.
Beecher, Lyman, 1775–1863.

LAC 40042
1645–1656. Portsmouth records. A transcript of the first thirty five pages of the earliest town book, Portsmouth, New Hampshire. With notes by Frank W. Hackett. Portsmouth, Priv. print. [Washington, D. C., R. O. Polkinhorn, printer] 1886.
Portsmouth, *N.H.*

LAC 16697
Sixteen months at the gold diggings. New York, Harper & brothers, 1851.
Woods, Daniel B.

LAC 10610
Sixty-five years in the life of a teacher, 1841–1906. By Edward Hicks Magill, ex-president of Swarthmore college. Boston and New York, Houghton, Mifflin & company, 1907.
Magill, Edward Hicks, 1825–1907.

LAC 16228
Sixty years of the theater; an old critic's memories. New York and London, Funk & Wagnalls company, 1916.
Towse, John Ranken, 1845–1933.

LAC 40049
Sketch of Charles Pinckney's plan for a constitution, 1787. [New York? 1904]
McLaughlin, Andrew Cunningham, 1861–1947, *ed.*

LAC 15116
A sketch of Chester Harding, artist, drawn by his own hand, ed. by his daughter Margaret E. White. Boston and New York, Houghton, Mifflin and company, 1890.
Harding, Chester, 1792–1866.

LAC 16949
Sketch of the civil engineering of North America; comprising remarks on the harbours, river and lake navigation, lighthouses, steam-navigation, water-works, canals, roads, railways, bridges, and other works in that country. London, J. Weale, 1838.
Stevenson, David, 1815–1886.

LAC 16075
Sketch of the erection and formation of the state of West Virginia from the territory of Virginia. Reprinted from vol. I, West Virginia Supreme court report. [Charleston, W. Va., 1927]
Hagans, John Marshall, 1838–1900.

LAC 15216
Sketch of the evolution of our native fruits... 2d ed. New York, The Macmillan co.; London, Macmillan & co., ltd.; 1906, [c1898]
Bailey, Liberty Hyde, 1858–

LAC 40143
Sketch of the geographical rout [!] of a great railway, by which it is proposed to connect the canals and navigable waters of the states of New-York, Pennsylvania, Ohio, Indiana, Illinois. Missouri; and the Michigan, North-west, and Missouri territories; opening thereby a free communication, at all seasons of the year, between the Atlantic states and the great valley of the Mississippi. New-York, G. & C. & H. Carvill, 1829.
Redfield, William C   1789–1857.

LAC 14089
A sketch of the history of Attleborough, from its settlement to the division. By John Daggett. Ed. and completed by his daughter. Boston, Press of S. Usher, 1894.
Daggett, John, 1805–1885.

LAC 13012
A sketch of the history of Harvard college. And of its present state. Boston, C. C. Little and J. Brown, 1848.
Eliot, Samuel Atkins, 1798–1862.

LAC 11701
A sketch of the history of Newbury, Newburyport, and West Newbury, from 1635 to 1845. Boston, S. G. Drake, 1845.
Coffin, Joshua, 1792–1864.

LAC 13489
A sketch of the laws relating to slavery in the several States of the United States of America. Philadelphia, Kimber and Sharpless, 1827.
Stroud, George McDowell, 1795–1875.

LAC 15327
A sketch of the life and a list of some of the works of John Singleton Copley. [Boston] Priv. print., 1873.
Perkins, Augustus Thorndike, 1827–1891.

LAC 15172
A sketch of the life of Com. Robert F. Stockton; with an appendix, comprising his correspondence with the Navy department respecting his conquest of California; and extracts from the defence of Col. J. C. Fremont, in relation to the same subject; together with his speeches in the Senate of the United States, and his political letters. New York, Derby & Jackson, 1856.
Bayard, Samuel John, d. 1879.

LAC 40102
Sketch of the life of J. F. D. Lanier. (Printed for the use of his family only) New York, 1870.
Lanier, James Franklin Doughty, 1800–1881.

LAC 40045
Sketch of the Norse discovery of America, at the festival of the Scandinavian societies assembled May 18, 1891, in Boston, on the occasion of presenting a testimonial to Eben Norton Horsford in recognition of the finding of the landfall of Leif Erikson, the site of his Vineland home and of the ancient Norse city of Norumbega, in Massachusetts, in the 43d degree. [Boston? 1891?]
Horsford, Eben Norton, 1818–1893.

LAC 10289
A sketch of the origin and progress of steam navigation from authentic documents. London, Taylor, Walton, and Maberly, 1848.
Woodcroft, Bennet, 1803–1879.

LAC 40054
Sketch of the philosophy of American literature. Boston, Ginn and co., 1891, [c1890]
White, Greenough, 1863–1901.

LAC 10867
Sketch of the resources of the city of New-York. With a view of its municipal government, population, &c. &c. from the foundation of the city to the date of the latest statistical accounts. New-York, G. & C. Carvill, 1827.
Dix, John Adams, 1798–1879.

LAC 40137
A sketch of the 29th regiment of Connecticut colored troops, by J. [!] J. Hill, giving a full account of its formation; of all the battles through which it passed, and its final disbandment. Baltimore, Printed by Daugherty, Maguire & co., 1867.
Hill, Isaac J   1826–

LAC 11233
Sketches and reminiscences of the Radical club of Chestnut street, Boston. Ed. by Mrs. John T. Sargent. Boston, J. R. Osgood and company, 1880.
Sargent, Mary Elizabeth, 1827–1904, ed.

LAC 16310
Sketches, essays and translations. By the late Francis Walker Gilmer. Baltimore, F. Lucas, jun., 1828.
Gilmer, Francis Walker, 1790–1826.

LAC 13620
Sketches from America. Part I.–Canada. Part II.–A pic-nic to the Rocky Mountains. Part III.–The Irish in America. London, S. Low, son, and Marston, 1870.
White, John, 1839–

LAC 15446
Sketches from Roman history. [Atlanta? Ga.] The author, 1908.
Watson, Thomas Edward, 1856–1922.

LAC 13326
Sketches from "Texas siftings". By Sweet and Knox. Illustrated by W. H. Caskie. New York, Texas siftings publishing company, 1882.
Sweet, Alexander Edwin, 1841–1901.

LAC 13321
Sketches, historical and descriptive, of Louisiana. By Major Amos Stoddard. Philadelphia: Published by Mathew Carey. A. Small, printer, 1812.
Stoddard, Amos, 1762–1813.

LAC 12174
Sketches of a tour to the western country, through the states of Ohio and Kentucky; a voyage down the Ohio and Mississippi rivers, and a trip through the Mississippi territory, and part of West Florida. Commenced at Philadelphia in the winter of 1807, and concluded in 1809. With notes and an appendix, containing some interesting facts, together with a notice of an expedition through Louisiana. Pittsburgh, Printed and pub. by Cramer, Spear & Eichbaum, 1810.
Cuming, Fortescue, 1762–1828.

LAC 13611
Sketches of America. A narrative of a journey of five thousand miles through the eastern and western states of America; contained in eight reports addressed to the thirty-nine English families by whom the author was deputed, in June 1817, to ascertain whether any, and what part of the United States would be suitable for their residence. With remarks on Mr. Birkbeck's "Notes" and "Letters". 3d ed. London, Longman, Hurst, Rees, Orme, and Brown, 1819.
Fearon, Henry Bradshaw, *b. ca.* 1770.

LAC 40017
Sketches of American policy (1785) [by] Noah Webster, edited with introduction and bibliographical note by Harry R. Warfel. New York, N. Y., Scholars' facsimiles & reprints, 1937.
Webster, Noah, 1758–1843.

LAC 11313
Sketches of eighteenth century America; more "Letters from an American farmer", by St. John de Crevecoeur, edited by Henri L. Bourdin, Ralph H. Gabriel and Stanley T. Williams. New Haven, Yale university press; [etc., etc.] 1925.
Crevecoeur, Michel Guillaume St. Jean de, *called* Saint John de Crevecoeur, 1735–1813.

LAC 40130
Sketches of French and English politicks in America, in May, 1797. By a member of the old Congress. Charleston: Printed for the author, by W. P. Young, Franklin's head, no. 43, Broad-street, 1797.
Beresford, Richard, 1755–1803, *supposed author.*

LAC 10895
Sketches of Louisville and its environs; including ... a Florula louisvillensis... To which is added an appendix, containing an accurate account of the earthquakes experienced here from the 16th December, 1811, to the 7th February, 1812, extracted principally from the papers of the late J. Brookes, esq. 1st ed. Louisville [Ky.] Printed by S. Penn, jun., Main-street, 1819.
McMurtrie, Henry, 1793–1865.

LAC 16437
Sketches of Lower Canada, historical and descriptive; with the author's recollections of the soil, and aspect; the morals, habits, and religious institutions, of that isolated country; during a tour to Quebec, in the month of July, 1817. New-York: Printed for Kirk & Mercein, 1817.
Sansom, Joseph, 1765 *or* 6–1826.

LAC 10267
Sketches of North Carolina, historical and biographical, illustrative of the principles of a portion of her early settlers. By Rev. William Henry Foote. New York, R. Carter, 1846.
Foote, William Henry, 1794–1869.

LAC 12715
Sketches of printers and printing in colonial New York. With numerous illustrations. New York, Dodd, Mead & company [De Vinne press] 1895.
Hildeburn, Charles Swift Riche, 1855–1901.

LAC 13838
Sketches of reforms and reformers, of Great Britain and Ireland. New York, J. Wiley, 1849.
Stanton, Henry Brewster, 1805–1887.

LAC 14077
Sketches of Rochester.
Settlement in the West. Sketches of Rochester; with incidental notices of western New-York... Arranged by Henry O'Reilly [!] Rochester, W. Alling, 1838.
O'Rielly, Henry, 1806–1886.

LAC 12182
Sketches of scenery and manners in the United States. By the author of the "Northern traveller." New-York, A. T. Goodrich, 1829.
Dwight, Theodore, 1796–1866.

LAC 40113
Sketches of slave life: or, Illustrations of the 'peculiar institution.' By Peter Randolph, an emancipated slave. 2d ed., enl. Boston, Pub. for the author, 1855.
Randolph, Peter.

LAC 16368
Sketches of the campaign in northern Mexico. In eighteen hundred forty-six and seven. By an officer of the First regiment of Ohio volunteers. New York, For the author by G. P. Putnam & co., 1853.
Giddings, Luther.

LAC 40041
Sketches of the city of Detroit, state of Michigan, past and present. 1855. Detroit, R. F. Johnstone & co., printers, 1855.
Roberts, Robert Ellis, 1809–1888.

LAC 40033
Sketches of the early history of Amherst college, prepared by President Heman Humphrey, D. D. at the request of the trustees. [Northampton, Mass., Kingsbury box & printing co., 1905]
Humphrey, Heman, 1779–1861.

LAC 40087
Sketches of the great West. A journal of the Santa-Fe expedition, under Col. Doniphan, which left St. Louis in June 1846. Kept by Jacob S. Robinson ... a member of the expedition. [Portsmouth, N. H.] Portsmouth journal press, 1848. [Tarrytown, N. Y., Reprinted, W. Abbatt, 1927]
Robinson, Jacob S.

LAC 22210

Sketches of the history, manners, and customs of the North American Indians with a plan for their melioration. New York, W. Borradaile, 1824.
Buchanan, James, *British consul at New York.*

LAC 13830

Sketches of the judicial history of Massachusetts from 1630 to the revolution in 1775. Boston, C. C. Little and J. Brown, 1840.
Washburn, Emory, 1800–1877.

LAC 12565

Sketches of the life and character of Patrick Henry. 8th ed., corr. by the author. New York, M'Elrath & Bangs, 1835, [c1832]
Wirt, William, 1772–1834.

LAC 12837

Sketches of the life and writings of James Gillespie Birney. Utica, N. Y., Jackson & Chaplin, 1844.
Green, Beriah, 1795–1874.

LAC 14977

Sketches of the life, times, and character of the Rt. Rev. Benedict Joseph Flaget, first bishop of Louisville. Louisville, Ky., Webb & Levering, 1852.
Spalding, Martin John, *abp.*, 1810–1872.

LAC 13496

Sketches of the lives and judicial services of the chief justices of the Supreme court of the United States. New York, C. Scribner, 1854.
Van Santvoord, George, 1819–1863.

LAC 10241

Sketches of the rise, progress, and decline of secession; with a narrative of personal adventures among the rebels. Philadelphia, G. W. Childs; Cincinnati, Applegate & co., 1862.
Brownlow, William Gannaway, 1805–1877.

LAC 10674

Sketches of Turkey in 1831 and 1832. By an American. New-York, J. & J. Harper, 1833.
De Kay, James Ellsworth, 1792–1851.

LAC 13082

Sketches of western Methodism: biographical, historical, and miscellaneous. Illustrative of pioneer life. By Rev. James B. Finley. Edited by W. P. Strickland, D. D. Cincinnati, Printed at the Methodist book concern, for the author, 1854.
Finley, James Bradley, 1781–1856.

LAC 16185

The Slav invasion and the mine workers; a study in immigration. Philadelphia and London, J. B. Lippincott company, 1904.
Warne, Frank Julian, 1874–

LAC 40132

The slave-auction. By Dr. John Theophilus Kramer, late of New Orleans, La. Boston, R. F. Wallcut, 1859.
Kramer, John Theophilus.

LAC 15837

Slave life in Georgia: a narrative of the life, sufferings, and escape of John Brown, a fugitive slave, now in England. Ed. by L. A. Chamerovzow. London [W. M. Watts] 1855.
Brown, John, *fl.* 1854.

LAC 12850

The slave: or, Memoirs of Archy Moore, [*pseud.*] 2d ed. Boston, Whipple and Damrell, 1840.
Hildreth, Richard, 1807–1865.

LAC 12799

The slave power: its character, career, and probable designs, being an attempt to explain the real issues involved in the American contest. [American ed.] New York, Carleton; [etc., etc.] 1862.
Cairnes, John Elliott, 1823–1875.

LAC 12778

Slave songs of the United States. New York, J. Ross & co. (Nation Press), 1871.
Allen, William Francis, 1830–1889, *comp.*

LAC 20965–66

The slave states of America. London, Paris, Fisher, son & co. [1842]
Buckingham, James Silk, 1786–1855.

LAC 12802

The slave trade, domestic and foreign: why it exists, and how it may be extinguished. Philadelphia, H. C. Baird, 1867.
Carey, Henry Charles, 1793–1879.

LAC 12805

Slavery. 4th ed. rev. Boston, J. Munroe and company, 1836, [c1835]
Channing, William Ellery, 1780–1842.

LAC 40111

Slavery and abolitionism, as viewed by a Georgia slave. By Harrison Berry, the property of S. W. Price. Covington, Georgia. Atlanta, Franklin printing house, Wood, Hanleiter, Rice & co., 1861. [Philadelphia, Rhistoric Publications, c1969]
Berry, Harrison, *b.* 1816.

LAC 12833

Slavery and anti-slavery; a history of the great struggle in both hemispheres; with a view of the slavery question in the United States. New-York, W. Goodell, 1853, [c1852]
Goodell, William, 1792–1878.

LAC 12854

Slavery and the church. Auburn [N.Y.] W. J. Moses, 1853.
Hosmer, William.

LAC 12787

Slavery and the domestic slave-trade in the United States. In a series of letters addressed to the Executive committee of the American union for the relief and improvement of the colored race. Boston, Light & Stearns, 1836.
Andrews, Ethan Allen, 1787–1858.

LAC 40068
Slavery and the domestic slave trade, in the United States. By the committee appointed by the late Yearly meeting of Friends held in Philadelphia, in 1839. Philadelphia, Printed by Merrihew and Thompson, 1841.
Friends, Society of. *Philadelphia Yearly Meeting.*

LAC 16497
Slavery and the internal slave trade in the United States. New York, Arno Press, 1969.
Weld, Theodore Dwight, 1803–1895.

LAC 16893
Slavery and the slave trade in Africa. New York, Harper & brothers, 1893.
Stanley, *Sir* Henry Morton, 1841–1904.

LAC 16628
Slavery as an industrial system; ethnological researchers. 2d, rev. ed. The Hague, M. Nijhoff, 1910.
Nieboer, Herman Jeremias.

LAC 13509
Slavery discussed in occasional essays, from 1833 to 1846. New York, Baker and Scribner, 1846.
Bacon, Leonard, 1802–1881.

LAC 12822
Slavery doomed: or, The contest between free and slave labour in the United States. London, Smith, Elder and co., 1860.
Edge, Frederick Milnes.

LAC 40103
Slavery in New York, a historical sketch; by ex-Judge A. Judd Northrup. [Albany, University of the state of New York, 1900]
Northrup, Ansel Judd, 1833–1919.

LAC 12829
Slavery in South Carolina and the ex-slaves; or, The Port Royal mission. New York, W. M. French, 1862.
French, Austa Malinda, 1810–1880.

LAC 14385
Slavery in the District of Columbia; the policy of Congress and the struggle for abolition. New York [etc.] G. P. Putnam's sons, 1892.
Tremain, Mary.

LAC 12869
Slavery in the United States. New-York, Harper & brothers, 1836.
Paulding, James Kirke, 1778–1860.

LAC 40076
Slavery in the United States. A sermon delivered in Amory hall, on Thanksgiving day, November 24, 1842. (Printed by friends for gratuitous distribution.) Boston, B. H. Greene, 1843.
Clarke, James Freeman, 1810–1888.

LAC 40133
Slavery inconsistent with justice and good policy; proved by a speech delivered in the convention, held at Danville, Kentucky. New York, Printed by Isaac Collins and son, 1804.
Rice, David, 1733–1816.

LAC 40076
Slavery: its origin, nature, and history, considered in the light of Bible teachings, moral justice, and political wisdom... By Rev. Thornton Stringfellow, D. D., of Culpeper county, Virginia. New York, J. F. Trow, printer, 1861.
Stringfellow, Thornton.

LAC 40138
Slavery justified; by a southerner... Fredericksburg, Va., Recorder printing office, 1850.
Fitzhugh, George, 1806–1881.

LAC 12884
Slavery ordained of God... By Rev. Fred A. Ross. Philadelphia, J. B. Lippincott & co., 1857.
Ross, Frederick Augustus, 1796–1883.

LAC 16865
Slavery unmasked; being a truthful narrative of a three years' residence and journeying in eleven Southern States; to which is added the invasion of Kansas, including the last chapter of her wrongs. New York, Negro Universities Press [1969]
Tower, Philo.

LAC 14389
Sloan's homestead architecture, containing forty designs for villas, cottages, and farm houses, with essays on style, construction, landscape gardening, furniture, etc., etc. Illustrated with upwards of 200 engravings. Philadelphia, J. B. Lippincott & co., 1861.
Sloan, Samuel, 1815–1884.

LAC 10914
The slums of Baltimore, Chicago, New York, and Philadelphia. Prepared in compliance with a joint resolution of the Congress of the United States, approved July 20, 1892. By Carroll D. Wright, commissioner of labor. Washington, Govt. print. off., 1894.
U.S. *Bureau of Labor.*

LAC 20920–22
The Smithsonian Institution: documents relative to its origin and history. 1835–1899. Comp. and ed. by William Jones Rhees. Washington, Gov't. print. off., 1901.
Smithsonian Institution.

LAC 12640
The Smithsonian institution, 1846–1896. The history of its first half century. Ed. by George Brown Goode. Washington, 1897.
Smithsonian Institution.

LAC 10031
Social and industrial conditions in the North during the civil war. New York, The Macmillan company, 1910.
Fite, Emerson David, 1874–1953.

LAC 13659
Social and mental traits of the Negro; research into the conditions of the Negro race in southern towns, a study in race traits, tendencies and prospects. New York, Columbia university; [etc., etc.] 1910.
Odum, Howard Washington, 1884–1954.

LAC 14362

Social aspects of Christianity, and other essays. New and enl. ed. New York, T. Y. Crowell & company [c1889]
Ely, Richard Theodore, 1854–1943.

LAC 11080

The social basis of religion. New York, The Macmillan company, 1911.
Patten, Simon Nelson, 1852–1922.

LAC 11043

Social consciousness.
Theology and the social consciousness; a study of the relations of the social consciousness to theology. New York, The Macmillan company; London, Macmillan & co., ltd., 1902.
King, Henry Churchill, 1858–1934.

LAC 13102

Social destiny of man; or, Association and reorganization of industry... Philadelphia, C. F. Stollmeyer, 1840.
Brisbane, Albert, 1809–1890.

LAC 13803

Social engineering; a record of things done by American industrialists employing upwards of one and one half million of people, by William H. Tolman. With an introduction by Andrew Carnegie. New York, McGraw Publishing company, 1909.
Tolman, William Howe, 1861–

LAC 10729

The social evil, with special reference to conditions existing in the city of New York, a report prepared under the direction of the Committee of fifteen. New York and London, G. P. Putnam's sons, 1902.
New York. *(City) Committee of Fifteen*, 1900.

LAC 11585

Social evolution. New ed. with a new preface. New York and London, Macmillan and co., 1895, [c1894]
Kidd, Benjamin, 1858–1916.

LAC 10528

Social evolution and political theory. New York, The Columbia university press, 1911.
Hobhouse, Leonard Trelawney, 1864–1929.

LAC 15919

The social gospel. Philadelphia, Boston [etc.] The Griffith & Rowland press [c1910]
Mathews, Shailer, 1863–1941.

LAC 40144

The social influence of Christianity.
A discourse on the social influence of Christianity, delivered at Providence, R. I., Sept. 1838, at the instance of the Phi beta kappa society of Brown university. Andover, Printed by Gould and Newman, 1839.
Cushing, Caleb, 1800–1879.

LAC 13651

Social insurance, a program of social reform. The Kennedy lectures for 1910, in the School of philanthropy, conducted by the Charity organization society of the city of New York. New York, The Macmillan company, 1910.
Seager, Henry Rogers, 1870–1930.

LAC 16536

Social insurance, with special reference to American conditions. New York, H. Holt and company, 1913.
Rubinow, Isaac Max, 1875–1936.

LAC 11312

Social life in old New England. Boston, Little, Brown, and company, 1915, [c1914]
Crawford, Mary Caroline, 1874–1930.

LAC 14372

Social life of Virginia in the seventeenth century. An inquiry into the origin of the higher planter class, together with a description of the habits, customs, and diversions of the people. 2d ed. rev. and enl. Lynchburg, Va., J. P. Bell, 1927, [c1907]
Bruce, Philip Alexander, 1856–1933.

LAC 16779

The social message of the modern pulpit. New York, C. Scribner's sons, 1906.
Brown, Charles Reynolds, 1862–1950.

LAC 13527

Social New York under the Georges, 1714–1776; houses, streets and country homes, with chapters on fashions, furniture, china, plate, and manners. New York, D. Appleton and company, 1902.
Singleton, Esther, *d.* 1930.

LAC 40073

The social pioneer, and herald of progress. Published under the superintendence of the society. Boston, J. P. Mendum [1844]
New England Social Reform Society.

LAC 13834

The social problem at the Chicago stock yards... Chicago, The University of Chicago press, 1902.
Bushnell, Charles Joseph, 1875–

LAC 20413–14

Social progress; a year book and encyclopedia of economic, industrial, social and religious statistics. 1904–06... New York, The Baker and Taylor co. [c1904–06]

LAC 10731

Social reform and the church, by John R. Commons. With an introduction by Prof. Richard T. Ely. New York, T. Y. Crowell & company [1894]
Commons, John Rogers, 1862–1945.

LAC 11099

Social regeneration the work of Christianity, by the Rev. W. N. Sloan, PH. D. Philadelphia, The Westminster press, 1902.
Sloan, William Niccolls, 1849–

LAC 12342

Social relations in our southern states. New-York, H. B. Price, 1860.
Hundley, Daniel Robinson, 1832–1899.

LAC 11073
Social religion; an interpretation of Christianity in terms of modern life. From an address delivered before the Friends' general conference, Ocean Grove, New Jersey, July 7, 1910. New York, The Macmillan company, 1913.
Nearing, Scott, 1883–

LAC 10775
Social salvation. Boston and New York, Houghton, Mifflin and company, 1902.
Gladden, Washington, 1836–1918.

LAC 11200
Social settlements. New York, Lentilhon & company [c1899]
Henderson, Charles Richmond, 1848–1915.

LAC 40134
The social significance of our institutions: an oration delivered by request of the citizens at Newport, R. I., July 4th, 1861. Boston, Ticknor and Fields, 1861.
James, Henry, 1811–1882.

LAC 11201
The social spirit in America. [2d ed.] Chicago, Scott, Foresman and company, 1907, [c1901]
Henderson, Charles Richmond, 1848–1915.

LAC 11835
Social strugglers; a novel. New York, C. Scribner's sons, 1893.
Boyesen, Hjalmar Hjorth, 1848–1895.

LAC 11219
Social studies. New York & London, G. P. Putnam's sons, 1887.
Newton, Richard Heber, 1840–1914.

LAC 40134
The social survey... New York, The Russell Sage foundation library [1913]
Potter, Zenas L

LAC 40134
The social survey. Papers by Paul U. Kellogg, Shelby M. Harrison [and] George T. Palmer. Reprinted from the proceedings of the Academy of Political Science, volume 11. No. 4. July, 1912. 2d ed. New York [n.d.]
Russell Sage Foundation, *New York. Dept. of Surveys and Exhibits.*

LAC 40081
The social system. An address pronounced before the House of convocation, of Trinity college, Hartford, August 2, 1848. By Daniel D. Barnard, LL. D. Pub. at the request of Convocation. Hartford, S. Hanmer, jr., 1848.
Barnard, Daniel Dewey, 1797–1861.

LAC 13785
Social theory. A grouping of social facts and principles. New York, Boston, T. Y. Crowell & company [c1895]
Bascom, John, 1827–1911.

LAC 11263
The social unrest; studies in labor and socialist movements. New York, The Macmillan company; [etc., etc.] 1903.
Brooks, John Graham, 1846–1938.

LAC 15190
Socialism; an examination of its nature, its strength and its weakness, with suggestions for social reform. New York, T. Y. Crowell & co. [c1894]
Ely, Richard Theodore, 1854–1943.

LAC 10940
Socialism and Christianity; New York, Baker & Taylor [c1886]
Behrends, Adolphus Julius Frederick, 1839–1900.

LAC 14000
Socialism and success; some uninvited messages. New York, John Lane company, 1910.
Ghent, William James, 1866–1942.

LAC 13951
Socialism and the American spirit. Boston and New York, Houghton, Mifflin and company, 1893.
Gilman, Nicholas Paine, 1849–1912.

LAC 11128
Socialism and the ethics of Jesus. New York, The Macmillan company, 1912.
Vedder, Henry Clay, 1853–1935.

LAC 40073
Socialism and the intellectuals. Brooklyn, New York labor news, 1967.
Lafargue, Paul, 1842–1911.

LAC 40006
Socialism and the labor problem; a plea for social democracy. Terre Haute, Ind., Debs Publishing co., 1901, [c1900]
McGrady, Thomas, 1863–

LAC 40152
Socialism and the worker. [London] Modern Press, 1884.
Sorge, Frederich Adolf, 1828–1906.

LAC 14047
Socialism as an incubus on the American labor movement, by J. W. Sullivan and Hayes Robbins. New York, B. H. Tyrrel, print, 1918.
Sullivan, James William, 1848–

LAC 10566
Socialism as it is; a survey of the world-wide revolutionary movement. New York, The Macmillan company, 1912.
Walling, William English, 1877–1936.

LAC 13956
Socialism in German American literature. Philadelphia, Americana germanica press, 1917.
Kamman, William Frederic, 1885–

LAC 13470
Socialism in theory and practice. New York, The Macmillan company, 1909.
Hillquit, Morris, 1869–1933.

LAC 14280
Socialism inevitable (Wilshire editorials) New York, Wilshire book company [c1907]
Wilshire, Henry Gaylord, 1861–

LAC 13984
Socialism or empire, a danger. [Omaha, Klopp & Bartlett company, c1906]
Browne, Edward Frederick, 1843–

LAC 14108
Socialism: positive and negative. Chicago, C. H. Kerr & company, 1907.
La Monte, Robert Rives.

LAC 15455
Socialism; promise or menace? By Morris Hillquit and John A. Ryan. New York, The Macmillan company, 1914.
Hillquit, Morris, 1869–1933.

LAC 13739
Socialism summed up. New York, The H. K. Fly company [c1913]
Hillquit, Morris, 1869–1933.

LAC 15785
Socialism versus Christianity. New York, Cochrane publishing co., 1909.
Hartman, Edward Randolph, 1878–

LAC 10505
Socialism, with preludes on current events. Boston, Houghton, Mifflin and company, 1880.
Cook, Joseph, 1838–1901.

LAC 40006
Socialist versus ultramontane economics and politics.
Abolition of poverty; socialist versus ultramontane economics and politics. New York city, New York labor news co. [1911?]
DeLeon, Daniel, 1852–1914.

LAC 15671
Socialistic, communistic, mutualistic, and financial fragments. Boston, Lee and Shepard; New York, Lee, Shepard, and Dillingham, 1875.
Greene, William Batchelder, 1819–1878.

LAC 15024
The socialized church; addresses before the first national conference of the social workers of Methodism, St. Louis, November 17–19, 1908; ed. by the secretary, Worth M. Tippy, D. D., for the Methodist federation for social service. New York, Eaton & Mains; Cincinnati, Jennings & Graham [c1909]
Tippy, Worth Marion, 1867–   *ed.*

LAC 12210
Society as I have found it. New York, Cassell publishing company [c1890]
McAllister, Ward, 1827–1895.

LAC 40017
A society for the special study of political economy, the philosophy of history, and the science of government, proposed by a citizen of Boston. Boston, Printed by A. Mudge & son, 1857.
Foster, William, 1772–1863.

LAC 20695
Society in America. New York, Saunders and Otley, 1837.
Martineau, Harriet, 1802–1876.

LAC 12166
Society, manners and politics in the United States. being a series of letters on North America. By Michael Chevalier. Tr. from the 3d Paris ed., by Thomas Gamaliel Bradford. Boston, Weeks, Jordan and company, 1839.
Chevalier, Michel, 1806–1879.

LAC 23207
The Society of Friends in the nineteenth century: a historical view of the successive convulsions and schisms therein during that period. Philadelphia, For sale by Smith, English & co., and by the author, 1875–76.
Hodgson, William.

LAC 10494
Sociology. New York & London, G. P. Putnam's sons [c1887]
Bascom, John, 1827–1911.

LAC 11209
Sociology, Experimental.
Experimental sociology. Descriptive and analytical. Delinquents. New York, The Macmillan company; London, Macmillan & co., ltd., 1901.
Kellor, Frances Alice, 1873–1952.

LAC 11185
Sociology for the South; or, The failure of free society. Richmond, Va., A. Morris, 1854.
Fitzhugh, George, 1806–1881.

LAC 11285
The sociology of a New York city block. New York, The Columbia university press, The Macmillan company, agents; [etc., etc.] 1904.
Jones, Thomas Jesse, 1873–

LAC 12422
Sociology; or, The reconstruction of society, government, and property, upon the principles of the equality, the perpetuity, and the individuality of the private ownership of life, person, government, homestead and the whole product of labor, by organizing all nations into townships of self-governed homestead democracies—self-employed in farming and mechanism, giving all the liberty and happiness to be found on earth. New York, The author, 1877.
Masquerier, Lewis, *b.* 1802.

LAC 10437
Sociology, The principles of.
The principles of sociology. An analysis of the phenomena of association and of social organization. [3d ed.] New York, The Macmillan company; London, Macmillan & co., ltd., 1921, [c1896]
Giddings, Franklin Henry, 1855–1931.

LAC 14733
Soil exhaustion as a factor in the agricultural history of Virginia and Maryland, 1606–1860. Urbana, The University of Illinois [c1926]
Craven, Avery Odelle, 1886–

LAC 11775
The soil, its nature, relations, and fundamental principles of management. New York and London, Macmillan and co., 1895.
King, Franklin Hiram, 1848–1911.

LAC 40080
Soldier and pioneer; a biographical sketch of Lt.-Col. Richard C. Anderson of the Continental army. New York, G. P. Putnam's sons, 1879.
Anderson, Edward Lowell, 1842–

LAC 11892
Soldiers of fortune, by Richard Harding Davis; with illustrations by C. D. Gibson. New York, C. Scribner's sons 1897.
Davis, Richard Harding, 1864–1916.

LAC 14774
Soldiers of the cross. Notes on the ecclesiastical history of New-Mexico, Arizona and Colorado, by Most Rev.J. B. Salpointe. Banning, Cal., St. Boniface's industrial school, 1898.
Salpointe, Jean Baptiste, *abp.* 1825–1898.

LAC 14907
A soldier's reminiscenses in peace and war. By Brig.-Gen. R. W. Johnson. Philadelphia, Press of J. B. Lippincott, company, 1886.
Johnson, Richard W   1827–1897.

LAC 40028
A solemn review of the custom of war; showing that war is the effect of popular delusion, and proposing a remedy. By Philo Pacificus [*pseud.*] 5th ed. Cambridge [Mass.] Printed by Hilliard and Metcalf, 1816.
Worcester, Noah, 1758–1837.

LAC 23490–91
Solon Robinson, pioneer and agriculturist; selected writings, edited by Herbert Anthony Kellar. Indianapolis, Indiana historical bureau, 1936.
Robinson, Solon, 1803–1880.

LAC 15626
Some account of the bills of credit or paper money of Rhode Island, from the first issue in 1710, to the final issue, 1786, by Elisha R. Potter and Sidney S. Rider. With twenty illustrations. Providence, S. S. Rider, 1880.
Potter, Elisha Reynolds, 1811–1882.

LAC 13869
Some account of the conduct of the Religious society of Friends towards the Indian tribes in the settlement of the colonies of East and West Jersey and Pennsylvania: with a brief narrative of their labours for the civilization and Christian instruction of the Indians, from the time of their settlement in America, to the year 1843. Published by the Aborigines' committee of the Meeting for sufferings. London, E. Marsh, 1844.
Friends, Society of. *London Yearly Meeting. Meeting for Sufferings. Aborigines' Committee.*

LAC 10812
Some account of the life and services of William Blount, an officer of the revolutionary army, member of the Continental congress, and of the convention which framed the Constitution of the United States, also governor of the territory south of the Ohio river, and senator in Congress U.S. 1783–1797. Together with a full account of his impeachment and trial in Congress, and his expulsion from the U.S. Senate. Washington, E. J. Gray [c1884]
Wright, Marcus Joseph, 1831–1922.

LAC 13597
Some account of the life, writings, and speeches of William Pinkney. By Henry Wheaton. New-York, E. Bliss & E. White, 1826.
Pinkney, William, 1764–1822.

LAC 16211
Some account of the Pennsylvania hospital; from its first rise to the beginning of the fifth month, called May, 1754. Philadelphia, Printed at the office of the United States' gazette, 1817.
Franklin, Benjamin, 1706–1790.

LAC 11968
Some adventures of Captain Simon Suggs, late of the Tallapoosa volunteers; together with "Taking the census," and other Alabama sketches. By a country editor. With a portrait from life, and other illustrations, by Darley. Philadelphia, Carey and Hart, 1846.
Hooper, Johnson Jones, 1815?–1863.

LAC 40141
Some aspects of the immigration problem. [Ithaca, N. Y., American economic association, 1914]
Kohler, Max James, 1871–1934.

LAC 13291
Some aspects of the religious life of New England with special reference to Congregationalists; lectures delivered on the Carew foundation before Hartford theological seminary in 1896. New York, Silver, Burdett, 1897.
Walker, George Leon, 1830–1900.

LAC 40064
Some Civil War documents, A. D. 1862–1864. Philadelphia, The Society, 1903.
American Catholic Historical Society of Philadelphia.

LAC 22264–65
Some colonial mansions and those who lived in them, with genealogies of the various families mentioned. Edited by Thomas Allen Glenn. Philadelphia, H. T. Coates, 1898–99.
Glenn, Thomas Allen, 1864–   *ed.*

LAC 40067
Some consequences of the last treaty of Paris; advances in international law and changes in national policy. London and New York, J. Lane, 1899.
Reid, Whitelaw, 1837–1912.

LAC 14339
Some correspondence between the governors and treasurers of the New England company in London and the commissioners of the United Colonies in America, the missionaries of the Company and others, between the years 1657 and 1712. To which are added the journals of

the Rev. **Experience Mayhew in 1713 and 1714.** London, Printed from the originals in the possession of the New England company by Spottiswoode & co., 1896.
Company for Propagation of the Gospel in New England and the Parts Adjacent in America.

LAC 40087
Some cursory remarks made by James Birket in his voyage to North America, 1750–1751. New Haven, Yale university press; [etc., etc.] 1916.
Birket, James.

LAC 40082
Some early writings of Jonathan Edwards, A. D. 1714–1726. [Worcester, Mass., American antiquarian society, 1896]
Smyth, Egbert Coffin, 1829–1904.

LAC 14161
Some eighteenth century tracts concerning North Carolina, with introductions and notes by William K. Boyd. Raleigh, Edwards & Broughton company, 1927.
Boyd, William Kenneth, 1879–1938, *ed.*

LAC 13973
Some ethical gains through legislation. New York, The Macmillan company; London, Macmillan & co., ltd., 1905.
Kelley, Florence, 1859–1932.

LAC 16776
Some historical account of Guinea, its situation, produce, and the general disposition of its inhabitants. With an inquiry into the rise and progress of the slave trade, its nature and lamentable effects... A new edition. London, printed and sold by J. Phillips, 1788.
Benezet, Anthony, 1713–1784.

LAC 11427
Some information respecting America collected by Thomas Cooper. The 2d ed. London, Printed for J. Johnson, 1795.
Cooper, Thomas, 1759–1839.

LAC 16487
Some interesting papers of John McDonogh, chiefly concerning the Louisiana purchase and the Liberian colonization, ed. by James T. Edwards. McDonogh, Md., Printed by boys of McDonogh School, 1898.
McDonogh, John, 1779–1850.

LAC 40005
Some letters of Edgar Allan Poe to E. H. N. Patterson of Oquawka, Illinois, with comments by Eugene Field...
Chicago, The Caxton club, 1898.
Poe, Edgar Allan, 1809–1849.

LAC 12031
Some letters of William Vaughn Moody; ed., with an introduction by Daniel Gregory Mason. Boston and New York, Houghton Mifflin company, 1913.
Moody, William Vaughn, 1869–1910.

LAC 12120
Some old Puritan love-letters—John and Margaret Winthrop—1618–1638; ed. by Joseph Hopkins Twichell.
New York, Dodd, Mead and company, 1893.
Winthrop, John, 1588–1649.

LAC 40027
Some phases of sexual morality & church discipline in colonial New England. Boston, Massachusetts historical society, 1891.
Adams, Charles Francis, 1835–1915.

LAC 20231
Some political writings of James Otis, collected with an introduction by Charles F. Mullett. Columbia, The University of Missouri, 1929.
Otis, James, 1725–1783.

LAC 40052
Some reasons for Chinese exclusion; meat vs. rice. American manhood against Asiatic coolieism; which shall survive? Washington, American federation of labor [1901?]
American Federation of Labor.

LAC 40011
Some reasons for the immediate establishment of a national system of education for the United States. 2d ed. Boston, Press of J. Wilson and son, 1869.
Brooks, Charles, 1795–1872.

LAC 40119
Some reasons why the American republic may endure.
New York, Forum pub. co., 1894.
Eliot, Charles William, 1834–1926.

LAC 10469
Some recollections by Captain Charles P. Low, commanding the clipper ships "Houqua," "Jacob Bell," "Samuel Russell," and "N. B. Palmer," in the China trade, 1847–1873... Boston, Geo. H. Ellis co., 1906, [c1905]
Low, Charles Porter, 1824–

LAC 16904
Some recollections of a western ranchman; New Mexico, 1883–1899. New York, Frederick A. Stokes company [1928]
French, William, 1854–1928.

LAC 12503
Some recollections of our antislavery conflict. Boston, Fields, Osgood, & co., 1869.
May, Samuel Joseph, 1797–1871.

LAC 40091
Some remarks on the internal improvement system of the South. Philadelphia, 1839.
Trautwine, John Cresson, 1810–1883.

LAC 14431
Some reminiscences. New York and Washington, The Neale publishing company, 1909.
Royall, William Lawrence, 1844–

LAC 40125
Some thoughts on the method of improving and securing the advantages which accrue to Great-Britain from the northern colonies. London, Printed for J. Wilkie, 1765.
Mauduit, Israel, 1708–1787.

LAC 40056
Some thoughts on the present dispute between Great Britain and America. Philadelphia: Printed for the author, and for sale by the principal booksellers, 1807.
Fessenden, Thomas Green, 1771–1837.

LAC 40014
Some types of modern educational theory, by Ella Flagg Young. Chicago, The University of Chicago press, 1902.
Young, Ella, 1845–1918.

LAC 15153
Something of men I have known, with some papers of a general nature, political, historical, and retrospective. Chicago, A. C. McClurg & co., 1909.
Stevenson, Adlai Ewing, 1835–1914.

LAC 16585
The son of Royal Langbrith, a novel. New York and London, Harper & brothers, 1904.
Howells, William Dean, 1837–1920.

LAC 15485
A son of the forest. The experience of William Apes, a native of the forest. Written by himself. 2d ed., rev. and cor. New-York, The author, 1831.
Apes, William, *b.* 1798.

LAC 11349
Songs and ballads of the American revolution. With notes and illustrations by Frank Moore. New York [etc.] D. Appleton & company, 1856.
Moore, Frank, 1828–1904, *ed.*

LAC 40089
Songs and dances of the Kwakiutl; on certain songs and dances of the Kwakiutl of British Columbia. Boston, Published for the American Folk-Lore society by Houghton, Mifflin, 1888. Reprinted with permission of the society by Kraus Reprint Corporation, New York, 1963.
Boas, Franz, 1858–1941.

LAC 10637
Songs and song writers. New York, C. Scribner's sons, 1900.
Finck, Henry Theophilus, 1854–1926.

LAC 40004
Songs for the grange. Dedicated to the order of Patrons of husbandry in the United States. Washington, D. C., Gibson brothers, printers, 1872.
Hall, Caroline Arabella, *b.* 1838.

LAC 11346
Songs for the great campaign of 1860; comprising a choice collection of original and selected solos, glees, choruses, &c., &c., from the best authors. Words and music. Edited by G. W. Civis. New York, Tribune office, 1860.
Civis, George W   *ed.*

LAC 11344
Songs for the new age. New York, The Century co., 1914.
Oppenheim, James, 1882–1932.

LAC 10526
Songs from the ghetto, [by] Morris Rosenfeld, with prose translation, glossary, and introduction, by Leo Wiener. New & enl. ed. Boston, Small, Maynard and company, 1900.
Rosenfeld, Morris, 1862–1923.

LAC 40015
Songs from Vagabondia [by] Bliss Carman [and] Richard Hovey; designs by Tom B. Meteyard. Boston, Copeland and Day; London, E. Mathews and John Lane, 1894.
Carman, Bliss, 1861–1929.

LAC 11345
Songs of the free, and hymns of Christian freedom... Boston, I. Knapp, 1836.
Chapman, Maria, 1806–1885, *comp.*

LAC 11350
Songs of the soldiers, arranged and ed. by Frank Moore. New York, G. P. Putnam, 1864.
Moore, Frank, 1828–1904, *ed.*

LAC 15918
Sonnets and other verses. New York, Duffield, 1906.
Santayana, George, 1863–1952.

LAC 15742
Sons of Italy; a social and religious study of the Italians in America. New York, Missionary education movement of the United States and Canada, 1917.
Mangano, Antonio, 1869–

LAC 13416
The Sons of liberty in New York. A paper read before the New York historical society, May 3, 1859. [Poughkeepsie, Platt & Schram, printers] 1859.
Dawson, Henry Barton, 1821–1889.

LAC 22259
The Sons of temperance offering: for 1850–51... Ed. by T. S. Arthur. New York, Nafis & Cornish [c1849–50]

LAC 14105
The sons of the sires; a history of the rise, progress, and destiny of the American party, and its probable influence on the next presidential election. To which is added a review of the letter of the Hon. Henry A. Wise, against the Know-nothings. By an American. Philadelphia, Lippincott, Grambo & co., 1855

LAC 10124
Sorgho and imphee, the Chinese and African sugar canes. A treatise upon their origin, varieties and culture; their value as a forage crop; and the manufacture of sugar... New York, A. O. Moore, 1858.
Olcott, Henry Steel, 1832–1907.

LAC 10110
Sorgo, or The northern sugar plant, by Isaac A. Hedges. With an introduction by William Clough. Sorgo culture. Cincinnati, Applegate & co., 1863.
Hedges, Isaac A.

LAC 40147

The sot-weed factor: or, A voyage to Maryland. A satyr. In which is describ'd the laws, government, courts and constitutions of the country; and also the buildings, feasts, frolicks, entertainments and drunken humours of the inhabitants of that part of America. In burlesque verse. By Eben. Cook, gent. London, Printed and sold by B. Bragg, 1708.
Cook, Ebenezer, *fl.* 1708–1732.

LAC 10972

The soul of America; a constructive essay in the sociology of religion. New York, The Macmillan company, 1914.
Coit, Stanton, 1857–

LAC 14991

The soul of an immigrant. New York, The Macmillan company, 1921.
Panunzio, Constantine Maria, 1884–

LAC 14531

The souls of black folk; essays and sketches. by W. E. Burghardt Du Bois. Chicago, A. C. McClurg & co., 1903.
Du Bois, William Edward Burghardt, 1868–1963.

LAC 40028

The sources of military delusion, and the practicability of their removal. An address before the Connecticut peace society; delivered at their second anniversary ... May 5, 1833 ... in ... Hartford. By Rev. Laurens P. Hickok. Hartford, Printed by P. Canfield, 1833.
Hickok, Laurens Perseus, 1798–1888.

LAC 13487

Sources of the Constitution of the United States, considered in relation to colonial and English history. New York and London, Macmillan and co., 1894.
Stevens, Charles Ellis, 1853–1906.

LAC 15187

The South: a tour of its battlefields and ruined cities, a journey through the desolated states, and talks with the people: being a description of the present state of the country—its agriculture—railroads—business and finances... Hartford, Conn., L. Stebbins, 1866.
Trowbridge, John Townsend, 1827–1916.

LAC 40111

The South alone, should govern the South. And African slavery should be controlled by those only, who are friendly to it. [Charleston? S. C., 1860]
Townsend, John.

LAC 15840

The South and its people.
My southern home; or, The South and its people. Upper Saddle River, N. J., Gregg Press [1968]
Brown, William Wells, 1815–1884.

LAC 10263

The South and its people. Richmond, Va., P. Keenan, printer, 1890.
Falkiner, William Robbins.

LAC 10227

South and North; or, Impressions received during a trip to Cuba and the South. New York, Abbey & Abbot, 1860.
Abbott, John Stevens Cabot, 1805–1877.

LAC 12958

The South as it is, or Twenty-one years' experience in the southern states of America. By the Rev. T. D. Ozanne, M. A. London, Saunders, Otley, and co., 1863.
Ozanne, T   D.

LAC 12386

South Carolina as a royal province, 1719–1776. New York, The Macmillan company; London, Macmillan & co., ltd., 1903.
Smith, William Roy, 1876–1938.

LAC 40133

A South Carolina protest against slavery: being a letter from Henry Laurens, second president of the Continental Congress, to his son, Colonel John Laurens; dated Charleston, S. C., August 14th, 1776. Now first published from the original. New York, G. P. Putnam, 1861.
Laurens, Henry, 1724–1792.

LAC 12388

South Carolina. Resources and population. Institutions and industries. Published by the State board of agriculture of South Carolina. Governor Hugh S. Thompson, chairman. A. P. Butler, commissioner. Charleston, S. C., Walker, Evans & Cogswell, printers, 1883.
South Carolina. *Dept. of Agriculture (1880–1890)*

LAC 40152

The south: her peril, and her duty. A discourse delivered in the First Presbyterian church, New Orleans, on Thursday, November 29, 1860. New Orleans, Printed at the office of the true witness and sentinel, 1860.
Palmer, Benjamin Morgan, 1818–1902.

LAC 16305

The South: its industrial, financial, and political condition. Philadelphia, J. B. Lippincott company, 1886.
McClure, Alexander Kelly, 1828–1909.

LAC 10232

The South since the war, as shown by fourteen weeks of travel and observation in Georgia and the Carolinas. Boston, Ticknor and Fields, 1866.
Andrews, Sidney, 1837–1880.

LAC 15020

South songs: from the lays of later days. Collected and edited by T. C. De Leon. New-York, Blelock & co., 1866.
De Leon, Thomas Cooper, 1839–1914, *comp.*

LAC 15862

The South vindicated; being a series of letters written for the American press during the canvass for the presidency in 1860, with a letter to Lord Brougham on the John Brown raid, and a survey of the result of the presidential contest, and its consequences, by the Hon. James Williams. With an introduction by John Baker Hopkins. London, Longman, Green, Longman, Roberts, & Green, 1862.
Williams, James, 1796–1869.

LAC 40008
Southern agricultural exhaustion and its remedies.
Washington, Govt. print. off., 1853.
Ruffin, Edmund, 1794-1865.

LAC 16066
Southern agriculture. New York, The Macmillan company, 1908.
Earle, Franklin Sumner, 1856–

LAC 10708
The southern business directory and general commercial advertiser... Vol. I. Charleston, Press of Walker & James, 1854.
Campbell, John P.

LAC 10113
The southern farmer and market gardener; being a compilation of useful articles on these subjects from the most approved writers... New improved and enl. ed. Charleston, Wm. R. Babcock [c1852]
Holmes, Francis Simmons, 1815-1882.

LAC 12420
A southern girl in '61; the war-time memories of a Confederate senator's daughter, by Mrs. D. Giraud Wright, illustrated from contemporary portraits. New York, Doubleday, Page & company, 1905.
Wright, Louise.

LAC 16542
The southern harmony songbook... Reproduced, with an introduction by the Federal writers' project of Kentucky, Works progress administration; sponsored by the Young men's progress club, Benton, Kentucky. New York, N. Y., Hastings house, 1939.
Walker, William, 1809-1875.

LAC 15185
Southern history of the war. The last year of the war. New York, C. B. Richardson, 1866.
Pollard, Edward Alfred, 1831-1872.

LAC 31088-119
The Southern literary messenger; devoted to every department of literature and the fine arts. v. 1-36; Aug. 1834-June 1864. Richmond, T. W. White [etc.]

LAC 40131
Southern planters and the freedmen. New York, American tract society [186–]
Waterbury, Jared Bell, 1799-1876.

LAC 40036
The southern platform; or, Manual of southern sentiment on the subject of slavery. Boston, J. P. Jewett & co., 1858.
Goodloe, Daniel Reaves, 1814-1902.

LAC 12027
The Southern poems of the war. Collected and arranged by Miss Emily V. Mason. Baltimore, J. Murphy & co., 1867.
Mason, Emily Virginia, 1815-1909, *comp.*

LAC 30992-013
The Southern quarterly review. v. 1-16, Jan. 1842-Jan. 1850; v. 17-28 (new ser., v. 1-12), Apr. 1850-Oct.? 1855; v. 29-30 (new ser., v. 1-2), Apr. 1856-Feb. 1857. New Orleans, The Proprietors; [etc., etc.]

LAC 40096
The southern question. A view of the policy and constitutional powers of the President, as to the southern states. Cleveland, O., Printed by Fairbanks & company, 1877.
Bishop, Jesse Phelps, 1815-1881.

LAC 14563
The southern side; or, Andersonville prison. Compiled from official documents by R. Randolph Stevenson, M. D. Together with an examination of the Wirz trial; a comparison of the mortality in northern and southern prisons; remarks on the exchange bureau, etc. Baltimore, Turnbull brothers, 1876.
Stevenson, R   Randolph.

LAC 12344
Southern sidelights; a picture of social and economic life in the South a generation before the war. New York, Boston, T. Y. Crowell & company [1896]
Ingle, Edward, 1861-1924.

LAC 10702
The southern South. New York and London, D. Appleton and company, 1910.
Hart, Albert Bushnell, 1854-1943.

LAC 10255
The southern states of the American union considered in their relations to the Constitution of the United States and to the resulting union. New York [etc.] G. P. Putnam's sons, 1894.
Curry, Jabez Lamar Monroe, 1825-1903.

LAC 12387
The southern states since the war. 1870-1. London & New York, Macmillan and co., 1871.
Somers, Robert, 1822-1891.

LAC 40059
The southern states, their present peril, and their certain remedy. Why do they not right themselves? And so fulfil their glorious destiny. Charleston, Printed by E. C. Councell, 1850.
Townsend, John.

LAC 14152
Southern wealth and northern profits, as exhibited in statistical facts and official figures: showing the necessity of union to the future prosperity and welfare of the republic. New York, G. W. & J. A. Wood, 1860.
Kettell, Thomas Prentice.

LAC 10833
Southern women in the recent education movement in the South. Washington, Govt. print. off., 1892.
Mayo, Amory Dwight, 1823-1907.

LAC 13807
Southern writers; selections in prose and verse. New York, The Macmillan company; London, Macmillan & co., ltd., 1928, [c1905]
Trent, William Peterfield, 1862–   ed.

LAC 12413
The Southland; an exposition of the present resources and development of the South. [New York?] The Southern railway co., 1898.
Presbrey, Frank Spencer, 1855–

LAC 23407-8
Southold town records, copied, and explanatory notes added, by J. Wickham Case. Printed by order of the towns of Southold and Riverhead. [New York, S. W. Green's son, printer, etc.] 1882–84.
Southold, N.Y.

LAC 40030
The South's redemption. From poverty to prosperity. In 1860 the richest part of the country–in 1870 the poorest–in 1880 signs of improvement–in 1889 regaining the position of 1860. Baltimore, Md., The Manufacturers' record co., 1890.
Edmonds, Richard Hathaway, 1857–1930.

LAC 12777
A south-side view of slavery; or, Three months at the South, in 1854. Boston, T. R. Marvin [etc.] 1855, [c1854]
Adams, Nehemiah, 1806–1878.

LAC 16961
Southward ho! A spell of sunshine. Chicago, Donohue, Henneberry, 1890.
Simms, William Gilmore, 1806–1870.

LAC 13235
The South-west. by a Yankee. New-York, Harper & brothers, 1835.
Ingraham, Joseph Holt, 1809–1860.

LAC 11387
Souvenirs of a diplomat. Private letters from America during the administrations of Presidents Van Buren, Harrison, and Tyler, by the chevalier de Bacourt, minister from France, with a memoir of the author by the Comtesse de Mirabeau. Tr. from the French. New York, H. Holt and company, 1885.
Bacourt, Adolphe Fourier de, 1801–1865.

LAC 40044
The soveraign efficacy of divine providence (1682) With an introd. by Joseph L. Blau. Los Angeles, William Andrews Clark Memorial Library, University of California, 1955.
Oakes, Urian, 1631–1681.

LAC 40058
Spain, Cuba, and the United States. Recognition and the Monroe doctrine. By Americus [pseud.] New York, Printed by C. A. Alvord, 1870.
Kingsley, Vine Wright.

LAC 12425
Spain in America, 1450–1580. New York and London, Harper & brothers, 1904.
Bourne, Edward Gaylord, 1860–1908.

LAC 14421
The Spanish-American war. New York and London, Harper & bros., 1901.
Alger, Russell Alexander, 1836–1907.

LAC 10661
The Spanish-American war. A collection of documents relative to the squadron operations in the West Indies. Arranged by Rear-Admiral Pascual Cervera y Topete. Translated from the Spanish. Office of naval intelligence. Washington, Govt. print. off., 1899.
Cervera y Topete, Pascual, 1839–1909.

LAC 23473
The Spanish dependencies in South America; an introduction to the history of their civilization. New York and London, Harper & brothers, 1914.
Moses, Bernard, 1846–1930.

LAC 15776
Spanish diplomatic correspondence and documents 1896–1900. Presented to the Cortes by the minister of state. (Translation) Washington, Gov't print. off., 1905.
Spain. Ministerio de Estado.

LAC 21124
The Spanish regime in Missouri; a collection of papers and documents relating to upper Louisiana principally within the present limits of Missouri during the dominion of Spain, from the Archives of the Indies at Seville, etc., translated from the original Spanish into English, and including also some papers concerning the supposed grant to Col. George Morgan at the mouth of the Ohio, found in the Congressional library; ed. and with an introduction and notes, biographical and explanatory, by Louis Houck. Chicago, Ill., R. R. Donnelley & sons company, 1909.
Houck, Louis, 1840–1925, ed.

LAC 40067
Spanish rule in Cuba. Laws governing the island. Review published by the Colonial office in Madrid, with data and statistics compiled from official records. (Authorized translation, with additional notes.) New York, 1896.
Spain. Ministerio de Ultramar.

LAC 15530
The Spanish settlements within the present limits of the United States, 1513–1561. New York & London, G. P. Putnam's sons, 1911, [c1901]
Lowery, Woodbury, 1853–1906.

LAC 13759
The speaking telephone, talking phonograph, and other novelties. New York, D. Appleton & company, 1878.
Prescott, George Bartlett, 1830–1894.

LAC 15610
Special report on immigration; accompanying information for immigrants relative to the prices and rentals of land, the staple products, facilities of access to market, cost of farm stock, kind of labor in demand in the western and southern states, etc., etc. To which are appended tables showing the average weekly wages paid in the several states and sections for factory, mechanical, and farm labor; the cost of provisions, groceries, dry goods, and house rent in the various manufacturing districts of the country, in the year 1869–'70. By Edward Young, PH. D., chief of the Bureau of statistics. Washington, Govt. print. off., 1872.
U.S. Bureau of Statistics (Treasury Dept.)

LAC 14541-42
Special report on the history and present condition of the sheep industry of the United States. Prepared under the direction of Dr. D. E. Salmon, chief of the Bureau of animal industry, by Ezra A. Carman, H. A. Heath, and John Minto. Published by authority of the secretary of agriculture. Washington, Gov't print. off., 1892.
U.S. *Bureau of Animal Industry.*

LAC 12113
Specimen days & Collect. Philadelphia, R. Welsh & co., 1882-83.
Whitman, Walt, 1819-1892.

LAC 20634-35
Specimens of American poetry, with critical and biographical notices. In three volumes. Boston, S. G. Goodrich and co., 1829.
Kettell, Samuel, 1800-1855.

LAC 10028
Speculation on the stock and produce exchange of the United States. New York, 1896.
Emery, Henry Crosby, 1872-1924.

LAC 10298
Speculations on the New York stock exchange, September, 1904-March, 1907. New York, Columbia University; [etc., etc.] 1913.
Osborne, Algernon Ashburner, 1882-

LAC 40097
Speculative consequences of evolution. Ann Arbor, Andrews & company, 1888.
Winchell, Alexander, 1824-1891.

LAC 40068
The speech of Charles Jas. Faulkner, (of Berkeley) in the House of delegates of Virginia, on the policy of the state with respect to her slave population. Delivered January 20, 1832. Richmond, T. W. White, printer, 1832.
Faulkner, Charles James, 1806-1884.

LAC 40103
Speech of James M'Dowell, jr. (of Rockbridge,) in the House of delegates of Virginia, on the slave question: delivered Saturday January 21, 1832. 2d ed. ... Richmond, Printed by T. W. White [1832]
McDowell, James, 1795-1851.

LAC 40070
Speech of the Hon. James Emott, in the House of representatives of the United States; delivered the 12th January, 1813. On the bill in addition to the act entitled "An act to raise an additional military force," and for other purposes. Boston: Printed by Russell & Cutler, 1813.
Emott, James, 1771-1850.

LAC 40119
A speech on the principles of social freedom, delivered in Steinway Hall, Monday, Nov. 20, 1871, and Music Hall, Boston, Wednesday, Jan. 3, '72. New York, Woodhull & Claflin, 1874.
Martin, Victoria Woodhull, 1838-1927.

LAC 11442
Speeches and addresses delivered in the Congress of the United States, and on several public occasions [1856-1865] by Henry Winter Davis, of Maryland. Preceded by a sketch of his life, public services, and character, being an oration by the Hon. J. A. J. Cresswell... With notes, introductory and explanatory. New York, Harper & brothers, 1867.
Davis, Henry Winter, 1817-1865.

LAC 12523
Speeches and addresses of William E. Russell. Selected and ed. by Charles Theodore Russell, jr. With an introduction by Thomas Wentworth Higginson. Boston, Little, Brown, and company, 1894.
Russell, William Eustis, 1857-1896.

LAC 15683
Speeches and addresses of William McKinley, from March 1, 1897, to May 30, 1900. New York, Doubleday & McClure co., 1900.
McKinley, William, *pres. U.S.*, 1843-1901.

LAC 20209
Speeches and occasional addresses. New York, D. Appleton and company, 1864.
Dix, John Adams, 1798-1879.

LAC 15251
Speeches, arguments, addresses, and letters of Clement L. Vallandigham. New York, J. Walter & co., 1864.
Vallandigham, Clement Laird, 1820-1871.

LAC 40075
Speeches by Henry Cabot Lodge. Boston and New York, Houghton Mifflin and company, 1892.
Lodge, Henry Cabot, 1850-

LAC 20837-40
Speeches, correspondence and political papers of Carl Schurz; selected and ed. by Frederic Bancroft on behalf of the Carl Schurz memorial committee... New York [etc.] G. P. Putnam's sons, 1913.
Schurz, Carl, 1829-1906.

LAC 20211-12
Speeches, correspondence, etc., of the late Daniel S. Dickinson, of New York. Including: addresses on important public topics; speeches in the state and United States Senate, and in support of the government during the rebellion; correspondence, private and political (collected and arranged by Mrs. Dickinson), poems (collected and arranged by Mrs. Mygatt), etc. Edited, with a biography, by his brother, John R. Dickinson. New York, G. P. Putnam & sons, 1867.
Dickinson, Daniel Stevens, 1800-1866.

LAC 10326
Speeches, debates, resolutions, list of the delegates, committees, etc. Held September 13th, 14th, 15th, 16th, 1899. Chicago, Civic federation of Chicago, 1900.
Chicago Conference on Trusts, 1899.

LAC 11472
Speeches in Congress. Boston, J. P. Jewett and company; Cleveland, O., Jewett, Proctor and Worthington; [etc., etc.] 1853.
Giddings, Joshua Reed, 1795-1864.

LAC 20256-57

Speeches, lectures, and letters. Boston, Lee and Shepard, 1892.
Phillips, Wendell, 1811-1884.

LAC 14162

Speeches, messages, and other writings of the Hon. Albert G. Brown, a senator in Congress from the state of Mississippi. Edited by M. W. Cluskey. Philadelphia, J. B. Smith & co., 1859.
Brown, Albert Gallatin, 1813-1880.

LAC 15253

Speeches of Andrew Johnson, president of the United States. With a biographical introduction by Frank Moore. Boston, Little, Brown, and company, 1865.
Johnson, Andrew, *pres. U.S.*, 1808-1875.

LAC 11501

Speeches of Daniel W. Voorhees, of Indiana, embracing his most prominent forensic, political, occasional and literary addresses, comp. by his son Charles S. Voorhees, with a short biographical sketch. Cincinnati, R. Clarke & co., printers, 1875.
Voorhees, Daniel Wolsey, 1827-1897.

LAC 11505

The speeches of Hon. John Wanamaker on Quayism and boss domination in Pennsylvania politics. Published under the direction of the Business men's Republican league of the state of Pennsylvania. [Philadelphia, 1898?]
Wanamaker, John, 1838-1922.

LAC 15249

Speeches of the governors of Massachusetts, from 1765 to 1775; and the answers of the House of representatives, to the same; with their resolutions and addresses for that period. And other public papers, relating to the dispute between this country and Great Britain, which led to the independence of the United States. Boston, Printed by Russell and Gardner, proprietors of the work, 1818.
Bradford, Alden, 1765-1843, *ed.*

LAC 16713

Speeches on the Jew bill, in the House of delegates of Maryland, by H. M. Brackenridge, Col. W. G. D. Worthington, and John S. Tyson, esquire. Together with an argument on the chancery powers, and an eulogy on Thomas Jefferson and John Adams, &c. Philadelphia, J. Dobson (agent) 1829.
Brackenridge, Henry Marie, 1786-1871.

LAC 10749

Speeches, poems, and miscellaneous writings, on subjects connected with temperance and the liquor traffic. Boston, J. P. Jewett, 1849.
Jewett, Charles, 1807-1879.

LAC 13902

The sphere and duties of woman. A course of lectures. 3d ed., cor. and enl. Baltimore, J. Murphy; Philadelphia, Kay & Troutman; [etc., etc.] 1851.
Burnap, George Washington, 1802-1859.

LAC 16940

The spirit of American government; a study of the Constitution: its origin, influence and relation to democracy. New York, The Macmillan company; London, Macmillan & co., ltd., 1911, [c1907]
Smith, James Allen, 1860-1926.

LAC 40044

Spirit of New England.
A looking glass for the times; or, The former spirit of New England revived in this generation. Providence, S. S. Rider, 1883.
Folger, Peter, 1617?-1690.

LAC 16557

The spirit of old West Point, 1858-1862. Boston and New York, Houghton, Mifflin and company, 1907.
Schaff, Morris, 1840-1929.

LAC 12050

The spirit of romance: an attempt to define somewhat the charm of the pre-renaissance literature of Latin Europe. London, J. M. Dent & sons, ltd.; [New York, E. P. Dutton & co., 1910]
Pound, Ezra Loomis, 1885-

LAC 15515

The spirit of the Ghetto; studies of the Jewish quarter in New York, by Hutchins Hapgood; with drawings from life by Jacob Epstein. New York and London, Funk & Wagnalls company, 1902.
Hapgood, Hutchins, 1869-1944.

LAC 16614

The spirit of youth and the city streets. New York, The Macmillan company, 1916, [c1909]
Addams, Jane, 1860-1935.

LAC 12214

Spiritual direction and auricular confession; their history, theory and consequences. Being a translation of Du pretre, de la femme, de la famille. Philadelphia, J. M. Campbell, 1845.
Michelet, Jules, 1798-1874.

LAC 40082

Spiritual milk for Boston babes in either England. Drawn out of the breasts of both Testaments for their souls nourishment. But may be of like use to any children. Cambridg [!] [Mass.] Printed by S. G. for Hezekiah Vsher at Boston in New-England, 1656. [Boston, 1939]
Cotton, John, 1584-1652.

LAC 40006

The spiritual significance of modern socialism. New York, B. W. Huebsch, 1908.
Spargo, John, 1876-1966.

LAC 20352

Spiritual wives. 4th ed., with a new pref. London, Hurst and Blackett, 1868.
Dixon, William Hepworth, 1821-1879.

LAC 11818

The splendid idle forties; stories of old California, by Gertrude Atherton, with illustrations by Harrison Fisher. New York, The Macmillan company; London, Macmillan & co., ltd., 1902.
Atherton, Gertrude Franklin, 1857-1948.

LAC 15139

The sport of the gods. New York, Dodd, Mead and co., 1902.
Dunbar, Paul Laurence, 1872-1906.

LAC 14737

The spraying of plants; a succinct account of the history, principles and practice of the application of liquids and powders to plants, for the purpose of destroying insects and fungi; by E. G. Lodeman. With a preface by B. T. Galloway. New York and London, Macmillan and co., 1896.
Lodeman, Ernest Gustavus, d. 1896.

LAC 14645

The spy of the rebellion; being a true history of the spy system of the United States army during the late rebellion. Revealing many secrets of the war hitherto not made public. Comp. from official reports prepared for President Lincoln, General McClellan and the provost-marshal-general. Chicago, A. G. Nettleton & co., 1884.
Pinkerton, Allan, 1819–1884.

LAC 15002

The squadron of Admiral Cervera, by Captain Victor M. Concas y Palau. Translated from the Spanish. Office of naval intelligence. Washington, Govt. print. off., 1900.
Concas y Palau, Victor Maria, 1845–1916.

LAC 11897

The Squibob papers. By John Phoenix. [Capt. Geo. H. Derby.] With comic illustrations by the author. New York, Carleton, 1865.
Derby, George Horatio, 1823–1861.

LAC 15114

The stage in America, 1897–1900. New York, The Macmillan company; London, Macmillan & co., ltd., 1901.
Hapgood, Norman, 1868–1937.

LAC 16612

The stage, or, Recollections of actors and acting from an experience of fifty years; a series of dramatic sketches. (With an appendix) Philadelphia, J. M. Stoddart & co., 1880.
Murdoch, James Edward, 1811–1893.

LAC 13183

Stage-coach and tavern days, by Alice Morse Earle. New York, The Macmillan company; London, Macmillan & co., ltd., 1915, [c1900]
Earle, Alice, 1851–1911.

LAC 11603

Standard against Uncle Sam [by] H. H. Tucker, jr. Kansas City, Kan., H. H. Tucker, jr. [c1907]
Tucker, Henry Harrison, jr., 1878–

LAC 12164

The standard of living among workingmen's families in New York city. New York, Charities publication committee, 1909.
Chapin, Robert Coit, 1863–

LAC 15437

Standard oil or the people; the end of corporate control in America. New York city, The author [c1914]
Klein, Henry H., 1879–

LAC 10518

Standards of public morality. The Kennedy lectures for 1906, in the School of philanthropy, conducted by the Charity organization society of the city of New York. New York, The Macmillan company; London, Macmillan & co., ltd., 1907.
Hadley, Arthur Twining, 1856–1930.

LAC 14055

Stanford White. New York, Dodd, Mead & company, 1931.
Baldwin, Charles Crittenton, 1888–

LAC 16560

The star corps; or, Notes of an army chaplain, during Sherman's famous "march to the sea." Rev. G. S. Bradley. Milwaukee, Jermain & Brightman, printers, 1865.
Bradley, George S.

LAC 14290

A star in the West; or, A humble attempt to discover the long lost ten tribes of Israel, preparatory to their return to their beloved city, Jerusalem. Trenton, N. J., Published by D. Fenton, S. Hutchinson and J. Dunham. George Sherman, Printer, 1816.
Boudinot, Elias, 1740–1821.

LAC 11415

The star of the west; or, National men and national measures. 3d ed., rev. and enl. New York, Miller, Orton & co., 1857.
Carroll, Anna Ella, 1815–1894.

LAC 10939

Star papers; or, Experiences of art and nature. New York, J. C. Derby; Boston, Phillips, Sampson & co.; [etc., etc.] 1855.
Beecher, Henry Ward, 1813–1887.

LAC 16507

"The star spangled banner" (revised and enlarged from the "Report" on the above and other airs, issued in 1909) Washington, Govt. print. off., 1914.
Sonneck, Oscar George Theodore, 1873–1928.

LAC 13697

Startling facts for native Americans called "Knownothings", or A vivid presentation of the dangers to American liberty, to be apprehended from foreign influence. New York, Pub. at 128 Nassau st., 1855.

LAC 11620

State aid to railways in Missouri. Chicago, The University of Chicago press, 1896.
Million, John Wilson, 1863–

LAC 40011

State aid to the U.S. land-grant colleges. An address in behalf of the University of Vermont and State agricultural college, delivered in the hall of the House of Representatives, at Montpelier, October 10, 1888. Montpelier, Vt., Argus and Patriot printing house, 1888.
Morrill, Justin Smith, 1810–1898.

LAC 21187–88
State and federal control of persons and property.
A treatise on state and federal control of persons and property in the United States, considered from both a civil and criminal standpoint. [2d ed.] St. Louis, The F. H. Thomas law book co., 1900.
Tiedeman, Christopher Gustavus, 1857–1903.

LAC 10605
The state and higher education; phases of their relationship, by Fred J. Kelly and John H. McNeely with an introduction by Howard J. Savage. New York city, 1933.
Kelly, Frederick James, 1880–1959.

LAC 16032
The state and the farmer. New York, The Macmillan company; London, Macmillan & co., ltd., 1908.
Bailey, Liberty Hyde, 1858–1954.

LAC 15895
State banking before the civil war, by Davis R. Dewey and The safety fund banking system in New York, 1829–1866, by Robert E. Chaddock. Washington, Govt. print. off., 1910 [i.e. 1911]
Dewey, Davis Rich, 1858–1942.

LAC 40026
State banking in Indiana, 1814–1873. [Bloomington, Ind., 1912]
Esarey, Logan, 1874–1942.

LAC 12570
State control of trade and commerce by national or state authority. New York, Baker, Voorhis & company, 1897.
Stickney, Albert, 1839–1908.

LAC 12564
The state. Elements of historical and practical politics. A sketch of institutional history and administration. Boston, D. C. Heath & co., 1889.
Wilson, Woodrow, *pres. U.S.*, 1856–1924.

LAC 40045
The state of England, anno Dom. 1600, by Thomas Wilson. Edited from the manuscripts among the state papers in the Public record office, by F. J. Fisher. London, Offices of the Society, 1936.
Wilson, *Sir* Thomas, 1560?–1629.

LAC 40042
A state of the province of Georgia, attested upon oath in the court of Savannah, November 10, 1740. London, Printed for W. Meadows, 1742. [Washington, P. Force, 1835]
Stephens, William, 1671–1753, *comp.*

LAC 40037
The state of trade in the northern colonies considered; with an account of their produce, and a particular description of Nova Scotia... London, Printed by G. Woodfall, 1748.
Little, Otis, 1712–1754.

LAC 14323
State platforms of the two dominant political parties in Indiana, 1850–1900; compiled by W. E. Henry. Indianapolis [Press of W. B. Burford] 1902.
Henry, William Elmer, 1857–1936, *comp.*

LAC 10014
State railroad commissions, and how they may be made effective. [Baltimore] American economic association, 1891.
Clark, Frederick Converse.

LAC 10148
State railroad control, with a history of its development in Iowa, by Frank H. Dixon. With an introduction by Henry C. Adams. New York, T. Y. Crowell & company [1896]
Dixon, Frank Haigh, 1869–

LAC 40059
State sovereignty and the doctrine of coercion, by the Hon. Wm. D. Porter; together with a letter from Hon. J. K. Paulding, former sec. of navy. The right to secede, by "States" [*pseud.*] [Charleston, S. C., Evans & Cogswell's steam-power presses, 1860]
Porter, William Dennison, 1810–1883.

LAC 14999
State trials of the United States during the administrations of Washington and Adams. With references, historical and professional, and preliminary notes on the politics of the times. Philadelphia, Carey and Hart [c1849]
Wharton, Francis, 1820–1889.

LAC 16013
Stately homes in America from colonial times to the present day, by Harry W. Desmond and Herbert Croly. New York, D. Appleton and company, 1903.
Desmond, Harry William, 1863–1913.

LAC 15518
A statement for non-exclusion, by Patrick J. Healy and Ng Poon Chew. San Francisco, 1905.
Healy, Patrick Joseph, *b.* 1838?

LAC 40131
Statement of Br. Maj. Gen. O. O. Howard, before the Committee on education and labor, in defense against the charges presented by Hon. Fernando Wood, and argument of Edgar Ketchum, esq., of counsel for Gen. Howard in summing up the case upon the testimony before the committee. New York, Bradstreet press, 1870.
Howard, Oliver Otis, 1830–1909.

LAC 16299
A statement of reasons for not believing the doctrines of Trinitarians, concerning the nature of God and the person of Christ. 2d. ed., with additions, and a biographical notice of the author. Boston, American Unitarian association, 1856.
Norton, Andrews, 1786-1853.

LAC 14609
Statement of some new principles on the subject of political economy, exposing the fallacies of the system of free trade, and of some other doctrines maintained in the "Wealth of nations." Boston, Hilliard, Gray, and co., 1834.
Rae, John. 1796–1872.

LAC 10093
A statement of the arts and manufactures of the United States of America, for the year 1810: digested and prepared by Tench Coxe, esquire, of Philadelphia. Philadelphia, Printed by A. Cornman, junr. 1814.
U.S. *Treasury Dept.*

LAC 14926

Statement of the origin, organization and progress of the Russian-American telegraph, Western union extension, Collins' overland line, via Behring strait and Asiatic Russia to Europe. Collated and prepared from official documents on file in the "Russian bureau" of the Western union telegraph company, by order of the Board of directors. Rochester, "Evening express" printing office, 1866.
Western Union Telegraph Company.

LAC 13189

The states and territories of the great West ... their geography, history, advantages, resources ... comprising their local history, institutions, and laws. Giving a table of distances, and the most direct routes ... also, pointing out the best districts for agricultural, commercial, lumbering, and mining operations... New York [etc.] Miller, Orton, and Mulligan; Buffalo, E. F. Beadle, 1856.
Ferris, Jacob.

LAC 11370

Statesman and friend; correspondence of John Adams with Benjamin Waterhouse, 1784-1822, edited by Worthington Chauncey Ford. Boston, Little, Brown, and company, 1927.
Adams, John, *pres, U.S.*, 1735-1826.

LAC 13906

The statesmanship of Andrew Jackson as told in his writings and speeches; ed. by Francis Newton Thorpe. New York, The Tandy-Thomas company [c1909]
Jackson, Andrew, *pres. U.S.*, 1767-1845.

LAC 14895

Statesmen and soldiers of the civil war; a study of the conduct of war, by Major General Sir Frederick Maurice. Boston, Little, Brown, and company, 1926.
Maurice, *Sir* Frederick Barton, 1871-

LAC 21275-76

Statistical abstract of the United States. 1st no., 1878; 35th no., 1912. Washington, U.S. Government Printing Office, 1879-1913.
U.S. *Bureau of the Census.*

LAC 16067

A statistical account of the county of Middlesex, in Connecticut. Pub. by the Connecticut academy of arts and sciences. Middletown, Conn., Printed by Clark & Lyman, April, 1819.
Field, David Dudley, 1781-1867.

LAC 13330

Statistical and other information for the Constitutional convention of Pennsylvania. Prepared by Francis Jordan, secretary of the commonwealth; in compliance with the act of Assembly authorizing said Convention. 2d ed. Harrisburg, B. Singerly, state printer, 1872.
Pennsylvania. *Secretary of the Commonwealth.*

LAC 12269

Statistical history of the first century of American Methodism: with a summary of the origin and present operations of other denominations. By Rev. C. C. Goss. New York, Carlton & Porter, 1866.
Goss, Charles C.

LAC 40138

A statistical inquiry into the condition of the people of colour, of the city and districts of Philadelphia. Philadelphia, Printed by Kite & Walton, 1849.

LAC 10480

Statistical tables, exhibiting the commerce of the United States with European countries from 1790 to 1890. Prepared by the chief of the Bureau of statistics, Treasury department. Washington, Gov't print. off., 1893.
U. S. *Bureau of Statistics. (Treasury Dept.)*

LAC 40008

A statistical view of American agriculture, its home resources and foreign markets, with suggestions for the schedules of the federal census in 1860. An address delivered at New York, before the American geographical and statistical society, on the organization of the Agricultural section. New York, D. Appleton & company, 1859.
Jay, John, 1817-1894.

LAC 11636

A statistical view of the commerce of the United States of America: including also an account of banks, manufactures and internal trade and improvements... New Haven, Durrie & Peck, 1835.
Pitkin, Timothy, 1766-1847.

LAC 10814

A statistical view of the district of Maine; more especially with reference to the value and importance of its interior. Addressed to the consideration of the legislators of Massachusetts. Boston: Published by Cummings and Hilliard, at the Boston bookstore, no. 1, Cornhill, 1816.
Greenleaf, Moses, 1777-1834.

LAC 10538

Statistics and economics. An outline of statistical science, with especial reference to the use of statistics in political economy and social science. [Baltimore] American economic association, 1888.
Mayo-Smith, Richmond, 1854-1901.

LAC 10912

Statistics of cities having a population of over 30,000: 1904. Washington, Govt. print. off., 1906.
U.S. *Bureau of the Census.*

LAC 11649

Statistics of coal: including mineral bituminous substances employed in arts and manufactures; with their geographical, geological and commercial distribution, and amount of production and consumption on the American continent. With incidental statistics of the iron manufacture. 2d ed., rev. and brought down to 1854, by S. S. Haldeman. Philadelphia, J. W. Moore, 1855.
Taylor, Richard Cowling, 1789-1851.

LAC 15102

Statistics of Indian tribes, Indian agencies, and Indian schools of every character. Comp. under the direction of the secretary of the interior. Corrected to January 1, 1899. [Washington, Govt. print. off., 1899]
U.S. *Dept. of the Interior.*

LAC 10475
Statistics of mines and mining in the states and territories west of the Rocky mountains, by Rossiter W. Raymond. Washington, Govt. print. off., 1870.
U.S. *Treasury Dept.*

LAC 12398
Statistics of the state of Georgia: including an account of its natural, civil, and ecclesiastical history; together with a particular description of each county, notices of the manners and customs of its aboriginal tribes, and a correct map of the state. Savannah, W. T. Williams, 1849.
White, George, 1802–1887.

LAC 13182
Statistics of the state of Oregon; containing a description of its agricultural development, and natural and industrial resources. Together with the physical, geographical, geological, and mineral statistics of the state. Compiled and published by order of the State agricultural society by A. J. Dufur. Salem, Ore., Printed at the "Willamette farmer" office, 1869.
Oregon State Agricultural Society.

LAC 20561–70
The statutes at large; being a collection of all the laws of Virginia, from the first session of the legislature, in the year 1619. Published pursuant to an act of the General assembly of Virginia, passed on the fifth day of February one thousand eight hundred and eight... New-York: Printed for the editor, by R. & W. & G. Bartow, 1819–23.
Virginia. *Laws, statutes, etc.*

LAC 16804
The statutes at large of the provisional government of the Confederate States of America, from the institution of the government, February 8, 1861, to its termination, February 18, 1862, inclusive. Arranged in chronological order. Together with the constitution for the provisional government, and the permanent constitution of the Confederate States, and the treaties concluded by the Confederate States with Indian tribes. Ed. by James M. Matthews. Richmond, R. M. Smith, printer to Congress, 1864.
Confederate States of America. *Laws, statutes, etc.*

LAC 23345–47
The statutes of Ohio and of the Northwestern territory, adopted or enacted from 1788 to 1833 inclusive: together with the Ordinance of 1787; the constitutions of Ohio and of the United States, and various public instruments and acts of Congress: illustrated by a preliminary sketch of the history of Ohio; numerous references and notes and copious indexes... Ed. by Salmon P. Chase. Cincinnati, Corey & Fairbank, 1833–35.
Ohio. *Laws, statutes, etc.*

LAC 10193
Steam navigation, and its relation to the commerce of Canada and the United States. Toronto, W. Briggs; [etc., etc.] 1898.
Croil, James, 1821–1916.

LAC 10400
Steamboat disasters and railroad accidents in the United States. To which is appended accounts of recent shipwrecks, fires at sea, thrilling incidents, &c. 2d ed. Worcester [Mass.] Dorr, Howland & co., 1840.
Howland, S   A.

LAC 10356
Stelligeri, and other essays concerning America. New York, C. Scribner's sons, 1893.
Wendell, Barrett, 1855–1921.

LAC 20527
Stephen Hopkins, a Rhode Island statesmen. A study in the political history of the eighteenth century. Providence, S. S. Rider, 1884.
Foster, William Eaton, 1851–1930.

LAC 15121
Stiegel glass, by Frederick William Hunter, A. M.; illustrated with twelve plates in color from autochromes by J. B. Kerfoot, and with one hundred and fifty-nine half-tones. Boston and New York, Houghton Mifflin company, 1914.
Hunter, Frederick William, 1865–1919.

LAC 10044
Stocks and the stock market... Philadelphia, American academy of political and social science, 1910.
American Academy of Political and Social Science, *Philadelphia.*

LAC 22566–67
Stonewall Jackson and the American civil war, by Lieut.-Col. G. F. R. Henderson. With an introduction by Field-Marshal the Right Hon. Viscount Wolseley. New impression. New York, London [etc.] Longmans, Green and co., 1900.
Henderson, George Francis Robert, 1854–1903.

LAC 13484
Stories of the great railroads. Chicago, C. H. Kerr & company, 1912.
Russell, Charles Edward, 1860–

LAC 14170
Stories of the struggle. Chicago, C. H. Kerr & company, 1908.
Winchevsky, Morris, 1856–

LAC 14908
The storming of Stony Point on the Hudson, midnight, July 15, 1779; its importance in the light of unpublished documents. New York, J. T. White & co., 1900.
Johnston, Henry Phelps, 1842–1923.

LAC 10359
The story of a border city during the civil war. With twelve portraits and views. Boston, Little, Brown, and company, 1908.
Anderson, Galusha, 1832–1918.

LAC 11969
The story of a country town. By E. W. Howe. Illustrated from original designs by W. L. Wells. Atchison, Kas., Howe & co., 1883.
Howe, Edgar Watson, 1853–1937.

LAC 14314
The story of a house. Tr. from the French of Viollet-Le-Duc by George M. Towle. Illustrated by the author. Boston, J. R. Osgood and company, 1874.
Viollet-Le-Duc, Eugene Emmanuel, 1814–1879.

LAC 11265
The story of a labor agitator. New York, The Outlook company, 1903.
Buchanan, Joseph Ray, 1851–1924.

LAC 13700
The story of a New England town; a record of the commemoration, July second and third, 1890 on the two hundred and fiftieth anniversary of the settlement of Haverhill, Massachusetts... Boston, J. G. Cupples, 1891.
Haverhill, *Mass.*

LAC 16077
The story of a regiment; a history of the campaigns, and associations in the field, of the Sixth regiment Ohio volunteer infantry. Cincinnati, The author, 1868.
Hannaford, Ebenezer, 1840–

LAC 15286
The story of a trooper. With much of interest concerning the campaign on the Peninsula, not before written. Washington, D. C., McGill & Witherow, 1864.
Adams, Francis Colburn.

LAC 10342
The story of American coals. [2d ed.] Philadelphia and London, J. B. Lippincott company, 1904.
Nicolls, William Jasper, 1854–1916.

LAC 15017
The story of Aunt Becky's army-life. New York, New York printing company, 1871, [1867]
Palmer, Sarah A.

LAC 15218
The story of corn and the westward migration. Chicago, New York [etc.] Rand, McNally & company [c1916]
Brooks, Eugene Clyde, 1871–1947.

LAC 15421
The story of cotton and the development of the cotton states. Chicago, New York [etc.] Rand, McNally & company [c1911]
Brooks, Eugene Clyde, 1871–1947.

LAC 10681
The story of Cuba: her struggles for liberty; the cause, crisis and destiny of the Pearl of the Antilles. Graphically illustrated with numerous typical photographic reproductions and original drawings. 6th ed.–rev. to date. Akron, O., The Werner company [1898]
Halstead, Murat, 1829–1908.

LAC 13837
The story of Jerry Simpson. Wichita, Kan., Jane Simpson [c1908]
Diggs, Annie Le Porte, 1853–

LAC 15678
The story of life insurance. London, W. Heineman, 1907.
Hendrick, Burton Jesse, 1870–1949.

LAC 16469
The story of my boyhood and youth. With illustrations from sketches by the author. Boston and New York, Houghton Mifflin company [c1913]
Muir, John, 1838–1914.

LAC 16743
The story of my life and work, Booker T. Washington, with an introduction by Dr. J. L. M. Curry; illustrated by Frank Beard. New York, Negro Universities Press [1969]
Washington, Booker Taliaferro, 1859?–1915.

LAC 10604
The story of my life, by Helen Keller, with her letters (1837–1901) and a supplementary account of her education, including passages from the reports and letters of her teacher, Anne Mansfield Sullivan, by John Albert Macy. New York, Doubleday, Page & company, 1903.
Keller, Helen Adams, 1880–

LAC 12443–44
The story of our post office; the greatest government department in all its phases. Boston, Mass., A. M. Thayer & co., 1893.
Cushing, Marshall Henry, 1860–1915.

LAC 14930
The story of Panama. Hearings on the Rainey resolution before the Committee on foreign affairs of the House of representatives... Washington, Govt. print. off., 1913.
U.S. *Congress. House. Committee on Foreign Affairs.*

LAC 10391
The story of paper-making; an account of paper-making from its earliest known record down to the present time... Chicago, J. W. Butler paper company, 1901.
Butler, Frank O.

LAC 14025
The story of the American board; an account of the first hundred years of the American board of commissioners for foreign missions. Boston, New York [etc.] The Pilgrim press; Boston, American board of commissioners for foreign missions [c1910]
Strong, William Ellsworth, 1860–

LAC 13255
The story of the American merchant marine. New York, The Macmillan company, 1910.
Spears, John Randolph, 1850–1936.

LAC 14082
Story of the Cherokee Bible. An address, with additional ... notes, delivered before the meeting of the Ladies' missionary society of the First Congregational church, Ithaca, N. Y., Feb. 5, 1897. 2d ed., enl. Ithaca, N. Y., Democrat press, 1899.
Foster, George Everett, 1849–

LAC 13748
The story of the Commonweal. Complete and graphic narrative of the origin and growth of the movement... Chicago, W. B. Conkey company, 1894.
Vincent, Henry.

LAC 14526
The story of the cowboy, by E. Hough, illustrated by William L. Wells and C. M. Russell. New York, D. Appleton and company, 1898, [c1897]
Hough, Emerson, 1857–1923.

LAC 11886
The story of the files; a review of Californian writers and literature, by Ella Sterling Cummins. [San Francisco, Co-operative printing co.] c1893.
Mighels, Ella Sterling, 1853–1934.

LAC 11752
The story of the first decade in Imperial valley, California, by Edgar F. Howe and Wilbur Jay Hall. Imperial, E. F. Howe & sons, 1910.
Howe, Edgar F.

LAC 12456
The story of the great march. From the diary of a staff officer. With a map and illustrations. New York, Harper & brothers, 1865.
Nichols, George Ward, 1837–1885.

LAC 10132–33
The story of the Herefords; an account of the origin and development of the breed in Herefordshire, a sketch of its early introduction into the United States and Canada, and subsequent rise to popularity in the western cattle trade, with sundry notes on the management of breeding herds. Chicago, The Breeder's gazette, 1914.
Sanders, Alvin Howard, 1860–

LAC 23394
Story of the Hutchinsons (tribe of Jesse) By John Wallace Hutchinson; comp. and ed. by Charles E. Mann, with an introduction by Frederick Douglass. Boston, Lee and Shepard, 1896.
Hutchinson, John Wallace, 1821–

LAC 40018
The story of the invention of steel pens, with a description of the manufacturing processes by which they are produced. New York, Ivison, Blakeman & company, 1890.
Bore, Henry.

LAC 14870
The story of the Irish in Boston: together with biographical sketches of representative men and noted women, ed. and comp. by James Bernard Cullen. Boston, J. B. Cullen & company, 1889.
Cullen, James Bernard, 1857– ed.

LAC 14797
The story of the Jubilee singers; with their songs. Rev. ed. Boston, Houghton, Osgood, 1880.
Marsh, J   B   T.

LAC 16927
The story of the life of John Anderson, the fugitive slave. Ed. by Harper Twelvetrees, M. A., chairman of the John Anderson committee. London, W. Tweedie, 1863.
Twelvetrees, Harper, 1823–1881, ed.

LAC 13315
The story of the mine, as illustrated by the great Comstock lode of Nevada. New York, D. Appleton and company, 1896.
Shinn, Charles Howard, 1852–1924.

LAC 11052
The story of the Mormons, from the date of their origin to the year 1901. New York, The Macmillan company; London, Macmillan & co., ltd., 1902.
Linn, William Alexander, 1846–1917.

LAC 15066
The story of the Pennsylvania Germans; embracing an account of their origin, their history, and their dialect. Easton, Penna., Express book print, 1898.
Beidelman, William.

LAC 13578
The story of the Pilgrim fathers, 1606–1623 A. D.; as told by themselves, their friends, and their enemies. Edited from the original texts, by Edward Arber. London, Ward and Downey, limited; Boston [etc.] Houghton, Mifflin & co., 1897.
Arber, Edward, 1836–1912, ed.

LAC 12612
The story of the telegraph, and a history of the great Atlantic cable; a complete record of the inception, progress, and final success of that undertaking. A general history of land and oceanic telegraphs. Descriptions of telegraphic apparatus, and biographical sketches of the principal persons connected with the great work. By Charles F. Briggs and Augustus Maverick. New York, Rudd & Carleton, 1858.
Briggs, Charles Frederick, 1804–1877.

LAC 11632
The story of the trust companies. New York and London, G. P. Putnam's sons, 1916.
Perine, Edward Ten Broeck, 1870–1941.

LAC 15037
The story of the volunteer fire department of the city of New York. With one hundred and forty-five illustrations. New York, Harper & brothers, 1882.
Sheldon, George William, 1843–1914.

LAC 13169
Story of the wild West and camp-fire chats, by Buffalo Bill, (Hon. W. F. Cody.) A full and complete history of the renowned pioneer quartette, Boone, Crockett, Carson and Buffalo Bill. Including a description of Buffalo Bill's conquests in England with his Wild West exhibition... Philadelphia, Chicago [etc.] Historical publishing co. 1890, [c1888]
Cody, William Frederick, 1846–1917.

LAC 40085
Strange news from Virginia; Being a full and true account of the life and death of Nathaniel Bacon Esquire, Who was the only Cause and Original of all the late troubles in that country. With a full Relation of all the Accidents which have happened in the late War there between the Christians and Indians. London, Printed for William Harris, next door to the Turn-Stile without Moor-gate, 1677. [Boston, 1926]

LAC 23221

The stranger in America: comprising sketches of the manners, society, and national peculiarities of the United States, in a series of letters to a friend in Europe. London, R. Bentley, 1835.
Lieber, Francis, 1800–1872.

LAC 12203

The stranger in America: containing observations made during a long residence in that country, on the genius, manners and customs of the people of the United States; with biographical particulars of public characters; hints and facts relative to the arts, sciences, commerce, agriculture, manufactures, emigration, and the slave trade. Illustrated by engravings. London, Printed for J. Cundee, 1807.
Janson, Charles William.

LAC 10283

The strategy of great railroads. New York, C. Scribner's sons, 1904.
Spearman, Frank Hamilton, 1859–1937.

LAC 16898

Stray leaves from strange literature; stories reconstructed from the Anvari-Soheili, Baital-Pachisi, Mahabharata, Pantchatantra Gulistan, Talmud, Kalewala, etc. Boston and New York, Houghton Mifflin company [c1912]
Hearn, Lafcadio, 1850–1904.

LAC 12465

Streaks of squatter life, and far-West scenes. A series of humorous sketches descriptive of incidents and character in the wild West. To which are added other miscellaneous pieces. By "Solitaire", (John S. Robb, of St. Louis, Mo.) Philadelphia, Carey and Hart, 1847.
Robb, John S.

LAC 14945

Street-cleaning and the disposal of a city's wastes: methods and results and the effect upon public health, public morals, and municipal prosperity, by George E. Waring, jr. New York, Doubleday & McClure co., 1897.
Waring, George Edwin, 1833–1898.

LAC 15343

Street pavements and paving materials. A manual of city pavements: the methods and materials of their construction. For the use of students, engineers, and city officials. 2d ed. 1st thousand. New York, J. Wiley & sons; [etc., etc.] 1912.
Tillson, George William, 1852–

LAC 10864

The street railways of Chicago; report of the Civic federation of Chicago, ed. by Milo Roy Maltbie, PH. D. Accountant's report by Edmund F. Bard. [New York] 1901.
Civic Federation of Chicago.

LAC 40104

Streets and slums. A study in local municipal geography... Baltimore, Cushing & company [c1892]
Brown, Frederick J.

LAC 13021

Strength and beauty. Discussions for young men. New York, Dodd & Mead [c1874]
Hopkins, Mark, 1802–1887.

LAC 40107

Strength out of weakness: or, A glorious manifestation of the further progress of the gospel among the Indians in New England. By Henry Whitfield. New York, Reprinted for J. Sabin, 1865.
Society for Propagation of the Gospel in New England.

LAC 14180

The strenuous life; essays and addresses. New York, The Century co., 1901.
Roosevelt, Theodore, *pres. U.S.*, 1858–1919.

LAC 40062

Strictures on a pamphlet, entitled, a "Friendly address to all reasonable Americans, on the subject of our political confusions." Addressed to the people of America... Philadelphia: Printed and sold by William and Thomas Bradford, at the London coffee-house, M.DCC.LXXIV.
Lee, Charles, 1731–1782.

LAC 40019

Strictures on Montgomery on the cotton manufactures of Great Britain and America. Also, a practical comparison of the cost of steam and water power in America. Newburyport, Morss and Brewster, 1841.
Frearson, John.

LAC 13032

Strictures on the modern system of female education. With a view of the principles and conduct prevalent among women of rank and fortune. New York, E. Duyckinck, 1813.
More, Hannah, 1745–1833.

LAC 40106

Strictures on the necessity of inviolably maintaining the navigation and colonial system of Great Britain. London, Printed for J. Debrett, 1804.
Sheffield, John Baker Holroyd, *1st earl of*, 1735–1821.

LAC 40062

Strictures upon the Declaration of the Congress at Philadelphia; in a letter to a noble lord, &c. London, Printed in the year 1776.
Hutchinson, Thomas, 1711–1780.

LAC 14165

The strike at Lawrence, Mass. Hearings before the Committee on rules of the House of representatives on House resolutions 409 and 433, March 2–7, 1912...
Washington, Govt. print. off., 1912.
U.S. *Congress. House. Committee on Rules.*

LAC 40021

The strike at Pullman. Statements of President Geo. M. Pullman and Second Vice-President T. H. Wickes, before the U.S. strike commission. Also published statements of the company relating to the strike. [n.p., 1894?]
Pullman, George Mortimer.

LAC 13383
A strike of millionaires against miners; or, The story of Spring Valley. An open letter to the millionaires. Chicago, Belford-Clarke co., 1890.
Lloyd, Henry Demarest, 1847–1903.

LAC 13742
Strikers, communists, tramps and detectives. New York, G. W. Dillingham co., 1900, [c1878]
Pinkerton, Allan, 1819–1884.

LAC 40136
Strikes in Massachusetts. [Boston, Rand, Avery, & co., printers to the commonwealth, 1880]
Massachusetts. *Bureau of Statistics of Labor.*

LAC 11268
Strikes; when to strike, how to strike; a book of suggestion for the buyers and sellers of labour. New York and London, G. P. Putnam's sons, 1910.
Crosby, Oscar Terry, 1861–1947.

LAC 13402
Striking for life: labor's side of the labor question; the right of the workingman to a fair living, by John Swinton, and articles specially contributed by Samuel Gompers, Eugene V. Debs [and] John W. Hayes. [n.p.] American Manufacturing and Publishing co., 1894.
Swinton, John, 1829–1901.

LAC 16579
Strive and succeed; or, The progress of Walter Conrad. By Horatio Alger, jr. Philadelphia, Porter & Coates [c1872]
Alger, Horatio, 1832–1899.

LAC 11170
Strong drink; the curse and the cure. Philadelphia [etc.] Hubbard brothers; St. Louis, Mo., N. D. Thompson & co.; [etc., etc., c1877]
Arthur, Timothy Shay, 1809–1885.

LAC 22269–70
The struggle for American independence. London, Siegle, Hill, 1908.
Fisher, Sydney George, 1856–1927.

LAC 14261
The struggle for existence. Chicago, Ill., International school of social economy [1904]
Mills, Walter Thomas, 1856–1942.

LAC 13258
The struggle for Missouri. Washington, D. C., The National tribune co., 1909.
McElroy, John, 1846–1929.

LAC 13721
The struggle for self-government; being an attempt to trace American political corruption to its sources in six states of the United States, with a dedication to the czar. New York, McClure, Phillips & co., 1906.
Steffens, Joseph Lincoln, 1866–1936.

LAC 14764
The struggle of '72. The issues and candidates of the present political campaign: containing biographical sketches of all the candidates for president and vice-president; history and platforms of the great political parties; facts about public men and measures; review of Grant's administration; the queer record of Horace Greeley. Chicago [etc.] Union publishing company; San Francisco, Cal., A. L. Bancroft & co., 1872.
Chamberlin, Everett.

LAC 16144
Struggles and triumphs; or, Forty years' recollections of P. T. Barnum. Written by himself. Author's ed. (Biography complete to April, 1871.)... Buffalo, Warren, Johnson & co., 1872.
Barnum, Phineas Taylor, 1810–1891.

LAC 12017
The struggles (social, financial and political) of Petroleum V. Nasby [*pseud.*]... Embracing his trials and troubles, ups and downs, rejoicings and wailings; likewise his views of men and things. Together with the lectures "Cussed be Canaan," "The struggles of a conservative with the woman question," and "In search of the man of sin." With an introduction by Hon. Charles Sumner. Illustrated by Thomas Nast. Boston, I. N. Richardson and company, 1872.
Locke, David Ross, 1833–1888.

LAC 16418
Stuart's cavalry in the Gettysburg campaign. New York, Moffat, Yard & company, 1908.
Mosby, John Singleton, 1833–1916.

LAC 12996
Student life at Amherst college. Its organizations, their membership and history... Amherst, Hatch & Williams. 1871.
Cutting, George Rugg, 1848–

LAC 11946
Studies and appreciations. New York [etc.] The Macmillan company, 1900.
Gates, Lewis Edwards, 1860–1924.

LAC 13016
Studies in American education. New York and London, Longmans, Green, and co., 1898, [c1895]
Hart, Albert Bushnell, 1854–

LAC 13737
Studies in American trade unionism, edited by Jacob H. Hollander and George E. Barnett. New York, H. Holt and company, 1907, [c1906]
Hollander, Jacob Harry, 1871–1940, *ed.*

LAC 15222
Studies in early graduate education, the Johns Hopkins, Clark university, the University of Chicago, by W. Carson Ryan. With a preface by Walter A. Jessup. New York, The Carnegie foundation for the advancement of teaching, 1939.
Ryan, Will Carson, 1885–

LAC 16818
Studies in enterprise; a selected bibliography of American and Canadian company histories and biographies of businessmen. Lorna M. Daniells, compiler. Boston, 1957.
Harvard University. *Graduate School of Business Administration. Baker Library.*

LAC 12127
Studies in letters and life. Boston and New York, Houghton, Mifflin and company, 1890.
Woodberry, George Edward, 1855–1930.

LAC 10509
Studies in logical theory, by John Dewey with the co-operation of members and fellows of the Department of philosophy. Chicago, The University of Chicago press, 1903.
Dewey, John, 1859–1952.

LAC 10522
Studies in philosophy and theology. Andover [Mass.] W. F. Draper, 1869.
Haven, Joseph, 1816–1874.

LAC 10245
Studies in the constitutional history of Tennessee. 2d. ed., rev. and enl. Cincinnati, The Robert Clarke company, 1907.
Caldwell, Joshua William, 1856–1909.

LAC 12394
Studies in the South and West, with comments on Canada. New York, Harper & brothers, 1889.
Warner, Charles Dudley, 1829–1900.

LAC 10549
Studies of good and evil: a series of essays upon problems of philosophy and of life. New York, D. Appleton and company, 1899, [c1898]
Royce, Josiah, 1855–1916.

LAC 15851
Studies on slavery, in easy lessons. Compiled into eight studies, and subdivided into short lessons for the convenience of readers. Natchez, J. Warner, 1852.
Fletcher, John, 1791–1862.

LAC 13540
The study of city government; an outline of the problems of municipal functions, control and organization. New York, The Macmillan company; London, Macmillan & co., ltd., 1897.
Wilcox, Delos Franklin, 1873–1928.

LAC 11454
A study of "monarchical" tendencies in the United States, from 1776 to 1801. Urbana, University of Illinois [c1923]
Dunbar, Louise Burnham, 1894–

LAC 13543
A study of the population of Manhattanville... New York, 1909.
Woolston, Howard Brown, 1876–

LAC 40049
A study of the Twelfth amendment of the Constitution of the United States... Philadelphia, 1901.
House, Lolabel.

LAC 11661
A study of the United States steel corporation in its industrial and legal aspects; being three lectures delivered to the class in private corporations, in the University of Michigan, June 3, 4 and 5, 1901. Chicago, Callaghan & company, 1901.
Wilgus, Horace La Fayette, 1859–1935.

LAC 10523
The subjective idea and the objective law of all intelligence.
Rational psychology: or, The subjective idea and the objective law of all intelligence. Schenectady, G. Y. Van Debogert, 1854, [c1848]
Hickok, Laurens Perseus, 1798–1888.

LAC 14305
The substance of a journal during a residence at the Red River Colony, British North America; and frequent excursions among the North-west American Indians, in the years 1820, 1821, 1822; 1823. London, L. B. Seeley and Son, 1824.
West, John, 1779?–1845.

LAC 40101
The substance of two reports of the faculty of Amherst college, to the Board of trustees, with the doings of the Board thereon. Amherst, Carter and Adams, printers, 1827.
Amherst College.

LAC 10773
Substitutes for the saloon, by Raymond Calkins; an investigation made for the Committee of fifty under the direction of Francis G. Peabody, Elgin R. L. Gould and William M. Sloane, sub-committee on substitutes for the saloon. Boston and New York, Houghton, Mifflin and company [1901]
Calkins, Raymond, 1869–

LAC 11988
Suburban sketches. 13th ed. With illustrations by Augustus Hoppin. Boston, Houghton, Mifflin, 1893, [c1872]
Howells, William Dean, 1837–1920.

LAC 14709
The subways and tunnels of New York, methods and costs, with an appendix on tunneling machinery and methods and tables of engineering data, by Gilbert H. Gilbert, Lucius I. Wightman and W. L. Saunders. 1st ed., 1st thousand. New York, J. Wiley & sons; [etc., etc.] 1912.
Gilbert, Gilbert Haskell, 1866–

LAC 10312
Success and its conditions. Boston, J. R. Osgood and company, 1871.
Whipple, Edwin Percy, 1819–1886.

LAC 16060
Suffolk in the XVIIth century: the Breviary of Suffolk, by Robert Reyce, 1618; now published for the first time from the ms. in the British museum, with notes, by Lord Francis Hervey. London, J. Murray, 1902.
Reyce, Robert, d. 1638.

LAC 12495
The suffrage franchise in the thirteen English colonies in America. Philadelphia, For the University; Boston, Ginn & co., agents, 1905.
McKinley, Albert Edward, 1870–1936.

LAC 15966
The sugar industry of the United States. Introduction. Part I.–Cane sugar. Part II.–Beet sugar. Part III.–Sorghum sugar. Part IV.–Maple sugar. Washington, Govt. print. off., 1885.
Wiley, Harvey Washington, 1844–1930.

LAC 10102
The sugar-planter's manual; being a treatise on the art of obtaining sugar from the sugar-cane. By W. J. Evans, M. D. Philadelphia, Lea and Blanchard, 1848.
Evans, William Julian.

LAC 11657
The sugar refining industry in the United States. Its development and present condition. Philadelphia, Pub. for the University, 1908.
Vogt, Paul Leroy, 1878–

LAC 40106
The sugar tax. [Boston, Printed at the Boston press, 1832]
Lee, Henry, 1782–1867.

LAC 40026
Suggestions respecting the reformation of the banking system. By R. Hare, M. D. Philadelphia, J. C. Clark, 1837.
Hare, Robert, 1781–1858.

LAC 10631
A summary history of New-England, from the first settlement at Plymouth, to the acceptance of the federal Constitution. Comprehending a general sketch of the American war. Dedham [Mass.] Printed for the author, by H. Mann and J. H. Adams, 1799.
Adams, Hannah, 1755–1831.

LAC 12160
A summary view of America: comprising a description of the face of the country, and of several of the principal cities; and remarks on the social, moral and political character of the people: being the result of observations and enquiries during a journey in the United States. By an Englishman. London, T. Cadell; [etc., etc.] 1824.
Candler, Isaac.

LAC 40008
A summary view of the courses of crops, in the husbandry of England & Maryland; with a comparison of their products; and a system of improved courses, proposed for farms in America. Philadelphia, Printed by Charles Cist, 1784.
Bordley, John Beale, 1727–1804.

LAC 11092
A summary view of the Millennial church, or United society of believers, (commonly called Shakers.) comprising the rise, progress and practical order of the society; together with the general principles of their faith and testimony. Published by order of the ministry, in union with the church... Albany, Printed by Packard & Van Benthuysen, 1823.
Shakers.

LAC 13318
A summer journey in the West. New York, J. S. Taylor and co., 1841.
Steele, Eliza R.

LAC 13144
Summer suns in the far West; a holiday trip to the Pacific slope. London, New York [etc.] T. Nelson and sons, 1890.
Blaikie, William Garden, 1820–1899.

LAC 14957
Sunday legislation; its history to the present time and its results. New ed., rev. to date and enl. New York, D. Appleton and co., 1902.
Lewis, Abram Herbert, 1836–1908.

LAC 14223
The Sunday-school: its origin, mission, methods, and auxiliaries. Philadelphia, J. D. Wattles, 1888.
Trumbull, Henry Clay, 1830–1903.

LAC 15405
Sunday-school movements in America. New York, Chicago [etc.] Fleming H. Revell co. [c1901]
Brown, Marianna Catherine, d. 1916.

LAC 11192
Sunlight and shadow; or, Gleanings from my life work. Comprising personal experiences and opinions, anecdotes, incidents, and reminiscences, gathered from thirty-seven years' experience on the platform and among the people, at home and abroad. With full-page engravings, and steel-plate portrait of the author. Hartford, Conn., A. D. Worthington and company; New York, C. Drew; [etc., etc.] 1881.
Gough, John Bartholomew, 1817–1886.

LAC 11995
The sunny South; or, The southerner at home, embracing five years' experience of a northern governess in the land of the sugar and the cotton. Ed. by Professor J. H. Ingraham. Philadelphia, G. G. Evans, 1860.
Ingraham, Joseph Holt, 1809–1860.

LAC 11301
Sunshine and shadow in New York. By Matthew Hale Smith, (Burleigh.) Hartford, J. B. Burr and company, 1868.
Smith, Matthew Hale, 1810–1879.

LAC 11056
The supernatural in relation to the natural. By the Rev. James M'Cosh. New York, Robert Carter & brothers, 1862.
McCosh, James, 1811–1894.

LAC 16619
The suppressed book about slavery! Prepared for publication in 1857,–never published until the present time. New York, Carleton, 1864.

LAC 15307
The suppression of the African slave-trade to the United States of America, 1638–1870. New York, London [etc.] Longmans, Green, and co., 1896.
Du Bois, William Edward Burghardt, 1868–1963.

LAC 16744
The Supreme court and unconstitutional legislation. New York, Columbia university; [etc., etc.] 1913.
Moore, Blaine Free, 1879–1941.

LAC 12732
The Supreme court of the United States: its history by Hampton L. Carson ... and its centennial celebration, February 4th, 1890. Prepared under direction of the Judiciary centennial committee. Philadelphia, A. R. Keller company, 1892.
Carson, Hampton Lawrence, 1852–1929.

LAC 12736

The Supreme court of the United States. With a review of certain decisions relating to its appellate power under the Constitution. Albany, N. Y., M. Bender & company, 1913.
Countryman, Edwin, 1833–1914.

LAC 13525

Surprising accounts of the revival of religion, in the United States of America, in different parts of the world, and among different denominations of Christians. With a number of interesting occurrences of divine Providence. Collected by the publisher. [Philadelphia] Printed and published by William W. Woodward, no. 52, South Second street; at the book-store lately occupied by Mr. William Young, 1802.
Woodward, William Wallis, *comp.*

LAC 11877

Surry of Eagle's-nest; or, The memoirs of a staff-officer serving in Virginia. Edited, from the mss. of Colonel Surry, by John Estern Cooke. With four illustrations by Winslow Homer. New York, Bunce and Huntington, 1866.
Cooke, John Esten, 1830–1886.

LAC 40041

A survey of the activities of municipal health departments in the United States, by Franz Schneider, jr. New York city, Dept. of surveys and exhibits, Russell Sage foundation [1916]
Schneider, Franz, 1887–

LAC 40057

A survey of the Japanese question in California, by J. Soyeda and T. Kamiya. San Francisco, 1913.
Soyeda, Juichi.

LAC 40041

A survey of the public health situation, Ithaca, New York, 1914, by Franz Schneider, jr. Ithaca, N. Y., Central committee for Ithaca survey, 1915.
Schneider, Franz, 1887–

LAC 16328

A survey of the roads of the United States of America, 1789. Edited by Walter W. Ristow. Cambridge, Mass., Belknap Press of Harvard University Press, 1961.
Colles, Christopher, 1738–1816.

LAC 14368

A survey of the summe of church-discipline. Wherein the way of the churches of New-England is warranted out of the Word, and all exceptions of weight, which are made against it, answered: Whereby also it will appear to the judicious reader, that something more must be said, then yet hath been, before their principles can be shaken, or they should be unsetled in their practice. London, Printed by A. M. for John Bellamy, at the Three Golden Lions in Cornhill, near the Royall exchange, 1648.
Hooker, Thomas, 1586–1647.

LAC 20942–43

Susan Lenox, her fall and rise ... with a portrait of the author. New York [etc.] D. Appleton and company, 1917.
Phillips, David Graham, 1867–1911.

LAC 13088

Sut Lovingood. Yarns spun by a "nat'ral born durn'd fool." Warped and wove for public wear. New York, Fitzgerald Publishing Corporation [c1867]
Harris, George Washington, 1814–1869.

LAC 13324

Sutter's own story; the life of General John Augustus Sutter and the history of New Helvetia in the Sacramento valley ... by Erwin G. Gudde. New York, G. P. Putnam's sons, 1936.
Sutter, John Augustus, 1803–1880.

LAC 40086

The sweating system. [Washington, Govt. print. off., 1896]
White, Henry, 1866–

LAC 15070

Swedes in America, 1638–1938, edited by Adolph B. Benson and Naboth Hedin. Published for the Swedish American tercentenary association. New Haven, Yale university press; London, H. Milford, Oxford university press, 1938.
Benson, Adolph Burnett, 1881–   *ed.*

LAC 40090

The Swedes in Kansas; address delivered, July 5, 1886, at the celebration of Independence Day, by the Swedes of Lindsborg, Kansas. [Topeka, Kansas publishing house, 1888]
Martin, John Alexander, 1839–1889.

LAC 14874

Swedish immigration. 1840–1930.
The background of Swedish immigration, 1840–1930...
[Chicago, Ill., The University of Chicago press, 1931]
Janson, Florence Edith.

LAC 23050–51

The Swedish settlements on the Delaware, 1638–1664.
Philadelphia, Swedish colonial society, 1911.
Johnson, Amandus, 1877–

LAC 12018

"Swingin round the cirkle." By Petroleum V. Nasby [*pseud.*] His ideas of men, politics, and things, as set forth in his letters to the public press, during the year 1866. Illustrated by Thomas Nast. Boston, Lee and Shepard, 1867.
Locke, David Ross, 1833–1888.

LAC 13150

The Switzerland of America. A summer vacation in the parks and mountains of Colorado. Springfield, Mass., S. Bowles & co.; New York, The American news co.; [etc., etc.] 1869.
Bowles, Samuel, 1826–1878.

LAC 12021

Sword blades and poppy seed. New York, The Macmillan company, 1914.
Lowell, Amy, 1874–1925.

LAC 11954

Sybaris and other homes. Boston, Fields, Osgood, & co., 1869.
Hale, Edward Everett, 1822–1909.

LAC 11816

The sylphs of the seasons, with other poems. First American from the London edition. Boston, Cummings and Hilliard, 1813.
Allston, Washington, 1779–1843.

LAC 40073

Syndicalism, by Earl C. Ford & Wm. Z. Foster. Chicago, W. Z. Foster [1913?]
Ford, Earl C.

LAC 11262

Syndicalism, American.
American syndicalism; the I. W. W. New York, The Macmillan company, 1913.
Brooks, John Graham, 1846–1938.

LAC 15617

Syndicalism, industrial unionism and socialism. New York, B. W. Huebsch, 1913.
Spargo, John, 1876–1966.

LAC 40006

Syndicalism, the modern menace to capitalism... New York, Mother earth publishing association, 1913.
Goldman, Emma, 1869–1940.

LAC 40087

Synopsis of the cruise of the U.S. exploring expedition, during the years 1838, '39, '40, '41 & '42; delivered before the National institute, by its commander, Charles Wilkes, esq., on the twentieth of June 1842. To which is added a list of officers and scientific corps attached to the expedition. Washington, Printed by P. Force, 1842.
Wilkes, Charles, 1798–1877.

LAC 14715

"The system," as uncovered by the San Francisco graft prosecution. San Francisco, Press of the James H. Barry company, 1915.
Hichborn, Franklin, 1869–

LAC 14260

A system of intellectual philosophy: by Rev. Asa Mahan. 2d ed. New York, Harper & brothers, 1847.
Mahan, Asa, 1800–1889.

LAC 12623

A system of mineralogy, comprising the most recent discoveries. With numerous woodcuts and four copper plates. 2d ed. New York and London, Wiley & Putnam, 1844.
Dana, James Dwight, 1813–1895.

LAC 10524

A system of moral science. Schenectady, G. Y. Van Debogert; [etc., etc.] 1853.
Hickok, Laurens Perseus, 1798–1888.

LAC 40026

A system of national finance. Notes explanatory of Mr. Chase's plan of national finance. Washington, Govt. print. off., 1861.
Stilwell, Silas Moore, 1800–1881.

LAC 16050

A system of penal law for the United States of America: consisting of a Code of crimes and punishments; a Code of procedure in criminal cases; a Code of prison discipline; and a Book of definitions. Prepared and presented to the House of representatives of the United States. Printed by order of the House of representatives. Washington, Printed by Gales & Seaton, 1828.
Livingston, Edward, 1764–1836.

LAC 15207

System of public instruction and primary school law of Michigan, with explanatory notes, forms, regulations and instructions; a digest of decisions, a detailed history of public instruction ... the history of and laws relating to incorporated institutions of learning &c. &c. Prepared by Francis W. Shearman, superintendent of public instruction. Lansing, Mich., Ingals, Hedges & co., printers to the state, 1852.
Michigan. *Dept. of Public Instruction.*

LAC 20367–69

Systematic theology. New York, C. Scribner and company, 1887.
Hodge, Charles, 1797–1878.

LAC 15639

A systematic treatise, historical, etiological and practical, on the principal diseases of the interior valley of North America, as they appear in the Caucasian, African, Indian, and Esquimaux varieties of its population. Cincinnati, W. B. Smith & co.; New York, Mason & Law; [etc., etc.] 1850.
Drake, Daniel, 1785–1852.

LAC 15658

A systematic treatise, historical, etiological, and practical, on the principal diseases of the interior valley of North America, as they appear in the Caucasian, African, Indian, and Esquimaux varieties of its population. By Daniel Drake, M. D. Ed. by S. Hanbury Smith and Francis G. Smith. 2d ser. Philadelphia, Lippincott, Grambo & co., 1854.
Drake, Daniel, 1785–1852.

LAC 15718

Systems, institutions and statistics of scientific instruction, applied to national industries.
Science and art. Systems, institutions and statistics of scientific instruction, applied to national industries in different countries. Vol. I... New York, E. Steiger, 1872.
Barnard, Henry, 1811–1900.

LAC 11809

Table-talk. Boston, Roberts brothers, 1877.
Alcott, Amos Bronson, 1799–1888.

LAC 10555

Tables of and annotated index to the congressional series of United States public documents. Prepared in the office of the superintendent of documents, Government printing office. Washington, Gov't. print. off., 1902.
U.S. *Superintendent of Documents.*

LAC 15611

Tables showing arrivals of alien passengers and immigrants in the United States from 1820 to 1888. Washington, Govt. print. off., 1889.
U.S. *Bureau of Statistics (Treasury Dept.)*

LAC 40060
A tabular view of the financial affairs of Pennsylvania, from the commencement of her public works to the present time; in which are included the cost, revenue and expenditures of the several lines of canals and railroads, &c. The whole prepared from the official records. Philadelphia, E. C. Biddle, 1844.
Hammond, John W.

LAC 14037
Tah-koo wah-kan; or, The gospel among the Dakotas. By Stephen R. Riggs. With an introduction, by S. B. Treat. Boston, Congregational publishing society [c1869]
Riggs, Stephen Return, 1812–1883.

LAC 16816
Taking Manila; or, In the Philippines with Dewey, giving the life and exploits of Admiral George Dewey, U.S.N. New York, Hurst & company [c1899]
Williams, Henry Llewellyn, 1842–

LAC 14826
A tale of the Huguenots; or, Memoirs of a French refugee family. Tr. and comp. from the original manuscripts of James Fontaine, by one of his descendants [Ann Maury] With an introduction, by F. L. Hawks. New York, J. S. Taylor, 1838.
Fontaine, Jacques, b. 1658.

LAC 11406
A tale of two conventions; being an account of the Republican and Democratic national conventions of June, 1912, with an outline of the Progressive national convention of August in the same year, by William Jennings Bryan, with selections of notable speeches, including those of Theodore Roosevelt, Mr. Bryan, Elihu Root and Alton B. Parker, ed. by Virgil V. McNitt, illustrated from contemporary cartoons. New York and London, Funk & Wagnalls company, 1912.
Bryan, William Jennings, 1860–1925.

LAC 15311
Tales about the United States of America, by Peter Parley [pseud.] London, T. Tegg, 1839.
Goodrich, Samuel Griswold, 1793–1860.

LAC 12011
Tales and sketches. By a country schoolmaster. New-York, Printed by J. & J. Harper, 1829.
Leggett, William, 1801–1839.

LAC 11822
Tales of the Puritans. The regicides.–The fair Pilgrim.–Castine. New-Haven, A. H. Maltby; New-York, G. and C. and H. Carvill, and J. Leavitt; [etc., etc.] 1831.
Bacon, Delia Salter, 1811–1859.

LAC 10394
Tales of the road, by Charles N. Crewdson; illustrated by J. J. Gould. Chicago, Thompson & Thomas, 1905.
Crewdson, Charles Newman, 1870–

LAC 10481
Talks for the times; by W. H. Crogman, South Atlanta, Ga. [Atlanta, Press of Franklin prtg. & pub. co., 1896]
Crogman, William Henry, 1841–1931.

LAC 10615
Talks on pedagogies. An outline of the theory of concentration. New York and Chicago, E. L. Kellogg & co. [1894]
Parker, Francis Wayland, 1837–1902.

LAC 11264
Talks on the labor troubles. By Rev. C. O. Brown. Chicago, F. H. Revell [c1886]
Brown, Charles Oliver.

LAC 12882
Talks with slaves in the southern states.
The roving editor: or, Talks with slaves in the southern states. New York, Negro Universities Press [1968]
Redpath, James, 1833–1891.

LAC 14070
The Tammany hall democracy of the city of New York, and the general committee for 1875, being a brief history of the Tammany hall democracy from 1834 to the present time... New York, M. B. Brown, printer, 1875.
Gover, William C.

LAC 13477
The tariff controversy in the United States, 1789–1833. With a summary of the period before the adoption of the Constitution. Palo Alto, Cal., Published by the University, 1892.
Elliott, Orrin Leslie, 1860–1940.

LAC 10214
The tariff history of the United States; a series of essays. New York & London, G. P. Putnam's sons, [1888]
Taussig, Frank William, 1859–1940.

LAC 40002
The tariff policy of England and of the United States contrasted. Boston, Little, Brown and company, 1877.
Bigelow, Erastus Brigham, 1814–1879.

LAC 20094–100
Tariff schedules. Hearings before the Committee on ways and means, House of representatives... Washington, Govt. print. off., 1913.
U.S. Congress. House. Committee on Ways and Means.

LAC 40069
Taxation; a plain talk for plain people. New York, The Society for political education, 1883.
Canfield, James Hulme, 1847–1909.

LAC 10027
Taxation in American states and cities. By Richard T. Ely. Assisted by John H. Finley, A. B. New York, T. Y. Crowell & co. [c1888]
Ely, Richard Theodore, 1854–1943.

LAC 40018
Taylor and other systems of shop management... Report. [Washington, Govt. print. off., 1912]
U.S. Congress. House. Special Committee to Investigate the Taylor and Other Systems of Shop Management.

LAC 10582
The teaching and history of mathematics in the United States. Washington, Govt. print. off., 1890.
Cajori, Florian, 1859–1930.

LAC 12806
Teachings of patriots and statesmen; or, The "founders of the republic" on slavery. Philadelphia, J. W. Bradley, 1861, [c1860]
Chase, Ezra B.

LAC 12685
The telegraph in America. Its founders, promoters, and noted men. New York, Derby brothers, 1879.
Reid, James D.

LAC 10299
The telegraph monopoly. Philadelphia, Pa., C. F. Taylor [1899]
Parsons, Frank, 1854–1908.

LAC 10913
Telephones and telegraphs and municipal electric fire-alarm and police-patrol signaling systems. 1912. Washington, Govt. print. off., 1915.
U.S. *Bureau of the Census.*

LAC 10774
The temperance reform and its great reformers. An illustrated history ... with over twenty portraits of the chief reformers, and characteristic selections from their best writings and addresses. Ed. by Rev. W. H. Daniels, A. M. With an introduction by Rev. Theodore L. Cuyler, D. D. Pub. by subscription. New York [etc.] Nelson & Phillips; Cincinnati [etc.] Hitchcock & Walden, 1878.
Daniels, William Haven, 1836–   *ed.*

LAC 15607
The temperance reformation: its history, from the organization of the first temperance society to the adoption of the liquor law of Maine, 1851; and the consequent influence to the promulgation of that law on the political interest of the state of New York, 1852. By Rev. Lebbeus Armstrong. New York, Boston [etc.] Fowlers and Wells, 1853.
Armstrong, Lebbeus, 1775–1860.

LAC 40015
The tempers. London, E. Mathews, 1913.
Williams, William Carlos, 1883–1963.

LAC 40046
The temporal power of the pope. A full and authentic report of the brilliant speech of the Hon. Joseph R. Chandler, of Pennsylvania. In the House of representatives of the United States. January 11, 1855. Philadelphia, H. & C. M'Grath, 1855.
Chandler, Joseph Ripley, 1792–1880.

LAC 40013
Ten-hour maximum working-day for women and young persons. April 10, 1913. Washington, Govt. print. off., 1913.
U.S. *Bureau of Labor Statistics.*

LAC 40079
Ten men of Money island, or The primer of finance. Chicago, The Chicago sentinel publishing co. [1891]
Norton, Seymour F.

LAC 11129
Ten New England leaders. New York, Boston [etc.] Silver, Burdett and company, 1901.
Walker, Williston, 1860–1922.

LAC 13963
Ten nights in a bar-room, and what I saw there. Philadelphia, G. G. Evans, 1860.
Arthur, Timothy Shay, 1809–1883.

LAC 13323
Ten thousand miles with a dog sled; a narrative of winter travel in interior Alaska. New York, C. Scribner's sons, 1914.
Stuck, Hudson, 1863–1920.

LAC 16133
Ten years a cowboy. By C. C. Post; addenda by Tex Bender, the cowboy fiddler. Chicago, Rhodes & McClure publishing company, 1906.
Post, Charles Clement.

LAC 16190
Ten years in Nevada; or, Life on the Pacific coast. Buffalo, Baker, Jones & co., printers, 1880.
Mathews, Mary McNair.

LAC 16670
Ten years in Oregon. By D. Lee and J. H. Frost. New-York, Pub. for the authors, J. Collord, printer, 1844.
Lee, Daniel, 1806–1895.

LAC 16909
Ten years in Oregon. Travels and adventures of Doctor E. White and lady, west of the Rocky mountains, with incidents of two sea voyages via Sandwich islands around cape Horn, containing, also, a brief history of the missions and settlement of the country ... description of the soil, production and climate. Ithaca, N. Y., Andrus, Gauntlett, & co., 1850.
Allen, *Miss* A   J   *comp.*

LAC 12352
Ten years on a Georgia plantation since the war. London, R. Bentley & son, 1883.
Leigh, Frances, 1838–1910.

LAC 13648
A ten years' war; an account of the battle with the slum in New York. Boston and New York, Houghton, Mifflin and company, 1900.
Riis, Jacob August, 1849–1914.

LAC 40041
The tendency of men to live in cities. Boston, Damrell & Upham, 1895.
Kingsbury, Frederick John, 1823–1910.

LAC 40005
Tender buttons: objects, food, rooms. New York, Claire Marie, 1914.
Stein, Gertrude, 1874–1946.

LAC 15452
Tenement conditions in Chicago. Report by the investigating committee of the City homes association. Text by Robert Hunter. Chicago, City homes association, 1901.
City Homes Association, *Chicago.*

LAC 13026
Tenth annual report covering the year 1846 [by] Horace Mann. Facsimile ed. [1952]
Massachusetts. *Board of Education.*

LAC 15794
Tenting on the plains; or, General Custer in Kansas and Texas, by Elizabeth B. Custer. New York, C. L. Webster and company, 1889, [c1887]
Custer, Elizabeth, *d.* 1933.

LAC 14982
Tenure and toil; or, Land, labor and capital. [2d ed.]
Chicago, Law journal print, 1894.
Gibbons, John, 1848–1917.

LAC 40093
The Tercentenary pamphlet series and its contributors. [New Haven] Published for the Tercentenary commission by the Yale university press, 1936.
Connecticut. *Tercentenary Commission. Committee on Historical Publications.*

LAC 22888
Teresina in America. By Therese Yelverton (viscountess Avonmore) London, R. Bentley and son, 1875.
Longworth, Maria Theresa, 1832?–1881.

LAC 12917
The territorial acquisitions of the United States; an historical review. Boston, Small, Maynard & co., 1899.
Bicknell, Edward.

LAC 21781–809
The territorial papers of the United States. Washington, U.S. Govt. Print. Off., 1934–69.
Carter, Clarence Edwin, 1881–1961, *comp.*

LAC 11163
Territories and dependencies of the United States, their Government and administration. New York, The Century co., 1905.
Willoughby, William Franklin, 1867–

LAC 14194
Testimonies concerning slavery. By M. D. Conway, a native of Virginia. London, Chapman and Hall, 1864.
Conway, Moncure Daniel, 1832–1907.

LAC 11093
Testimonies concerning the character and ministry of Mother Ann Lee and the first witnesses of the gospel of Christ's second appearing; given by some of the aged brethren and sisters of the United society, including a few sketches of their own religious experience: approved by the church... Albany, Printed by Packard & Van Benthuysen, 1827.
Shakers.

LAC 15453
Testimonies of the life, character, revelations and doctrines of Mother Ann Lee, and the elders with her, through whom the word of eternal life was opened in this day of Christ's second appearing, collected from living witnesses, in union with the church... 2d ed. Albany, N. Y., Weed, Parsons & co., printers, 1888.
Shakers.

LAC 16492
The testimony and practice of the Presbyterian church in reference to American slavery: with an appendix: containing the position of the General assembly (New school), Free Presbyterian church, Reformed Presbyterian, Associate, Associate reformed, Baptist, Protestant Episcopal, and Methodist Episcopal churches. By Rev. John Robinson. Cincinnati, J. D. Thorpe, 1852.
Robinson, John, 1814–1888.

LAC 14779
Testimony in relation to the Ute Indian outbreak, taken by the committee on Indian affairs of the House of representatives. [Washington, Govt. print. off., 1880]
U.S. *Congress. House. Committee on Indian Affairs.*

LAC 20454–58
Testimony taken before the Senate committee on cities, pursuant to resolution of the Senate, adopted January 20, 1890. Albany, J. B. Lyon, 1891.
New York *(State) Legislature. Senate.*

LAC 10103
Testing milk and its products. A manual for dairy students, creamery and cheese factory operators and dairy farmers, by E. H. Farrington and F. W. Woll. 6th rev. enl. ed. Madison, Wis., Mendota book company, 1900, [c1899]
Farrington, Edward Holyoke, 1860–1934.

LAC 15722
Tests of divine inspiration: or, The rudimental principles by which true and false revelation, in all eras of the world, can be unerringly discriminated... New Lebanon [N. Y.] United society called Shakers, 1853.
Evans, Frederick William, 1808–1893.

LAC 16647
Texas; a contest of civilizations. Boston and New York, Houghton, Mifflin and company [c1903]
Garrison, George Pierce, 1853–1910.

LAC 22357
Texas and the Texans; or, Advance of the Anglo-Americans to the South-West; including a history of leading events in Mexico, from the conquest by Fernando Cortes to the termination of the Texan revolution... Philadelphia, Thomas, Cowperthwait & co., 1841.
Foote, Henry Stuart, 1804–1880.

LAC 16570
A Texas cow boy [!]; or, Fifteen years on the hurricane deck of a Spanish pony. Taken from real life. Chicago, Ill., M. Umbdenstock & co., 1885.
Siringo, Charles A   1855–1928.

LAC 16944
Texas. Observations, historical, geographical and descriptive, in a series of letters, written during a visit to Austin's colony, with a view of a permanent settlement in

that country, in the autumn of 1831. With an appendix containing specific answers to certain questions, relative to colonization in Texas, issued some time since by the London geographical society. Also, some notice of the recent political events in that quarter. Baltimore, Armstrong & Plaskitt, 1833.
Holley, Mary Austin, *d.* 1846.

LAC 15992
A text-book in the history of education. New York, The Macmillan company; London, Macmillan & co., ltd., 1905.
Monroe, Paul, 1869–1947.

LAC 10127
Text-book of scientific agriculture: with practical deductions. Intended for the use of colleges, schools, and private students. New York, A. S. Barnes & company, 1876, [c1874]
Pendleton, Edmund Monroe, 1815–1884.

LAC 11243
Text-book of the new reformation.
Municipal reform movements in the United States, by William Howe Tolman, with an introductory chapter by the Rev. Charles H. Parkhurst. New-York, Chicago [etc.] Fleming H. Revell company, 1895.
Tolman, William Howe, 1861–

LAC 40138
Text book of the origin and history, &c. &c. of the colored people. Hartford, L. Skinner, printer, 1841.
Pennington, James W   C.

LAC 10162
The textile industries of the United States, including sketches and notices of cotton, woolen, silk, and linen manufacturers in the colonial period. V. I., 1639–1810. Boston, W. B. Clarke & co. [c1893]
Bagnall, William R   1819–1892.

LAC 40062
A thanksgiving sermon on the total repeal of the Stamp-act. Preached in Cambridge, New-England, May 20th, in the afternoon preceding the public rejoicings of the evening upon that great occasion. Published by the desire of the audience, and at the expence of the Honorable Brigadier General Brattle. Boston, Printed and sold by Edes and Gill, in Queenstreet, 1766.
Appleton, Nathaniel, 1693–1784.

LAC 12108
That fortune. Hartford, The American publishing co., 1904.
Warner, Charles Dudley, 1829–1900.

LAC 15972
Theatrical and circus life; or, Secrets of the stage, green-room and sawdust arena... New and rev. ed. St. Louis, [Sun publishing co., c1822]
Jennings, John Joseph, 1853–1909.

LAC 15975
The theatrical apprenticeship and anecdotical recollections of Sol. Smith ... comprising a sketch of the first seven years of his professional life; together with some sketches of adventure in after years... Philadelphia, Carey and Hart, 1847, [c1845]
Smith, Solomon Franklin, 1801–1869.

LAC 15132
Theatrical biography: or, The life of an actor and manager. Interspersed with sketches, anecdotes, and opinions of the professional merits of the most celebrated actors and actresses of our day. Glasgow, R. Griffin, 1848.
Wemyss, Francis Courtney, 1797–1859.

LAC 15976
The theatrical journey-work and anecdotical recollections of Sol. Smith. Comprising a sketch of the second seven years of his professional life; together with sketches of adventure in after years; with a portrait of the author. Philadelphia, T. B. Peterson [c1854]
Smith, Solomon Franklin, 1801–1869.

LAC 15126
Theatrical management in the West and South for thirty years. Interspersed with anecdotical sketches: autobiographically given by Sol. Smith. With fifteen illustrations and a portrait of the author. New York, Harper & brothers, 1868.
Smith, Solomon Franklin, 1801–1869.

LAC 11989
Their wedding journey. By W. D. Howells. With illustrations by Augustus Hoppin. Boston, J. R. Osgood and company, 1872.
Howells, William Dean, 1837–1920.

LAC 14338
Theodore Parker. Boston, Little, Brown, and company, 1936.
Commager, Henry Steele, 1902–

LAC 16308
Theodore Parker: a biography. New York, G. P. Putnam's sons, 1880.
Frothingham, Octavius Brooks, 1822–1895.

LAC 13103
Theodore Parker, preacher and reformer. Boston and New York, Houghton, Mifflin and company, 1901, [c1900]
Chadwick, John White, 1840–1904.

LAC 11537
Theodore Roosevelt, the citizen. New York, Macmillan company; London, Macmillan & co., ltd., 1918, [c1904]
Riis, Jacob August, 1849–1914.

LAC 23075–90
The theological and miscellaneous works of Joseph Priestley... edited, with notes, by John Towill Rutt. [London, Printed by G. Smallfield, 1817–32]
Priestley, Joseph, 1733–1804.

LAC 14119
The theological aspect of reformed Judaism. Baltimore, The Friedenwald company, 1904.
Margolis, Max Leopold, 1866–1932.

LAC 11043
Theology and the social consciousness; a study of the relations of the social consciousness to theology. New York, The Macmillan company; London, Macmillan & co., ltd., 1902.
King, Henry Churchill, 1858–1934.

LAC 11582

The theoretical system by Karl Marx in the light of recent criticism. Chicago, C. H. Kerr & company, 1920, [c1907]
Boudin, Louis Boudianoff, 1874–1952.

LAC 15072

Theories of Americanization; a critical study, with special reference to the Jewish group. New York city, Teachers college, Columbia university, 1920.
Berkson, Isaac Baer, 1891–

LAC 10420

The theory and practice of taxation. New York, D. Appleton and company, 1907, [c1900]
Wells, David Ames, 1828–1898.

LAC 10614

Theory and practice of teaching; or, the motives and methods of good school keeping, by David P. Page. Edited by E. C. Branson. New York [etc.] American book company [c1899]
Page, David Perkins, 1810–1848.

LAC 40024

Theory and practice of the American system of through fast freight transportation, as illustrated in the operations of the Empire transportation company. Philadelphia, Press of Helfenstein, Lewis & Greene, 1876.
Empire Transportation Company, *Philadelphia.*

LAC 40014

The theory of American education. Washington, J. H. Holmes, 1871.
Harris, William Torrey, 1835–

LAC 10562

The theory of business enterprise. New York, C. Scribner's sons, 1904.
Veblen, Thorstein, 1857–1929.

LAC 10525

Theory of morals: an inquiry concerning the law of moral distinctions and the variations and contradictions of ethical codes. Boston, C. C. Little & J. Brown, 1844.
Hildreth, Richard, 1807–1865.

LAC 12991

A theory of motives, ideals, and values in education. Boston and New York, Houghton, Mifflin and company, 1907.
Chancellor, William Estabrook, 1867–

LAC 10574

Theory of politics: an inquiry into the foundations of governments, and the causes and progress of political revolutions. New-York, Harper & brothers, 1853.
Hildreth, Richard, 1807–1865.

LAC 10563

The theory of the leisure class; an economic study in the evolution of institutions. New York, The Macmillan company; London, Macmillan & co., ltd., 1899.
Veblen, Thorstein, 1857–1929.

LAC 10508

The theory of thought. A treatise on deductive logic...
New York, Harper & brothers, 1880.
Davis, Noah Knowles, 1830–1910.

LAC 16458

The Theosophical congress held by the Theosophical society at the Parliament of religions, World's fair of 1893, at Chicago, Ill., September 15, 16, 17. Report of proceedings and documents. New York, 1893.
Theosophical Society.

LAC 16701

They who knock at our gates; a complete gospel of immigration, by Mary Antin, with illustrations by Joseph Stella. Boston and New York, Houghton Mifflin company, 1914.
Antin, Mary, 1881–1949.

LAC 12163

Things as they are in America. London and Edinburgh, W. and R. Chambers, 1854.
Chambers, William, 1800–1883.

LAC 16123

Things as they are: or, Notes of a traveller through some of the middle and northern states. New York, Harper, 1834.
Dwight, Theodore, 1796–1866.

LAC 14854

Things Korean; a collection of sketches and anecdotes, missionary and diplomatic. New York, Chicago [etc.] F. H. Revell company [c1908]
Allen, Horace Newton, 1858–1932.

LAC 10495

Things learned by living. New York and London, G. P. Putnam's sons, 1913.
Bascom, John, 1827–1911.

LAC 13464

Things of the mind. Chicago, A. C. McClurg and company, 1894.
Spalding, John Lancaster, 1840–1916.

LAC 14480

The thinking bayonet. Boston, Walker, Fuller, and company, 1865.
Hosmer, James Kendall, 1834–1927.

LAC 16767

The third violet. New York, D. Appleton and company, 1897.
Crane, Stephen, 1871–1900.

LAC 10923

Thirteen historical discourses, on the completion of two hundred years, from the beginning of the First church in New Haven, with an appendix. New Haven, Durrie & Peck; New York, Gould, Newman & Saxton, 1839.
Bacon, Leonard, 1802–1881.

LAC 12971
The 13th district; a story of a candidate. Indianapolis, The Bowen-Merrill company [c1902]
Whitlock, Brand, 1869–1934.

LAC 13181
Thirty-one years on the plains and in the mountains; or, The last voice from the plains. An authentic record of a life time of hunting, trapping, scouting and Indian fighting in the far West, by Capt. William F. Drannan. Copiously illustrated by H. S. De Lay. Chicago, Rhodes & McClure publishing company, 1901, [c1900]
Drannan, William F   1832–1913.

LAC 10019
Thirty-six voyages to various parts of the world, made between the years 1799 and 1841. By George Coggeshall. Selected from his ms. journal of eighty voyages. 3d ed. Rev., cor. and enl., with additional notes and explanations. New York, The author, G. P. Putnam, agent, 1858.
Coggeshall, George, 1784–1861.

LAC 16251
Thirty years a slave, from bondage to freedom; autobiography. New York, Negro Universities Press [1969]
Hughes, Louis, 1832–

LAC 40105
Thirty years in California; a contribution to the history of the state from 1849 to 1879. San Francisco, A. L. Bancroft & co., printers, 1879.
Willey, Samuel Hopkins.

LAC 10870
Thirty years in Topeka; a historical sketch. Topeka, Kan., G. W. Crane & co., 1886.
Giles, Frye Williams, 1819–1898.

LAC 14490
Thirty years of army life on the border. Comprising descriptions of the Indian nomads of the plains; explorations of new territory; a trip across the Rocky mountains in the winter; descriptions of the habits of different animals found in the West, and the methods of hunting them: with incidents in the life of different frontier men, &c., &c. By Colonel R. B. Marcy. With numerous illustrations. New York, Harper & brothers, 1866.
Marcy, Randolph Barnes, 1812–1887.

LAC 13393
Thirty years of labor. 1859 to 1889. In which the history of the attempts to form organizations of workingmen for the discussion of political, social, and economic questions is traced. The National labor union of 1866, the Industrial brotherhood of 1874, and the order of the Knights of labor of America and the world. The chief and most important principles in the preamble of the Knights of labor discussed and explainedwith views of the author on land, labor and transportation... Columbus, O., Excelsior publishing house, 1890.
Powderly, Terence Vincent, 1849–1924.

LAC 11398
Thirty years of New York politics up-to-date... New York, The author, 1899.
Breen, Matthew Patrick.

LAC 16461
Thirty years passed among the players in England and America: interspersed with anecdotes and reminiscences of a variety of persons, directly or indirectly connected with the drama during the theatrical life of Joe Cowell, comedian. New York, Harper & brothers [1843]
Cowell, Joseph, 1792–1863.

LAC 20316–17
Thirty years' view; or, A history of the working of the American government for thirty years, from 1820 to 1850. Chiefly taken from the Congress debates, the private papers of General Jackson, and the speeches of ex-Senator Benton, with his actual view of the men and affairs: with historical notes and illustrations, and some notices of eminent deceased contemporaries: by a senator of thirty years. New York, D. Appleton and company; Boston, F. Parker, 1854–56.
Benton, Thomas Hart, 1782–1858.

LAC 15411
Thomas Hazard, son of Robt, call'd College Tom. A study of life in Narragansett in the XVIIIth century, by his grandson's granddaughter, Caroline Hazard. Boston and New York, Houghton, Mifflin and company, 1893.
Hazard, Caroline, 1856–1945.

LAC 11503
Thomas Hooker: preacher, founder, democrat. New York, Dodd, Mead, and company [c1891]
Walker, George Leon, 1830–1900.

LAC 40066
Thomas Jefferson and James Thomson Callender, 1798–1802. Ed. by Worthington Chauncey Ford. Brooklyn, N. Y., Historical printing club, 1897.
Callender, James Thomson, 1758–1803.

LAC 40122
Thomas Jefferson and the first monument of the classical revival in America... [Harrisburg, Pa., and Washington, D. C., 1915]
Kimball, Sidney Fiske, 1888–1955.

LAC 14667
Thomas Jefferson, architect; original designs in the collection of Thomas Jefferson Coolidge, junior, with an essay and notes by Fiske Kimball. Boston, Printed for private distribution at the Riverside press, Cambridge, 1916.
Jefferson, Thomas, *pres. U.S.*, 1743–1826.

LAC 12180
Thomas Jefferson as an architect and a designer of landscapes, by William Alexander Lambeth, M. D., and Warren H. Manning. Boston and New York, Houghton Mifflin company, 1913.
Lambeth, William Alexander, 1867–

LAC 13768
Th. Nast, his period and his pictures. New York, The Macmillan company; London, Macmillan & co., ltd., 1904.
Paine, Albert Bigelow, 1861–1937.

LAC 11860
Thoreau: the poet-naturalist. With memorial verses. Boston, Roberts brothers, 1873.
Channing, William Ellery, 1817–1901.

LAC 16884
Thoughts and details on the high and low prices of the thirty years, from 1793 to 1822... 2d ed. London, J. Murray, MDCCCXXIV.
Tooke, Thomas, 1774–1858.

LAC 13592
Thoughts and theories of life and education. Chicago, A. C. McClurg and company, 1897.
Spalding, John Lancaster, *abp.*, 1840–1916.

LAC 14356
Thoughts and things at home and abroad. By Elihu Burritt. With a memoir, by Mary Howitt. Boston, Phillips, Sampson, and company; New York, J. C. Derby, 1856, [c1854]
Burritt, Elihu, 1810–1879.

LAC 11638
Thoughts for the young men of America: or, A few practical words of advice to those born in poverty and destined to be reared in orphanage. 2d ed., rev. and enl. New York, S. R. Wells, 1873.
Reavis, Logan Uriah, 1831–1889.

LAC 15999
Thoughts on African colonization: or, An impartial exhibition of the doctrines, principles and purposes of the American colonization society. Together with the resolutions, addresses and remonstrances of the free people of color... Boston, Printed and pub. by Garrison and Knapp, 1832.
Garrison, William Lloyd, 1805–1879.

LAC 12986
Thoughts on educational topics and institutions. Boston, Phillips, Sampson and company, 1859.
Boutwell, George Sewall, 1818–1905.

LAC 40081
Thoughts on instinctive impulses... Philadelphia: Printed by Jane Aitken, no. 71, North Third street, 1810.
Law, Thomas, 1756–1834.

LAC 14837
Thoughts on institutions of the higher education, with a chapter on classical studies. New York, S. & D. A. Huebsch, 1893.
Leverson, Montague Richard, 1830–

LAC 16564
Thoughts on physical education: being a discourse delivered to a convention of teachers in Lexington, Ky., on the 6th & 7th of Nov., 1833. By Charles Caldwell, M. D. Boston, Marsh, Capen & Lyon, 1834.
Caldwell, Charles, 1772–1853.

LAC 14611
Thoughts on political economy. In two parts. Baltimore, F. Lucas, jun'r., 1820.
Raymond, Daniel, 1786–1849.

LAC 15790
Thoughts on popery... By Rev. William Nevins. New York, American tract society [c1836]
Nevins, William, 1797–1835.

LAC 40094
Thoughts on the condition and prospects of popular education in the United States. By a citizen of Pennsylvania. Philadelphia, Printed by A. Waldie, 1836.
Packard, Frederick Adolphus, 1794–1867.

LAC 14723
Thoughts on the future civil policy of America. 3d ed. New York, Harper & brothers 1867.
Draper, John William, 1811–1882.

LAC 40069
Thoughts on the increasing wealth and national economy of the United States of America. City of Washington, Printed by Way and Groff, North E street, near the Post-office, 1801.
Blodget, Samuel, 1757–1814.

LAC 40062
Thoughts on the origin and nature of government. Occasioned by the late disputes between Great Britain and her American colonies. Written in the year 1766... London, Printed for T. Becket [etc.] 1769.
Ramsay, Allan, 1713–1784.

LAC 14680
Thoughts on the present collegiate system in the United States. Boston, Gould, Kendall & Lincoln, 1842.
Wayland, Francis, 1796–1865.

LAC 40017
Thoughts on the study of political economy as connected with the population, industry and paper currency of the United States. To which is added an appendix drydocks consisting of a series of articles first published in the Columbian Centinel, 1804. New York, Augustus M. Kelley, 1968 [Cambridge, Hilliard & Metcalf, 1809]
Baldwin, Loammi, 1780–1838.

LAC 40152
Thoughts upon female education, accommodated to the present state of society, manners, and government, in the United States of America. Addressed to the visitors of the Young ladies' academy in Philadelphia, 28 July, 1787, at the close of the quarterly examination, by Benjamin Rush, M. D., professor of chemistry in the University of Pennsylvania. To which is added, a prayer, by Samuel Magaw, D. D., rector of St. Paul's church, and vice-provost of the University of Pennsylvania; delivered upon the same occasion. Philadelphia: Printed by Prichard & Hall, 1787.
Rush, Benjamin, 1745–1813.

LAC 40025
Thoughts upon the conduct of our administration, in relation both to Great Britain and France, more especially in reference to the late negotiation, concerning the attack on the Chesapeake. By a friend to peace. Boston, Printed at the Repertory office, 1808.
Lowell, John, 1769–1840.

LAC 15267
Thoughts upon the political situation of the United States of America, in which that of Massachusetts is more particularly considered. With some observations on the Constitution for a federal government. Addressed to the people of the Union. By a native of Boston. Printed at Worcester, Mass., by I. Thomas, 1788.
Jackson, Jonathan, 1743–1810.

LAC 40108

Three addresses on the relations subsisting between the white and colored people of the United States. Washington [D. C.] Gibson bros., printers, 1886.
Douglass, Frederick, 1817?–1895.

LAC 15374

The three constitutions of Connecticut, 1638–9, 1662, 1818... With notes on town representation, by Charles J. Hoadly, 1892. Compiled in Comptroller's office. Hartford, Conn., Printed by order of the comptroller [by The Case, Lockwood & Brainard company] 1901.
Connecticut. *Comptroller.*

LAC 11430

Three decades of federal legislation, 1865–1898.
Union–disunion–reunion. Three decades of federal legislation, 1855 to 1885. Personal and historical memories of events preceding, during, and since the American civil war, involving slavery and secession, emancipation and reconstruction, with sketches of prominent actors during these periods. Illustrated with thirty-six portraits engraved on steel expressly for this work. Providence, R. I., J. A. & R. A. Reid, 1888, [c1885]
Cox, Samuel Sullivan, 1824–1889.

LAC 22191–92

Three episodes of Massachusetts history: the settlement of Boston bay; the Antinomian controversy; a study of church and town government. Boston and New York, Houghton, Mifflin and company, 1892.
Adams, Charles Francis, 1835–1915.

LAC 40025

Three letters, written, and originally published, under the signature of A South Carolina planter. The first, on the case of Jonathan Robbins... The second, on the recent captures of American vessels by British cruisers... The third, on the right of expatriation. By Charles Pinckney, esquire, senator in Congress, for South-Carolina. To which is added, an appendix, containing sundry documents concerning Jonathan Robbins. Philadelphia: Aurora-office, 1799.
Pinckney, Charles, 1758–1824.

LAC 12101

Three men of letters. New York [etc.] G. P. Putnam's sons, 1895.
Tyler, Moses Coit, 1835–1900.

LAC 15178

Three months in the southern states, April–June, 1863. By Lieut.-Col. Fremantle. With portraits engraved from photographs. Edinburgh and London, W. Blackwood and sons, 1863.
Fremantle, *Sir* Arthur James Lyon, 1835–1901.

LAC 11341

Three Phi beta kappa addresses:A college fetich, 1883; "Shall Cromwell have a statue?" 1902; Some modern college tendencies, 1906. Boston and New York, Houghton, Mifflin and company, 1907.
Adams, Charles Francis, 1835–1915.

LAC 16708

Three philosophical poets: Lucretius, Dante, and Goethe. Cambridge, Harvard university, 1910.
Santayana, George, 1863–1952.

LAC 14405

Threescore years: an autobiography, containing incidents of voyages and travels, including six years in a man-of-war. Details of the war between the United States and the Algerine government, bombardment of Algiers by Lord Exmouth, and its subjugation by the French. Also, two years in California, a visit to the Crimea during the bombardment and capture of Sebastopol, journey through Asia Minor, Syria, Palestine and Egypt... Boston, J. French and company, 1857.
Holbrook, Samuel F   *b.* 1793.

LAC 13345

"Three score years and ten," life-long memories of Fort Snelling, Minnesota, and other parts of the West. [Minneapolis, Printing house of Harrison & Smith] 1895, [c1888]
Van Cleve, Charlotte Ouisconsin, 1819–1907.

LAC 14357

Three thousand miles through the Rocky mountains. Philadelphia, J. P. Lippincott & co., 1869.
McClure, Alexander Kelly, 1828–1909.

LAC 40142

Three tracts respecting the conversion and instruction of the free Indians and negroe slaves in the colonies. Addressed to the venerable Society for propagation of the gospel in foreign parts, in the year 1768. A new ed. London, Printed for J. Debrett, M.DCC.LXXXIX.
Knox, William, 1732–1810.

LAC 12329

The three voyages of William Barents to the Arctic regions, (1594, 1595, and 1596) By Gerrit de Veer. First edition ed. by Charles T. Beke, 1853. 2d ed., with an introduction, by Lieutenant Koolemans Beynen. London, Printed for the Hakluyt society, 1876.
Veer, Gerrit de.

LAC 40022

Three weeks in the gold mines.
The emigrant's guide to the gold mines. Three weeks in the gold mines, or Adventures with the gold diggers of California. New York, Joyce and co., 1848. [Tarrytown, N. Y., Reprinted W. Abbatt, 1932]
Simpson, Henry I.

LAC 13237

Three years among the Indians and Mexicans, by General Thomas James, of Monroe county, Illinois; ed., with notes and biographical sketches, by Walter B. Douglas. Saint Louis, Missouri historical society, 1916.
James, Thomas, 1782–1847.

LAC 13732

Three years among the working-classes in the United States during the war. By the author of "The autobiography of a beggar-boy". London, Smith, Elder and co., 1865.
Burn, James Dawson.

LAC 11328

[Three years in Arkansaw]... A complete history of ... my three years of life liberty and pursuit of hapiness [!] along the rocky path of life down in old Arkansaw... Chicago, M. A. Donohue & company [c1904]
Hughes, Marion.

LAC 13356

Three years in California [1846-1849] By Rev. Walter Colton, U. S. N. New York, A. S. Barnes & co.; Cincinnati, H. W. Derby & co., 1850.
Colton, Walter, 1797-1851.

LAC 16862

Three years in Europe: or, Places I have seen and people I have met. By W. Wells Brown, a fugitive slave. With a memoir of the author, by William Farmer, esq. London, C. Gilpin; [etc., etc.] 1852.
Brown, William Wells, 1815-1884.

LAC 40063

Three years in Texas. Including a view of the Texan revolution and an account of the principal battles, together with descriptions of the soil, commercial and agricultural advantages, &c. By Dr. Joseph E. Field, one of the few survivors of Fannin's command. Greenfield, Mass., J. Jones; Boston, A. Tompkins, 1836. Tarrytown, N. Y., Reprinted, W. Abbatt, 1925.
Field, Joseph E.

LAC 15048

Three years in the Federal Cavalry. New York, R. H. Ferguson, 1872.
Glazier, Willard, 1841-1905.

LAC 16383

Three years in the Sixth corps. A concise narrative of events in the Army of the Potomac, from 1861 to the close of the rebellion, April 1865. Albany, S. R. Gray, 1866.
Stevens, George Thomas, 1832-1921.

LAC 16577

A thrilling and truthful history of the pony express; or, Blazing the westward way, and other sketches and incidents of those stirring times. Chicago, Rand, McNally & co. [c1908]
Visscher, William Lightfoot, 1842-1924.

LAC 40078

A thrilling narrative from the lips of the sufferers of the late Detroit riot, March 6, 1863, with the hair breadth escapes of men, women and children, and destruction of colored men's property, not less than $15,000. Detroit, Mich. Published by the author. 1863. Hattiesburg, Miss., The Book farm, 1945.

LAC 12788

Through Afro-America, an English reading of the race problem. London, Chapman & Hall, ltd., 1910.
Archer, William, 1856-1924.

LAC 11435

Through five administrations; reminiscences of Colonel William H. Crook, body-guard to President Lincoln, comp. and ed. by Margarita Spalding Gerry. New York and London, Harper & brothers, 1910.
Crook, William Henry, 1839-1915.

LAC 10513

Through nature to God. Boston and New York, Houghton, Mifflin and company [1899]
Fiske, John, 1842-1901.

LAC 11846

Through one administration. By Frances Hodgson Burnett. New York, C. Scribner's sons 1901, [c1883]
Burnett, Frances, 1849-1924.

LAC 11102

Through science to faith. New ed. New York, C. Scribner's sons, 1904, [c1902]
Smyth, Newman, 1843-1925.

LAC 13815

Through the air: a narrative of forty years' experience as an aeronaut. Comprising a history of the various attempts in the art of flying by artificial means from the earliest period down to the present time. With an account of the author's most important air-voyages and his many thrilling adventures and hairbreadth escapes. Also an appendix, in which are given full instructions for the manufacture and management of balloons. Philadelphia, New York [etc.] To-day publishing company, 1873.
Wise, John, 1808-1879.

LAC 21049-50

Through the Dark continent: or, The sources of the Nile, around the great lakes of equatorial Africa, and down the Livingstone river to the Atlantic ocean. With ten maps and one hundred and fifty woodcuts... New York, Harper & brothers, 1878.
Stanley, *Sir* Henry Morton, 1841-1904.

LAC 16627

Through unknown African countries; the first expedition from Somaliland to lake Lamu. By A. Donaldson Smith. London, New York, E. Arnold, 1897.
Smith, Arthur Donaldson, 1864-1939.

LAC 16186

The tide of immigration. New York [etc.] D. Appleton and company, 1916.
Warne, Frank Julian, 1874-

LAC 10088

The Tim Bunker papers; or, Yankee farming. By Timothy Bunker [*pseud.*] With illustrations by Hoppin. New York, O. Judd and company [c1868]
Clift, William, *b.* 1817.

LAC 16288

The "Times" on the American war: a historical study. By L. S. London, W. Ridgway, 1865.
Stephen, *Sir* Leslie, 1832-1904.

LAC 13246

Timothy Flint, pioneer, missionary, author, editor, 1780-1840; the story of his life among the pioneers and frontiersmen in the Ohio and Mississippi valley and in New England and the South. New York, Burt Franklin, 1968.
Kirkpatrick, John Ervin, 1869-1931.

LAC 14581

The Titan. New York, John Lane company; London, John Lane; [etc., etc.] 1914.
Dreiser, Theodore, 1871-1945.

LAC 13122

To and fro in Southern California. With Sketches in Arizona and New Mexico. Cincinnati, W. M. B. C. press, 1887.
Adams, Emma Hildreth.

LAC 40072

To Nebraska in '57; a diary of Erastus F. Beadle, printed from the original manuscript by courtesy of its owner, Dr. Frank P. O'Brien. [New York] The New York public library, 1923.
Beadle, Erastus Flavel, 1821–1894.

LAC 40065

To the people of the state of South-Carolina. [Charleston, 1832]
Grimke, Thomas Smith, 1786–1834.

LAC 40039

To the rescue of American commerce. Boston, J. E. Farwell & co., 1869.
Blake, Alpheus P.

LAC 12345

The tobacco industry in the United States. New York, The Columbia university press, the Macmillan company, agents; [etc., etc.] 1907.
Jacobstein, Meyer, 1880–

LAC 10076

Tobacco. Its history, varieties, culture, manufacture and commerce, with an account of its various modes of use, from its first discovery until now. Hartford, Conn., American publishing company, 1875.
Billings, E   R.

LAC 40019

Tobacco, the bane of Virginia husbandry. Richmond, Macfarlane & Fergusson, 1860.
Cocke, John Hartwell, 1780–1866.

LAC 15014

Tobias Wilson: a tale of the great rebellion. By Hon. Jere. Clemens. Philadelphia, J. B. Lippincott & co., 1865.
Clemens, Jeremiah, 1814–1865.

LAC 40016

Tolls and transportation. A free canal essential to the state's prosperity: and the water route demonstrated to be superior to the railways. August 10, 1877. Buffalo, Matthews & Warren, 1877.
Richmond, Alonzo.

LAC 12939

To-morrow in Cuba. New York and London, Harper & brothers, 1899.
Pepper, Charles Melville, 1859–1930.

LAC 11014

Tools and the man; property and industry under the Christian law. Boston and New York, Houghton, Mifflin and company, 1893.
Gladden, Washington, 1836–1918.

LAC 22282

The Topeka improvement survey ... [reports] Department of surveys and exhibits, Russell Sage foundation, New York city, to the Topeka improvement survey committee, Topeka, Kansas... [Topeka, Kan., Mail printing house] 1914.
Russell Sage Foundation, *New York. Dept. of Surveys and Exhibits.*

LAC 13173

A topographical description of the state of Ohio, Indiana Territory, and Louisiana. Comprehending the Ohio and Mississippi rivers, and their principal tributary streams: the face of the country, soils, waters, natural productions, animal, vegetable, and mineral; towns, villages, settlements and improvements: and a concise account of the Indian tribes west of the Mississippi. To which is added, an interesting journal of Mr. Chas. Le Raye, while a captive with the Sioux nation, on the waters of the Missouri River. By a late officer in the U.S. army. Boston: Published by Charles Williams. J. Belcher, printer, 1812.
Cutler, Jervis, 1768–1844.

LAC 40105

A topographical description of Virginia, Pennsylvania, Maryland, and North Carolina, comprehending the rivers Ohio, Kenhawa, Sioto, Cherokee, Wabash, Illinois, Mississippi, &c.; the climate, soil and produce, whether animal, vegetable, or mineral; the mountains, creeks, roads, distances, latitudes, &c., and of every part laid down in the annexed map. Published by Thomas Hutchins, captain in the 60th regiment of foot. With a plan of the rapids of the Ohio, a plan of the several villages in the Illinois country, a table of the distances between Fort Pitt and the mouth of the Ohio, all engraved upon copper. And an appendix, containing Mr. Patrick Kennedy's Journal up the Illinois river, and a correct list of the different nations and tribes of Indians, with the number of fighting men, &c. London, Printed for the author, and sold by J. Almon, 1778.
Hutchins, Thomas, 1730–1789.

LAC 40053

Torpedo war, and submarine explosions. New-York, Printed by W. Elliot, 1810.
Fulton, Robert, 1765–1815.

LAC 16836

Totem tales. Indian stories Indian told, gathered in the Pacific Northwest. Fully illustrated by the author. Chicago, Star publishing co., 1896.
Phillips, Walter Shelley, 1867–1940.

LAC 10091

A tour from the city of New York, to Detroit in the Michigan Territory, made between the 2d of May and the 22d of September, 1818. The tour is accompanied with a map upon which the route will be designated; a particular map of the falls and river of Niagara, and the environs of the city of Detroit. New York, Kirk and Mercein, 1819.
Darby, William, 1775–1854.

LAC 20022

A tour in America in 1798, 1799, and 1800. Exhibiting sketches of society and manners, and a particular account of the American system of agriculture, with its recent improvements. London, Printed for J. Harding [etc.] 1805.
Parkinson, Richard, 1748–1815.

LAC 11309
A tour in the United States, Cuba, and Canada. A course of lectures delivered before the members of the Bolton mechanics' institution. London, A. W. Bennett; [etc., etc., 1861]
Ashworth, Henry, 1794–1880.

LAC 16683
A tour of duty in California; including a description of the gold region; and an account of the voyage around cape Horn; with notices of lower California, the Gulf and Pacific coasts, and the principal events attending the conquest of the Californias. By Joseph Warren Revere. Ed. by Joseph N. Balestier. With a map and plates from original designs. New York, C. S. Francis & co.; Boston, J. H. Francis, 1849.
Revere, Joseph Warren, 1812–1880.

LAC 22298
Tour of the American lakes, and among the Indians of the North-west territory, in 1830: disclosing the character and prospects of the Indian race. London, F. Westley and A. H. Davis, 1833.
Colton, Calvin, 1789–1857.

LAC 11996
A tour on the prairies. New York, F. M. Lupton [n. d.]
Irving, Washington, 1783–1859.

LAC 12142
Tour through parts of the United States and Canada. By a British subject. London, Longman, Rees, Orme, Brown, and Green, 1828.
Beaufoy.

LAC 13292
A tour through the southern and western territories of the United States of North-America; the Spanish dominions on the river Mississippi, and the Floridas; the countries of the Creek nations; and many uninhabited parts. Richmond, Printed by J. Dixon, for the author, 1792. [New York, C. L. Woodward, 1888]
Pope, John.

LAC 40105
A tour, through upper and lower Canada. By a citizen of the United States. Containing a view of the present state of religion, learning, commerce, agriculture, colonization, customs and manners, among the English, French and Indian settlements. Printed at Litchfield, (according to Act of Congress) 1799. Tarrytown, N. Y., Reprinted, W. Abbatt, 1917.
Ogden, John Cosens, 1751–1800.

LAC 21827–29
The town and city of Waterbury, Connecticut, from the aboriginal period to the year eighteen hundred and ninety-five. New Haven, The Price & Lee company, 1896.
Anderson, Joseph, 1836–1916, ed.

LAC 16649
The town down the river; a book of poems. New York, Charles Scribner's sons, 1910.
Robinson, Edwin Arlington, 1869–1935.

LAC 10869
The town of Roxbury: its memorable persons and places, its history and antiquities, with numerous illustrations of its old landmarks and noted personages. Roxbury, Pub. by the author, 1878.
Drake, Francis Samuel, 1828–1885.

LAC 11373
The town proprietors of the New England colonies; a study of their development, organization, activities and controversies, 1620–1770. Philadelphia, Press of the University of Pennsylvania, 1924.
Akagi, Roy Hidemichi, 1892–

LAC 14137
Town records of Derby, Connecticut, 1655–1710; copied and compared with the original by Nancy O. Phillips. Derby, Sarah Riggs Humphreys chapter, Daughters of the American revolution, 1901.
Derby, *Conn.*

LAC 20507
Town records of Salem, Massachusetts. [v. 1]–3, 1634–1691. Salem, Mass., The Essex institute, 1868–1934.
Salem, *Mass.*

LAC 40145
The track of Ponce de Leon in 1513. [New York] American Geographical Society, 1913.
Scisco, Louis Dow, 1868–

LAC 12324
Tractatus de globis et eorum usu. A treatise descriptive of the globes constructed by Emery Molyneux and published in 1592 (*i.e.* 1594) By Robert Hues. Edited, with annotated indices and an introduction, by Clements R. Markham, C. B., F. R. S. London, Printed for the Hakluyt society, 1889.
Hues, Robert, 1553–1632.

LAC 21433–36
Tracts and other papers relating principally to the origin, settlement, and progress of the colonies in North America, from the discovery of the country to the year 1776. Collected by Peter Force. Washington, Printed by P. Force, 1836–46.
Force, Peter, 1790–1868, *comp.*

LAC 16298
Tracts concerning Christianity. Cambridge, Mass., John Bartlett, 1852.
Norton, Andrews, 1786–1853.

LAC 40103
Tracts for the times, in relation to African labor, the future supply of cotton and popular government in North America. New York, Printed for the author, 1861.

LAC 14606
Tracts on Sundry topics of political economy. 1834. New York, A. M. Kelley, 1970.
Putnam, Oliver, 1777–1826.

LAC 10425
Tracts relating to the currency of the Massachusetts Bay, 1682–1720; ed. by Andrew McFarland Davis. Boston and New York, Houghton, Mifflin and company, 1902.
Davis, Andrew McFarland, 1833–1920, *ed.*

LAC 12293
Trade and navigation between Spain and the Indies in the time of the Hapsburgs. Cambridge, Harvard university press; [etc., etc.] 1918.
Haring, Clarence Henry, 1885–

LAC 13799
Trade unionism and labor problems; edited with an introduction, by John R. Commons. Boston, New York [etc.] Ginn & company [c1905]
Commons, John Rogers, 1862–1945, *ed.*

LAC 14300
Traditions of the Arapaho, collected under the auspices of the Field Columbian museum and of the American museum of natural history, by George A. Dorsey and Alfred L. Kroeber. Chicago, 1903.
Dorsey, George Amos, 1868–1931.

LAC 40039
A traffic history of the Mississippi River system. Washington, Govt. print. off., 1909.
Dixon, Frank Haigh, 1869–

LAC 12890
The tragedy of the negro in America. A condensed history of the enslavement, sufferings, emancipation, present condition and progress of the negro race in the United States of America... by Rev. P. Thomas Stanford. Boston, Author's edition, 1898.
Stanford, Peter Thomas.

LAC 13564
Traits of American life. Philadelphia, E. L. Carey & A. Hart, 1835.
Hale, Sarah Josepha, 1788–1879.

LAC 12069
Traits of the aborigines of America. A poem. Cambridge [Mass.] Hilliard and Metcalf, printers, 1822.
Sigourney, Lydia Howard, 1791–1865.

LAC 13254
A tramp across the continent. New York, C. Scribner's sons, 1892.
Lummis, Charles Fletcher, 1859–1928.

LAC 14044
The tramp at home. New York, Harper & brothers [c1889]
Meriwether, Lee, 1862–

LAC 11474
A tramp trip; how to see Europe on fifty cents a day. New York [etc.] Harper & brothers, 1887.
Meriwether, Lee, 1862–

LAC 22998–99
Transactions of the 4th–10th annual meetings of the Western literary institute and college of professional teachers... 1834–40. Cincinnati, 1835–41.
Western Literary Institute and College of Professional Teachers.

LAC 22498–99
Transactions of the Society for the promotion of useful arts, in the state of New York. [v. 1]–4. Albany, 1801–1819.
Society for the Promotion of Useful Arts, *Albany, N.Y.*

LAC 20592
Transatlantic sketches, comprising visits to the most interesting scenes in North and South America, and the West Indies. With notes on Negro slavery and Canadian emigration. By Capt. J. E. Alexander. London, R. Bentley, 1833.
Alexander, *Sir* James Edward, 1803–1885.

LAC 13612
Transatlantic wanderings: or, A last look at the United States. By Capt. Oldmixon. London, New York, G. Routledge & co., 1855.
Oldmixon, John W.

LAC 14114
Transcendentalism in New England; a history. Boston, American Unitarian Association [1876]
Frothingham, Octavius Brooks, 1822–1895.

LAC 15564
Transcontinental sketches; legends, lyrics and romances gleaned on vacation tours in northeastern and middle Canada and the Pacific states. Illustrated from pencil and water-color drawings by the writer. Philadelphia, The John C. Winston company [c1909]
Chase, Eliza Brown.

LAC 11720
Transcript of original documents in the English archives relating to the early history of the state of New Hampshire. Ed. by John Scribner Jenness. New York, Priv. print., 1876.
Jenness, John Scribner, 1827–1879, *ed.*

LAC 12187
The transit of civilization from England to America in the seventeenth century. New York, D. Appleton and company, 1901.
Eggleston, Edward, 1837–1902.

LAC 15296
The transition in Virginia from colony to commonwealth. New York, 1910.
Lingley, Charles Ramsdell, 1877–1934.

LAC 10684
Translation of the constitution and laws of the Hawaiian islands, established in the reign of Kamehameha III. Lahainaluna, 1842.
Hawaiian Islands. *Constitution.*

LAC 10058
Transportation and industrial development in the Middle West. New York, Columbia university, Longmans, Green & co., agents; [etc., etc.] 1909.
Gephart, William Franklin, 1877–

LAC 13039
Transylvania university; its origin, rise, decline, and fall. Prepared for the Filson club by Robert Peter, M. D., and his daughter, Miss Johanna Peter. Louisville, Ky., J. P. Morton and company, printers, 1896.
Peter, Robert, 1805–1894.

LAC 40098
Traps baited with orphan; or, What is the matter with life insurance? Boston, J. R. Osgood and company, 1877.
Wright, Elizur, 1804–1885.

LAC 10736
Traps for the young. By Anthony Comstock. With introduction by J. M. Buckley, D. D. New York and London, Funk & Wagnalls [c1883]
Comstock, Anthony, 1844–1915.

LAC 13351
Travel and adventure in the territory of Alaska, formerly Russian America—now ceded to the United States—and in various other parts of the north Pacific. New York, Harper & brothers, 1869.
Whymper, Frederick.

LAC 13958
A traveler at forty, by Theodore Dreiser; illustrated by W. Glackens. New York, The Century co., 1914, [c1913]
Dreiser, Theodore, 1871–1945.

LAC 11206
A traveler from Altruria, romance by W. D. Howells. New York, Harper & brothers, 1894.
Howells, William Dean, 1837–1920.

LAC 14191
Travellers and outlaws; episodes in American history. Boston, Lee and Shepard; New York, C. T. Dillingham, 1889.
Higginson, Thomas Wentworth, 1823–1911.

LAC 40007
The traveller's directory: or, A pocket companion, shewing the course of the main road from Philadelphia to New York; and from Philadelphia to Washington... From actual survey. By S. S. Moore and T. W. Jones. 2d ed. Philadelphia: Printed for Mathew Carey, no. 122 Market-street, 1804.
Moore, S   S.

LAC 40048
Travelling salesmen: their opportunities and their dangers. An address delivered before the Boston young men's Christian union. [Boston] For the Boston young men's Christian union [1874]
Baldwin, William Henry, 1826–1909.

LAC 13221
Travels & adventures in Canada and the Indian territories between the years 1760 and 1776, by Alexander Henry, fur trader. New ed., edited with notes, illustrative and biographical, by James Bain. Boston, Little, Brown, & company, 1901.
Henry, Alexander, 1739–1824.

LAC 23046–47
Travels and works of Captain John Smith... Edited by Edward Arber. A new ed., with a biographical and critical introduction by A. G. Bradley. Edinburgh, J. Grant, 1910.
Smith, John, 1580–1631.

LAC 13274
Travels in Alaska. Boston and New York, Houghton Mifflin company [1915]
Muir, John, 1838–1914.

LAC 21266
Travels in America and Italy. London, H. Colburn, 1828.
Chateaubriand, Francois Auguste Rene, *vicomte* de, 1768–1848.

LAC 11322
Travels in America 100 years ago. Being notes and reminiscences. New York, Harper & brothers, 1894.
Twining, Thomas, 1776–1861.

LAC 12162
Travels in America. The poetry of Pope. Two lectures delivered to the Leeds mechanics' institution and literary society, December 5th and 6th, 1850. By the Right Honorable the Earl of Carlisle, (Lord Morpeth.) New-York, G. P. Putnam, 1851.
Carlisle, George William Frederick Howard, *7th earl of*, 1802–1864.

LAC 11317
Travels in Canada, and the United States, in 1816 and 1817. By Lieut. Francis Hall. 2d ed. London, Longman, Hurst, Rees, Orme, and Brown, 1819.
Hall, Francis, *d.* 1833.

LAC 11146
Travels in England, France, Spain, and the Barbary states, in the years 1813–14 and 15. New-York, Kirk and Mercein; London, J. Miller, 1819.
Noah, Mordecai Manuel, 1785–1851.

LAC 10236
Travels in Louisiana and the Floridas, in the year, 1802, giving a correct picture of those countries. Tr. from the French, with notes, &c. by John Davis. New-York: Printed by and for I. Riley & co., 1806.
Berquin-Duvallon,

LAC 23194–96
Travels; in New-England and New-York. New-Haven, T. Dwight, 1821–22.
Dwight, Timothy, 1752–1817.

LAC 20700
Travels in North America during the years 1834, 1835 & 1836, including a summer residence with the Pawnee Tribe of Indians in the remote prairies of the Missouri and a visit to Cuba and the Azore Islands. New York, Harper & brothers, 1839.
Murray, *Sir* Charles Augustus, 1806–1895.

LAC 13140
Travels in North America, from modern writers. With remarks and observations; exhibiting a connected view of the geography and present state of that quarter of the globe. By the Rev. William Bingley. Designed for the use of young persons. London, Printed for Harvey and Darton, 1821.
Bingley, William, 1774–1823.

LAC 12209

Travels in North America, in the years 1841-2; with geological observations on the United States, Canada and Nova Scotia. New-York, Wiley and Putnam, 1845.
Lyell, *Sir* Charles, *bart.*, 1797-1875.

LAC 12165

Travels in North-America, in the years 1780-81-82. Tr. from the French, by an English gentleman, who resided in America at that period. With notes by the translator. Also, a biographical sketch of the author: letters from Gen. Washington to the Marquis de Chastellux: and notes and corrections, by the American editor. New-York, White, Gallaher, & White, 1827.
Chastellux, Francois Jean, *marquis* de, 1734-1788.

LAC 12213

Travels in the American colonies, ed. under the auspices of the National society of the colonial dames of America, by Newton D. Mereness. New York, The Macmillan company, 1916.
Mereness, Newton Dennison, *ed.*

LAC 14298

Travels in the interior inhabited parts of North America in the years 1791 and 1792, by P. Campbell; edited with an introduction, by H. H. Langton, and with notes by H. H. Langton and W. F. Ganong. Toronto, The Champlain society, 1937.
Campbell, Patrick.

LAC 12227

Travels in the United States of America; commencing in the year 1793 and ending in 1797. With the author's journals of his two voyages across the Atlantic. London, Printed for J. Johnson, 1802.
Priest, William, *musician.*

LAC 20681-82

Travels into North America; containing its natural history, and a circumstantial account of its plantations and agriculture in general, with the civil, ecclesiastical and commercial state of the country, the manners of the inhabitants, and several curious and important remarks on various subjects. By Peter Kalm. Tr. into English by John Reinhold Forster. London, Printed for the editor, 1770-71.
Kalm, Pehr, 1716-1779.

LAC 15113

The travels, observations, and experience of a Yankee stonecutter. By Horace Bender [*pseud.*] Part I... New York, G. P. Putnam, 1852.
Greenough, Horatio, 1805-1852.

LAC 13562

Travels of four years and a half in the United States of America; during 1798, 1799, 1800, 1801, and 1802... London, Sold by T. Ostell [etc.] and New York, H. Caritat; for R. Edwards, printer, Bristol, 1803.
Davis, John, 1774-1854.

LAC 23242

Travels through that part of North America formerly called Louisiana. By Mr. Bossu. Tr. from the French, by John Reinhold Forster. Illustrated with notes relative chiefly to natural history. To which is added by the translator a systematic catalogue of all the known plants of English North-America, or, A flora Americae Septentrionalis. Together with an abstract of the most useful and necessary articles contained in Peter Loefling's Travels through Spain and Cumana in South America. Referred to the pages of the original Swedish edition... London, Printed for T. Davies, 1771.
Bossu, Jean Bernard, 1720-1792.

LAC 20594

Travels through the interior parts of America. In a series of letters. By an officer. A new ed. London, Printed for W. Lane, 1791.
Anburey, Thomas.

LAC 13164

Travels through the interior parts of North America, in the years 1766, 1767, and 1768. Illustrated with copper plates, coloured. The 3d ed. To which is added, some account of the author, and a copious index. London, C. Dilly [etc.] 1781.
Carver, Jonathan, 1710-1780.

LAC 12158

Travels through the middle settlements in North America, in the years 1759, and 1760. With observations upon the state of the colonies. London, T. Payne, 1775.
Burnaby, Andrew, 1734?-1812.

LAC 21135-36

Travels through the United States of North America, the country of the Iroquois, and Upper Canada, in the years 1795, 1796, and 1797; with an authentic account of Lower Canada. By the Duke de La Rochefoucault Liancourt. London, R. Phillips, 1799.
La Rochefoucauld Liancourt, Francois Alexandre Frederic, *duc* de, 1747-1827.

LAC 13784

Travels through the western country in the summer of 1816. Including notices of the natural history, antiquities, topography, agriculture, commerce and manufactures: with a map of the Wabash country, now settling. Auburn (N. Y.) Printed by David Rumsey, 1819.
Thomas, David, 1776-1859.

LAC 13267

Travels to the westward of the Allegany mountains, in the states of the Ohio, Kentucky, and Tennessee, and return to Charlestown, through the upper Carolinas; containing details on the present state of agriculture and the natural productions of these countries; as well as information relative to the commercial connections of these states with those situated to the eastward of the mountains and with lower Louisiana. Undertaken in the year X, 1802, under the auspices of His Excellency M. Chaptal, minister of the interior. With a very correct map of the states in the centre, west and south of the United States. By F. A. Michaux. Faithfully tr. from the original French, by B. Lambert. London, J. Mawman, 1805.
Michaux, Francois Andre, 1770-1855.

LAC 16406

A travers l'Amerique; impressions d'un musicien. Paris, E. Lachaud, 1872.
Kowalski, Henri, *b.* 1841.

LAC 16595

The treasures of the Metropolitan museum of art of New York, described by Arthur Hoeber. New York, R. H. Russell, 1899.
Hoeber, Arthur, 1854-1915.

LAC 12944
Treaties and conventions with or concerning China and Korea, 1894–1904, together with various state papers and documents affecting foreign interests. Washington, Govt. print. off., 1904.
Rockhill, William Woodville, 1854–1914, *ed.*

LAC 22195–97
Treaties, conventions, international acts, protocols and agreements between the United States of America and other powers, 1776–1909. Compiled by William M. Malloy under resolution of the Senate of January 18, 1909... Washington, Govt. print. off., 1910.
U.S. *Treaties, etc.*

LAC 13500
A treatise concerning political enquiry, and the liberty of the press. New-York, Printed by G. Forman for the author, 1800.
Wortman, Tunis, *d.* 1822.

LAC 13846
A treatise of practical surveying; which is demonstrated from its first principles. Wherein everything that is useful and curious in that art, is fully considered and explained... The whole illustrated with copper-plates. 8th ed. With alterations and amendments, adapted to the use of American surveyors. Philadelphia, Printed by J. & J. Crukshank, 1803.
Gibson, Robert.

LAC 16143
A treatise on American citizenship. Northport, Long island, N. Y., Edward Thompson company, 1906.
Wise, John Sergeant, 1846–1913.

LAC 10930
A treatise on atonement; in which the finite nature of sin is argued, its cause and consequences as such; the necessity and nature of atonement; and, its glorious consequences, in the final reconciliation of all men to holiness and happiness. 14th ed. Boston, The Universalist publishing house, 1902.
Ballou, Hosea, 1771–1852.

LAC 12668
A treatise on chemistry applied to the manufacture of soap and candles; being a thorough exposition, in all their minutiae, of the principles and practice of the trade, based upon the most recent discoveries in science and art. New and improved ed., illus. with two hundred and sixty engravings on wood. Philadelphia, Parry and McMillan, 1856.
Morfit, Campbell, 1820–1897.

LAC 16089
A treatise on cocking, giving a history of the various breeds of imported and American game fowls; the manner of feeding and training them for the pit, a scientific mode of gafting for battle, together with rules of the pit and for breeding, and the proper treatment of the various diseases incident to game fowls. Media, Pa., Cooper & Vernon, prs., 1859.
Cooper, J   W.

LAC 10474
A treatise on currency and banking. Philadelphia, Grigg & Elliot, 1839.
Raguet, Condy, 1784–1842.

LAC 12144
A treatise on domestic economy, for the use of young ladies at home, and at school. Boston, T. H. Webb & co., 1842.
Beecher, Catharine Esther, 1800–1878.

LAC 16661
A treatise on field fortification, containing instructions on the methods of laying out, constructing, defending, and attacking intrenchments, with the general outlines also of the arrangement, the attack and defence of permanent fortifications. 3d ed., rev. and enl. New York, J. Wiley, 1862.
Mahan, Dennis Hart, 1802–1871.

LAC 40032
A treatise on gardening, by a citizen of Virginia, John Randolph, jr. (1727–1784) reprinted from the American gardener by John Gardiner and David Hepburn, 3d ed., 1826; edited by M. F. Warner. Richmond, Reprinted by Appeals press, inc. for the William Parks club, 1924.
Randolph, John, 1727?–1784.

LAC 13491
A treatise on government, and constitutional law; being an inquiry into the source and limitation of governmental authority, according to the American theory. Albany, W. C. Little, 1867.
Tiffany, Joel, 1811–1893.

LAC 10428
A treatise on logic; or, The laws of pure thought; comprising both the Aristotelic and Hamiltonian analyses of logical forms, and some chapters of applied logic. Cambridge [Mass.] Sever and Francis, 1864.
Bowen, Francis, 1811–1890.

LAC 15675–76
A treatise on medical jurisprudence. By Francis Wharton and Moreton Stille. The medical part revised and corrected, with numerous additions, by Alfred Stille, M. D. 2d and rev. ed. Philadelphia, Kay & brother, 1860.
Wharton, Francis, 1820–1889.

LAC 15438
A treatise on military law and the jurisdiction, constitution, and procedure of military courts, with a summary of the rules of evidence as applicable to such courts. By Lieutenant Rollin A. Ives. New York, D. Van Nostrand, 1879.
Ives, Rollin Augustus, 1849–1881.

LAC 12644
A treatise on military surgery and hygiene. Illustrated with 127 engravings. New York, Bailliere brothers; London, H. Bailliere; [etc., etc.] 1865.
Hamilton, Frank Hastings, 1813–1886.

LAC 16719
Treatise on rail-roads and internal communications...
Philadelphia, J. Grigg [etc.] 1830.
Earle, Thomas, 1796–1849.

LAC 13752
A treatise on roads, their history, character, and utility; being the substance of two lectures delivered before the Young men's association of the city of Albany. Albany, O. Steele, 1838.
Bloodgood, Simeon De Witt, 1799–1866.

LAC 21187–88
A treatise on state and federal control of persons and property in the United States, considered from both a civil and criminal standpoint. [2d ed.] St. Louis, The F. H. Thomas law book co., 1900.
Tiedeman, Christopher Gustavus, 1857–1903.

LAC 15580
A treatise on surveying, containing the theory and practice: to which is prefixed a perspicuous system of plane trigonometry. The whole clearly demonstrated and illustrated by a large number of appropriate examples, particularly adapted to the use of schools. 5th ed., improved. Philadelphia, Kimber & Sharpless, 1828.
Gummere, John, 1784–1845.

LAC 15589
A treatise on the Christian doctrine of marriage. By Hugh Davey Evans, LL. D. With a biographical sketch of the author, and an appendix containing Bishop Andrewes' "Discourse against second marriage," etc., now printed for the first time in this country. New York, Cambridge, Hurd and Houghton, 1870.
Evans, Hugh Davey, 1792–1868.

LAC 15364
A treatise on the constitutional limitations which rest upon the legislative power of the states of the American union. 2d ed., with considerable additions, giving the results of the recent cases. Boston, Little, Brown, and company, 1871.
Cooley, Thomas McIntyre, 1824–1898.

LAC 22500–2
A treatise on the criminal law of the United States. 7th and rev. ed. Philadelphia, Kay and brother, 1874.
Wharton, Francis, 1820–1889.

LAC 40008
A treatise on the culture of lucerne. By Jacqulin [!] Ambler. Richmond, Printed by T. Nicolson [1800?]
Ambler, Jacquelin.

LAC 10634
A treatise on the federal income tax under the act of 1894. By Roger Foster and Everett V. Abbot. Boston, The Boston book company, 1895.
Foster, Roger, 1857–1924.

LAC 12630
A treatise on the forces which produce the organization of plants. With an appendix containing several memoirs on capillary attraction, electricity, and the chemical action of light. New York, Harper & brothers, 1845, [c1844]
Draper, John William, 1811–1882.

LAC 15431
A treatise on the improvement of canal navigation; exhibiting the numerous advantages to be derived from small canals... London, I. & J. Taylor, 1796.
Fulton, Robert, 1765–1815.

LAC 40133
A treatise on the intellectual character, and civil and political condition of the colored people of the U. States; and the prejudice exercised towards them: with a sermon on the duty of the church to them. By Rev. H. Easton. Boston, I. Knapp, 1837.
Easton, Hosea.

LAC 16797
A treatise on the law of boundaries and fences including the rights of property on the sea-shore and in the lands of public rivers and other streams, and the law of window lights. Albany, W. Gould & son, 1874.
Tyler, Ransom Hebbard, 1813–1881.

LAC 12735
A treatise on the law of libel and the liberty of the press; showing the origin, use, and abuse of the law of libel: with copious notes and references to authorities in Great Britain and the United States: as applicable to individuals and to political and ecclesiastical bodies and principles. New York, Printed by G. F. Hopkins & son, 1830.
Cooper, Thomas, 1759–1839.

LAC 10711–12
A treatise on the law of stock-brokers and stock-exchanges. New York, Harper & brothers, 1882.
Dos Passos, John Randolph, 1844–1917.

LAC 12596
A treatise on the marine boilers of the United States. Philadelphia, R. W. Barnard & sons, printers, 1851.
Bartol, Barnabas H.

LAC 12605
A treatise on the materia medica, intended as a sequel to the Pharmacopoeia of the United States: being an account of the origin, qualities and medical uses of the articles and compounds, which constitute that work, with their modes of prescription and administration. Boston, C. Ewer, 1822.
Bigelow, Jacob, 1787–1879.

LAC 16716
A treatise on the military law of the United States. Together with the practice and procedure of courts-martial and other military tribunals. By Lieutenant-Colonel George B. Davis. 2d ed., rev. 1st thousand. New York, J. Wiley & sons; [etc., etc.] 1899.
Davis, George Breckenridge, 1847–1914.

LAC 13965
A treatise on the millennium; in which the prevailing theories on that subject are carefully examined; and the true scriptural doctrine attempted to be elicited and established. New-York, J. & J. Harper, 1832.
Bush, George, 1796–1859.

LAC 40076
A treatise on the patriarchal, or co-operative, system of society as it exists in some governments, and colonies in America, and in the United States, under the name of slavery, with its necessity and advantages. By an inhabitant of Florida. 2d ed. [n.p.] 1829.
Kingsley, Z.

LAC 14652
A treatise on the practice of the Pension bureau governing the adjudication of the army and navy pensions. Compiled by order of the commissioner of pensions, under the authority of the Secretary of the interior. Washington, Govt. print. off., 1898.
U.S. *Pension Bureau.*

LAC 11644
A treatise on the right of personal liberty, and on the writ of habeas corpus and the practice connected with it: with a view of the law of extradition of fugitives. Albany, W. C. Little & co., 1858.
Hurd, Rollin Carlos, *b.* 1815.

LAC 12729
A treatise on the rights and privileges guaranteed by the fourteenth amendment to the Constitution of the United States. Cincinnati, W. H. Anderson & co., 1901.
Brannon, Henry, 1837–1914.

LAC 40144
A treatise on the second coming of Christ... Putney, Vt., 1840.
Noyes, John Humphrey, 1811–1886.

LAC 16887
A treatise on the unconstitutionality of American slavery: together with the powers and duties of the federal government in relation to that subject. Cleveland, O., J. Calyer, printer [1849]
Tiffany, Joel.

LAC 12695
A treatise on water-works for conveying and distributing supplies of water; with tables and examples. Boston, Hilliard, Gray, and co., 1835.
Storrow, Charles Storer, 1809–1904.

LAC 15096
The treaty–its merits and demerits fairly discussed and displayed. [Boston? 1795?]

LAC 21076–77
The treaty making power of the United States. New York, The Banks law pub. co., 1902.
Butler, Charles Henry, 1859–1940.

LAC 40031
A treaty of peace between the United States and Spain. Message from the President of the United States transmitting a treaty of peace between the United States and Spain, signed at the city of Paris on December 10, 1898... Washington, Gov't print. off., 1899.
U.S. *Treaties, etc., 1897–1901 (McKinley)*

LAC 11143
The Treaty of Washington: its negotiation, execution, and the discussions relating thereto. New York, Harper & brothers, 1873.
Cushing, Caleb, 1800–1879.

LAC 40063
Treaty with Mexico. Message of the President of the United States transmitting a copy of the treaty of peace, friendship, limits, and settlement, between the United States and the republic of Mexico, ratifications of which were exchanged at the city of Queretaro, in Mexico, on the 30th of May, 1848. [Washington, Govt. print. off., 1848]
U.S. *Treaties, etc., 1845–1849 (Polk)*

LAC 40010
The treaty with Spain: should it be ratified? [n.p.] 1898.
Seward, George Frederick, 1840–1910.

LAC 40118
Trees and other poems. Garden City, New York, Doubleday & company, inc. [c1914]
Kilmer, Joyce, 1886–1918.

LAC 14933
The Trent affair, including a review of English and American relations at the beginning of the civil war, by Thomas L. Harris, A. M. With an introduction by James A. Woodburn. Indianapolis, Bobbs-Merrill [c1896]
Harris, Thomas Le Grand, 1863–

LAC 40075
The trial, execution, autopsy and mental status of Leon F. Czolgosz, alias Fred Nieman, the assassin of President McKinley. Baltimore, The Johns Hopkins press, 1902.
Mac Donald, Carlos Frederick, 1845–

LAC 14099
The trial of a new society, being a review of the celebrated Ettor-Giovannitti-Caruso case, beginning with the Lawrence textile strike that caused it and including the general strike that grew out of it. Illustrated with portraits, posters and cartoons. Cleveland, O., I. W. W. publishing bureau [1913]
Ebert, Justus, 1869–

LAC 16175
The trial of Alexander McLeod, for the murder of Amos Durfee, at the burning and destruction of the steamboat Caroline, by the Canadians, December 29th, 1837. Reported by Marcus T. C. Gould. Assisted by H. Fowler. New York, Gould, Banks & co.; Albany, W. A. Gould & co., 1841.
McLeod, Alexander, *defendant.*

LAC 22480–81
Trial of Andrew Johnson, president of the United States, before the Senate of the United States, on impeachment by the House of representatives for high crimes and misdemeanors. Pub. by order of the Senate... Washington, Govt. print. off., 1868.
Johnson, Andrew, *pres. U.S.,* 1808–1875.

LAC 16633
Trial of Captain Kidd. Edited by Graham Brooks. Edinburgh, W. Hodge [1930]
Kidd, *Capt.* William, *d.* 1701, *defendant.*

LAC 12745
The trial of the Constitution. Philadelphia, J. B. Lippincott & co.; [etc., etc.] 1862.
Fisher, Sidney George, 1809–1871.

LAC 12688
Trials of a public benefactor, as illustrated in the discovery of etherization. New York, Pudney & Russell, 1859.
Rice, Nathan P.

LAC 12234
The Tribune book of open-air sports. Prepared by the New York tribune with the aid of acknowledged experts. Edited by Henry Hall. New York, The Tribune association, 1887, [c1886]
Hall, Henry, 1845–1920, *ed.*

LAC 16499
A tribute for the Negro; being a vindication of the moral, intellectual, and religious capabilities of the coloured portion of mankind; with particular reference to the African race. Illustrated by numerous biographical sketches, facts, anecdotes, etc. ... Manchester, W. Irwin; American agent, W. Harned, New York; [etc., etc.] 1848.
Armistead, Wilson, 1819?–1868.

LAC 13511
Tribute to Gallaudet. A discourse in commemoration of the life, character and services, of the Rev. Thomas H. Gallaudet, LL. D., delivered before the citizens of Hartford, Jan. 7th, 1852. With an appendix, containing history of deaf-mute instruction and institutions, and other documents. 2d ed. New York, F. C. Brownell; Hartford, Hutchinson & Bullard, 1859.
Barnard, Henry, 1811–1900.

LAC 11628
A tribute to the life and character of Jonas Chickering. "By one who knew him well"... Boston, W. P. Tewksbury, 1854.
Parker, Richard Green, 1798–1869.

LAC 14771
A tribute to the principles, virtues, habits and public usefulness of the Irish and Scotch early settlers of Pennsylvania. By a descendant. Chambersburg, Pa., M. Kieffer, 1856.
Chambers, George, 1786–1866.

LAC 40046
The trinity, in its theological, scientific, and practical aspects, analyzed and illustrated, by Dr. M. Edgeworth Lazarus. New York, Published for the author by Fowlers and Wells, 1851.
Lazarus, M   Edgeworth.

LAC 40067
Trip through the island of Luzon. Letter from the Secretary of the navy, transmitting ... a copy of the report of paymaster W. B. Wilcox and naval cadet L. R. Sargent on a trip through the island of Luzon.
U.S. *Congress. Senate. Committee on the Philippines.*

LAC 13284
Trip to the West and Texas. Comprising a journey of eight thousand miles, through New York, Michigan, Illinois, Missouri, Louisiana and Texas, in the autumn and winter of 1834–5. Interspersed with anecdotes, incidents and observations. Concord, N. H., White & Fisher, 1835.
Parker, Amos Andrew, 1791–1893.

LAC 13594
Tripoli. First war with the United States. Inner history. Letter book by James Leander Cathcart, first consul to Tripoli, and last letters from Tunis, comp. by his daughter, J. B. Cathcart Newkirk, D. A. R. LaPorte, Ind., Herald print [1901]
Cathcart, James Leander, 1767–1843.

LAC 40064
Triumphal march of Sergeant Bates from Vicksburg to Washington. Washington, Intelligencer printing house, 1868.
Bates, Gilbert H.

LAC 11683
Triumphant democracy; or, Fifty years' march of the republic. New York, Scribner, 1886.
Carnegie, Andrew, 1835–1919.

LAC 40021
A trooper's narrative of service in the anthracite coal strike, 1902. Philadelphia, G. W. Jacobs & co. [c1903]
Culin, Stewart, 1858–1929.

LAC 15965
Tropical agriculture; the climate, soils, cultural methods, crops, live stock, commercial importance and opportunities of the tropics. New York and London, D. Appleton and company, 1916.
Wilcox, Earley Vernon, 1869–

LAC 12239
The trotting horse of America; how to train and drive him. With reminiscences of the trotting turf. By Hiram Woodruff. Ed. by Charles J. Foster, including an introductory notice by George Wilkes, and a biographical sketch by the editor. New York, J. B. Ford and company, 1868.
Woodruff, Hiram Washington, 1817–1867.

LAC 13533
Troy's one hundred years. 1789–1889. Troy, N. Y., W. H. Young, 1891.
Weise, Arthur James, 1838–1910, *or* 11.

LAC 10123
Truck-farming at the South. A guide to the raising of vegetables for northern markets. New York, Orange Judd company, 1884, [c1883]
Oemler, A.

LAC 40001
The true American system of finance; the rights of labor and capital, and the common sense way of doing justice to the soldiers and their families. No banks: greenbacks the exclusive currency. Chicago, Evening journal book and job print, 1864.
Campbell, Alexander.

LAC 15806
True and false democracy. New York, The Macmillan company; London, Macmillan & co., ltd., 1907.
Butler, Nicholas Murray, 1862–1947.

LAC 12417
A true and historical narrative of the colony of Georgia in America, from the first settlement thereof until this present period. Containing the most authentic facts, matters, and transactions therein; together with His Majesty's charter, representations of the people, letters, etc. ... By Pat Tailfer, M. D., Hugh Anderson, M. A., Da. Douglas, and others. Charles-town, South Carolina: Printed by P. Timothy, for the authors, 1741. [Rochester, G. P. Humphrey, 1897]
Tailfer, Patrick.

LAC 14278

True civilization an immediate necessity, and the last ground of hope for mankind. Being the results and conclusions of thirty-nine years' laborious study and experiments in civilization as it is, and in different enterprises for reconstruction. Boston, J. Warren, 1863.
Warren, Josiah, 1798–1874.

LAC 40093

A trve discovrse of the present estate of Virginia, and the successe of the affaires there till the 18 of Iune, 1614. Together. With a relation of the seuerall English townes and fortes, the assured hopes of that countrie and the peace concluded with the Indians. The christening of Powhatans daughter and her marriage with an Englishman. Written by Raphe Hamor the yonger, late secretarie in that colony. London, Printed by Iohn Beale for W. Welby, 1615 [Albany, J. Munsell, 1860]
Hamor, Ralph, *the younger.*

LAC 13916

The true English interest: or An account of the chief national improvements; in some political observations, demonstrating an infallible advance of this nation to infinite wealth and greatness, trade and populacy, with imployment, and preferment for all persons. London, Printed for Giles Widdowes at the Green Dragon in St. Paul's Church-Yard, 1674.
Reynell, Carew, 1636–1690.

LAC 11464

The true George Washington. [4th ed.] Philadelphia, J. B. Lippincott company, 1897, [c1896]
Ford, Paul Leicester, 1865–1902.

LAC 40002

The true issue: industrial depression and political corruption caused by tariff monopolies. Reform demanded in the interest of manufacturers, farmers, and workingmen. New York & London, G. P. Putnam's sons, 1884.
Donnell, Ezekiel J.

LAC 40055

A true picture of emigration; or, Fourteen years in the interior of North America; being a full and impartial account of the various difficulties and ultimate success of an English family who emigrated from Barwick-in-Elmet, near Leeds, in the year 1831. London, G. Berger; [etc., etc., 1848]
Burlend, Rebecca, 1793–1872.

LAC 15099

A true picture of the United States of America; being a brief statement of the conduct of the government and people of that country, towards Great Britain, from the peace concluded in 1783, to the present time. By a British subject. London, Jordan and Maxwell [etc.] 1807.

LAC 15082

True stories of New England captives carried to Canada during the old French and Indian wars. Cambridge [Greenfield, Mass., Press of E. A. Hall & co.] 1897.
Baker, Charlotte Alice, 1833–1909.

LAC 15016

The true story of Andersonville prison: a defense of Major Henry Wirz, by James Madison Page, late 2d lieut. Company A, Sixth Michigan cavalry, in collaboration with M. J. Haley. With portraits. New York and Washington, The Neale publishing company, 1908.
Page, James Madison, 1839–

LAC 13635

The true William Penn. Philadelphia, J. B. Lippincott company [c1899]
Fisher, Sydney George, 1856–1927.

LAC 15868

Trust finance; a study of the genesis, organization, and management of industrial combinations. New York, D. Appleton and company, 1906, [c1903]
Mead, Edward Sherwood, 1874–

LAC 10051

The trust: its book; being a presentation of the several aspects of the latest form of industrial evolution, by Charles R. Flint, James J. Hill, James H. Bridge, S. C. T. Dodd, and Francis B. Thurber, with numerous expressions of representative opinion and a bibliography, ed. by James H. Bridge. New York, Doubleday, Page & company, 1902.
Bridge, James Howard, 1858–   *ed.*

LAC 23557–59

Trust legislation. Hearings before the Committee on the judiciary, House of representatives, Sixty-third Congress, second session, on trust legislation. In two volumes. Serial 7–parts 1 to [35] inclusive [and Appendix] [Dec. 9, 1913–April 6, 1914] Washington, Govt. print. off., 1914.
U.S. *Congress. House. Committee on the Judiciary.*

LAC 11607

The trust problem. New York, McClure, Phillips & co., 1900.
Jenks, Jeremiah Whipple, 1856–1929.

LAC 10039

Trusts and the public. [Popular ed.] New York, D. Appleton and company, 1899.
Gunton, George, 1845–1919.

LAC 10176

Trusts of to-day; facts relating to their promotion, financial management and the attempts at state control. New York, McClure, Phillips & co., 1904.
Montague, Gilbert Holland, 1880–1961.

LAC 10061

Trusts, or industrial combinations and coalitions in the United States, New York, The Macmillan company; London, Macmillan & co., ltd., 1899, [c1895]
Halle, Ernst von, 1868–1909.

LAC 15811

Trusts, pools and corporations; ed. with an introduction by William Z. Ripley. Boston, New York [etc.] Ginn & company [1905]
Ripley, William Zebina, 1867–1941, *ed.*

LAC 10306–7
Trusts. Proceedings of the Committee on manufactures, House of Representatives of the United States, in relation to trusts, etc. Washington, Govt. print. off., 1888.
U. S. *Congress. House. Committee on Manufactures.*

LAC 40048
The truth about Mr. Rockefeller and the Merritts. [New York, The Knickerbocker press, n.d.]
Gates, Frederick Taylor, 1853–1929.

LAC 40074
The truth about the I. W. W. Facts in relation to the trial at Chicago, by competent industrial investigators and noted economists... New York city, National civil liberties bureau, 1918.
American Civil Liberties Union.

LAC 10178
The truth about the trusts; a description and analysis of the American trust movement. New-York, Chicago, Moody publishing company [c1904]
Moody, John, 1868–1958.

LAC 40113
The truth at last. History corrected. Reminiscences of old John Brown. Thrilling incidents of border life in Kansas; with an appendix, containing statements and full details of the Pottawotomie massacre, by Gov. Crawford, Col. Blood, Jas. Townsley, Col. Walker, and others, to which is added a review: by Hon. Eli Thayer. By G. W. Brown. Rockford, Ill., Stereotyped and printed by A. E. Smith, 1880.
Brown, George Washington, 1820–1915.

LAC 12846
Truth stranger than fiction. Father Henson's story of his own life. With an introduction by Mrs. H. B. Stowe. Boston, J. P. Jewett and company; Cleveland, O., H. P. B. Jewett, 1858.
Henson, Josiah, 1789–1883.

LAC 40149
Truth will out! The foul charges of the Tories against the editor of the Aurora repelled by positive proof and plain truth and his base calumniators put to shame. [Philadelphia, 1798]
Bache, Benjamin Franklin, 1769–1798.

LAC 23471
Turkistan; notes of a journey in Russian Turkistan, Khokand, Bukhara, and Kuldja. New York, Scribner, Armstrong & co., 1877, [c1876]
Schuyler, Eugene, 1840–1890.

LAC 11487
Turning on the light. A dispassionate survey of President Buchanan's administration, from 1860 to its close. Including a biographical sketch of the author, eight letters from Mr. Buchanan never before published, and numerous miscellaneous articles. Philadelphia, J. B. Lippincott co., 1895.
King, Horatio, 1811–1897.

LAC 12585
The turnpikes of New England and evolution of the same through England, Virginia, and Maryland. Boston, Marshall Jones company, 1919.
Wood, Frederic James, 1867–

LAC 13069
Tuskegee & its people: their ideals and achievements. New York, D. Appleton, 1905.
Washington, Booker Taliaferro, 1859?–1915, *ed.*

LAC 13048
Tuskegee; its story and its work, by Max Bennett Thrasher, with an introduction by Booker T. Washington. Boston, Small, Maynard & company, 1900.
Thrasher, Max Bennett, 1860–1903.

LAC 15465
The twelve decisive battles of the war; a history of the eastern and western campaigns, in relation to the actions that decided their issue. New York, Dick & Fitzgerald [c1867]
Swinton, William, 1833–1892.

LAC 14258
Twelve lectures on the natural history of man, and the rise and progress of philosophy. By Alexander Kinmont, A. M. With a biographical sketch of the author... Cincinnati, U. P. James, 1839.
Kinmont, Alexander, 1799–1838.

LAC 40009
Twelve letters on the future of New York. New York, M. B. Brown, printer, 1877.
Andrews, George Henry.

LAC 15013
Twelve months in Andersonville. On the march–in the battle–in the Rebel prison pens, and at last in God's country. Huntington, Ind., T. and M. Butler, 1886.
Long, Lessel.

LAC 16047
Twelve months in New-Harmony; presenting a faithful account of the principal occurrences which have taken place there within that period; interspersed with remarks. Cincinnati, W. H. Woodward, 1827.
Brown, Paul.

LAC 14193
Twelve years a slave. Narrative of Solomon Northup, a citizen of New-York, kidnapped in Washington city in 1841, and rescued in 1853, from a cotton plantation near the Red river, in Louisiana. Auburn, Derby and Miller; Buffalo, Derby, Orton and Mulligan; [etc., etc.] 1853.
Northup, Solomon, *b.* 1808.

LAC 13723
The twentieth century city. By Rev. Josiah Strong. New York, The Baker and Taylor co. [c1898]
Strong, Josiah, 1847–1916.

LAC 16477
Twentieth century Negro literature; or, A cyclopedia of thought on the vital topics relating to the American Negro, by one hundred of America's greatest Negroes. Naperville, Ill., Toronto, Can. [etc.] J. L. Nichols & co. [1902]
Culp, Daniel Wallace, *ed.*

LAC 14256
Twentieth century socialism; what it is not; what it is; how it may come. New York [etc.] Longmans, Green, and co., 1910.
Kelly, Edmond, 1851–1909.

LAC 16053
Twenty-five years a parson in the wild West: being the experience of Parson Ralph Riley [*pseud.*] by Rev. John Brown. Fall River, Mass., The author, 1896.
Brown, John, 1843–

LAC 14684
Twenty-five years in the mail order business; or, The experiences of a mail order man. Chicago, A. E. Swett [c1902]
Lee, James, *of the mail order business.*

LAC 11562
Twenty-five years in the secret service; the recollections of a spy, by Major Henri Le Carone [*pseud.*] 2d ed. London, W. Heinemann, 1892.
Beach, Thomas Miller, 1841–1894.

LAC 10337
Twenty-five years of brewing, with an illustrated history of American beer, dedicated to the friends of George Ehret. [New York, The Gast lithograph & engraving company, 1891]
Ehret, George, 1835–

LAC 40055
Twenty-four letters from labourers in America to their friends in England. London, E. Rainford, 1829.
Smith, Benjamin, *of Mountfield, England, ed.*

LAC 11225
Twenty-seven years of autobiography. Threading my way. New York, G. W. Carleton & co.; [etc., etc.] 1874.
Owen, Robert Dale, 1801–1877.

LAC 16731
Twenty-two years a slave, and forty years a freeman; embracing a correspondence of several years, while president of Wilberforce colony, London, Canada West. New York, Negro Universities press [1968]
Steward, Austin, *b.* 1794.

LAC 14282
Twenty-two years of protection. September, 1888. New York, H. V. & H. W. Poor [1888]
Poor, Henry Varnum, 1812–1905.

LAC 16877
Twenty-two years' work of the Hampton normal and agricultural institute at Hampton, Virginia. Records of negro and Indian graduates and ex-students, with historical and personal sketches and testimony on important race questions from within and without, to which are added ... some of the songs of the races gathered in the school. Illustrated with views and maps. Hampton, Normal school press, 1893.
Hampton Institute, *Hampton, Va.*

LAC 13698
Twenty years in the press gallery; a concise history of important legislation from the 48th to the 58th Congress: the part played by the leading men of that period and the interesting and impressive incidents. Impressions of official and political life in Washington, by O. O. Stealey. With an introduction by Henry Watterson. Also crisp and vivid character sketches of the men prominent in public life, by well-known Washington correspondents; illustrated by Clifford K. Berryman. New York, The author, Publishers printing company, printers, 1906.
Stealey, Orlando Oscar, 1842–1928.

LAC 20319–20
Twenty years of Congress: from Lincoln to Garfield. With a review of the events which led to the political revolution of 1860. Norwich, Conn., The Henry Bill publishing company, 1884–86.
Blaine, James Gillespie, 1830–1893.

LAC 11623
Twenty years of Kansas City's live stock trade and traders. [Kansas City, Mo., Pearl printing company, 1893]
Powell, Cuthbert.

LAC 14770
Twenty years of the republic, 1885–1905. New York, Dodd, Mead & company, 1907, [c1906]
Peck, Harry Thurston, 1856–1914.

LAC 21267
Two centuries of costume in America, MDCXX–MDCCCXX, by Alice Morse Earle. New York, The Macmillan company; London, Macmillan & co., ltd. [c1903]
Earle, Alice, 1851–1911.

LAC 13141
Two crowded years; being selected addresses, pastorals, and letters issued during the first twenty-four months of the episcopate of the Most Rev. George William Mundelein, D. D., as archbishop of Chicago. Foreword by the Right Rev. Francis C. Kelley, D. D. Chicago, Extension press, 1918.
Mundelein, George William, *cardinal,* 1872–1939.

LAC 14067
Two evil isms, Pinkertonism and anarchism, by a cowboy detective who knows, as he spent twenty-two years in the inner circle of Pinkerton's national detective agency. Chicago, Ill., C. A. Siringo, c1915.
Siringo, Charles A 1855–

LAC 11140
The two Hague conferences. Princeton, Princeton university press; [etc., etc.] 1913.
Choate, Joseph Hodges, 1832–1917.

LAC 13621
Two hundred years: the history of the Society for promoting Christian knowledge, 1698–1898, by W. O. B. Allen and Edmund McClure. London, Society for promoting Christian knowledge; New York, E. & J. B. Young, 1898.
Allen, William Osborne Bird.

LAC 40027
Two in a bed: America's greatest indoor sport; or, The super-specialist's handbook on bundling with the Pennsylvania Dutch. Harrisburg, Pa., Aurand press [c1930]
Aurand, Ammon Monroe, 1895–

LAC 40101
Two lectures: I. History of the introduction of state normal schools in America. II. A prospective system of national education for the United States. Boston, Printed by J. Wilson and son, 1864.
Brooks, Charles, 1795–1872.

LAC 40020

Two lectures on combustion: supplementary to a course of lectures on chemistry. Read at Nassau-hall. Containing an examination of Dr. Priestley's Considerations on the doctrine of phlogiston, and the decomposition of water. Philadelphia, T. Dobson, 1797.
Maclean, John, 1771–1814.

LAC 12708

Two lectures on comets, by Professor Winthrop, also an Essay on comets, by A. Oliver jun. esq., with sketches of the lives of Professor Winthrop and Mr. Oliver. Likewise, a supplement, relative to the present comet of 1811. Boston, W. Wells and T. B. Wait and co., 1811.
Winthrop, John, 1714–1779.

LAC 13271

Two lectures on intemperance. I.–The effects of intemperance on the poor and ignorant. II.–The effects of intemperance on the rich and educated. New York, Fowler and Wells, 1859, [c1852]
Mann, Horace, 1796–1859.

LAC 40069

Two lectures on political economy, delivered at Clinton hall, before the Mercantile library association of the city of New York, on the 23d and 30th of December, 1831. New York, G. & C. & H. Carvill, 1832.
Lawrence, William Beach, 1800–1881.

LAC 16833

Two lectures on the connection between the Biblical and physical history of man, delivered by invitation, from the Chair of Political Economy, etc., of the Louisiana University, in December, 1848. New York, Negro Universities Press [1969]
Nott, Josiah Clark, 1804–1873.

LAC 40128

Two lectures on the parallax and distance of the sun, as deducible from the transit of Venus. Read in Holden-chapel at Harvard-college in Cambridge, New-England, in March 1769. Published by the general desire of the students. Boston: Printed and sold by Edes & Gill, in Queen-street, M,DCC,LXIX.
Winthrop, John, 1714–1779.

LAC 40126

Two letters addressed to the Hon. J. Quincy Adams; embracing a history of the re-charter of the Bank of the United States; and a view of the present condition of the currency. London, P. Richardson, 1837.
Biddle, Nicholas, 1786–1844.

LAC 40080

Two letters from Agricola to Sir William Howe; to which are annexed, by the same author, Political observations... London, Printed for J. Millidge, 1779.
Agricola, *pseud.*

LAC 12043

Two little Confederates. New York, C. Scribner's sons, 1888.
Page, Thomas Nelson, 1853–1922.

LAC 16057

Two months in the Confederate states; including a visit to New Orleans under the domination of General Butler. By an English merchant. London, R. Bentley, 1863.

LAC 14732

Two pages from Roman history. I. Plebs leaders and labor leaders. II. The warning of the Gracchi. New York, National Executive Committee Socialist Labor Party, 1915.
De Leon, Daniel, 1852–1914.

LAC 40034

Two remarkable lectures delivered in Boston, by Dr. C. Knowlton, on the day of his leaving the jail at East Cambridge, March 31, 1833, where he had been imprisoned, for publishing a book. Boston, A. Kneeland, 1833.
Knowlton, Charles, 1800–1850.

LAC 15502

Two sides of the Atlantic. London, Simpkin, Marshall & co. [1880]
Burnley, James, 1842–1919.

LAC 40076

Two tracts for the times. The one entitled "Negro-slavery no evil," by B. F. Stringfellow, of Missouri. The other, an answer to the inquiry "Is it expedient to introduce slavery into Kansas?" by D. R. Goodloe, of North Carolina. Republished by the N. E. Emigrant Aid Co. Boston, A. Mudge and Son, printers, 1855.
New England Emigrant Aid Company, *Boston.*

LAC 40084

Two tracts: On the proposed alteration of the tariff; and On weights & measures... Charleston, A. E. Miller, printer, 1823.
Cooper, Thomas, 1759–1839.

LAC 11887

Two years before the mast. A personal narrative of life at sea. London, E. Maxon, 1841.
Dana, Richard Henry, 1815–1882.

LAC 11962

Two years in the French West Indies. New York, Harper & brothers, 1890.
Hearn, Lafcadio, 1850–1904.

LAC 15637

A two years journal in New York, and part of its territories in America. By Charles Wooley, A. M. A new ed., with an introduction and copious historical notes by E. B. O'Callaghan. New York, W. Gowans, 1860.
Wolley, Charles.

LAC 14925

Two years on the Alabama. With over thirty illustrations. 2d ed. Boston, Lee and Shepard, 1896.
Sinclair, Arthur, *(C.S.N.)*

LAC 13212

Two years' residence in the new settlements of Ohio, North America: with directions to emigrants. London, Westley and Davis; [etc., etc.] 1835.
Griffiths, D   *jr.*

LAC 40051

Types of Indian culture in California. Berkeley, The University press, 1904.
Kroeber, Alfred Louis, 1876–1960.

LAC 12588
Typographia; or, The printer's instructor: a brief sketch of the origin, rise, and progress of the typographic art, with practical directions for conducting every department in an office, hints to authors, publishers, &c. [New ed.] Philadelphia, L. Johnson & co., 1864.
Adams, Thomas F.

LAC 12549
Tyranny unmasked. Washington City, Davis and Force, 1822.
Taylor, John, 1753–1824.

LAC 15511
Ukrainians in the United States. Chicago, Ill., The University of Chicago press [1937]
Halich, Wasyl.

LAC 12268
Ultimate conceptions of faith. Boston and New York, Houghton, Mifflin and company, 1903.
Gordon, George Angier, 1853–1929.

LAC 12452
Ulysses S. Grant; his life and character. New York, Doubleday & McClure co., 1898.
Garland, Hamlin, 1860–1940.

LAC 15491
Un-American immigration: its present effects and future perils. A study from the census of 1890. By Rena Michaels Atchison. With an introduction by Rev. Joseph Cook. Chicago, C. H. Kerr & company, 1894.
Atchison, Rena, 1856–

LAC 15092
Uncas and Miantonomoh; a historical discourse, delivered at Norwich, (Conn.,) on the fourth day of July, 1842, on the occasion of the erection of a monument to the memory of Uncas, the white man's friend, and first chief of the Mohegans. New York, Dayton & Newman, 1842.
Stone, William Leete, 1792–1844.

LAC 40095
Uncivil liberty: an essay to show the injustice and impolicy of ruling woman without her consent. 20th thousand. Princeton, Mass., Cooperative publishing company, 1870.
Heywood, Ezra Hervey, 1829–1893.

LAC 15953
"Uncle Jerry." Life of General Jeremiah M. Rusk, stage driver, farmer, soldier, legislator, governor, cabinet officer. By Henry Casson. With a chapter by ex-President Benjamin Harrison. Madison, Wis., J. W. Hill, 1895.
Casson, Henry, 1843–

LAC 11961
Uncle Remus, his songs and his sayings; the folklore of the old plantation, by Joel Chandler Harris; with illustrations by Frederick S. Church and James H. Moser. New York, D. Appleton and company, 1881, [c1880]
Harris, Joel Chandler, 1848–1908.

LAC 14195
"Uncle Tom's cabin" contrasted with Buckingham hall, the planter's home, or, A fair view of both sides of the slavery question. New York, D. Fanshaw, 1852.
Criswell, Robert.

LAC 40005
Uncollected lectures by Ralph Waldo Emerson; reports of lectures on American life and Natural religion, reprinted from the Commonwealth. Edited by Clarence Gohdes. New York, W. E. Rudge, 1932.
Emerson, Ralph Waldo, 1803–1882.

LAC 14048
Uncollected writings, edited with an introduction by Olov W. Fryckstedt. Uppsala [Distributed by Almquist & Wiksell, Stockholm] 1963.
Crane, Stephen, 1871–1900.

LAC 11240
The unconstitutionality of slavery. Boston, B. Marsh, 1860, [c1845]
Spooner, Lysander, 1808–1887.

LAC 16634
Unconstitutionality of the Fugitive slave act. Decisions of the Supreme court of Wisconsin in the cases of Booth and Rycraft. Milwaukee, R. King & co., printers, 1855.
Wisconsin. *Supreme Court.*

LAC 10816
Under a colonial roof-tree; fireside chronicles of early New England. Syracuse, Wolcott and West, 1892, [c1891]
Huntington, Arria Sargent, 1848–

LAC 12538
Under four administrations, from Cleveland to Taft; recollections of Oscar S. Straus... Boston and New York, Houghton Mifflin company, 1922.
Straus, Oscar Solomon, 1850–1926.

LAC 13176
Under the black flag, by Captain Kit Dalton, a Confederate soldier, a guerilla captain under the fearless leader Quantrell, and a border outlaw for seventeen years following the surrender of the Confederacy. Associated with the most noted band of free booters the world has ever known. [Memphis, Tenn., Lockard publishing company, c1914]
Dalton, Kit, 1843–1920.

LAC 12079
Under the evening lamp. New York, C. Scribner's sons, 1892.
Stoddard, Richard Henry, 1825–1903.

LAC 22614–15
Under the old flag; recollections of military operations in the war for the Union, the Spanish war, the Boxer rebellion, etc., and James Harrison Wilson... New York and London, D. Appleton and company, 1912.
Wilson, James Harrison, 1837–1925.

LAC 11936
Under the skylights. New York, D. Appleton and company, 1901.
Fuller, Henry Blake, 1857–1929.

LAC 16604

The **Under-ground railroad.** Westport, Conn., Negro Universities Press [1970]
Mitchell, William M.

LAC 14537

The **underground rail road.** A record of facts, authentic narratives, letters, &c., narrating the hardships, hairbreadth escapes and death struggles of the slaves in their efforts for freedom, as related by themselves and others, or witnessed by the author; together with sketches of some of the largest stockholders, and most liberal aiders and advisers, of the road. Philadelphia, Porter & Coates, 1872.
Still, William, 1821–1902.

LAC 12887

The **underground railroad from slavery to freedom,** by Wilbur H. Siebert, with an introduction by Albert Bushnell Hart. New York, The Macmillan company [etc.,etc.] 1899, [c1898]
Siebert, Wilbur Henry, 1866–1961.

LAC 14942

Underground transmission and distribution for electric light and power. 1st ed. New York, McGraw-Hill book company, inc.; [etc., etc.] 1916.
Meyer, Edward Bernard, 1882–

LAC 12973

The **understanding reader: or, Knowledge before oratory.** Being a new selection of lessons, suited to the understandings and the capacities of youth, and designed for their improvement, I. In reading. II. In the definition of words. III. In spelling, particularly, compound and derivative words. 3d ed. Leominster, Mass., Printed by Salmon Wilder, for the author, 1805.
Adams, Daniel, 1773–1864.

LAC 40030

The **undeveloped South.** Its resources, and the importance of their development as a factor in determining the future prosperity and growth of wealth in the United States. Louisville, Ky., Printed by the Courier-Journal job printing company, 1887.
Cowlam, George B.

LAC 15458

The **undeveloped West; or, Five years in the territories:** being a complete history of that vast region between the Mississippi and the Pacific, its resources, climate, inhabitants, natural curiosities, etc., etc. Life and adventure on prairies, mountains, and the Pacific coast. With two hundred and forty illustrations, from original sketches and photographic views of the scenery ... of the great West. Philadelphia, Chicago [etc.] National publishing company [1873]
Beadle, John Hanson, 1840–1897.

LAC 11990

The **undiscovered country.** Boston, Houghton, Mifflin and company, 1880.
Howells, William Dean, 1837–1920.

LAC 40013

Unemployed and public employment agencies... Chicago [Cameron, Amberg & co., printers] 1914.
Sutherland, Edwin Hardin, 1883–1950.

LAC 40104

The **unemployed in American cities.** Boston, George H. Ellis, 1894.
Closson, Carlos C.

LAC 16266

Unforeseen tendencies of democracy. Boston and New York, Houghton, Mifflin and company, 1898.
Godkin, Edwin Lawrence, 1831–1902.

LAC 40096

The **union and its enemies.** Speech of Hon. Benjamin H. Hill, of Georgia, delivered in the Senate of the United States, Saturday, May 10, 1879. Washington, D. C., Globe printing and publishing house, 1879.
Hill, Benjamin Harvey, 1823–1882.

LAC 15062

The **Union cause in Kentucky, 1860–1865,** by Captain Thomas Speed, adjutant 12th Kentucky infantry and veteran infantry vols. 1861–65. New York and London, G. P. Putnam's sons, 1907.
Speed, Thomas, 1841–1906.

LAC 11430

Union–disunion–reunion. Three decades of federal legislation, 1855 to 1885. Personal and historical memories of events preceding, during, and since the American civil war, involving slavery and secession, emancipation and reconstruction, with sketches of prominent actors during these periods. Illustrated with thirty-six portraits engraved on steel expressly for this work. Providence, R. I., J. A. & R. A. Reid, 1888, [c1885]
Cox, Samuel Sullivan, 1824–1889.

LAC 16878

Union list of newspapers.
American newspapers, 1821–1936; a union list of files available in the United States and Canada, edited by Winifred Gregory under the auspices of the Bibliographical Society of America. New York, H. W. Wilson Co., 1937.

LAC 10054

The **Union Pacific railway; a study in railway politics, history, and economics.** Chicago, S. C. Griggs and company, 1894.
Davis, John Patterson, 1862–1903.

LAC 40059

The **Union, past and future: how it works, and how to save it.** By a citizen of Virginia. Charleston, Walker & James, 1850.
Garnett, Muscoe Russell Hunter, 1821–1864.

LAC 21072–74

Union university, its history, influence, characteristics and equipment, with the lives and works of its founders, benefactors, officers, regents, faculty, and the achievements of its alumni. Union college, Albany medical college, Albany law school, Dudley observatory, Albany college of pharmacy. New York, Lewis publishing company, 1907.
Raymond, Andrew Van Vranken, 1854–

LAC 14963

Unitarianism in America; a history of its origin and development. Boston, American Unitarian association, 1910, [c1902]
Cooke, George Willis, 1848–1923.

LAC 14227

Unitarianism: its origin and history. A course of sixteen lectures delivered in Channing hall, Boston, 1888-89. Boston, American Unitarian association, 1895, [c1889]

LAC 16491

The united Negro: his problems and his progress, containing the addresses and proceedings of the Negro young people's Christian and educational congress, held August 6-11, 1902; introduction by Bishop W. J. Gaines; edited by Prof. I. Garland Penn [and] Prof. J. W. E. Bowen. Atlanta, Ga., D. E. Luther publishing co., 1902.
Penn, Irvine Garland, 1867-1930, *ed.*

LAC 16873

The United States a Christian nation. Philadelphia, The J. C. Winston company, 1905.
Brewer, David Josiah, 1837-1910.

LAC 12940

The United States and Cuba. London, Pewtress & co.; New York, Sheldon, Blakeman, & co., 1857.
Phillippo, James Mursell, 1798-1879.

LAC 11626

The United States and Cuba: eight years of change and travel. London, R. Bentley, 1851.
Taylor, John Glanville, 1823-1851.

LAC 11142

The United States and foreign powers. Rev. ed. New York, C. Scribner's sons, 1900, [c1899]
Curtis, William Eleroy, 1850-1911.

LAC 21367-68

The United States and Mexico, 1821-1848; a history of the relations between the two countries from the independence of Mexico to the close of the war with the United States. New York, C. Scribner's sons, 1913.
Rives, George Lockhart, 1849-1917.

LAC 10679

The United States and Spain in 1790. An episode in diplomacy described from hitherto unpublished sources. With an introduction by Worthington Chauncey Ford. Brooklyn, Historical printing club, 1890.
Ford, Worthington Chauncey, 1858-1941, *ed.*

LAC 11519

The United States and the states under the Constitution. Philadelphia, T. & J. W. Johnson & co., 1888.
Patterson, Christopher Stuart, 1842-1924.

LAC 10139

The United States beet-sugar industry and the tariff. New York, Columbia university, Longmans, Green & co., agents; [etc., etc.] 1912.
Blakey, Roy Gillispie, 1880-

LAC 12693

The United States gazetteer: containing an authentic description of the several states. Their situation, extent, boundaries, soil, produce, climate, population, trade and manufactures. Together with the extent, boundaries and population of their respective counties... Illustrated with nineteen maps. Philadelphia: Printed by F. and R. Bailey, at Yorick's-Head, No. 116, High Street, 1795. (Published according to Act of Congress)
Scott, Joseph, *geographer.*

LAC 10688

The United States in the Far East; or, Modern Japan and the Orient. Richmond, Va., B. F. Johnson publishing co., 1899.
Hubbard, Richard Bennett, 1832-1901.

LAC 13833

The United States in the Orient; the nature of the economic problem. Boston and New York, Houghton, Mifflin and company, 1900.
Conant, Charles Arthur, 1861-1915.

LAC 12206

The United States in the twentieth century, by Pierre Leroy-Beaulieu; authorized translation by H. Addington Bruce. 3d ed. New York and London, Funk & Wagnalls company, 1906.
Leroy-Beaulieu, Pierre, 1871-1915.

LAC 30219-32

The United States magazine, and democratic review. v. 1-18; Oct. 1837-June 1846. Washington, D. C., Langtree and O'Sullivan, 1838-40; New York, J. & H. G. Langley [etc.] 1841-46.

LAC 14417

The United States naval academy, being the yarn of the American midshipman (naval cadet)... New York and London, G. P. Putnam's sons, 1900.
Benjamin, Park, 1849-1922.

LAC 10063

United States notes; a history of the various issues of paper money by the government of the United States, with an appendix containing the recent decision of the Supreme court of the United States and the dissenting opinion upon the legal tender question. 3d ed. rev. New York, C. Scribner's sons, 1899, [c1884]
Knox, John Jay, 1828-1892.

LAC 21857-58

The United States of America; a study of the American commonwealth, its natural resources, people, industries, manufactures, commerce, and its work in literature, science, education, and self-government. New York, D. Appleton and company, 1897, [c1894]
Shaler, Nathaniel Southgate, 1841-1906, *ed.*

LAC 13573

The United States of North America. By Achille Murat. With a Note on Negro slavery, by Junius redivivus [*pseud.* of W. B. Adams] 2d ed. London, E. Wilson [etc.] 1833.
Murat, Achille, *prince*, 1801-1847.

LAC 12136

The United States of North America as they are; not as they are generously described: being a cure for radicalism... London, Longman, Orme, Brown, Green & Longmans, 1840.
Brothers, Thomas.

LAC 15914

The U.S. sanitary commission in the valley of the Mississippi, during the war of the rebellion, 1861-1866. Final report of Dr. J. S. Newberry, secretary... Cleveland, Fairbanks, Benedict & co., printers, 1871.
United States Sanitary Commission. *Western Dept.*

LAC 15393

United States school and college directory for 1874. Containing a complete list of schools and colleges, and description of first-class educational institutions, and much other valuable information. New York, T. C. Pinckney [c1874]

LAC 10166

The United States steel corporation; a study of the growth and influence of combination in the iron and steel industry. New York, The Columbia university press, the Macmillan company, agents; [etc., etc.] 1907.
Berglund, Abraham, 1875–1942.

LAC 23326–34

United States steel corporation. Hearings before the Committee on investigation of United States steel corporation. House of representatives. Washington, Govt. print. off., 1911–12.
U.S. *Congress. House. Committee on Investigation of United States Steel Corporation.*

LAC 12212

The United States unmasked. A search into the causes of the rise and progress of these states, and an exposure of their present material and moral condition. With additions and corrections by the author. London, E. Stanford, 1879.
Manigault, Gabriel, 1809–1888.

LAC 10500

The unity of law; as exhibited in the relations of physical, social, mental, and moral science. Philadelphia, H. C. Baird, 1873, [c1872]
Carey, Henry Charles, 1793–1879.

LAC 14984

The unity of the human races proved to be the doctrine of Scripture, reason, and science. With a review of the present position and theory of Professor Agassiz. By the Rev. Thomas Smyth. New-York, G. P. Putnam, 1850.
Smyth, Thomas, 1808–1873.

LAC 14363

The universal restoration, exhibited in four dialogues between a minister and his friend: comprehending the substance of several real conversations which the author had with various persons, both in America and Europe, on that interesting subject, chiefly designed fully to state, and fairly to answer the most common objections that are brought against it, from the Scriptures. To this edition is prefixed, a brief account of the means and manner of the author's embracing these sentiments; intermixed with some sketches of his life during four years. Published at Worcester, Massachusetts: by Isaiah Thomas, jun. Sold wholesale and retail by him, at his printing office in Worcester, and by Thomas & Whipple, in Newburyport, October–1803.
Winchester, Elhanan, 1751–1797.

LAC 15403

Universalism false and unscriptural. An essay on the duration and intensity of future punishment. Philadelphia, Presbyterian board of publication [1851]

LAC 20353–54

Universalism in America. A history. Boston, Universalist publishing house, 1886.
Eddy, Richard, 1828–1906.

LAC 40033

University and school extension. A paper read before the National educational association at St. Paul, Minn., July, 1890. Syracuse, N. Y., C. W. Bardeen, 1890.
Harris, William Torrey, 1835–1909.

LAC 14679

University education. New York, G. P. Putnam, 1851.
Tappan, Henry Philip, 1805–1881.

LAC 40003

University extension in the United States. Washington, Govt. print. off., 1914.
Reber, Louis Ehrhart, 1858–

LAC 40003

The university library; its larger recognition in higher education. New York, Publication office, 1894.
Lowrey, C   E

LAC 10458

University problems in the United States. New York, The Century co., 1898.
Gilman, Daniel Coit, 1831–1908.

LAC 40010

The unlawful and unjustifiable conquest of the Filipinos. Boston, G. H. Ellis, 1901.
Brooks, Francis Augustus, 1824–1902.

LAC 10958

Unpublished letters of Charles Carroll of Carrollton, and his father, Charles Carroll of Doughoregan. Comp. and ed. with a memoir by Thomas Meagher Field. New York, The United States Catholic historical society, 1902.
Carroll, Charles, 1737–1832.

LAC 13490

The unwritten constitution of the United States. A philosophical inquiry into the fundamentals of American constitutional law. New York [etc.] G. P. Putnam's sons, 1890.
Tiedeman, Christopher Gustavus, 1857–1903.

LAC 16522

Up from slavery; an autobiography. New York, Doubleday, Page & co., 1902, [c1901]
Washington, Booker Taliaferro, 1859?–1915.

LAC 11637

Up the heights of fame and fortune, and the routes taken by the climbers to become men of mark. Edited by Fred'k Brent Read. Cincinnati, W. H. Moore & company, 1873.
Read, Frederick Brent, *ed.*

LAC 10709

The upper Tennessee; comprehending desultory records of river operations in the Tennessee valley, covering a period of one hundred fifty years, including pen and camera pictures of the hardy craft and the colorful characters who navigated them... T. J. Campbell, author and publisher. Chattanooga, Tenn., c1932.
Campbell, Thomas Jefferson, 1864–

LAC 11232

The uprising of the many. Illustrated from photographs. New York, Doubleday, Page & company, 1907.
Russell, Charles Edward, 1860–1941.

LAC 16643

Ups and downs of an army officer. By Col. George A. Armes, U.S.A. Washington, D. C., 1900.
Armes, George Augustus, 1844–1919.

LAC 21352

The useful arts, considered in connexion with the applications of science; with numerous engravings. New York, Harper, 1863, [c1840]
Bigelow, Jacob, 1787–1879.

LAC 14234

Utah and the Mormons. The history, government, doctrines, customs, and prospects of the Latter-day saints. From personal observation during a six months' residence at Great Salt Lake City. New York, Harper & brothers, 1854.
Ferris, Benjamin G.

LAC 40142

Ute, Pai-Ute, Go-si Ute, and Shoshone Indians. Letter from the acting secretary of the Interior in relation to the condition and wants of the Ute Indians of Utah; the Pai-Utes of Utah, northern Arizona, southern Nevada, and southeastern California; the Go-si Utes of Utah and Nevada; the northwestern Shoshones of Idaho and Utah, and the western Shoshones of Nevada. [Washington, Govt. print. off., 1874]
U.S. *Bureau of Indian Affairs.*

LAC 12237

A vacation tour in the United States and Canada. London, Longman, Brown, Green, and Longmans, 1855.
Weld, Charles Richard, 1813–1869.

LAC 12228

The vade mecum for America: or, A companion for traders and travellers... Boston, Printed by S. Kneeland, and T. Green for D. Henchman & T. Hancock, 1732.
Prince, Thomas, 1687–1758.

LAC 21061

The valley of decision; a novel. New York, C. Scribner's sons, 1902.
Wharton, Edith Newbold, 1862–1937.

LAC 10536

The valor of ignorance. With specially prepared maps. New York and London, Harper & brothers [c1909]
Lea, Homer, 1876–1912.

LAC 40094

The value of common school education to common labor, by Dr. Edward Jarvis ... together with illustrations of the same as shown by the answers to inquiries addressed to employers, workmen, and observers. Washington, Govt. print. off., 1879.
Jarvis, Edward, 1803–1884.

LAC 12038

Vandover and the brute. Garden City, N. Y., Doubleday, Page & company, 1914.
Norris, Frank, 1870–1902.

LAC 14299

The vanishing race, the last great Indian council: a record in picture and story of the last great Indian council, participated in by eminent Indian chiefs from nearly every Indian reservation in the United States, together with the story of their lives as told by themselves–their speeches and folklore tales–their solemn farewell and the Indians' story of the Custer fight, written and illustrated by Dr. Joseph K. Dixon, leader of the expeditions to the North American Indian to perpetuate the life story of these first Americans; the concept of Rodman Wanamaker. This volume is illustrated with eighty photogravures of Indian chiefs and Indian life. Garden City, N. Y., Doubleday, Page & company, 1914, [c1913]
Dixon, Joseph Kossuth.

LAC 16939

Van Zorn; a comedy in three acts. New York, The Macmillan company, 1914.
Robinson, Edwin Arlington, 1869–1935.

LAC 15255

The varieties of religious experience; a study in human nature, being the Gifford lectures on natural religion delivered at Edinburgh in 1901–1902. New York, London [etc.] Longmans, Green, and co., 1902.
James, William, 1842–1910.

LAC 40102

Various forms of local government in the District of Columbia. (Read before the Columbia historical society, April 4, 1898) Washington, Govt. print. off., 1898.
Bryan, Wilhelmus Bogart, 1854–1938.

LAC 14049

The various writings of Cornelius Mathews... New York, Harper & brothers, 1863 [*i.e.* 1843]
Mathews, Cornelius, 1817–1889.

LAC 16956

Vasconselos: a romance of the New World. Chicago [etc.] Belford, Clarke & Co., 1888.
Simms, William Gilmore, 1806–1870.

LAC 11991

Venetian life. 2d ed. New York, Hurd and Houghton, 1867.
Howells, William Dean, 1837–1920.

LAC 40124

The Venezuelan question and the Monroe doctrine. Washington, D. C., Gibson bros., printers, 1896.
Boutwell, George Sewall, 1818–1905.

LAC 40058

The Venezuelan question: British aggressions in Venezuela, or The Monroe doctrine on trial; Lord Salisbury's mistakes; Fallacies of the British "blue book" on the disputed boundary. Atlanta, Ga., The Franklin printing and publishing co., 1896.
Scruggs, William Lindsay, 1836–1912.

LAC 40007

Vermont; a glimpse of its scenery and industries. Montpelier, Vt., Argus and Patriot, 1893.
Spear, Victor Ira.

LAC 15900

Vermont: a study of independence. Boston and New York, Houghton, Mifflin and company, 1892.
Robinson, Rowland Evans, 1833–1900.

LAC 20536–42

The Vermont historical gazetteer: a magazine, embracing a history of each town, civil, ecclesiastical, biographical and military. Edited by Abby Maria Hemenway. Burlington, Vt., Miss A. M. Hemenway; [etc., etc.] 1868–91.

LAC 15656

Vermont state papers; being a collection of records and documents, connected with the assumption and establishment of government by the people of Vermont; together with the journal of the Council of safety, the first constitution, the early journals of the General assembly, and the laws from the year 1779 to 1786, inclusive. To which are added the Proceedings of the first and second Councils of censors. Comp. and pub. by William Slade. Middlebury, J. W. Copeland, printer, 1823.
Vermont.

LAC 40102

Vermont's appeal to the candid and impartial world. Containing, a fair stating of the claims of Massachusetts-Bay, New-Hampshire, and New-York. The right the state of Vermont has to independence. With an address to the honorable American Congress, and the inhabitants of the thirteen united states. Hartford, Printed by Hudson & Goodwin [1780]
Bradley, Stephen Row, 1754–1830.

LAC 14436

Verrazano the navigator; or, Notes on Giovanni da Verrazano and on a planisphere of 1529 illustrating his American voyage in 1524. With a reduced copy of the map... New York [The Argus co., printers, Albany] 1874.
Brevoort, James Carson, 1818–1887.

LAC 15375

Vestiges of civilization: or, The aetiology of history, religious, aesethetical, political, and philosophical... New York [etc.] H. Bailliere; [etc., etc.] 1851.
O'Connell, James.

LAC 14757

Vestiges of the natural history of creation. With a sequel. New York, Harper [1847?]
Chambers, Robert, 1802–1871.

LAC 11840

Victorian prose masters; Thackeray–Carlyle–George Eliot–Matthew Arnold–Ruskin–George Meredith. New York, C. Scribner's sons, 1928, [c1901]
Brownell, William Crary, 1851–1928.

LAC 40077

A view of exertions lately made for the purpose of colonizing the free people of colour, in the United States, in Africa, or elsewhere. City of Washington, Printed by Jonathan Elliot, Pennsylvania avenue, 1817.
American Colonization Society.

LAC 10321

A view of the commerce of the United States and the Mediterranean sea-ports, including the Adriatic and Morea; with maps of the principal harbours in those seas... From the manuscript of the late John Martin Baker, by his son, Louis Baker. Philadelphia, Barrington & Murphy, 1847.
Baker, John Martin.

LAC 15208

A view of the conduct of the executive, in the foreign affairs of the United States connected with the mission to the French republic, during the years 1794, 5, & 6. By James Monroe, late minister plenipotentiary to the said republic; illustrated by his instructions and correspondence and other authentic documents. Philadelphia: Printed by Benj. Franklin Bache, M,DCCXCVII.
Monroe, James, *pres. U.S.*, 1758–1831.

LAC 15980

A view of the constitution of the British colonies, in North-America and the West Indies, at the time the civil war broke out on the continent of America... London, Printed for the author and sold by B. White, 1783.
Stokes, Anthony, 1736–1799.

LAC 14749

A view of the Constitution of the United States of America. 2d ed. Philadelphia, P. H. Nicklin, 1829.
Rawle, William, 1759–1836.

LAC 13311

A view of the lead mines of Missouri; including some observations on the mineralogy, geology, geography, antiquities, soil, climate, population, and productions of Missouri and Arkansaw, and other sections of the western country. Accompanied by three engravings, by Henry R. Schoolcraft. New-York: Published by Charles Wiley & co. no. 3 Wall-street. J. Seymour, printer, 1819.
Schoolcraft, Henry Rowe, 1793–1864.

LAC 12302

View of the origin and migrations of the Polynesian nation; demonstrating their ancient discovery and progressive settlement of the continent of America. London, Cochrane and McCrone, 1834.
Lang, John Dunmore, 1799–1878.

LAC 11418

A view of the political conduct of Aaron Burr, esq., vice-president of the United States. By the author of the "Narrative." New-York, Printed by Denniston & Cheetham, 1802.
Cheetham, James, 1772–1810.

LAC 40088

View of the practicability and means of supplying the city of Philadelphia with wholesome water. In a letter to John Miller, esquire, from B. Henry Latrobe, engineer. December 29th, 1798. Printed by order of the Corporation of Philadelphia. Philadelphia: Printed by Zachariah Poulson, junior, no. 106, Chesnut-street, 1799.
Latrobe, Benjamin Henry, 1764–1820.

LAC 11440

View of the President's conduct concerning the conspiracy of 1806. A reprint, ed. by Isaac Joslin Cox and Helen A. Swineford. Cincinnati, The Abingdon press [1917]
Daveiss, Joseph Hamilton, 1774–1811.

LAC 40039

A view of the relative situation of Great Britain and the United States of North America: by a merchant. London, Printed by H. L. Galabin and sold by J. Debrett [etc.] 1794.
Bird, Henry Merttins.

LAC 14003

A view of the rights and wrongs, power and policy, of the United States of America... Philadelphia, O. & A. Conrad & co.; Baltimore, Conrad, Lucas & co., 1808.
Ingersoll, Charles Jared, 1782–1862.

LAC 12704

A view of the soil and climate of the United States of America: with supplementary remarks upon Florida; on the French colonies on the Mississippi and Ohio, and in Canada; and on the aboriginal tribes of America. By C. F. Volney. Tr., with occasional remarks, by C. B. Brown. With maps and plates. Philadelphia, Pub. by J. Conrad & co.; Baltimore, M. & J. Conrad & co.; [Philadelphia] Printed by T. & G. Palmer, 1804.
Volney, Constantin Francois Chasseboeuf, *comte* de, 1757–1820.

LAC 13670

A view of the state of parties in the United States of America; being an attempt to account for the present ascendancy of the French or Democratic party, in that country; in two letters to a friend. By a gentleman who has recently visited the United States. Edinburgh, J. Ballantyne and co.; [etc., etc.] 1812.
MacCormack, Samuel.

LAC 10190

A view of the United States of America, in a series of papers, written at various times, between the years 1787 and 1794; interspersed with authentic documents: the whole tending to exhibit the progress and present state of civil and religious liberty, population, agriculture, exports, imports, fisheries, navigation, ship-building, manufactures, and general improvement. Philadelphia, Printed for William Hall, no. 51, Market street, and Wrigley & Berriman, no. 149, Chesnut street, 1794.
Coxe, Tench, 1755–1824.

LAC 16774

Views a-foot.
Pedestrian tour in Europe. Views a-foot: or, Europe seen with knapsack and staff, by J. Bayard Taylor. With a preface by N. P. Willis. 8th ed., with additions, and a portrait from a sketch by T. B. Read. New York, G. P. Putnam, 1848.
Taylor, Bayard, 1825–1878.

LAC 10533

Views and reviews, by Henry James, now first collected; introduction by Le Roy Phillips. Boston, The Ball publishing company, 1908.
James, Henry, 1843–1916.

LAC 15220

Views and reviews in American literature, history and fiction. By the author of "The Yemassee". 1st [and 2d] series. New York, Wiley and Putnam, 1845.
Simms, William Gilmore, 1806–1870.

LAC 13860

Views in theology. Published by request of the synod of Cincinnati. Cincinnati, Truman and Smith; New York, Leavitt, Lord and co., 1836.
Beecher, Lyman, 1775–1863.

LAC 12834

Views of American constitutional law in its bearing upon American slavery. 2d ed.: rev., with additions...
Utica, N. Y., Lawson & Chaplin, 1845.
Goodell, William, 1792–1878.

LAC 15265

Views of an ex-president, by Benjamin Harrison; being his addresses and writings on subjects of public interest since the close of his administration as president of the United States, comp. by Mary Lord Harrison. Indianapolis, The Bowen-Merrill company [c1901]
Harrison, Benjamin, *pres. U.S.*, 1833–1901.

LAC 12175

Views of society and manners in America; in a series of letters from that country to a friend in England, during the years 1818, 1819, and 1820. By an Englishwoman. From the 1st London ed. with additions and corrections by the author... New York, E. Bliss and E. White, 1821.
D'Arusmont, Frances, 1795–1852.

LAC 40031

Views of the American press on the Philippines. Edited by T. Bruce [*pseud.*] New York, Esty & Esty, 1899.
Esty, Thomas Bruce, *ed.*

LAC 13632

Views of the prophecies and prophetic chronology, selected from manuscripts of William Miller, with a memoir of his life, by Joshua V. Himes. Boston, Joshua V. Himes, 1842.
Miller, William, 1782–1849.

LAC 40060

Views on the subject of internal improvement, between the Atlantic and western states. Baltimore, Printed by W. Wooddy, 1825.
Hollins, William.

LAC 22363–64

Vigilante days and ways; the pioneers of the Rockies; the makers and making of Montana, Idaho, Oregon, Washington, and Wyoming. New York, D. D. Merrill, 1893.
Langford, Nathaniel Pitt, 1832–1911.

LAC 11824

Village life in New England.
Norwood; or, Village life in New England. New York, C. Scribner & company, 1868.
Beecher, Henry Ward, 1813–1887.

LAC 14310

Villas and cottages. A series of designs prepared for execution in the United States. By Calvert Vaux, architect, late Downing & Vaux. Illustrated by 370 engravings. New York, Harper & Brothers, 1867.
Vaux, Calvert, 1824–1895.

LAC 10328

A vindication by Cadwallader D. Colden, of the steam boat right granted by the state of New-York [to Livingston and Fulton] in the form of an answer to the letter of Mr. Duer, addressed to Mr. Colden. Albany, Printed by Websters and Skinners, 1818.
Colden, Cadwallader David, 1769–1834.

LAC 40095

A vindication of the character and condition of the females employed in the Lowell mills, against the charges contained in the Boston times, and the Boston quarterly review. By Elisha Bartlett, M. D. Lowell, L. Huntress, printer, 1841.
Bartlett, Elisha, 1804–1855.

LAC 40143

Vindication of the claim of Elkanah Watson, Esq. to the merit of projecting the Lake canal policy, as created by the Canal act of March, 1792. And also a vindication of the claim of the late General Schuyler, to the merit of drawing that act, and procuring its passage through the legislature. Geneva, N. Y., J. Bogert, 1821.
Troup, Robert, 1757–1832.

LAC 15596

A vindication of the government of New England churches. Boston, John Boyles, 1772.
Wise, John, 1652–1725.

LAC 40092

A vindication of the measures of the present administration. By Algernon Sidney [pseud.] Portsmouth: N. H., Printed by N. S. & W. Pierce, 1803.
Granger, Gideon, 1767–1822.

LAC 13377

Violence and the labor movement. New York, The Macmillan company, 1914.
Hunter, Robert, 1874–1942.

LAC 10685

Virginalia, songs of my summer nights. [Brooklyn, E. L. Schwaab, 1942]
Chivers, Thomas Holley, 1809–1858.

LAC 12307

Virginia Carolorum: the colony under the rule of Charles the First and Second, A. D. 1625–A. D. 1685, based upon manuscripts and documents of the period. Albany, N. Y., J. Munsell's sons, 1886.
Neill, Edward Duffield, 1823–1893.

LAC 10276

The Virginia convention of 1776. A discourse delivered before the Virginia Alpha of the Phi beta kappa society, in the chapel of William and Mary college, in the city of Williamsburg, on the afternoon of July the 3rd, 1855. (Published by a resolution of the Society.) Richmond, J. W. Randolph, 1855.
Grigsby, Hugh Blair, 1806–1881.

LAC 10906

Virginia, especially Richmond, in by-gone days; with a glance at the present: being reminiscences and last words of an old citizen. 2d ed., with many corrections and additions. Richmond, West & Johnston, 1860.
Mordecai, Samuel.

LAC 13682

The Virginia house-wife: or, Methodical cook... Philadelphia, E. H. Butler & co., 1871.
Randolph, Mary.

LAC 40127

Virginia in 1616. Richmond, Macfarlane & Fergusson, 1848.
Rolfe, John, 1585–1622.

LAC 14449

Virginia land grants, a study of conveyancing in relation to colonial politics. Richmond, Priv. print., The Old Dominion press, 1925.
Harrison, Fairfax, 1869–

LAC 40012

Virginia: more especially the south part thereof, richly and truly valued: viz. The fertile Carolana, and no lesse excellent isle of Roanoak, of latitude from 31. to 37. degr. relating the meanes of raysing infinite profits to the adventurers and planters. The 2d ed., with addition of the Discovery of silkworms, with their benefit. And implanting of mulberry trees. Also the dressing of vines, for the rich trade of making wines in Virginia. Together with the making of the sawmill, very usefull in Virginia, for cutting of timber and clapboard to build withall, and its conversion to many as profitable uses. By E. W. gent. London, Printed by T. H. for J. Stephenson, 1650.
Williams, Edward, fl. 1650.

LAC 13827

The Virginia report of 1799–1800, touching the Alien and sedition laws; together with the Virginia resolutions of December 21, 1798, the debate and proceedings thereon in the House of delegates of Virginia, and several other documents illustrative of the report and resolutions. Richmond, J. W. Randolph, 1850.
Virginia. General Assembly. House of Delegates.

LAC 16675

Virginia under the Stuarts, 1607–1688. Princeton, Princeton university press; [etc., etc.] 1914.
Wertenbaker, Thomas Jefferson, 1879–1966.

LAC 12123

The Virginian, a horseman of the plains, by Owen Wister, with illustrations by Arthur I. Keller. New York, The Macmillan company; London, Macmillan & Co., ltd., 1902.
Wister, Owen, 1860–1938.

LAC 16520

The Virginian history of African colonization. Richmond, Macfarlane & Fergusson, 1855.
Slaughter, Philip, 1808–1890.

LAC 16027

Visible speech: the science ... of universal alphabets; or Self-interpreting physiological letters, for the writing of all languages in one alphabet... Inaugural ed. London, Simpkin, Marshall & co., 1867.
Bell, Alexander Melville, 1819–1905.

LAC 15316

The vision of Columbus; a poem in nine books. 2d ed. Hartford: Printed by Hudson and Goodwin, for the author. M.DCC.LXXXVII.
Barlow, Joel, 1754–1812.

LAC 11993
Visionaries. New York, Charles Scribner's sons, 1905.
Huneker, James Gibbons, 1860–1921.

LAC 16690
A visit to Salt Lake; being a journey across the plains, and a residence in the Mormon settlements at Utah. London, Smith, Elder, and co., 1857.
Chandless, William.

LAC 14703
A visit to the cities and camps of the Confederate States. Edinburgh and London, W. Blackwood and sons, 1865.
Ross, Fitzgerald.

LAC 14950
A visit to the Philadelphia prison; being an accurate and particular account of the wise and humane administration adopted in every part of that building; containing also an account of the gradual reformation, and present improved state, of the penal laws of Pennsylvania: with observations on the impolicy and injustice of capital punishments. In a letter to a friend. Philadelphia printed; London, Re-printed and sold by J. Phillips & son, 1797.
Turnbull, Robert James, 1775–1833.

LAC 15905
A visit to the United States in 1841. New York, A. M. Kelley, 1969.
Sturge, Joseph, 1793–1859.

LAC 14841
Visitation and search; or, An historical sketch of the British claim to exercise a maritime police over the vessels of all nations in peace as well as in war... Boston, Little, Brown, and company, 1858.
Lawrence, William Beach, 1800–1881.

LAC 12047
A vocabulary; or, Collection of words and phrases, which have been supposed to be peculiar to the United States of America. To which is prefixed an essay on the present state of the English language in the United States. Originally published in the Memoirs of the American academy of arts and sciences: and now republished with corrections and additions. Boston: Published by Cummings and Hilliard, No. 1 Cornhill ... Cambridge ... Hilliard and Metcalf, 1816.
Pickering, John, 1777–1846.

LAC 40113
A voice from Harper's Ferry. A narrative of events at Harper's Ferry; with incidents prior and subsequent to its capture by Captain Brown and his men. By Osborne P. Anderson, one of the number. Boston, Printed for the author, 1861.
Anderson, Osborne Perry, 1830–1872.

LAC 40126
A voice from old Tammany! Meeting of the people! [New York, J. M. Marsh, printer, 1838]
Democratic Party. *New York. New York (City) General Committee of Young Men.*

LAC 16618
A voice from South Carolina. Twelve chapters before Hampton. Two chapters after Hampton. With a journal of a reputed Ku-klux, and an appendix. Charleston, S. C., Walker, Evans & Cogswell, 1879.
Leland, John A.

LAC 14815
The voice of America on Kishineff. Philadelphia, The Jewish publication society of America, 1904.
Adler, Cyrus, 1863–1940, *ed.*

LAC 13461
The voice of labor; containing special contributions by leading workingmen throughout the United States ... plain talk by men of intellect on labor's rights, wrongs, remedies, and prospects. History of the Knights of labor. Illustrated with fine portraits and engravings. Chicago, A. B. Gehman & co., 1887.
Jelley, Symmes M.

LAC 11949
The voice of the people. New York, Doubleday, Page & co., 1900.
Glasgow, Ellen Anderson Gholson, 1873–1945.

LAC 40066
The voice of warning, to Christians, on the ensuing election of a president of the United States... New-York, Baker and Scribner, 1849.
Mason, John Mitchell, 1770–1829.

LAC 12527
A voice to America; or, The model republic, its glory, or its fall: with a review of the causes of the decline and failure of the republics of South America, Mexico, and of the Old world; applied to the present crisis in the United States... New York, E. Walker, 1855.
Saunders, Frederick, 1807–1902.

LAC 13072
A voice to Universalists. Boston, J. M. Usher, 1849.
Ballou, Hosea, 1771–1852.

LAC 14641
The volunteer soldier of America. With Memoir of the author and Military reminiscences from General Logan's private journal. Chicago and New York, R. S. Peale & company, 1887.
Logan, John Alexander, 1826–1886.

LAC 40064
"A volunteer's reminiscences of life in the North Atlantic blockading squadron, 1862-'5," prepared by Companion Acting Master Francis P. B. Sands, and read at the stated meeting of April 4, 1894. [Washington, 1894]
Sands, Francis Preston Blair, 1842–

LAC 40076
The votes and speeches of Martin Van Buren, on the subjects of the right of suffrage, the qualifications of coloured persons to vote, and the appointment or election of justices of the peace. In the Convention of the state of New-York (assembled to amend the constitution in 1821.)... Albany, Printed by T. Weed, 1840.
Van Buren, Martin, *pres. U.S.*, 1782–1862.

LAC 16168
Voyage a la Louisiane, et sur le continent de l'Amerique septentrionale, fait dans les annees 1794 a 1798; contenant un tableau historique de la Louisiane... Par B— D—. Orne d'une belle carte... Paris, Dentu, an XI.– 1802.
Baudry des Lozieres, Louis Narcisse, 1761–1841.

LAC 21270–72
Voyage dans les Etats-Unis d'Amerique, fait en 1795, 1796 et 1797. Par La Rochefoucauld Liancourt. Paris, Du Pont [etc.] l'an VII de la Republique [1799]
La Rochefoucauld Liancourt, Francois Alexandre Frederic, *duc* de, 1747–1827.

LAC 15202
Voyage en Californie, 1852–1853. Paris, L. Hachette, 1854.
Auger, Edouard.

LAC 40072
Voyage in a six-oared skiff to the Falls of Saint Anthony in 1817. St. Paul, Minnesota historical society, 1889.
Long, Stephen Harriman, 1784–1864.

LAC 12330
The voyage of Robert Dudley, afterwards styled Earl of Warwick and Leicester and Duke of Northumberland, to the West Indies, 1594–1595, narrated by Capt. Wyatt, by himself, and by Abram Kendall, master. Ed. by George F. Warner. London, Printed for the Hakluyt society, 1899.
Warner, *Sir* George Frederic, 1845–1936, *ed.*

LAC 12606
Voyage of the paper canoe: a geographical journey of 2500 miles, from Quebec to the Gulf of Mexico, during the years 1874–5. Boston, Lee and Shepard: New York, C. T. Dillingham, 1878.
Bishop, Nathaniel Holmes, 1837–1902.

LAC 13761
Voyage of the United States frigate Potomac, under the command of Commodore John Downes, during the circumnavigation of the globe, in the years 1831, 1832, 1833, and 1834... New York, Harper & brothers, 1835.
Reynolds, Jeremiah N   1799–1858.

LAC 12252
A voyage round the world; including an embassy to Muscat and Siam, in 1835, 1836, and 1837. Philadelphia, Carey, Lea & Blanchard, 1838.
Ruschenberger, William Samuel Waithman, 1807–1895.

LAC 13618
A voyage to North America, perform'd by G. Taylor, of Sheffield, in the years 1768 and 1769, with an account of his tedious passage ... manner of trading with the Indians ... his setting sail from Philadelphia to New Orleans ... and other matters worthy of notice... Nottingham, Printed by S. Creswell for the author, 1771.
Taylor, G   *of Sheffield, Eng.*

LAC 20743
A voyage to South America. Describing at large, the Spanish cities, towns, provinces, &c. on that extensive continent. Interspersed throughout with reflexions on whatever is peculiar in the religion and civil policy; in the genius, customs, manners, dress, &c. &c. of the several inhabitants; whether natives, Spaniards, creoles, Indians, mulattoes, or negroes. Together with the natural as well as commercial history of the country. And an account of their gold and silver mines. Undertaken by command of the king of Spain, by Don George Juan, and Don Antonio de Ulloa. Translated from the original Spanish. Illustrated with copper plates... The 2d ed., rev. and cor. London, L. Davis and C. Reymers, 1760.
Ulloa, Antonio de, 1716–1795.

LAC 20499
Voyage to South America, performed by order of the American government, in the years 1817 and 1818, in the frigate Congress. By H. M. Brackenridge, esq., secretary to the mission. London, Printed for J. Miller, 1820.
Brackenridge, Henry Marie, 1786–1871.

LAC 21114–15
A voyage to the Pacific Ocean; undertaken by command of his majesty, for making discoveries in the northern hemisphere. Performed under the direction of Captains Cook, Clerke, and Gore, in the years 1776, 1777, 1778, 1779, and 1780. Being a copious, comprehensive, and satisfactory abridgement of the voyage written by Captain James Cook and Captain James King. Illustrated with cuts. London, Printed for J. Stockdale, Scratcherd and Whitaker, J. Fielding, and J. Hardy, 1784.
Cook, James, 1728–1779.

LAC 20893
The voyages and explorations of Samuel de Champlain, 1604–1616, narrated by himself; translated by Annie Nettleton Bourne; together with the voyage of 1603, reprinted from Purchas his pilgrimes; ed. with introduction and notes by Edward Gaylord Bourne. New York, Allerton book co., 1922.
Champlain, Samuel de, 1567–1635.

LAC 14029
Voyages and travels of an Indian interpreter and trader, describing the manners and customs of the North American Indians; with an account of the posts situated on the river Saint Laurence, lake Ontario, &c. To which is added a vocabulary of the Chippeway language ... a list of words in the Iroquois, Mohegan, Shawanee, and Esquimeaux tongues, and a table, shewing the analogy between the Algonkin and Chippeway languages. London, Printed for the author, and sold by Robson [etc.] 1791.
Long, John, *Indian trader.*

LAC 11316
The voyages, dangerous adventures and imminent escapes of Captain Richard Falconer... Intermix'd with the voyages and adventures of Thomas Randal... Written by himself... London, W. Chetwood [etc.] 1720.
Chetwood, William Rufus, *d.* 1766.

LAC 16929
Voyages d'un Francois...
Un Francais en Virginie; Voyages d'un Francois exile pour la religion, avec une description de la Virgine & Marilan dans l'Amerique, d'apres l'edition originale de 1687; avec une introduction et des notes par Gilbert Chinard. Paris, E. Droz; Baltimore, The Johns Hopkins press; [etc., etc.] 1932.
Durand,   *of Dauphine, fl.* 1685–1687.

LAC 12305
Voyages from Asia to America, for completing the discoveries of the north west coast of America. To which is prefixed, a summary of the voyages made by the Russians on the Frozen sea, in search of a north east passage. Serving as an explanation of a map of the Russian discoveries, published by the Academy of sciences at Petersburgh. Tr. from the High Dutch of S. [*i.e.* G.] Muller. With the addition of three new maps... By Thomas Jefferys. London, T. Jefferys, 1761.
Muller, Gerhard Friedrich, 1705–1783.

LAC 12936
Voyages made in the years 1788 and 1789, from China to the north west coast of America. To which are prefixed, an introductory narrative of a voyage performed in 1786, from Bengal, in the ship Nootka; observations on the probable existence of a north west passage; and some account of the trade between the north west coast of America and China; and the latter country and Great Britain. London, Printed at the Logographic press, 1790.
Meares, John, 1756?–1809.

LAC 23203
The voyages of Captain Luke Foxe of Hull, and Captain Thomas James of Bristol, in search of a north-west passage, in 1631–32; with narratives of the earlier north-west voyages of Frobisher, Davis, Weymouth, Hall, Knight, Hudson, Button, Gibbons, Bylot, Baffin, Hawkridge, and others... New York, B. Franklin [1963?]
Christy, Miller, 1861–   ed.

LAC 12310
Voyages of Peter Esprit Radisson, being an account of his travels and experiences among the North American Indians, from 1652–1684. Transcribed from original manuscript in the Bodleian library and the British museum. With historical illustrations and an introduction, by Gideon D. Scull. Boston, The Prince society, 1885.
Radisson, Pierre Esprit, 1620?–1710.

LAC 12317
The voyages of the Cabots and the English discovery of North America under Henry VII and Henry VIII. Illustrated with thirteen maps. London, The Argonaut press, 1929.
Williamson, James Alexander, 1886–

LAC 12285
The voyages of the Cabots, latest phases of the controversy. [Ottawa, J. Hope & co.; London, B. Quaritch] 1897.
Dawson, Samuel Edward, 1833–1916.

LAC 16913
Voyages of the slavers St. John and Arms of Amsterdam, 1659, 1663; together with additional papers illustrative of the slave trade under the Dutch. Tr. from the original manuscripts, with an introduction and index, by E. B. O'Callaghan. Albany, N. Y., J. Munsell, 1867.
O'Callaghan, Edmund Bailey, 1797–1880, comp.

LAC 12331
The voyages of the Venetian brothers, Nicolo & Antonio Zeno, to the northern seas, in the XIVth century, comprising the latest known accounts of the lost colony of Greenland; and of the Northmen in America before Columbus. Tr. and ed., with notes and an introduction, by Richard Henry Major, F. S. A., &c. London, Printed for the Hakluyt society, 1873.
Zeno, Niccolo, 1515–1565.

LAC 12326
The voyages of William Baffin, 1612–1622. Ed., with notes and an introduction, by Clements R. Markham. London, Printed for the Hakluyt society, 1881.
Markham, Sir Clements Robert, 1830–1916, ed.

LAC 12247
Voyages round the world; with selected sketches of voyages to the South seas, north and south Pacific oceans, China. New York, Collins & Hannay, 1833.
Fanning, Edmund, 1769–1841.

LAC 22578
Voyages to the New England coasts.
Forerunners and competitors of the Pilgrims and Puritans; or, Narratives of voyages made by persons other than the Pilgrims and Puritans of the Bay colony to the shores of New England during the first quarter of the seventeenth century, 1601–1625, with especial reference to the labors of Captain John Smith in behalf of the settlement of New England. Ed. for the New England society of Brooklyn by Charles Herbert Levermore. Brooklyn, N. Y., Pub. for the Society, 1912.
Levermore, Charles Herbert, 1856–1927, ed.

LAC 22680
The Wabash: or, Adventures of an English gentleman's family in the interior of America... London, Hurst and Blackett, 1855.
Beste, John Richard Digby, 1806–1885.

LAC 10905
Wacker's manual of the plan of Chicago; municipal economy. Especially prepared for study in the schools of Chicago, auspices of the Chicago Plan commission. [Chicago, Printed by H. C. Sherman & co.] 1912, [c1911]
Moody, Walter Dwight, 1874–1920.

LAC 13389
Wage-earners' budgets: a study of standards and cost of living in New York city, by Louise Bolard More, with a preface by Franklin H. Giddings. New York, H. Holt and company, 1907.
More, Louise Bolard.

LAC 40013
Wages and family budgets in the Chicago stockyards district, with wage statistics from other industries employing unskilled labor, by J. C. Kennedy and others. Chicago, Ill., The University of Chicago press [1914]
Kennedy, John Curtis, 1884–

LAC 40013
The wages of unskilled labor in the United States, 1850–1900... Chicago, The University of Chicago press, 1905.
Abbott, Edith, 1876–1957.

LAC 13411
The wages question; a treatise on wages and the wages class. New York, H. Holt and company; Boston, C. Schoenhof, 1891.
Walker, Francis Amasa, 1840–1897.

LAC 40016
Wagon roads as feeders to railways. Boston, Albert A. Pope, 1892.
Pope, Albert Augustus, 1843–1909.

LAC 10598
Walden. With an introductory note by Will H. Dircks. London, W. Scott, ltd. [1886]
Thoreau, Henry David, 1817–1862.

LAC 15400
The Walker Expedition to Quebec, 1711. Edited, with an introduction, by Gerald S. Graham. [London] Navy Records Society, 1953.
Walker, Sir Hovenden, 1656?–1728.

LAC 12960
Walker's expedition to Nicaragua; a history of the Central American war; and the Sonora and Kinney expeditions, including all the recent diplomatic correspondence, together with a new and accurate map of Central America, and a memoir and portrait of General William Walker. New York, Stringer and Townsend, 1856.
Wells, William Vincent, 1826–1876.

LAC 11759
Walks and talks of an American farmer in England. London, D. Bogue, 1852.
Olmsted, Frederick Law, 1822–1903.

LAC 10824
Wall street and the country, a study of recent financial tendencies. New York and London, G. P. Putnam's sons, 1904.
Conant, Charles Arthur, 1861–1915.

LAC 12172
The Wall street point of view. New York, Boston [etc.] Silver, Burdett & co. [c1900]
Clews, Henry, 1836–1923.

LAC 11795
Wall-street to Cashmere. A journal of five years in Asia, Africa, and Europe; comprising visits, during 1851, 2, 3, 4, 5, 6, to the Danemora iron mines, the "Seven churches", plains of Troy, Palmyra, Jerusalem, Petra, Seringapatam, Surat; with the scenes of the recent mutinies (Benares, Agra, Cawnpore, Lucknow, Delhi, etc., etc.), Cashmere, Peshawur, the Khyber Pass to Afghanistan, Java, China, and Mauritius. With nearly one hundred illustrations, from sketches made on the spot by the author. New York, S. A. Rollo & co.; [etc., etc.] 1859.
Ireland, John B.

LAC 16401
Walls and bars. Chicago, Ill., Socialist party [c1927]
Debs, Eugene Victor, 1855–1926.

LAC 11843
Walt Whitman, by Richard Maurice Bucke. To which is added English critics on Walt Whitman; ed. by Edward Dowden. Glasgow, Wilson & McCormick, 1884.
Bucke, Richard Maurice, 1837–1902.

LAC 12081
Walt Whitman, a study. With portrait and four illustrations. London, J. C. Nimmo, 1893.
Symonds, John Addington, 1840–1893.

LAC 40005
Walt Whitman's diary in Canada, with extracts from other of his diaries and literary note-books; ed. by William Sloane Kennedy. Boston, Small, Maynard & company, 1904.
Whitman, Walt, 1819–1892.

LAC 15302
Wandering recollections of a somewhat busy life. An autobiography... Boston, Roberts brothers, 1869.
Neal, John, 1793–1876.

LAC 40028
War and Christianity: an address before the American peace society, on the fourteenth anniversary in Boston, Mass., May 23, 1842. Boston, American peace society, 1842.
Coues, Samuel Elliott, 1797–1867.

LAC 40028
War and peace: the evils of the first and a plan for preserving the last. Reprinted from the original edition of 1842, with an introductory note by James Brown Scott. New York [etc.] Oxford University press, 1919.
Jay, William, 1789–1858.

LAC 15052
A war diary of events in the war of the great rebellion. 1863–1865. Boston, J. R. Osgood and company, 1882.
Gordon, George Henry, 1825?–1886.

LAC 12550
War government, federal and state, in Massachusetts, New York, Pennsylvania and Indiana, 1861–1865. Boston and New York, Houghton, Mifflin and company, 1906.
Weeden, William Babcock, 1834–1912.

LAC 15705
The war in America: being an historical and political account of the southern and northern states: showing the origin and cause of the present secession war. With a large map of the United States... London, Hamilton, Adams, and co. [1862]
Shaffner, Taliaferro Preston, 1818–1881.

LAC 11545
War in disguise; or, The frauds of the neutral flags. London, printed: New York: Re-printed by Hopkins & Seymour, for I. Riley and co. New-York; Hugh Maxwell, Philadelphia; Anderson and Jeffries, Baltimore; Samuel C. Carpenter, Charleston, S. C. and John West, Boston, January, 1806.
Stephen, James, 1758–1832.

LAC 11158
The war in Nicaragua. Written by Gen'l William Walker. Mobile, New York, S. H. Goetzel & co., 1860.
Walker, William, 1824–1860.

LAC 13108
War inconsistent with the religion of Jesus Christ, by David Low Dodge; with an introduction by Edwin D. Mead. Boston, Pub. for the International union, Ginn & company, 1905.
Dodge, David Low, 1774–1852.

LAC 40118
War is kind. Drawings by W. Bradley. New York, F. A. Stokes Co., 1899.
Crane, Stephen, 1871–1900.

LAC 16369
War letters, 1862–1865, of John Chipman Gray ... and John Codman Ropes ... with portraits. Boston and New York, Houghton Mifflin company, 1927.
Gray, John Chipman, 1839–1915.

LAC 40131

War of races. By whom it is sought to be brought about. Considered in two letters, with copious extracts from the recent work of Hilton [!] R. Helper. Richmond, 1867.
Gilmer, John H.

LAC 12020

War of the classes. New York, The Macmillan company; London, Macmillan & co., ltd., 1912, [c1905]
London, Jack, 1876–1916.

LAC 22140–74

The war of the rebellion: a compilation of the official records of the Union and Confederate armies. Pub. under the direction of the ... secretary of war. Washington, Govt. print. off., 1880–1901.
U.S. *War Dept.*

LAC 11461

War of the rebellion; or, Scylla and Charybdis. Consisting of observations upon the causes, course, and consequences of the late civil war in the United States. New York, Harper & brothers, 1866.
Foote, Henry Stuart, 1804–1880.

LAC 11677

The war on the Bank of the United States; or, A review of the measures of the administration against that institution and the prosperity of the country. New York, B. Franklin [1967]
Gordon, Thomas Francis, 1787–1860.

LAC 14878

War on the Detroit; the chronicles of Thomas Vercheres de Boucherville and The capitulation, by an Ohio volunteer, edited by Milo Milton Quaife. Chicago, The Lakeside press, R. R. Donnelley & sons co., 1940.
Vercheres de Boucherville, Rene Thomas.

LAC 12406

War pictures from the South. New York, D. Appleton and company, 1863.
Estvan, Bela, *b.* 1827.

LAC 12556

The war powers of the President, and the legislative powers of Congress in relation to rebellion, treason and slavery. 6th ed., pub for the Emancipation league. Boston, J. L. Shorey, 1863.
Whiting, William, 1813–1873.

LAC 13498

War powers under the Constitution of the United States. Military arrests, reconstruction and military government. Also, now first published, War claims of aliens. With notes on the acts of the executive and legislative departments during our civil war, and a collection of cases decided in the national courts. 43d ed. Boston, Lee and Shepard; New York, Lee, Shepard and Dillingham, 1871.
Whiting, William, 1813–1873.

LAC 40064

War-songs for freemen. Dedicated to the army of the United States... 2d ed. Boston, Ticknor and Fields, 1863.
Child, Francis James, 1825–1896, *ed.*

LAC 10231

The war-time journal of a Georgia girl, 1864–1865. Illustrated from contemporary photographs. New York, D. Appleton and company, 1908.
Andrews, Eliza Frances, *b.* 1840.

LAC 12420

War time memories of a Confederate senator's daughter.
A southern girl in '61; the war-time memories of a Confederate senator's daughter, by Mrs. D. Giraud Wright, illustrated from contemporary portraits. New York, Doubleday, Page & company, 1905.
Wright, Louise.

LAC 40028

War unchristian; or, The custom of war compared with the standard of christian duty. Hartford, W. Watson, 1834.
Connecticut Peace Society.

LAC 22464–65

The war with Mexico. New York, Harper & brothers, 1849.
Ripley, Roswell Sabine, 1823–1887.

LAC 22296–97

The war with Mexico. New York, The Macmillan company, 1919.
Smith, Justin Harvey, 1857–1930.

LAC 14638

The war with Mexico reviewed. Seventh thousand. Boston, American peace society, 1850.
Livermore, Abiel Abbot, 1811–1892.

LAC 12929

The war with Spain. New York and London, Harper brothers, 1900, [c1899]
Lodge, Henry Cabot, 1850–1924.

LAC 40031

I. The war with Spain. II. The Venezuelan dispute. Reprinted from the Baltimore American. Baltimore, J. Murphy & co., 1898.
Marburg, Theodore, 1862–1946.

LAC 11769

Waring's book of the farm; being a rev. ed. of the Handy-book of husbandry. A guide for farmers... By George E. Waring, jr. Philadelphia, Porter & Coates [c1877]
Waring, George Edwin, 1833–1898.

LAC 23201

Warrants for lands in South Carolina, 1672–1711; edited by A. S. Salley, jr., secretary of the Historical commission of South Carolina. Columbia, S. C., Printed for the Historical commission of South Carolina by the State co., 1910–15.
South Carolina *(Colony) Governor and Council.*

LAC 12515

"Warrington" pen-portraits: a collection of personal and political reminiscences from 1848 to 1876, from the writings of William S. Robinson. Ed. by Mrs. W. S. Robinson. Boston, Lee and Shepherd; New York, C. T. Dillingham, 1877.
Robinson, William Stevens, 1818–1876.

LAC 40074

Was it a fair trial? An appeal to the Governor of Illinois by Gen. M. M. Trumbull in behalf of the condemned anarchists. [1887?]
Trumbull, Matthew Mark, *d.* 1894.

LAC 22394

Washington and his generals. New York, C. Scribner, 1853–64.
Headley, Joel Tyler, 1813–1897.

LAC 40110

Washington in domestic life. From original letters and manuscripts. Philadelphia, J. B. Lippincott and co., 1857.
Rush, Richard, 1780–1859.

LAC 10850

Washington in Lincoln's time. New York, The Century co., 1895.
Brooks, Noah, 1830–1903.

LAC 16555

Washington the soldier. With illustrations, maps, chronological index and appendices... New York, C. Scribner's sons, 1899.
Carrington, Henry Beebee, 1824–1912.

LAC 16058

The Washoe giant in San Francisco, being heretofore uncollected sketches by Mark Twain [*pseud.*] published in the Golden era in the sixties, including Those blasted children, The Lick house ball, The Kearny street ghost story, Fitz Smythe's horse, and thirty-four more items by the wild humorist of the Pacific slope. With many drawings by Lloyd Hoff. Collected and edited, with an introduction, by Franklin Walker. San Francisco, G. Fields, 1938.
Clemens, Samuel Langhorne, 1835–1910.

LAC 13756

The watch factories of America, past and present. A complete history of watchmaking in America, from 1809 to 1888 inclusive... By Henry G. Abbott *pseud.* Chicago, G. K. Hazlitt & co., 1888.
Hazlitt, George Henry Abbott, 1858–1905.

LAC 13532

The water supply of the city of New York. 1658–1895. 1st ed. 1st thousand. New York, J. Wiley & sons; [etc., etc.] 1896.
Wegmann, Edward, 1850–

LAC 10199

Waterways of westward expansion, the Ohio River and its tributaries. [Large paper ed.] Cleveland, O., The A. H. Clark company, 1903.
Hulbert, Archer Butler, 1873–1933.

LAC 13244

Wau-bun, the "early day" in the North-west. New York, Derby & Jackson; Cincinnati, H. W. Derby & co., 1856.
Kinzie, Juliette Augusta, 1806–1870.

LAC 15232

The way of life; or, Gods way and course, in bringing the soule into, keeping it in, and carrying it on, in the wayes of life and peace. Laid downe in foure severall treatises on foure texts of Scripture... London, Printed by M. F. for L. Fawne and S. Gellibrand, 1641.
Cotton, John, 1584–1652.

LAC 10822

The ways and means of payment; a full analysis of the credit system, with its various modes of adjustment. Philadelphia, J. B. Lippincott & co., 1859.
Colwell, Stephen, 1800–1871.

LAC 15409

Ways of the spirit, and other essays. Boston, Roberts brothers, 1878, [c1877]
Hedge, Frederic Henry, 1805–1890.

LAC 13642

Wealth against commonwealth. New York, Harper & brothers [c1894]
Lloyd, Henry Demarest, 1847–1903.

LAC 40104

Wealth and biography of the wealthy citizens of New York city, comprising an alphabetical arrangement of persons estimated to be worth $100,000, and upwards. With the sums appended to each name... 6th ed. ... containing brief biographical and genealogical notices of the principal persons in this catalogue. Also, a valuable table of statistics. New York, The Sun office, 1845.
Beach, Moses Yale, 1800–1868, *ed.*

LAC 10170

The wealth and income of the people of the United States. New York, The Macmillan company; London, Macmillan & co., ltd., 1915.
King, Willford Isbell, 1880–1962.

LAC 40086

Wealth and misery. London, J. Watson [n.d.]
Owen, Robert Dale, 1801–1877.

LAC 10347

Wealth and moral law... Hartford, Conn., Hartford seminary press, 1894.
Andrews, Elisha Benjamin, 1844–1917.

LAC 13736

Wealth and progress; a critical examination of the labor problem; the natural basis for industrial reform, or how to increase wages without reducing profits or lowering rents: the economic philosophy of the eight hour movement. New York, D. Appleton and company, 1887.
Gunton, George, 1845–1919.

LAC 40002

Wealth: of what does it consist? Philadelphia, H. C. Baird, 1870.
Carey, Henry Charles, 1793–1879.

LAC 13691

A week in the White House with Theodore Roosevelt; a study of the President at the nation's business. New York and London, G. P. Putnam's sons, 1908.
Hale, William Bayard, 1869–1924.

LAC 10827

A week in Wall street. By one who knows. New York, For the booksellers, 1841.
Jackson, Frederick.

LAC 31232–35

The Weekly register, containing political, historical, geographical, scientifical, astronomical, statistical and biographical documents, essays and facts; together with notices of the arts and manufactures, and a record of the events of the time. v. 1–6; Sept. 7, 1811–Aug. 27, 1814. Baltimore.

LAC 15597

The well-bred girl in society, by Mrs. Burton Harrison. Philadelphia, Curtis publishing company; New York, Doubleday & McClure co. [c1898]
Harrison, Constance, 1843–1920.

LAC 15587

The well-dressed woman: a study in the practical application to dress of the laws of health, art, and morals. 2d ed., rev. and enl. ... New York, Fowler & Wells co., 1893.
Ecob, Helen Gilbert.

LAC 15507

Welshmen as factors.
Facts about Welsh factors... Welshmen as factors. The successful prize essay at the international Eisteddfod of the World's Columbia [!] exposition, Chicago, 1893. By "William Penn" [pseud.] [Utica, N. Y., Press of T. J. Griffiths, 1899]
Edwards, Ebenezer.

LAC 10753

Wendell Phillips: the agitator. With an appendix containing three of the orator's masterpieces, never before published in book form, viz.: "The lost arts." "Daniel O'Connell." "The scholar in a republic." Special ed. rev. New York [etc.] Funk & Wagnalls, 1890.
Martyn, Carlos, 1841–1917.

LAC 13293

The West: from the census of 1880, a history of the industrial, commercial, social, and political development of the states and territories of the West from 1800 to 1880. By Robert P. Porter. Assisted by Henry Gannett and Wm. P. Jones. Chicago, Rand, McNally & company; [etc., etc.] 1882.
Porter, Robert Percival, 1852–1917.

LAC 40152

The west in American history. [Columbus, The Ohio state archaeological and historical society, 1915]
Webster, John Lee, 1847–

LAC 13218

The West; its commerce and navigation. Cincinnati, H. W. Derby & co., 1848.
Hall, James, 1793–1868.

LAC 40115

West Point and the Military academy. 2d ed.–Rev. New York, W. C. & F. P. Church [etc.] 1879.
Farrow, Edward Samuel, 1855–1926.

LAC 40074

Western arbitration award.
Interpretation by Conference committee of managers of the western arbitration award as applied to certain questions and answers of the Brotherhood of locomotive engineers and the Brotherhood of locomotive firemen and enginemen. Chicago, July 1st, 1915. [Chicago? 1915?]
Conference Committee of Managers. (Railroads of Western Territory) 1914–1915.

LAC 16323

Western characters; or, Types of border life in the western states, by J. L. McConnel. With illustrations by Darley. New York, Redfield, 1853.
McConnel, John Ludlum, 1826–1862.

LAC 10438

Western civilisation.
Principles of western civilisation. New York, The Macmillan company; London, Macmillan & co., ltd., 1902.
Kidd, Benjamin, 1858–1916.

LAC 12005

Western clearings. by Mrs. C. M. Kirkland. New York, Wiley and Putnam, 1845.
Kirkland, Caroline Matilda, 1801–1864.

LAC 13157

The western gazetteer; or, emigrant's directory, containing a geographical description of the western states and territories, viz. the states of Kentucky, Indiana, Louisiana, Ohio, Tenessee [!] and Mississippi: and the territories of Illinois, Missouri, Alabama, Michigan, and North-Western. With an appendix, containing sketches of some of the western counties of New-York, Pennsylvania and Virginia; a description of the great northern lakes; Indian annuities, and directions to emigrants. Auburn, N. Y., Printed by H. C. Southwick, 1817.
Brown, Samuel R   1775–1817.

LAC 13204

Western lands and western waters. With illustrations from designs by eminent artists. London, S. O. Beeton, 1864.
Gerstacker, Friedrich Wilhelm Christian, 1816–1872.

LAC 13726

The western merchant. A narrative... By Luke Shortfield [pseud.] Philadelphia, Grigg, Elliot & co., 1849.
Jones, John Beauchamp, 1810–1866.

LAC 30572–76

The Western messenger; devoted to religion, life and literature. v. 1–8; June 1835–Apr. 1841. Louisville, Western Unitarian association; [etc., etc.] 1836–41.

LAC 11100

Western missions and missionaries: a series of letters, by Rev. P. J. de Smet. New York, James B. Kirker, late E. Dunigan and brother, 1863, [c1859]
Smet, Pierre Jean de, 1801–1873.

LAC 21110

A western pioneer: or, Incidents of the life and times of Rev. Alfred Brunson, embracing a period of over seventy years. Written by himself. Cincinnati, Hitchcock and Walden; New York, Carlton and Lanahan, 1872–[79]
Brunson, Alfred, 1793–1882.

LAC 15415

The western tourist and emigrant's guide through the states of Ohio, Michigan, Indiana, Illinois, Missouri, Iowa, and Wisconsin, and the territories of Minesota [!], Missouri, and Nebraska. Being an accurate and concise description of each state and territory; and containing the routes and distances on the great lines of travel... Accompanied with a large and minute map... New York, J. H. Colton, 1854.
Colton, Joseph Hutchins, 1800–1893.

LAC 20687
The western world; or, Travels in the United States in 1846–47: exhibiting them in their latest development, social, political, and industrial; including a chapter on California. From the 2d London ed. Philadelphia, Lea & Blanchard, 1849.
Mackay, Alexander, 1808–1852.

LAC 13297
Westward by rail: the new route to the East. New York, D. Appleton & company, 1871.
Rae, William Fraser, 1835–1905.

LAC 16908
Westward empire; or, The great drama of human progress. New-York, Harper & brothers, 1856.
Magoon, Elias Lyman, 1810–1886.

LAC 13353
The westward movement... The colonies and the republic west of the Alleghanies, 1763–1798. With full cartographical illustrations from contemporary sources. Boston and New York, Houghton, Mifflin and company, 1897.
Winsor, Justin, 1831–1897.

LAC 40073
What Christian socialism is. Reprinted from The Dawn of February, 1894. Boston, Office of the Dawn, 1894.
Bliss, William Dwight Porter, 1856–1926.

LAC 13905
What dress makes of us. By Dorothy Quigley. Illustrations by Annie Blakeslee. New York, E. P. Dutton & company [c1897]
Quigley, Dorothy.

LAC 40067
What followed the flag in the Philippines. An address delivered by Hon. Chas. E. Magoon, before the Patria club of the city of New York, at the Hotel Savoy, New York city. Friday evening, February 19, 1904. [New York, The Freitag printing co., 1904]
Magoon, Charles Edward, 1861–1920.

LAC 15632
The what, how and why of church building. New York, 1897.
Kramer, George W   1847–

LAC 11748
What I know of farming: a series of brief and plain expositions of practical agriculture as an art based upon science. New York, The Tribune association, 1871.
Greeley, Horace, 1811–1872.

LAC 13159
What I saw in California: being the journal of a tour, by the emigrant route and South pass of the Rocky mountains, across the continent of North America, the great desert basin, and through California, in the years, 1846–1847... 7th ed. With an appendix, containing accounts of the gold mines, various routes, outfit, etc., etc. New York, D. Appleton, 1849.
Bryant, Edwin, 1805–1869.

LAC 10529
What is Darwinism? New York, Scribner, Armstrong, and company, 1874.
Hodge, Charles, 1797–1878.

LAC 10593
What is it to be educated? Boston and New York, Houghton Mifflin company [c1914]
Henderson, Charles Hanford, 1861–1941.

LAC 40082
What is Presbyterianism? An address delivered before the Presbyterian historical society at their anniversary meeting in Philadelphia, on Tuesday evening, May 1, 1855. By Rev. Charles Hodge, D.D. Philadelphia, Presbyterian board of publication [c1855]
Hodge, Charles, 1797–1878.

LAC 40036
What makes slavery a question of national concern? A lecture, delivered, by invitation, at New York, January 30, at Syracuse, February 1, 1855. Boston, Little, Brown, and co., 1855.
Adams, Charles Francis, 1807–1886.

LAC 40006
?What means this strike? Address delivered by Daniel De Leon in the City hall of New Bedford, Massachusetts, February 11th, 1898. New York city, National executive committee, Socialist labor party, 1920.
De Leon, Daniel, 1852–1914.

LAC 40067
What shall we do with the Filipinos? Another view. Chicago, G. E. Marshall & co., 1899.
Rice, William Henry, 1840–1911.

LAC 40067
What shall we do with the Philippine islands? This problem solved. Seward, Neb., 1900.
Woodward, James H.

LAC 10552
What social classes owe to each other. New York, Harper & brothers [c1883]
Sumner, William Graham, 1840–1910.

LAC 40125
What think ye of the Congress now? or, An enquiry, how far the Americans are bound to abide by, and execute the decisions of, the late Congress?... New-York: Printed by James Rivington, 1775.
Chandler, Thomas Bradbury, 1726–1790.

LAC 40027
What to wear? By Elizabeth Stuart Phelps. Boston, J. R. Osgood and company, 1873.
Ward, Elizabeth Stuart, 1844–1911.

LAC 11765
Wheat fields and markets of the world. Saint Louis, The Modern miller company, 1908.
Smith, Rollin Edson, 1862–

LAC 10011
The wheat plant: its origin, culture, growth, development, composition, varieties, diseases, etc., etc. Together with a few remarks on Indian corn, its culture, etc. One hundred illustrations. Cincinnati, Moore, Wilstach, Keys & co., 1860, [c1859]
Klippart, John Hancock, 1823–1878.

LAC 11950
The wheel of life. New York, Doubleday, Page & company, 1906.
Glasgow, Ellen Anderson Gholson, 1874–

LAC 15574
Wheels and wheeling; an indispensable handbook for cyclists, with over two hundred illustrations. Boston, Wheelman company, 1892.
Porter, Luther Henry.

LAC 15525
When I was a boy in China. Boston, Lothrop, Lee & Shepard co. [c1887]
Lee, Yan Phou, 1861–

LAC 15744
When I was a child. London, Constable & company, 1913.
Markino, Yoshio, 1874–

LAC 10243
When railroads were new, by Charles Frederick Carter, with introductory note by Logan G. McPherson. New York, H. Holt and company; [etc., etc.] 1909.
Carter, Charles Frederick, 1863–1939.

LAC 14863
Where to emigrate and why, describes the climate-soil-productions-minerals and general resources ... in nearly all sections of the United States; and contains a description of the Pacific railroad ... rates of wages ... etc. ... New York, F. B. Goddard, 1869.
Goddard, Frederick Bartlett, 1834–

LAC 16897
Whilomville stories, by Stephen Crane. Illustrated by Peter Newell. New York and London, Harper & brothers, 1900.
Crane, Stephen, 1871–1900.

LAC 13440
Whisky frauds. Testimony before the Select committee concerning the whisky frauds... [Washington, Govt. print. off., 1876]
U. S. *Congress. House. Select Committee Concerning Whisky Frauds.*

LAC 14028
Whistler as I knew him. London, A. and C. Black, 1904.
Menpes, Mortimer, 1859–1938.

LAC 12800
White and black; the outcome of a visit to the United States, by Sir George Campbell, M. P. New York, R. Worthington, 1879.
Campbell, *Sir* George, 1824–1892.

LAC 22863
White conquest. London, Chatto and Windus, 1876.
Dixon, William Hepworth, 1821–1879.

LAC 15836
White diamonds better than "black diamonds"; slave states impoverished by slave labor. Read the appendix, and decide from fact. By Isaac V. Brown, D. D. Trenton, N. J., Printed by Murphy & Bechtel, 1860.
Brown, Isaac Van Arsdale, 1784–1861.

LAC 13243
The White hills; their legends, landscape, and poetry. By Thomas Starr King. With sixty illustrations, engraved by Andrew, from drawings by Wheelock. New York, Hurd and Houghton; Cambridge, H. O. Houghton and company, 1870.
King, Thomas Starr, 1824–1864.

LAC 16412
White-jacket; or, The world in a man-of-war. New York, Harper & brothers; London, R. Bentley, 1850.
Melville, Herman, 1819–1891.

LAC 40030
The White league conspiracy against free government. [New Orleans, New Orleans Republican, 1875]
Campbell, Hugh J

LAC 20701
White, red, black. Sketches of American society in the United States during the visit of their guests. By Francis and Theresa Pulszky. New York, Redfield, 1853.
Pulszky, Ferencz Aurelius, 1814–1897.

LAC 13371
White servitude in Pennsylvania: indentured and redemption labor in colony and commonwealth. Philadelphia, J. J. McVey, 1926.
Herrick, Cheesman Abiah, 1866–1956.

LAC 14687
The white slaves of monopolies; or, John Fitz Patrick, the miner, soldier and workingman's friend. A history of his struggles with mine owners, corporations [etc.]... Harrisburg, Pa., L. S. Hart, printer, 1884.

LAC 10719
White slaves; or, The oppression of the worthy poor. Boston, Lee and Shepard, 1893, [c1891]
Banks, Louis Albert, 1855–1933.

LAC 15573
The White Sulphur papers; or, Life at the springs of western Virginia. By Mark Pencil, esq. New York, S. Colman, 1839.
Pencil, Mark, *pseud.*

LAC 12896
White supremacy and Negro subordination; or, Negroes a subordinate race, and (so-called) slavery its normal condition. With an appendix, showing the past and present condition of the countries south of us. New York, Van Evrie, Horton & co., 1868, [c1867]
Van Evrie, John H   1814–1896.

LAC 40150
Whittier as a politician; illustrated by his letters to Professor Elizur Wright, jr. Now first published. Ed., with explanatory text, by Samuel T. Pickard. Boston, C. E. Goodspeed, 1900.
Whittier, John Greenleaf, 1807–1892.

LAC 11015
Who wrote the Bible? A book for the people. Boston and New York, Houghton, Mifflin and company, 1891.
Gladden, Washington, 1836–1918.

LAC 20101–3
Wholesale prices, wages, and transportation. Report by Mr. Aldrich, from the Committee on finance, March 3, 1893... Washington, Govt. print. off., 1893.
U. S. *Congress. Senate. Committee on Finance.*

LAC 14867
Why and how. Why the Chinese emigrate, and the means they adopt for the purpose of reaching America. With sketches of travel, amusing incidents, social customs, &c. By Russell H. Conwell. With illustrations by Hammatt Billings. Boston, Lee and Shepard; New York, Lee, Shepard and Dillingham, 1871.
Conwell, Russell Herman, 1843–1925.

LAC 40108
Why disfranchisement is bad. [Philadelphia, Press of E. A. Wright, 1904?]
Grimke, Archibald Henry, 1849–1930.

LAC 40037
Why is Canada not a part of the United States? Read before the U.S. Catholic historical society, Nov. 25th, 1889. New York, Geo. E. O'Hara, 1890.
Shea, John Dawson Gilmary, 1824–1892.

LAC 10006
Why is the dollar shrinking? A study in the high cost of living. New York, The Macmillan company, 1914.
Fisher, Irving, 1867–1947.

LAC 14762
Why should we change our form of government? Studies in practical politics. New York, C. Scribner's sons, 1912.
Butler, Nicholas Murray, 1862-1947.

LAC 16448
Why soldiers desert from the United States army.
Philadelphia, W. F. Fell & company, 1903.
Bergey, Ellwood.

LAC 12335
Why the solid South? or, Reconstruction and its results. By Hilary A. Herbert, M. C., Alabama; Zebulon B. Vance, U. S. senator, North Carolina; John J. Hemphill, M. C., South Carolina; Henry G. Turner, M. C., Georgia; Samuel Pasco, U. S. senator, Florida; Ira P. Jones, Tennessee; Robert Stiles, esq., Virginia; O. S. Long and William L. Wilson, M. C., West Virginia; George G. Vest, U. S. senator, Mo.; William M. Fishback, Arkansas; Ethelbert Barksdale, ex-M. C., Miss.; Charles Stewart, M. C., Texas; B. J. Sage, Louisiana. Baltimore, R. H. Woodward & company, 1890.
Herbert, Hilary Abner, 1834–1919, *ed.*

LAC 15769
Wicked city [Chicago] Chicago, 1906.
Stevens, Grant Eugene.

LAC 20663
The wide, wide world. By Elizabeth Wetherell [*pseud.*] Thirtieth thousand. New York, G. P. Putnam, 1854, [c1852]
Warner, Susan, 1819–1885.

LAC 14570
Wider use of the school plant, by Clarence Arthur Perry; introduction by Luther Halsey Gulick, M. D. New York, Charities publication committee, 1911, [c1910]
Perry, Clarence Arthur, 1872–

LAC 12135
The widow Rugby's husband, A night at the ugly man's, and other tales of Alabama. By Johnson J. Hooper. With engravings from original designs by Elliott. Philadelphia, T. B. Peterson and brothers [c1851]
Hooper, Johnson Jones, 1815?–1863.

LAC 16970
The wigwam and the cabin. New and rev. ed. Chicago, Belford, Clarke, & co., 1885.
Simms, William Gilmore, 1806–1870.

LAC 14035
Wigwam and war-path; or, The royal chief in chains.
Boston, J. P. Dale and company, 1875.
Meacham, Alfred Benjamin, 1826–1882.

LAC 16551
Wild life on the plains and horrors of Indian warfare. By a corps of competent authors and artists. Being a complete history of Indian life, warfare and adventure in America. Making specially prominent the late Indian war, with full descriptions of the Messiah craze, ghost dance, life of Sitting Bull... St. Louis, Mo., Continental Publishing co. [c1891]
Custer, George Armstrong, 1839–1876.

LAC 23697
Wild scenes in the forest and prairie. With sketches of American life. New York, W. H. Colyer, 1843.
Hoffman, Charles Fenno, 1806–1884.

LAC 13205
Wild sports in the far West. By Frederick Gerstaecker. Tr. from the German. With tinted illustrations, by H. Weir. London, New York, G. Routledge & co., 1854.
Gerstacker, Friedrich Wilhelm Christian, 1816–1872.

LAC 11685
The will to believe, and other essays in popular philosophy. New York, London [etc.] Longmans, Green and co., 1931, [c1896]
James, William, 1842–1910.

LAC 11353
Willard's practical butter book: a complete treatise on butter-making at factories and farm dairies, including the selection, feeding and management of stock for butter dairying–with plans for dairy rooms and creameries, dairy fixtures, utensils, etc. New York, Rural publishing company, 1875.
Willard, Xerxes Addison, 1820–1882.

LAC 10318
Willem Usselinx, founder of the Dutch and Swedish West India companies. New York and London, G. P. Putnam's sons, 1887.
Jameson, John Franklin, 1859–1937.

LAC 40009
William B. Ogden; and early days in Chicago: a paper read before the Chicago historical society, Tuesday, December 20, 1881... By Hon. Isaac N. Arnold. Chicago, Fergus printing company, 1882.
Arnold, Isaac Newton, 1815–1884.

LAC 16841
William Clayton's journal; a daily record of the journey of the original company of "Mormon" pioneers from Nauvoo, Illinois, to the valley of the Great Salt Lake, pub. by the Clayton family association. Salt Lake City, Utah, The Deseret news, 1921.
Clayton, William, 1814–1879.

LAC 10963
William Ellery Channing, minister of religion. Boston and New York, Houghton, Mifflin and company, 1903.
Chadwick, John White, 1840–

LAC 12096
William Gilmore Simms. Boston and New York, Houghton, Mifflin and company, 1892.
Trent, William Peterfield, 1862–1939.

LAC 11586
William James, and other essays on the philosophy of life. New York, The Macmillan company, 1912, [c1911]
Royce, Josiah, 1855–1916.

LAC 40034
William James as philosopher. Philadelphia, International journal of ethics, 1911.
Lovejoy, Arthur Oncken, 1873–1962.

LAC 10765
William Jay, and the constitutional movement for the abolition of slavery. By Bayard Tuckerman, with a preface by John Jay. New York, Negro universities press [c1893]
Tuckerman, Bayard, 1855–1923.

LAC 20091–93
William Lloyd Garrison, 1805–1879; the story of his life told by his children... New-York, The Century co., 1885–1889.
Garrison, Wendell Phillips, 1840–1907.

LAC 40093
William Penn: a bibliography, a tentative list of publications about him and his work. Harrisburg, 1932.
Spence, Mary Kirk.

LAC 13929
William Penn: an historical biography. With an extra chapter on "The Macaulay charges." London, Chapman and Hall, 1851.
Dixon, William Hepworth, 1821–1879.

LAC 11697
William Penn as the founder of two commonwealths. New York, D. Appleton and company, 1904.
Buell, Augustus C., 1847–1904.

LAC 40093
William Penn's journal: Kent and Sussex, 1672. [Philadelphia, The Historical society of Pennsylvania, 1944]
Penn, William, 1644–1718.

LAC 23193
William Wetmore Story and his friends; from letters, diaries, and recollections. Boston, Houghton, Mifflin & co., 1904.
James, Henry, 1843–1916.

LAC 14051
Winds of doctrine; studies in contemporary opinion. New York, C. Scribner's sons; London, J. M. Dent & sons, ltd. [c1913]
Santayana, George, 1863–1952.

LAC 22616
Winnowings in American history. Brooklyn, Historical printing club, 1890–91.

LAC 40047
Winslow Homer. New York, Priv. print., 1914.
Cox, Kenyon, 1856–1919.

LAC 13451
Winslow papers, A. D. 1776–1826. Printed under the auspices of the New Brunswick historical society. Ed. by Rev. W. O. Raymond, M. A. St. John, N. B., The Sun printing company, ltd., 1901.
Raymond, William Odber, 1853–1923, *ed.*

LAC 40044
A winter evening's conversation upon the doctrine of original sin, between a minister and three of his neighbours accidentally met together... Boston, Green and Russell, 1757.
Webster, Samuel, 1719–1796.

LAC 16438
A winter in Central America and Mexico. Boston, Lee and Shepard, 1887, [c1886]
Sanborn, Helen Josephine, 1857–1917.

LAC 21123
A winter in the West. By a New Yorker. New York, Harper & brothers, 1835.
Hoffman, Charles Fenno, 1806–1884.

LAC 40127
Winthrop's Conclusions for the plantation in New England. [Boston, Directors of the Old South work, 1896]
Winthrop, John, 1588–1649.

LAC 11203
Wisconsin; an experiment in democracy. New York, C. Scribner's sons, 1912.
Howe, Frederic Clemson, 1867–1940.

LAC 11495
The Wisconsin idea. New York, The Macmillan company, 1912.
McCarthy, Charles, 1873–1921.

LAC 23467–68
Wisconsin in three centuries, 1634–1905; narrative of three centuries in the making of an American commonwealth illustrated with numerous engravings of historic scenes and landmarks, portraits and facsimiles of rare prints, documents and old maps... New York, The Century history company [c1906]
Campbell, Henry Colin, 1862–

LAC 22528–31
Wisconsin, its story and biography, 1848–1913. Chicago and New York, The Lewis publishing company, 1914.
Usher, Ellis Baker, 1852–

LAC 13332
Wisconsin; the Americanization of a French settlement. Boston and New York, Houghton Mifflin company, 1908.
Thwaites, Reuben Gold, 1853–1913.

LAC 40072
Wisconsin. What it offers to the immigrant. An official report published by the State board of immigration of Wisconsin... Milwaukee, Cramer, Aikens & Cramer, printers, 1879.
Wisconsin. *State Board of Immigration.*

LAC 22240
The witchcraft delusion in New England: its rise, progress, and termination, as exhibited by Dr. Cotton Mather, in The wonders of the invisible world; and by Mr. Robert Calef, in his More wonders of the invisible world. With a preface, introduction, and notes, by Samuel G. Drake. Roxbury, Mass., Printed for W. E. Woodward, 1866.
Drake, Samuel Gardner, 1798–1875, *comp.*

LAC 14881
With Dewey at Manila; being the plain story of the glorious victory of the United States squadron over the Spanish fleet, Sunday morning, May 1st, 1898, as related in the notes and correspondence of an officer on board the flagship Olympia. New York, R. F. Fenno & company, [c1898]
Vivian, Thomas Jondrie, 1855–   *ed.*

LAC 16436
With fly-rod and camera. Illustrated with one hundred and fifty plates, from photographs by the author. New York, Forest and stream publishing co., 1890.
Samuels, Edward Augustus, 1836–1908.

LAC 15050
With Sampson through the war, by W. A. M. Goode; being an account of the naval operations of the North Atlantic squadron during the Spanish-American war of 1898. With contributed chapters by Rear-Admiral Sampson, U. S. N., Captain Robley D. Evans, U. S. N., Commander C. C. Todd, U. S. N. New York, Doubleday & McClure co., 1899.
Goode, *Sir* William Athelstane Meredith, 1875–

LAC 16452
With the battle fleet; cruise of the sixteen battleships of the United States Atlantic fleet from Hampton Roads to the Golden Gate, December, 1907–May, 1908, by Franklin Matthews; illustrated by Henry Reuterdahl (courtesy of Collier's weekly) New York, B. W. Huebsch, 1908.
Matthews, Franklin, 1858–1917.

LAC 12500
With the fathers; studies in the history of the United States. New York, D. Appleton and company, 1896.
McMaster, John Bach, 1852–1932.

LAC 11937
With the procession, a novel. New York, Harper & brothers, 1895.
Fuller, Henry Blake, 1857–1929.

LAC 16842
Within prison walls; being a narrative of personal experience during a week of voluntary confinement in the state prison at Auburn, New York, by Thomas Mott Osborne (Thomas Brown, Auburn no. 33,333X) New York and London, D. Appleton and company, 1940, [c1914]
Osborne, Thomas Mott, 1859–1926.

LAC 14109
Wolfville days, by Alfred Henry Lewis, with frontispiece by Frederic Remington. New York, Grosset & Dunlap [c1902]
Lewis, Alfred Henry, 1857–1914.

LAC 12013
Wolfville nights. New York, Frederick A. Stokes company [1902]
Lewis, Alfred Henry, 1857–1914.

LAC 11218
Woman and social progress; a discussion of the biologic, domestic, industrial and social possibilities of American women, by Scott Nearing and Nellis M. S. Nearing. New York, The Macmillan company, 1912.
Nearing, Scott, 1883–1946.

LAC 16029
Woman and the higher education. New York, Harper & brothers, 1893.
Brackett, Anna Callender, 1836–1911, *ed.*

LAC 13936
Woman and the republic; a survey of the woman-suffrage movement in the United States and a discussion of the claims and arguments of its foremost advocates, by Helen Kendrick Johnson. A new and enl. ed., with an index. New York, The Guidon club opposed to woman suffrage, 1913, [c1909]
Johnson, Helen, 1844–1917.

LAC 16668
Woman, church and state: a historical account of the status of woman through the Christian ages: with reminiscences of the matriarchate: by Matilda Joslyn Gage. Chicago, C. H. Kerr & company, 1893.
Gage, Matilda, 1826–1898.

LAC 11220

Woman in all ages and nations; a complete and authentic history of the manners and customs, character and condition of the female sex, in civilized and savage countries, from the earliest ages to the present time. By Thomas L. Nichols, M. D. With a preface, by Stephen Pearl Andrews. New York, Boston [etc.] Fowlers and Wells [c1849]
Nichols, Thomas Low, 1815–1901.

LAC 16146

Woman in America; being an examination into the moral and intellectual condition of American female society... New York, Harper and brothers, 1858, [c1841]
Graves, A   J.

LAC 13839

Woman in prison. New York, Hurd and Houghton, 1869.
Woods, Caroline H.

LAC 11224

Woman in the nineteenth century. By S. Margaret Fuller. London, G. Slater, 1850.
Ossoli, Sarah Margaret, *marchesa* d', 1810–1850.

LAC 10769

A woman of the century; fourteen hundred-seventy biographical sketches accompanied by portraits of leading American women in all walks of life; ed. by Frances E. Willard and Mary A. Livermore, assisted by a corps of able contributors. Buffalo, New York [etc.] C. W. Moulton, 1893.
Willard, Frances Elizabeth, 1839–1898, *ed.*

LAC 15214

A woman rice planter [by] Patience Pennington [*pseud.*] with an introduction by Owen Wister and illustrations by Alice R. H. Smith. New York, The Macmillan company, 1922, [c1913]
Pringle, Elizabeth Waties, 1845–1921.

LAC 16048

Woman suffrage. The argument of Carrie S. Burnham before Chief Justice Reed, and Associate Justices Agnew, Sharswood and Mercur, of the Supreme court of Pennsylvania, in banc, on the third and fourth of April, 1873. With an appendix containing the opinion of Hon. George Sharswood and a complete history of the case. Also, a compilation of the laws of Pennsylvania touching the rights of women. Philadelphia, Citizen's suffrage association, 1873.
Burnham, Carrie S.

LAC 13410

The woman who toils; being the experiences of two ladies as factory girls, by Mrs. John Van Vorst and Marie Van Vorst. New York, Doubleday, Page & company, 1903.
Van Vorst, Bessie, 1873–1928.

LAC 13614

The woman's book of sports; a practical guide to physical development and outdoor recreation. Illustrated from photographs taken by the author. New York, D. Appleton and company, 1901.
Paret, Jahial Parmly, 1870–

LAC 16481

A woman's life-work: labors and experiences of Laura S. Haviland. Cincinnati, Printed by Walden & Stowe, for the author, 1882, [c1881]
Haviland, Laura, 1808–1898.

LAC 11992

A woman's reason, a novel. Boston and New York, Houghton Mifflin company [c1882]
Howells, William Dean, 1837–1920.

LAC 13333

A woman's story of pioneer Illinois, by Christiana Holmes Tillson; edited by Milo Milton Quaife, with two portraits. Chicago, R. R. Donnelley & sons company, 1919.
Tillson, Christiana Holmes, 1798–1872.

LAC 10754

Woman's work in America, ed. by Annie Nathan Meyer; with an introduction by Julia Ward Howe. New York, H. Holt and company, 1891.
Meyer, Annie 1867–1951, *ed.*

LAC 14251

Woman's work in the civil war: a record of heroism, patriotism and patience. By L. P. Brockett and Mrs. Mary C. Vaughan. With an introduction, by Henry W. Bellows. Philadelphia, Zeigler, McCurdy & co.; Boston [etc.] R. H. Curran, 1867.
Brockett, Linus Pierpont

LAC 13109

Woman's wrongs: a counter-irritant. By Gail Hamilton [*pseud.*] Boston, Ticknor and Fields, 1868.
Dodge, Mary Abigail, 1833–1896.

LAC 13191

Women in industry; a study in American economic history, by Edith Abbott, with an introductory note by Sophonisba P. Breckinridge. New York and London, D. Appleton and company, 1910.
Abbott, Edith, 1876–1957.

LAC 13872

Women in industry; decision of the United States Supreme court in Curt Muller vs. state of Oregon, upholding the constitutionality of the Oregon ten hour law for women and brief for the state of Oregon, by Louis D. Brandeis assisted by Josephine Goldmark. Reprinted for the National consumers' league. New York [1908]
Brandeis, Louis Dembitz, 1856–1941.

LAC 13637

Women in public life... Editor in charge of this volume, James P. Lichtenberger, PH. D. Philadelphia, American academy of political and social science [c1914]
American Academy of Political and Social Science, *Philadelphia.*

LAC 14799

The women of the Confederacy, in which is presented the heroism of the women of the Confederacy with accounts of their trials during the war and the period of reconstruction, with their ultimate triumph over adversity. Their motives and their achievements as told by writers and orators now preserved in permanent form. By Rev. J. L. Underwood. New York and Washington, The Neale publishing company, 1906.
Underwood, John Levi.

LAC 14893

Women of the war; their heroism and self-sacrifice.
Hartford, Conn., S. S. Scranton & co.; Chicago, R. C.
Trent; [etc., etc.] 1866.
Moore, Frank, 1828–1904.

LAC 16176

Women's suffrage; the reform against nature. New
York, C. Scribner and company, 1869.
Bushnell, Horace, 1802–1876.

LAC 15925

**Wonder-working providence of Sions Saviour in New
England** (by Captain Edward Johnson of Woburn, Mas-
sachusetts bay) London, 1654. With an historical intro-
duction and an index by William Frederick Poole.
Andover [Mass.] W. F. Draper, 1867.
Johnson, Edward, 1599–1672.

LAC 16539

The wonderful wizard of Oz, by L. Frank Baum, with
pictures by W. W. Denslow. Chicago, New York, G. M.
Hill co., 1900.
Baum, Lyman Frank, 1856–1919.

LAC 15305

**The wonders of the invisible world. Being an account
of the tryals of several witches lately executed in New-
England.** London, John Russell Smith, 1862.
Mather, Cotton, 1663–1728.

LAC 16460

**The wood-carver of Salem; Samuel McIntire, his life
and work,** by Frank Cousins and Phil M. Riley. Boston,
Little, Brown, and company, 1916.
Cousins, Frank, 1851–

LAC 16968

**Woodcraft; or, Hawks about the dovecote; a story of
the South at the close of the revolution.** New and rev. ed.
New York, W. J. Widdleton [187–]
Simms, William Gilmore, 1806–1870.

LAC 40088

Wood-engraving; three essays, by A. V. S. Anthony,
Timothy Cole and Elbridge Kingsley, with a list of
American books illustrated with woodcuts. New York,
The Grolier club, 1916.

LAC 14429

**Woodrow Wilson; his career, his statesmanship, and
his public policies,** by Hester E. Hosford. 2d ed., rev. and
enl.; with a preface by Thomas P. Gore. With 16 illustrations. New York and London, G. P. Putnam's sons, 1912.
Hosford, Hester Eloise, 1892–

LAC 10421

**Wool-growing and the tariff; a study in the economic
history of the United States.** Awarded the David A.
Wells prize for the year 1907–08, and published from the
income of the David A. Wells fund. Boston and New
York, Houghton Mifflin company, 1910.
Wright, Chester Whitney.

LAC 40066

**A word to Federalists and to those who love the memory
of Washington.** [Boston, 1810]

LAC 11847

Work and play; or, Literary varieties. New York, C.
Scribner, 1864.
Bushnell, Horace, 1802–1876.

LAC 10221

**The work of the Interstate commerce commission.
With which have been reprinted certain editorial and
other articles throwing light upon the proposed amendment of the Interstate commerce law.** Washington, Press
of Gibson brothers, 1905.
Newcomb, Harry Turner, 1867–1944.

LAC 15204

The work of the rural school, by J. D. Eggleston and
Robert W. Bruere. New York and London, Harper &
brothers [c1913]
Eggleston, Joseph Dupuy, 1867–

LAC 14326

**Work, wages, and profits; their influence on the cost
of living.** New York, The Engineering magazine, 1910.
Gantt, Henry Laurence, 1861–1919.

LAC 13430

The workers; an experiment in reality. The West. New
York, C. Scribner's sons, 1898.
Wyckoff, Walter Augustus, 1865–1908.

LAC 11257

The working-class movement in America. By Edward
& Eleanor Marx Aveling. 2d ed., enl. London, S. Son-
nenschein & co., 1891.
Aveling, Edward Bibbins, 1851–1898.

LAC 13873

**The working girls of Boston. From the fifteenth An-
nual report of the Massachusetts Bureau of statistics of
labor for 1884.** By Carroll D. Wright. Boston, Wright &
Potter printing co., 1889.
Massachusetts. *Bureau of Statistics of Labor.*

LAC 14334

Working people and their employers. New York, Funk
& Wagnalls, 1888, [c1885]
Gladden, Washington, 1836–1918.

LAC 16496

**Working with the hands; being a sequel to "Up from
Slavery," covering the author's experiences in industrial
training at Tuskegee,** by Booker T. Washington; illus-
trated from photographs by Frances Benjamin Johnston.
New York, Doubleday, Page & company, 1904.
Washington, Booker Taliaferro, 1859?–1915.

LAC 11110

The working man and social problems. Chicago [etc.]
F. H. Revell company, 1903.
Stelzle, Charles, 1869–1941.

LAC 13740

The working man's political economy, founded upon the principle of immutable justice, and the inalienable rights of man... Cincinnati, T. Varney, 1847.
Pickering, John.

LAC 14451

The working man's way to wealth; a practical treatise on building associations: what they are and how to use them. 5th ed. Philadelphia, J. K. Simon, 1872.
Wrigley, Edmund.

LAC 15457

Workingmen's insurance. New York, Boston, T. Y. Crowell & company [1898]
Willoughby, William Franklin, 1867–

LAC 16231

The workingmen's party of California. An epitome of its rise and progress... San Francisco, Bacon & company, printers, 1878.

LAC 16651

Workmen's compensation. Hearings before the Committee on the judiciary. House of representatives, Sixty-first Congress, on H. R. 1, February 17 and March 15, 1910. Washington, Govt. print. off., 1910.
U.S. *Congress. House. Committee on the Judiciary.*

LAC 13800

Workmen's compensation. Report upon operation of state laws. Investigation by Commission of the American federation of labor and the National civic federation. Commission's findings, views of employers and workmen, digest of laws, rules of state boards of award. Washington, Govt. print. off., 1914.
Commission on Workmen's Compensation Laws (American Federation of Labor and National Civic Federation)

LAC 23386–93

[Works] New York, The Century co. [1909–15]
Mitchell, Silas Weir, 1829–1914.

LAC 22305–20

Works. [Boston, Little, Brown, and company, 1901–07]
Parkman, Francis, 1823–1893.

LAC 12044

The works in verse and prose, of the late Robert Treat Paine, jun., esq. With notes. To which are prefixed, sketches of his life, character and writings... Boston: Printed and published by J. Belcher, 1812.
Paine, Robert Treat, 1773–1811.

LAC 21323–29

The works of Alexander Hamilton, ed. by Henry Cabot Lodge. [Federal ed.] New York and London, G. P. Putnam's sons, 1904.
Hamilton, Alexander, 1757–1804.

LAC 22516–20

The works of Alexander Hamilton; comprising his correspondence, and his political and official writings, exclusive of the Federalist, civil and military. Published from the original manuscripts deposited in the Department of state, by order of the Joint library committee of Congress. Edited by John C. Hamilton. New-York, J. F. Trow, printer, 1850–51.
Hamilton, Alexander, 1757–1804.

LAC 11836

The works of Anne Bradstreet in prose and verse, ed. by John Harvard Ellis. Charlestown, A. E. Cutter, 1867.
Bradstreet, Anne, 1612?–1672.

LAC 21082–84

The works of Charles Follen, with a memoir of his life... Boston, Hilliard, Gray and company, 1841–42.
Follen, Charles Theodore Christian, 1796–1840.

LAC 21832–40

The works of Charles Sumner... Boston, Lee and Shepard, 1870–83.
Sumner, Charles, 1811–1874.

LAC 21954

Works of Fisher Ames. With a selection from his speeches and correspondence. Ed. by his son, Seth Ames. Boston, Little, Brown and company, 1854.
Ames, Fisher, 1758–1808.

LAC 23863–66

The works of Francis J. Grimke, edited by Carter G. Woodson. Washington, D. C., The Associated publishers, inc. [1942]
Grimke, Francis James, 1850–1937.

LAC 22716–20

The works of Henry Clay comprising his life, correspondence and speeches, ed. by Calvin Colton, LL. D. With an introduction by Thomas B. Reed and a history of tariff legislation, 1812–1896, by William McKinley. New York and London, G. P. Putnam's sons, 1904.
Clay, Henry, 1777–1852.

LAC 23566–73

The works of Henry Wadsworth Longfellow, with bibliographical and critical notes and his life, with extracts from his journals and correspondence, edited by Samuel Longfellow. In fourteen volumes. [Boston and New York, Houghton, Mifflin and company, c1886–91]
Longfellow, Henry Wadsworth, 1807–1882.

LAC 22129–36

The works of Herman Melville. Standard ed. [London, etc., Constable and company, 1922–24]
Melville, Herman, 1819–1891.

LAC 23265–303

The works of Hubert Howe Bancroft... San Francisco, A. L. Bancroft & company, 1882–90.
Bancroft, Hubert Howe, 1832–1918.

LAC 20788–89

The works of James Abram Garfield, ed. by Burke A. Hinsdale. Boston, J. R. Osgood and company; Cleveland, Cobb, Andrews & co., 1882–1883.
Garfield, James Abram, *pres. U.S.*, 1831–1881.

LAC 21256–63

The works of James Buchanan, comprising his speeches, state papers, and private correspondence; collected and ed. by John Bassett Moore. Philadelphia & London, J. B. Lippincott company, 1908–11.
Buchanan, James, *pres. U.S.*, 1791–1868.

LAC 14083
The works of James Houstoun, M. D., containing memoirs of his life and travels in Asia, Africa, America, and most parts of Europe. From the year 1690 to the present time. Giving a particular account of the Scotch expedition to Darien in America ... the rise, progress, and fall of the two great trading African and South-Sea companies; the late expedition to the Spanish West-Indies; the taking and restitution of Cape-Breton. Some curious anecdotes of the Spanish court... London, Printed for the author; and sold by S. Bladon, 1753.
Houstoun, James, *b. ca.* 1690.

LAC 14553
The works of James McNeill Whistler, a study by Elisabeth Luther Cary, with a tentative list of the artist's works. New York, Moffat, Yard & company, 1913, [c1907]
Cary, Elisabeth Luther, 1867–

LAC 20283–92
The works of John Adams, second President of the United States: with a life of the author, notes and illustrations, by his grandson Charles Francis Adams. Boston, Little, Brown and company [etc.] 1850–56 [v. 1, '56]
Adams, John, *pres. U.S.*, 1735–1826.

LAC 20324–29
The works of John C. Calhoun... New York, D. Appleton and company [1851]–56.
Calhoun, John Caldwell, 1782–1850.

LAC 21193–95
The works of John Robinson, pastor of the pilgrim fathers. With a memoir and annotations by Robert Ashton. Boston, Doctrinal tract and book society, 1851.
Robinson, John, 1575?–1625.

LAC 11252
The works of John Woolman. In two parts. Philadelphia, Printed by Joseph Crukshank, in Market-street, between Second and Third streets, M.DCC.LXXIV.
Woolman, John, 1720–1772.

LAC 22822–23
The works of Joseph Bellamy, D. D., first pastor of the church in Bethlem, Conn., with a memoir of his life and character... Boston, Doctrinal tract and book society, 1853, '50.
Bellamy, Joseph, 1719–1790.

LAC 22218–22
The works of Leonard Woods. Boston, Jewett, 1850–1851 [v. 5, 1850]
Woods, Leonard, 1774–1854.

LAC 20355–60
The works of Nathanael Emmons, D. D. With a memoir of his life. Edited by Jacob Ide, D. D. Boston, Crocker and Brewster, 1842.
Emmons, Nathanael, 1745–1840.

LAC 22741–47
The works of Oliver Wendell Holmes. [Standard library ed. Boston and New York, Houghton, Mifflin and company, c1892]
Holmes, Oliver Wendell, 1809–1894.

LAC 22845–58
The works of Orestes A. Brownson, collected and arranged by Henry F. Brownson. Detroit, T. Nourse, 1882–1887.
Brownson, Orestes Augustus, 1803–1876.

LAC 10983
The works of Orville Dewey, D. D. With a biographical sketch. New and complete ed. Boston, American Unitarian association, 1883.
Dewey, Orville, 1794–1882.

LAC 22682–84
The works of Philip Lindsley... Edited by Le Roy J. Halsey. With introductory notices of his life and labours. By the editor. Philadelphia, J. B. Lippincott & co., 1866.
Lindsley, Philip, 1786–1855.

LAC 23072–74
The works of President Edwards... A reprint of the Worcester edition, with valuable additions and a copious general index, to which, for the first time, has been added, at great expense, a complete index of Scripture texts. 8th ed. ... New York, Leavitt & Allen, 1851–52.
Edwards, Jonathan, 1703–1758.

LAC 23613–20
The works of Robert G. Ingersoll. New York, The Ingersoll league, 1912–1929.
Ingersoll, Robert Green, 1833–1899.

LAC 20780–81
The works of Rufus Choate, with a memoir of his life. By Samuel Gilman Brown. Boston, Little, Brown and company, 1862.
Choate, Rufus, 1799–1859.

LAC 20716–19
The works of Samuel de Champlain... reprinted, translated and annotated by six Canadian scholars under the general editorship of H. P. Biggar. Toronto, The Champlain society, 1922–36.
Champlain, Samuel de, 1567–1635.

LAC 23686–87
The works of Samuel Hopkins... With a memoir of his life and character... Boston, Doctrinal tract and book society, 1852.
Hopkins, Samuel, 1721–1803.

LAC 21966–69
The works of the Reverend George Whitefield ... containing all his sermons and tracts which have been already published: with a select collection of letters... Also some other pieces of important subjects never before printed... To which is prefixed an account of his life... London, E. and C. Dilly, 1771–72.
Whitefield, George, 1714–1770.

LAC 23062–69
[The works of Theodore Parker] Centenary ed. Boston, American Unitarian Association, 1907–11.
Parker, Theodore, 1810–1860.

LAC 21297–99
The works of Thomas Shepard, first pastor of the First church, Cambridge, Mass., with a memoir of his life and character... Boston, Doctrinal tract and book society, 1853.
Shepard, Thomas, 1605–1649.

LAC 21556-76
[Works of Washington Irving] New York, G. P. Putnam, 1857-1897.
Irving, Washington, 1783-1859.

LAC 20605-7
The works of William E. Channing. 23d complete ed. With an introduction. Boston, American unitarian association, 1874.
Channing, William Ellery, 1780-1842.

LAC 22118-22
The works of William H. Seward, ed. by George E. Baker. New York, Redfield, 1853-84.
Seward, William Henry, 1801-1872.

LAC 14007
The world a department store; a story of life under a cooperative system. By Bradford Peck. With illustrations by Harry C. Wilkinson. Lewiston, Me., & Boston, B. Peck [1900]
Peck, Bradford.

LAC 10545
The world as it is: containing a view of the present condition of its principal nations ... with ... numerous engravings. 6th ed. [New Haven] T. Belknap, 1841, [c1836]
Perkins, Samuel, 1767-1850.

LAC 12286
The world encompassed by Sir Francis Drake, being his next voyage to that to Nombre de Dios. Collated with an unpublished manuscript of Francis Fletcher, chaplain to the expedition. With appendices illustrative of the same voyage, and introduction, by W. S. W. Vaux, esq., M. A. London, Printed for the Hakluyt society, 1854.
Drake, *Sir* Francis, *bart., d.* 1637.

LAC 11231
World peace.
Selected articles on world peace including international arbitration and disarmament. White Plains, N. Y., and New York city, The H. W. Wilson company, 1914.
Reely, Mary Katharine, 1881-   *comp.*

LAC 11148
World politics at the end of the nineteenth century, as influenced by the oriental situation. New York, The Macmillan company; London, Macmillan and co., ltd., 1908, [c1900]
Reinsch, Paul Samuel, 1869-1923.

LAC 13499
The world's crisis. Cincinnati, Miami printing and publishing co., print., 1868.
Woolfolk, L.   B.

LAC 40046
The world's first parliament of religions; its Christian spirit, historic greatness and manifold results. A brief summary of testimonies gathered from many lands, indicating what the world has said of this memorable congress of the creeds, of its organizer and chairman, John Henry Barrows, and of the official literature of the parliament. Chicago, Hill & Shuman [c1895]
Goodspeed, George Stephen, 1860-1905, *ed.*

LAC 20341-42
The World's parliament of religions; an illustrated and popular story of the World's first parliament of religions, held in Chicago in connection with the Columbian exposition of 1893. Ed. by the Rev. John Henry Barrows. Chicago, The Parliament publishing company, 1893.
Barrows, John Henry, 1847-1902, *ed.*

LAC 10295
Worth and wealth: a collection of maxims, morals and miscellanies for merchants and men of business. New York, Stringer & Townsend, 1856.
Hunt, Freeman, 1804-1858.

LAC 12114
The wound dresser; a series of letters written from the hospitals in Washington during the war of the rebellion, by Walt Whitman, ed. by Richard Maurice Bucke. Boston, Small, Maynard & company [etc.] 1898.
Whitman, Walt, 1819-1892.

LAC 16268
Wounds in the rain; war stories. New York, Frederick A. Stokes company [c1900]
Crane, Stephen, 1871-1900.

LAC 16427
Wreck of the Glide, with recollections of the Fijiis, and of Wallis Island. New York and London, Wiley & Putnam, 1848.
Oliver, James, *d.* 1845.

LAC 22703-12
The writings and speeches of Daniel Webster... National ed. ... Boston, Little, Brown, & company, 1903.
Webster, Daniel, 1782-1852.

LAC 12441
The writings and speeches of Grover Cleveland; selected and edited, with an introduction, by George F. Parker. New York, Cassell publishing company [c1892]
Cleveland, Grover, *pres. U.S.*, 1837-1908.

LAC 20235-36
The writings and speeches of Samuel J. Tilden. Ed. by John Bigelow. New York, Harper and brothers, 1885.
Tilden, Samuel Jones, 1814-1886.

LAC 20232-34
Writings; collected and edited by Moncure Daniel Conway. New York, Putnam [c1894-96.]
Paine, Thomas, 1737-1809.

LAC 20385-87
The writings of Albert Gallatin. Edited by Henry Adams. Philadelphia [etc.] J. B. Lippincott & co., 1879.
Gallatin, Albert, 1761-1849.

LAC 21085-94
The writings of Benjamin Franklin; collected and ed., with a life and introduction, by Albert Henry Smyth. New York, The Macmillan company; London, Macmillan & co., ltd., 1905-07.
Franklin, Benjamin, 1706-1790.

LAC 15844
The writings of Cassius Marcellus Clay, including speeches and addresses. Edited, with a pref. and memoir, by Horace Greeley. New York, Negro Universities Press [1969]
Clay, Cassius Marcellus, 1810–1903.

LAC 14093
Writings of Christopher Columbus, descriptive of the discovery and occupation of the New world; ed., with an introduction, by Paul Leicester Ford. New York, C. L. Webster & co., 1892.
Colombo, Cristoforo.

LAC 21209–34
The writings of George Washington from the original manuscript sources, 1745–1799; prepared under the direction of the United States George Washington bicentennial commission and published by authority of Congress; John C. Fitzpatrick, editor. Washington, U.S. Govt. print. off. [1931–44]
Washington, George, *pres. U.S.*, 1732–1799.

LAC 22540–48
The writings of Harriet Beecher Stowe, with biographical introductions, portraits, and other illustrations. In sixteen volumes. Boston, Houghton, Mifflin and co., 1896–1900.
Stowe, Harriet Elizabeth, 1811–1896.

LAC 24011–29
The writings of Henry David Thoreau... Boston and New York, Houghton, Mifflin, 1906.
Thoreau, Henry David, 1817–1862.

LAC 20437–38
Writings of Hugh Swinton Legare ... consisting of a diary of Brussels, and journal of the Rhine; extracts from his private and diplomatic correspondence; orations and speeches; and contributions to the New-York and Southern reviews. Prefaced by a memoir of his life. Edited by his sister. Charleston, S. C., Burges & James; New York, D. Appleton & co.; [etc., etc.] 1846, 45.
Legare, Hugh Swinton, 1797?–1843.

LAC 22645–50
The writings of James Madison, comprising his public papers and his private correspondence, including numerous letters and documents now for the first time printed. Ed. by Gaillard Hunt. New York [etc.] G. P. Putnam's sons, 1900–10.
Madison, James, *pres. U.S.*, 1751–1836.

LAC 20247–50
The writings of James Monroe, including a collection of his public and private papers and correspondence now for the first time printed. Ed. by Stanislaus Murray Hamilton. New York, London, G. P. Putnam's sons, 1898–1903.
Monroe, James, *pres. U. S.*, 1758–1831.

LAC 24035–51
The writings of John Fiske. Ed. de luxe. [Cambridge, Mass., Printed at the Riverside press, 1902]
Fiske, John, 1842–1901.

LAC 22512–15
The writings of John Greenleaf Whittier. Riverside ed. [Boston and New York, Houghton, Mifflin and company, 1893–94]
Whittier, John Greenleaf, 1807–1892.

LAC 23740–48
The writings of John Lothrop Motley. Netherlands ed. New York and London, Harper and brothers [1900]
Motley, John Lothrop, 1814–1877.

LAC 20293–99
Writings of John Quincy Adams, edited by Worthington Chauncey Ford. New York, The Macmillan company, 1913–17.
Adams, John Quincy, *pres. U.S.*, 1767–1848.

LAC 22843–44
Writings of Levi Woodbury, LL.D. Political, judicial and literary. Now first selected and arranged. Boston, Little, Brown and company, 1852.
Woodbury, Levi, 1789–1851.

LAC 23713–39
The writings of Mark Twain [*pseud.*] Definitive edition. New York, G. Wells, 1922–25.
Clemens, Samuel Langhorne, 1835–1910.

LAC 21304–5
Writings of Professor B. B. Edwards, with a memoir by Edwards A. Park. Boston, J. P. Jewett and company; Cleveland, O., Jewett, Proctor, and Worthington; [etc., etc.] 1853.
Edwards, Bela Bates, 1802–1852.

LAC 20650
The writings of Robert C. Sands, in prose and verse. With a memoir of the author. New-York, Harper & brothers, 1834.
Sands, Robert Charles, 1799–1832.

LAC 21125–30
The writings of Sam Houston, 1813–1863; edited by Amelia W. Williams and Eugene C. Barker. Austin, Tex., The University of Texas press, 1938–43.
Houston, Samuel, 1793–1863.

LAC 11050
The writings of the late Elder John Leland, including some events in his life, written by himself, with additional sketches, &c., by L. F. Greene. New York, G. W. Wood, 1845.
Leland, John, 1754–1841.

LAC 22691–94
The writings of Thomas Bailey Aldrich. [Large-paper ed.] [Cambridge, Printed at the Riverside press, 1897–1907]
Aldrich, Thomas Bailey, 1836–1907.

LAC 22697–702
The writings of Thomas Jefferson; collected and ed. by Paul Leicester Ford. New York [etc.] G. P. Putnam's sons, 1892–99.
Jefferson, Thomas, *pres. U.S.*, 1743–1826.

LAC 10810

Written music remodeled, and invested with the simplicity of an exact science... A system of short hand accompaniment introduced... Boston, J. P. Jewett and company, 1860.
Warren, Josiah, 1798–1874.

LAC 11226

The wrong of slavery, the right of emancipation, and the future of the African race in the United States. Philadelphia, J. B. Lippincott & co., 1864.
Owen, Robert Dale, 1801–1877.

LAC 40025

The X.Y.Z. letters. Ed. by Herman V. Ames and John Bach McMaster. Philadelphia, Pa., The Department of history of the University of Pennsylvania, 1899.
Ames, Herman Vandenburg, 1865–1935, *ed.*

LAC 11311

Yachts and yachting. With over one hundred and ten illustrations. New York, Cassell & company, ltd. [c1887]
Cozzens, Frederick Schiller, 1846–

LAC 20333–34

Yale college, a sketch of its history, with notices of its several departments, instructors, and benefactors, together with some account of student life and amusements, by various authors. Ed. by William L. Kingsley. Illustrated with views and portraits... New York, H. Holt and company, 1879.
Kingsley, William Lathrop, 1824–1896, *ed.*

LAC 14223

Yale lectures on the Sunday-school.
The Sunday-school: its origin, mission, methods, and auxiliaries. Philadelphia, J. D. Wattles, 1888.
Trumbull, Henry Clay, 1830–1903.

LAC 14817

Yankee travels through the island of Cuba; or, The men and government, the laws and customs of Cuba, as seen by American eyes. New-York, D. Appleton & co., 1856.
Philalethes, Demoticus, *pseud.*

LAC 13574

The Yankey in London, being the first part of a series of letters written by an American youth, during nine months' residence in the city of London... vol. I. New-York: Printed and published by Isaac Riley, 1809.
Tyler, Royall, 1757–1826.

LAC 12366

Yazoo; or, On the picket line of freedom in the South. A personal narrative... Washington, D. C., The author, 1884.
Morgan, Albert Talmon.

LAC 23246–47

A year in Europe. Comprising a journal of observations in England, Scotland, Ireland, France, Switzerland, the north of Italy, and Holland. In 1818 and 1819. New-York, Collins & co.; Philadelphia, H. C. Carey & J. Lea; [etc., etc.] 1823.
Griscom, John, 1774–1852.

LAC 13201

A year of American travel; narrative of personal experience. Voyage to California in 1848: impressions of Panama, San Francisco, Monterey, San Jose, &c., and a letter from Colonel John Fremont, describing his expedition to the Rocky Mountains made during the winter of 1848–49. With an introd. by Patrice Manahan, and engravings by Ernest Freed. San Francisco, The Book Club of California, 1960.
Fremont, Jessie, 1824–1902.

LAC 12131

A year of wreck; a true story, by a victim. New York, Harper & brothers, 1880.
Benham, George Chittenden.

LAC 40146

Yearbook. [New York, 1911–12]
New York Peace Society *(Founded 1906)*

LAC 21664–83

Yearbook of Agriculture. 1894–1915. Washington, U.S. Govt. print. off., 1895–1916.
U.S. *Dept. of Agriculture.*

LAC 15819

Years of experience: an autobiographical narrative, by Georgiana Bruce Kirby. New York & London, G. P. Putnam's sons, 1887.
Kirby, Georgiana, *b.* 1818.

LAC 16586

Years of my youth. New York and London, Harper & brothers [c1917]
Howells, William Dean, 1837–1920.

LAC 12173

A year's residence, in the United States of America. Treating of the face of the country, the climate, the soil, the products, the mode of cultivating the land, the prices of land, of labour, of food, of raiment; of the expenses of housekeeping, and of the usual manner of living; of the manners and customs of the people; and of the institutions of the country, civil, political, and religious. Belfast, Printed at the Ulster Register Office, from an American copy, 1818.
Cobbett, William, 1763–1835.

LAC 16930

Yekl; a tale of the New York ghetto. New York, D. Appleton and company, 1896.
Cahan, Abraham, 1860–1951.

LAC 15459

The Yellowstone national park: historical and descriptive... 7th ed., rev. and enl. Cincinnati, Stewart & Kidd, 1912, [c1903]
Chittenden, Hiram Martin, 1858–1917.

LAC 16957

The Yemassee; a romance of Carolina. New and rev. ed. Chicago, Donohue, Henneberry, 1890.
Simms, William Gilmore, 1806–1870.

LAC 11913

Yesterdays with authors. Boston, J. R. Osgood and company, 1872.
Fields, James Thomas, 1816–1881.

LAC 14399

The Yorktown campaign and the surrender of Cornwallis, 1781. New York, Harper & brothers, 1881.
Johnston, Henry Phelps, 1842–1923.

LAC 16914

The Yosemite. New York, The Century co., 1912.
Muir, John, 1838–1914.

LAC 16311

Youma: the story of a West-Indian slave. New York, Harper & brothers, 1890.
Hearn, Lafcadio, 1850–1904.

LAC 16415

The young carpenter's assistant; or, A system of architecture, adapted to the style of building in the United States. Philadelphia, B. Johnson, 1805.
Biddle, Owen.

LAC 12137

The young husband, or Duties of man in the marriage relation. 20th stereotype ed. Boston, C. D. Strong, 1851.
Alcott, William Andrus, 1798–1859.

LAC 12979

The young ladies' class book; a selection of lessons for reading, in prose and verse. 16th stereotyped ed. Boston, Gould, Kendall, and Lincoln, 1837.
Bailey, Ebenezer, 1795–1839.

LAC 40123

The young lady's accidence; or, A short and easy introduction to English grammar... 5th ed. corrected. Boston, Printed by I. Thomas and E. T. Andrews, 1791.
Bingham, Caleb, 1757–1817.

LAC 15605

The young lady's friend. By a lady. Boston, American stationers' company, 1836.
Farrar, Eliza Ware, 1791–1870.

LAC 11615

The young man entering business. New York, T. Y. Crowell & co. [c1903]
Marden, Orison Swett, 1848–1924.

LAC 15570

The young man's friend. Boston, J. Munroe and company, 1836.
Muzzey, Artemas Bowers, 1802–1892.

LAC 12138

The young man's guide. 16th ed. Boston, T. R. Marvin, 1844.
Alcott, William Andrus, 1798–1859.

LAC 15592

The young merchant... Philadelphia, R. W. Pomeroy, 1839.
Frost, John, 1800–1859.

LAC 15029

The young mill-wright and miller's guide; illus. by twenty-eight descriptive plates. 9th ed., with additions and corrections, by Thomas P. Jones, and a description of an improved merchant flour-mill, with engravings, by C. and O. Evans, engineers. Philadelphia, Carey, Lea & Blanchard, 1836.
Evans, Oliver, 1755–1819.

LAC 10625

A young scholar's letters; being a memoir of Byron Caldwell Smith, ed. by D. O. Kellogg. New York, London, G. P. Putnam's sons, 1897.
Smith, Byron Caldwell, 1849–1877.

LAC 12139

The young woman's guide to excellence. 13th ed. Boston, C. H. Peirce, Binney and Otheman [etc.] 1847, [c1836]
Alcott, William Andrus, 1798–1859.

LAC 15300

The younger American poets. Illustrated with portraits. Boston, Little, Brown, and company, 1906, [c1904]
Rittenhouse, Jessie Belle, 1869–1948.

LAC 14437

The Youngers' fight for freedom; a southern soldier's twenty years' campaign to open northern prison doors—with anecdotes of war days, by W. C. Bronaugh, who spent the period from 1882 to 1902 to secure the release of Cole, Jim and Bob Younger from the Minnesota state penitentiary... Columbia, Mo., Printed for the author by E. W. Stephens publishing company, 1906.
Bronaugh, Warren Carter, b. 1839.

LAC 13603

Youth and life. Boston and New York, Houghton Mifflin company, 1913.
Bourne, Randolph Silliman, 1886–1918.

LAC 15660

Youth; its education, regimen, and hygiene. New York, D. Appleton and company, 1906.
Hall, Granville Stanley, 1844–1924.

LAC 14587

Yvernelle, a legend of feudal France. Philadelphia, J. B. Lippincott company, 1892.
Norris, Frank, 1870–1902.

LAC 12008

Zury: the meanest man in Spring county; a novel of western life. Boston and New York, Houghton, Mifflin and company, 1889, [c1887]

WITHDRAWAL